THE **SPORT AMERICANA**®

Baseball Card

PRICE GUIDE

NO. 3

By

DR. JAMES BECKETT
AND
DENNIS W. ECKES

D0064392

ISBN 0-937424-07-2

ACKNOWLEDGEMENTS

As we have stated in the previous two editions of the Price Guide, it is impossible to write a book of this magnitude without considerable help. Aside from being major contributors, several collectors have provided exceptional assistance with the special articles in this book. We should like to thank them specifically — Chris Benjamin (for the physical preparation of the book, and the Harry Stovey article), Barry and Steve Halper (for the One Man's Collection article and the color sections), and Mike Aronstein, Larry Fritsch, Lew Lipset Tom Reid, Herb Ross and Nick Shoff (for the 1952 Topps article).

In addition to the cooperation of the gentlemen listed above, major contributions — in the form of set descriptions, checklists, price input and a vast amount of personal time — were unselfishly made to us by: Frank & Vivian Barning, Buck Barker, Bill Dodge, Rich Egan, Gervise Ford, Mike Gordon, Jim Horne, Dave & Rosie Jones, Larry Kelly, Don Lepore, Irv Lerner, Lew Lipset, B. A. Murry, Ralph Nozaki, Tom Pfirrman, Jack Pollard, Andrew Pywowarczuk, Dick Reuss, Gavin Riley, Dave Ring, Randall Root, Bill Rothney, John Rumierz, Elwood Scharf, Geoff Sindelar, Sal Vasali and Bill Zekus.

Many others have contributed in the form of price input, error corrections, and picture donations, we should like to thank them: Jeff Alcorn, Mark Allen, Mike Berkus, Phil Bolsta, Lonny Brewer, Andy Brookens, Tom Burderi, Mark Burrell, Jim Callis, Ray Carson, Steve Carter, Ira Cetron, Mark Christiansen, Derrick Clark, Jerry Clark, Mark Colby, Chuck Cole, Peck Dean, Tony DeFiore, Tommie Dotson, Brian Dyet, Dennis William Eckes, Darryl Fischbeck, Ira Frankel, Steve Friedman, J. Frye, Dick Goddard, Danny Greenberg, Bill Hall, Hershell Hanks, Lincoln Harold, C. E. Harsha, Bill Heitman, Christian Iversen, Dave Jenkins, Kevin Johnson, Gary Kessel, Steve Kessinger, David Kinnard, T. J. Kulaga, Robert Lecrone, Aaron Lee, Howie Levy, Bob Lydon, Bud Lynch, George Lyons, Paul Marchant, Don McPherson, Michael Olenick, Ted Patterson, Carroll Plunk, Pat Quinn, Bob Rathgeber, Edward Reed, Owen Ricker, Robert Rossini, Daryl Slade, Nick Snider, Ted Sobocinski, Mel Soloman, Bob Solon, Don Steinback, Webb Thomas, Tom Tuschak, Richard West, Richard Weston, Andy White, Bill Zihlmann, and other contributors we have inadvertently not included.

Finally, though far from least, we should like to thank the skilled and patient typists who endured the authors moods, their rewrites, and their other whims long enough to type the many preliminary drafts and the final version of this manuscript: Karen Brantley, Denise Delss, Rae McDonald, Millie "Slick" Phillips, Carollyn Roach, Margaret Schutz, and Doris Wheeler.

Special thanks are extended to the Topps Chewing Gum Company (specifically Messrs. Sy Berger and Bill Haber), The Fleer Corporation (specifically Mr. Arnold Harris) and The Donruss Company (specifically Mr. Stewart F. Lyman) for providing 1981 checklists in order that the 1981 national issues could be included in this Price Guide.

SPORT AMERICANA BASEBALL CARD
PRICE GUIDE
TABLE OF CONTENTS

1981 BASEBALL CARDS

OUR 34TH YEAR IN CARDS—AMERICA'S MOST RELIABLE CARD DEALER

WITH OVER 25 MILLION CARDS IN STOCK ... WE HAVE AMERICA'S MOST COMPLETE STOCK OF SPORTS TRADING CARDS. All sets and singles are available ... 1948-1981. We have thousands of Pre-1948 cards available also.

SUPER SERVICE! ! We have four full-time employees ready and able to process your order with the maximum of efficiency and speed ... TRY OUR SERVICE & SEE ... You'll agree ... it's the best you have ever had! ! ! Full Money back guarantee if you are not completely satisfied with our service and products. YOU, the customer are always NO. 1 to us! ! !

To receive Super Service it is necessary to send a POSTAL MONEY ORDER with your order, (all personal checks are held 15 days for clearance).

TOPPS
1. Complete Set (726 cards) only $22.00 + $1.75 shipping.
2. 1000 mint cards in never before opened boxes. $17.00 + $1.50 shipping.
2. Team Sets—$3.50 each ppd. Phillies, Pirates, Reds, Yankees $5.00 each ppd. Dodgers, Orioles, Red Sox $4.25 each ppd.

FLEER
1. Complete Set (660 cards) only $20.00 + $1.75 shipping.
2. 1000 mint cards in never before opened boxes. $16.50 + $1.50 shipping.
3. Team Sets — $3.25 each ppd. Phillies, Pirates, Reds, Yankees $4.75 each ppd. Dodgers, Orioles, Red Sox $4.00 each ppd.

DONRUSS
1. Complete Set (605 cards) only $16.00 + $1.75 shipping.
2. Team sets — $3.00 each ppd. Phillies, Pirates, Reds, Yankees $4.00 ppd. Dodgers, Orioles, Red Sox $3.50 each ppd.

PARTIAL LIST OF SETS AVAILABLE
(All sets are in mint condition)
All sets are shipped in numerical order, postpaid, via UPS, in damage-free boxes.

BASEBALL SETS	
Topps (726)	$22.00
1980 Topps Superstars (60)	25.00
1979 Topps (726) w/Willis Rangers	35.00
1979 Topps (726) w/Willis Bluejays	28.50
1978 Topps (726)	36.00
1977 Topps (660)	45.00
1976 Topps (660)	60.00
1975 Topps (660)	100.00
1974 Topps (660)	125.00
1973 Topps (660)	160.00
1979 Topps Comics (33)	14.00
1977 Topps Patches & C/L (73)	25.00
1974 Topps Traded (44)	5.00
1974 Topps Traded (44)	6.00
1974 Topps Washington (11)	42.50
1971 Topps Super (63)	80.00
1970 Topps Super (41) w/# 38	72.50
1980 Kellogg's 3D (60)	10.00
1979 Kellogg's 3D (60)	12.50
1978 Kellogg's 3D (57)	26.00
1977 Kellogg's 3D (57)	25.00
1974 Kellogg's 3ZD (54)	27.50
1973 Kellogg's 3D (54)	90.00
1972 Kellogg's 3D (54)	30.00
1972 3D Baseball Greats (15)	7.50
1975 Fleer Pioneers of BB (28)	8.50
1974 Fleer World Series (68)	32.50
1970 Fleer World Series (67)	35.00
1958 Fleer (79) w/o #68)	80.00
1976 Sport Stars (630)	75.00

FOOTBALL SETS	
1980 Topps (528)	$18.00
1980 Topps Superstars (30)	12.50
1979 Topps (528)	20.00
1978 Topps (528)	22.50
1977 Topps (528)	25.00
1976 Topps (528)	28.00
1975 Topps (528)	33.00
1974 Topps (528)	40.00
1973 Topps (528)	47.50
1972 Topps (351)	80.00
1971 Topps (263)	62.50
1970 Topps (263)	65.00
1970 Topps Super (35)	30.00
1969 Topps (Nos. 89-176)	45.00
1976 Wonder Bread (24)	8.50
1975 Wonder Bread (24)	9.50
1974 Wonder Bread (24)	14.50
1980 Fleer NFL in Action (70)	7.50
1979 Fleer NFL in Action (69)	10.50
1978 Fleer NFL in Action (68)	13.50
1977 Fleer NFL in Action (67)	17.50
1974 Fleer Hall of Fame (50)	8.50
1972 Fleer AFL (132)	60.00
1972 Canadian League (132)	22.50
1971 Canadian League (132)	25.00
1972 Kellogg's 3D (60)	27.50
1974 Nabisco Pro Faces (25)	11.00
1972 Sunoco-DX Stamps w/album	27.50
1969 Trester-Comet Bengals (19)	22.50
1968 KDKA Steelers (15)	17.50

BASKETBALL SETS	
1980-81 Topps (88)	$ 6.00
1970-80 Topps (132)	8.00
1978-79 Topps (132)	10.00
1977-78 Topps (132)	12.50
1976-77 Topps (144-Large)	20.00
1975-76 Topps (330)	37.50
1974-75 Topps (264)	30.00
1973-74 Topps (264)	35.00
1972-73 Topps (264)	45.00
1971-72 Topps (233)	47.50
1970-71 Topps (175)	55.00
1970-71 Topps Pin Ups (24)	13.50
1969-70 Topps Pin Ups (23)	12.50

HOCKEY SETS	
1980-81 Topps (264)	10.50
1979-80 Topps (264)	12.00
1978-79 Topps (264)	13.50
1977-78 Topps (264)	15.50
1977-78 Topps Inserts (22)	9.00
1975-76 Topps (264)	18.00
1976-77 Topps Inserts (22)	10.00
1975-76 Topps (264)	27.50
1974-75 Topps (264)	28.00
1973-74 Topps (198)	30.00
1972-73 Topps (176)	40.00
1971-72 Topps (132)	50.00
1968-69 Topps (132)	65.00
1974-75 O-Pee-Cee (WHA) (66)	15.00

CANADA, ALASKA, HAWAII, APO, FPO, & P.O. BOX CUSTOMERS: Add an additional $3.00 per set for sets over 250 cards and $1.50 per set for sets under 250 cards for shipping and handling. Prices of all items are U.S. Funds only. CANADIAN ORDERS: POSTAL MONEY ORDERS IN U.S. FUNDS ONLY.

BASEBALL CARD CHECKLIST BOOK

• The new BASEBALL CARD CHECKLIST BOOK is available now for immediate shipment. Illustrated checklists of all regular issue baseball cards of Topps, Bowman, Fleer and Leaf from 1948 through 1980 (including the 1964, 1969-71 Super sets). It has over 18,000 players names listed.

• The new BASEBALL CARD CHECKLIST BOOK lists the card number and name of every player issued in the above sets, plus the varieties in each set. A card of each year and manufacturer is illustrated to help you identify the cards you have.

• NEW FEATURE! The book has a plastic binder which allows for adding of new pages each year as the new baseball sets are issued. These pages can be purchased each year to keep your checklist book up-to-date ... No need to buy the entire book each year! Your checklist book is always current.

A MUST FOR ANY CARD COLLECTOR ... $8.50 Postpaid $9.75 Air Mail

The ALL NEW BASEBALL CARD TEAM CHECKLIST is here! ! !

• This new book lists all Bowman and Topps regular issues by team!

• Contains 112 pages of fully illustrated team lists along with a list of all the wrong pictures printed by Topps and Bowman.

• The BASEBALL CARD TEAM CHECKLIST is printed on high quality, glossy paper with a removable binding to allow the addition of the current pages as they come out every year! ! !

• With the BASEBALL CARD TEAM CHECKLIST it will not be necessary to page through regular checklist books or alpha books to find players on your favorite team — find them at a GLANCE! ! !

$7.98 Postpaid $9.48 Air Mail

FINEST QUALITY PLASTIC SHEETS
FEATURING
• NON-MIGRATING PLASTIC IN ALL SHEETS
• PLASTIC THAT DOES NOT STICK TOGETHER
• STIFFNESS TO PREVENT CARD CURLING
• INTELLIGENT DESIGN
• RESISTANCE TO CRACKING
• FULL COVERAGE OF CARDS, PHOTOS & POSTCARDS
SHEETS FIT ANY 3 RING BINMDER

* ONE-YEAR WINNERS *
NOW TWO COMPLETELY DIFFERENT SERIES OF ONE YEAR WINNERS!
• BOTH SERIES FEATURE PLAYERS WHOSE BIG LEAGUE CAREERS WERE VERY SHORT.
• MOST OF THE PLAYERS IN BOTH SERIES WERE NEVER MADE ON A BASEBALL CARD.
• EACH CARD CONTAINS THE COMPLETE VITAL STATISTICS OF THE PLAYER ALONG WITH A SHORT BIOGRAPHY AND COMPLETE BIG LEAGUE RECORDS ON THE BACK.

SERIES ONE—CONTAINS 18 CARDS IN BLACK & WHITE $3.50 shipped
SERIES TWO—CONTAINS 36 CARDS IN FULL COLOR ($7.50 shipped)

With the great number of cards we have in stock it is possible to list only a few items. Please send 25¢ for EACH of the following lists of what we have available and prices.

1. Sets not listed below), singles (baseball, football, hockey, basketball) 1970-81

2. NEED BASEBALL CARDS or FOOTBALL CARDS from 1948-1972 ? ? We have over 7 million in stock. Ask for "new concept to obtain older cards" (specify sport) for complete details.

3. BASEBALL TEAM SET COLLECTORS—are you looking for your favorite team in older sets! ! ! We have all team sets (all the players issued on your favorite team) 1948-1979 available. List team and years wanted most more than 5 at one time).

4. NON-SPORTS CARDS—Sets and singles available 1948-1975. Your want list would be helpful and appreciated.

5. SPORTING NEWS, SPORTS ILLUSTRATED, SPORT MAGAZINE, BASEBALL DIGEST—We have back issues 1954 to date available.

BUYING CARDS! ! ! Top prices paid for cards issued prior to 1968. Please send list.

(Also buying APBA Baseball playing cards (complete sets, loose singles, or sample cards from 1950 to the present)

LARRY FRITSCH

DEPT. 556   735 OLD WAUSAU ROAD   STEVENS POINT, WIS. 54481

PREFACE

During the first two years that this Price Guide has been published, the baseball card collecting hobby has grown by leaps and bounds; prices have fluctuated upward and downward; new card sets have been produced in unprecedented amounts; and our National Pastime itself continues to flourish with attendance records being set every year. While there might be a temptation to alter the purpose or format of this third edition of the Price Guide, in retrospect, the purpose of the book is the same as it was for the first edition, even though the size of the book has more than doubled. The format has proven useful and workable; therefore, the authors see no reason to change it.

The prime purpose of this Price Guide is to provide a functional tool to the hobbyist, not to entertain as would a novel. The Guide is about baseball cards, not the personalities pictured on them, albeit the value of a card is determined to a great extent by who is pictured on the card. However, while the prime purpose of the Guide is not to entertain, we do hope you find it interesting and useful.

The Sport Americana Baseball Card Price Guide has been successful when other attempts have failed because of its completeness, currentness, and validity. This Price Guide contains three prices, by condition, for all baseball cards in the issues which account for almost all of the post-1900 baseball cards that exist today. Not only does it list prices for the so-called common player cards in each issue, but also it distinguishes the common player cards from the high value cards (Star, Superstar, Team and Special cards). These high value cards form the foundation upon which the price structure of the baseball card collecting hobby is currently based. The Guide is current; prices were added to the card lists in 1981, just prior to printing. And, the prices are valid. The prices reflect not the authors' opinions or desires but the "going" retail prices for each card based on the marketplace—hobby papers, sports memorabilia conventions, local club meetings, and dealers' catalogues and price lists.

To facilitate your use of this book, please read the "How to Use The Price Guide" and "Glossary" sections before going to the pricing data.

Sports memorabilia collecting in general and baseball card collecting in particular is popular. We've read on numerous occasions that sports collecting is the third most popular hobby in the country; whether it is or not is irrelevant. We collect baseball cards because we enjoy collecting them, not because the hobby is popular. That others also enjoy our hobby gives us the opportunity to find new and interesting hobby material and meet new and interesting people with similar interests to ours. Who could ask for more from one's hobby?

Sincerely,
Jim Beckett
Denny Eckes

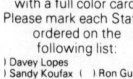

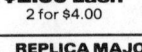
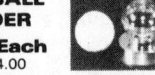

2

INTRODUCTION

This third edition of the Sport Americana Baseball Card Price Guide has been expanded to include most of the E—card sets, Exhibits from 1939 to 1966, Burger King sets, the 1981 Topps, Fleer and Donruss sets, and many other lesser known but interesting baseball card sets. Collector issues have again been omitted except in exceptional instances which are explained later in the book. All prices have, of course, been updated to reflect the 1981 market value.

As more information has become available concerning variations, double and triple card printing frequencies, scarcities and anomalies, they have been incorporated into the Guide. New, and the authors believe interesting, articles have been added, as have different and unusual baseball cards and uncut sheets. Features such as "Last Year in Brief" and "What's New for This Year" have been retained.

Illustrations for sets checklisted are almost all at 57% of original size. Several illustrations in the listed sets are at 50% or less, reductions necessary to accommodate the illustration to the page size. Illustration for cards not in listed sets are normally at 50% of original sizes; however, here again some further reduction was necessary for some of these illustrations (e.g., uncut sheets) to accommodate the page size.

The authors would like to overemphasize some points mentioned at different spots later in the book, but which are so important as to deserve specific reference here:

This book is a guide. It is not the "for sale" list of anyone. The prices are not the thoughts or desires of the authors, publisher, distributors or advertisers. They are what the market place, through the law of supply and demand, has determined. Throughout the year prices on "any" card might increase or decrease. You and you alone are the final judge as to whether you should or should not buy or sell a particular card at a particular price.

Prices vary widely on many of the higher priced cards—particularly the truly scarce cards of which there are very few available for purchase (T206 Wagner and Plank; 1951 Topps current stars Roberts, Konstanty and Stanky; 1933 Goudey Lajoie) and the speculator cards which are reasonably plentiful but for which there is an incredible demand (e.g., 1952 Topps Mantle, 1967 Brooks Robinson, 1970 Topps Johnny Bench, 1954 Topps Aaron).

3

No. 1 $6⁹⁵

THE SPORT AMERICANA™

Football & Basketball Card
PRICE GUIDE

By
Dr. James Beckett
and Dennis W. Eckes

Contains prices for virtually all football and basketball cards in existence, condition guide, glossary of terms, and how to obtain cards.

INCLUDES CANADIAN FOOTBALL LEAGUE

THE 1979-1980 SPORT AMERICANA FOOTBALL AND BASKETBALL CARD PRICE GUIDE

by
Dr. James Beckett
&
Dennis W. Eckes

$ 6.95 plus postage and handling

THE NEW SPORT AMERICANA FOOTBALL & BASKETBALL CARD PRICE GUIDE CONTAINS ALL POPULAR FOOTBALL AND BASKETBALL CARDS ISSUED IN THE U.S. PLUS ALL POPULAR CANADIAN FOOTBALL ISSUES. THE FORMAT OF THE GUIDE IS SIMILAR TO THE PHENOMENALLY SUCCESSFUL BASEBALL CARD PRICE GUIDE, WHICH WAS ALSO WRITTEN BY DR. JAMES BECKETT AND DENNIS W. ECKES. THE NUMBER, PLAYER & THREE PRICES EACH, BASED ON CONDITION, ARE LISTED FOR EACH CARD IN EACH SET.

SPORTS MEMORABILIA
$ 6.50 plus postage and handling

Den's Collectors Den has purchased the remaining inventory of the book SPORTS MEMORABILIA, by John Douglas. This book has been touted by the Price Guide as "probably the best single volume introduction to the sports collectables hobby for the novice". Unfortunately, when it was published it had a $12.95 cover price on it. This price precluded many people from purchasing the book. Now the book can be purchased by all at the very reasonable price of $6.50 plus $1.00 postage. In addition to having the best type-set, in color, of any book ever published (the type-set includes Baseball, Football, Basketball & Hockey cards), it contains information on autographs, programs, yearbooks, uniforms, guides, postcards and more.

While the book is of immeasurable help to the novice, it also contains quite a bit of material for the veteran or advanced collector. The section on cards, the largest section of the book, gives a chronology of sports cards by decade beginning in the 19th Century.

THE SPORTS COLLECTORS BIBLE
NEW 3rd EDITION

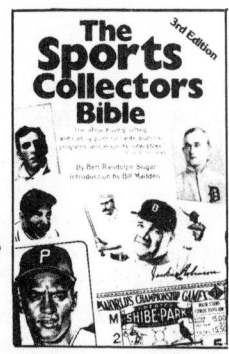

it's Here

The Sports Collectors Bible
3rd Edition

By Bert Randolph Sugar
Introduction by Bill Madden

$ 11.95 plus postage and handling

THE BIBLE IS THE SECOND LARGEST SELLING COLLECTORS AID TO THE HOBBY (THE PRICE GUIDE BEING FAR AND AWAY THE LARGEST SELLING AID), AND THIS 3rd EDITION SHOULD PROVE TO BE THE BEST BIBLE YET. MANY OF THE ERRORS AND OMISSIONS OF THE FIRST TWO VERSIONS HAVE BEEN CORRECTED, AND THE CHECKLISTS FOR THE POPULAR CARD SETS HAVE BEEN PUT IN THE MORE READABLE VERTICAL FORMAT. THE BIBLE REMAINS THE BEST SOURCE OF CHECKLISTS FOR PRE-1900, SCARCE ISSUE AND NON-LEGITIMATE CARD ISSUES. AND THE BIBLE IS NOT LIMITED TO SPORTS CARDS AS AUTOGRAPHS, YEARBOOKS, PINS AND OTHER BITS OF SPORTS MEMORABILIA ARE PRESENTED.

FREE CATALOGUE
Send name, address and 25¢ postage to: **DEN'S COLLECTORS DE**
P.O. Box 606, dept PG3 ,Laurel, Maryland 208

HISTORY OF CARD COLLECTING

The current version of the baseball card, with its full color front and statistic laden back, is a far cry from its earliest ancestors issued nearly a century ago. The mid 1800's gave birth to the institution of the baseball card, presumably because the mood of the American public turned against the "risque" cards of actresses and entertainers then being packed with cigarettes. As to actually which was the first baseball card, the issue is cloudy. These early issues were generally printed on heavy cardboard, with the quality of photography, drawing and printing being quite poor.

Goodwin & Co., of New York, makers of Gypsy Queen, Old Judge, and other cigarette brands is usually considered to be among, if not the, first issuers of baseball cards. Their issues, predominately in the 1 1/2" X 2 1/2" size, generally consisted of photographs of baseball players, boxers, wrestlers and non-sport subjects mounted on stiff cardboard stock. Over 2000 different photos of baseball players alone have been identified. The "Old Judges", a collective name commonly used for the Goodwin & Co. cards, were issued from 1886-1890 and are treasured parts of many collections. Among the other cigarette companies issuing baseball cards which still command attention today are Allen & Ginter, D. Buchner & Co. (Gold Coin Chewing Tobacco), and P. H. Mayo & Brother. The first two issued colored line drawing cards while the Mayo's are sepia photographs on black cardboard. In addition to the small sized cards from this era, several tobacco companies issued cabinet sized baseball cards. These "cabinets" were considerably larger than the small cards, usually about 4 1/4" X 6 1/2", and were printed on heavy stock. Goodwin & Co's Old Judge cabinets and the National Tobacco Works' "Newsboy" baseball photos are two that remain popular today.

The American Tobacco Company, formed in 1890, so dominated the tobacco industry that by 1895 baseball card inserts to cigarette packages (actually slide boxes in those days) were discontinued. The lack of competition in the then burgeoning cigarette market had made "freebie" inserts unnecessary. The end of the first era of the baseball card had come.

The dawn of the twentieth century saw a few scattered baseball cards issued; however, it remained for the cigarette companies, particularly the American Tobacco Co., and, to a lesser extent, the candy and gum makers to revive the baseball card. The period from 1909 to 1915 saw the bulk of these T cards (American Card Catalog, designated hereinafter as ACC, for the Twentieth Century Tobacco issues) and E cards (ACC for Early Candy and Gum issues) released. This era, probably the most romantic if not the most popular (other than today) period of baseball card collecting gave use the fabled T-206 Honus Wagner card, card collecting's most prized treasure; the T-206 Plank card, long the second most valuable baseball card (recently relinquishing its number two position to the more distinctive and aesthetically pleasing Napoleon Lajoie card from the 1933 (34) Goudey Gum series); and the T-206 Magee error card (Magee misspelled Magie on the card), card collecting's most famous blooper card.

The ingenuity and distinctiveness of this era has yet to be surpassed. The T-202 Hassan Triple-folders, probably the best looking, certainly the most distinctive card ever issued; the durable T-201 Mecca double folders, one of the first sets with the player's records on the back; the T-3 Turkey Reds, collecting's most popular cabinet card; the E-145 Cracker Jacks, the only major set containing Federal League player cards, and the T-204 Ramlys, with their distinctive black and white oval photos and ornate gold borders, were but a few of the variety of cards issued during this period. While the American Tobacco Co. dominated the field, several other tobacco companies, clothing manufacturers, newspapers and periodicals, game makers, and companies whose identity remains anonymous did issue cards during this period before World War I. In fact, the Collins-McCarthy Candy Company, makers of the Zeenuts Pacific Coast League baseball cards remains today the manufacturer other than the Topps Chewing Gum Company with the most continuous years of baseball card issuances (1911-1938).

The coming of World War I, possibly coupled with the realization by the American Tobacco Co. that those who collected baseball card inserts to their cigarettes were youngsters, who, presumably, did not indulge in the smoking of their product (the influence of the son on Dad and Grandpa notwithstanding), meant an end to the last era of tobacco cards, although Red Man Chewing Tobacco did produce sets from 1952-1955.

The next flurry of card issues began in the roaring and prosperous 1920's. The caramel companies (National Caramel, American Caramel, York Caramel) led the way during this era of the E card; however, the strip card, a continous strip with several or many cards seperated by dotted lines or other sectioning features, did flourish. While the E cards and the strip cards are generally considered less imaginative than the T Cards or the recent candy and gum issues, they are still sought after by many advanced collectors. Another "event" of significance that occurred during the 1920's was the introduction of the arcade card or "Exhibit" as it is known, taking this designation from its issuer the Exhibit Supply Company of Chicago. The Exhibit machines, once a trademark of the penny arcades, amusement parks and county fairs across the country, dispensed for one penny a large (close to the size of a postcard) picture card on thick stock of your favorite cowboy, actor, actress, or baseball player. The Exhibit Supply or one of its associated companies produced baseball cards over a longer span of years, though discontinous, than any other manufacturer. Its first cards were produced in 1921 while the last Exhibit issue was in 1966. In 1979 the Exhibit Supply Company was bought by a collector/dealer who has since issued other Exhibit cards, reprinted from Exhibit photos of the past.

If the T card period from 1909-1915 can be called the Golden Age of baseball card collecting, the period beginning at the height of the depression in 1933 and ending with the beginning of American formal involvement in World War II in 1941 can certainly be called the Silver Age. The forerunner of today's baseball bubble gum card in size, packaging, and distribution, was introduced by the Goudey Gum Company of Boston in 1933. With its Big League Gum series of 240 cards (239 issued in 1933), an extremely well done, full color, line drawing set on thick card stock, Goudey started an era in which some of the most attractive and sought after cards in the history of collecting were produced. The 1933 Goudey Big League Gum series was the largest single issue since the T-206 white border tobacco set and ranks as one of the four of five hallmark baseball card issued. The set contained over 40 Hall of Fame players, including four cards of Babe Ruth and two of Lou Gehrig. In 1934 Goudey continued its reign with a 96 card set, in color, plus the remaining card to the 1933 series—no. 106, the Napoleon Lajoie card. This rare and attractive card just recently passed the T-206 Plank card in value to become the second most valuable baseball card. Goudey also issued player cards in 1935, 1936, 1938, and 1941 with all but 1941 issued being well done and still quite popular.

In addition to Goudey, several other bubble gum manufacturers issued baseball cards during this era. DeLong Gum Company issued an extremely attractive set in 1933. National Chicle Company issued the largest die-cut set ever with their 192 card Batter-Up series of 1934-1936, and they also issued the extremely popular Diamond Stars series from 1934-1936. Other popular sets of this period were the Tattoo-Orbit set of 60 color cards issued in 1933 and Gum Products' 75 card Double Play set, a sepia colored set consisting of two players per card (although there were only 75 cards, each player was numbered separately giving the set numbers from 1 to 150).

In 1939, Gum, Inc., which later became Bowman Gum, issued their first of three sets, taking over from Goudey Gum as the leading producer of baseball cards. Their 1939 set of 162, entitled Play Ball-America, and their 1940 set of 240 entitled Play Ball, were both in black & white, and the latter is still considered by many to be the best looking black and white card sets ever produced. In 1941 Gum, Inc., issued their only color set, a very popular 72 card set entitled Play Ball Sports Hall of Fame. Many of the poses in this set were colored repeats of the 1940 series.

Besides regular gum cards, many manufacturers distributed "premium" issues during the 1930's. These premiums were printed on paper or photograph stock rather than card stock and were much larger in size than the regular cards. They were sold across the counter with gum (which was packaged separately from the premium) for a penny, or more often, they were redeemed at the store or through the mail in exchange for the wrappers of previously purchased gum cards, a la the proof-of-purchase box top premiums of today. The premiums are much scarcer than the card issues of the 1930's and, in most cases, no manufacturer's identification is present on the issue. Among the more common of these issues were the thin, postcard sized "fine pen" and "wide pan" premiums (called "fine" and "wide" pen depending on the boldness of the facsimile autographs on the premium); Diamond Star Gum (issued by Goudey Gum) in both sepia (4" X 6 1/4") and black and white (4 3/4" X 7 5/16"); and Diamond Star Premiums, issued anonymously by National Chicle Company.

World War II brought an end to this popular era of card collecting. Paper and rubber shortages curtailed bubble gum baseball cards until the Bowman Gum Company, the direct descendant of Gum, Inc., resurrected the baseball card in 1948, the beginning of the modern era of card collecting.

In 1948, Bowman Gum issued a 48 card black & white set available in 1c packs in which one card and one slab of gum were contained. That same year the Leaf Gum Co. also issued a set of cards in color (although rather poor color). A squabble over the rights to use players' pictures on the cards developed between Bowman and Leaf. Leaf eventually dropped out of the baseball card producing market, but not before it had left an impression on the hobby and issued some of the rarest cards in existence. Leaf's baseball card series of 1948—1949 contained 98 cards, skip numbered to no. 168 (not all numbers were printed). Of the 98 cards, 49 are relatively plentiful; however, the other 49 are rare, and quite valuable.

Bowman continued its production of cards in 1949 with a color series of 240 cards. This series remains the most difficult Bowman regular issue to complete. Its "high numbers" are both numerous and scarce. Although the set was in color and today commands quite a bit of interest because of its scarcity, aesthetically it is considered a bit inferior to the Goudey and National Chicle issues of the 1930's. In addition to the regular issue of 1949, Bowman issued a set of 36 Pacific Coast League players. While it is not a regular issue, it is still prized by collectors and has become, by far, the most valuable Bowman issue.

In 1950, Bowman's one year monopoly in the baseball card field, it began a string of excellent quality cards which it continued until its demise in 1955. The 1950 series itself contained somewhat of an oddity because the more difficult numbers to obtain were the "low numbers" rather than the traditional high numbers.

The year 1951 began the most competitive, and perhaps highest quality period of baseball card production. It was the year Topps Chewing Gum Company of Brooklyn entered the market. Topps' 1951 series consisted of two sets of 52 cards each, one set with red backs and one set with blue backs. In addition, it issued 31 insert cards, three of which (current stars Konstanty, Roberts and Stanky) remain the rarest cards of any major set. The 1951 Topps cards were quite homely and paled in comparison to the 1951 Bowman issues; however, they were successful enough for Topps to continue producing cards, which they have done every year since. In 1952 Topps issued a larger and much more attractive card. This size was to be the standard for the next five years as Bowman also began issuing larger baseball cards in 1953. This first truly major set by Topps has become, like the 1933 Goudey series and the T-206 white border series, the classic set of its era. The 407 card set is a collector's dream of scarcities, rarities, errors, and variations. It also contains the first Topps issues of Mickey Mantle and Willie Mays (in a rare and scarce series, respectively), who along with Hank Aaron and Ted Williams form card collecting's "big four" of the modern era.

As with Bowman and Leaf in the late 1940's, competition over player rights arose. Ensueing court battles between Topps and Bowman and the splitting of the market caused by stiff competition led, in January 1956, to the purchase of Bowman by Topps. From that time to the present, Topps has remained virtually unchallenged as the leader in the production of baseball cards. Fleer Gum, with small sets in 1959, 1960, 1961 and 1963, and several cartoon sets in the 1970's and more recently Kellogg cereal and Hostess Cakes have issued baseball cards for promotional purposes.

So, the story of major baseball card sets from 1956 to the present is by and large the story of Topps issues, with the single exception coming in 1976 with the issue by Sports Stars Publishing Company of a 630 card set of current players. In 1957, Topps changed the standard size of the baseball card to 3 1/2" X 2 1/2" in dimensions. That size has remained with us to the present time. In addition to their regular yearly series of current players, Topps has issued many auxiliary sets—Giant or Super sized cards in 1964, 1970 and 1971, die-cut stand-ups in 1964, an embossed set in 1977, a smaller version of its regular set (mini's) in 1975 and several others. From 1977-1980, Topps reprinted (a few cards contain different poses than the regular set and different numbers are on the back) several teams for use by the Burger King Restaurant Chain for promotional purposes. These auxiliary sets—many of which are called Test Sets — are also collectible and sometimes sought after fiercely.

What you have just read is a thumbnail sketch of card collecting from its inception in the 1880's to the present. These few pages can't begin to tell you that about which entire books have been written. If you are interested in the history of card collecting, there are many excellent books and catalogues, many of which are advertised within this Price Guide, that are available. Virtually all serious collectors subscribe to at least one of the sports collecting hobby papers. Send off for samples if you are not sure which hobby paper is appropriate for you. Also, try to attend a sport collectibles convention in your area. Card collecting is still a young and informal hobby, and the chances are good that you will run into one or more of the "experts" in the field; they're usually more than happy to share their knowledge with you.

B18 BLANKET

 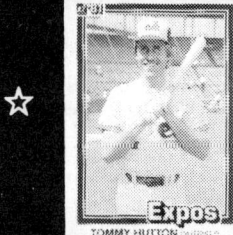

HOBBY GROWTH

As in previous years, the year 1980 witnessed continued growth in the hobby. The number of sports collectors shows and conventions increased to a point where each week provided the card collector with his choice of several shows being held somewhere in the country. The hobby papers continued to flourish with each adding many new subscribers monthly. This Price Guide more than doubled its circulation—a fact which shows the continued growing interest of the general public in baseball card collecting.

The First National Sports Collectors Convention was held in late August in Los Angeles. While no concrete national organization was formalized at this convention, the groundwork for such an organization was established. The 1981 National Convention will be held in Plymouth, Michigan, a suburb of Detroit, on July 9—12. For those of you who are interested, the inside front cover of this book provides details about the Second National Convention.

The hobby received quite a bit of ink in the media again this year, with several national magazines carrying major articles on card collecting. Unfortunately, most of the articles stressed the price of baseball cards rather than the enjoyable aspects of the hobby. Also unfortunate was the seemingly endless use of journalistic sensationalism, both in magazine and newspaper stories across the country, in which the media often presented information on prices and card scarcities which was of dubious factual origin.

PRICES

The year 1980 will quite possibly be remembered as the year rationality and stabilization came to the card collecting hobby. In early March, the ridiculous price spiraling of early Topps and Bowman superstar cards came to an abrupt halt. Whether the reasons for this turnaround were the recession that existed in the country in 1980, the abundance of cards which surfaced from the heretofore untouched caches in attics, garages, and basements of the general public, or the fact that many get-rich-quick speculators decided to desert the market at this particular time, the results were quite sobering. In essence what had happened was an awakening of novice collectors and dealers to what veteran collectors and dealers had known for some time—there are no scarce Topps or Bowman regular issue cards, whether they be common player cards or superstar cards. By definition, the fact that Topps and Bowman cards are national issues precludes any limited printing or distribution of their regular issue cards. Later on in this book, the authors have presented some logical reasoning concerning scarcity of regular nationally issued cards of which the new collector or dealer should be aware.

Prices for MINT condition cards (not excellent to mint or excellent condition) have held the price line much better than lower condition cards. This edition of the Price Guide attempts to show this fact, particularly in the Topps and Bowman issues, by a widening of the price gap between mint condition cards and lower condition cards. While a definite decrease in card prices was felt in the spring, at year's end card prices which had fallen appeared to be stabilizing or increasing moderately.

Older (pre-World War II) issues and all regionals held their own on prices much better than post-World War II regular issues. Goudeys, Play Balls, Diamond Stars, and T— and N—Card issues justifiably witnessed an increase in price because of their relative scarcities when compared to recent issues.

A distressing factor that came to bear during 1980 was an increased emphasis being placed on the plentiful rookie cards of 1970's superstars. While rookie cards have traditionally been viewed with particular desirability, the multitude of post-1970 cards of all players is making a mockery of the scarcity factor in the hobby.

NEW CARD ISSUES

Topps, Kellogg and O-Pee-Chee continued to provide issues on current baseball players; however, Hostess, which had issued sets over the last five years, dropped from the card producing market. Once again this year the Burger King fast food chain, in conjunction with Topps, issued small sets as promotional items in their retail outlets. In Philadelphia, Burger King issued a set of 1980 Phillies, and in Baltimore they issued a set entitled "Pitch, Hit and Run," which contained 33 star or superstar players including 11 pitchers, 11 hitters and 11 runners. In addition to these issues, at least one significant collector issue was produced: The Sports Stars Publishing Company (SSPC) set entitled "Baseball Immortals Hall of Fame," which features 173 cards depicting each member of the Hall of Fame through 1980. This set is in full color and utilizes portions of old baseball cards for many of its pictures.

The highlight of the new card sets produced in 1980 was a set of 60 5 x 7 Superstar Photo cards issued by Topps during the late spring or early summer time period. This set is considered by many the most attractive nationally issued card set in more than a decade. Besides being attractive, the set has some interesting collector appeal because of the way in which it was distributed. Originally, it was available in limited sections of the country in packs of three cards (to our knowledge, gum was never distributed with these cards). Several methods were available and elaborated on in the packages by which a collector could obtain an entire set of these cards by a mail order method. These cards were issued on relatively thick white stock and contained only the player's name and number on the back of the card. Presumably, due to the popularity of these cards or the rising cost of this thicker stock, Topps reprinted these cards on a thinner gray cardboard and placed a large Topps logo on the back. While the fronts of the cards were identical, the originally issued white back set is thought to be available in lesser quantities than the subsequently issued gray back set.

1980 also witnessed a continuance of the many collector issues which, over the past few years, have flooded the market. While these collector issues show varying degrees of excellence, the SSPC Baseball Immortals Hall of Fame set is the only one the authors believe significant enough to deserve mention in this Price Guide.

HOBBY LITERATURE

Besides the second issue of this Price Guide, several significant reference contributions to the hobby were produced in 1980. Bill Heitman released his planned Sport Americana T—206 Guide and Checklist in May. While this book does not claim to be the last word on the T—206 card set, it certainly is the most informative and elaborate reference of this popular card issue.

The Sport Americana Baseball Address List was issued by Jack Smalling and Denny Eckes in April of 1980. The format of this address list was changed from the previous address lists issued by Mr. Smalling to a more compact and convenient size. It also features dictionary-type headings for ease of use and is filled with interesting photos, facsimile autographs and informative material. The price of the book was reduced considerably because of mass production methods, making it available to the average collector and autograph hound at a modest price. It contains the names and addresses or dates and places of death of all players who debuted in the big leagues since 1910.

Veteran collector Dan Even and Sports Collectors Digest publisher John Stommen released a Sports Collectors Directory at mid-year. The names, but unfortunately, not the addresses, of collectors by state are included in a format of articles, photos and cursory card prices for baseball, football, hockey and basketball memorabilia. Andy Pywowarczuk released his Hockey Checklist and Price Guide late in the year. This publication contains the most thorough list of hockey issue checklists ever published. While each and every card is not priced individually, the prices listed do present a workable guide for the hockey card collector.

Chris Benjamin issued a wrapper checklist book which illustrates nearly all popular baseball card wrappers plus most football, basketball, boxing and many non-sports wrappers. At year's end, Dick and Mark Sikes released the third edition of their non-sports card checklist and price guide. This guide was increased in scope to include over 1000 non-sports card issues dating from the pre-1900 time period to the present. Also at year's end, Ralph Nozaki released his updated errors and variations book entitled "The Mistake Manual." (The previous edition was called the Master Errors and Variations Checklist). Although a book like this could never be complete because of the thousands of errors being made annually on baseball cards, some of which are so minor they will never be found, this book is the best of its type available at this time.

WHAT'S IN STORE FOR 1981

Not since 1955, the last year both Topps and Bowman produced major sets of current players, has the card collecting public been faced with more than one significant national regular issue in one year. This year three gum companies are issuing major card sets of current players. Topps is producing a 726 card set; Fleer, which has not produced a card set containing current players since their 66 card set released in 1963, is producing a 660 card set; and Donruss (who had heretofore limited their card producing activities to non-sports sets) is issuing its first baseball card set containing 600 numbered cards and five un-numbered checklist cards. Checklists and prices for these major 1981 issues are included in this Price Guide.

Although not yet official at the time of printing of this Price Guide, it is expected that Kellogg will again issue a 60-odd card set as it has for the last eleven years, and that O-Pee-Chee of Canada will quite probably issue a 350-400 card set which, hopefully, will include player poses different from the 1981 Topps set issued in this country. That Burger King will again issue team sets as local promotional items for its retail outlets is not yet known.

As we have come to expect, there will probably be quite a few collector issue sets again in 1981, although the authors have not been able to confirm any major collector issues planned for this year. We can only hope that "someone" will produce in 1981 a set as aesthetically pleasing as 1980's Topps Superstar Photo set.

A new Sport Americana Football Card Price Guide will be issued in the fall with revised prices and a few surprises. Even and Stommen plan to update their collector's directory about mid-year, while Jeff Fritsch will add the 1980 and 1981 sets to his Topps-Bowman Team Checklist Book.

The most ambitious reference project scheduled for this year is a Baseball Memorabilia Price Guide to be written and compiled by the authors of this Price Guide. Baseball memorabilia other than popular card issues—press pins, programs, yearbooks, World Series bats, coins, uniforms, autographed balls, Hartland statues and more—will be featured in this 200-300 page book.

A LOGICAL LOOK AT RECENT CARD SCARCITY

While it is not the policy of the authors to editorialize about card prices but to report card prices, we have an obligation to the readers of this Price Guide, particularly the novice collectors and dealers, to explain some of the reasoning behind the price structure in the hobby. We hope this information will help the collector or dealer determine for himself whether or not he should buy, sell or trade a card at a given price.

The value of any collectible is based on two factors—desirability and scarcity. The desirability factor is subjective, a collector's personal attraction to the physical item being collected. With baseball cards desirability is manifested in the preference of most collectors for mint condition cards rather than fair condition cards, for Mickey Mantle cards rather than Whammy Douglas cards, for 1953 Bowman color cards rather than 1949 MP & Co., cards. The scarcity factor is objective, being, quite logically, how many of that given card are available to collectors. Within any hobby, price is eventually determined by a combination of both of these factors.

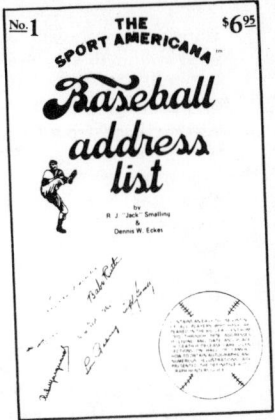

HOBBY REFERENCE LITERATURE

The SPORT AMERICANA

T 206, THE MONSTER
GUIDE & CHECKLIST
BY
BILL HEITMAN

$ 2.50 POSTPAID

This 32-page pamphlet describes, discusses, theorizes and checklists the fronts, backs, abundances and scarcities of the possible 7000 odd T 206 cigarette cards. Bill's own theories form the basis for the multi-page checklist included. A must for any serious T 206 collector or any card collector interested in the mysteries behind this, quite possibly, most popular of all baseball card issues.

Baseball address list
by
R. J. "Jack" Smalling
&
Dennis W. Eckes

$ 6.95 plus postage & handling

CONTAINS AN EASY TO USE LISTING OF ALL PLAYERS WHO HAVE APPEARED IN THE BIG LEAGUES FROM 1910 THROUGH 1979. ADDRESSES IF LIVING AND DATE AND PLACE OF DEATH IF DECEASED ARE GIVEN. SECTIONS ON HALL OF FAMERS, HOW TO OBTAIN AUTOGRAPHS, AND NUMEROUS ILLUSTRATIONS ARE PRESENTED. THE DEFINITIVE AUTOGRAPH HUNTERS GUIDE.

COMIC BOOK PRICE GUIDE

What SCOTT is to stamps, SPORT AMERICANA is to baseball cards, the OVERSTREET PRICE GUIDE is to comics

$ 9.95 plus postage & handling

This guide contains over 500 pages listing three prices each for all comic books known to exist. Feature articles, full color sections, background information and dealer ads and wants comprise this book. A must for every comic lover.

$3.00

ILLUSTRATED WRAPPER CHECKLIST
$ 3.00 plus postage & handling

This new Illustrated Wrapper Checklist is an invaluable aid to the card collecting hobbyist. Over 325 different wrappers are pictured and identified. Over 100 baseball wrappers through 1980 are listed, with virtually all Topps, Bowman, Fleer, Goudey, and Play Ball wrappers included. Football, Hockey, Basketball and non-sport wrappers comprise the remainder of the checklist. Checklist boxes are provided for cataloging your collection.

We are still in the infancy or rapid growth stage of card collecting. Predictably, the desirability factor recently has had the dominating effect on price. During 1980 we began to see the influence of scarcity in the price structure of cards. Some of the plentiful 1950's superstars, which were over-valued from the scarcity view point, witnessed noticeable leveling or decreases in their prices, for example, the 1952 Topps high numbers and particularly the 1952 Topps Mantle card. More recently, there has been increased emphasis placed on 1970's rookie cards of superstars (or potential superstars) and plentiful 1970's variation cards. While superstar rookie cards are indeed desirable, and as variation cards might well be desirable, this emphasis completely ignores the scarcity factor of these cards. Two examples are presented below which the authors believe places these recent "phenomena" in the proper perspective.

In 1975 Topps produced all regular issue cards at the same time on five different 132-card sheets. There were no doubly printed cards and all sheets were produced, within normal statistical variances, in the same quantity. A conservative estimate of the total number of regular issue cards Topps produced in 1975 is 250 million, which means at least 380,000 of each numbered card was produced. The George Brett, Jim Rice and Fred Lynn rookie cards are contained in this set. If by attrition as many as 25% are no longer in existence, we are still left with 285,000 of each card available to collectors—enough so that each collector who desired could possess at least one. A youngster in 1975 could get any card for about a penny apiece, with wrapper and bubble gum, at any local candy store. Dealers who bought directly from Topps paid less than four-tenths of a cent apiece for these cards. If a dealer today sells a 1975 card of a common player, which is neither more nor less scarce than a Brett, Lynn or Rice card, at the current retail rate of six cents, he would realize a profit of 1,500%, quite gratifying and certainly more than enough to cover overhead costs of sorting, storage and advertising, but still 100 times less than that which he would realize if he sold at $6.00 an equally plentiful "Brett", "Lynn" or "Rice" card. While we encourage collectors and dealers to interpret prices in terms of the multiplicative factor based on the desirability of one player card (superstar card) to another player card (common player card), we question whether a factor of 100 is at present appropriate for any recent, widely distributed, mass produced card.

The 1979 Topps Bump Wills card presents an even more striking example of the misplaced logic which results in high prices being paid for recent cards which are not scarce. The current retail value for the correct version (Rangers) of the 1979 Topps Bump Wills card is $6.00, or 200 times the value of a common player card. The error card (with the incorrect Blue Jays team name on the front) is valued at $3.00, 100 times the price of a common player card. Using the same conservative print run of 250 million cards elaborated upon in the above example, and considering the larger set size and double printings in the 1979 Topps set, 315,000 Bump Wills cards were initially available to the card collecting public. Certainly, in but two years, no significant amount of these cards were lost or destroyed. From the retail price listed one might presume that, because Wills is neither a star or superstar, that the Wills cards are higher price totally due to scarcity. But such is not the case, as there are as many Wills cards as of any other (single printed) player. Even the question of which of the Wills variation cards is the scarcer is sometimes disputed among dealers and collectors. No matter which one is the scarcer, the fact is that there are more than enough of each variation available so that every collector desiring a 1979 Bump Wills card could have at least one of each type.

Both of the above examples are presented here not to invalidate the current baseball card price structure, because the "prices" listed in this Guide are the "prices" which currently exist. The examples are presented to inform the reader, particularly the novice collector or dealer, that in this young hobby, emotion and moments of irrationality sometimes cause one to loose track of logic. Baseball cards are a collectible, and like all collectibles, the scarcity factor will eventually surface and have its proper effect.

HOW TO COLLECT

There are no set rules on how to collect baseball cards. Card collecting is a hobby, a leisure pastime. What you collect, how much you collect, and how much time and money you spend collecting are entirely up to you. The amount of time you wish to spend, the funds you have available for collecting, and your own personal likes and dislikes determine how you collect. What will be presented here is information and ideas that might help you in your enjoyment of the hobby.

OBTAINING CARDS

Several avenues are open to you to obtain cards. You can purchase the current cards in the traditional way at the local candy, grocery, or drug store, with the bubble gum or other products included. You can purchase complete recent sets from the many mail order advertisers found in sports media publications; e.g., The Sporting News, Baseball Digest, Street & Smith's Baseball Yearbook, Baseball Magazine and others. Occasionally, a few older cards and sets are advertised in these same publications. However, most serious card collectors obtain older cards from one or more of the following three sources—other collectors or dealers, the hobby papers, and/or sports collectibles shows or conventions.

NOMENCLATURE

Each hobby has its own nomenclature to describe the collectibles that particular hobby contains. The nomenclature traditionally used for baseball cards is derived from the American Card Catalog, published in 1960 by Nostalgia Press. This catalog, written by Jefferson Burdick (who is called the Father of Card Collecting), uses letter and number descriptions for each separate set of cards. For example, the American Card Catalog (ACC) number for the popular 1933 Goudey set of 240 cards is R319.

The letter used in the ACC number refers to the generic type of card. While both sport and non-sport issues are classified in the ACC, we shall confine ourselves in this description to the sport issues which appear in The Sport Americana Price Guide. The following list defines the letters and their meanings as used by the American Card Catalog.

              T — 20th Century U.S. Tobacco
       (none) — 19th Century U.S. Tobacco
              B — Blankets
              D — Bakery Inserts
              E — Early Candy & Gum
              F — Food Inserts
              H — Advertising
              M — Periodicals
              PC— Postcards
              R — Candy & Gum Cards 1930—Present
              UO—Gas & Oil Inserts
              V — Canadian Candy & Gum
              W — Exhibits, Strip Cards, Team Issues
              N — 19th Century U.S. Tobacco (not ACC designation)

Following the letter designation and an optional hyphen is a one, two, or three digit number, i.e., 1—999.

In several cases, the ACC number is further addended by an additional hyphen and another one or two digit number, i.e., 1—99.

As an example, consider the Topps regular series baseball card issue of 1957. The ACC designation is R414—12. The "R" indicates a Candy or Gum Card produced after 1929. The "414" is the ACC designation for Topps Chewing Gum Baseball Issues; the "12" is the ACC designation for the 1957 regular issue.

15

As with other traditional methods of identification, there is some rhyme and reason in the system; however, most serious collectors learn the ACC designation of the popular sets by rote, rather than by attempting to "figure out" what they might or should be.

Within the description in the Price Guide included with the price data and checklists for each set before 1948, the ACC designation is given along with the year, maker and/or common name identification for the set.

From 1948 forward all sets are normally referred to by their year and maker, if the set is a regular issue, or by their year, maker and another distinguishing characteristic, if the set is not a regular issue or if more than one type of regular issue were issued by the same maker that year. For example, in 1964 Topps issued three distinctly different baseball card sets. The regular issue is referred to as 1964 Topps; the postcard sized issue is referred to as 1964 Topps Giants; and the die-cut issue is referred to as 1964 Topps Stand-Ups. No ACC designations are given in the set description for regular issue sets from 1948 to the present; however, for regionals, the ACC or SCB description is mentioned.

In order to be consistent with the nomenclature used most frequently in the hobby and by the reference books used in the hobby for sets issued after 1960, (which may not have a logical ACC number), the Sport Americana Baseball Card Price Guide has opted to use the numbering system similar to that used in the 3rd Edition of the Sports Collector's Bible (SCB), which uses the ACC designations as its base.

OTHER AVAILABLE LITERATURE

There have been several other more recent books which have either augmented or elaborated on material in the American Card Catalog. Among the better and more popular of these are:

The Sport Americana Alphabetical Baseball Card Checklist
Den's Collectors Den, Publisher

The Sport Americana Football and Basketball Card Price Guide
Den's Collectors Den, Publisher

The Stirling Sport Card Catalog
John C. Stirling, Jr., Publisher

The Sports Collectors Bible
Bobbs-Merrill, Publisher

Sports Memorabilia
Wallace-Homestead Book Co., Publisher

Baseball Card Team Checklist
Jeff Fritsch, Publisher

The Sport Americana Alphabetical Baseball Card Checklist, by Dr. James Beckett and Dennis W. Eckes, is an illustrated, alphabetical listing, by the last name of the player portrayed on the card, of all baseball cards appearing in the first issue of this Price Guide. It is the most complete alphabetical listing on baseball cards in existence and covers baseball cards from 1909 through 1979.

The Sport Americana Football and Basketball Card Price Guide, also by Dr. James Beckett and Dennis W. Eckes, is similar in format and content to this Price Guide; however, it covers all popular American and Canadian football and American basketball card issues.

Stirling's book, published in 1977, updates the sports issue in the American Card Catalog, including non-baseball issues. The illustrations are excellent, and although the book uses a different nomenclature, conversions to the ACC nomenclature are given. A supplemental, single price per issue list is included in this book.

The Sports Collectors Bible, Third Edition published in October 1979, contains sections on cards, pins, post cards, yearbooks, programs, autographs, and other collectibles. In the card area, this book contains the best single-volume source of pre-1900 card issues, non-legitimate/collector issues and reprinted set checklists available. This third edition shows a marked improvement over the first two editions as many of the errors and omissions were corrected, and Topps-Bowman-Fleer checklists were put into the most readable vertical formats. Guideline prices for cards and other sports collectibles are also presented.

John Douglas's Sports Memorabilia is an extremely well-written and formatted guide to sports memorabilia collecting with an abundance of color illustrations of cards and other collectibles. Cards, autographs, post cards, yearbooks, and other collectibles are given excellent presentations. This book is probably the best single-volume introduction to the sports collectibles hobby for the novice.

The Baseball Card Team Checklist, by Jeff Fritsch, lists all Topps and Bowman baseball cards by the teams of the players portrayed on the cards. Players who appear with one team on the front of the card and with another team on the back of the card (because of trades) are cross-referenced with both teams. Both the year of issue and the number on the card are listed.

In addition to guide books, there are several excellent standard checklist books for baseball cards. The checklist books list the producer, year issued, and each card by number (if the issue is numbered, alphabetically if not) and player portrayed. The checklist is utilized by the collector to "check off" the cards that he possesses, while the unchecked numbers become the record of which cards he does not possess.

VALUE

The value of a baseball card is determined by many factors. Among these factors are age of the card, player portrayed on the card, the amount of the card printed (initial scarcity), the attractiveness and popularity of the set in which the card is a part, and perhaps most important, the physical condition of the card.

In general, the older the card, the more renown the player on the card, the lower the quantity of the card printed, the more attractive and popular the set in which the card is a part, and the better the condition of the card, the higher the value of the card. There are exceptions (many) to all of these factors, except the condition factor. Given two of the same card, the one in the best condition always has the higher value.

So, while there are certain guidelines that establish the value of a baseball card, the exceptions and peculiarities make a simple mathematical formula to determine value impossible. But, that's why the Sport Americana Baseball Card Price Guide was written.

EXTREMELY VALUABLE CARDS

Cards with extremely high value are valued so because of their desirability and relative scarcity, both of which cause a high demand for these cards. For example, all of the cards of the "Top Ten" (pictured elsewhere in this book) are truly rare, except the 1952 Topps Mickey Mantle card, which though far from plentiful derives its value from the extreme desirability of possessing the Topps rookie card of Mickey Mantle. Many (possibly most) of the extremely high value cards are already in the hands of collectors, who have no intention of parting with them. Therefore, the opportunity to purchase them does not frequently occur, and for lengthy time periods some may be unavailable at any price.

EXTREMELY INEXPENSIVE CARDS

At the other end of the spectrum lie the cards with extremely low values. Recent Topps double-printed cards picturing common players are the best examples of this group. These cards were produced in enormous quantities and are readily available. In the case of these cards, the supply is much greater than the demand; hence, the low price. These cards are frequently sold in bricks of several hundred cards.

PRICES AND DEALERS

The prices in the Price Guide are the "retail" going rates for baseball cards as of the beginning of 1981. Dealers are profit seekers who perform the very important service of providing collectors with cards. They have overhead expenses—advertising, postage, convention fees, etc. A dealer cannot and will not buy cards at the retail rate. Normally he will pay from 30 to 70% of the retail rate, the higher rate being paid for the more popular cards that he can sell in a short period of time. Occasionally, a dealer will pay full retail for extremely scarce, popular or currently 'hot" cards, with the thought that the value of these cards is increasing rapidly, and by holding the cards for a reasonably short time, a sufficient profit can be realized.

INDIVIDUAL VS. SET PRICES

A somewhat paradoxical situation exists in the cost of a set versus the combined cost of the individual cards in the set. In nearly every case, the sum of the prices for the individual cards in the set is higher than the cost for the complete set. The reasons behind this anomaly lie in the habits of collectors and the carrying costs of dealers. Many collectors do not collect complete sets. Many collect only stars, superstars or particular teams. Because each card in the set is normally produced in the same quantity (scarcities and rare series notwithstanding) the dealer is left with a shortage of cards of certain players and an abundance of cards of many others. As a dealer, the cards that he has are intended for sale. If he cannot sell them, he can make no profit (or even recoup his costs) on these cards. Indeed, he has an expense in simply "carrying" these cards. The sale of a complete set offers the dealer a way to sell a large number of cards at a single time, any of which he might otherwise "carry" indefinitely. Therefore, he is willing to receive less than the retail for each and every individual card in the set, but benefits from the recovery of all his costs and also receives some profit on all cards in the set.

SCARCE SERIES

The term scarce series is derived from the fact that most pre-1974 card issues were made available to the public in more than one series, each of a finite number of cards, rather than all cards of the set being available for purchase at one time. At some point during the year, usually near the end of the baseball season, interest in baseball cards of that year wanes; consequently, the manufacturers produce a smaller number of these later series of cards. Nearly all national issues from the post-World War II manufacturers (1948 to 1973) can be recognized in series. For example, Bowman used 36 cards on its standard printed sheets. (While the number of cards on printed sheets is usually the same as the number of cards in a particular series, such is not always the case as will be explained below.) Topps series have been comprised of many different numbers of cards, including 55, 66, 80, 88, and others. Recently Topps has settled on what is now their standard sheet size of 132 cards.

While we have stated that the number of cards within a particular series usually has the same number of cards as the number of cards on one printed sheet, this is not always the case. As early as 1948, Bowman substituted 12 cards during later print runs of its 1948 baseball cards. Twelve of the cards from the initial sheet of 36 cards were removed and replaced by 12 different cards giving, in effect, a first series of 36 cards and a second series of 12 new cards. This replacement phenomenon in the 1948 Bowman series produced a scarcity of 24 cards in the series—the 12 cards removed from the original sheet and the 12 new cards added to the sheet. A full sheet of 1948 Bowman cards (second printing) is reproduced later in this book and one can see that card numbers 37—48 have replaced 12 of the cards on the first printing sheet. The Topps Gum Company has also created scarcities and/or excesses of certain cards in many of their sets. Topps, however, has most frequently used the double printing procedure to do this. The double printing procedure involves the act of printing more than one card of the same player and number on a particular sheet. This causes an abundance of the cards of the players who are on the sheet more than one time. During the past few years, Topps has double printed 66 cards which will likely be quite plentiful for many years to come. The Topps double printing of cards in other years is the most logical explanation for the known scarcities of particular cards in some of the Topps sets.

PRICE VARIATIONS IN DIFFERENT PARTS OF THE COUNTRY

Two different types of price variations exist among the sections of the country in which a card is bought or sold. The first is the general price variation on all cards bought and sold in one geographical area compared to another; the second is the specific player card price variations found in a certain geographical area and not in others.

Unlike OHIO which is high (Hi) in the middle, card prices are slightly higher on the ends, on the East and West coast, and slightly lower in the middle, in the Southwest and Midwest portions of the country. This variation is what is referred to as the general variation among different sections of the country. The specific variation in prices refers to cards with particular players portrayed on them which command a higher price in one area of the country than in all (or most all) other areas of the country. An Al Kaline card would be valued higher in Detroit than in Cincinnati because Kaline played in Detroit and the demand for an Al Kaline card is higher in Detroit than it is in Cincinnati. On the other hand, a Johnny Bench card would be priced higher in Cincinnati than in Detroit for similar reasons.

The prices in this Guide are neither East or West coast prices nor Southwest or Midwest prices but consensus prices among all sections of the country. Likewise, the prices for a particular player's cards are not the prices for that player's cards in his home team town, as even common player cards command a higher price to home town collectors, but the price of that player's cards in all other parts of the country.

An exception to this pricing policy exists with regional cards. Because regional issues are by definition released in but a limited area of the country and usually feature, to a large extent, players of the team in the area in which it is released, the preponderance of that regional are found and extensively collected only in that particular area. Therefore, Glendale prices are essentially Detroit area prices; Briggs prices are essentially Washington, D.C. area prices; and Esskay prices are essentially Baltimore area prices.

PRICES IN THE SPORT AMERICANA PRICE GUIDE

The prices in this Guide are not the "for sale" prices of the authors, the publisher, the distributors, the advertisers or any card dealers connected with the Guide. No one is in any way obligated to buy, sell or trade his or her cards based on these prices. The price listings were compiled by the authors from actual buy-sell transactions at sports conventions, buy-sell advertisements in the hobby papers, and for sale prices from dealer catalogues and price lists.

SOME INTERSTING NOTES ON CARDS AND PRICES

The numerically first card of an issue is the single card most likely to receive excessive wear; consequently, you will find the price on the number one card to be somewhat higher than its inherent status would justify. Similarly, but to a lesser extent, the numerically last card of an issue is also prone to abnormal wear. Logically, this phenomenon can be explained simply by the fact that the first and last cards are exposed to the elements (human element included) more than any other cards. They are generally end cards in any brick formations, rubber bandings, stackings on wet surfaces, and like activities.

Baseball cards have no intrinsic value. They are functionally worthless as are cancelled stamps, knick knacks, empty beer cans, the Mona Lisa and pearl earrings. The value of a baseball card, as the value of these other collectibles, can only be assessed by you and your enjoyment in viewing and possessing these cardboard swatches.

Inflation is something with which we all live. The prices in this Guide are early 1981 prices. It would be foolhearty to believe prices will stay at this level throughout the year. Baseball cards and other collectibles are hardly immune to inflation. Indeed, many investors purchase works of art, antiques, and other collectibles, including baseball cards, as a hedge against inflation. However, do not be lulled into believing prices must only go up. Last year was a case in point as many of the so-called glamor cards remained at a constant price or decreased through the course of the year.

There is no such thing as an excellent-mint (Ex-Mt) individual card; a card is either mint or not mint. However, a card could be graded very good-excellent (Vg-Ex) as two individuals could disagree on the condition (one rates very good while the other rates the card excellent) or the card may contain a mixture of attributes of excellent and very good cards. Thus a strict excellent card is more valuable than a very good-excellent card but not as valuable as a mint card— the strict excellent condition card would be valued halfway between the mint and very good-excellent prices (first and second columns of the Price Guide).

Remember, you the buyer ultimately determine the price of each baseball card. You have the supreme weapon in your ability to say NO to the price of any card. And when the cost of a baseball card, or anything else, exceeds the enjoyment or utility you will receive from that item, your answer should be "no". The authors of this Price Guide are reporters of prices. You are the ones who set the prices.

ADVERTISING IN THE PRICE GUIDE

Throughout this Price Guide you will see advertisements for sports memorabilia material, hobby paper subscriptions, upcoming sports collectibles conventions, and mail order and retail sports collectibles establishments. All advertisements were accepted in good faith based on the reputations of the advertiser: however, neither the authors, the publisher, the distributors nor the other advertisers in the Price Guide accept any responsibility for any particular advertiser not complying with the terms of his or her ad.

Should you come into contact with any of the advertisers in this Guide as a result of their advertisement herein, please mention to them this source as your contact.

ERRATA

As with any book of over 40,000 names, 125,000 prices, and untold words in prose, there are going to be a few typographical errors, a few mispellings (sic) and possibly, a number or two out of order. If you catch a blooper, drop one of the authors a line, in care of the publisher, and we shall try to correct the error in next year's issue.

H801-5 PACKARD—BELL

TOPPS BASEBALL CARD LOTS — ALL CARDS AND COMPLETE SETS IN EX-MT CONDITION

YEAR	1954	1955	1956	1957	1958	1959	1960	1961	1962	1963	1964	1965	1966	1967	1968	1969	1970	1971	1972	1973	1974
Henry Aaron	175.00	35.00	28.00	30.00	20.00	13.00	14.00	13.00	12.00	28.00	10.00	10.00	10.00	7.00	6.00	6.00	5.50	5.00	4.00	3.50	4.00
Ernie Banks	40.00	10.00	9.00	8.00	8.00	7.00	4.00	4.00	4.00	7.00	7.00	7.00	9.00	6.00	3.00	2.50	4.00	4.00	3.00	2.75	
Yogi Berra	20.00	30.00	10.00	9.00	8.00	6.00	5.00	5.00	4.00	7.00	4.50	5.00	3.50	3.00	3.00	2.50	3.50	3.50	3.00	1.50	2.50
Roy Campanella		100.00	20.00	12.00																	
Roberto Clemente		100.00	18.00	15.00	13.00	18.00	8.50	7.00	7.00	40.00	8.00	6.00	7.00 Bench↑	6.00	5.00	3.00	4.50	3.00	1.75	1.50	2.75
Don Drysdale	14.00			10.00	5.00	3.75	3.50	3.50	3.50	5.00	3.50	3.00	3.00	3.00	2.50	2.00	4.50	3.00	2.50	3.00	1.50
Whitey Ford			8.00	7.50	7.00			3.75	15.00	6.00	3.75	3.00	3.00	Garvey↑	2.75	Baylor↑	2.50	3.00	2.50	2.00	2.00
Bob Feller			12.00	Gibson↑		15.00		2.75	2.50	3.00	2.75	3.00	1.75	2.75	1.50	1.50	2.50	2.25	1.25	2.00	1.50
Gil Hodges	12.00	28.00	7.00	6.00	5.00	3.75	3.00	5.00	15.00	6.00	3.00	3.00	3.00	3.00	2.75	2.50	2.50	2.25	2.00	1.75	
Monte Irvin	6.00	5.00	4.00		McCovey↑		17.00	2.75	2.50	18.00	2.75	2.75	1.75	1.75	1.50	1.50	1.50	1.25	2.00	1.50	1.50
Al Kaline	50.00	12.00	10.00	8.00	7.00	5.50	4.00	5.00	3.00	9.00	2.50	2.50	30.00	2.75	2.25	2.50	7.00	2.50	2.50	1.75	1.50
Harmon Killebrew	6.00		6.00		5.00	7.00	6.50	3.00	2.50	9.00	3.50	2.50	2.50	3.00	2.25	8.50	2.00	1.75	2.75	1.50	2.00
Sandy Koufax			25.00	75.00	9.00	7.00	6.50	6.00	6.00	9.00	5.00	7.00	9.00	10.00	9.00		3.50	3.00	2.75	2.50	2.00
Mickey Mantle	14.00	10.00	70.00	40.00	28.00	25.00	22.00	18.00	17.00	28.00	12.00	14.00	9.00	10.00	9.00	8.50 G. Foster↑	3.50	3.50	2.00	1.75	1.50
Ed Mathews	80.00	150.00	30.00	28.00	20.00	15.00	13.00	11.00	12.00	20.00	9.00	10.00	11.00	R. Jackson↑	7.00	Lunzinski↑	2.00	2.00	4.00	1.75	
Willie Mays			6.00	5.00	Musial↑	8.00	6.00	8.00	6.00	8.00	7.00	10.00	2.50	8.00	7.00	7.00	2.00	8.00	4.00	4.00	
Bob Lemon			5.00	5.00	4.50	4.00	Brock↑	2.50	2.50	2.50	2.00	2.00	11.00	Ryan↑	6.00	7.00	8.00	2.00	1.75	1.75	1.75
Robin Roberts	10.00	18.00	7.00 B. Robby↑		8.00	4.50	4.00	3.00	2.50	8.00 Morgan↑	2.00	2.75	2.75	130.00	2.50	4.00	8.00	2.50	2.50	2.00	1.75
Phil Rizzuto	8.00	3.00 F. Robby↑		7.00	8.00	4.50	4.00	3.00	2.50	5.00	2.75	2.75	2.75	2.75	2.25	6.00	7.00	3.00	3.50	1.75	2.50
Al Rosen	22.00	20.00	18.00	Maris↑	8.00	4.50	4.00	4.00	6.00	3.50	2.75	2.50	2.50	2.50	2.50	6.00	3.00	3.00	3.50	3.00	2.50
Jackie Robinson	14.00	7.00	6.00	9.00	6.50	4.50	4.50	3.00	3.00	4.00	3.00	3.00 Carew↑	Seaver↑	80.00	5.00	Munson↑	8.00	2.50	3.50	2.50	1.75
Warren Spahn	14.00	100.00	11.00	9.00	7.00	5.00	4.50	3.50	6.00	14.00	17.00	12.00	8.00	30.00	6.00	4.00	3.00	3.00	35.00	2.50	2.00
Duke Snider	35.00	25.00	23.00	28.00	22.00	10.00	Yaz↑	Rose↑	Stargell↑	65.00	4.00	8.00	8.00	9.00	4.50	5.00	3.50	4.50	5.00	2.50	2.00
Pee Wee Reese			4.00	3.50	7.00	5.00	25.00	18.00	20.00	10.00	3.00	8.00	8.00	8.00	4.50	3.00	3.50	2.50	3.00	2.50	1.50
Ted Williams	35.00	25.00		28.00	22.00	Yaz↑	3.00	2.50	Stargell↑	15.00	4.00	3.50									
Early Wynn																					

Lower-left card lots

YEAR	25 Diff.	50 Diff.	Comp. Set
1953	37.50	75.00	1600.00
1954	25.00	50.00	700.00
1955	12.50	25.00	650.00
1956	12.50	25.00	450.00

YEAR	1957	1958	1959	1960	1961	1962	1963	1964	1965	1966	1967	1968	1969	1970	1971	1972	1973	1974
50 Diff.	20.00	14.00	12.00	20.00	20.00	10.00	10.00	9.00	9.00	9.00	9.00	5.50	5.00	5.00	4.75	4.50	4.00	3.50
100 Diff.	40.00	28.00	25.00	40.00	40.00	20.00	20.00	18.00	18.00	16.00	16.00	11.00	10.00	10.00	9.50	9.00	8.00	7.00
200 Diff.	100.00	60.00	45.00	80.00	70.00	40.00	40.00	36.00	36.00	36.00	36.00	22.00	20.00	20.00	19.00	18.00	16.00	14.00
300 Diff.		100.00	80.00	125.00	125.00	70.00	90.00	60.00	60.00	115.00	115.00	35.00	35.00	35.00	30.00	27.00	24.00	21.00
400 Diff.			150.00			125.00	150.00	115.00	115.00	115.00	115.00	70.00	60.00	55.00	45.00	38.00	35.00	30.00
500 Diff.													75.00	70.00	60.00	50.00	50.00	40.00
Complete Set	650.00	360.00	375.00	325.00	650.00	375.00	500.00	260.00	275.00	400.00	575.00	200.00	200.00	200.00	200.00	225.00	125.00	80.00

ORDERING INSTRUCTIONS

Minimum Order is **$8.00**. Please be sure to **print** your name, address and zip code with your order. Money orders are preferred. Personal check will delay order 7-10 days.

All cards listed are original and in Excellent Mint condition. All Star, Super Star cards are regular issue. Cards contained in lots are our choice only.

Please choose alternates when possible.

All orders over **$15.00** are sent out insured via speedy UPS, others by USPS unless otherwise specified. Add $1.50 to all Star, Super Star orders to cover postage and insurance. Add 50¢ per 50 cards ordered on card lots to cover postage and handling (Maximum $7.00). California residents add 6% sales tax.

ALL PRICES IN THIS AD SUBJECT TO CHANGE WITHOUT NOTICE.

SPECIAL ANNOUNCEMENT: We have opened two Sports Memorabilia Shops. One in La Habra at 107 No. Valencia, near the intersection of Harbor and La Habra Blvd. The second in Temple City at 9163 Las Tunas, near the intersection of Rosemead and Las Tunas.

WANTED — All Star, Super Star Cards listed above (in most cases). We will pay 50% of the price shown for cards selling under $30 and 70% of price shown for cards selling for $30 and more. All cards sent must be in excellent condition or better. This means sharp corners, no creases or wear marks, no pen or pencil marks, and no discoloration of other defects. We are also interested in large and small collections, complete sets, and all sports memorabilia. Drop us a line and let us know who you have to sell. Send all cards insured, postage will be refunded. Minimum shipment is $6.00. Send all orders to:

COMPLETE SETS

1975 (660) $80.00 Ppd.
1976 (704) $60.00 Ppd.
1977 (660) $50.00 Ppd.
1978 (726) $38.00 Ppd.
1979 (726) $30.00 Ppd.
1980 (726) 24.00 Ppd.
1980 SuperStar Set
(60 Cards) $18.50 Ppd.

1981 BASEBALL MINT COMPLETE SETS

TOPPS (726 Cards) $16.50*
DONRUSS (605 Cards) $14.50*
FLEER (660 Cards) $14.50*

*Plus $1.50 postage

★ ★ ★ ★ ★
SPECIAL: ORDER ALL THREE SETS
A $50.00 Value for $42.50!!
(Plus $2.50 postage)
SAVE $5.00!!

SPORTS NOSTALGIA SHOP, 107 N. Valencia St., #9, La Habra, CA 90631 / 1-213-691-4221

HOW TO USE THE PRICE GUIDE

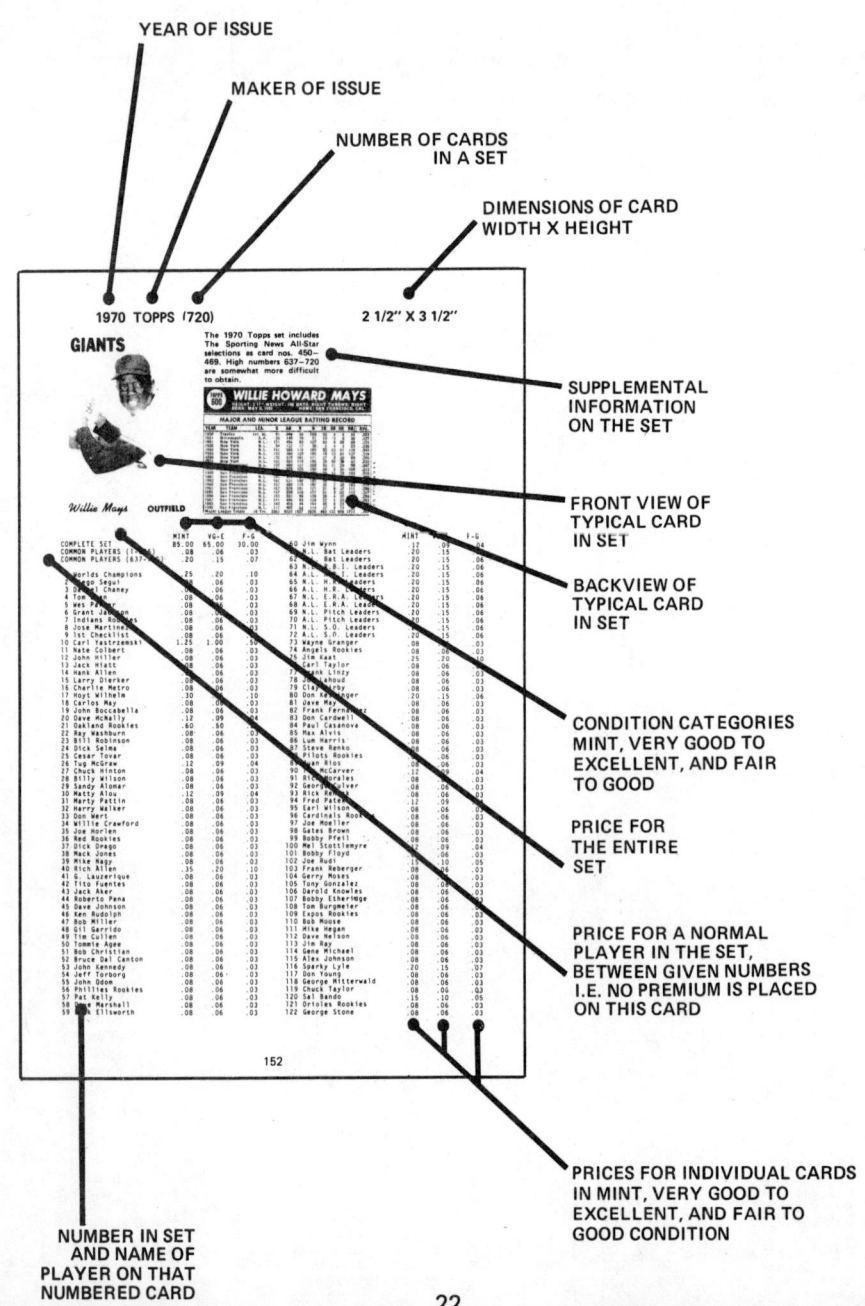

YEAR OF ISSUE

MAKER OF ISSUE

NUMBER OF CARDS
IN A SET

DIMENSIONS OF CARD
WIDTH X HEIGHT

1970 TOPPS (720)

2 1/2" X 3 1/2"

SUPPLEMENTAL
INFORMATION
ON THE SET

FRONT VIEW OF
TYPICAL CARD
IN SET

BACKVIEW OF
TYPICAL CARD
IN SET

CONDITION CATEGORIES
MINT, VERY GOOD TO
EXCELLENT, AND FAIR
TO GOOD

PRICE FOR
THE ENTIRE
SET

PRICE FOR A NORMAL
PLAYER IN THE SET,
BETWEEN GIVEN NUMBERS
I.E. NO PREMIUM IS PLACED
ON THIS CARD

PRICES FOR INDIVIDUAL CARDS
IN MINT, VERY GOOD TO
EXCELLENT, AND FAIR TO
GOOD CONDITION

NUMBER IN SET
AND NAME OF
PLAYER ON THAT
NUMBERED CARD

22

1948 BABE RUTH STORY (28)

2" X 2 1/2"

The 1948 Babe Ruth Story set of 28 black and white, numbered cards was issued by the Philadelphia Chewing Gum Company to commemorate the 1949 movie of the same name which starred William Bendix. Babe Ruth himself appears on card No. 1. The last 12 cards (17 to 28) are more difficult to obtain than other cards in the set. The ACC designation is R421.

	MINT	VG-E	F-G
COMPLETE SET	250.00	200.00	75.00
COMMON CARDS (1-16)	6.00	4.50	2.00
COMMON CARDS (17-28)	12.00	9.00	4.00
1 "The Babe Ruth Story" In the Making	15.00	11.00	5.00
2 Bat Boy Becomes the Babe	6.00	4.50	2.00
3 Claire Hodgson / Claire Trevor	6.00	4.50	2.00
4 Babe Ruth / William Bendix; Claire Hodgson / Claire Trevor	6.00	4.50	2.00
5 Brother Matthias / Charles Bickford	6.00	4.50	2.00
6 Phil Conrad / Sam Levene	6.00	4.50	2.00
7 Night Club Singer / Gertrude Niesen	6.00	4.50	2.00
8 Baseball's Famous Deal	6.00	4.50	2.00
9 Babe Ruth / William Bendix; Mrs. Babe Ruth / Claire Trevor	6.00	4.50	2.00
10 Babe Ruth, Mrs. Babe Ruth, Brother Matthias / actors	6.00	4.50	2.00
11 Babe Ruth / William Bendix; Miller Huggins / Fred Lightner	6.00	4.50	2.00
12 Babe Ruth / William Bendix; Johnny Sylvester / George Marshall	6.00	4.50	2.00
13 Mr. Sylvester, Mrs. Sylvester, Johnny Sylvester / actors	6.00	4.50	2.00
14 "When A Feller Needs A Friend"	6.00	4.50	2.00
15 Dramatic Home Run!	6.00	4.50	2.00
16 The Homer That Set the Record!	6.00	4.50	2.00
17 "The Slap That Started Babeball's Most Famous Career"	12.00	9.00	4.00
18 The Babe Plays Santa Claus	12.00	9.00	4.00
19 Ed Barrow, Jacob Ruppert, Miller Huggins / actors for same	12.00	9.00	4.00
20 "Broken Window Paid Off"	12.00	9.00	4.00
21 (no title) "Regardless of the generation, Babe Ruth..."	12.00	9.00	4.00
22 Charley Grimm and William Bendix	12.00	9.00	4.00
23 Ted Lyons and William Bendix	12.00	9.00	4.00
24 Lefty Gomez, William Bendix, and Bucky Harris	12.00	9.00	4.00
25 Babe Ruth and Bill Bendix	15.00	11.00	5.00
26 Babe Ruth and William Bendix	15.00	11.00	5.00
27 Babe Ruth and Claire Trevor	15.00	11.00	5.00
28 William Bendix, Babe Ruth, Claire Trevor	15.00	11.00	5.00

1934—36 BATTER-UP (192)

2 3/8" X 3 1/4"
2 3/8" X 3 "

The National Chicle Co. 1934-36 Batter-Up set, ACC designation R-318, contains die-cut cards which have been seen in tints of sepia, brown, red, purple, green, blue, or basic black & white. Numbers 1–80 are 2 3/8" X 3 1/4" in size while the higher numbers 81–192 are 2 3/8" X 3". The higher numbers are more difficut to obtain. As with other die-cut cards, if the backs have been removed, the condition of the card is at best fair.

	MINT	VG-E	F-G			MINT	VG-E	F-G
COMPLETE SET	3500.00	2500.00	1000.00		4 Dick Bartell	9.50	6.25	2.25
COMMON PLAYER (1-80)	9.50	6.25	2.25		5 Carl Hubbell	20.00	15.00	6.50
COMMON PLAYER (81-192)	22.00	16.00	6.00		6 Bill Terry	20.00	15.00	6.50
					7 Pepper Martin	12.00	8.75	4.00
1 Wally Berger	11.00	8.00	3.50		8 Jim Bottomley	15.00	11.00	5.00
2 Ed Brandt	9.50	6.25	2.25		9 Tom Bridges	9.50	6.25	2.25
3 Al Lopez	13.50	10.00	4.50		10 Rick Ferrell	9.50	6.25	2.25

BATTER -UP (CONTINUED)

#	Name	MINT	VG-E	F-G		#	Name	MINT	VG-E	F-G
11	Ray Benge	9.50	6.25	2.25		102	Pep Young	22.00	16.00	6.00
12	Wes Ferrell	9.50	6.25	2.25		103	Willis Hudlin	22.00	16.00	6.00
13	Chalmer Cissell	9.50	6.25	2.25		104	Mickey Haslin	22.00	16.00	6.00
14	Pie Traynor	20.00	15.00	6.50		105	Oswald Bluege	22.00	16.00	6.00
15	Leroy Mahaffey	9.50	6.25	2.25		106	Paul Andrews	22.00	16.00	6.00
16	Chick Hafey	15.00	11.00	5.00		107	Ed Brandt	22.00	16.00	6.00
17	Lloyd Waner	15.00	11.00	5.00		108	Don Taylor	22.00	16.00	6.00
18	Jack Burns	9.50	6.25	2.25		109	Thornton Lee	22.00	16.00	6.00
19	Buddy Myer	9.50	6.25	2.25		110	Hal Schumacher	22.00	16.00	6.00
20	Bob Johnson	9.50	6.25	2.25		111	Hayes & Lyons	30.00	22.50	10.50
21	Arky Vaughan	12.00	8.75	4.00		112	Odell Hale	22.00	16.00	6.00
22	Red Rolfe	11.00	8.00	3.50		113	Earl Averill	30.00	22.50	10.50
23	Lefty Gomez	18.00	13.50	6.00		114	Italo Chelini	22.00	16.00	6.00
24	Earl Averill	15.00	11.00	5.00		115	Andrews & Bottomley	30.00	22.50	10.50
25	Mickey Cochrane	20.00	15.00	6.50		116	Bill Walker	22.00	16.00	6.00
26	Van Mungo	11.00	8.00	3.50		117	Bil Dickey	45.00	34.00	15.00
27	Mel Ott	25.00	18.50	8.75		118	Gerald Walker	22.00	16.00	6.00
28	Jimmy Foxx	30.00	22.50	10.50		119	Ted Lyons	30.00	22.50	10.50
29	Jimmy Dykes	11.00	8.00	3.50		120	Eldon Auker	22.00	16.00	6.00
30	Bill Dickey	24.00	18.00	8.50		121	Bill Hallahan	22.00	16.00	6.00
31	Lefty Grove	24.00	18.00	8.50		122	Fred Lindstrom	27.00	20.00	9.00
32	Joe Cronin	20.00	15.00	6.50		123	Oral Hildebrand	22.00	16.00	6.00
33	Frank Frisch	20.00	15.00	6.50		124	Luke Appling	30.00	22.50	10.50
34	Al Simmons	20.00	15.00	6.50		125	Pepper Martin	25.00	18.50	8.75
35	Rogers Hornsby	30.00	22.50	10.50		126	Rick Ferrell	22.00	16.00	6.00
36	Ted Lyons	15.00	11.00	5.00		127	Ival Goodman	22.00	16.00	6.00
37	Rabbit Maranville	14.00	10.50	4.75		128	Joe Kuhel	22.00	16.00	6.00
38	Jimmy Wilson	9.50	6.25	2.25		129	Ernie Lombardi	27.00	20.00	9.00
39	Willie Kamm	9.50	6.25	2.25		130	Charlie Gehringer	35.00	26.00	12.00
40	Bill Hallahan	9.50	6.25	2.25		131	Van Lingle Mungo	22.00	16.00	6.00
41	Gus Suhr	9.50	6.25	2.25		132	Larry French	22.00	16.00	6.00
42	Charlie Gehringer	18.00	13.50	6.00		133	Buddy Myer	22.00	16.00	6.00
43	Joe Heving	9.50	6.25	2.25		134	Mel Harder	22.00	16.00	6.00
44	Adam Comorosky	9.50	6.25	2.25		135	Augie Galan	22.00	16.00	6.00
45	Tony Lazzeri	12.00	8.75	4.00		136	Gabby Hartnett	30.00	22.50	10.50
46	Sam Leslie	9.50	6.25	2.25		137	Stan Hack	25.00	18.50	8.75
47	Bob Smith	9.50	6.25	2.25		138	Billy Herman	27.00	20.00	9.00
48	Willis Hudlin	9.50	6.25	2.25		139	Bill Jurges	22.00	16.00	6.00
49	Carl Reynolds	9.50	6.25	2.25		140	Bill Lee	22.00	16.00	6.00
50	Fred Schulte	9.50	6.25	2.25		141	Zeke Bonura	22.00	16.00	6.00
51	Cookie Lavagetto	9.50	6.25	2.25		142	Tony Piet	22.00	16.00	6.00
52	Hal Schumacher	9.50	6.25	2.25		143	Paul Dean	25.00	18.50	8.75
53	Roger Cramer	9.50	6.25	2.25		144	Jimmy Foxx	50.00	38.00	17.00
54	Sylvester Johnson	9.50	6.25	2.25		145	Joe Medwick	35.00	26.00	12.00
55	Ollie Bejma	9.50	6.25	2.25		146	Rip Collins	22.00	16.00	6.00
56	Sam Byrd	9.50	6.25	2.25		147	Mel Almada	22.00	16.00	6.00
57	Hank Greenberg	20.00	15.00	6.50		148	Allan Cooke	22.00	16.00	6.00
58	Bill Knickerbocker	9.50	6.25	2.25		149	Moe Berg	22.00	16.00	6.00
59	Bill Urbanski	9.50	6.25	2.25		150	Dolph Camilli	22.00	16.00	6.00
60	Eddie Morgan	9.50	6.25	2.25		151	Oscar Melillo	22.00	16.00	6.00
61	Robbit McNair	9.50	6.25	2.25		152	Bruce Campbell	22.00	16.00	6.00
62	Ben Chapman	9.50	6.25	2.25		153	Lefty Grove	40.00	30.00	13.00
63	Roy Johnson	9.50	6.25	2.25		154	Johnny Murphy	22.00	16.00	6.00
64	"Dizzy" Dean	50.00	38.00	17.00		155	Luke Sewell	22.00	16.00	6.00
65	Zeke Bonura	9.50	6.25	2.25		156	Leo Durocher	25.00	18.50	8.75
66	Fred Marberry	9.50	6.25	2.25		157	Lloyd Waner	30.00	22.50	10.50
67	Gus Mancuso	9.50	6.25	2.25		158	Gus Bush	22.00	16.00	6.00
68	Joe Vosmik	9.50	6.25	2.25		159	Jimmy Dykes	25.00	18.50	8.75
69	Earl Grace	9.50	6.25	2.25		160	Steve O'Neil	22.00	16.00	6.00
70	Tony Piet	9.50	6.25	2.25		161	General Crowder	22.00	16.00	6.00
71	Rollie Hemsley	9.50	6.25	2.25		162	Joe Cascarella	22.00	16.00	6.00
72	Fred Fitzsimmons	9.50	6.25	2.25		163	Bud Hafey	30.00	22.50	10.50
73	Jack Wilson	9.50	6.25	2.25		164	Gilly Campbell	22.00	16.00	6.00
74	Chick Fullis	9.50	6.25	2.25		165	Ray Hayworth	22.00	16.00	6.00
75	Fred Frankhouse	9.50	6.25	2.25		166	Frank Demaree	22.00	16.00	6.00
76	Ethan Allen	9.50	6.25	2.25		167	John Babich	22.00	16.00	6.00
77	Heine Manush	14.00	10.50	4.75		168	Marvin Owen	22.00	16.00	6.00
78	Rip Collins	9.50	6.25	2.25		169	Ralph Kress	22.00	16.00	6.00
79	Tony Cuccinello	9.50	6.25	2.25		170	Mule Haas	22.00	16.00	6.00
80	Joe Kuhel	9.50	6.25	2.25		171	Frank Higgins	22.00	16.00	6.00
81	Tom Bridges	22.00	16.00	6.00		172	Wally Berger	22.00	16.00	6.00
82	Clint Brown	22.00	16.00	6.00		173	Frank Frisch	35.00	26.00	12.00
83	Albert Blanche	22.00	16.00	6.00		174	Wes Ferrell	22.00	16.00	6.00
84	Boze Berger	22.00	16.00	6.00		175	Pete Fox	22.00	16.00	6.00
85	Goose Goslin	27.00	20.00	9.00		176	John Vergez	22.00	16.00	6.00
86	Lefty Gomez	35.00	26.00	12.00		177	Billy Rogell	22.00	16.00	6.00
87	Joe Glenn	22.00	16.00	6.00		178	Don Brennan	22.00	16.00	6.00
88	Cy Blanton	22.00	16.00	6.00		179	Jim Bottomley	30.00	22.50	10.50
89	Tom Carey	22.00	16.00	6.00		180	Travis Jackson	22.00	16.00	6.00
90	Ralph Birkofer	22.00	16.00	6.00		181	Red Rolfe	22.00	16.00	6.00
91	Fred Gabler	22.00	16.00	6.00		182	Frank Crosetti	25.00	18.50	8.75
92	Dick Coffman	22.00	16.00	6.00		183	Joe Cronin	30.00	22.50	10.50
93	Ollie Bejma	22.00	16.00	6.00		184	Schoolboy Rowe	25.00	18.50	8.75
94	Leroy Parmelee	22.00	16.00	6.00		185	Chuck Klein	27.00	20.00	9.00
95	Carl Reynolds	22.00	16.00	6.00		186	Lou Warneke	22.00	16.00	6.00
96	Ben Cantwell	22.00	16.00	6.00		187	Gus Suhr	22.00	16.00	6.00
97	Curtis Davis	22.00	16.00	6.00		188	Ben Chapman	22.00	16.00	6.00
98	Webb & Moses	30.00	22.50	10.50		189	Clint Brown	22.00	16.00	6.00
99	Ray Benge	22.00	16.00	6.00		190	Paul Derringer	25.00	18.50	8.75
100	Pie Traynor	35.00	26.00	12.00		191	John Burns	22.00	16.00	6.00
101	Phil Cavaretta	25.00	18.50	8.75		192	John Broaca	22.00	16.00	6.00

1959 BAZOOKA (23)

The 1959 Bazooka set of 23 full color, unnumbered, blank backed cards were issued on boxes containing 25 individual pieces of Bazooka gum. Originally, nine cards were issued. Later 14 more cards were issued. These later issued cards are indicated in the checklist below by an asterisk and are more difficult to obtain than the originally issued nine cards.

	MINT	VG-E	F-G
COMPLETE SET	2100.00	1650.00	800.00
COMMON PLAYER	45.00	35.00	15.00
1 Hank Aaron	160.00	120.00	55.00
2 Richie Ashburn*	90.00	70.00	30.00
3 Ernie Banks*	130.00	95.00	40.00
4 Ken Boyer*	90.00	70.00	30.00
5 Orlando Cepeda	50.00	38.00	17.00
6 Bob Cerv*	80.00	60.00	25.00
7 Rocco Colavito*	90.00	70.00	30.00
8 Del Crandall	45.00	35.00	15.00
9 Jim Davenport	45.00	35.00	15.00
10 Don Drysdale*	100.00	70.00	30.00
11 Nellie Fox*	80.00	60.00	25.00
12 Jackie Jensen*	80.00	60.00	25.00
13 Harvey Kuenn*	80.00	60.00	25.00
14 Mickey Mantle	250.00	180.00	80.00
15 Willie Mays	160.00	120.00	55.00
16 Bill Mazeroski	45.00	35.00	15.00
17 Roy McMillan	45.00	35.00	15.00
18 Billy Pierce*	80.00	60.00	25.00
19 Roy Sievers*	80.00	60.00	25.00
20 Duke Snider*	160.00	120.00	55.00
21 Gus Triandos*	80.00	60.00	25.00
22 Bob Turley	45.00	35.00	15.00
23 Vic Wertz*	80.00	60.00	25.00

1960 BAZOOKA (36)

The 1960 Bazooka set of 36 full color, blanked backed, numbered cards was issued on boxes of Bazooka bubble gum. The cards were issued in panels of three cards per panel. The cards could be cut from the panel; therefore, individual cards plus full panels are in existence. The checklist below indicates prices for both individual cards and panels of three.

WARREN SPAHN
MILWAUKEE BRAVES pitcher
NO. 19 OF 36 CARDS

HARMON KILLEBREW
WASH. SENATORS 3rd base
NO. 20 OF 36 CARDS

JACKIE JENSEN
BOSTON RED SOX outfield
NO. 21 OF 36 CARDS

	AS INDIVIDUALS			AS PANELS		
	MINT	VG-E	F-G	MINT	VG-E	F-G
COMPLETE SET	150.00	110.00	50.00	200.00	150.00	70.00
COMMON PLAYER	2.75	2.00	.90	xxxx	xxxx	xxxx
COMMON PANEL	xxxx	xxxx	xxxx	13.00	10.00	4.00
1 Ernie Banks	10.00	7.00	3.00			
2 Bud Daley	2.75	2.00	.90	17.00	12.50	6.00
3 Wally Moon	2.75	2.00	.90			
4 Hank Aaron	20.00	15.00	6.50			
5 Milt Pappas	2.75	2.00	.90	27.00	20.00	9.00
6 Dick Stuart	2.75	2.00	.90			
7 Bob Clemente	12.50	9.00	4.00			
8 Yogi Berra	11.00	8.00	3.50	30.00	22.50	10.50
9 Ken Boyer	4.00	3.00	1.50			
10 Orlando Cepeda	4.00	3.00	1.50			
11 Gus Triandos	2.75	2.00	.90	13.00	10.00	4.00
12 Frank Malzone	2.75	2.00	.90			
13 Willie Mays	20.00	15.00	6.50			
14 Camilo Pascual	2.75	2.00	.90	25.00	18.50	8.75
15 Bob Cerv	2.75	2.00	.90			
16 Vic Power	2.75	2.00	.90			
17 Larry Sherry	2.75	2.00	.90	16.00	12.00	5.50
18 Al Kaline	10.00	7.00	3.00			
19 Warren Spahn	9.00	6.75	3.00			
20 Harmon Killebrew	8.00	6.00	2.50	22.00	16.50	7.50
21 Jackie Jensen	4.00	3.00	1.50			

1960 BAZOOKA (CONTINUED)

	MINT	VG-E	F-G	MINT	VG-E	F-G
22 Luis Aparicio	4.00	3.00	1.50			
23 Gil Hodges	7.00	5.25	2.50	16.00	12.00	5.50
24 Richie Ashburn	3.50	2.50	1.20			
25 Nellie Fox	4.00	3.00	1.50			
26 Robin Roberts	7.00	5.25	2.50	15.00	11.00	5.00
27 Joe Cunningham	2.75	2.00	.90			
28 Early Wynn	6.00	4.50	2.00			
29 Frank Robinson	8.00	6.00	2.50	20.00	15.00	6.50
30 Rocky Colavito	4.00	3.00	1.50			
31 Mickey Mantle	25.00	18.50	8.75			
32 Glen Hobbie	2.75	2.00	.90	30.00	22.50	10.50
33 Roy McMillan	2.75	2.00	.90			
34 Harvey Kuenn	2.75	2.00	.90			
35 Johnny Antonelli	2.75	2.00	.90	13.00	10.00	4.00
36 Del Crandall	2.75	2.00	.90			

1961 BAZOOKA (36)

1 13/16" X 2 3/4"
2 3/4" X 5 1/2"

The 1961 Bazooka set contains 36 full color, blank backed, numbered cards. The set is almost identical in format to the 1960 Bazooka set except that the cards are not in focus quite as clearly as the 1960 set.

	AS INDIVIDUALS			AS PANELS		
	MINT	VG-E	F-G	MINT	VG-E	F-G
COMPLETE SET	120.00	90.00	40.00	150.00	110.00	50.00
COMMON PLAYER	2.50	1.75	.75	xxxx	xxxx	xxxx
COMMON PANEL	xxxx	xxxx	xxxx	12.00	9.00	4.00
1 Art Mahaffey	2.50	1.75	.75			
2 Mickey Mantle	22.00	16.50	7.50	27.00	20.00	9.00
3 Ron Santo	3.00	2.25	1.00			
4 Bud Daley	2.50	1.75	.75			
5 Roger Maris	7.00	5.25	2.50	12.00	9.00	4.00
6 Eddie Yost	2.50	1.75	.75			
7 Minnie Minoso	3.00	2.25	1.00			
8 Dick Groat	3.00	2.25	1.00	12.00	9.00	4.00
9 Frank Malzone	2.50	1.75	.75			
10 Dick Donovan	2.50	1.75	.75			
11 Ed Mathews	7.00	5.25	2.50	12.00	9.00	4.00
12 Jim Lemon	2.50	1.75	.75			
13 Chuck Estrada	2.50	1.75	.75			
14 Ken Boyer	3.00	2.25	1.00	12.00	9.00	4.00
15 Harvey Kuenn	2.50	1.75	.75			
16 Ernie Broglio	2.50	1.75	.75			
17 Rocky Colavito	3.50	2.50	1.20	12.00	9.00	4.00
18 Ted Kluszewski	3.50	2.50	1.20			
19 Ernie Banks	9.00	6.75	3.00			
20 Al Kaline	9.00	6.75	3.00	22.00	16.50	7.50
21 Ed Bailey	2.50	1.75	.75			
22 Jim Perry	2.50	1.75	.75			
23 Willie Mays	18.00	13.50	6.00	25.00	18.50	8.75
24 Bill Mazeroski	3.00	2.25	1.00			
25 Gus Triandos	2.50	1.75	.75			
26 Don Drysdale	5.00	3.75	1.75	12.00	9.00	4.00
27 Frank Herrera	2.50	1.75	.75			
28 Earl Battey	2.50	1.75	.75			
29 Warren Spahn	7.50	5.75	2.50	15.00	11.00	5.00
30 Gene Woodling	2.50	1.75	.75			
31 Frank Robinson	7.00	5.25	2.50			
32 Pete Runnels	2.50	1.75	.75	12.00	9.00	4.00
33 Woodie Held	2.50	1.75	.75			
34 Norm Larker	2.50	1.75	.75			
35 Luis Aparicio	4.00	3.00	1.40	12.00	9.00	4.00
36 Bill Tuttle	2.50	1.75	.75			

1962 BAZOOKA (45)

1 13/16" X 2 3/4"

2 3/4" X 5 1/2"

JOHNNY ROMANO — ERNIE BANKS — NORM SIEBERN

The 1962 Bazooka set of 45 full color, blank backed, un-numbered cards was issued in panels of three on Bazooka bubble gum boxes. The cards below are numbered by panel alphabetically based on the last name of the player pictured on the far left card of the panel. The cards with an asterisk in the checklist below are more difficult to obtain than other cards in the set.

	AS INDIVIDUALS			AS PANELS		
	MINT	VG-E	F-G	MINT	VG-E	F-G
COMPLETE SET	175.00	130.00	60.00	350.00	250.00	120.00
COMMON PLAYER	2.25	1.65	.75	xxxx	xxxx	xxxx
COMMON PANEL	xxxx	xxxx	xxxx	10.00	7.00	3.00
1 Bob Allison *	5.00	3.75	1.75			
2 Ed Mathews *	20.00	15.00	6.50	75.00	55.00	24.00
3 Vada Pinson *	6.00	4.50	2.00			
4 Earl Battey	2.25	1.65	.75			
5 Warren Spahn	7.00	5.25	2.50	13.00	9.50	4.00
6 Lee Thomas	2.25	1.65	.75			
7 Orlando Cepeda	3.50	2.50	1.20			
8 Woodie Held	2.25	1.65	.75	10.00	7.00	3.00
9 Bob Aspromonte	2.25	1.65	.75			
10 Dick Howser	3.00	2.25	1.00			
11 Bob Clemente	11.00	8.00	3.50	25.00	18.50	8.75
12 Al Kaline	9.00	6.75	3.00			
13 Joe Jay	2.25	1.65	.75			
14 Roger Maris	6.50	5.00	2.25	15.00	11.00	5.00
15 Frank Howard	4.00	3.00	1.40			
16 Sandy Koufax	9.00	6.75	3.00			
17 Jim Gentile	2.25	1.65	.75	15.00	11.00	5.00
18 Johnny Callison	2.25	1.65	.75			
19 Jim Landis	2.25	1.65	.75			
20 Ken Boyer	3.00	2.25	1.00	10.00	7.00	3.00
21 Chuck Schilling	2.25	1.65	.75			
22 Art Mahaffey	2.25	1.65	.75			
23 Mickey Mantle	20.00	15.00	6.50	27.00	20.00	9.00
24 Dick Stuart	2.25	1.65	.75			
25 Ken McBride	2.25	1.65	.75			
26 Frank Robinson	7.00	5.25	2.50	17.00	12.50	6.00
27 Gil Hodges	6.00	4.50	2.50			
28 Milt Pappas	3.00	2.25	1.00			
29 Hank Aaron	15.00	11.00	5.00	25.00	18.50	8.75
30 Luis Aparicio	4.00	3.00	1.40			
31 Johnny Romano*	5.00	3.75	1.75			
32 Ernie Banks *	30.00	22.50	10.50	75.00	55.00	24.00
33 Norm Siebern *	5.00	3.75	1.75			
34 Ron Santo	3.00	2.25	1.00			
35 Norm Cash	3.00	2.25	1.00	10.00	7.00	3.00
36 Jim Piersall	3.00	2.25	1.00			
37 Don Schwall	2.25	1.65	.75			
38 Willie Mays	15.00	11.00	5.00	22.00	16.50	7.50
39 Norm Larker	2.25	1.65	.75			
40 Bill White	2.25	1.65	.75			
41 Whitey Ford	7.00	5.25	2.50	15.00	11.00	5.00
42 Rocky Colavito	4.00	3.00	1.40			
43 Don Zimmer*	7.00	5.25	2.50			
44 Harmon Killebrew *	20.00	15.00	6.50	75.00	55.00	24.00
45 Gene Woodling *	5.00	3.75	1.75			

Watch the hobby papers and your local bookstores for the release later this year of the Sport Americana Baseball Memorabilia Price Guide. This book will contain prices and descriptions of baseball memorabilia other than the popular baseball card issues — yearbooks, baseball coins, programs, press pins, uniforms, statues, postcards, etc.

1963 BAZOOKA (36)

	NORM SIEBERN	WARREN SPAHN	BILL MAZEROSKI
	K.C. ATHLETICS 1B	MIL. BRAVES PITCHER	PITTS. PIRATES 2B
	NO. 4 OF 36 CARDS	NO. 5 OF 36 CARDS	NO. 6 OF 36 CARDS

The 1963 Bazooka set of full color, blank backed, numbered cards was issued Bazooka bubble gum box This year marked a cha... in format from previ... Bazooka issues with a sma... sized card being issued. ... card features a white s... with the player's name prin... in red and the team posi... printed in black on the ca... The number appears in white border at the bott... of the card. Three ca... were issued per panel

	AS INDIVIDUALS			AS PANELS		
	MINT	VG-E	F-G	MINT	VG-E	F-G
COMPLETE SET	130.00	100.00	40.00	170.00	130.00	60.00
COMMON PLAYER	2.00	1.50	.65	xxxx	xxxx	xxxx
COMMON PANEL	xxxx	xxxx	xxxx	8.50	6.25	3.00
1 Mickey Mantle	20.00	15.00	6.50			
2 Bob Rodgers	2.00	1.50	.65	32.00	24.00	11.00
3 Ernie Banks	8.00	6.00	2.50			
4 Norm Siebern	2.00	1.50	.65			
5 Warren Spahn	6.00	4.50	2.00	12.00	8.75	4.00
6 Bill Mazeroski	3.00	2.25	1.00			
7 Harmon Killebrew	6.00	4.50	2.50			
8 Dick Farrell	2.00	1.50	.65	25.00	18.50	8.75
9 Hank Aaron	15.00	11.00	5.00			
10 Dick Donovan	2.00	1.50	.65			
11 Jim Gentile	2.00	1.50	.65	22.00	16.50	7.50
12 Willie Mays	15.00	11.00	5.00			
13 Camilo Pascual	3.00	2.25	1.00			
14 Bob Clemente	10.00	7.00	3.00	17.00	12.50	6.00
15 Johnny Callison	3.00	2.25	1.00			
16 Carl Yastrzemski	10.00	7.00	3.00			
17 Don Drysdale	4.50	3.50	1.60	18.00	13.50	6.00
18 Johnny Romano	2.00	1.50	.65			
19 Al Jackson	2.00	1.50	.65			
20 Ralph Terry	2.00	1.50	.65	8.50	6.25	3.00
21 Bill Monbouquette	2.00	1.50	.65			
22 Orlando Cepeda	3.00	2.25	1.00			
23 Stan Musial	15.00	11.00	5.00	22.00	16.50	7.50
24 Floyd Robinson	2.00	1.50	.65			
25 Chuck Hinton	2.00	1.50	.65			
26 Bob Purkey	2.00	1.50	.65	8.50	6.25	3.00
27 Ken Hubbs	3.00	2.25	1.00			
28 Bill White	2.00	1.50	.65			
29 Ray Herbert	2.00	1.50	.65	15.00	11.00	5.00
30 Brooks Robinson	8.00	6.00	2.50			
31 Frank Robinson	7.00	5.25	2.50			
32 Lee Thomas	2.00	1.50	.65	15.00	11.00	5.00
33 Rocky Colavito	4.00	3.00	1.40			
34 Al Kaline	8.00	6.00	2.50			
35 Art Mahaffey	2.00	1.50	.65	15.00	11.00	5.00
36 Tommy Davis	3.00	2.25	1.00			

1963 BAZOOKA (41)
ALL—TIME GREATS

EDDIE COLLINS
PHILA—CHICAGO   2B

41 EDDIE COLLINS
2B   Phila.-Chicago

BORN: MAY 2, 1887

HOME: MILLERTOWN, NEW YORK

Eddie first joined the Athlet ics in 1906, but he didn't be come a big star until 1909 when he batted .346. Then the second baseman batted over 300 for eight consecu tive seasons. Eddie was traded to the White Sox in 1915 and had his best year in the majors in 1920 when he hit .369. At the end of the 1926 season, the lefthanded hitter was dealt back to the Philadelphia Athletics. An exciting ballplayer, Eddie ob tained a lifetime batting mark of .333.

©T.C.G. PRINTED IN U.S.A.

The 1963 Bazooka All-Time Greats set contains 41 black and white, numbered cards issued as inserts in boxes of Bazooka bubble gum. The cards feature bust shots with gold trim. The backs are yellow with black print containing vital information and a biography of the player. Many of the players are pictured not as they looked during their playing careers but as they looked many years after their playing days were through.

	MINT	VG-E	F-G
COMPLETE SET	70.00	50.00	20.00
COMMON PLAYER	1.50	1.10	.50
1 Joe Tinker	1.50	1.10	.50
2 Harry Heilmann	1.50	1.10	.50
3 Jack Chesbro	1.50	1.10	.50

4 Christy Mathewson	3.00	2.25	1.00
5 Herb Pennock	1.50	1.10	.50
6 Cy Young	1.75	1.25	.55
7 Ed Walsh	1.50	1.10	.50
8 Nap Lajoie	2.00	1.50	.60
9 Eddie Plank	1.75	1.25	.55

1963 BAZOOKA (CONTINUED)

	MINT	VG-E	F-G			MINT	VG-E	F-G
10 Honus Wagner	3.00	2.25	1.00	26 Fred Clarke		1.50	1.10	.50
11 Chief Bender	1.50	1.10	.50	27 Wilbert Robinson		1.50	1.10	.50
12 Walter Johnson	3.00	2.25	1.00	28 Dazzy Vance		1.50	1.10	.50
13 Mordecai Brown	1.50	1.10	.50	29 Pete Alexander		2.00	1.50	.60
14 Rabbit Maranville	1.50	1.10	.50	30 Judge Landis		1.50	1.10	.50
15 Lou Gehrig	5.00	3.75	1.75	31 Willie Keeler		1.50	1.10	.50
16 Ban Johnson	1.50	1.10	.50	32 Rogers Hornsby		3.00	2.25	1.00
17 Babe Ruth	8.00	6.00	2.50	33 Hugh Duffy		1.50	1.10	.50
18 Connie Mack	2.00	1.50	.60	34 Mickey Cochrane		2.00	1.50	.60
19 Hank Greenberg	1.75	1.25	.55	35 Ty Cobb		5.00	3.75	1.75
20 John McGraw	1.75	1.25	.55	36 Mel Ott		2.50	1.80	.80
21 Johnny Evers	1.50	1.10	.50	37 Clark Griffith		1.50	1.10	.50
22 Al Simmons	1.50	1.10	.50	38 Ted Lyons		1.50	1.10	.50
23 Jimmy Collins	1.50	1.10	.50	39 Cap Anson		1.50	1.10	.50
24 Tris Speaker	1.75	1.25	.55	40 Bill Dickey		2.00	1.50	.60
25 Frank Chance	1.75	1.25	.55	41 Eddie Collins		1.50	1.10	.50

1964 BAZOOKA (36)

1 9/16" X 2 1/2"
2 1/2" X 4 11/16"

The 1964 Bazooka set of 36 full color, blank backed, numbered cards were issued in panels of three on the backs of Bazooka bubble gum boxes. Many players from the 1963 set have the same numbers; however, the pictures are different.

	AS INDIVIDUALS			AS PANELS		
	MINT	VG-E	F-G	MINT	VG-E	F-G
COMPLETE SET	120.00	90.00	40.00	150.00	110.00	50.00
COMMON PLAYER	2.00	1.50	.65	xxxx	xxxx	xxxx
COMMON PANEL	xxxx	xxxx	xxxx	7.50	5.50	2.50
1 Mickey Mantle	20.00	15.00	6.50			
2 Dick Groat	2.00	1.50	.65	26.00	19.00	9.00
3 Steve Barber	2.00	1.50	.65			
4 Ken McBride	2.00	1.50	.65			
5 Warren Spahn	6.00	4.50	2.00	12.00	8.75	4.00
6 Bob Friend	2.00	1.50	.65			
7 Harmon Killebrew	6.00	4.50	2.00			
8 Dick Farrell	2.00	1.50	.65	25.00	18.50	8.75
9 Hank Aaron	14.00	10.50	4.75			
10 Rich Rollins	2.00	1.50	.65			
11 Jim Gentile	2.00	1.50	.65	20.00	15.00	6.50
12 Willie Mays	14.00	10.50	4.75			
13 Camilo Pascual	2.00	1.50	.65			
14 Bob Clemente	10.00	7.00	3.00	15.00	11.00	5.00
15 Johnny Callison	2.00	1.50	.65			
16 Carl Yastrzemski	10.00	7.00	3.00			
17 Billy Williams	3.00	2.25	1.00	17.00	12.50	6.00
18 Johnny Romano	2.00	1.50	.65			
19 Jim Maloney	2.00	1.50	.65			
20 Norm Cash	2.00	1.50	.65	10.00	7.00	3.00
21 Willie McCovey	5.00	3.75	1.75			
22 Jim Fregosi	3.00	2.25	1.10			
23 George Altman	2.00	1.50	.65	7.50	5.50	2.50
24 Floyd Robinson	2.00	1.50	.65			
25 Chuck Hinton	2.00	1.50	.65			
26 Ron Hunt	2.00	1.50	.65	7.50	5.50	2.50
27 Gary Peters	2.00	1.50	.65			
28 Dick Ellsworth	2.00	1.50	.65			
29 Elston Howard	3.00	2.25	1.10	15.00	11.00	5.00
30 Brooks Robinson	8.00	6.00	2.50			
31 Frank Robinson	7.00	5.25	2.50			
32 Sandy Koufax	9.00	6.75	3.00	22.00	16.50	7.50
33 Rocky Colavito	3.50	2.50	1.20			
34 Al Kaline	8.00	6.00	2.50			
35 Ken Boyer	3.00	2.25	1.10	15.00	11.00	5.00
36 Tommy Davis	2.00	1.50	.65			

REMEMBER THE NATIONAL CONVENTION IS BEING HELD JULY 9 - 12, 1981, IN PLYMOUTH, MICHIGAN

1965 BAZOOKA (36)

1 9/16″ X 2 1/2″
2 1/2″ X 4 11/16″

The 1965 Bazooka set of 36 full color, blank backed, numbered cards was issued in panels of three on the backs of Bazooka bubble gum boxes. As in the previous two years, some of the players have the same numbers on their cards; however, all pictures are different from the previous two years.

	AS INDIVIDUALS			AS PANELS		
	MINT	VG-E	F-G	MINT	VG-E	F-G
COMPLETE SET	115.00	85.00	40.00	140.00	105.00	50.00
COMMON PLAYER	1.75	1.30	.60	xxx	xxx	xxx
COMMON PANEL	xxx	xxx	xxx	6.75	5.00	2.00
1 Mickey Mantle	16.00	12.00	5.50			
2 Larry Jackson	1.75	1.30	.60	22.00	16.50	7.50
3 Chuck Hinton	1.75	1.30	.60			
4 Tony Oliva	3.00	2.25	1.00			
5 Dean Chance	1.75	1.30	.60	6.75	5.00	2.00
6 Jim O'Toole	1.75	1.30	.60			
7 Harmon Killebrew	5.50	4.25	2.00			
8 Pete Ward	1.75	1.30	.60	22.00	16.50	7.50
9 Hank Aaron	13.00	9.50	4.00			
10 Dick Radatz	1.75	1.30	.60			
11 Boog Powell	3.00	2.25	1.00	20.00	15.00	6.50
12 Willie Mays	13.00	9.50	4.00			
13 Bob Veale	1.75	1.30	.60			
14 Bob Clemente	9.00	6.75	3.00	14.00	10.50	4.75
15 Johnny Callison	1.75	1.30	.60			
16 Joe Torre	3.00	2.25	1.00			
17 Billy Williams	3.00	2.25	1.00	9.00	6.75	3.00
18 Bob Chance	1.75	1.30	.60			
19 Bob Aspromonte	1.75	1.30	.60			
20 Joe Christopher	1.75	1.30	.60	6.75	5.00	2.00
21 Jim Bunning	3.00	2.25	1.00			
22 Jim Fregosi	3.00	2.25	1.00			
23 Bob Gibson	4.50	3.50	1.60	13.00	9.50	4.00
24 Juan Marichal	3.50	2.50	1.20			
25 Dave Wickersham	1.75	1.30	.60			
26 Ron Hunt	1.75	1.30	.60	6.75	5.00	2.00
27 Gary Peters	1.75	1.30	.60			
28 Ron Santo	3.00	2.25	1.00			
29 Elston Howard	3.00	2.25	1.00	15.00	11.00	5.00
30 Brooks Robinson	7.50	5.75	2.50			
31 Frank Robinson	6.50	5.00	2.25			
32 Sandy Koufax	8.50	6.50	3.00	20.00	15.00	6.50
33 Rocky Colavito	3.00	2.25	1.00			
34 Al Kaline	7.50	5.75	2.50			
35 Ken Boyer	3.00	2.25	1.00	14.00	10.50	4.75
36 Tommy Davis	1.75	1.30	.60			

1966 BAZOOKA (48)

1 9/16″ X 2 1/2″
2 1/2″ X 4 11/16″

The 1966 Bazooka set of 48 full color, blank backed, numbered cards was issued in panels of three on the backs of Bazooka bubble gum boxes. The set is distinguishable from the previous years by mention of a "48 card set" at the bottom of the card

	AS INDIVIDUALS			AS PANELS		
	MINT	VG-E	F-G	MINT	VG-E	F-G
COMPLETE SET	120.00	90.00	40.00	150.00	110.00	50.00
COMMON PLAYER	1.75	1.30	.60	xxx	xxx	xxx
COMMON PANEL	xxx	xxx	xxx	6.25	4.50	2.00
1 Sandy Koufax	8.00	6.00	2.50			
2 Willie Horton	1.75	1.30	.60	15.00	11.00	5.00
3 Frank Howard	3.00	2.25	1.00			

1966 BAZOOKA (CONTINUED)

	MINT	VG-E	F-G	MINT	VG-E	F-G
4 Richie Allen	3.00	2.25	1.00			
5 Mel Stottlemyre	1.75	1.30	.60	7.00	5.25	2.00
6 Tony Conigliaro	1.75	1.30	.60			
7 Mickey Mantle	15.00	11.00	5.00			
8 Leon Wagner	1.75	1.30	.60	21.00	15.50	7.00
9 Ed Kranepool	1.75	1.30	.60			
10 Juan Marichal	3.00	2.25	1.00			
11 Harmon Killebrew	5.00	3.75	1.75	11.00	8.00	3.50
12 Johnny Callison	1.75	1.30	.60			
13 Roy McMillan	1.75	1.30	.60			
14 Willie McCovey	4.50	3.50	1.60	11.00	8.00	3.50
15 Rocky Colavito	3.00	2.25	1.00			
16 Willie Mays	12.00	8.75	4.00			
17 Sammy McDowell	1.75	1.30	.60	17.00	12.50	6.00
18 Vern Law	1.75	1.30	.60			
19 Jim Fregosi	3.00	2.25	1.00			
20 Ron Fairly	1.75	1.30	.60	11.00	8.00	3.50
21 Bob Gibson	4.50	3.50	1.60			
22 Carl Yastrzemski	8.50	6.50	3.00			
23 Bill White	1.75	1.30	.60	14.00	10.50	4.75
24 Bob Aspromonte	1.75	1.30	.60			
25 Dean Chance	1.75	1.30	.60			
26 Bob Clemente	8.50	6.50	3.00	14.00	10.50	4.75
27 Tony Cloninger	1.75	1.30	.60			
28 Curt Blefary	1.75	1.30	.60			
29 Milt Pappas	1.75	1.30	.60	17.00	12.50	6.00
30 Hank Aaron	12.00	8.75	4.00			
31 Jim Bunning	2.50	1.80	.80			
32 Frank Robinson	6.00	4.50	2.00	13.00	9.50	4.00
33 Bill Skowron	2.50	1.80	.80			
34 Brooks Robinson	7.00	5.25	2.50			
35 Jim Wynn	1.75	1.30	.60	13.00	9.50	4.00
36 Joe Torre	2.50	1.80	.80			
37 Jim Grant	1.75	1.30	.60			
38 Pete Rose	12.00	8.75	4.00	18.00	13.50	6.00
39 Ron Santo	2.50	1.80	.80			
40 Tom Tresh	1.75	1.30	.60			
41 Tony Oliva	2.50	1.80	.80	10.00	7.00	3.00
42 Don Drysdale	4.00	3.00	1.50			
43 Pete Richert	1.75	1.30	.60			
44 Bert Campaneris	1.75	1.30	.60	6.25	4.50	2.00
45 Jim Maloney	1.75	1.30	.60			
46 Al Kaline	7.00	5.25	2.50			
47 Eddie Fisher	1.75	1.30	.60	14.00	10.50	4.75
48 Billy Williams	3.00	2.25	1.00			

1967 BAZOOKA (48)

1 9/16″ X 2 1/2″
2 1/2 X 4 11/16″

The 1967 Bazooka set of 48 full color, blank backed, numbered cards was issued in panels of three on the backs of Bazooka bubble gum boxes. This set is virtually identical to the 1966 set with the exception of 10 new cards as replacements for ten 1966 cards. The remaining 38 cards are identical in both pose and number. The replacement cards are listed in the checklist below with an asterisk.

TOMMY DAVIS NEW YORK METS OF — NO. 37 OF 48 CARDS

PETE ROSE CINCINNATI REDS 2B — NO. 38 OF 48 CARDS

RON SANTO CHICAGO CUBS 3B — NO. 39 OF 48 CARDS

	AS INDIVIDUALS			AS PANELS		
	MINT	VG-E	F-G	MINT	VG-E	F-G
COMPLETE SET	105.00	75.00	35.00	135.00	100.00	45.00
COMMON PLAYER	1.75	1.30	.60	xxx	xxx	xxx
COMMON PANEL	xxx	xxx	xxx	6.00	4.50	2.00
1 Rick Reichardt*	1.75	1.30	.60			
2 Tommy Agee*	1.75	1.30	.60	7.00	5.25	2.50
3 Frank Howard*	3.00	2.25	1.00			
4 Richie Allen	2.50	1.80	.80			
5 Mel Stottlemyre	1.75	1.30	.60	6.00	4.50	2.00
6 Tony Conigliaro	1.75	1.30	.60			
7 Mickey Mantle	15.00	11.00	5.00			
8 Leon Wagner	1.75	1.20	.60	20.00	15.00	6.50
9 Gary Peters*	1.75	1.20	.60			
10 Juan Marichal	3.00	2.25	1.00			
11 Harmon Killebrew	5.00	3.75	1.75	10.00	7.00	3.00
12 Johnny Callison	1.75	1.20	.60			
13 Denny McLain*	2.50	1.80	.80			
14 Willie McCovey	4.50	3.50	1.60	10.00	7.00	3.00
15 Rocky Colavito	2.50	1.80	.80			
16 Willie Mays	12.00	8.75	4.00			
17 Sammy McDowell	1.75	1.30	.60	18.00	13.50	6.00
18 Jim Kaat*	2.50	1.80	.80			

31

	MINT	VG-E	F-G	MINT	VG-E	F-G
19 Jim Fregosi	3.00	2.25	1.00			
20 Ron Fairly	1.75	1.30	.60	10.00	7.00	3.00
21 Bob Gibson	4.00	3.00	1.40			
22 Carl Yastrzemski	8.50	6.50	3.00			
23 Bill White	1.75	1.30	.60	14.00	10.50	4.75
24 Bob Aspromonte	1.75	1.30	.60			
25 Dean Chance	1.75	1.30	.60			
26 Bob Clemente	8.50	6.50	3.00	14.00	10.50	4.75
27 Tony Cloninger	1.75	1.30	.60			
28 Curt Blefary	1.75	1.30	.60			
29 Phil Regan*	1.75	1.30	.60	18.00	13.50	6.00
30 Hank Aaron	12.00	8.75	4.00			
31 Jim Bunning	2.50	1.80	.80			
32 Frank Robinson	6.00	4.50	2.00	13.00	9.50	4.00
33 Ken Boyer*	2.50	1.80	.80			
34 Brooks Robinson	7.00	5.25	2.50			
35 Jim Wynn	1.75	1.30	.60	13.00	9.50	4.00
36 Joe Torre	2.50	1.80	.80			
37 Tommy Davis*	1.75	1.30	.60			
38 Pete Rose	12.00	8.75	4.00	18.00	13.50	6.00
39 Ron Santo	2.50	1.80	.80			
40 Tom Tresh	1.75	1.30	.60			
41 Tony Oliva	2.50	1.80	.80	10.00	7.00	3.00
42 Don Drysdale	4.00	3.00	1.40			
43 Pete Richert	1.75	1.30	.60			
44 Bert Campaneris	1.75	1.30	.60	6.00	4.50	2.00
45 Jim Maloney	1.75	1.30	.60			
46 Al Kaline	6.50	5.00	2.25			
47 Matty Alou*	1.75	1.30	.60	13.00	9.50	4.00
48 Billy Williams	3.00	2.25	1.00			

1968 BAZOOKA (15)
TIPPS FROM THE TOPPS

3" X 6 1/4"
1 1/4" X 3 1/8"
5 1/2" X 6 1/4"

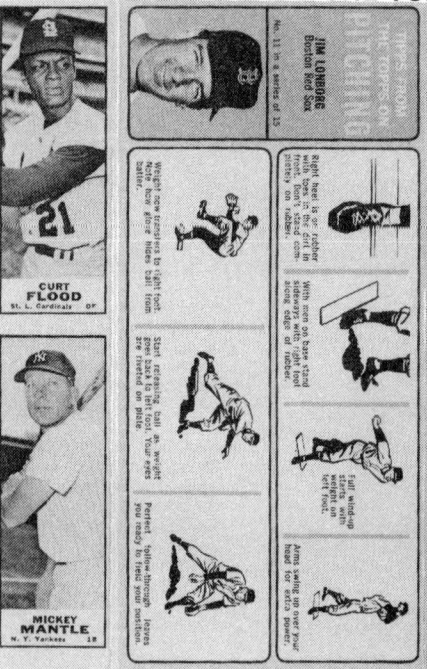

The 1968 Bazooka Tipps from the Topps is a set of 15 numbered boxes, each containing on the back panel a baseball playing tip from a star, and on the side panels four mini cards, two per side, in full color, measuring 1 1/4" X 3". Although the set contains a total of 60 of these small cards, 4 are repeated; therefore, there are but 56 different small cards.

	MINT	VG-E	F-G	AS COMPLETE BOX MINT	VG-E	F-G
COMPLETE SET	120.00	90.00	40.00	150.00	110.00	50.00
COMMON PANEL	xxx	xxx	xxx	7.00	5.25	2.50
COMMON PLAYER	1.00	.75	.35	xxx	xxx	xxx
1 Maury Wills, Bunting	1.50	1.10	.50			
Kaline	4.00	3.00	1.40			
Casanova	1.00	.75	.35	12.00	8.75	4.00
C. Boyer	1.00	.75	.35			
Seaver	4.00	3.00	1.40			
2 Carl Yastrzemski, Batting	6.00	4.50	2.00			
Hunter	2.00	1.50	.60			
Freehan	1.00	.75	.35	12.00	8.75	4.00
M. Alou	1.00	.75	.35			
Lefebvre	1.00	.75	.35			
3 Bert Campaneris, Stealing Bases	1.50	1.10	.50			
McCarver	1.00	.75	.35			
Veale	1.00	.75	.35	8.00	6.00	2.50
Fr. Robinson	3.25	2.40	1.10			
Knoop	1.00	.75	.35			

1968 BAZOOKA (CONTINUED)

	MINT	VG-E	F-G	MINT	VG-E	F-G
4 Maury Wills, Sliding	1.50	1.10	.50			
Holtzman	1.00	.75	.35			
Azcue	1.00	.75	.35	7.00	5.25	4.00
T. Conigliaro	1.00	.75	.35			
White	1.00	.75	.35			
5 Julian Javier, The Double Play	1.25	.90	.40			
Marichal	1.50	1.10	.50			
Petrocelli	1.00	.75	.35	12.00	8.75	4.00
Pepitone	1.00	.75	.35			
Aaron	6.00	4.50	2.00			
6 Orlando Cepeda, Playing 1st Base	1.50	1.10	.50			
Santo	1.25	.90	.40			
Drysdale	2.50	1.80	.80	13.00	9.50	4.00
Rose	6.00	4.50	2.00			
Agee	1.00	.75	.35			
7 Bill Mazeroski, Playing 2nd Base	1.50	1.10	.50			
Roseboro	1.00	.75	.35			
Bunning	1.25	.90	.40	7.00	5.25	4.00
F. Howard	1.50	1.10	.50			
Scott	1.00	.75	.35			
8 Brooks Robinson, Playing 3rd Base	5.00	3.75	1.75			
Gonzalez	1.00	.75	.35			
McGlothlin	1.00	.75	.35	12.00	8.75	4.00
Horton	1.00	.75	.35			
Killebrew	2.50	1.80	.80			
9 Jim Fregosi, Playing Shortstop	1.50	1.10	.50			
Alvis	1.00	.75	.35			
Gibson	2.50	1.80	.80	9.00	6.75	3.00
Oliva	2.00	1.50	.60			
Pinson	1.50	1.10	.50			
10 Joe Torre, Catching	1.50	1.10	.50			
Chance	1.00	.75	.35			
Jenkins	1.50	1.10	.50	7.00	5.25	2.50
T. Davis	1.25	.90	.40			
Monday	1.00	.75	.35			
11 Jim Lonborg, Pitching	1.25	.90	.40			
Horlen	1.00	.75	.35			
Wynn	1.00	.75	.35	15.00	11.00	5.00
Flood	1.25	.90	.40			
Mantle	9.00	6.75	3.00			
12 Mike McCormick, Fielding Pitcher	1.25	.90	.40			
Mincher	1.00	.75	.35			
Perez	1.50	1.10	.50	12.00	8.75	4.00
Clemente	5.00	3.75	1.75			
Downing	1.00	.75	.35			
13 Frank Crosetti, Coaching	1.50	1.10	.50			
Carew	4.00	3.00	1.40			
Wilson	1.00	.75	.35	12.00	8.75	4.00
Swoboda	1.00	.75	.35			
McCovey	3.25	2.50	1.10			
14 Willie Mays, Playing the Outfield	6.00	4.50	2.00			
Allen	1.50	1.10	.50			
Peters	1.00	.75	.35	13.00	9.50	4.00
B. Williams	2.00	1.50	.60			
Staub	1.50	1.10	.50			
15 Lou Brock, Base Running	5.00	3.75	1.75			
Agee	1.00	.75	.35			
Rose	6.00	4.50	2.00	17.00	12.50	6.00
Santo	1.25	.90	.40			
Drysdale	2.50	1.80	.80			

WASHINGTON TIMES

1969–70 BAZOOKA (12)
BASEBALL EXTRA

3″ X 6 1/4″
1 1/4″ X 3 1/8″
5 1/2″ X 6 1/4″

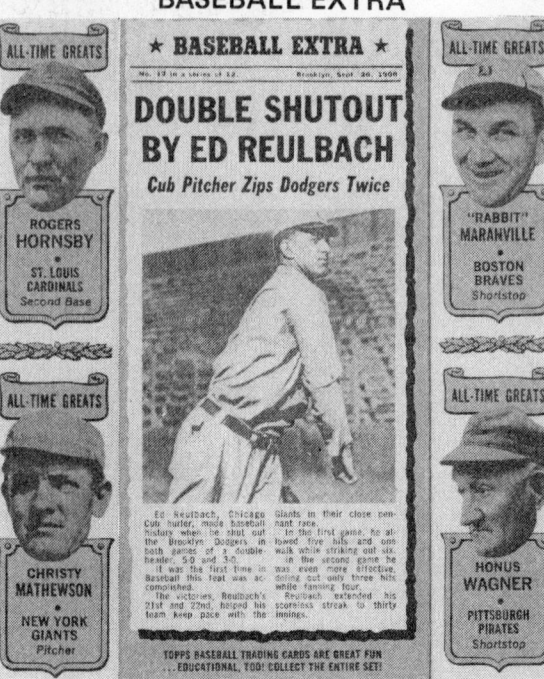

The 1969-1970 Bazooka Baseball Extra News cards contain 12 complete panels, each comprising a large action shot of a significant event in baseball history and four small cards, comparable to those in the "Tipps from the Topps set of 1968", of Hall of Fame baseball players.

	AS INDIVIDUALS			AS COMPLETE BOXES		
	MINT	VG-E	F-G	MINT	VG-E	F-G
COMPLETE SET	100.00	70.00	30.00	125.00	90.00	40.00
COMMON PANEL	xxx	xxx	xxx	7.00	5.25	2.50
COMMON PLAYER	.60	.45	.20	xxx	xxx	xxx
1 No-Hit Duel by Toney & Vaughn	1.00	.70	.30			
Cobb	4.00	3.00	1.50			
Keeler	.60	.45	.20	7.00	5.25	2.50
Brown	.60	.45	.20			
Plank	1.00	.70	.30			
2 Alexander Conquers Yanks	2.50	1.80	.80			
Simmons	.60	.45	.20			
B. Johnson	.60	.45	.20	10.00	7.00	3.00
W. Johnson	3.00	2.25	1.00			
Hornsby	2.50	1.80	.80			
3 Yanks' Lazzeri Sets AL Record	1.00	.70	.30			
Mathewson	2.50	1.80	.80			
Bender	.60	.45	.20	8.00	6.00	2.50
Alexander	2.00	1.50	.60			
Young	1.50	1.10	.50			
4 HR Almost Hit Out of Stadium	4.00	3.00	1.50			
Gehrig	5.00	3.75	1.75			
Duffy	.60	.45	.20	12.00	8.75	4.00
Speaker	1.50	1.10	.50			
Tinker	.60	.45	.20			
5 Four Cons. Homers by Lou	8.00	6.00	2.50			
McGraw	1.00	.70	.30			
Chance	1.00	.70	.30	18.00	13.50	6.00
Ruth	6.50	5.00	2.25			
Cochrane	1.00	.70	.30			
6 No-Hit Game by Walter Johnson	5.00	3.75	1.75			
Young	1.50	1.10	.50			
W. Johnson	3.00	2.25	1.00	12.00	8.75	4.00
Evers	1.00	.70	.30			
McGraw	1.00	.70	.30			
7 Twelve RBIs by Bottomley	1.00	.70	.30			
Evers	1.00	.70	.30			
Collins	.60	.45	.20	12.00	8.75	4.00
Gehrig	5.00	3.75	1.75			
Cobb	4.00	3.00	1.50			
8 Ty Ties Record	8.00	6.00	2.50			
Wagner	3.00	2.25	1.00			
Cochrane	1.00	.70	.30	15.00	11.00	5.00
Collins	.60	.45	.20			
Ott	2.00	1.50	.60			
9 Babe Ruth Hits 3 HR's in Game	10.00	7.00	3.00			
Anson	.60	.45	.20			
Speaker	1.50	1.10	.50	15.00	11.00	5.00
Chesbro	.60	.45	.20			
Simmons	.60	.45	.20			

35

	MINT	VG-E	F-G		MINT	VG-E	F-G
10 Calls Shot in Series Game	10.00	7.00	3.00				
Maranville	.60	.45	.20				
Walsh	.60	.45	.20		16.00	12.00	5.50
Lajoie	2.00	1.50	.60				
Mack	2.00	1.50	.60				
11 Ruth's 60th HR Sets New Record	10.00	7.00	3.00				
Tinker	.60	.45	.20				
Lajoie	2.00	1.50	.60		16.00	12.00	5.50
Ott	2.00	1.50	.60				
Chance	1.00	.70	.30				
12 Double Shutout by Ed Reulbach	1.00	.70	.30				
Hornsby	2.50	1.80	.80				
Maranville	.60	.45	.20		10.00	7.00	3.00
Mathewson	2.50	1.80	.80				
Wagner	3.00	2.25	1.00				

1971 BAZOOKA (36)

2" X 2 5/8"
2 5/8" X 5 5/16"

RANDY HUNDLEY   WILLIE MAYS   JIM HUNTER

The 1971 Bazooka set of 36 full color, unnumbered cards was issued in 12 panels of three cards each on the backs of boxes containing one cent Bazooka bubble gum. The panels are numbered in the checklist alphabetically by the player's last name on the left most card of the panel.

	AS INDIVIDUALS			AS PANELS		
	MINT	VG-E	F-G	MINT	VG-E	F-G
COMPLETE SET	45.00	35.00	15.00	65.00	48.00	22.00
COMMON PLAYER	.80	.60	.25	xxx	xxx	xxx
COMMON PANEL	xxx	xxx	xxx	3.50	2.50	1.00
1 Tommie Agee	.80	.60	.25			
2 Harmon Killebrew	3.00	2.25	1.10	9.00	6.75	3.00
3 Reggie Jackson	5.00	3.75	1.75			
4 Bert Campaneris	.80	.60	.25			
5 Pete Rose	6.00	4.50	2.00	8.00	6.00	2.50
6 Orlando Cepeda	1.00	.70	.30			
7 Rico Carty	.80	.60	.25			
8 Johnny Bench	5.00	3.75	1.75	7.00	5.25	2.50
9 Tommy Harper	.80	.60	.25			
10 Bill Freehan	.80	.60	.25			
11 Roberto Clemente	5.00	3.75	1.75	7.00	5.25	2.50
12 Claude Osteen	.80	.60	.25			
13 Jim Fregosi	1.25	.90	.40			
14 Billy Williams	1.75	1.25	.55	4.00	3.00	1.50
15 Dave McNally	.80	.60	.25			
16 Randy Hundley	.80	.60	.25			
17 Willie Mays	6.00	4.50	2.00	9.00	6.75	3.00
18 Jim Hunter	2.00	1.50	.60			
19 Juan Marichal	1.50	1.10	.50			
20 Frank Howard	1.25	.90	.40	3.50	2.50	1.00
21 Bill Melton	.80	.60	.25			
22 Willie McCovey	3.00	2.25	1.10			
23 Carl Yastrzemski	6.00	4.50	2.00	10.00	7.00	3.00
24 Clyde Wright	.80	.60	.25			
25 Jim Merritt	.80	.60	.25			
26 Luis Aparicio	1.25	.90	.40	3.50	2.50	1.00
27 Bobby Murcer	1.00	.70	.30			
28 Rico Petrocelli	.80	.60	.25			
29 Sam McDowell	1.00	.70	.30	3.50	2.50	1.00
30 Clarence Gaston	.80	.60	.25			
31 Brooks Robinson	5.00	3.75	1.75			
32 Hank Aaron	6.00	4.50	2.00	12.00	8.75	4.00
33 Larry Dierker	.80	.60	.25			
34 Rusty Staub	1.25	.90	.40			
35 Bob Gibson	2.50	1.80	.80	5.00	3.75	1.75
36 Amos Otis	1.00	.70	.30			

Attend a Sports Memorabilia Show or Convention in your area sometime this year. They are both interesting and enjoyable to all members of the family.

1958 BELL BRAND (10)

3" X 4"

ROY CAMPANELLA
Catcher LOS ANGELES DODGERS

Height: 5'10"   Weight: 218
Home: Glen Cove, New York
Throws: Right   Bats: Right
Born: November 19, 1921

Roy Campanella has been named The Most Valuable Player in the National League on 3 occasions! His finest season was in 1953 when he hit 41 home runs and piled up 142 runs batted in — an all-time high in Dodger history. In his ten campaigns with the Dodgers, Roy has hit 242 homers and only twice has dropped below 20.

MAJOR LEAGUE RECORD

YEAR	CLUB	GAMES	HITS	HR	RBI	AVG.
1948	Dodgers	83	72	9	45	.258
1949	"	130	125	22	82	.287
1950	"	126	123	31	89	.281
1951	"	143	164	33	108	.325
1952	"	128	126	22	97	.269
1953	"	144	162	41	142	.312
1954	"	111	82	19	51	.207
1955	"	123	142	32	107	.318
1956	"	124	85	20	73	.219
1957	"	103	80	13	62	.242

ROY CAMPANELLA

The 1958 Bell Brand Potato Chips set of 10 unnumbered cards features Los Angeles Dodgers only. The set is distinguished by a 1/4" dark green border. The Cimoli, Podres, and Snider cards are quite scarce. The ACC designation is F339-1.

	MINT	VG-E	F-G
COMPLETE SET	480.00	340.00	150.00
COMMON PLAYER	25.00	19.00	8.00

	MINT	VG-E	F-G			MINT	VG-E	F-G
1 Roy Campanella	55.00	40.00	15.00	6 Sandy Koufax		55.00	40.00	15.00
2 Gino Cimoli	75.00	55.00	24.00	7 Johnny Podres		110.00	85.00	40.00
3 Don Drysdale	35.00	28.00	12.00	8 Pee Wee Reese		35.00	28.00	12.00
4 Jim Gilliam	30.00	24.00	10.00	9 Duke Snider		90.00	70.00	30.00
5 Gil Hodges	35.00	28.00	12.00	10 Don Zimmer		25.00	19.00	8.00

1960 BELL BRAND (20)

2 1/2" X 3 1/2"

SANDY KOUFAX
Left-Hand Pitcher   L.A. Dodgers

9   SANDY KOUFAX
Left-Hand Pitcher

Sandy tied the all-time record for strike-outs in a single game when he fanned eighteen Giants, matching the record held by Cleveland's Bob Feller. Sandy has the best strike-out average among currently active National League pitchers.

Start your collection of L. A. Dodger players! There's one in each package of 39c, 49c and 59c Bell Brand Potato Chips and the 29c, 49c Corn Chips.

Los Angeles Dodgers 1960 Home Game Schedule

The 1960 Bell Brand Potato Chips set of 20 full color, numbered cards features Los Angeles Dodgers only. Because these cards were issued in packages of potato chips, many cards suffered from stains. Labine, Klippstein, and Alston are somewhat more difficult to obtain than other cards in the set. The ACC designation is F339-2.

	MINT	VG-E	F-G
COMPLETE SET	150.00	110.00	50.00
COMMON PLAYER	6.50	5.00	2.25

	MINT	VG-E	F-G			MINT	VG-E	F-G
1 Norm Larker	6.50	5.00	2.25	11 Chuck Essegian		6.50	5.00	2.25
2 Duke Snider	15.00	11.00	5.00	12 John Klippstein		16.00	12.00	5.50
3 Danny McDevitt	6.50	5.00	2.25	13 Ed Roebuck		6.50	5.00	2.25
4 Jim Gilliam	8.00	6.00	2.50	14 Don Demeter		6.50	5.00	2.25
5 Rip Repulski	6.50	5.00	2.25	15 Roger Craig		6.50	5.00	2.25
6 Clem Labine	12.50	9.00	4.00	16 Stan Williams		6.50	5.00	2.25
7 John Roseboro	6.50	5.00	2.25	17 Don Zimmer		8.00	6.00	2.50
8 Carl Furillo	8.00	6.00	2.50	18 Walt Alston		15.00	11.00	5.00
9 Sandy Koufax	20.00	15.00	6.50	19 Johnny Podres		8.00	6.00	2.50
10 Joe Pignatano	6.50	5.00	2.25	20 Maury Wills		10.00	7.00	3.00

1961 BELL BRAND (20)

2 7/16" X 3 1/2"

DUKE SNIDER
OUTFIELDER   L.A. DODGERS

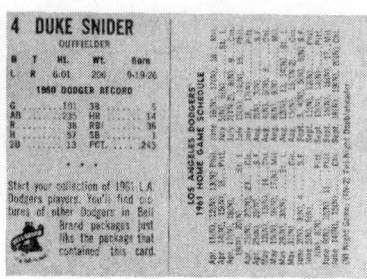

The 1961 Bell Brand Potato Chips set of 20 full color cards features Los Angeles Dodger players only and is numbered by the uniform numbers of the players. The cards are slightly smaller than the 1960 cards and are on thinner paper stock. The ACC designation is F339-3.

	MINT	VG-E	F-G
COMPLETE SET	125.00	90.00	40.00
COMMON PLAYER	5.50	4.25	2.00

		MINT	VG-E	F-G			MINT	VG-E	F-G
3	Willie Davis	6.50	5.00	2.25	22 John Podres	6.50	5.00	2.25
4	Duke Snider	12.50	9.00	4.00	24 Walt Alston	6.50	5.00	2.25
5	Norm Larker	5.50	4.25	2.00	30 Maury Wills	9.00	6.75	3.00
8	John Roseboro	5.50	4.25	2.00	32 Sandy Koufax	15.00	11.00	5.00
9	Wally Moon	5.50	4.25	2.00	34 Norm Sherry	5.50	4.25	2.00
11	Bob Lillis	5.50	4.25	2.00	37 Ed Roebuck	5.50	4.25	2.00
12	Tom Davis	6.50	5.00	2.25	38 Roger Craig	5.50	4.25	2.00
14	Gil Hodges	10.00	7.00	3.00	40 Stan Williams	5.50	4.25	2.00
16	Don Demeter	5.50	4.25	2.00	43 Charlie Neal	5.50	4.25	2.00
19	Jim Gilliam	7.00	5.25	2.50	51 Larry Sherry	5.50	4.25	2.00

1962 BELL BRAND (20)

2 7/16" X 3 1/2"

DON DRYSDALE
PITCHER   L.A. DODGERS

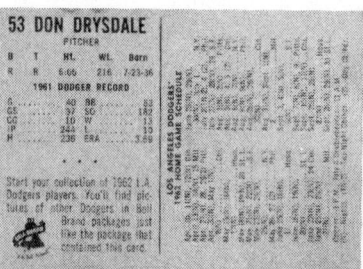

The 1962 Bell Brand set of 20 full color cards features Los Angeles Dodger players only and is numbered by the uniform numbers of the players. These cards were printed on a high quality glossy paper, much better than the previous two years, virtually eliminating the grease stains. This set is distinguished by a schedule on the backs of the cards. The ACC designation is F339-4.

	MINT	VG-E	F-G
COMPLETE SET	110.00	85.00	35.00
COMMON PLAYER	4.75	3.50	1.50

		MINT	VG-E	F-G			MINT	VG-E	F-G
3	Willie Davis	6.00	4.50	2.00	24 Walt Alston	6.00	4.50	2.00
4	Duke Snider	12.00	8.75	4.00	25 Frank Howard	7.00	5.25	2.50
6	Ron Fairly	4.75	3.50	1.50	30 Maury Wills	8.00	6.00	2.50
8	John Roseboro	4.75	3.50	1.50	32 Sandy Koufax	13.50	10.00	4.50
9	Wally Moon	4.75	3.50	1.50	34 Norm Sherry	4.75	3.50	1.50
12	Tom Davis	6.00	4.50	2.00	37 Ed Roebuck	4.75	3.50	1.50
16	Ron Perranoski	4.75	3.50	1.50	40 Stan Williams	4.75	3.50	1.50
19	Jim Gilliam	6.50	5.00	2.25	51 Larry Sherry	4.75	3.50	1.50
20	Daryl Spencer	4.75	3.50	1.50	53 Don Drysdale	10.00	7.00	3.00
22	John Podres	6.00	4.50	2.00	56 Lee Walls	4.75	3.50	1.50

1951 BERK ROSS (72)　　　　　2 1/16″ X 2 1/2″

The 1951 Berk Ross Set is a 72 card set composed of four series designated in the checklist as A, B, C, and D. Other sports stars are depicted along with the baseball players.

	MINT	VG-E	F-G
COMPLETE SET	125.00	90.00	40.00
COMMON BASEBALL	1.25	1.00	.40
COMMON NON-BB	.80	.60	.25
A1 Al Rosen	3.50	2.50	1.20
A2 Bob Lemon	4.00	3.00	1.40
A3 Phil Rizzuto	4.00	3.00	1.40
A4 Hank Bauer	2.50	1.80	.80
A5 Billy Johnson	1.25	.90	.40
A6 Jerry Coleman	1.75	1.25	.55
A7 Johnny Mize	3.00	2.25	1.00
A8 Dom DiMaggio	2.50	1.80	.80
A9 Richie Ashburn	2.00	1.40	.60
A10 Del Ennis	1.25	1.00	.40
A11 Bob Cousy	2.00	1.40	.60
A12 Dick Schnittker	.80	.60	.25
A13 Ezzard Charles	1.00	.70	.30
A14 Leon Hart	1.25	1.00	.40
A15 James Martin	.80	.60	.25
A16 Ben Hogan	2.00	1.40	.60
A17 Bill Durnan	.80	.60	.25
A18 Bill Quackenbush	.80	.60	.25
B1 Stan Musial	12.00	8.75	4.00
B2 Warren Spahn	6.00	4.50	2.10
B3 Tom Henrich	2.50	1.80	.80
B4 Yogi Berra	8.00	6.00	2.75
B5 Joe DiMaggio	20.00	14.00	6.00
B6 Bobby Brown	1.25	1.00	.40
B7 Granny Hamner	1.25	1.00	.40
B8 Willie Jones	1.25	1.00	.40
B9 Stan Lopata	1.25	1.00	.40
B10 Mike Goliat	1.25	1.00	.40
B11 Sherman White	.80	.60	.25
B12 Joe Maxim	.80	.60	.25
B13 Ray Robinson	3.00	2.25	1.00
B14 Doak Walker	1.75	1.25	.55
B15 Emil Sitko	.80	.60	.25
B16 Jack Stewart	.80	.60	.25
B17 Dick Button	1.00	.70	.30

	MINT	VG-E	F-G
B18 Melvin Patton	.80	.60	.25
C1 Ralph Kiner	4.00	3.00	1.40
C2 Billy Goodman	1.25	1.00	.40
C3 Allie Reynolds	2.50	1.80	.80
C4 Vic Raschi	2.00	1.40	.60
C5 Joe Page	2.00	1.40	.60
C6 Eddie Lopat	2.00	1.40	.60
C7 Andy Seminick	1.25	1.00	.40
C8 Dick Sisler	1.25	1.00	.40
C9 Eddie Waitkus	1.25	1.00	.40
C10 Ken Heintzelman	1.25	1.00	.40
C11 Paul Unruh	.80	.60	.25
C12 Jake LaMotta	2.00	1.40	.60
C13 Ike Williams	.80	.60	.25
C14 Wade Walker	.80	.60	.25
C15 Rodney Franz	.80	.60	.25
C16 Sid Abel	1.00	.70	.30
C17 Claire Sherman	.80	.60	.25
C18 Jesse Owens	3.00	2.25	1.00
D1 Gene Woodling	1.50	1.10	.50
D2 Cliff Mapes	1.25	1.00	.40
D3 Fred Sontort	1.25	1.00	.40
D4 Tommy Byrne	1.25	1.00	.40
D5 Whitey Ford	6.00	4.50	2.10
D6 Jim Konstanty	1.75	1.25	.55
D7 Russ Meyer	1.25	1.00	.40
D8 Robin Roberts	4.00	3.00	1.40
D9 Curt Simmons	1.25	1.00	.40
D10 Sam Jethroe	1.25	1.00	.40
D11 Bill Sharman	1.75	1.25	.55
D12 Sandy Saddler	.80	.60	.25
D13 Margaret DuPont	.80	.60	.25
D14 Arnold Galiffa	1.00	.70	.30
D15 Charlie Justice	1.50	1.10	.50
D16 Glen Cunningham	1.25	1.00	.40
D17 Gregory Rice	.80	.60	.25
D18 Harrison Dillard	.80	.60	.25

HAL SMITH

DICK GROAT

HOCUS FOCUS, SMALL & LARGE, PLUS ALBUM

1952 BERK ROSS (72)

2" X 3"

HIT PARADE OF CHAMPIONS
Trade Mark Reg. U.S. Pat. Off.
MICKEY MANTLE
Outfielder, New York Yankees
Member of the N. Y. Yankees
World Champions

Born Commerce, Oklahoma
October 20, 1931
Height 5-10, Weight 175
Throws Right, Bats Left or Right
1951 Hit .267 in 96 Games

The 1952 Berk Ross set contains most of the top stars of the era. The backs of the Ewell Blackwell and Nelson Fox cards are transposed; this error was never corrected. Rizzuto appears twice in the set: swinging a bat and bunting.

	MINT	VG-E	F-G		MINT	VG-E	F-G
COMPLETE SET	800.00	610.00	250.00	Ed Lopat	6.50	5.00	2.25
COMMON PLAYER	5.50	4.00	1.50	Sal Maglie	6.00	4.50	2.00
				Mickey Mantle	160.00	125.00	30.00
Richie Ashburn	6.50	5.00	2.25	Billy Martin	15.00	11.00	5.00
Hank Bauer	6.50	5.00	2.25	Willie Mays	120.00	90.00	40.00
Yogi Berra	24.00	18.00	8.50	Gil McDougald	6.50	5.00	2.25
Ewell Blackwell	6.00	4.50	2.00	Minnie Minoso	6.50	5.00	2.25
Bobby Brown	5.50	4.00	1.50	Johnny Mize	8.00	6.00	2.50
Jim Busby	5.50	4.00	1.50	Tom Morgan	5.50	4.00	1.50
Roy Campanella	32.00	24.00	11.00	Don Mueller	5.50	4.00	1.50
Chico Carrasquel	5.50	4.00	1.50	Stan Musial	65.00	48.00	22.00
Jerry Coleman	6.00	4.50	2.00	Don Newcombe	6.50	5.00	2.25
Joe Collins	5.50	4.00	1.50	Ray Noble	5.50	4.00	1.50
Alvin Dark	6.00	4.50	2.00	Joe Ostrowski	5.50	4.00	1.50
Dom DiMaggio	8.00	6.00	2.50	Mel Parnell	5.50	4.00	1.50
Joe DiMaggio	160.00	125.00	50.00	Vic Raschi	6.50	5.00	2.25
Larry Doby	6.50	5.00	2.25	Pee Wee Reese	9.00	6.75	3.00
Bobby Doerr	6.00	4.50	2.00	Allie Reynolds	6.50	5.00	2.25
Bob Elliott	5.50	4.00	1.50	Bill Rigney	5.50	4.00	1.50
Del Ennis	5.50	4.00	1.50	Phil Rizzuto (2)	12.50	9.00	4.00
Ferris Fain	5.50	4.00	1.50	Robin Roberts	10.00	7.00	3.00
Bob Feller	24.00	18.00	8.50	Eddie Robinson	6.50	5.00	2.25
Nellie Fox	7.50	5.75	2.50	Jackie Robinson	65.00	48.00	22.00
Ned Garver	5.50	4.00	1.50	Preacher Roe	7.00	5.25	2.50
Clint Hartung	5.50	4.00	1.50	Johnny Sain	6.50	5.00	2.25
Jim Hearn	5.50	4.00	1.50	Red Schoendienst	6.50	5.00	2.25
Gil Hodges	12.00	8.75	4.00	Duke Snider	21.00	15.50	7.00
Monte Irvin	9.00	6.75	3.00	George Spencer	5.50	4.00	1.50
Larry Jansen	5.50	4.00	1.50	Eddie Stanky	6.50	5.00	2.25
Sheldon Jones	5.50	4.00	1.50	Hank Thompson	5.50	4.00	1.50
George Kell	6.50	5.00	2.25	Bobby Thomson	6.50	5.00	2.25
Monte Kennedy	5.50	4.00	1.50	Vic Wertz	5.50	4.00	1.50
Ralph Kiner	11.00	8.00	3.50	Wally Westlake	5.50	4.00	1.50
Dave Koslo	5.50	4.00	1.50	Wes Westrum	5.50	4.00	1.50
Bob Kuzava	5.50	4.00	1.50	Ted Williams	90.00	70.00	30.00
Bob Lemon	10.00	7.00	3.00	Gene Woodling	5.50	4.00	1.50
Whitey Lockman	5.50	4.00	1.50	Gus Zernial	5.50	4.00	1.50

1958 BOND BREAD (9) 2 1/2" X 3 1/2"

1958 Bond Bread set of nine unnumbered cards features players from the Buffalo Bisons of the International League. The ACC designation is D301.

	MINT	VG-E	F-G		MINT	VG-E	F-G
COMPLETE SET	80.00	60.00	25.00	4 Rip Coleman	6.00	4.50	2.00
COMMON PLAYER	6.00	4.50	2.00	5 Luke Easter	40.00	30.00	13.00
				6 Ken Johnson	6.00	4.50	2.00
1 Al Aber	6.00	4.50	2.00	7 L. Ortiz	6.00	4.50	2.00
2 Joe Caffie	6.00	4.50	2.00	8 Jack Phillips	6.00	4.50	2.00
3 Phil Cavaretta	10.00	7.00	3.00	9 Jim Small	6.00	4.50	2.00

1947 BOND BREAD (13) JACKIE ROBINSON 2 1/4" X 3 1/2"

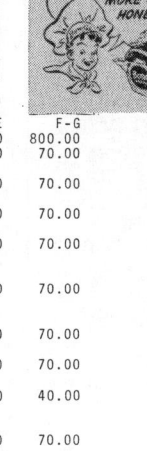

The 1947 Bond Bread Jackie Robinson set features 13 cards of Jackie in different action or portrait poses. Card number 7 was issued in greater quantity than other cards in the set. The ACC designation is D302.

	MINT	VG-E	F-G
COMPLETE SET	2500.00	1800.00	800.00
COMMON CARD	200.00	150.00	70.00
1 Sliding into base, cap ump in photo (horiz.)	200.00	150.00	70.00
2 Running down 3rd base line (vert.)	200.00	150.00	70.00
3 Batting, bat behind head, facing camera (vert.)	200.00	150.00	70.00
4 Moving towards second, throw almost to glove (horiz.)	200.00	150.00	70.00
5 Taking throw at first (horiz.)	200.00	150.00	70.00
6 Jumping high in air for ball (vert.)	200.00	150.00	70.00
7 Profile with glove in front of head, auto-graphed (vert.)	125.00	100.00	40.00
8 Leaping over 2nd base, ready to throw (vert)	200.00	150.00	70.00
9 Portrait--holding glove over head	200.00	150.00	70.00
10 Portrait--holding bat perpendicular to body	200.00	150.00	70.00
11 Reaching for throw, glove near ankle	200.00	150.00	70.00
12 Leaping for throw, no scoreboard in back-ground.	200.00	150.00	70.00
13 Portrait--holding bat parallel to body.	200.00	150.00	70.00

1948 BOWMAN (48) B&W

2 1/8" X 2 1/2"

18 — WARREN SPAHN
Pitcher—Boston Braves
Born: Buffalo, N. Y.   1922
Bats: Left   Throws: Left
Height: 6:00   Weight: 165

Beginning his career with Bradford in
the Pony League in 1940, his record
was not spectacular though he did
strike out 62 batters in 66 innings.
Next year he led the Three I League in
games won. After that his Hartford
record for the Eastern League was
17-12. In rejoining the Braves after
the war, he won 8 and lost 5. Last
year he really clicked—winning 21—
losing 10.

ASK FOR BLONY BUBBLE GUM
The Bubble Gum with
the three different flavors
BOWMAN GUM, INC. Copyright 1948

The 1948 Bowman set is considered to be the first set of
the modern era. This black
& white set contains twelve
cards which are relatively
more difficult to obtain than
the other 36. These cards
are marked with an (*) on
the checklist below.

	MINT	VG-E	F-G
COMPLETE SET	580.00	310.00	140.00
COMMON PLAYERS (1-36)	3.25	2.50	1.00
COMMON PLAYERS (37-48)	4.50	3.50	1.50

No.	Player	MINT	VG-E	F-G
1	Bob Elliot	7.50	3.50	1.50
2	Ewell Blackwell	3.25	2.50	1.00
3	Ralph Kiner	13.00	9.50	4.00
4	Johnny Mize	8.00	6.00	2.50
5	Bob Feller	21.00	15.50	7.00
6	"Yogi" Berra	22.00	16.50	7.50
7	Peter Reiser*	12.50	9.00	4.00
8	Phil Rizzuto*	32.00	24.00	11.00
9	Walker Cooper	3.25	2.50	1.00
10	Buddy Rosar	3.25	2.50	1.00
11	Johnny Lindell	3.25	2.50	1.00
12	Johnny Sain	5.00	3.75	1.75
13	Willard Marshall*	10.50	7.50	3.50
14	Allie Reynolds	6.00	4.50	2.00
15	Eddie Joost	3.25	2.50	1.00
16	Jack Lohrke*	10.50	7.50	3.50
17	Enos Slaughter	7.50	5.75	2.50
18	Warren Spahn	17.00	12.50	6.00
19	Tommy Henrich	6.00	4.50	2.00
20	Buddy Kerr*	10.50	7.50	3.50
21	Ferris Fain	3.25	2.50	1.00
22	Floyd Bevins*	10.50	7.50	3.50
23	Larry Jansen	3.25	2.50	1.00
24	"Dutch" Leonard*	10.50	7.50	3.50
25	Barney McCoskey	3.25	2.50	1.00
26	Frank Shea*	10.50	7.50	3.50
27	Sid Gordon	3.25	2.50	1.00
28	Emil Verbam*	10.50	7.50	3.50
29	Joe Page*	12.50	9.00	4.00
30	Whitey Lockman*	10.50	7.50	3.50
31	Bill McCahan	3.25	2.50	1.00
32	Bill Rigney	3.25	2.50	1.00
33	Bill Johnson	3.25	2.50	1.00
34	Sheldon Jones*	10.50	7.50	3.50
35	"Snuffy" Sternweiss	3.25	2.50	1.00
36	Stan Musial	55.00	42.00	19.00
37	Clint Hartung	4.50	3.50	1.50
38	"Red" Schoendienst	6.00	4.50	2.00
39	Augie Galan	4.50	3.50	1.50
40	Marty Marion	4.50	3.50	1.50
41	Rex Barney	6.00	4.50	2.00
42	Ray Pope	4.50	3.50	1.50
43	Bruce Edwards	4.50	3.50	1.50
44	Johnny Wyrostek	4.50	3.50	1.50
45	Hank Sauer	6.00	4.50	2.00
46	Herman Wehmeier	4.50	3.50	1.50
47	Bobby Thomson	7.50	5.75	2.50
48	"Dave" Koslo	4.50	3.50	1.50

1949 BOWMAN PCL (36)

2 1/8" X 2 1/2"

PCL No. 24
CHARLES "Red" ADAMS
Pitcher—Los Angeles Angels
Born: Parlier, Calif., October 7, 1921
Bats: Right Throws: Right Ht.: 6:2 Wt.: 195

First joined Los Angeles in 1942 after three seasons in lower minors. In 1945 he won 21 games
for Angels, losing 15. Had a trial with Chicago
Cubs at beginning of 1946 season. Rejoined
Angels and has been with them ever since. In
1947 his record was 14 wins and 12 losses, and
last season it read 14-11. Hobby is catching and
training mountain lions.

#202—OFFICIAL BASEBALL RING
Made of durable metal. Adjustable—fits any size
finger. Silverplate oxidized finish shows detail of
official Baseball Emblem. Baseball of white
plastic. Sides show Baseball and
Crossed Bats design. Send only 15c
and 3 Baseball wrappers to:
BASEBALL, P.O. BOX 491
NEW YORK 46, N. Y.

(Not valid where contrary to State laws.)
Offer expires 12/31/49 ©Bowman Gum, Inc., 1949

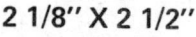

1949 Bowman Pacific Coast
League set is one of the
scarcest sets of modern times.
It is not a Bowman regular
issue, and there is still considerable doubt as to whether or not this set was of-
ficially released for sale. Pacific League players only are
portrayed.

	MINT	VG-E	F-G
COMPLETE SET	7000.00	5400.00	2500.00
COMMON PLAYERS	200.00	150.00	70.00

No.	Player	MINT	VG-E	F-G
1	Lee Anthony	200.00	150.00	70.00
2	George Metkovich	200.00	150.00	70.00
3	Ralph Hodgin	200.00	150.00	70.00
4	George Woods	200.00	150.00	70.00
5	Xavier Rescigno	200.00	150.00	70.00
6	Mickey Grasso	200.00	150.00	70.00
7	Johnny Rucker	200.00	150.00	70.00
8	Jack Brewer	200.00	150.00	70.00
9	Dom D'Allessandro	200.00	150.00	70.00
10	Charlie Gassaway	200.00	150.00	70.00
11	Tony Freitas	200.00	150.00	70.00
12	Gordon Maltzberger	200.00	150.00	70.00
13	John Jensen	200.00	150.00	70.00
14	Joyner White	200.00	150.00	70.00
15	Harvey Storey	200.00	150.00	70.00
16	Dick Lajeski	200.00	150.00	70.00
17	Albie Glosson	200.00	150.00	70.00
18	Bill Raimondi	200.00	150.00	70.00
19	Ken Holcombe	200.00	150.00	70.00
20	Don Ross	200.00	150.00	70.00
21	Pete Coscarart	200.00	150.00	70.00
22	Tony York	200.00	150.00	70.00
23	Jake Mooty	200.00	150.00	70.00
24	Charles Adams	200.00	150.00	70.00
25	Les Scarsella	200.00	150.00	70.00
26	Joe Marty	200.00	150.00	70.00
27	Frank Kelleher	200.00	150.00	70.00
28	Lee Handley	200.00	150.00	70.00
29	Herman Besse	200.00	150.00	70.00
30	John Lazor	200.00	150.00	70.00
31	Eddie Malone	200.00	150.00	70.00
32	Maurice Van Robays	200.00	150.00	70.00
33	Jim Tabor	200.00	150.00	70.00
34	Gene Handiley	200.00	150.00	70.00
35	Tom Seats	200.00	150.00	70.00
36	Ora Burnett	200.00	150.00	70.00

Hall's Nostalgia

If you're looking for those missing baseball cards in your collection, why not try buying them from Hall's Nostalgia? We have several hundred thousand cards from 1880 to date. If you can visit our store, you are welcome to browse around. However, we also serve over 10,000 mail order customers and would be happy to add your name to the growing list. Just send a stamped - self addressed - envelope, and 50¢ for handling, along with your want list, and we will promptly send out a price quote for your specific needs. We also carry thousands of sport publications so send $1.00 for our current publication list.

BASEBALL CARDS WANTED

Paying 35% up to 100% of this guide.
Always check with us before you sell.

43

No. 50 of a Series of 240
JACKIE ROBINSON
Second Base—Brooklyn Dodgers
Born: Cairo, Georgia, January 31, 1919
Bats: Right Throws: Right Ht.: 6:0 Wt.: 190

When Brooklyn signed him to Montreal Royal contract, he became first Negro to enter rank of pro ball. As Royals' regular second baseman for 1946 he led International League in batting with .349. When he joined Dodgers in 1947 he was switched to first base. Led National League in stolen bases with 29, hit .296 and was named Rookie of Year. Last year he finished with same average, .296 and batted in 85 runs.

#202—OFFICIAL BASEBALL RING
Made of durable metal. Adjustable—fits any size finger. Beautiful silverplate oxidized finish brings out detail of official Baseball Emblem. Baseball of white plastic. Sides of ring show Baseball and Crossed Bats design. Send only 15c and 3 Baseball wrappers to BASEBALL, P.O. BOX 491 NEW YORK 46, N. Y.

(Not valid where contrary to State laws)
Offer expires 12/31/49 ©Bowman Gum, Inc., 1949

The 1949 Set is Bowman's first color set and the most difficult Bowman regular issue to complete. The high numbers 145-240 are somewhat scarce. Card nos. 4, 78, 83, 85, 86, 88, and 98 exist with or without the player's name printed on the front of the card, i.e., no name on front (NNOF). Card nos. 109, 124, 126, 127, 132, and 143 exist with printed (PR) or script (SCR) name on the back of the card. Cards up to no. 144 were issued in series of 36 cards except that no. 4 was included with the third series.

	MINT	VG-E	F-G
COMPLETE SET	2650.00	2100.00	900.00
COMMON (1-37, 74-108)	3.25	2.50	1.00
COMMON PLAYER (38-73)	4.25	3.00	1.25
COMMON PLAYER (109-144)	2.25	1.60	.70
COMMON PLAYER (145-240)	14.50	11.00	4.50
1 Vern Bickford	10.00	4.00	1.50
2 Whitey Lockman	3.25	2.50	1.00
3 Bob Porterfield	3.25	2.50	1.00
4A Jerry Priddy(NNOF)	4.00	3.00	1.40
4B Jerry Priddy(NOF)	10.00	7.00	3.00
5 Hank Sauer	4.00	3.00	1.40
6 Phil Cavaretta	4.00	3.00	1.40
7 Joe Dobson	3.25	2.50	1.00
8 Murray Dickson	3.25	2.50	1.00
9 Ferris Fain	4.00	3.00	1.40
10 Ted Gray	3.25	2.50	1.00
11 Lou Boudreau	10.00	2.50	1.00
12 Cass Michaels	3.25	2.50	1.00
13 Bob Chesnes	3.25	2.50	1.00
14 Curt Simmons	4.00	2.50	1.00
15 Ned Garver	3.25	2.50	1.00
16 Al Kozar	3.25	2.50	1.00
17 Earl Torgeson	3.25	2.50	1.00
18 Bobby Thomson	6.00	4.50	2.00
19 Bobby Brown	3.25	2.50	1.00
20 Gene Hermanski	3.25	2.50	1.00
21 Frank Baumholtz	3.25	2.50	1.00
22 "Peanuts" Lowrey	3.25	2.50	1.00
23 Bobby Doerr	4.00	3.00	1.40
24 Stan Musial	55.00	42.00	19.00
25 Carl Scheib	3.25	2.50	1.00
26 George Kell	4.00	3.00	1.40
27 Bob Feller	22.00	16.50	7.50
28 Don Kolloway	3.25	2.50	1.00
29 Ralph Kiner	11.00	8.00	3.50
30 Andy Seminick	3.25	2.50	1.00
31 Dick Kokos	3.25	2.50	1.00
32 Eddie Yost	3.25	2.50	1.00
33 Warren Spahn	16.00	12.00	5.50
34 Dave Koslo	3.25	2.50	1.00
35 Vic Raschi	5.00	3.75	1.75
36 "Peewee" Reese	10.00	7.00	3.00
37 John Wyrostek	3.25	2.50	1.00
38 Emil Verban	4.25	3.00	1.25
39 Billy Goodman	4.25	3.00	1.25
40 "Red" Munger	4.25	3.00	1.25
41 Lou Brissie	4.25	3.00	1.25
42 "Hoot" Evers	4.25	3.00	1.25
43 Dale Mitchell	4.25	3.00	1.25
44 Dave Philley	4.25	3.00	1.25
45 Wally Westlake	4.00	3.00	1.25
46 Robin Roberts	11.00	8.00	3.50
47 Johnny Sain	5.50	4.25	2.00
48 Willard Marshall	4.25	3.00	1.25
49 Frank Shea	4.25	3.00	1.25
50 Jackie Robinson	55.00	42.00	19.00
51 Herman Wehmeier	4.25	3.00	1.25
52 Johnny Schmitz	4.25	3.00	1.25
53 Jack Kramer	4.25	3.00	1.25
54 Marty Marion	5.50	4.25	2.00
55 Eddie Joost	4.25	3.00	1.25
56 Pat Mullin	4.25	3.00	1.25
57 Gene Bearden	4.25	3.00	1.25
58 Bob Elliott	4.25	3.00	1.25
59 Jack Lohrke	4.25	3.00	1.25
60 "Yogi" Berra	30.00	22.50	10.50
61 Rex Barney	4.25	3.00	1.25
62 Grady Hatton	4.25	3.00	1.25
63 Andy Pafko	4.25	3.00	1.25
64 Dom DiMaggio	7.50	5.75	2.50
65 Enos Slaughter	7.50	5.75	2.50

	MINT	VG-E	F-G
66 Elmer Valo	4.25	3.00	1.25
67 Alvin Dark	5.50	4.25	2.00
68 Sheldon Jones	4.25	3.00	1.25
69 Tommy Henrich	6.50	5.00	2.25
70 Carl Furillo	6.50	5.00	2.25
71 Vern Stephens	4.25	3.00	1.25
72 Tommy Holmes	5.50	4.25	2.00
73 Billy Cox	4.25	3.00	1.25
74 Tom McBride	3.25	2.50	1.00
75 Eddie Mayo	3.25	2.50	1.00
76 Bill Nicholson	3.25	2.50	1.00
77 Ernie Donham	3.25	2.50	1.00
78A Sam Zoldak(NNOF)	4.00	3.00	1.40
78B Sam Zoldak(NOF)	10.00	7.00	3.00
79 Ron Northey	3.25	2.50	1.00
80 Bill McCahan	3.25	2.50	1.00
81 Virgil Stallcup	3.25	2.50	1.00
82 Joe Page	4.00	3.00	1.40
83A Bob Scheffing(NNOF)	4.00	3.00	1.40
83B Bob Scheffing(NOF)	10.00	7.00	3.00
84A Roy Campanella(NNOF)	40.00	30.00	13.00
84B Roy Campanella(NOF)	not verified		xxxx
85A Johnny Mize(NNOF)	8.00	6.00	2.50
85B Johnny Mize(NOF)	20.00	15.00	6.50
86A Johnny Pesky(NNOF)	4.00	3.00	1.40
86B Johnny Pesky(NOF)	10.00	7.00	3.00
87 Randy Gumpert	3.25	2.50	1.00
88A Bill Salkeld(NNOF)	4.00	3.00	1.40
88B Bill Salkeld(NOF)	10.00	7.00	3.00
89 Mizell Platt	3.25	2.50	1.00
90 Gil Coan	3.25	2.50	1.00
91 Dick Wakefield	3.25	2.50	1.00
92 Willie Jones	3.25	2.50	1.00
93 Ed Stevens	3.25	2.50	1.00
94 "Mickey" Vernon	4.00	3.00	1.40
95 Howie Pollet	3.25	2.50	1.00
96 Taft Wright	3.25	2.50	1.00
97 Danny Litwhiler	3.25	2.50	1.00
98A Phil Rizzuto(NNOF)	12.00	8.75	4.00
98B Phil Rizzuto(NOF)	30.00	22.50	10.50
99 Frank Gustine	3.25	2.50	1.00
100 Gil Hodges	11.00	8.00	3.50
101 Sid Gordon	3.25	2.50	1.00
102 Stan Spence	3.25	2.50	1.00
103 Joe Tipton	3.25	2.50	1.00
104 Ed Stanky	4.00	3.00	1.40
105A Bill Kennedy(NNOF)	3.25	2.50	1.00
105B Bill Kennedy(NOF)	not verified		xxxx
106 Jake Early	3.25	2.50	1.00
107 Eddie Lake	3.25	2.50	1.00
108 Ken Heintzleman	3.25	2.50	1.00
109A Ed Fitzgerald(PR)	3.00	2.50	1.00
109B Ed Fitzgerald(SCR)	8.00	6.00	2.50
110 Early Wynn	8.00	6.00	2.50
111 "Red" Schoendienst	4.00	3.00	1.40
112 Sam Chapman	2.25	1.60	.70
113 Ray LaManno	2.25	1.60	.70
114 Allie Reynolds	4.50	3.50	1.60
115 "Dutch" Leonard	2.25	1.60	.70
116 Joe Hatton	2.25	1.60	.70
117 Walker Cooper	2.25	1.60	.70
118 Sam Mele	2.25	1.60	.70
119 Floyd Baker	2.25	1.60	.70
120 Cliff Fannin	2.25	1.60	.70
121 Mark Christman	2.25	1.60	.70
122 George Vico	2.25	1.60	.70
123 Johnny Blatnick	2.25	1.60	.70
124A Danny Murtaugh(PR)	3.00	2.50	1.00
124B Danny Murtaugh(SCR)	8.00	6.00	2.50
125 Ken Keltner	2.25	1.60	.70
126A Al Brazle(PRINT)	3.00	2.50	1.00
126B Al Brazle(SCRIPT)	8.00	6.00	2.50

	MINT	VG-E	F-G
127A "Hank" Majeski(PRINT)	3.00	2.25	1.00
127B "Hank" Majeski(SCR)	8.00	6.00	2.50
128 Johnny Vander Meer	4.00	3.00	1.40
129 Bill Johnson	2.25	1.60	.70
130 Harry Walker	2.25	1.60	.70
131 Paul Lehner	2.25	1.60	.70
132A Al Evans(PRINT)	3.00	2.25	1.00
132B Al Evans(SCRIPT)	8.00	6.00	2.50
133 Aaron Robinson	2.25	1.60	.70
134 Hank Borowy	2.25	1.60	.70
135 Stan Rojek	2.25	1.60	.70
136 "Hank" Edwards	2.25	1.60	.70
137 Ted Wilks	2.25	1.60	.70
138 "Buddy" Rosar	2.25	1.60	.70
139 Hank Arft	2.25	1.60	.70
140 Rae Scarborough	2.25	1.60	.70
141 Ulysses Lupien	2.25	1.60	.70
142 Eddie Waitkus	2.25	1.60	.70
143A Bob Dillinger(PRINT)	3.00	2.25	1.00
143B Bob Dillinger(SCRIPT)	8.00	6.00	2.50
144 "Mickey" Haefner	2.25	1.60	.70
145 Sylvester Donnelly	14.50	11.00	4.50
146 "Mike" McCormick	14.50	11.00	4.50
147 "Bert" Singleton	14.50	11.00	4.50
148 Bob Swift	14.50	11.00	4.50
149 Roy Partee	14.50	11.00	4.50
150 Allie Clark	14.50	11.00	4.50
151 Mickey Harris	14.50	11.00	4.50
152 Clarence Maddern	14.50	11.00	4.50
153 Phil Masi	14.50	11.00	4.50
154 Clint Hartung	14.50	11.00	4.50
155 "Mickey" Guerra	14.50	11.00	4.50
156 Al Zarilla	14.50	11.00	4.50
157 Walt Masterson	14.50	11.00	4.50
158 Harry Brecheen	16.00	12.00	5.50
159 Glen Moulder	14.50	11.00	4.50
160 Jim Blackburn	14.50	11.00	4.50
161 "Jocko" Thompson	14.50	11.00	4.50
162 "Preacher" Roe	21.00	15.50	7.00
163 Clyde McCullough	14.50	11.00	4.50
164 Vic Wertz	14.50	11.00	4.50
165 "Snuffy" Stirnweiss	14.50	11.00	4.50
166 Mike Tresh	14.50	11.00	4.50
167 "Babe" Martin	14.50	11.00	4.50
168 Doyle Lake	14.50	11.00	4.50
169 Jeff Heath	14.50	11.00	4.50
170 Bill Rigney	14.50	11.00	4.50
171 Dick Fowler	14.50	11.00	4.50
172 Eddie Pellagrini	14.50	11.00	4.50
173 Eddie Stewart	14.50	11.00	4.50
174 Terry Moore	16.00	12.00	5.50
175 Luke Appling	25.00	18.50	8.75
176 Ken Raffensberger	14.50	11.00	4.50
177 Stan Lopata	14.50	11.00	4.50
178 Tommy Brown	14.50	11.00	4.50
179 Hugh Casey	14.50	11.00	4.50
180 Connie Berry	14.50	11.00	4.50
181 Gus Niarhos	14.50	11.00	4.50

	MINT	VG-E	F-G
182 Hall Peck	14.50	11.00	4.50
183 Lou Stringer	14.50	11.00	4.50
184 Bob Chipman	14.50	11.00	4.50
185 Pete Reiser	18.00	13.50	6.00
186 "Buddy" Kerr	14.50	11.00	4.50
187 Phil Marchildon	14.50	11.00	4.50
188 Karl Drews	14.50	11.00	4.50
189 Earl Wooten	14.50	11.00	4.50
190 Jim Hearn	14.50	11.00	4.50
191 Joe Haynes	14.50	11.00	4.50
192 Harry Gumbert	14.50	11.00	4.50
193 Ken Trinkle	14.50	11.00	4.50
194 Ralph Branca	16.00	12.00	5.50
195 Eddie Bockman	14.50	11.00	4.50
196 Fred Hutchinson	18.00	13.50	6.00
197 Johnny Lindell	14.50	11.00	4.50
198 Steve Gromek	14.50	11.00	4.50
199 "Tex" Hughson	14.50	11.00	4.50
200 Jess Dobernic	14.50	11.00	4.50
201 Sibby Sisti	14.50	11.00	4.50
202 Larry Jansen	14.50	11.00	4.50
203 Barney McCosky	14.50	11.00	4.50
204 Bob Savage	14.50	11.00	4.50
205 Dick Sisler	14.50	11.00	4.50
206 Bruce Edwards	14.50	11.00	4.50
207 Johnny Hopp	14.50	11.00	4.50
208 "Dizzy" Trout	14.50	11.00	4.50
209 Charlie Keller	18.00	13.50	6.00
210 Joe Gordon	14.50	11.00	4.50
211 "Boo" Ferriss	14.50	11.00	4.50
212 Ralph Hamner	14.50	11.00	4.50
213 "Red" Barrett	14.50	11.00	4.50
214 Richie Ashburn	24.00	18.00	8.50
215 Kirby Higbe	14.50	11.00	4.50
216 "Schoolboy" Rowe	18.00	13.50	6.00
217 Marion Pieretti	14.50	11.00	4.50
218 Dick Kryhoski	14.50	11.00	4.50
219 "Fire" Trucks	14.50	11.00	4.50
220 Johnny McCarthy	14.50	11.00	4.50
221 Bob Muncrief	14.50	11.00	4.50
222 Alex Kellner	14.50	11.00	4.50
223 Bobby Hofmann	14.50	11.00	4.50
224 "Satchell" Paige	375.00	275.00	125.00
225 Gerry Coleman	16.00	12.00	5.50
226 "Duke" Snider	200.00	150.00	65.00
227 Fritz Ostermueller	14.50	11.00	4.50
228 Jackie Mayo	14.50	11.00	4.50
229 Ed Lopat	22.00	16.50	7.50
230 Augie Galan	14.50	11.00	4.50
231 Earl Johnson	14.50	11.00	4.50
232 George McQuinn	14.50	11.00	4.50
233 Larry Doby	22.00	16.50	7.50
234 "Rip" Sewell	14.50	11.00	4.50
235 Jim Russell	14.50	11.00	4.50
236 Fred Sanford	14.50	11.00	4.50
237 Monte Kennedy	14.50	11.00	4.50
238 Bob Lemon	75.00	55.00	24.00
239 Frank McCormick	14.50	11.00	4.50
240 "Babe" Young	14.50	11.00	4.50

1950 BOWMAN (252)   2 1/8" X 2 1/2"

ROY CAMPANELLA
Catcher—Brooklyn Dodgers
Born: Philadelphia, Nov. 19, 1921
Height: 5-9½   Weight: 180
Bats: Right   Throws: Right
In his second big-league year (1949)
Roy led National League catchers
appearing in 100 or more games with a
fielding percentage of .985. Hit .287
in 130 games, banged 22 homers, drove
in 82 runs. Was the NL all-star catcher.
Dodgers first noted Roy when he played
against them on an all-star Negro team
in an exhibition game.
No. 75 in the 1950 SERIES of BASEBALL Picture Cards
© 1950 Bowman Gum, Inc., Phila., Pa., U.S.A.

The Bowman set of 252 color cards showed a marked improvement in the quality and color over the 1949 issue. The "low numbers", 1-72, are more difficult to obtain than the higher numbers.

	MINT	VG-E	F-G
COMPLETE SET	875.00	700.00	300.00
COMMON PLAYER (1-72)	4.75	3.75	1.75
COMMON PLAYER (73-252)	2.00	1.50	.60
1 Mel Parnell	20.00	15.00	6.50
2 Vern Stephens	4.75	3.75	1.75
3 Dom DiMaggio	8.00	6.00	2.50
4 Gus Zernial	4.75	3.75	1.75
5 Bob Kuzava	4.75	3.75	1.75
6 Bob Feller	26.00	19.00	9.00

	MINT	VG-E	F-G
7 Jim Hegan	4.75	3.75	1.75
8 George Kell	6.00	4.50	2.00
9 Vic Wertz	4.75	3.75	1.75
10 Tommy Henrich	7.50	5.75	2.50
11 Phil Rizzuto	15.00	11.00	5.00
12 Joe Page	6.50	5.00	2.25
13 Ferris Fain	6.00	4.50	2.00
14 Alex Kellner	4.75	3.75	1.75
15 Al Kozar	4.75	3.75	1.75
16 Roy Sievers	4.75	3.75	1.75

	MINT	VG-E	F-G
17 Sid Hudson	4.75	3.75	1.75
18 Eddie Robinson	4.75	3.75	1.75
19 Warren Spahn	17.00	12.50	6.00
20 Bob Elliott	4.75	3.75	1.75
21 "Peewee" Reese	12.00	8.75	4.00
22 Jackie Robinson	50.00	38.00	17.00
23 Don Newcombe	8.50	6.50	3.00
24 Johnny Schmitz	4.75	3.75	1.75
25 Hank Sauer	5.50	4.25	2.00
26 Grady Hatton	4.75	3.75	1.75
27 Herman Wehmeier	4.75	3.75	1.75
28 Bobby Thomson	7.50	5.75	2.50
29 Eddie Stanky	5.50	4.25	2.00
30 Eddie Waitkus	4.75	3.75	1.75
31 Del Ennis	5.50	4.25	2.00
32 Robin Roberts	13.00	9.50	4.00
33 Ralph Kiner	12.00	8.75	4.00
34 Murry Dickson	4.75	3.75	1.75
35 Enos Slaughter	8.00	6.00	2.50
36 Eddie Kazak	4.75	3.75	1.75
37 Luke Appling	7.50	5.75	2.50
38 Bill Wight	4.75	3.75	1.75
39 Larry Doby	6.00	4.50	2.00
40 Bob Lemon	11.50	8.25	3.75
41 "Hoot" Evers	4.75	3.75	1.75
42 Art Houtteman	4.75	3.75	1.75
43 Bobby Doerr	6.00	4.50	2.00
44 Joe Dobson	4.75	3.75	1.75
45 Al Zarilla	4.75	3.75	2.00
46 "Yogi" Berra	27.00	20.00	9.00
47 Jerry Coleman	6.00	4.50	2.00
48 Lou Brissie	4.75	3.75	1.75
49 Elmer Valo	4.75	3.75	1.75
50 Dick Kokos	4.75	3.75	1.75
51 Ned Garver	4.75	3.75	1.75
52 Sam Mele	4.75	3.75	1.75
53 Clyde Vollmer	4.75	3.75	1.75
54 Gil Coan	4.75	3.75	1.75
55 "Buddy" Kerr	4.75	3.75	1.75
56 Del Crandell	5.50	4.25	2.00
57 Vern Bickford	4.75	3.75	1.75
58 Carl Furillo	6.00	4.50	2.00
59 Ralph Branca	5.50	4.25	2.00
60 Andy Pafko	4.75	3.75	1.75
61 Bob Rush	4.75	3.75	1.75
62 Ted Kluszewski	6.00	4.50	2.00
63 Ewell Blackwell	5.50	4.25	2.00
64 Al Dark	6.00	4.50	2.00
65 Dave Koslo	4.75	3.75	1.75
66 Larry Jansen	4.75	3.75	1.75
67 Willie Jones	4.75	3.75	1.75
68 Curt Simmons	5.50	4.25	2.00
69 Wally Westlake	4.75	3.75	1.75
70 Bob Chesnes	4.75	3.75	1.75
71 "Red" Schoendienst	6.00	4.50	2.00
72 Howie Pollet	4.75	3.75	1.75
73 Willard Marshall	2.00	1.50	.60
74 Johnny Antonelli	5.50	4.25	2.00
75 Roy Campanella	30.00	22.50	10.50
76 Rex Barney	2.00	1.50	.60
77 Duke Snider	17.00	12.50	6.00
78 Mickey Owen	2.00	1.50	.60
79 Johnny Vandermeer	3.50	2.50	1.20
80 Howard Fox	2.00	1.50	.60
81 Ron Northey	2.00	1.50	.60
82 Whitey Lockman	2.00	1.50	.60
83 Sheldon Jones	2.00	1.50	.60
84 Richie Ashburn	4.00	3.00	1.40
85 Ken Heintzleman	2.00	1.50	.60
86 Stan Rojek	2.00	1.50	.60
87 Bill Werle	2.00	1.50	.60
88 Marty Marion	3.00	2.25	1.00
89 "Red" Munger	2.00	1.50	.60
90 Harry Brecheen	2.50	1.80	.80
91 Cass Michaels	2.00	1.50	.60
92 Hank Majeski	2.00	1.50	.60
93 Gene Bearden	2.00	1.50	.60
94 Lou Boudreau	8.50	6.50	3.00
95 Aaron Robinson	2.00	1.50	.60
96 Virgil Trucks	2.00	1.50	.60
97 Maurice McDermott	2.00	1.50	.60
98 Ted Williams	65.00	48.00	22.00
99 Billy Goodman	2.00	1.50	.60
100 Vic Raschi	3.00	2.25	1.00
101 Bobby Brown	2.00	1.50	.60
102 Billy Johnson	2.00	1.50	.60
103 Eddie Joost	2.00	1.50	.60
104 Sam Chapman	2.00	1.50	.60
105 Bob Dillinger	2.00	1.50	.60
106 Cliff Fannin	2.00	1.50	.60
107 Sam Dente	2.00	1.50	.60
108 Ray Scarborough	2.00	1.50	.60
109 Sid Gordon	2.00	1.50	.60

	MINT	VG-E	F-G
110 Tommy Holmes	3.00	2.25	1.00
111 Walker Cooper	2.00	1.50	.60
112 Gil Hodges	12.00	8.75	4.00
113 Gene Hermanski	2.00	1.50	.60
114 Wayne Terwilliger	2.00	1.50	.60
115 Roy Smalley	2.00	1.50	.60
116 Virgil Stallcup	2.00	1.50	.60
117 Bill Rigney	2.00	1.50	.60
118 Clint Hartung	2.00	1.50	.60
119 Dick Sisler	2.00	1.50	.60
120 John Thompson	2.00	1.50	.60
121 Andy Seminick	2.00	1.50	.60
122 Johnny Hopp	2.50	1.80	.80
123 Dino Restelli	2.00	1.50	.60
124 Clyde McCullough	2.00	1.50	.60
125 Del Rice	2.00	1.50	.60
126 Al Brazle	2.00	1.50	.60
127 Dave Philley	2.00	1.50	.60
128 Phil Masi	2.00	1.50	.60
129 Joe Gordon	2.00	1.50	.60
130 Dale Mitchell	2.00	1.50	.60
131 Steve Gromek	2.00	1.50	.60
132 James Vernon	3.00	2.25	1.00
133 Don Kolloway	2.00	1.50	.60
134 Paul Trout	2.00	1.50	.60
135 Pat Mullin	2.00	1.50	.60
136 Warren Rosar	2.00	1.50	.60
137 Johnny Pesky	2.50	1.80	.80
138 Allie Reynolds	4.00	3.00	1.40
139 Johnny Mize	6.50	5.00	2.25
140 Pete Suder	2.00	1.50	.60
141 Joe Coleman	2.00	1.50	.60
142 Sherman Lollar	2.00	1.50	.60
143 Eddie Stewart	2.00	1.50	.60
144 Al Evans	2.00	1.50	.60
145 Jack Graham	2.00	1.50	.60
146 Floyd Baker	2.00	1.50	.60
147 Mike Garcia	2.50	1.80	.80
148 Early Wynn	10.00	7.00	3.00
149 Bob Swift	2.00	1.50	.60
150 George Vico	2.00	1.50	.60
151 Fred Hutchinson	3.00	2.25	1.00
152 Ellis Kinder	2.00	1.50	.60
153 Walt Masterson	2.00	1.50	.60
154 Gus Niarhos	2.00	1.50	.60
155 Frank Shea	2.00	1.50	.60
156 Fred Sanford	2.00	1.50	.60
157 Mike Guerra	2.00	1.50	.60
158 Paul Lehner	2.00	1.50	.60
159 Joe Tipton	2.00	1.50	.60
160 Mickey Harris	2.00	1.50	.60
161 Sherry Robertson	2.00	1.50	.60
162 Eddie Yost	2.00	1.50	.60
163 Earl Torgeson	2.00	1.50	.60
164 Sibby Sisti	2.00	1.50	.60
165 Bruce Edwards	2.00	1.50	.60
166 Joe Hatton	2.00	1.50	.60
167 "Preacher" Roe	3.50	2.50	1.20
168 Bob Scheffing	2.00	1.50	.60
169 Hank Edwards	2.00	1.50	.60
170 "Dutch" Leonard	2.00	1.50	.60
171 Harry Gumbert	2.00	1.50	.60
172 "Peanuts" Lowery	2.00	1.50	.60
173 Lloyd Merriman	2.00	1.50	.60
174 Hank Thompson	2.00	1.50	.60
175 Monte Kennedy	2.00	1.50	.60
176 Sylvester Donnelly	2.00	1.50	.60
177 Hank Borowy	2.00	1.50	.60
178 Eddie Fitzgerald	2.00	1.50	.60
179 Chuck Diering	2.00	1.50	.60
180 Harry Walker	2.00	1.50	.60
181 Marino Pieretti	2.00	1.50	.60
182 Sam Zoldak	2.00	1.50	.60
183 Mickey Haefner	2.00	1.50	.60
184 Randy Gumpert	2.00	1.50	.60
185 Howie Judson	2.00	1.50	.60
186 Ken Keltner	2.00	1.50	.60
187 Lou Stringer	2.00	1.50	.60
188 Earl Johnson	2.00	1.50	.60
189 Owen Friend	2.00	1.50	.60
190 Ken Wood	2.00	1.50	.60
191 Dick Starr	2.00	1.50	.60
192 Bob Chipman	2.00	1.50	.60
193 "Pete" Reiser	3.00	2.25	1.00
194 Billy Cox	2.00	1.50	.60
195 Phil Cavaretta	3.00	2.25	1.00
196 Doyle Lade	2.00	1.50	.60
197 Johnny Wyrostek	2.00	1.50	.60
198 Danny Litwiler	2.00	1.50	.60
199 Jack Kramer	2.00	1.50	.60
200 Kirby Higby	2.00	1.50	.60
201 Pete Castiglione	2.00	1.50	.60
202 Cliff Chambers	2.00	1.50	.60
203 Danny Murtaugh	2.00	1.50	.60

1950 BOWMAN (CONTINUED)

	MINT	VG-E	F-G
204 Granny Hamner	2.00	1.50	.60
205 Mike Goliat	2.00	1.50	.60
206 Stan Lopata	2.00	1.50	.60
207 Max Lanier	2.00	1.50	.60
208 Jim Hearn	2.00	1.50	.60
209 Johnny Lindell	2.00	1.50	.60
210 Ted Gray	2.00	1.50	.60
211 Charley Keller	3.00	2.25	1.00
212 Gerry Priddy	2.00	1.50	.60
213 Carl Scheib	2.00	1.50	.60
214 Dick Fowler	2.00	1.50	.60
215 Ed Lopat	4.50	3.50	1.60
216 Bob Porterfield	2.00	1.50	.60
217 Casey Stengel	18.00	13.50	6.00
218 Cliff Mapes	2.00	1.50	.60
219 Hank Bauer	3.50	2.50	1.20
220 Leo Durocher	8.00	6.00	2.50
221 Don Mueller	2.00	1.50	.60
222 Bobby Morgan	2.00	1.50	.60
223 Jim Russell	2.00	1.50	.60
224 Jack Banta	2.00	1.50	.60
225 Eddie Sawyer	3.00	2.25	1.00
226 Jim Konstanty	5.00	3.75	1.75
227 Bob Miller	2.00	1.50	.60
228 Bill Nicholson	2.00	1.50	.60
229 Frank Frisch	9.00	6.75	3.00
230 Bill Serena	2.00	1.50	.60
231 Preston Ward	2.0C	1.50	.60
232 Al Rosen	6.50	5.00	2.25
233 Allie Clark	2.00	1.50	.60
234 Bobby Shantz	2.50	1.80	.80
235 Harold Gilbert	2.00	1.50	.60
236 Bob Cain	2.00	1.50	.60
237 Bill Salkeld	2.00	1.50	.60
238 Vernal Jones	2.00	1.50	.60
239 Bill Howerton	2.00	1.50	.60
240 Eddie Lake	2.00	1.50	.60
241 Neil Berry	2.00	1.50	.60
242 Dick Kryhoski	2.00	1.50	.60
243 Johnny Groth	2.00	1.50	.60
244 Dale Coogan	2.00	1.50	.60
245 Al Papai	2.00	1.50	.60
246 Walt Dropo	2.00	1.50	.60
247 Irv Noren	2.00	1.50	.60
248 Sam Jethroe	3.00	2.25	1.00
249 "Snuffy" Stirnweiss	2.00	1.50	.60
250 Ray Coleman	2.00	1.50	.60
251 John Moss	2.00	1.50	.60
252 Billy DeMars	6.00	4.50	2.00

1951 BOWMAN (324)   2 1/8" X 3 1/8"

TED WILLIAMS

Outfield—Boston Red Sox
Born: San Diego, Calif., Oct. 30, 1918
Height: 6-3   Weight: 190
Bats: Left   Throws: Right

Because of a broken elbow, received in the All-Star game, Ted was in only 89 games in 1950. But he made good use of those 89 appearances. He batted .317. Slammed 28 homers. Knocked in 97 runs. In 1949, led the League in homers (49), runs scored (160), total bases (368), two-base hits (39). Tied for lead in runs driven in (159). Voted League's most valuable player, 1949 and 1946.

No. 165 in the 1951 SERIES
BASEBALL
PICTURE CARDS
©1951 Bowman Gum, Inc., Phila., Pa., U.S.A.

The 1951 Bowman set, many of the cards of which are exact poses taken from the 1950 set, is Bowman's largest single issue. Its high nos., 253-324 are much more difficult to obtain than the low numbers, and the high numbers contain the "true" rookie cards of Mickey Mantle and Willie Mays. Card no. 195 portrays a caricature sketch of Paul Richards rather than the normal line drawing likeness as players on the other cards in the set are portrayed. The full name of the player appears on the face of the card.

	MINT	VG-E	F-G
COMPLETE SET	1600.00	1200.00	500.00
COMMON PLAYER (1-252)	2.00	1.50	.60
COMMON PLAYER (253-324)	7.00	5.25	2.25
1 Whitey Ford	50.00	30.00	13.00
2 "Yogi" Berra	27.00	20.00	9.00
3 Robin Roberts	10.00	7.00	3.00
4 Del Ennis	2.50	1.80	.80
5 Dale Mitchell	2.50	1.80	.80
6 Don Newcombe	6.00	4.50	2.00
7 Gil Hodges	11.00	8.00	3.50
8 Paul Lehner	2.50	1.80	.80
9 Sam Chapman	2.50	1.80	.80
10 "Red" Schoendienst	4.00	3.00	1.40
11 "Red" Munger	2.00	1.50	.60
12 Hank Majeski	2.00	1.50	.60
13 Eddie Stanky	2.50	1.80	.80
14 Al Dark	2.50	1.80	.80
15 Johnny Pesky	2.00	1.50	.60
16 Maurice McDermott	2.00	1.50	.60
17 Pete Castiglione	2.00	1.50	.60
18 Gil Coan	2.00	1.50	.60
19 Sid Gordon	2.00	1.50	.60
20 Del Crandall	2.50	1.80	.80
21 "Snuffy" Stirnweiss	2.00	1.50	.60
22 Hank Sauer	2.50	1.80	.80
23 "Hoot" Evers	2.00	1.50	.60
24 Ewell Blackwell	2.50	1.80	.80
25 Vic Raschi	3.50	2.50	1.20
26 Phil Rizzuto	12.50	9.00	4.00
27 Jim Konstanty	2.50	1.80	.80
28 Eddie Waitkus	2.00	1.50	.60
29 Allie Clark	2.00	1.50	.60
30 Bob Feller	20.00	15.00	6.50
31 Roy Campanella	28.00	21.00	10.00
32 Duke Snider	16.00	12.00	5.50
33 Bob Hooper	2.00	1.50	.60
34 Marty Marion	3.00	2.25	1.00
35 Al Zarilla	2.00	1.50	.60
36 Joe Dobson	2.00	1.50	.60
37 Whitey Lockman	2.00	1.50	.60
38 Al Evans	2.00	1.50	.60
39 Ray Scarborough	2.00	1.50	.60
40 Gus Bell	2.00	1.50	.60
41 Eddie Yost	2.00	1.50	.60
42 Vern Bickford	2.00	1.50	.60
43 Billy DeMars	2.00	1.50	.60
44 Roy Smalley	2.00	1.50	.60
45 Art Houtteman	2.00	1.50	.60
46 George Kell (1941 Back)	6.00	4.50	2.00
47 Grady Hatton	2.00	1.50	.60
48 Ken Raffensberger	2.00	1.50	.60
49 Jerry Coleman	2.50	1.80	.80
50 Johnny Mize	6.00	4.50	2.00
51 Andy Seminick	2.00	1.50	.60
52 Dick Sisler	2.00	1.50	.60
53 Bob Lemon	10.00	7.00	3.00
54 Ray Boone	2.00	1.50	.60
55 Gene Hermanski	2.00	1.50	.60
56 Ralph Branca	2.50	1.80	.80
57 Alex Kellner	2.00	1.50	.60
58 Enos Slaughter	6.00	4.50	2.00
59 Randy Gumpert	2.00	1.50	.60
60 "Chico" Carrasquel	2.00	1.50	.60
61 Jim Hearn	2.00	1.50	.60
62 Lou Boudreau	8.00	6.00	2.50
63 Bob Dillinger	2.00	1.50	.60
64 Bill Werle	2.00	1.50	.60
65 "Mickey" Vernon	2.50	1.80	.80
66 Bob Elliott	2.00	1.50	.60
67 Roy Sievers	2.00	1.50	.60
68 Dick Kokos	2.00	1.50	.60
69 Johnny Schmitz	2.00	1.50	.60
70 Ron Northey	2.00	1.50	.60
71 Jerry Priddy	2.00	1.50	.60
72 Lloyd Merriman	2.00	1.50	.60

	MINT	VG-E	F-G
73 Tommy Byrne	2.00	1.50	.60
74 Billy Johnson	2.00	1.50	.60
75 Russ Meyer	2.00	1.50	.60
76 Stan Lopata	2.00	1.50	.60
77 Mike Goliat	2.00	1.50	.60
78 Early Wynn	10.00	7.00	3.00
79 Jim Hegan	2.00	1.50	.60
80 "Peewee" Reese	9.00	6.75	3.00
81 Carl Furillo	4.50	3.50	1.60
82 Joe Tipton	2.00	1.50	.60
83 Carl Scheib	2.00	1.50	.60
84 Barney McCoskey	2.00	1.50	.60
85 Eddie Kazak	2.00	1.50	.60
86 Harry Brecheen	2.50	1.80	.80
87 Floyd Baker	2.00	1.50	.60
88 Eddie Robinson	2.00	1.50	.60
89 "Hank" Thompson	2.00	1.50	.60
90 Dave Koslo	2.00	1.50	.60
91 Clyde Vollmer	2.00	1.50	.60
92 Vern Stephens	2.00	1.50	.60
93 Danny O'Connell	2.00	1.50	.60
94 Clyde McCullough	2.00	1.50	.60
95 Sherry Robertson	2.00	1.50	.60
96 Sandy Consuegra	2.00	1.50	.60
97 Bob Kuzava	2.00	1.50	.60
98 Willard Marshall	2.00	1.50	.60
99 Earl Torgeson	2.00	1.50	.60
100 Sherm Lollar	2.00	1.50	.60
101 Owen Friend	2.00	1.50	.60
102 "Dutch" Leonard	2.00	1.50	.60
103 Andy Pafko	2.00	1.50	.60
104 Virgil Trucks	2.00	1.50	.60
105 Don Kolloway	2.00	1.50	.60
106 Pat Mullin	2.00	1.50	.60
107 Johnny Wyrostek	2.00	1.50	.60
108 Virgil Stallcup	2.00	1.50	.60
109 Allie Reynolds	4.00	3.00	1.40
110 Bobby Brown	2.00	1.50	.60
111 Curt Simmons	2.50	1.80	.80
112 Willie Jones	2.00	1.50	.60
113 Bill Nicholson	2.00	1.50	.60
114 Sam Zoldak	2.00	1.50	.60
115 Steve Gromek	2.00	1.50	.60
116 Bruce Edwards	2.00	1.50	.60
117 Eddie Miksis	2.00	1.50	.60
118 Preacher Roe	3.50	2.50	1.20
119 Eddie Joost	2.00	1.50	.60
120 Joe Coleman	2.00	1.50	.60
121 Gerry Staley	2.00	1.50	.60
122 Joe Garagiola	9.00	6.75	3.00
123 Howie Judson	2.00	1.50	.60
124 Gus Niarhos	2.00	1.50	.60
125 Bill Rigney	2.00	1.50	.60
126 Bobby Thomson	4.50	3.50	1.60
127 Sal Maglie	2.50	1.80	.80
128 Ellis Kinder	2.00	1.50	.60
129 Matt Batts	2.00	1.50	.60
130 Tom Saffell	2.00	1.50	.60
131 Cliff Chambers	2.00	1.50	.60
132 Cass Michaels	2.00	1.50	.60
133 Sam Dente	2.00	1.50	.60
134 Warren Spahn	14.00	10.50	4.75
135 Walker Cooper	2.00	1.50	.60
136 Ray Coleman	2.00	1.50	.60
137 Dick Starr	2.00	1.50	.60
138 Phil Cavaretta	2.50	1.80	.80
139 Doyle Lade	2.00	1.50	.60
140 Eddie Lake	2.00	1.50	.60
141 Fred Hutchinson	2.50	1.80	.80
142 Aaron Robinson	2.00	1.50	.60
143 Ted Kluszewski	4.00	3.00	1.40
144 Herman Wehmeier	2.00	1.50	.60
145 Fred Sanford	2.00	1.50	.60
146 Johnny Hopp	2.50	1.80	.80
147 Ken Heintzelman	2.00	1.50	.60
148 Granny Hamner	2.00	1.50	.60
149 "Bubba"Church	2.00	1.50	.60
150 Mike Garcia	2.50	1.80	.80
151 Larry Doby	3.50	2.50	1.20
152 Cal Abrams	2.00	1.50	.60
153 Rex Barney	2.00	1.50	.60
154 Pete Suder	2.00	1.50	.60
155 Lou Brissie	2.00	1.50	.60
156 Del Rice	2.00	1.50	.60
157 Al Brazle	2.00	1.50	.60
158 Chuck Diering	2.00	1.50	.60
159 Eddie Stewart	2.00	1.50	.60
160 Phil Masi	2.00	1.50	.60
161 Wes Westrum	2.00	1.50	.60
162 Larry Jansen	2.00	1.50	.60
163 Monte Kennedy	2.00	1.50	.60
164 Bill Wight	2.00	1.50	.60

	MINT	VG-E	F-G
165 Ted Williams	55.00	42.00	19.00
166 Stan Rojek	2.00	1.50	.60
167 Murry Dickson	2.00	1.50	.60
168 Sam Mele	2.00	1.50	.60
169 Sid Hudson	2.00	1.50	.60
170 Sibby Sisti	2.00	1.50	.60
171 Buddy Kerr	2.00	1.50	.60
172 Ned Garver	2.00	1.50	.60
173 Hank Arft	2.00	1.50	.60
174 Mickey Owen	2.50	1.80	.80
175 Wayne Terwilliger	2.00	1.50	.60
176 Vic Wertz	2.50	1.80	.80
177 Charlie Keller	2.50	1.80	.80
178 Ted Gray	2.00	1.50	.60
179 Danny Litwiler	2.00	1.50	.60
180 Howie Fox	2.00	1.50	.60
181 Casey Stengel	16.00	12.00	5.50
182 Tom Ferrick	2.00	1.50	.60
183 Hank Bauer	3.00	2.25	1.00
184 Eddie Sawyer	2.50	1.80	.80
185 Jimmy Bloodworth	2.00	1.50	.60
186 Richie Ashburn	4.00	3.00	1.40
187 Al Rosen	5.50	4.25	2.00
188 Bobby Avila	2.00	1.50	.60
189 Erv Palica	2.00	1.50	.60
190 Joe Hatton	2.00	1.50	.60
191 Billy Hitchcock	2.00	1.50	.60
192 Hank Wyse	2.00	1.50	.60
193 Ted Wilks	2.00	1.50	.60
194 "Peanuts" Lowery	2.00	1.50	.60
195 Paul Richards	6.00	4.50	2.00
196 Billy Pierce	3.50	2.50	1.20
197 Bob Cain	2.00	1.50	.60
198 Monte Irvin	7.00	5.25	2.50
199 Sheldon Jones	2.00	1.50	.60
200 Jack Kramer	2.00	1.50	.60
201 Steve O'Neill	2.00	1.50	.60
202 Mike Guerra	2.00	1.50	.60
203 Vernon Law	2.50	1.80	.80
204 Vic Lombardi	2.00	1.50	.60
205 Mickey Grasso	2.00	1.50	.60
206 Conrado Marrero	2.00	1.50	.60
207 Billy Southworth	2.00	1.50	.60
208 Blix Donnelly	2.00	1.50	.60
209 Ken Wood	2.00	1.50	.60
210 Les Moss	2.00	1.50	.60
211 Hal Jeffcoat	2.00	1.50	.60
212 Bob Rush	2.00	1.50	.60
213 Neil Berry	2.00	1.50	.60
214 Bob Swift	2.00	1.50	.60
215 Ken Peterson	2.00	1.50	.60
216 Connie Ryan	2.00	1.50	.60
217 Joe Page	3.00	2.25	1.00
218 Ed Lopat	4.00	3.00	1.40
219 Gene Woodling	2.50	1.80	.80
220 Bob Miller	2.00	1.50	.60
221 Dick Whitman	2.00	1.50	.60
222 Thurman Tucker	2.00	1.50	.60
223 Johnny Vandermeer	4.00	3.00	1.40
224 Billy Cox	2.00	1.50	.60
225 Dan Bankhead	2.00	1.50	.60
226 Jimmy Dykes	2.50	1.80	.80
227 Bobby Shantz	2.50	1.80	.80
228 Cloyd Boyer	2.00	1.50	.60
229 Bill Howerton	2.00	1.50	.60
230 Max Lanier	2.00	1.50	.60
231 Luis Aloma	2.00	1.50	.60
232 Nelson Fox	4.50	3.50	1.60
233 Leo Durocher	6.00	4.50	2.00
234 Clint Hartung	2.00	1.50	.60
235 Jack Lohrke	2.00	1.50	.60
236 Warren Rosar	2.00	1.50	.60
237 Billy Goodman	2.00	1.50	.60
238 Peter Reiser	2.50	1.80	.80
239 Bill MacDonald	2.00	1.50	.60
240 Joe Haynes	2.00	1.50	.60
241 Irv Noren	2.00	1.50	.60
242 Sam Jethroe	2.00	1.50	.60
243 Johnny Antonelli	2.50	1.80	.80
244 Cliff Fannin	2.00	1.50	.60
245 John Berardino	2.50	1.80	.80
246 Bill Serena	2.00	1.50	.60
247 Bob Ramazotti	2.00	1.50	.60
248 Johnny Klippstein	2.00	1.50	.60
249 Johnny Groth	2.00	1.50	.60
250 Hank Borowy	2.00	1.50	.60
251 Billy Ramsdell	2.00	1.50	.60
252 Dixie Howell	2.00	1.50	.60
253 Mickey Mantle	400.00	300.00	150.00
254 Jackie Jensen	10.00	7.00	3.00
255 Milo Candini	7.00	5.25	2.25
256 Ken Sylvestri	7.00	5.25	2.25
257 Birdie Tebbetts	8.00	6.00	2.50

		MINT	VG-E	F-G
258	Luke Easter	8.00	6.00	2.50
259	Chuck Dressen	8.00	6.00	2.50
260	Carl Erskine	11.00	8.00	3.50
261	Wally Moses	8.00	6.00	2.50
262	Gus Zernial	8.00	6.00	2.50
263	Howie Pollet	7.00	5.25	2.25
264	Don Richmond	7.00	5.25	2.25
265	Steve Bilko	7.00	5.25	2.25
266	Harry Dorish	7.00	5.25	2.25
267	Ken Holcomb	7.00	5.25	2.25
268	Don Mueller	7.00	5.25	2.25
269	Ray Noble	7.00	5.25	2.25
270	Willard Nixon	7.00	5.25	2.25
271	Tommy Wright	7.00	5.25	2.25
272	Billy Meyer	7.00	5.25	2.25
273	Danny Murtaugh	8.00	6.00	2.50
274	George Metkovich	7.00	5.25	2.25
275	Bucky Harris	13.00	9.50	4.00
276	Frank Quinn	7.00	5.25	2.25
277	Roy Hartsfield	7.00	5.25	2.25
278	Norman Roy	7.00	5.25	2.25
279	Jim Delsing	7.00	5.25	2.25
280	Frank Overmire	7.00	5.25	2.25
281	Al Widmar	7.00	5.25	2.25
282	Frank Frisch	16.00	12.00	5.50
283	Walt Dubiel	7.00	5.25	2.25
284	Gene Bearden	7.00	5.25	2.25
285	Johnny Lipon	7.00	5.25	2.25
286	Bob Usher	7.00	5.25	2.25
287	Jim Blackburn	7.00	5.25	2.25
288	Bobby Adams	7.00	5.25	2.25
289	Cliff Mapes	7.00	5.25	2.25
290	Bill Dickey	27.00	20.00	9.00

		MINT	VG-E	F-G
291	Tommy Henrich	15.00	11.00	5.00
292	Eddie Pellegrini	7.00	5.25	2.25
293	Ken Johnson	7.00	5.25	2.25
294	Jocko Thompson	7.00	5.25	2.25
295	Al Lopez	16.00	12.00	5.50
296	Bob Kennedy	8.00	6.50	2.00
297	Dave Philley	7.00	5.25	2.25
298	Joe Astroth	7.00	5.25	2.25
299	Clyde King	7.00	5.25	2.25
300	Hal Rice	7.00	5.25	2.25
301	Tommy Glaviano	7.00	5.25	2.25
302	Jim Busby	7.00	5.25	2.25
303	Marv Rotblatt	7.00	5.25	2.25
304	Al Gettel	7.00	5.25	2.25
305	Willie Mays	370.00	300.00	140.00
306	Jim Piersall	16.00	12.00	5.50
307	Walt Masterson	7.00	5.25	2.25
308	Ted Beard	7.00	5.25	2.25
309	Mel Queen	7.00	5.25	2.25
310	Erv Dusak	7.00	5.25	2.25
311	Mickey Harris	7.00	5.25	2.25
312	Gene Mauch	12.00	8.75	4.00
313	Ray Mueller	7.00	5.25	2.25
314	Johnny Sain	11.00	8.00	3.50
315	Zack Taylor	7.00	5.25	2.25
316	Duane Pillette	7.00	5.25	2.25
317	"Smoky" Burgess	8.00	6.00	2.50
318	Warren Hacker	7.00	5.25	2.25
319	"Red" Rolfe	8.00	6.00	2.50
320	Hal White	7.00	5.25	2.25
321	Earl Johnson	7.00	5.25	2.25
322	Luke Sewell	8.00	6.00	2.50
323	Joe Adcock	8.00	6.00	2.50
324	Johnny Pramesa	10.00	7.00	3.00

1952 BOWMAN (252)　　　　2 1/8" X 3 1/8"

STAN MUSIAL

Outfield—St. Louis Cardinals
Born: Donora, Pa., Nov. 21, 1920
Height: 6 ft   Weight: 175
Bats: Left   Throws: Left

Led the National League batters for the fifth time in 1951. His average was .355. Tied for lead in scoring most runs (124), hit for most total bases (355), tied for most triples (12). Extended own National League record by scoring 100 or more runs for 8th straight year.

No. 196 in the 1952 SERIES

BASEBALL®

PICTURE CARDS

Get a $1.00 value Baseball Cap at your favorite major league team by sending 5 wrappers and 50 cents to BOWMAN Baseball, P. O. BOX 234, New York 23, N. Y. State size: small, medium or large.

© 1952 Bowman Gum Division, Haelan Laboratories, Inc., Phila. 44, Pa.—Ptd. in U. S. A.

The 1952 Bowman issue of 252 cards contains a series of high numbers (Nos. 217—252) which are more difficult to obtain than the other cards in the set. A facsimile autograph of the player is printed on the face of the card.

	MINT	VG-E	F-G
COMPLETE SET	850.00	675.00	275.00
COMMON PLAYER (1—216)	2.00	1.50	.60
COMMON PLAYER (217—252)	4.25	3.25	1.50
1 "Yogi" Berra	45.00	25.00	10.00
2 Bobby Thomson	5.00	3.75	1.75
3 Fred Hutchinson	3.00	2.25	1.00
4 Robin Roberts	10.00	7.00	3.00
5 "Minnie" Minoso	4.00	3.00	1.40
6 Virgil Stallcup	2.50	1.80	.80
7 Mike Garcia	2.50	1.80	.80
8 "Peewee" Reese	10.00	7.00	3.00
9 Vern Stephens	2.50	1.80	.80
10 Bob Hooper	2.50	1.80	.80
11 Ralph Kiner	10.00	7.00	3.00
12 Max Surkont	2.00	1.50	.60
13 Cliff Mapes	2.00	1.50	.60
14 Cliff Chambers	2.00	1.50	.60
15 Sam Mele	2.00	1.50	.60
16 "Turk" Lown	2.00	1.50	.60
17 Ed Lopat	4.00	3.00	1.40
18 Don Mueller	2.00	1.50	.60
19 Bob Cain	2.00	1.50	.60
20 Willie Jones	2.00	1.50	.60
21 Nelson Fox	4.00	3.00	1.40
22 Willard Ramsdell	2.00	1.50	.60
23 Bob Lemon	10.00	7.00	3.00
24 Carl Furillo	4.00	3.00	1.40
25 "Mickey" McDermott	2.00	1.50	.60

	MINT	VG-E	F-G
26 Eddie Joost	2.00	1.50	.60
27 Joe Garagiola	8.00	6.00	2.50
28 Ray Hartsfield	2.00	1.50	.60
29 Ned Garver	2.00	1.50	.60
30 "Red" Schoendienst	3.00	2.25	1.00
31 Eddie Yost	2.00	1.50	.60
32 Eddie Miksis	2.00	1.50	.60
33 Gil McDougald	3.00	2.25	1.00
34 Alvin Dark	2.50	1.80	.80
35 Granny Hamner	2.00	1.50	.60
36 Cass Michaels	2.00	1.50	.60
37 Vic Raschi	3.00	2.25	1.00
38 Whitey Lockman	2.00	1.50	.60
39 Vic Wertz	2.00	1.50	.60
40 "Bubba" Church	2.00	1.50	.60
41 Chico Carrasquel	2.00	1.50	.60
42 Johnny Wyrostek	2.00	1.50	.60
43 Bob Feller	18.00	13.50	6.00
44 Roy Campanella	27.00	20.00	9.00
45 Johnny Pesky	2.00	1.50	.60
46 Carl Scheib	2.00	1.50	.60
47 Pete Castiglione	2.00	1.50	.60
48 Vern Bickford	2.00	1.50	.60
49 Jim Hearn	2.00	1.50	.60
50 Gerry Staley	2.00	1.50	.60
51 Gil Coan	2.00	1.50	.60
52 Phil Rizzuto	11.00	8.00	3.50
53 Richie Ashburn	3.50	2.50	1.20
54 Billy Pierce	2.50	1.80	.80

1952 BOWMAN (CONTINUED)

		MINT	VG-E	F-G
55	Ken Raffensberger	2.00	1.50	.60
56	Clyde King	2.00	1.50	.60
57	Clyde Vollmer	2.00	1.50	.60
58	Hank Majeski	2.00	1.50	.60
59	Murry Dickson	2.00	1.50	.60
60	Sid Gordon	2.00	1.50	.60
61	Tommy Byrne	2.00	1.50	.60
62	Joe Presko	2.00	1.50	.60
63	Irv Noren	2.00	1.50	.60
64	Roy Smalley	2.00	1.50	.60
65	Hank Bauer	3.00	2.25	1.00
66	Sal Maglie	2.50	1.80	.80
67	Johnny Groth	2.00	1.50	.60
68	Jim Busby	2.00	1.50	.60
69	Joe Adcock	2.50	1.80	.80
70	Carl Erskine	3.00	2.25	1.00
71	Vernon Law	2.50	1.80	.80
72	Earl Torgeson	2.00	1.50	.60
73	Gerry Coleman	2.00	1.50	.60
74	Wes Westrum	2.00	1.50	.60
75	George Kell	2.50	1.50	.60
76	Del Ennis	2.00	1.50	.60
77	Eddie Robinson	2.00	1.50	.60
73	Lloyd Merriman	2.00	1.50	.60
79	Lou Brissie	2.00	1.50	.60
80	Gil Hodges	11.00	8.00	3.50
81	Billy Goodman	2.00	1.50	.60
82	Gus Zernial	2.00	1.50	.60
83	Howie Pollet	2.00	1.50	.60
84	Sam Jethroe	2.00	1.50	.60
85	Marty Marion	3.00	2.25	1.00
86	Cal Abrams	2.00	1.50	1.00
87	Mickey Vernon	2.50	1.80	.80
88	Bruce Edwards	2.00	1.50	.60
89	Billy Hitchcock	2.00	1.50	.60
90	Larry Jansen	2.00	1.50	.60
91	Don Kolloway	2.00	1.50	.60
92	Eddie Waitkus	2.00	1.50	.60
93	Paul Richards	2.50	1.80	.80
94	Luke Sewell	2.00	1.50	.60
95	Luke Easter	2.50	1.80	.80
96	Ralph Branca	2.50	1.80	.80
97	Willard Marshall	2.00	1.50	.60
98	Jimmy Dykes	2.50	1.80	.80
99	Clyde McCullough	2.00	1.50	.60
100	Sibby Sisti	2.00	1.50	.60
101	Mickey Mantle	200.00	150.00	/0.00
102	"Peanuts" Lowery	2.00	1.50	.60
103	Joe Haynes	2.00	1.50	.60
104	Hal Jeffcoat	2.00	1.50	.60
105	Bobby Brown	2.00	1.50	.60
106	Randy Gumpert	2.00	1.50	.60
107	Del Rice	2.00	1.50	.60
108	George Metkovich	2.00	1.50	.60
109	Tom Morgan	2.00	1.50	.60
110	Max Lanier	2.00	1.50	.60
111	"Hoot" Evers	2.00	1.50	.60
112	"Smokey" Burgess	2.00	1.50	.60
113	Al Zarilla	2.00	1.50	.60
114	Frank Hiller	2.00	1.50	.60
115	Larry Doby	3.00	2.25	1.00
116	Duke Snider	16.00	12.00	5.50
117	Bill Wight	2.00	1.50	.60
118	Ray Murray	2.00	1.50	.60
119	Bill Howerton	2.00	1.50	.60
120	Chet Nichols	2.00	1.50	.60
121	Al Corwin	2.00	1.50	.60
122	Billy Johnson	2.00	1.50	.60
123	Sid Hudson	2.00	1.50	.60
124	"Birdie" Tebbetts	2.00	1.50	.60
125	Howie Fox	2.00	1.50	.60
126	Phil Cavaretta	2.50	1.80	.80
127	Dick Sisler	2.00	1.50	.60
128	Don Newcombe	5.50	4.25	2.00
129	Gus Niarhos	2.00	1.50	.60
130	Allie Clark	2.00	1.50	.60
131	Bob Swift	2.00	1.50	.60
132	Dave Cole	2.00	1.50	.60
133	Dick Kryhoski	2.00	1.50	.60
134	Al Brazle	2.00	1.50	.60
135	Mickey Harris	2.00	1.50	.60
136	Gene Hermanski	2.00	1.50	.60
137	Stan Rojek	2.00	1.50	.60
138	Ted Wilks	2.00	1.50	.60
139	Jerry Priddy	2.00	1.50	.60
140	Ray Scarborough	2.00	1.50	.60
141	Hank Edwards	2.00	1.50	.60
142	Early Wynn	10.00	7.00	3.00
143	Sandy Consuegra	2.00	1.50	.60
144	Joe Hatton	2.00	1.50	.60
145	Johnny Mize	6.00	4.50	2.00
146	Leo Durocher	6.00	4.50	2.00
147	Marlin Stuart	2.00	1.50	.60
148	Ken Heintzelman	2.00	1.50	.60
149	Howie Judson	2.00	1.50	.60
150	Herman Wehmeier	2.00	1.50	.60
151	Al Rosen	6.00	4.50	2.00
152	Billy Cox	2.00	1.50	.60
153	Fred Hatfield	2.00	1.50	.60
154	Ferris Fain	2.50	1.80	.80
155	Billy Meyer	2.00	1.50	.60
156	Warren Spahn	12.00	8.75	4.00
157	Jim Delsing	2.00	1.50	.60
158	Bucky Harris	6.00	4.50	2.00
159	"Dutch" Leonard	2.00	1.50	.60
160	Eddie Stanky	2.50	1.80	.80
161	Jackie Jensen	3.00	2.25	1.00
162	Monte Irvin	7.00	5.25	2.50
163	Johnny Lipon	2.00	1.50	.60
164	Connie Ryan	2.00	1.50	.60
165	Saul Rogovin	2.00	1.50	.60
166	Bobby Adams	2.00	1.50	.60
167	Bobby Avila	2.00	1.50	.60
168	"Preacher" Roe	3.50	2.50	1.20
169	Walt Dropo	2.00	1.50	.60
170	Joe Astroth	2.00	1.50	.60
171	Mel Queen	2.00	1.50	.60
172	Ebba St. Claire	2.00	1.50	.60
173	Gene Bearden	2.00	1.50	.60
174	Mickey Grasso	2.00	1.50	.60
175	Ransom Jackson	2.00	1.50	.60
176	Harry Brecheen	2.50	1.80	.80
177	Gene Woodling	2.50	1.80	.80
178	Dave Williams	2.00	1.50	.60
179	Pete Suder	2.00	1.50	.60
180	Eddie Fitzgerald	2.00	1.50	.60
181	Joe Collins	2.00	1.50	.60
182	Dave Koslo	2.00	1.50	.60
183	Pat Mullin	2.00	1.50	.60
184	Curt Simmons	2.50	1.80	.80
185	Eddie Stewart	2.00	1.50	.60
186	Frank Smith	2.00	1.50	.60
187	Jim Hegan	2.00	1.50	.60
188	Charlie Dressen	2.50	1.80	.80
189	Jim Piersall	3.00	2.25	1.00
190	Dick Fowler	2.00	1.50	.60
191	Bob Friend	2.50	1.80	.80
192	John Cusick	2.00	1.50	.60
193	Bobby Young	2.00	1.50	.60
194	Bob Porterfield	2.00	1.50	.60
195	Frank Baumholtz	2.00	1.50	.60
196	Stan Musial	60.00	45.00	20.00
197	Charlie Silvera	2.00	1.50	.60
198	Chuck Diering	2.00	1.50	.60
199	Ted Gray	2.00	1.50	.60
200	Ken Silvestri	2.00	1.50	.60
201	Ray Coleman	2.00	1.50	.60
202	Harry Perkowski	2.00	1.50	.60
203	Steve Gromek	2.00	1.50	.60
204	Andy Pafko	2.00	1.50	.60
205	Walt Masterson	2.00	1.50	.60
206	Elmer Valo	2.00	1.50	.60
207	George Strickland	2.00	1.50	.60
208	Walker Cooper	2.00	1.50	.60
209	Dick Littlefield	2.00	1.50	.60
210	Archie Wilson	2.00	1.50	.60
211	Paul Minner	2.00	1.50	.60
212	Solly Hemus	2.00	1.50	.60
213	Monte Kennedy	2.00	1.50	.60
214	Ray Boone	2.00	1.50	.60
215	Sheldon Jones	2.00	1.50	.60
216	Matt Batts	2.00	1.50	.60
217	Casey Stengel	24.00	18.00	8.50
218	Willie Mays	225.00	170.00	80.00
219	Neil Berry	4.25	3.25	1.50
220	Russ Meyer	4.25	3.25	1.50
221	Lou Kretlow	4.25	3.25	1.50
222	"Dixie" Howell	4.25	3.25	1.50
223	Harry Simpson	4.25	3.25	1.50
224	Johnny Schmitz	4.25	3.25	1.50
225	Del Wilber	4.25	3.25	1.50
226	Alex Kellner	4.25	3.25	1.50
227	Clyde Sukeforth	4.25	3.25	1.50
228	Bob Chipman	4.25	3.25	1.50
229	Hank Arft	4.25	3.25	1.50
230	Frank Shea	4.25	3.25	1.50
231	Dee Fondy	4.25	3.25	1.50
232	Enos Slaughter	12.50	9.00	4.00
233	Bob Kuzava	4.25	3.25	1.50
234	Fred Fitzsimmons	4.25	3.25	1.50
235	Steve Souchock	4.25	3.25	1.50
236	Tommy Brown	4.25	3.25	1.50
237	Sherman Lollar	4.25	3.25	1.50
238	Roy McMillan	4.25	3.25	1.50
239	Dale Mitchell	4.25	3.25	1.50
240	Billy Loes	4.25	3.25	1.50

	MINT	VG-E	F-G			MINT	VG-E	F-G
241 Mel Parnell	4.25	3.25	1.50	247 John Pramesa		4.25	3.25	1.50
242 Everett Kell	4.25	3.25	1.50	248 Bill Werle		4.25	3.25	1.50
243 "Red Munger	4.25	3.25	1.50	249 "Hank" Thompson		4.25	3.25	1.50
244 Lew Burdette	9.00	6.75	3.00	250 Ivan Delock		4.25	3.25	1.50
245 George Schmees	4.25	3.25	1.50	251 Jack Lohrke		4.25	3.25	1.50
246 Jerry Snyder	4.25	3.25	1.50	252 Frank Crosetti		20.00	12.00	5.00

1953 BOWMAN COLOR (160)   2 1/2" X 3 3/4"

The 1953 Bowman Color set, considered by many to be the best looking set of the modern era, contains Kodachrome photographs with no names or facsimile autographs on the face. Numbers 113-160 are somewhat more difficult to obtain. Card no. 159 is actually a picture of Floyd Baker.

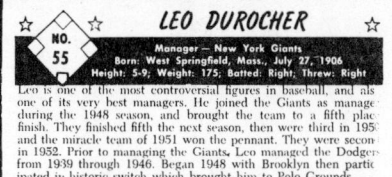

	MINT	VG-E	F-G		MINT	VG-E	F-G
COMPLETE SET	1600.00	1200.00	500.00	55 Leo Durocher	8.00	6.00	2.50
COMMON PLAYER (1-112)	4.00	2.75	1.00	56 Bob Cain	4.00	2.75	1.00
COMMON PLAYER (113-160)	8.00	6.00	2.50	57 Lou Boudreau	9.00	6.75	3.00
				58 Willard Marshall	4.00	2.75	1.00
1 Dave Williams	10.00	4.00	1.50	59 Mickey Mantle	200.00	150.00	65.00
2 Vic Wertz	4.00	2.75	1.00	60 Granny Hamner	4.00	2.75	1.00
3 Sam Jethroe	4.00	2.75	1.00	61 George Kell	6.00	4.50	2.00
4 Art Houtteman	4.00	2.75	1.00	62 Ted Kluszewski	6.50	5.00	2.25
5 Sid Gordon	4.00	2.75	1.00	63 Gil McDougald	6.00	4.50	2.00
6 Joe Ginsberg	4.00	2.75	1.00	64 Curt Simmons	5.00	3.75	1.75
7 Harry Chiti	4.00	2.75	1.00	65 Robin Roberts	12.00	8.75	4.00
8 Al Rosen	7.00	5.25	2.50	66 Mel Parnell	4.00	2.75	1.00
9 Phil Rizzuto	16.00	12.00	5.50	67 Mel Clark	4.00	2.75	1.00
10 Richie Ashburn	6.50	5.00	2.25	68 Allie Reynolds	7.00	5.25	2.50
11 Bobby Shantz	5.00	3.75	1.75	69 Charley Grimm	4.00	2.75	1.00
12 Carl Erskine	6.00	4.50	2.00	70 Clint Courtney	4.00	2.75	1.00
13 Gus Zerniel	4.00	2.75	1.00	71 Paul Minner	4.00	2.75	1.00
14 Billy Loes	4.00	2.75	1.00	72 Ted Gray	4.00	2.75	1.00
15 Jim Busby	4.00	2.75	1.00	73 Billy Pierce	6.00	4.50	2.00
16 Bob Friend	5.00	3.75	1.75	74 Don Mueller	4.00	2.75	1.00
17 Jerry Staley	4.00	2.75	1.00	75 Saul Rogovin	4.00	2.75	1.00
18 Nelson Fox	7.50	5.75	2.50	76 Jim Hearn	4.00	2.75	1.00
19 Alvin Dark	5.00	3.75	1.75	77 Mickey Grasso	4.00	2.75	1.00
20 Don Lenhardt	4.00	2.75	1.00	78 Carl Furillo	7.00	5.25	2.50
21 Joe Garagiola	11.00	8.00	3.50	79 Ray Boone	4.00	2.75	1.00
22 Bob Porterfield	4.00	2.75	1.00	80 Ralph Kiner	12.00	8.75	4.00
23 Herman Wehmeier	4.00	2.75	1.00	81 Enos Slaughter	9.00	6.75	3.00
24 Jackie Jensen	6.00	4.50	2.00	82 Joe Astroth	4.00	2.75	1.00
25 "Hoot" Evers	4.00	2.75	1.00	83 Jack Daniels	4.00	2.75	1.00
26 Roy McMillan	4.00	2.75	1.00	84 Hank Bauer	7.00	5.25	2.50
27 Vic Raschi	6.00	4.50	2.00	85 Solly Hemus	4.00	2.75	1.00
28 "Smoky" Burgess	4.00	2.75	1.00	86 Harry Simpson	4.00	2.75	1.00
29 Bobby Avila	4.00	2.75	1.00	87 Harry Perkowski	4.00	2.75	1.00
30 Phil Cavaretta	5.00	3.75	1.75	88 Joe Dobson	4.00	2.75	1.00
31 Jimmy Dykes	5.00	3.75	1.75	89 Sandy Consuegra	4.00	2.75	1.00
32 Stan Musial	80.00	60.00	25.00	90 Joe Nuxhall	5.00	3.75	1.75
33 "Peewee" Reese	16.00	12.00	5.50	91 Steve Souchock	4.00	2.75	1.00
34 Gil Coan	4.00	2.75	1.00	92 Gil Hodges	15.00	11.00	5.00
35 Maurice McDermott	4.00	2.75	1.00	93 Rizzuto & Martin	28.00	21.00	10.00
36 "Minnie" Minoso	7.50	5.75	2.50	94 Bob Addis	4.00	2.75	1.00
37 Jim Wilson	4.00	2.75	1.00	95 Wally Moses	4.00	2.75	1.00
38 Harry Byrd	4.00	2.75	1.00	96 Sal Maglie	5.00	3.75	1.75
39 Paul Richards	5.00	3.75	1.75	97 Ed Mathews	16.00	12.00	5.50
40 Larry Doby	6.00	4.50	2.00	98 Hector Rodriguez	4.00	2.75	1.00
41 Sammy White	4.00	2.75	1.00	99 Warren Spahn	16.00	12.00	5.50
42 Tommy Brown	4.00	2.75	1.00	100 Bill Wight	4.00	2.75	1.00
43 Mike Garcia	5.00	3.75	1.75	101 Red Schoendienst	6.50	5.00	2.25
44 Bauer, Berra, Mantle	50.00	38.00	17.00	102 Jim Hegan	4.00	2.75	1.00
45 Walt Dropo	4.00	2.75	1.00	103 Del Ennis	4.00	2.75	1.00
46 Roy Campanella	32.00	24.00	11.00	104 Luke Easter	5.00	3.75	1.75
47 Ned Garver	4.00	2.75	1.00	105 Eddie Joost	4.00	2.75	1.00
48 Hank Sauer	5.00	3.75	1.75	106 Ken Raffensberger	4.00	2.75	1.00
49 Eddie Stanky	5.00	3.75	1.75	107 Alex Kellner	4.00	2.75	1.00
50 Lou Kretlow	4.00	2.75	1.00	108 Bobby Adams	4.00	2.75	1.00
51 Monte Irvin	9.00	6.75	3.00	109 Ken Wood	4.00	2.75	1.00
52 Marty Marion	6.00	4.50	2.00	110 Bob Rush	4.00	2.75	1.00
53 Del Rice	4.00	2.75	1.00	111 Jim Dyck	4.00	2.75	1.00
54 Chico Carrasquel	4.00	2.75	1.00	112 Toby Atwell	4.00	2.75	1.00

1953 BOWMAN COLOR (CONT.)

	MINT	VG-E	F-G			MINT	VG-E	F-G
113 Karl Drews	8.00	6.00	2.50		137 Sam Dente	8.00	6.00	2.50
114 Bob Feller	65.00	48.00	22.00		138 Bubba Church	8.00	6.00	2.50
115 Cloyd Boyer	8.00	6.00	2.50		139 Pete Runnels	8.00	6.00	2.50
116 Eddie Yost	8.00	6.00	2.50		140 Al Brazle	8.00	6.00	2.50
117 Duke Snider	160.00	120.00	55.00		141 Frank Shea	8.00	6.00	2.50
118 Billy Martin	40.00	30.00	13.00		142 Larry Miggins	8.00	6.00	2.50
119 Dale Mitchell	8.00	6.00	2.50		143 Al Lopez	16.00	12.00	5.50
120 Marlin Stuart	8.00	6.00	2.50		144 Warren Hacker	8.00	6.00	2.50
121 Yogi Berra	110.00	80.00	35.00		145 George Shuba	8.00	6.00	2.50
122 Bill Serena	8.00	6.00	2.50		146 Early Wynn	28.00	21.00	10.00
123 Johnny Lipon	8.00	6.00	2.50		147 Clem Koshorek	8.00	6.00	2.50
124 Charlie Dressen	9.00	6.75	3.00		148 Billy Goodman	8.00	6.00	2.50
125 Ray Hatfield	8.00	6.00	2.50		149 Al Corwin	8.00	6.00	2.50
126 Al Corwin	8.00	6.00	2.50		150 Carl Scheib	8.00	6.00	2.50
127 Dick Kryhoski	8.00	6.00	2.50		151 Joe Adcock	9.00	6.75	3.00
128 Whitey Lockman	8.00	6.00	2.50		152 Clyde Vollmer	8.00	6.00	2.50
129 Russ Meyer	8.00	6.00	2.50		153 Whitey Ford	60.00	45.00	20.00
130 Cass Michaels	8.00	6.00	2.50		154 Turk Lown	8.00	6.00	2.50
131 Connie Ryan	8.00	6.00	2.50		155 Allie Clark	8.00	6.00	2.50
132 Fred Hutchinson	10.00	7.00	3.00		156 Max Surkont	8.00	6.00	2.50
133 Willie Jones	8.00	6.00	2.50		157 Sherman Lollar	8.00	6.00	2.50
134 Johnny Pesky	8.00	6.00	2.50		158 Howard Fox	8.00	6.00	2.50
135 Bobby Morgan	8.00	6.00	2.50		159 Mickey Vernon	9.00	6.75	3.00
136 Jim Brideweiser	8.00	6.00	2.50		160 Cal Abrams	10.00	7.00	3.00

1953 BOWMAN B&W (64)   2 1/2" X 3 3/4"

The 1953 Bowman Black and White set contains photograph fronts exactly like the color set of 1953. Although they suffer aesthetically from the lack of color, the '53 Black and Whites are popular among collectors because of the difficulty in completing the set.

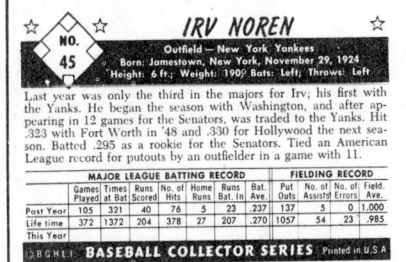

	MINT	VG-E	F-G			MINT	VG-E	F-G
COMPLETE SET	850.00	600.00	250.00		32 Rocky Bridges	10.00	7.00	3.00
COMMON PLAYERS	10.00	7.00	3.00		33 Bob Kuzava	10.00	7.00	3.00
					34 Ebba St. Claire	10.00	7.00	3.00
1 Gus Bell	25.00	10.00	4.00		35 Johnny Wyrostek	10.00	7.00	3.00
2 Willard Nixon	10.00	7.00	3.00		36 Jim Piersall	20.00	15.00	6.50
3 Bill Rigney	10.00	7.00	3.00		37 Hal Jeffcoat	10.00	7.00	3.00
4 Pat Mullin	10.00	7.00	3.00		38 Dave Cole	10.00	7.00	3.00
5 Dee Fondy	10.00	7.00	3.00		39 Casey Stengel	125.00	90.00	40.00
6 Ray Murray	10.00	7.00	3.00		40 Larry Jansen	10.00	7.00	3.00
7 Andy Seminick	10.00	7.00	3.00		41 Bob Ramazotti	10.00	7.00	3.00
8 Pete Suder	10.00	7.00	3.00		42 Howie Judson	10.00	7.00	3.00
9 Walt Masterson	10.00	7.00	3.00		43 Hal Bevan	10.00	7.00	3.00
10 Dick Sisler	10.00	7.00	3.00		44 Jim Delsing	10.00	7.00	3.00
11 Dick Gernert	10.00	7.00	3.00		45 Irv Noren	10.00	7.00	3.00
12 Randy Jackson	10.00	7.00	3.00		46 Bucky Harris	20.00	15.00	6.50
13 Joe Tipton	10.00	7.00	3.00		47 Jack Lohrke	10.00	7.00	3.00
14 Bill Nicholson	10.00	7.00	3.00		48 Steve Ridzek	10.00	7.00	3.00
15 Johnny Mize	28.00	21.00	10.00		49 Floyd Baker	10.00	7.00	3.00
16 Stu Miller	10.00	7.00	3.00		50 Dutch Leonard	10.00	7.00	3.00
17 Virgil Trucks	10.00	7.00	3.00		51 Lou Burdette	18.00	13.50	6.00
18 Billy Hoeft	10.00	7.00	3.00		52 Ralph Branca	14.00	10.50	4.75
19 Paul Lapalme	10.00	7.00	3.00		53 Morris Martin	10.00	7.00	3.00
20 Eddie Robinson	10.00	7.00	3.00		54 Billy Miller	10.00	7.00	3.00
21 Clarence Podbielan	10.00	7.00	3.00		55 Don Johnson	10.00	7.00	3.00
22 Matt Batts	10.00	7.00	3.00		56 Roy Smalley	10.00	7.00	3.00
23 Wilmer Mizell	10.00	7.00	3.00		57 Andy Pafko	10.00	7.00	3.00
24 Del Wilber	10.00	7.00	3.00		58 Jim Konstanty	12.00	8.75	4.00
25 Johnny Sain	20.00	15.00	6.50		59 Duane Pillette	10.00	7.00	3.00
26 "Preacher" Roe	20.00	15.00	6.50		60 Billy Cox	10.00	7.00	3.00
27 Bob Lemon	30.00	22.50	10.50		61 Tom Gorman	10.00	7.00	3.00
28 Hoyt Wilhelm	21.00	15.50	7.00		62 Keith Thomas	10.00	7.00	3.00
29 Sid Hudson	10.00	7.00	3.00		63 Steve Gromek	10.00	7.00	3.00
30 Walker Cooper	10.00	7.00	3.00		64 Andy Hansen	10.00	7.00	3.00
31 Gene Woodling	11.00	8.00	3.50					

1954 BOWMAN (224)

2 1/2" X 3 3/4"

The 1954 Bowman set contains the modern era's most publicized variation card. Number 66 exists as both Ted Williams and Jim Piersall (who is also number 210 in the set). The Williams card is considered by some to be scarcest post-war regular issue card. The set price below does not include number 66 Williams.

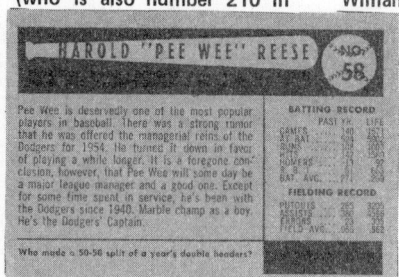

	MINT	VG-E	F-G
COMPLETE SET	500.00	380.00	150.00
COMMON PLAYER (1-128)	.75	.55	.25
COMMON PLAYER (129-224)	1.00	.70	.30

	MINT	VG-E	F-G
1 Phil Rizzuto	18.00	10.00	4.00
2 Jackie Jensen	2.50	1.80	.80
3 Marion Fricano	.75	.55	.25
4 Bob Hooper	.75	.55	.25
5 Bill Hunter	.75	.55	.25
6 Nelson Fox	3.00	2.25	1.00
7 Walt Dropo	.75	.55	.25
8 Jim Busby	.75	.55	.25
9 Davey Williams	.75	.55	.25
10 Carl Erskine	2.50	1.80	.80
11 Sid Gordon	.75	.55	.25
12 Roy McMillan	.75	.55	.25
13 Paul Minner	.75	.55	.25
14 Gerry Staley	.75	.55	.25
15 Richie Ashburn	3.00	2.25	1.00
16 Jim Wilson	.75	.55	.25
17 Tom Gorman	.75	.55	.25
18 "Hoot" Evers	.75	.55	.25
19 Bobby Shantz	1.50	1.10	.50
20 Art Houtteman	.75	.55	.25
21 Vic Wertz	.75	.55	.25
22 Sam Mele	.75	.55	.25
23 Harvey Kuenn	2.00	1.50	.60
24 Bob Porterfield	.75	.55	.25
25 Wes Westrum	.75	.55	.25
26 Billy Cox	.75	.55	.25
27 Dick Cole	.75	.55	.25
28 Jim Greengrass	.75	.55	.25
29 Johnny Klippstein	.75	.55	.25
30 Del Rice	.75	.55	.25
31 "Smokey" Burgess	1.00	.70	.30
32 Del Crandall	1.00	.70	.30
33 Vic Raschi	2.50	1.80	.80
34 Sammy White	.75	.55	.25
35 Eddie Joost	.75	.55	.25
36 George Strickland	.75	.55	.25
37 Dick Kokos	.75	.55	.25
38 "Minnie" Minoso	3.00	2.25	1.00
39 Ned Garver	.75	.55	.25
40 Gil Coan	.75	.55	.25
41 Alvin Dark	1.00	.70	.30
42 Billy Loes	.75	.55	.25
43 Bob Friend	1.00	.70	.30
44 Harry Perkowski	.75	.55	.25
45 Ralph Kiner	8.00	6.00	2.50
46 Rip Repulski	.75	.55	.25
47 Granny Hamner	.75	.55	.25
48 Jack Dittmer	.75	.55	.25
49 Harry Byrd	.75	.55	.25
50 George Kell	2.00	1.50	.60
51 Alex Kellner	.75	.55	.25
52 Joe Ginsberg	.75	.55	.25
53 Don Lenhardt	.75	.55	.25
54 Chico Carrasquel	.75	.55	.25
55 Jim Delsing	.75	.55	.25
56 Maurice McDermott	.75	.55	.25
57 Hoyt Wilhelm	3.00	2.25	1.00
58 "Peewee" Reese	9.00	6.75	3.00
59 Bob Schultz	.75	.55	.25
60 Fred Baczewski	.75	.55	.25

	MINT	VG-E	F-G
61 Eddie Miksis	.75	.55	.25
62 Enos Slaughter	4.50	3.50	1.60
63 Earl Torgeson	.75	.55	.25
64 Eddie Mathews	9.00	6.75	3.00
65 Mickey Mantle	85.00	65.00	30.00
66 Ted Williams	700.00	500.00	250.00
66 Jim Piersall	50.00	38.00	17.00
67 Carl Scheib	.75	.55	.25
68 Bobby Avila	.75	.55	.25
69 Clint Courtney	.75	.55	.25
70 Willard Marshall	.75	.55	.25
71 Ted Gray	.75	.55	.25
72 Eddie Yost	.75	.55	.25
73 Don Mueller	.75	.55	.25
74 Jim Gilliam	2.50	1.80	.80
75 Max Surkont	.75	.55	.25
76 Joe Nuxhall	1.00	.70	.30
77 Bob Rush	.75	.55	.25
78 Sal Yvars	.75	.55	.25
79 Curt Simmons	1.00	.70	.30
80 Johnny Logan	.75	.55	.25
81 Jerry Coleman	1.00	.70	.30
82 Billy Goodman	.75	.55	.25
83 Ray Murray	.75	.55	.25
84 Larry Doby	2.50	1.80	.80
85 Jim Dyck	.75	.55	.25
86 Harry Dorish	.75	.55	.25
87 Don Lund	.75	.55	.25
88 Tom Umphlett	.75	.55	.25
89 Willie Mays	75.00	55.00	24.00
90 Roy Campanella	21.00	15.50	7.00
91 Cal Abrams	.75	.55	.25
92 Ken Raffensberger	.75	.55	.25
93 Bill Serena	.75	.55	.25
94 Solly Hemus	.75	.55	.25
95 Robin Roberts	8.00	6.00	2.50
96 Joe Adcock	1.00	.70	.30
97 Gil McDougald	1.25	.90	.40
98 Ellis Kinder	.75	.55	.25
99 Pete Suder	.75	.55	.25
100 Mike Garcia	1.00	.70	.30
101 Don Larsen	2.00	1.50	.60
102 Billy Pierce	2.00	1.50	.60
103 Steve Souchock	.75	.55	.25
104 Frank Shea	.75	.55	.25
105 Sal Maglie	1.00	.70	.30
106 Clem Labine	.75	.55	.25
107 Paul LaPalme	.75	.55	.25
108 Bobby Adams	.75	.55	.25
109 Roy Smalley	.75	.55	.25
110 "Red" Schoendienst	2.00	1.50	.60
111 Murry Dickson	.75	.55	.25
112 Andy Pafko	.75	.55	.25
113 Allie Reynolds	3.00	2.25	1.00
114 Willard Nixon	.75	.55	.25
115 Don Bollweg	.75	.55	.25
116 Luke Easter	.75	.55	.25
117 Dick Kryhoski	.75	.55	.25
118 Bob Boyd	.75	.55	.25
119 Fred Hatfield	.75	.55	.25
120 Mel Hoderlein	.75	.55	.25
121 Ray Katt	.75	.55	.25

	MINT	VG-E	F-G
122 Carl Furillo	2.50	1.80	.80
123 Toby Atwell	.75	.55	.25
124 Gus Bell	.75	.55	.25
125 Warren Hacker	.75	.55	.25
126 Cliff Chambers	.75	.55	.25
127 Del Ennis	.75	.55	.25
128 Ebba St. Claire	.75	.55	.25
129 Hank Bauer	2.00	1.50	.60
130 Milt Bolling	1.00	.70	.30
131 Joe Astroth	1.00	.70	.30
132 Bob Feller	14.00	10.50	4.75
133 Duane Pillette	1.00	.70	.30
134 Luis Aloma	1.00	.70	.30
135 Johnny Pesky	1.00	.70	.30
136 Clyde Vollmer	1.00	.70	.30
137 Al Corwin	1.00	.70	.30
138 Gil Hodges	10.00	7.00	3.00
139 Preston Ward	1.00	.70	.30
140 Saul Rogovin	1.00	.70	.30
141 Joe Garagiola	7.50	5.75	2.50
142 Al Brazle	1.00	.70	.30
143 Wille Jones	1.00	.70	.30
144 Ernie Johnson	1.00	.70	.30
145 Billy Martin	8.00	6.00	2.50
146 Dick Gernert	1.00	.70	.30
147 Joe DeMaestri	1.00	.70	.30
148 Dale Mitchell	1.00	.70	.30
149 Bob Young	1.00	.70	.30
150 Cass Michaels	1.00	.70	.30
151 Pat Mullin	1.00	.70	.30
152 Mickey Vernon	1.25	.90	.40
153 Whitey Lockman	1.00	.70	.30
154 Don Newcombe	3.50	2.50	1.20
155 Frank Thomas	1.00	.70	.30
156 Rocky Bridges	1.00	.70	.30
157 "Turk" Lown	1.00	.70	.30
158 Stu Miller	1.00	.70	.30
159 Johnny Lindell	1.00	.70	.30
160 Danny O'Connell	1.00	.70	.30
161 "Yogi" Berra	17.00	12.50	6.00
162 Ted Lepcio	1.00	.70	.30
163 Dave Philley	1.00	.70	.30
164 Early Wynn	7.50	5.75	2.50
165 Johnny Groth	1.00	.70	.30
166 Sandy Consuegra	1.00	.70	.30
167 Billy Hoeft	1.00	.70	.30
168 Ed Fitzgerald	1.00	.70	.30
169 Larry Jansen	1.00	.70	.30
170 Duke Snider	15.00	11.00	5.00
171 Carlos Bernier	1.00	.70	.30
172 Andy Seminick	1.00	.70	.30

	MINT	VG-E	F-G
173 Dee Fondy	1.00	.70	.30
174 Pete Castiglione	1.00	.70	.30
175 Mel Clark	1.00	.70	.30
176 Vern Bickford	1.00	.70	.30
177 "Whitey" Ford	11.00	8.00	3.50
178 Del Wilber	1.00	.70	.30
179 Morris Martin	1.00	.70	.30
180 Joe Tipton	1.00	.70	.30
181 Les Moss	1.00	.70	.30
182 Sherman Lollar	1.00	.70	.30
183 Matt Batts	1.00	.70	.30
184 Mickey Grasso	1.00	.70	.30
185 Daryl Spencer	1.00	.70	.30
186 Russ Meyer	1.00	.70	.30
187 Vernon Law	1.00	.70	.30
188 Frank Smith	1.00	.70	.30
189 Randy Jackson	1.00	.70	.30
190 Joe Presko	1.00	.70	.30
191 Karl Drews	1.00	.70	.30
192 Lou Burdette	1.50	1.10	.50
193 Eddie Robinson	1.00	.70	.30
194 Sid Hudson	1.00	.70	.30
195 Bob Cain	1.00	.70	.30
196 Bob Lemon	8.00	6.00	2.50
197 Lou Kretlow	1.00	.70	.30
198 Virgil Trucks	1.00	.70	.30
199 Steve Gromek	1.00	.70	.30
200 Conrado Marrero	1.00	.70	.30
201 Bobby Thomson	3.50	2.50	1.20
202 George Shuba	1.00	.70	.30
203 Vic Janowicz	1.00	.70	.30
204 Jackie Collum	1.00	.70	.30
205 Hal Jeffcoat	1.00	.70	.30
206 Steve Bilko	1.00	.70	.30
207 Stan Lopata	1.00	.70	.30
208 Johnny Antonelli	1.00	.70	.30
209 Gene Woodling	1.00	.70	.30
210 Jim Piersall	4.00	3.00	1.40
211 Al Robertson	1.00	.70	.30
212 Owen Friend	1.00	.70	.30
213 Dick Littlefield	1.00	.70	.30
214 Ferris Fain	1.00	.70	.30
215 Johnny Bucha	1.00	.70	.30
216 Jerry Snyder	1.00	.70	.30
217 Henry Thompson	1.00	.70	.30
218 "Preacher" Roe	2.50	1.80	.80
219 Hal Rice	1.00	.70	.30
220 Hobie Landrith	1.00	.70	.30
221 Frank Baumholtz	1.00	.70	.30
222 Memo Luna	1.00	.70	.30
223 Steve Ridzik	1.00	.70	.30
224 Bill Bruton	2.00	1.50	.60

1955 BOWMAN (320)   2 1/2" X 3 3/4"

The 1955 Bowman set, also known as "the Television set" because all the players are portrayed within a T.V. border, includes the first cards of umpires in a major set. High numbers 225—320 are more difficult to obtain than the lower numbers. Card nos. 48 Milt Bolling and 204 Frank Bolling exist with each others backs, as do card nos. 101 Don Johnson and 157 Ernie Johnson. Card no. 132 Harvey Kuenn exsists with the name spelled correctly and also incorrectly spelled "Kueen".

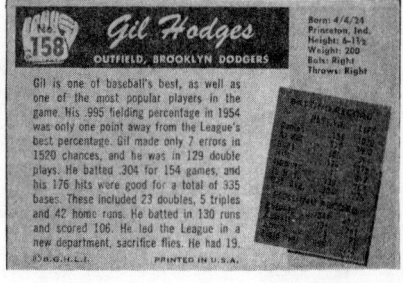

	MINT	VG-E	F-G
COMPLETE SET	425.00	330.00	150.00
COMMON PLAYER (1-96)	.50	.38	.16
COMMON PLAYER (97-224)	.40	.31	.13
COMMON PLAYER (225-320)	1.75	1.30	.60
UMPIRES	3.00	2.25	1.00
1 Hoyt Wilhelm	8.00	2.50	1.00
2 Alvin Dark	.60	.45	.20
3 Joe Coleman	.50	.38	.16
4 Eddie Waitkus	.50	.38	.16
5 Jim Robertson	.50	.38	.16
6 Pete Suder	.50	.38	.16

	MINT	VG-E	F-G
7 Gene Baker	.50	.38	.16
8 Warren Hacker	.50	.38	.16
9 Gil McDougald	1.25	.90	.40
10 Phil Rizzuto	8.00	6.00	2.50
11 Billy Bruton	.50	.38	.16
12 Andy Pafko	.50	.38	.16
13 Clyde Vollmer	.50	.38	.16
14 Gus Keriazakos	.50	.38	.16
15 Frank Sullivan	.50	.38	.16
16 Jim Piersall	1.50	1.10	.50
17 Del Ennis	.60	.45	.20

	MINT	VG-E	F-G		MINT	VG-E	F-G
18 Stan Lopata	.50	.38	.16	108 Lou Kretlow	.40	.31	.13
19 Bobby Avila	.50	.38	.16	109 Vern Stephens	.40	.31	.13
20 Al Smith	.50	.38	.16	110 Bob Miller	.40	.31	.13
21 Don Hoak	.50	.38	.16	111 Steve Ridzik	.40	.31	.13
22 Roy Campanella	13.50	10.00	4.50	112 Granny Hamner	.40	.31	.13
23 Al Kaline	10.00	7.00	3.00	113 Bob Hall	.40	.31	.13
24 Al Aber	.50	.38	.16	114 Vic Janowicz	.40	.31	.13
25 Minnie Minoso	2.50	1.80	.80	115 Roger Bowman	.40	.31	.13
26 Virgil Trucks	.50	.38	.16	116 Sandy Consuegra	.40	.31	.13
27 Preston Ward	.50	.38	.16	117 Johnny Groth	.40	.31	.13
28 Dick Cole	.50	.38	.16	118 Bobby Adams	.40	.31	.13
29 Red Schoendienst	1.50	1.10	.50	119 Joe Astroth	.40	.31	.13
30 Bill Sarni	.50	.38	.16	120 Ed Burtschy	.40	.31	.13
31 Johnny Temple	.50	.38	.16	121 Rufus Crawford	.40	.31	.13
32 Wally Post	.50	.38	.16	122 Al Corwin	.40	.31	.13
33 Nelson Fox	2.50	1.80	.80	123 Marv Grissom	.40	.31	.13
34 Clint Courtney	.50	.38	.16	124 Johnny Antonelli	.60	.45	.20
35 Bill Tuttle	.50	.38	.16	125 Paul Giel	.40	.31	.13
36 Wayne Belardi	.50	.38	.16	126 Billy Goodman	.40	.31	.13
37 Peewee Reese	8.00	6.00	2.50	127 Hank Majeski	.40	.31	.13
38 Early Wynn	7.00	5.25	2.50	128 Mike Garcia	.60	.45	.20
39 Bob Darnell	.50	.38	.16	129 Hal Naragon	.40	.31	.13
40 Vic Wertz	.60	.45	.20	130 Richie Ashburn	2.00	1.50	.60
41 Mel Clark	.50	.38	.16	131 Willard Marshall	.40	.31	.13
42 Bob Greenwood	.50	.38	.16	132a Harvey Kuenn(corr)	3.00	2.25	1.00
43 Bob Buhl	.50	.38	.16	132b Harvey Kuenn(Kueen)	1.25	.90	.40
44 Danny O'Connell	.50	.38	.16	133 Charles King	.40	.31	.13
45 Tom Umphlett	.50	.38	.16	134 Bob Feller	11.00	8.00	3.50
46 Mickey Vernon	.75	.55	.25	135 Lloyd Merriman	.40	.31	.13
47 Sammy White	.50	.38	.16	136 Rocky Bridges	.40	.31	.13
48a Milt Bolling(corr)	4.00	3.00	1.40	137 Bob Talbot	.40	.31	.13
48b Milt Bolling(error)	1.50	1.10	.50	138 Davey Williams	.40	.31	.13
49 Jim Greengrass	.50	.38	.16	139 Shantz Brothers	1.50	1.10	.50
50 Hobie Landrith	.50	.38	.16	140 Bobby Shantz	1.00	.70	.30
51 Elvin Tappe	.50	.38	.16	141 Wes Westrum	.40	.31	.13
52 Hal Rice	.50	.38	.16	142 Rudy Regalado	.40	.31	.13
53 Alex Kellner	.50	.38	.16	143 Don Newcombe	2.50	1.80	.80
54 Don Bollweg	.50	.38	.16	144 Art Houtteman	.40	.31	.13
55 Cal Abrams	.50	.38	.16	145 Bob Nieman	.40	.31	.13
56 Billy Cox	.50	.38	.16	146 Don Liddle	.40	.31	.13
57 Bob Friend	.75	.55	.25	147 Sam Mele	.40	.31	.13
58 Frank Thomas	.50	.38	.16	148 Bob Chakales	.40	.31	.13
59 Whitey Ford	10.00	7.00	3.00	149 Cloyd Boyer	.40	.31	.13
60 Enos Slaughter	4.50	3.50	1.60	150 Bill Klaus	.40	.31	.13
61 Paul LaPalme	.50	.38	.16	151 Jim Brideweser	.40	.31	.13
62 Royce Lint	.50	.38	.16	152 Johnny Klippstein	.40	.31	.13
63 Irv Noren	.50	.38	.16	153 Eddie Robinson	.40	.31	.13
64 Curt Simmons	.60	.45	.20	154 Frank Lary	.40	.31	.13
65 Don Zimmer	.75	.55	.25	155 Gerry Staley	.40	.31	.13
66 George Shuba	.50	.38	.16	156 Jim Hughes	.40	.31	.13
67 Don Larsen	2.00	1.50	.60	157a Ernie Johnson(corr)	3.00	2.25	1.00
68 Elston Howard	2.50	1.80	.80	157b Ernie Johnson(error)	1.25	.90	.40
69 Bill Hunter	.50	.38	.16	158 Gil Hodges	8.00	6.00	2.50
70 Lou Burdette	.75	.55	.25	159 Harry Byrd	.40	.31	.13
71 Dave Jolly	.50	.38	.16	160 Bill Skowron	1.50	1.10	.50
72 Chet Nichols	.50	.38	.16	161 Matt Batts	.40	.31	.13
73 Eddie Yost	.50	.38	.16	162 Charlie Maxwell	.40	.31	.13
74 Jerry Snyder	.50	.38	.16	163 Sid Gordon	.40	.31	.13
75 Brooks Lawrence	.50	.38	.16	164 Toby Atwell	.40	.31	.13
76 Tom Poholsky	.50	.38	.16	165 Maurice McDermott	.40	.31	.13
77 Jim McDonald	.50	.38	.16	166 Jim Busby	.40	.31	.13
78 Gil Coan	.50	.38	.16	167 Bob Grim	.40	.31	.13
79 Willie Miranda	.50	.38	.16	168 Yogi Berra	12.00	8.75	4.00
80 Lou Limmer	.50	.38	.16	169 Carl Furillo	3.00	2.25	1.00
81 Bob Morgan	.50	.38	.16	170 Carl Erskine	2.00	1.50	.60
82 Lee Walls	.50	.38	.16	171 Robin Roberts	6.50	5.00	2.25
83 Max Surkont	.50	.38	.16	172 Willie Jones	.40	.31	.13
84 George Freese	.50	.38	.16	173 Chico Carrasquel	.40	.31	.13
85 Cass Michaels	.50	.38	.16	174 Sherman Lollar	.40	.31	.13
86 Ted Gray	.50	.38	.16	175 Wilmer Shantz	.40	.31	.13
87 Randy Jackson	.50	.38	.16	176 Joe DeMaestri	.40	.31	.13
88 Steve Bilko	.50	.38	.16	177 Willard Nixon	.40	.31	.13
89 Lou Boudreau	6.00	4.50	2.00	178 Tom Brewer	.40	.31	.13
90 Art Ditmar	.50	.38	.16	179 Hank Aaron	30.00	22.50	10.50
91 Dick Marlowe	.50	.38	.16	180 Johnny Logan	.40	.31	.13
92 George Zuverink	.50	.38	.16	181 Eddie Miksis	.40	.31	.13
93 Andy Seminick	.50	.38	.16	182 Bob Rush	.40	.31	.13
94 Hank Thompson	.60	.45	.20	183 Ray Katt	.40	.31	.13
95 Sal Maglie	.75	.55	.25	184 Willie Mays	32.00	24.00	11.00
96 Ray Narleski	.40	.31	.13	185 Vic Raschi	1.50	1.10	.50
97 Johnny Podres	1.50	1.10	.50	186 Alex Grammas	.40	.31	.13
98 Jim Gilliam	2.50	1.80	.80	187 Fred Hatfield	.40	.31	.13
99 Jerry Coleman	.75	.55	.25	188 Ned Garver	.40	.31	.13
100 Tom Morgan	.40	.31	.13	189 Jack Collum	.40	.31	.13
101a Don Johnson(corr)	3.00	2.25	1.00	190 Fred Baczewski	.40	.31	.13
101b Don Johnson(error)	1.25	.90	.40	191 Bob Lemon	6.50	5.00	2.25
102 Bobby Thomson	2.50	1.80	.80	192 George Strickland	.40	.31	.13
103 Eddie Mathews	8.00	6.00	2.50	193 Howie Judson	.40	.31	.13
104 Bob Porterfield	.40	.31	.13	194 Joe Nuxhall	.60	.45	.20
105 Johnny Schmitz	.40	.31	.13	195a Erv Palica(w/tr)	4.00	3.00	1.40
106 Del Rice	.40	.31	.13	195b Erv Palica(w/o tr)	.75	.55	.25
107 Solly Hemus	.40	.31	.12	196 Russ Meyer	.40	.31	.13

1955 BOWMAN (CONTINUED)

	MINT	VG-E	F-G		MINT	VG-E	F-G
197 Ralph Kiner	6.50	5.00	2.25	258 John Stevens (UMP)	3.00	2.25	1.00
198 Dave Pope	.40	.31	.13	259 Don Mossi	1.75	1.30	.60
199 Vernon Law	.60	.45	.20	260 Edwin Hurley (UMP)	3.00	2.25	1.00
200 Dick Littlefield	.40	.31	.13	261 Walt Moryn	1.75	1.30	.60
201 Allie Reynolds	3.00	2.25	1.00	262 Jim Lemon	1.75	1.30	.60
202 Mickey Mantle	37.00	27.00	12.50	263 Eddie Joost	1.75	1.30	.60
203 Steve Gromek	.40	.31	.13	264 Bill Henry	1.75	1.30	.60
204a Frank Bolling(corr)	3.00	2.25	1.00	265 Albert Barlick (UMP)	3.00	2.25	1.00
204b Frank Bolling(error)	1.25	.90	.40	266 Mike Fornieles	1.75	1.30	.60
205 Rip Repulski	.40	.31	.13	267 George Honochick (UMP)	3.00	2.25	1.00
206 Ralph Beard	.40	.31	.13	268 Roy Lee Hawes	1.75	1.30	.60
207 Frank Shea	.40	.31	.13	269 Joe Amalfitano	1.75	1.30	.60
208 Eddy Fitzgerald	.50	.40	.18	270 Chico Fernandez	1.75	1.30	.60
209 Smokey Burgess	.40	.31	.13	271 Bob Hooper	1.75	1.30	.60
210 Earl Torgeson	.40	.31	.13	272 John Flaherty (UMP)	3.00	2.25	1.00
211 Sonny Dixon	.40	.31	.13	273 Bubba Church	1.75	1.30	.60
212 Jack Dittmer	.40	.31	.13	274 Jim Delsing	1.75	1.30	.60
213 George Kell	1.00	.70	.30	275 William Grieve (UMP)	3.00	2.25	1.00
214 Billy Pierce	1.50	1.10	.50	276 Ike Delock	1.75	1.30	.60
215 Bob Kuzava	.40	.31	.13	277 Ed Runge (UMP)	3.00	2.25	1.00
216 Preacher Roe	2.00	1.50	.60	278 Charles Neal	1.75	1.30	.60
217 Del Crandall	.50	.40	.18	279 Hank Soar (UMP)	3.00	2.25	1.00
218 Joe Adcock	.50	.40	.18	280 Clyde McCullough	1.75	1.30	.60
219 Whitey Lockman	.40	.31	.13	281 Charles Berry (UMP)	3.00	2.25	1.00
220 Jim Hearn	.40	.31	.13	282 Phil Cavaretta	3.00	2.25	1.00
221 Hector Brown	.40	.31	.13	283 Nestor Chylak (UMP)	3.00	2.25	1.00
222 Russ Kemmerer	.40	.31	.13	284 Bill Jackowski (UMP)	3.00	2.25	1.00
223 Hal Jeffcoat	.40	.31	.13	285 Walt Dropo	1.75	1.30	.60
224 Dee Fondy	.40	.31	.13	286 Frank Secory (UMP)	3.00	2.25	1.00
225 Paul Richards	4.00	3.00	1.40	287 Ron Mrozinski	1.75	1.30	.60
226 W. McKinley (UMP)	3.00	2.25	1.00	288 Dick Smith	1.75	1.30	.60
227 Frank Baumholtz	1.75	1.30	.60	289 Arthur Gore (UMP)	3.00	2.25	1.00
228 John Phillips	1.75	1.30	.60	290 Hershell Freeman	1.75	1.30	.60
229 Jim Brosnan	2.50	1.80	.80	291 Frank Dascoli (UMP)	3.00	2.25	1.00
230 Al Brazle	1.75	1.30	.60	292 Marv Blaylock	1.75	1.30	.60
231 Jim Konstanty	3.50	2.50	1.20	293 Thomas Gorman (UMP)	3.00	2.25	1.00
232 Birdie Tebbetts	1.75	1.30	.60	294 Wally Moses	1.75	1.30	.60
233 Bill Serena	1.75	1.30	.60	295 Lee Ballanfant (UMP)	3.00	2.25	1.00
234 Dick Bartell	1.75	1.30	.60	296 Bill Virdon	8.00	6.00	2.50
235 J. Paparella (UMP)	3.00	2.25	1.00	297 Dusty Boggess (UMP)	3.00	2.25	1.00
236 Murry Dickson	1.75	1.30	.60	298 Charlie Grimm	1.75	1.30	.60
237 Johnny Wyrostek	1.75	1.30	.60	299 Lon Warneke (UMP)	3.00	2.25	1.00
238 Eddie Stanky	3.00	2.25	1.00	300 Tommy Byrne	1.75	1.30	.60
239 Edwin Rommel (UMP)	3.00	2.25	1.00	301 William Engeln (UMP)	3.00	2.25	1.00
240 Billy Loes	1.75	1.30	.60	302 Frank Malzone	1.75	1.30	.60
241 Johnny Pesky	2.50	1.80	.80	303 Jocko Conlan (UMP)	7.50	5.75	2.50
242 Ernie Banks	50.00	38.00	17.00	304 Harry Chiti	1.75	1.30	.60
243 Gus Bell	1.75	1.30	.60	305 Frank Umont (UMP)	3.00	2.25	1.00
244 Duane Pillette	1.75	1.30	.60	306 Bob Cerv	1.75	1.30	.60
245 Bill Miller	1.75	1.30	.60	307 Babe Pinelli (UMP)	3.00	2.25	1.00
246 Hank Bauer	6.50	5.00	2.25	308 Al Lopez	9.00	6.75	3.00
247 Dutch Leonard	1.75	1.30	.60	309 Hal Dixon (UMP)	3.00	2.25	1.00
248 Harry Dorish	1.75	1.30	.60	310 Ken Lehman	1.75	1.30	.60
249 Billy Gardner	1.75	1.30	.60	311 Lawrence Goetz (UMP)	3.00	2.25	1.00
250 Larry Napp (UMP)	3.00	2.25	1.00	312 Bill Wight	1.75	1.30	.60
251 Stan Jok	1.75	1.30	.60	313 A. Donatelli (UMP)	4.00	3.00	1.40
252 Roy Smalley	1.75	1.30	.60	314 Dale Mitchell	1.75	1.30	.60
253 Jim Wilson	1.75	1.30	.60	315 Cal Hubbard (UMP)	10.00	7.00	3.00
254 Bennett Flowers	1.75	1.30	.60	316 Marion Fricano	1.75	1.30	.60
255 Pete Runnels	1.75	1.30	.60	317 William Summers (UMP)	3.00	2.25	1.00
256 Owen Friend	1.75	1.30	.60	318 Sid Hudson	1.75	1.30	.60
257 Tom Alston	1.75	1.30	.60	319 Albert Schroll	1.75	1.30	.60
				320 George Susce Jr.	1.75	1.30	.60

1952 TIP TOP (48)

2 3/4" X 2 1/2"

This set of 48 bread end-labels was issued by Tip Top in 1952. An album distributed with the labels names 47 ballplayers and has one blank slot with advertising. A second pose of Rizzuto—which appears "cropped" from the first photo—suggests either a last minute substitution for another player, or simply his popularity in the market area. The ACC designation is D290-1.

	MINT	VG-E	F-G
OMPLETE SET	2500.00	1750.00	800.00
OMMON PLAYER	35.00	25.00	10.00

	MINT	VG-E	F-G
1 Bauer - Yanks	40.00	30.00	13.00
2 Berra - Yanks	70.00	50.00	23.00
3 Branca - Dodgers	40.00	30.00	13.00
4 Brissie- Indians	35.00	25.00	10.00
5 Campanella - Dodgers	80.00	60.00	25.00
6 Cavaretta - Cubs	40.00	30.00	13.00
7 Dickson - Pirates	35.00	25.00	10.00
8 Fain - A's	35.00	25.00	10.00
9 Furillo - Dodgers	40.00	30.00	13.00
0 Garver - Browns	35.00	25.00	10.00
1 Gordon - Braves	35.00	25.00	10.00
2 Groth - Tigers	35.00	25.00	10.00
3 Hamner - Phils	35.00	25.00	10.00
4 Hearn - Giants	35.00	25.00	10.00
5 Hermanski - Cubs	35.00	25.00	10.00
6 Hodges - Dodgers	55.00	42.00	19.00
7 Jansen - Giants	35.00	25.00	10.00
8 Joost - A's	35.00	25.00	10.00
9 Kell - Tigers	40.00	30.00	13.00
0 Leonard - Cubs	35.00	25.00	10.00
1 Lockman - Giants	35.00	25.00	10.00
2 Lopat - Yanks	45.00	34.00	15.00
3 Maglie - Giants	35.00	25.00	10.00
4 Mantle - Yanks	500.00	375.00	175.00
25 McDougald - Yanks	40.00	30.00	13.00
26 Mitchell - Indians	35.00	25.00	10.00
27 Mueller - Giants	35.00	25.00	10.00
28 Pafko - Dodgers	35.00	25.00	10.00
29 Porterfield - Senators	35.00	25.00	10.00
30 Raffensberger - Reds	35.00	25.00	10.00
31 Reynolds - Yanks	45.00	34.00	15.00
32 Rizzuto - Yanks (large)	60.00	45.00	20.00
33 Rizzuto - Yanks (small)	60.00	45.00	20.00
34 Roberts - Phils	60.00	45.00	20.00
35 Rogovin - White Sox	35.00	25.00	10.00
36 Scarborough - Red Sox	35.00	25.00	10.00
37 Schoendienst - Cards	40.00	30.00	13.00
38 Sisler - Reds	35.00	25.00	10.00
39 Slaughter - Cards	45.00	34.00	15.00
40 Snider - Dodgers	75.00	55.00	24.00
41 Spahn - Braves	60.00	45.00	20.00
42 Stephens - Red Sox	35.00	25.00	10.00
43 Torgeson - Braves	35.00	25.00	10.00
44 Vernon - Senators	40.00	30.00	13.00
45 Waitkus - Phils	35.00	25.00	10.00
46 Westrum - Giants	35.00	25.00	10.00
47 Yost - Senators	35.00	25.00	10.00
48 Zarilla - White Sox	35.00	25.00	10.00

1952 NATIONAL TEA (48?)

2 3/4" X 2 11/16"

The bread labels in this set are often called "Red Borders" because of their distinctive trim. Issued with the bakery products of the National Tea Company, there are thought to be 48 different labels in the set, although only 39 have been cataloged to date. The labels are also known as the "Bread For Health" set and may have included an album. The SCB designation is D290-2.

	MINT	VG-E	F-G
OMPLETE SET	1400.00	1000.00	400.00
OMMON PLAYER	35.00	25.00	10.00

	MINT	VG-E	F-G
Bearden - Senators	35.00	25.00	10.00
Berra - Yankees	70.00	50.00	23.00
Lou Brissie - A's	35.00	25.00	10.00
Chapman - A's	35.00	25.00	10.00
Diering - Cards	35.00	25.00	10.00
DiMaggio - Red Sox	45.00	34.00	15.00
Edwards - Dodgers	35.00	25.00	10.00
Ennis - Phils	35.00	25.00	10.00
Fain - A's	35.00	25.00	10.00
Gordon - Braves	35.00	25.00	10.00
Groth - Tigers	35.00	25.00	10.00
Hamner - Phils	35.00	25.00	10.00
Jones - Giants	35.00	25.00	10.00
Judson - White Sox	35.00	25.00	10.00
Lollar - Browns	35.00	25.00	10.00
C. Marshall - Browns	35.00	25.00	10.00
Mueller - Giants	35.00	25.00	10.00
Murtaugh - Pirates	35.00	25.00	10.00
Philley - White Sox	35.00	25.00	10.00

	MINT	VG-E	F-G
20 Jerry Priddy - Tigers	35.00	25.00	10.00
21 Bill Rigney - Giants	35.00	25.00	10.00
22 Robin Roberts - Phils	60.00	45.00	20.00
23 Eddie Robinson - W.S.	35.00	25.00	10.00
24 Roe - Dodgers	35.00	25.00	10.00
25 Rojek - Pirates	35.00	25.00	10.00
26 Rosen - Indians	45.00	34.00	15.00
27 Rush - Cubs	35.00	25.00	10.00
28 Sauer - Cubs	35.00	25.00	10.00
29 Schmitz - Cubs	35.00	25.00	10.00
30 Slaughter - Cards	45.00	34.00	10.00
31 Snider - Dodgers	75.00	55.00	24.00
32 Spahn - Braves	65.00	48.00	22.00
33 Staley - Cards	35.00	25.00	10.00
34 Stallcup - Reds	35.00	25.00	10.00
35 Torgeson - Braves	35.00	25.00	10.00
36 Trout - Tigers	35.00	25.00	10.00
37 Vernon - Senators	35.00	25.00	10.00
38 Westlake - Pirates	35.00	25.00	10.00
39 Wyrostek - Reds	35.00	25.00	10.00
40 Yost - Senators	35.00	25.00	10.00

1951-52 FISCHER BAKING (32) 2 3/4" X 2 3/4"

CHICAGO
"CHICO"
CARRASQUEL
WHITE SOX
BREAD for ENERGY

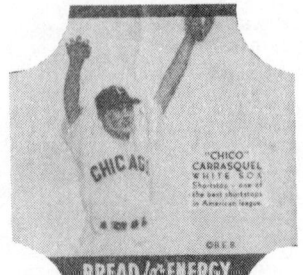

One of the popular "Bread For Energy" end-label sets, these labels are found with blue, red and yellow backgrounds. They were distributed mainly in the northeast section of the country and there may be an album associated with the set. The SCB designation is D290-3.

	MINT	VG-E	F-G
COMPLETE SET	1100.00	825.00	350.00
COMMON PLAYER	35.00	25.00	10.00
1 Bickford - Braves	35.00	25.00	10.00
2 Branca - Dodgers	35.00	25.00	10.00
3 Brecheen - Cards	35.00	25.00	10.00
4 Carrasquel - White Sox	35.00	25.00	10.00
5 Chambers - Pirates	35.00	25.00	10.00
6 Evers - Tigers	35.00	25.00	10.00
7 Garver - Browns	35.00	25.00	10.00
8 Goodman - Red Sox	35.00	25.00	10.00
9 Hodges - Dodgers	60.00	45.00	20.00
10 Jansen - Giants	35.00	25.00	10.00
11 Jones - Phils	35.00	25.00	10.00
12 Joost - A's	35.00	25.00	10.00
13 Kell - Tigers	40.00	30.00	13.00
14 Kellner - A's	35.00	25.00	10.00
15 Kluszewski - Reds	40.00	30.00	13.00
16 Konstanty - Phils	40.00	30.00	13.00

	MINT	VG-E	F-G
17 Lemon - Indians	60.00	45.00	20.00
18 Michaels - Senators	35.00	25.00	10.00
19 Mize - Yanks	50.00	38.00	17.00
20 Noren - Senators	35.00	25.00	10.00
21 Page - Yanks	40.00	30.00	13.00
22 Pafko - Cubs	35.00	25.00	10.00
23 Parnell - Red Sox	35.00	25.00	10.00
24 Sain - Braves	40.00	30.00	13.00
25 Schoendienst - Cards	40.00	30.00	13.00
26 Sievers - Browns	35.00	25.00	10.00
27 Smalley - Cubs	35.00	25.00	10.00
28 Wehmeier - Reds	35.00	25.00	10.00
29 Werle - Pirates	35.00	25.00	10.00
30 Westrum - Giants	35.00	25.00	10.00
31 Wynn - Indians	60.00	45.00	20.00
32 Zernial - White Sox	35.00	25.00	10.00

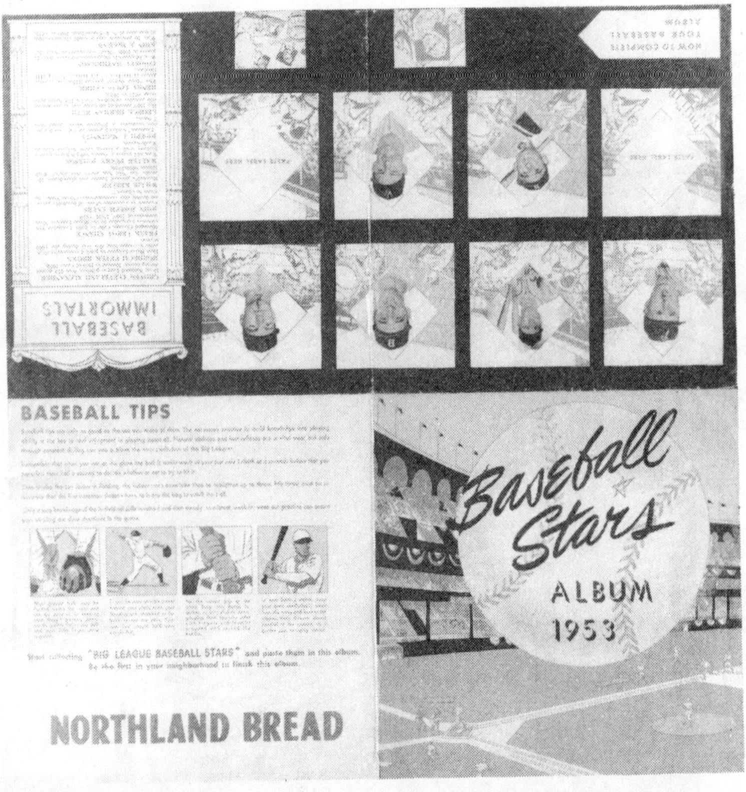
BASEBALL IMMORTALS
BASEBALL TIPS
Start collecting "BIG LEAGUE BASEBALL STARS" and paste them in this album.
Be the first in your neighborhood to finish this album.
NORTHLAND BREAD
Baseball Stars
ALBUM
1953

1953 NORTHLAND BREAD (32)   2 11/16" X 2 11/16"

This 32 label set features two players from each major league team and is one of the popular "Bread For Energy" sets. Although the labels are printed in black and white, the 1953 Northland Bread set includes a "Baseball Stars" album which provides additional information concerning "Baseball Immortals" and "Baseball Tips." The amended SCB designation is D290-3A.

	MINT	VG-E	F-G
COMPLETE SET	1050.00	825.00	350.00
COMMON PLAYER	35.00	25.00	10.00

		MINT	VG-E	F-G
1	Abrams - Pirates	35.00	25.00	10.00
2	Ashburn - Phils	40.00	30.00	13.00
3	Bell - Reds	35.00	25.00	10.00
4	Busby - Nationals	35.00	25.00	10.00
5	Courtney - Browns	35.00	25.00	10.00
6	Cox - Dodgers	35.00	25.00	10.00
7	Dyck - Browns	35.00	25.00	10.00
8	Fox - White Sox	40.00	30.00	13.00
9	Gordon - Braves	35.00	25.00	10.00
10	Hacker - Cubs	35.00	25.00	10.00
11	Hearn - Giants	35.00	25.00	10.00
12	Hutchinson - Tigers	40.00	30.00	13.00
13	Irvin - Giants	50.00	38.00	17.00
14	Jensen - Nationals	40.00	30.00	13.00
15	Kluszewski - Reds	40.00	30.00	13.00
16	Lemon - Indians	60.00	45.00	20.00

		MINT	VG-E	F-G
17	McDermott - Red Sox	35.00	25.00	10.00
18	Minoso - White Sox	40.00	30.00	13.00
19	Mize - Yanks	45.00	34.00	15.00
20	Parnell - Red Sox	35.00	25.00	10.00
21	Pollet - Pirates	35.00	25.00	10.00
22	Priddy - Tigers	35.00	25.00	10.00
23	Reynolds - Yanks	45.00	34.00	15.00
24	Roe - Dodgers	40.00	30.00	13.00
25	Rosen - Indians	45.00	34.00	15.00
26	Ryan - Phillies	35.00	25.00	10.00
27	Sauer - Cubs	35.00	25.00	10.00
28	Schoendienst - Cards	40.00	30.00	13.00
29	Schantz - A's	35.00	25.00	10.00
30	Slaughter - Cards	45.00	34.00	15.00
31	Spahn - Braves	65.00	48.00	22.00
32	Zernial - A's	35.00	25.00	10.00

1953-54 BRIGGS (37)

2 1/4" X 3 1/2"

ERWIN PORTERFIELD, Pitcher
Born August 10, 1924, at Newport, Va.
THROWS RIGHT — BATS RIGHT

Hank Bauer

HANK BAUER

The 1953-54 Briggs hot dog set of 37 full color, blank backed, unnumbered cards was issued in the Washington, D.C., area only. Twenty-five of the cards contain Washington Senator players while the other 12 cards portray players from the three New York teams. The poses are similar to those used in the Dan Dee Potato Chips issue. The ACC designation is F154.

	MINT	VG-E	F-G
COMPLETE SET	3600.00	2700.00	1200.00
COMMON PLAYERS (W)	75.00	55.00	25.00
COMMON PLAYERS (NY)	85.00	65.00	25.00
W 1 Jim Busby	75.00	55.00	25.00
W 2 Tommy Bryne	75.00	55.00	25.00
W 3 Sonny Dixon	75.00	55.00	25.00
W 4 Ed Fitzgerald	75.00	55.00	25.00
W 5 Mickey Grasso	75.00	55.00	25.00
W 6 Mel Hoderlein	75.00	55.00	25.00
W 7 Jackie Jensen	100.00	70.00	30.00
W 8 Connie Marrero	75.00	55.00	25.00
W 9 Carmen Mauro	90.00	70.00	30.00
W10 Walt Masterson	75.00	55.00	25.00
W11 Mickey McDermott	75.00	55.00	25.00
W12 Bob Oldis	75.00	55.00	25.00
W13 Bob Porterfield	75.00	55.00	25.00
W14 Pete Runnels	80.00	60.00	25.00
W15 Johnny Schmitz	75.00	55.00	25.00
W16 Angel Scull	75.00	55.00	25.00
W17 Spec Shea	75.00	55.00	25.00

	MINT	VG-E	F-G
W18 Chuck Stobbs	75.00	55.00	25.00
W19 Wayne Terwilliger	75.00	55.00	25.00
W20 Joe Tipton	75.00	55.00	25.00
W21 Tom Umphlett	75.00	55.00	25.00
W22 Mickey Vernon	90.00	70.00	30.00
W23 Clyde Vollmer	75.00	55.00	25.00
W24 Gene Werbil	90.00	70.00	30.00
W25 Eddie Yost	80.00	60.00	25.00
NY 1 Hank Bauer	100.00	70.00	30.00
NY 2 Carl Erskine	100.00	70.00	30.00
NY 3 Gil Hodges	140.00	100.00	45.00
NY 4 Monte Irvin	120.00	85.00	40.00
NY 5 Whitey Lockman	85.00	65.00	25.00
NY 6 Mickey Mantle	800.00	600.00	250.00
NY 7 Willie Mays	650.00	500.00	200.00
NY 8 Gil McDougald	100.00	70.00	30.00
NY 9 Don Mueller	85.00	65.00	25.00
NY10 Don Newcombe	100.00	70.00	30.00
NY11 Phil Rizzuto	140.00	100.00	45.00
NY12 Duke Snider	200.00	150.00	65.00

1977 BURGER KING YANKEES (24)   2 1/2" X 3 1/2"

The cards in this set marked with an asterisk have different poses than those cards in the regular Topps set. The checklist card is unnumbered and the Piniella card was issued subsequent to the original printing.

	MINT	VG-E	F-G
COMPLETE SET	17.00	13.00	5.00
COMMON PLAYER	.25	.20	.08

	MINT	VG-E	F-G
1 Team Card - Martin	.50	.40	.18
2 Thurman Munson*	1.50	1.10	.50
3 Fran Healy	.25	.20	.08
4 Jim Hunter	.50	.40	.18
5 Ed Figueroa	.25	.20	.08
6 Don Gullett*	.50	.40	.18
7 Mike Torrez*	.50	.40	.18
8 Ken Holtzman	.25	.20	.08
9 Dick Tidrow	.25	.20	.08
10 Sparky Lyle	.40	.30	.13
11 Ron Guidry	.75	.55	.25
12 Chris Chambliss	.40	.30	.13

	MINT	VG-E	F-G
13 Willie Randolph*	.50	.40	.18
14 Bucky Dent*	.50	.40	.18
15 Graig Nettles*	.50	.40	.18
16 Fred Stanley	.25	.20	.08
17 Reggie Jackson*	1.50	1.10	.50
18 Mickey Rivers	.40	.30	.13
19 Roy White	.25	.20	.08
20 Jim Wynn*	.50	.40	.18
21 Paul Blair*	.50	.40	.18
22 Carlos May	.25	.20	.08
Checklist Card	.05	.03	.01
23 Lou Piniella	11.00	7.00	3.00

1978 BURGER KING ASTROS (23)   2 1/2" X 3 1/2"

J. R. RICHARD

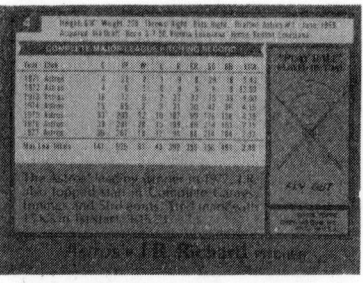

Released in local Burger King outlets during the 1978 season, this Astros series contains the standard 22 numbered player cards and one unnumbered checklist. The player poses found to differ from the regular Topps issue are marked with astericks.

	MINT	VG-E	F-G
COMPLETE SET	6.00	4.50	2.00
COMMON PLAYER	.25	.20	.08

	MINT	VG-E	F-G
1 Bill Virdon	.40	.30	.13
2 Joe Ferguson	.25	.20	.08
3 Ed Herrman	.25	.20	.08
4 J.R. Richard	.50	.40	.18
5 Joe Niekro	.30	.25	.10
6 Floyd Bannister	.25	.20	.08
7 Joaquin Andujar	.25	.20	.08
8 Ken Forsch	.25	.20	.08
9 Mark Lemongello	.25	.20	.08
10 Joe Sambito	.30	.25	.10
11 Gene Pentz	.25	.20	.08

	MINT	VG-E	F-G
12 Bob Watson	.30	.25	.10
13 Julio Gonzales	.25	.20	.08
14 Enos Cabell	.25	.20	.08
15 Roger Metzger	.25	.20	.08
16 Art Howe	.25	.20	.08
17 Jose Cruz	.25	.20	.08
18 Cesar Cedeno	.40	.30	.13
19 Terry Puhl	.30	.25	.10
20 Wilbur Howard	.25	.20	.08
21 Dave Bergman*	.25	.20	.08
22 Jesus Alou*	.25	.20	.08
Checklist	.03	.02	.01

1978 BURGER KING RANGERS (23)   2 1/2" X 3 1/2"

BUMP WILLS

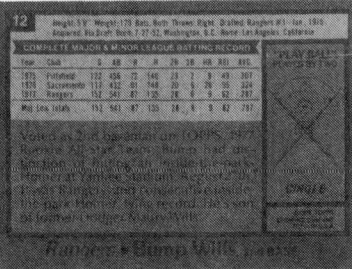

This set of 22 numbered player cards and one unnumbered checklist was issued regionally by Burger King in 1978. Astericks denote poses different than those found in the regular Topps cards of this year

	MINT	VG-E	F-G
COMPLETE SET	6.00	4.50	2.00
COMMON PLAYER	.25	.20	.08
1 Billy Hunter	.40	.30	.13
2 Jim Sundberg	.40	.30	.13
3 John Ellis	.25	.20	.08
4 Doyle Alexander	.25	.20	.08
5 Jon Matlack	.30	.25	.10
6 Doc Ellis	.25	.20	.08
7 Doc Medich	.25	.20	.08
8 Ferguson Jenkins	.40	.30	.13
9 Len Barker	.25	.20	.08
10 Reggie Cleveland	.25	.20	.08
11 Mike Hargrove	.25	.20	.08

	MINT	VG-E	F-G
12 Bump Wills	.30	.25	.10
13 Toby Harrah	.30	.25	.10
14 Bert Campaneris	.30	.25	.10
15 Sandy Alomar	.25	.20	.08
16 Kurt Bevacqua	.25	.20	.08
17 Al Oliver	.50	.40	.18
18 Juan Beniquez	.25	.20	.08
19 Claudell Washington	.25	.20	.08
20 Richie Zisk	.30	.25	.10
21 John Lowenstein	.25	.20	.08
22 Bobby Thompson	.25	.20	.08
Checklist	.03	.02	.01

1978 BURGER KING TIGERS (23)   2 1/2" X 3 1/2"

RUSTY STAUB

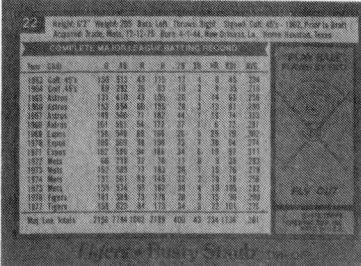

Twenty-three color cards—22 players and one numbered checklist—comprise the 1978 Burger King Tigers set issued in the Detroit area. The cards marked with an asterisk contain photos different from those appearing on the Topps regular issue cards of the year.

	MINT	VG-E	F-G
COMPLETE SET	6.00	4.50	2.00
COMMON PLAYER	.25	.20	.08
1 Ralph Houk	.30	.25	.10
2 Milt May	.25	.20	.08
3 John Wockenfuss	.25	.20	.08
4 Mark Fidrych	.40	.30	.13
5 Dave Rozema	.25	.20	.08
6 Jack Billingham*	.40	.30	.13
7 Jim Slaton*	.40	.30	.13
8 Jack Morris	.30	.25	.10
9 John Hiller	.25	.20	.08
10 Steve Foucault	.25	.20	.08
11 Milt Wilcox	.25	.20	.08

	MINT	VG-E	F-G
12 Jason Thompson	.30	.25	.10
13 Lou Whitaker	.30	.25	.10
14 Aurelio Rodriguez	.25	.20	.08
15 Alan Trammel*	.50	.40	.18
16 Steve Dillard	.25	.20	.08
17 Phil Mankowski	.25	.20	.08
18 Steve Kemp	.40	.30	.13
19 Ron LeFlore	.40	.30	.13
20 Tim Corcoran	.25	.20	.08
21 Mickey Stanley	.25	.20	.08
22 Rusty Staub	.40	.30	.13
Checklist	.03	.02	.01

1978 BURGER KING YANKEES (23)   2 1/2" X 3 1/2"

CLIFF JOHNSON

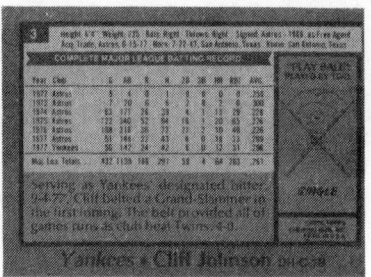

These cards were distributed in packs of three players plus a checklist at Burger King's New York area outlets. Cards with an asterisk have different poses than those in the Topps regular issue.

	MINT	VG-E	F-G
COMPLETE SET	5.00	3.50	1.50
COMMON PLAYER	.20	.15	.06

	MINT	VG-E	F-G
1 Billy Martin	.40	.30	.13
2 Thurman Munson	.75	.55	.25
3 Cliff Johnson	.20	.15	.06
4 Ron Guidry	.40	.30	.13
5 Ed Figueroa	.20	.15	.06
6 Dick Tidrow	.20	.15	.06
7 Jim Hunter	.30	.25	.10
8 Don Gullett	.20	.15	.06
9 Sparky Lyle	.25	.20	.08
10 Rich Gossage*	.50	.40	.18
11 Rawly Eastwick*	.40	.30	.13
12 Chris Chambliss	.25	.20	.08

	MINT	VG-E	F-G
13 Willie Randolph	.25	.20	.08
14 Graig Nettles	.25	.20	.08
15 Bucky Dent	.25	.20	.08
16 Jim Spencer*	.40	.30	.13
17 Fred Stanley	.20	.15	.06
18 Lou Piniella	.30	.25	.10
19 Roy White	.20	.15	.06
20 Mickey Rivers	.25	.20	.08
21 Reggie Jackson	.75	.55	.25
22 Paul Blair	.20	.15	.06
Checklist card	.03	.02	.01

1979 BURGER KING PHILLIES (23)   2 1/2" X 3 1/2"

PETE ROSE 18
PHILLIES

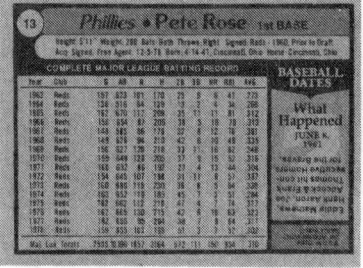

The 1979 Burger King Phillies set follows the regular format of 22 player cards and one unnumbered checklist card. The asterick indicates where the pose differs from the Topps card of that year.

	MINT	VG-E	F-G
COMPLETE SET	5.00	3.75	1.75
COMMON PLAYER	.20	.15	.06

	MINT	VG-E	F-G
1 Danny Ozark*	.30	.25	.10
2 Bob Boone	.25	.20	.08
3 Tim McCarver	.20	.15	.06
4 Steve Carlton	.50	.40	.18
5 Larry Christenson	.20	.15	.06
6 Dick Ruthven	.20	.15	.06
7 Ron Reed	.20	.15	.06
8 Randy Lerch	.20	.15	.06
9 Warren Brusstar	.20	.15	.06
10 Tug McGraw	.30	.25	.10
11 Nino Espinosa**	.20	.15	.06

	MINT	VG-E	F-G
12 Doug Bird*	.20	.15	.06
13 Pete Rose*	.75	.55	.25
14 Manny Trillo*	.25	.20	.08
15 Larry Bowa	.40	.30	.13
16 Mike Schmidt	.65	.50	.20
17 Pete Mackanin*	.20	.15	.06
18 Jose Cardenal	.20	.15	.06
19 Greg Luzinski	.40	.30	.13
20 Garry Maddox	.30	.25	.10
21 Bake McBride	.25	.20	.08
22 Greg Gross*	.20	.15	.06
Checklist	.03	.02	.01

1979 BURGER KING YANKEES (23) 2 1/2" X 3 1/2"

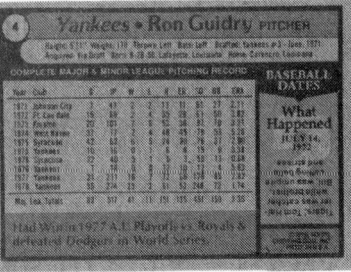

There are 22 numbered cards and one unnumbered check list in the 1979 Burger King Yankee set. The poses of Guidry, Tiant, John and Beniquez, marked with an asterisk below, are different from those poses appearing in the regular topps issue. The team card has a picture of Lemon rather than Martin.

	MINT	VG-E	F-G
COMPLETE SET	5.00	3.75	1.75
COMMON PLAYER	.20	.15	.06
1 Team Card - Lemon*	.30	.25	.10
2 Thurman Munson	.60	.45	.20
3 Cliff Johnson	.20	.15	.06
4 Ron Guidry*	.40	.30	.13
5 Jay Johnstone	.20	.15	.06
6 Jim Hunter	.30	.25	.10
7 Jim Beattie	.20	.15	.06
8 Luis Tiant*'	.25	.20	.08
9 Tommy John*	.30	.25	.10
10 Rich Gossage	.30	.25	.10

	MINT	VG-E	F-G
11 Ed Figueroa	.20	.15	.06
12 Chris Chambliss	.25	.20	.08
13 Willie Randolph	.25	.20	.08
14 Bucky Dent	.25	.20	.08
15 Graig Nettles	.25	.20	.08
16 Fred Stanley	.20	.15	.06
17 Jim Spencer	.20	.15	.06
18 Lou Piniella	.25	.20	.08
19 Roy White	.20	.15	.06
20 Mickey Rivers	.25	.20	.08
21 Reggie Jackson	.60	.45	.20
22 Juan Beniquez*.	.20	.15	.06
Check List	.03	.02	.01

1980 BURGER KING PHILLIES (23) 2 1/2" X 3 1/2"

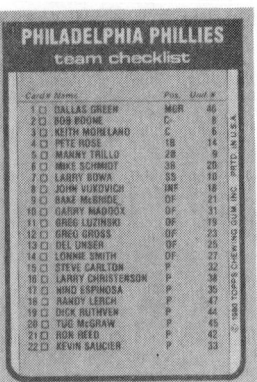

The 1980 edition of Burger King Phillies followed the established pattern of 22 numbered player cards and one unnumbered checklist. Cards marked with asterisks contain poses different from those found in regular 1980 Topps cards.

	MINT	VG-E	F-G
COMPLETE SET	4.00	3.00	1.25
COMMON PLAYER	.15	.11	.04
1 Dallas Green	.25	.20	.08
2 Bob Boone	.15	.11	.04
3 Keith Moreland	.15	.11	.04
4 Pete Rose	.75	.55	.25
5 Manny Trillo	.20	.15	.06
6 Mike Schmidt	.65	.50	.20
7 Larry Bowa	.25	.20	.08
8 John Vukovich	.15	.11	.04
9 Bake McBride	.20	.15	.06
10 Garry Maddox	.20	.15	.06
11 Greg Luzinski	.30	.25	.10

	MINT	VG-E	F-G
12 Greg Gross	.15	.11	.04
13 Del Unser	.15	.11	.04
14 Lonnie Smith	.15	.11	.04
15 Steve Carlton	.50	.40	.18
16 Larry Christenson	.15	.11	.04
17 Nino Espinosa	.15	.11	.04
18 Randy Lerch	.15	.11	.04
19 Dick Ruthven	.15	.11	.04
20 Tug McGraw	.30	.25	.10
21 Ron Reed	.15	.11	.04
22 Kevin Saucier	.15	.11	.04
Check List	.03	.02	.01

1980 BURGER KING (34) PITCH, HIT & RUN

2 1/2" X 3 1/2"

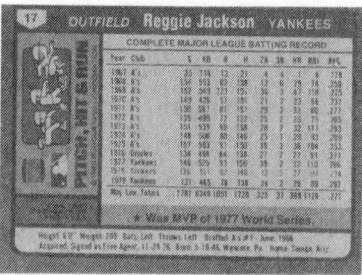

This Baltimore-area giveaway set was called "Pitch, Hit and Run," and featured a Burger King logo on the front. Those cards marked with an asterisk denote a different pose than found in the Topps regular issue. The unnumbered checklist card was given away with each group of three ballplayers, thus accounting for its wide availability with respect to the other cards.

	MINT	VG-E	F-G
COMPLETE SET	9.00	7.00	3.00
COMMON PLAYER	.20	.15	.06

	MINT	VG-E	F-G
Vida Blue*	.30	.25	.10
Steve Carlton	.40	.30	.13
Rollie Fingers	.30	.25	.10
Ron Guidry*	.40	.30	.13
Jerry Koosman*	.30	.25	.10
Phil Niekro	.30	.25	.10
Jim Palmer*	.40	.30	.13
J. R. Richard	.40	.30	.13
Nolan Ryan*	.50	.40	.18
Tom Seaver*	.50	.40	.18
Bruce Sutter	.30	.25	.10
Don Baylor	.30	.25	.10
George Brett	.50	.40	.18
Rod Carew	.50	.30	.13
George Foster	.30	.25	.10
Keith Hernandez*	.40	.30	.13

		MINT	VG-E	F-G
17	Reggie Jackson*	.50	.40	.18
18	Fred Lynn*	.50	.40	.18
19	Dave Parker	.40	.30	.13
20	Jim Rice	.40	.30	.13
21	Pete Rose	.40	.30	.13
22	Dave Winfield*	.50	.40	.18
23	Bobby Bonds*	.30	.25	.10
24	Enos Cabell	.20	.15	.06
25	Cesar Cedeno	.30	.25	.10
26	Julio Cruz	.20	.15	.06
27	Ron LeFlore*	.30	.25	.10
28	Dave Lopes*	.30	.25	.10
29	Omar Moreno*	.30	.25	.10
30	Joe Morgan*	.30	.25	.10
31	Bill North	.20	.15	.06
32	Frank Taveras	.20	.15	.06
33	Willie Wilson	.30	.25	.10

1933 R306 BUTTER CREAM (29)

1 1/4" X 3 1/2"

The small, elongated cards of this set are unnumbered and highly valued by collectors. They are black & white in color and are found with or without the producer's name printed on the reverse. The ACC stated 25 to be the number of cards in the set, but new additions have pushed the known total to 29.

	MINT	VG-E	F-G
COMPLETE SET	2400.00	1800.00	750.00
COMMON PLAYER	80.00	60.00	25.00

	MINT	VG-E	F-G
Earl Averill	100.00	70.00	30.00
Ed Brandt	80.00	60.00	25.00
Guy T. Bush	80.00	60.00	25.00
Gordon Cochrane	125.00	90.00	40.00
Joe Cronin	125.00	90.00	40.00
George Earnshaw	80.00	60.00	25.00
Wesley Ferrell	80.00	60.00	25.00
Jimmy E. Foxx	175.00	125.00	60.00
Frank C. Frisch	125.00	90.00	40.00
Charles M. Gelbert	80.00	60.00	25.00
"Lefty" Grove	150.00	110.00	50.00
Leo Charles Hartnett	125.00	90.00	40.00
"Babe" Herman	80.00	60.00	25.00
Charles Klein	100.00	70.00	30.00
Ray Kremer	80.00	60.00	25.00

		MINT	VG-E	F-G
16	Fred C. Lindstrom	100.00	70.00	30.00
17	Ted A. Lyons	100.00	70.00	30.00
18	"Pepper" Martin	80.00	60.00	25.00
19	Robert O'Farrell	80.00	60.00	25.00
20	Ed A. Rommell	80.00	60.00	25.00
21	Charles Root	80.00	60.00	25.00
22	Harold "Muddy" Ruel	80.00	60.00	25.00
23	"Al" Simmons	125.00	90.00	40.00
24	"Bill" N. Terry	125.00	90.00	40.00
25	George Uhle	80.00	60.00	25.00
26	Lloyd J. Waner	100.00	70.00	30.00
27	Paul C. Waner	125.00	90.00	40.00
28	"Hack" Wilson	100.00	70.00	30.00
29	Glenn Wright	80.00	60.00	25.00

1934 R310 BUTTERFINGER (65)   7 3/4" X 9 1/2"
7 7/16" X 9 7/16"

This large-size premium set comes either in paper or on heavy cardboard stock with advertising for Butterfinger or other candy at the top. The cards are unnumbered and Foxx exists as Fox or Foxx. The ACC designation is R310.

	MINT	VG-E	F-G
COMPLETE SET	500.00	350.00	150.00
COMMON PLAYER (THIN)	7.00	5.00	2.00
COMMON PLAYER (THICK)	15.00	12.00	5.00
1 Earl Averill	10.00	7.00	3.00
2 Richard Bartell	7.00	5.00	2.00
3 Lawrence Benton	7.00	5.00	2.00
4 Walter Berger	7.00	5.00	2.00
5 Jim Bottomley	10.00	7.00	3.00
6 Ralph Boyle	7.00	5.00	2.00
7 Tex Carleton	7.00	5.00	2.00
8 Owen T. Carroll	7.00	5.00	2.00
9 Ben Chapman	7.00	5.00	2.00
10 Mickey Cochrane	12.00	8.75	4.00
11 James Collins	7.00	5.00	2.00
12 Joe Cronin	11.00	8.00	3.50
13 Alvin Crowder	7.00	5.00	2.00
14 "Dizzy" Dean	18.00	13.50	6.00
15 Paul Derringer	7.00	5.00	2.00
16 William Dickey	14.00	10.50	4.75
17 Leo Durocher	10.00	7.00	3.00
18 George Earnshaw	7.00	5.00	2.00
19 Richard Ferrell	7.00	5.00	2.00
20 Lew Fonseca	7.00	5.00	2.00
21 Jimmy Foxx(2)	21.00	15.50	7.00
22 Benny Frey	7.00	5.00	2.00
23 Frankie Frisch	12.00	8.75	4.00
24 Lou Gehrig	25.00	18.50	8.75
25 Chas. Gehringer	12.00	8.75	4.00
26 Vernon Gomez	12.00	8.75	4.00
27 Ray Grabowski	7.00	5.00	2.00
28 Robert (Lefty) Grove	15.00	11.00	5.00
29 George (Mule) Haas	7.00	5.00	2.00
30 "Chick" Hafey	10.00	7.00	3.00
31 Stanley Harris	9.00	6.75	3.00
32 J. Francis Hogan	7.00	5.00	2.00

	MINT	VG-E	F-G
33 Ed Holley	7.00	5.00	2.00
34 Rogers Hornsby	16.00	12.00	5.50
35 Waite Hoyt	10.00	7.00	3.00
36 Walter Johnson	21.00	15.50	7.00
37 Jim Jordan	7.00	5.00	2.00
38 Joe Kuhel	7.00	5.00	2.00
39 Hal Lee	7.00	5.00	2.00
40 Gus Mancuso	7.00	5.00	2.00
41 Henry Manush	10.00	7.00	3.00
42 Fred Marberry	7.00	5.00	2.00
43 Pepper Martin	8.00	6.00	2.50
44 Oscar Melillo	7.00	5.00	2.00
45 Johnny Moore	7.00	5.00	2.00
46 Joe Morrisey	7.00	5.00	2.00
47 Joe Mowrey	7.00	5.00	2.00
48 Bob O'Farrell	7.00	5.00	2.00
49 Melvin Ott	15.00	11.00	5.00
50 Monte Pearson	7.00	5.00	2.00
51 Carl Reynolds	7.00	5.00	2.00
52 Chas. Ruffing	10.00	7.00	3.00
53 "Babe" Ruth	40.00	30.00	13.00
54 John "Blondy" Ryan	7.00	5.00	2.00
55 Al Simmons	12.00	8.75	4.00
56 Al Spohrer	7.00	5.00	2.00
57 Gus Suhr	7.00	5.00	2.00
58 Steve Swetonic	7.00	5.00	2.00
59 "Dazzy" Vance	10.00	7.00	3.00
60 Joe Vosmik	7.00	5.00	2.00
61 Lloyd Waner	10.00	7.00	3.00
62 Paul Waner	11.00	8.00	3.50
63 Sam West	7.00	5.00	2.00
64 Earl Whitehill	7.00	5.00	2.00
65 Jimmy Wilson	7.00	5.00	2.00

1950–56 CALLAHAN (82)

HALL OF FAME

1 3/4" X 2 1/2"

The 1950-56 Callahan Hall of Fame set was issued over a number of years at the Baseball Hall of Fame museum in Cooperstown, New York. New cards were added to the set each year when new members were inducted into the Hall of Fame. The cards with (2) in the checklist exist with two different biographies. The year of each card's first inclusion in the set is in ( ). The ACC designation is W576.

	MINT	VG-F	F-G
COMPLETE SET	120.00	85.00	35.00
COMMON PLAYER	1.00	.75	.30

	MINT	VG-F	F-G
1 Grover Alexander	2.00	1.50	.60
2 Cap Anson	1.00	.75	.30
3 Frank Baker('55)	2.00	1.50	.60
4 Edward Barrow ('54)	1.50	1.10	.50
5 Chief Bender(2)	1.50	1.10	.50
6 Roger Bresnahan	1.00	.75	.30
7 Dan Brouthers	1.00	.75	.30
8 Mordecai Brown	1.00	.75	.30
9 Morgan Bulkeley	1.00	.75	.30
10 Jesse Burkett	1.00	.75	.30
11 Alexander Cartwright	1.00	.75	.30
12 Henry Chadwick	1.00	.75	.30
13 Frank Chance	1.50	1.10	.50
14 Happy Chandler('52)	2.00	1.50	.60
15 Jack Chesbro	1.00	.75	.30
16 Fred Clarke	1.00	.75	.30
17 Ty Cobb	6.00	4.50	2.00
18A Mickey Cochran(sic)	5.00	3.75	1.75
18B Mickey Cochrane(2)	2.00	1.50	.60
19 Eddie Collins (2)	1.50	1.10	.50
20 Jimmie Collins	1.00	.75	.30
21 Charles Comiskey	1.00	.75	.30
22 Tom Connolly('54)	1.50	1.10	.50
23 Candy Cummings	1.00	.75	.30
24 Dizzy Dean ('52)	4.00	3.00	1.40
25 Ed Delahanty	1.00	.75	.30
26 Bill Dickey (2)('54)	2.50	1.80	.80
27 Joe DiMaggio ('55)	10.00	7.00	3.00
28 Hugh Duffy	1.00	.75	.30
29 Johnny Evers	1.50	1.10	.50
30 Buck Ewing	1.00	.75	.30
31 Jimmie Foxx	3.00	2.25	1.00
32 Frank Frisch	2.00	1.50	.60
33 Lou Gehrig	8.00	6.00	2.50
34 Charles Gehringer	6.50	5.00	2.25
35 Clark Griffith	1.00	.75	.30
36 Lefty Grove	2.50	1.80	.80
37 Gabby Hartnett ('55)	1.50	1.10	.50
38 Harry Heilmann ('52)	1.50	1.10	.50
39 Rogers Hornsby	2.50	1.80	.80
40 Carl Hubbell	2.00	1.50	.60

	MINT	VG-F	F-G
41 Hughy Jennings	1.00	.75	.30
42 Ban Johnson	1.00	.75	.30
43 Walter Johnson	3.00	2.25	1.00
44 Willie Keeler	1.00	.75	.30
45 Mike Kelly	1.00	.75	.30
46 Bill Klem('54)	1.50	1.10	.50
47 Napoleon Lajoie	2.00	1.50	.60
48 Kenesaw Landis	1.00	.75	.30
49 Ted Lyons('55)	1.50	1.10	.50
50 Connie Mack	2.00	1.50	.60
51 Walter Maranville('54)	1.50	1.10	.50
52 Christy Mathewson	3.00	2.25	1.00
53 Tommy McCarthy	1.00	.75	.30
54 Joe McGinnity	1.00	.75	.30
55 Charles Nichols	1.00	.75	.30
57 Jim O'Rourke	1.00	.75	.30
58 Mel Ott	2.00	1.50	.60
59 Herb Pennock	1.00	.75	.30
60 Eddie Plank	1.50	1.10	.50
61 Charles Radbourne	1.00	.75	.30
62 Wilbert Robinson	1.00	.75	.30
63 Babe Ruth	10.00	7.00	3.00
64 Ray Schalk('55)	1.50	1.10	.50
65 Al Simmons('52)	1.50	1.10	.50
66 George Sisler (2)	1.50	1.10	.50
67 A. G. Spalding	1.00	.75	.30
68 Tris Speaker	2.00	1.50	.60
69 Bill Terry('54)	2.00	1.50	.60
70 Joe Tinker	1.50	1.10	.50
71 Pie Traynor	1.50	1.10	.50
72 Dazzy Vance('55)	1.50	1.10	.50
73 Rube Waddell	1.00	.75	.30
74 Hans Wagner	3.00	2.25	1.00
75 Bobby Wallace('54)	1.50	1.10	.50
76 Ed Walsh	1.00	.75	.30
77 Paul Waner('52)	1.50	1.10	.50
78 George Wright	1.00	.75	.30
79 Harry Wright('54)	1.50	1.10	.50
80 Cy Young	1.50	1.10	.50
81 Museum Int. (2)('54)	2.00	1.50	.60
82 Museum Ext. (2)('54)	2.00	1.50	.60

GROVER ALEXANDER
P.—Chicago Nationals

D381-1 GASSLER'S BREAD

1914 CRACKER JACK 144 SERIES (144)   2 1/4 X 3"

135

William Killifer, catcher of the Philadelphia Nationals, was born at Paw Paw, Mich., April 13, 1886. In 1907 he began his playing career with Kalamazoo South Michigan League Club. He divided 1908 between Austin of Texas League, and San Francisco, of Pacific Coast. In 1909 he was with Houston Texas League Club, and the following year received his first trial with St. Louis Americans. He was sent to Buffalo by St. Louis in 1911, from which team the Philadelphia Nationals secured him. At the close of 1913 he signed with the Chicago Federals, but came back to Philadelphia before the start of the 1914 season.

This is one of a series of colored pictures of famous Ball Players and Managers given Free with Cracker Jack, "The Famous Popcorn Confection," one card in each package. Our first issue is 15,000,000 pictures. Complete set has 144 pictures of Stars in the American, National and Federal Leagues.

RUECKHEIM BROS. & ECKSTEIN
Brooklyn, N.Y.   Chicago, Ill.

KILLIFER, PHILADELPHIA - NATIONALS

The 1914 Cracker Jacks set, called the Cracker Jacks series of 144, was issued in Cracker Jacks candies. Many or most of the cards have product residues (stains) on them. The series of 144 can be distinguished from the 1915 Cracker Jacks series of 176 by the fact that the tops of both the obverse and reverse of the card are at the same end of the card. This series is one of the few major card sets which includes Federal League players. The ACC designation is E145.

	MINT	VG-E	F-G
COMPLETE SET	5000.00	4000.00	1600.00
COMMON PLAYER	32.00	24.00	10.00

		MINT	VG-E	F-G
1	Knabe	32.00	24.00	10.00
2	Baker	65.00	48.00	22.00
3	Tinker	65.00	48.00	22.00
4	Doyle	32.00	24.00	10.00
5	Wark Miller	32.00	24.00	10.00
6	Plank (Phil. A.L.)	90.00	70.00	30.00
7	Collins (Phil.A.L.)	75.00	55.00	24.00
8	Oldring	32.00	24.00	10.00
9	Artie Hoffman	32.00	24.00	10.00
10	McInnis	32.00	24.00	10.00
11	Stovall	32.00	24.00	10.00
12	Connie Mack	90.00	70.00	30.00
13	Wilson	32.00	24.00	10.00
14	Crawford	55.00	42.00	19.00
15	Russell	32.00	24.00	10.00
16	Camnitz	32.00	24.00	10.00
17	Bresnahan(Catcher)	60.00	45.00	20.00
18	Evers	65.00	48.00	22.00
19	Bender (Phil.A.L.)	65.00	48.00	22.00
20	Falkenberg	32.00	24.00	10.00
21	Zimmerman	32.00	24.00	10.00
22	Wood	32.00	24.00	10.00
23	Comiskey	55.00	42.00	19.00
24	Mullen	32.00	24.00	10.00
25	Simon	32.00	24.00	10.00
26	Scott	32.00	24.00	10.00
27	Carrigan	32.00	24.00	10.00
28	Barry	32.00	24.00	10.00
29	Gregg (Clev.)	32.00	24.00	10.00
30	Cobb	200.00	150.00	65.00
31	Wagner	32.00	24.00	10.00
32	M. Brown	55.00	42.00	19.00
33	Strunk	32.00	14.00	10.00
34	Thomas	32.00	24.00	10.00
35	Hooper	55.00	42.00	19.00
36	Ed Walsh	55.00	42.00	19.00
37	Alexander	90.00	70.00	30.00
38	Dooin (Phil. N.L.)	32.00	24.00	10.00
39	Gandil	32.00	24.00	10.00
40	Auston (St. L.A.L.)	32.00	24.00	10.00
41	Leach	32.00	24.00	10.00
42	Bridwell	32.00	24.00	10.00
43	Marquard (N.Y. Nat'l)	60.00	45.00	20.00
44	Testeau	32.00	24.00	10.00
45	Luderus	32.00	24.00	10.00
46	Groom	32.00	24.00	10.00
47	Devore (Phi. N.L.)	32.00	24.00	10.00
48	Lord	75.00	55.00	24.00
49	Miller	32.00	24.00	10.00
50	Hummell	32.00	24.00	10.00
51	Rucker	32.00	24.00	10.00
52	Wheat	55.00	42.00	19.00
53	Otto Miller	32.00	24.00	10.00
54	O'Toole	32.00	24.00	10.00
55	Hoblitzel (Cinn.)	32.00	24.00	10.00
56	Milan	32.00	24.00	10.00
57	Johnson	125.00	90.00	40.00
58	Schang	32.00	24.00	10.00
59	Gessler	32.00	24.00	10.00
60	Zeider	32.00	24.00	10.00

		MINT	VG-E	F-G
61	Schalk, Ray	55.00	42.00	19.00
62	Cashion	125.00	90.00	40.00
63	Adams	32.00	24.00	10.00
64	Archer, Jimmy	32.00	24.00	10.00
65	Speaker, Tris	100.00	70.00	30.00
66	Lajoie (Cleve.)	125.00	90.00	40.00
67	Crandall	32.00	24.00	10.00
68	Wagner, Honus	125.00	90.00	40.00
69	McGraw, John	75.00	55.00	24.00
70	Fred Clarke	55.00	42.00	19.00
71	Meyers	32.00	24.00	10.00
72	Boehling	32.00	24.00	10.00
73	Carey, Max	55.00	42.00	19.00
74	Frank Owens	32.00	24.00	10.00
75	Huggins, Miller	60.00	45.00	20.00
76	Claude Hendrix	32.00	24.00	10.00
77	Jennings, Hugh	55.00	42.00	19.00
78	Merkle, Fred	32.00	24.00	10.00
79	Bodie, Ping	32.00	24.00	10.00
80	Ruelbach	32.00	24.00	10.00
81	J. C. Delehanty	32.00	24.00	10.00
82	Cravath	32.00	24.00	10.00
83	Ford, Russ	32.00	24.00	10.00
84	E. E. Knetzer	32.00	24.00	10.00
85	Herzog, Buck	32.00	24.00	10.00
86	Shotten	32.00	24.00	10.00
87	Casey	32.00	24.00	10.00
88	Mathewson (Pitching)	250.00	185.00	87.50
89	Cheney	32.00	24.00	10.00
90	Frank Smith	32.00	24.00	10.00
91	Peckinpaugh, Roger	32.00	24.00	10.00
92	Demaree (N.Y. Nat.)	32.00	24.00	10.00
93	Pratt (Throwing)	75.00	55.00	24.00
94	Cicotte, Eddie	32.00	24.00	10.00
95	Keating	32.00	24.00	10.00
96	Becker, Beals	32.00	24.00	10.00
97	Benton	32.00	24.00	10.00
98	LaPorte	32.00	24.00	10.00
99	Chance, Frank	200.00	150.00	65.00
100	Seaton	32.00	24.00	10.00
101	Schulte	32.00	24.00	10.00
102	Fisher	32.00	24.00	10.00
103	Joe Jackson	125.00	90.00	40.00
104	Vic Saier	32.00	24.00	10.00
105	Lavender, James	32.00	24.00	10.00
106	Birmingham	32.00	24.00	10.00
107	Downey	32.00	24.00	10.00
108	Magee (Phi.N.L.)	32.00	24.00	10.00
109	Blanding, Fred	32.00	24.00	10.00
110	Bescher	32.00	24.00	10.00
111	Jim Callahan	100.00	70.00	30.00
112	Sweeney	32.00	24.00	10.00
113	Suggs	32.00	24.00	10.00
114	Geo. J. Moriarity	32.00	24.00	10.00
115	Brennan, Addison	32.00	24.00	10.00
116	Zeider	32.00	24.00	10.00
117	Easterly	32.00	24.00	10.00
118	Konetchy (Pitts.N.L.	32.00	24.00	10.00
119	Perring	32.00	24.00	10.00
120	Doolan	32.00	24.00	10.00

Most serious collectors subscribe to at least one of the hobby papers. Read the ads in this Guide for The Trader Speaks (for advanced collectors), Sports Collectors Digest, and Baseball Hobby News to determine which one or more appeal to you.

1914 CRACKERJACK (CONT)

	MINT	VG-E	F-G			MINT	VG-E	F-G
121 Perdue (Bos. N.L.)	32.00	24.00	10.00		133 Rickey, Branch	65.00	48.00	22.00
122 Bush	32.00	24.00	10.00		134 Marsans (Cin.)	32.00	24.00	10.00
123 Sallee	32.00	24.00	10.00		135 Killefer	32.00	24.00	10.00
124 Earl Moore	32.00	24.00	10.00		136 Maranville, Rabbit	55.00	42.00	19.00
125 Niehoff (Cinc.)	32.00	24.00	10.00		137 Raiden	32.00	24.00	10.00
126 Blair	32.00	24.00	10.00		138 Gowdy, Hank	32.00	24.00	10.00
127 Schmidt	32.00	24.00	10.00		139 Oakes	32.00	24.00	10.00
128 Evans	32.00	24.00	10.00		140 Murphy	32.00	24.00	10.00
129 Caldwell	32.00	24.00	10.00		141 Barger	32.00	24.00	10.00
130 Wingo, Ivy	32.00	24.00	10.00		142 Packard	32.00	24.00	10.00
131 Baumgardner	32.00	24.00	10.00		143 Daubert	32.00	24.00	10.00
132 Nunamaker	32.00	24.00	10.00		144 Walsh, James C.	32.00	24.00	10.00

1915 CRACKER JACK 176 SERIES (176)   2 1/4" X 3"

The 1915 Cracker Jacks set, called the Cracker Jacks series of 176, could be obtained from both boxes of Cracker Jacks and as a set directly from the company. An album could also be obtained for the set. The top of the obverse is at the same end of the card as the botton of the reverse in this series of 176. The ACC designation is E145.

	MINT	VG-E	F-G			MINT	VG-E	F-G
COMPLETE SET	4500.00	3500.00	1600.00		48 O'Neill	35.00	26.00	12.00
COMMON PLAYER	25.00	18.00	8.00		49 Miller	25.00	18.00	8.00
					59 Hummell, John	25.00	18.00	8.00
1 Knabe, Otto	25.00	18.00	8.00		51 Rucker, Nap	25.00	18.00	8.00
2 Baker, Frank	45.00	34.00	15.00		52 Wheat, Zach	40.00	30.00	13.00
3 Tinker, Joe	45.00	34.00	15.00		53 Otto Miller	25.00	18.00	8.00
4 Doyle, Larry	25.00	18.00	8.00		54 O'Toole, Marty	25.00	18.00	8.00
5 Ward Miller	25.00	18.00	8.00		55 Hoblitzel(Bos. A.L.)	25.00	18.00	8.00
6 Plank(St. L. Fed.)	65.00	48.00	22.00		56 Milan, Clyde	25.00	18.00	8.00
7 Collins(Chic. A.L.)	55.00	42.00	19.00		57 Johnson, Walter	100.00	70.00	30.00
8 Oldring, Rube	25.00	18.00	8.00		58 Schang	25.00	18.00	8.00
9 Artie Hoffman	25.00	18.00	8.00		59 Gessler	25.00	18.00	8.00
10 McInnis	25.00	18.00	8.00		60 Dugey	35.00	26.00	12.00
11 Stovall, George	25.00	18.00	8.00		61 Schalk, Ray	40.00	30.00	13.00
12 Connie Mack	75.00	55.00	24.00		62 Mitchell	35.00	26.00	12.00
13 Wilson	25.00	18.00	8.00		63 Adams	25.00	18.00	8.00
14 Crawford, Sam	45.00	34.00	15.00		64 Archer, Jimmy	25.00	18.00	8.00
15 Russell	25.00	18.00	8.00		65 Speaker, Tris	75.00	55.00	24.00
16 Camnitz, Howie	25.00	18.00	8.00		66 Lajoie(Phi. A.L.)	100.00	70.00	30.00
17 Bresnahan, Roger	45.00	34.00	15.00		67 Crandall	25.00	18.00	8.00
18 Evers, Johnny	50.00	38.00	17.00		68 Wagner, Honus	100.00	70.00	30.00
19 Bender(Balt. Fed.)	50.00	38.00	17.00		69 McGraw, John	50.00	38.00	17.00
20 Falkenberg	25.00	18.00	8.00		70 Fred Clarke	40.00	30.00	13.00
21 Zimmerman	25.00	18.00	8.00		71 Meyers	25.00	18.00	8.00
22 Wood, Joe	25.00	18.00	8.00		72 Boehling	25.00	18.00	8.00
23 Comiskey, Charles	40.00	30.00	13.00		73 Carey, Max	40.00	30.00	13.00
24 Mullen, George	25.00	18.00	8.00		74 Frank Owens	25.00	18.00	8.00
25 Simon	25.00	18.00	8.00		75 Huggins, Miller	45.00	34.00	15.00
26 Scott	25.00	18.00	8.00		76 Claude Hendrix	25.00	18.00	8.00
27 Carrigan, Bill	25.00	18.00	8.00		77 Jennings, Hugh	40.00	30.00	13.00
28 Barry, Jack	25.00	18.00	8.00		78 Merkle, Fred	25.00	18.00	8.00
29 Gregg(Bos. A.L.)	25.00	18.00	8.00		79 Bodie, Ping	25.00	18.00	8.00
30 Cobb, Ty	150.00	110.00	50.00		80 Ruelbach	25.00	18.00	8.00
31 Wagner, Heine	25.00	18.00	8.00		81 J. C. Delehanty	25.00	18.00	8.00
32 M. Brown	40.00	30.00	13.00		82 Cravath	25.00	18.00	8.00
33 Strunk, Amos	25.00	18.00	8.00		83 Ford, Russ	25.00	18.00	8.00
34 Thomas	25.00	18.00	8.00		84 E. E. Knetzer	25.00	18.00	8.00
35 Hooper, Harry	40.00	30.00	13.00		85 Herzog, Buck	25.00	18.00	8.00
36 Ed Walsh	40.00	30.00	13.00		86 Shotten	25.00	18.00	8.00
37 Alexander, Grover C.	70.00	50.00	23.00		87 Casey	25.00	18.00	8.00
38 Dooin(Cincin.)	25.00	18.00	8.00		88 Mathewson(Portrait)	100.00	70.00	30.00
39 Gandil, Chick	25.00	18.00	8.00		89 Cheney	25.00	18.00	8.00
40 Austin(Pit. Fed.)	25.00	18.00	8.00		90 Frank Smith	25.00	18.00	8.00
41 Leach, Tommy	25.00	18.00	8.00		91 Peckinpaugh, Roger	25.00	18.00	8.00
42 Bridwell, Al	25.00	18.00	8.00		92 Demaree(Phi. N.L.)	25.00	18.00	8.00
43 Marquard(Bkn. Fed.)	45.00	34.00	15.00		93 Pratt(Portrait)	35.00	26.00	12.00
44 Tesreau, Charles	25.00	18.00	8.00		94 Cicotte, Eddie	25.00	18.00	8.00
45 Luderus	25.00	18.00	8.00		95 Keating	25.00	18.00	8.00
46 Groom, Bob	25.00	18.00	8.00		96 Becker, Beals	25.00	18.00	8.00
47 Devore(Bos. N.L.)	25.00	18.00	8.00		97 Benton	25.00	18.00	8.00

1915 CRACKERJACK (CONTINUED)

		MINT	VG-E	F-G
98	LaPorte	25.00	18.00	8.00
99	Chase, Hal	40.00	30.00	13.00
100	Seaton	25.00	18.00	8.00
101	Schulte	25.00	18.00	8.00
102	Fisher	25.00	18.00	8.00
103	Joe Jackson	100.00	70.00	30.00
104	Vic Saier	25.00	18.00	8.00
105	Lavender, James	25.00	18.00	8.00
106	Birmingham	25.00	18.00	8.00
107	Downey	25.00	18.00	8.00
108	Magee(Bos. N.L.)	25.00	18.00	8.00
109	Blanding, Fred	25.00	18.00	8.00
110	Bescher	25.00	18.00	8.00
111	Moran	35.00	26.00	12.00
112	Sweeney	25.00	18.00	8.00
113	Suggs	25.00	18.00	8.00
114	Geo. J. Moriarity	25.00	18.00	8.00
115	Brennan, Addison	25.00	18.00	8.00
116	Zeider	25.00	18.00	8.00
117	Easterly	25.00	18.00	8.00
118	Konetchy(Pit. Fed.)	25.00	18.00	8.00
119	Perring	25.00	18.00	8.00
120	Doolan	25.00	18.00	8.00
121	Perdue(St. L. N.L.)	25.00	18.00	8.00
122	Bush	25.00	18.00	8.00
123	Sallee	25.00	18.00	8.00
124	Earl Moore	25.00	18.00	8.00
125	Niehoff(Phi. N.L.)	25.00	18.00	8.00
126	Blair	25.00	18.00	8.00
127	Schmidt	25.00	18.00	8.00
128	Evans	25.00	18.00	8.00
139	Caldwell	25.00	18.00	8.00
130	Wingo, Ivy	25.00	18.00	8.00
131	Baumgardner	25.00	18.00	8.00
132	Nunamaker	25.00	18.00	8.00
133	Rickey, Branch	45.00	34.00	15.00
134	Marsans(St. L. Fed.)	25.00	18.00	8.00
135	Killefer	25.00	18.00	8.00
136	Maranville, Rabbit	40.00	30.00	13.00

		MINT	VG-E	F-G
137	Rariden	25.00	18.00	8.00
138	Gowdy, Hank	25.00	18.00	8.00
139	Oakes	25.00	18.00	8.00
140	Murphy	25.00	18.00	8.00
141	Barger	25.00	18.00	8.00
142	Packard	25.00	18.00	8.00
143	Daubert	25.00	18.00	8.00
144	Walsh, James C.	25.00	18.00	8.00
145	Cather	25.00	18.00	8.00
146	Tyler	25.00	18.00	8.00
147	Lee Magee	25.00	18.00	8.00
148	Wilson	25.00	18.00	8.00
149	Janvrin	25.00	18.00	8.00
150	Johnston	25.00	18.00	8.00
151	Whitted	25.00	18.00	8.00
152	McQuillen	25.00	18.00	8.00
153	James	25.00	18.00	8.00
154	Rudolph	25.00	18.00	8.00
155	Connolly	25.00	18.00	8.00
156	Dubuc	25.00	18.00	8.00
157	Kaiserling	25.00	18.00	8.00
158	Maisel	25.00	18.00	8.00
159	Groh, Heine	25.00	18.00	8.00
160	Kauff	25.00	18.00	8.00
161	Rousch, Ed	40.00	30.00	13.00
162	Stallings	25.00	18.00	8.00
163	Waling	25.00	18.00	8.00
164	Shawkey	25.00	18.00	8.00
165	Murphy	25.00	18.00	8.00
166	Bush	25.00	18.00	8.00
167	Griffith, Clark	45.00	34.00	15.00
168	Campbell	25.00	18.00	8.00
169	Raymond Collins	25.00	18.00	8.00
170	Lobert	25.00	18.00	8.00
171	Hamilton	25.00	18.00	8.00
172	Mayer	25.00	18.00	8.00
173	Walker	25.00	18.00	8.00
174	Veach	25.00	18.00	8.00
175	Benz	25.00	18.00	8.00
176	Vaughn	25.00	18.00	8.00

1954 DAN DEE (29)　　　　2 1/2″ X 3 5/8″

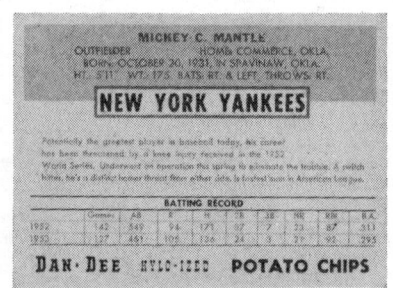

The 1954 Dan Dee P
Chips set contains 29 c
blank backed cards. The
Smith card and, to a l
extent, the Walker Cc
card are quite difficul
obtain. The poses on r
of these cards are simila
other regional cards is
during the mid-1950's.
ACC designation is F342.

		MINT	VG-E	F-G
	COMPLETE SET	1600.00	1100.00	450.00
	COMMON PLAYER	30.00	22.00	10.00
1	Bobby Avila	30.00	22.00	10.00
2	Hank Bauer	35.00	26.00	12.00
3	Walker Cooper	150.00	110.00	50.00
4	Larry Doby	35.00	26.00	12.00
5	Luke Easter	30.00	22.00	10.00
6	Bob Feller	65.00	48.00	22.00
7	Bob Friend	30.00	22.00	10.00
3	Mike Garcia	30.00	22.00	10.00
9	Sid Gordon	30.00	22.00	10.00
10	Jim Hegan	30.00	22.00	10.00
11	Gil Hodges	50.00	38.00	17.00
12	Art Houtteman	30.00	22.00	10.00
13	Monte Irvin	40.00	30.00	13.00
14	Paul LaPalme	30.00	22.00	10.00

		MINT	VG-E	F-G
15	Bob Lemon	40.00	30.00	13.00
16	Al Lopez	35.00	26.00	12.00
17	Mickey Mantle	600.00	400.00	150.00
18	Dale Mitchell	30.00	22.00	10.00
19	Phil Rizzuto	35.00	26.00	12.00
20	Curt Roberts	30.00	22.00	10.00
21	Al Rosen	35.00	26.00	12.00
22	Red Schoendienst	35.00	26.00	12.00
23	Paul Smith	300.00	225.00	100.00
24	Duke Snider	75.00	55.00	24.00
25	George Strickland	30.00	22.00	10.00
26	Max Surkont	30.00	22.00	10.00
27	Frank Thomas	35.00	26.00	12.00
28	Wally Westlake	30.00	22.00	10.00
29	Early Wynn	40.00	30.00	13.00

1959 DARIGOLD FARMS (22)

2 1/2" X 2 3/8"

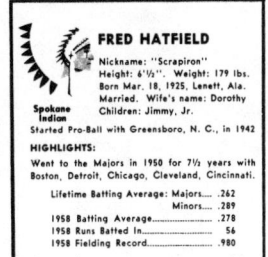

FRED HATFIELD, 3rd Base
Compliments of DARIGOLD FARMS

FRED HATFIELD

Nickname: "Scrapiron"
Height: 6'½". Weight: 179 lbs.
Born Mar. 18, 1925, Lanett, Ala.
Married. Wife's name: Dorothy
Children: Jimmy, Jr.

Started Pro-Ball with Greensboro, N. C., in 1942

HIGHLIGHTS:
Went to the Majors in 1950 for 7½ years with
Boston, Detroit, Chicago, Cleveland, Cincinnati.

Lifetime Batting Average.... Majors.... .262
Minors.... .289
1958 Batting Average........................ .278
1958 Runs Batted In........................ 56
1958 Fielding Record........................ .980

Featuring the Spokane Indians, this set of 22 unnumbered, black & white cards are found with yellow (1-8), red (9-16), and blue (17-22) backgrounds. The cards were attached to a milk carton by a tab. The SCB designation is F115-1.

	MINT	VG-E	F-G
COMPLETE SET	400.00	300.00	150.00
COMMON PLAYER	20.00	15.00	7.00

	MINT	VG-E	F-G		MINT	VG-E	F-G
1 Facundo Barragan	20.00	15.00	7.00	12 Larry Miller	20.00	15.00	7.00
2 Steve Bilko	20.00	15.00	7.00	13 Chris Nicolosi	20.00	15.00	7.00
3 Bobby Bragan	25.00	20.00	10.00	14 Allen Norris	20.00	15.00	7.00
4 Chuck Churn	20.00	15.00	7.00	15 Phil Ortega	20.00	15.00	7.00
5 Tom Davis	25.00	20.00	10.00	16 Phillips Paine	20.00	15.00	7.00
6 Dom Domenichelli	20.00	15.00	7.00	17 Bill Parsons	20.00	15.00	7.00
7 Bob Giallombardo	20.00	15.00	7.00	18 Hisel Patrick	20.00	15.00	7.00
8 Connie Grob	20.00	15.00	7.00	19 Tony Roig	20.00	15.00	7.00
9 Fred Hatfield	20.00	15.00	7.00	20 Tom Saffell	20.00	15.00	7.00
10 Bob Lillis	20.00	15.00	7.00	21 Norm Sherry	20.00	15.00	7.00
11 Lloyd Merritt	20.00	15.00	7.00	22 Ben Wade	20.00	15.00	7.00

1960 DARIGOLD FARMS (24)

2 3/8" X 2 9/16"

Compliments of DARIGOLD FARMS

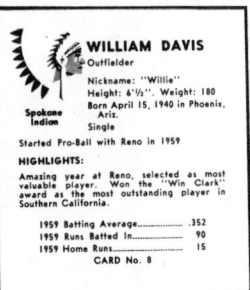

WILLIAM DAVIS
Outfielder

Nickname: "Willie"
Height: 6'½". Weight: 180
Born April 15, 1940 in Phoenix,
Ariz.
Single

Started Pro-Ball with Reno in 1959

HIGHLIGHTS:
Amazing year at Reno, selected as most
valuable player. Won the "Win Clark"
award as the most outstanding player in
Southern California.

1959 Batting Average................ .352
1959 Runs Batted In................ 90
1959 Home Runs.................... 15
CARD No. 8

This set is very similar to the 1959 issue, with background colors of yellow (1-8), green (9-16), and red (17-24). The cards feature only players of the Spokane Indians (PCL).

	MINT	VG-E	F-G
COMPLETE SET	360.00	260.00	125.00
COMMON PLAYER	16.00	12.00	6.00

	MINT	VG-E	F-G		MINT	VG-E	F-G
1 Chris Nicolosi	16.00	12.00	6.00	13 Clarence Churn	16.00	12.00	6.00
2 Jim Pagliaroni	16.00	12.00	6.00	14 Ramon Conde	16.00	12.00	6.00
3 Roy Smalley	16.00	12.00	6.00	15 George O'Donnell	16.00	12.00	6.00
4 Bill Bethee	16.00	12.00	6.00	16 Tony Roig	16.00	12.00	6.00
5 Joe Liscio	16.00	12.00	6.00	17 Frank Howard	25.00	20.00	10.00
6 Curt Roberts	16.00	12.00	6.00	18 Billy Harris	16.00	12.00	6.00
7 Ed Palmquist	16.00	12.00	6.00	19 Mike Brumley	16.00	12.00	6.00
8 William Davis	20.00	16.00	8.00	20 Earl Robinson	16.00	12.00	6.00
9 Bob Giallombardo	16.00	12.00	6.00	21 Ron Fairly	20.00	16.00	8.00
10 Pedro Gomez	16.00	12.00	6.00	22 Joe Frazier	16.00	12.00	6.00
11 Mel Nelson	16.00	12.00	6.00	23 Allen Norris	16.00	12.00	6.00
12 Charlie Smith	16.00	12.00	6.00	24 Ford Young	16.00	12.00	6.00

1933 DELONG (24)   2″ X 3″

The 1933 Delong Gum set, R333 (ACC), is a beautiful and scarce set of 24 cards. It is Delong Gum's only baseball card issue.

	MINT	VG-E	F-G
COMPLETE SET	1700.00	1300.00	600.00
COMMON PLAYER	50.00	38.00	16.00

		MINT	VG-E	F-G
1	McManus, Marty	50.00	38.00	16.00
2	Simmons, Al	65.00	48.00	22.00
3	Melillo, Oscar	50.00	38.00	16.00
4	W. Terry	75.00	55.00	24.00
5	Gehringer, Charlie	70.00	50.00	23.00
6	Cochrane, Mickey	80.00	60.00	25.00
7	Lou Gehrig	650.00	500.00	225.00
8	Cuyler, Kiki	65.00	48.00	22.00
9	Urbanski, Bill	50.00	38.00	16.00
10	O'Doul, Lefty	50.00	38.00	16.00
11	Lindstrom, Fred	75.00	55.00	24.00

		MINT	VG-E	F-G
12	Pie Traynor	70.00	50.00	23.00
13	Maranville, Rabbit	60.00	45.00	22.00
14	Gomez, Lefty	70.00	50.00	23.00
15	Stephenson, Riggs	60.00	45.00	20.00
16	Warneke, Lon	60.00	45.00	20.00
17	Martin, Pepper	50.00	38.00	16.00
18	Dykes, Jim	50.00	38.00	16.00
19	Hafey, Chick	60.00	45.00	20.00
20	Vosmik, Joe	60.00	45.00	20.00
21	Foxx, Jimmie	175.00	125.00	60.00
22	Klein, Chuck	65.00	48.00	22.00
23	Grove, Lefty	100.00	70.00	30.00
24	Goslin, Goose	65.00	48.00	22.00

1959 — ADVERTISING PANEL

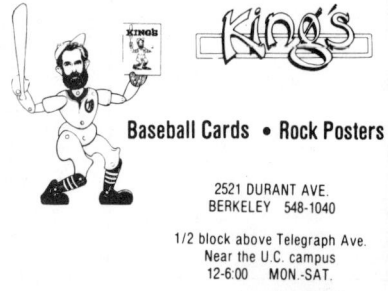

DIAMOND STARS, No. .16
Fielding Tips—Catching the High Fly.
One of the fastest and surest outfielders of the game is Lloyd Waner of the Pittsburgh Pirates. Like most great outfielders, Lloyd catches high flies with his arms and hands extended overhead, so that, in case the ball bounces out of his glove, he will have another chance to catch it before it reaches the ground. Fielders who catch such flies, basket fashion, at the waist have no second chance for the recovery. Line drives or low flies, must, of course, be caught basket fashion.

(signature) Boston American

LLOYD J. WANER. Born Harrah, Okla. 28 years old, 5 ft. 8 inches, 150 pounds. Bats left, throws right. Hit for .276 in 1933.

One of 240 major league players with playing tips. ©1934 National Chicle Co. Cambridge, Mass. U.S.A.

The Diamond Stars set produced by National Chicle from 1934-1936 is also known as R-327 (ACC). The year of production can be determined by the statistics contained on the back of the card. There are 168 possible front-back combinations counting blue and green backs over all three years. The last twelve cards are repeat players, and are quite scarce.

	MINT	VG-E	F-G
COMPLETE SET	1650.00	1200.00	500.00
COMMON PLAYERS (1-72)	8.00	5.50	2.50
COMMON PLAYERS (73-96)	10.00	7.00	3.00
COMMON PLAYERS (97-108)	45.00	35.00	15.00
1 Lefty Grove	40.00	22.00	9.00
2 Al Simmons	18.00	13.50	6.00
3 Rabbit Maranville	15.00	11.00	5.00
4 Buddy Myer	8.00	5.50	2.50
5 Tommy Bridges	8.00	5.50	2.50
6 Bishop, Max	8.00	5.50	2.50
7 Fonseca, Lew	8.00	5.50	2.50
8 Vosmik, Joe	8.00	5.50	2.50
9 Cochrane, Mickey	21.00	15.50	7.00
10 Mahaffey, Leroy	8.00	5.50	2.50
11 Dickey, Bill	27.00	20.00	9.00
12 F. Walker (Dixie)	8.00	5.50	2.50
13 Blaeholder, George	8.00	5.50	2.50
14 Terry, Bill	21.00	15.50	7.00
15 Bartell, Dick	8.00	5.50	2.50
16 L. Waner	16.00	12.00	5.50
17 Frisch, Frank	21.00	15.50	7.00
18 Hafey, Chick	15.00	11.00	5.00
19 Mungo, Van Lingle	9.00	6.75	3.75
20 Hogan, Frank	8.00	5.50	2.50
21 Vergez, Johnny	8.00	5.50	2.50
22 J. Wilson	8.00	5.50	2.50
23 Hallahan, Bill	8.00	5.50	2.50
24 Adams, Earl	8.00	5.50	2.50
25 Berger, Wally	8.00	5.50	2.50
26 Martin, Pepper	10.00	7.00	3.00
27 Traynor, Pie	19.00	14.50	6.50
28 Lopez, Al	14.00	10.50	4.75
29 Rolfe, Red	9.00	6.75	3.00
30 Manush, Heine	15.00	11.00	5.00
31 Cuyler, Kiki	15.00	11.00	5.00
32 Rice, Sam	15.00	11.00	5.00
33 Rowe, Schoolboy	9.00	6.75	3.00
34 Hack, Stan	9.00	6.75	3.00
35 Averill, Earl	15.00	11.00	5.00
36 Lombardi, Ernie	10.00	7.00	3.00
37 Urbanski, Billy	8.00	5.50	2.50
38 B. Chapman	8.00	5.50	2.50
39 Hubbell, Carl	21.00	15.50	7.00
40 Ryan, Blondy	8.00	5.50	2.50
41 Hendrick, Harvey	8.00	5.50	2.50
42 Dykes, Jimmy	9.00	6.75	3.00
43 Lyons, Ted	15.00	11.00	5.00
44 Hornsby, Rogers	30.00	22.50	10.50
45 White, Jo-Jo	8.00	5.50	2.50
46 Lucas, Red	8.00	5.50	2.50
47 Bob Bolton	8.00	5.50	2.50
48 Rick Ferrell	8.00	5.50	2.50
49 Buck Jordan	8.00	5.50	2.50
50 Mel Ott	27.00	20.00	9.00
51 Burgess Whitehead	8.00	5.50	2.50

	MINT	VG-E	F-G
52 Tuck Stainback	8.00	5.50	2.50
53 Oscar Melillo	8.00	5.50	2.50
54 Hank Greenberg	21.00	15.50	7.00
55 Tony Cuccinello	8.00	5.50	2.50
56 Gus Suhr	8.00	5.50	2.50
57 Cy Blanton	8.00	5.50	2.50
58 Myatt, Glenn	8.00	5.50	2.50
59 Bottomley, Jim	15.00	11.00	5.00
60 Ruffing, Red	15.00	11.00	5.00
61 Werber, Bill	8.00	5.50	2.50
62 Frankhouse, Fred	8.00	5.50	2.50
63 Jackson, Travis	8.00	5.50	2.50
64 Foxx, Jimmy	35.00	26.00	12.00
65 Bonura, Zeke	8.00	5.50	2.50
66 Medwick, Ducky	20.00	15.00	6.50
67 Owen, Mickey	8.00	5.50	2.50
68 Leslie, Sam	8.00	5.50	2.50
69 Grace, Earl	8.00	5.50	2.50
70 Trosky, Hal	8.00	5.50	2.50
71 Bluege, Ossie	8.00	5.50	2.50
72 Piet, Tony	8.00	5.50	2.50
73 Ostermueller, Fritz	10.00	7.00	3.00
74 Lazzeri, Tony	13.00	9.50	4.00
75 Burns, Jack	10.00	7.00	3.00
76 Rogell, Billy	10.00	7.00	3.00
77 Gehringer, Charlie	22.00	16.50	7.50
78 Kuhel, Joe	10.00	7.00	3.00
79 Hudlin, Willis	10.00	7.00	3.00
80 Chiozza, Lou	10.00	7.00	3.00
81 Delancey, Bill	10.00	7.00	3.00
82 Babich, Johnny	10.00	7.00	3.00
83 P. Waner	20.00	15.00	6.50
84 Byrd, Sam	10.00	7.00	3.00
85 Solters, Moose	10.00	7.00	3.00
86 Crosetti, Frank	13.00	9.50	4.00
87 O'Neill, Steve	10.00	7.00	3.00
88 Selkirk, George	10.00	7.00	3.00
89 Stripp, Joe	10.00	7.00	3.00
90 Hayworth, Ray	10.00	7.00	3.00
91 Harris, Bucky	18.00	13.50	6.00
92 E. Allen	10.00	7.00	3.00
93 Crowder, General	10.00	7.00	3.00
94 W. Ferrell	11.00	8.00	3.50
95 Appling, Luke	18.00	13.50	6.00
96 Riggs, Lew	10.00	7.00	3.00
97 Lopez	60.00	45.00	20.00
98 Rowe	50.00	38.00	17.00
99 Traynor	100.00	70.00	30.00
100 Averill	70.00	50.00	23.00
101 Bartell	45.00	34.00	15.00
102 Mungo	45.00	34.00	15.00
103 Dickey	110.00	80.00	35.00
104 Rolfe	45.00	34.00	15.00
105 Lombardi	50.00	38.00	17.00
106 Lucas	45.00	34.00	15.00
107 Hack	45.00	34.00	15.00
108 Berger	50.00	38.00	17.00

Produced under the auspices of Michael Schlecter Associates (MSA) in 1976, the ballplayer-on-disc format was distributed by a number of different advertisers - such as Crane's, Isaly's and Towne Club - and can be found in various regions of the country.

	MINT	VG-E	F-G			MINT	VG-E	F-G
COMPLETE SET	6.50	5.00	2.00	35 Doc Medich		.07	.05	.02
COMMON PLAYER	.07	.05	.02	36 Andy Messersmith		.10	.07	.03
				37 Rick Monday		.07	.05	.02
1 Henry Aaron	.50	.40	.15	38 John Montefusco		.07	.05	.02
2 Johnny Bench	.40	.30	.13	39 Jerry Morales		.07	.05	.02
3 Vida Blue	.20	.15	.06	40 Joe Morgan		.20	.15	.06
4 Larry Bowa	.15	.10	.04	41 Thurman Munson		.30	.25	.10
5 Lou Brock	.30	.25	.10	42 Bobby Murcer		.15	.10	.04
6 Jeff Burroughs	.10	.07	.03	43 Al Oliver		.15	.10	.04
7 John Candelaria	.10	.07	.03	44 Jim Palmer		.25	.20	.08
8 Jose Cardenal	.07	.05	.02	45 Dave Parker		.30	.25	.10
9 Rod Carew	.30	.25	.10	46 Tony Perez		.15	.10	.04
10 Steve Carlton	.25	.20	.08	47 Jerry Reuss		.10	.07	.03
11 Dave Cash	.07	.05	.02	48 Brooks Robinson		.35	.27	.12
12 Cesar Cedeno	.15	.10	.04	49 Frank Robinson		.30	.25	.10
13 Ron Cey	.15	.10	.04	50 Steve Rogers		.10	.07	.03
14 Carlton Fisk	.20	.15	.06	51 Pete Rose		.50	.40	.15
15 Tito Fuentes	.07	.05	.02	52 Nolan Ryan		.30	.25	.10
16 Steve Garvey	.30	.25	.10	53 Manny Sanguillen		.07	.05	.02
17 Ken Griffey	.15	.10	.04	54 Mike Schmidt		.30	.25	.10
18 Don Gullett	.07	.05	.02	55 Tom Seaver		.30	.25	.10
19 Willie Horton	.07	.05	.02	56 Ted Simmons		.20	.15	.06
20 Al Hrabosky	.10	.07	.03	57 Reggie Smith		.15	.10	.04
21 Catfish Hunter	.20	.15	.06	58 Willie Stargell		.25	.20	.08
22 Reggie Jackson	.30	.25	.10	59 Rusty Staub		.10	.07	.03
23 Randy Jones	.10	.07	.03	60 Rennie Stennett		.07	.05	.02
24 Jim Kaat	.10	.07	.03	61 Don Sutton		.15	.10	.04
25 Don Kessinger	.10	.07	.03	62 Andy Thornton		.10	.07	.03
26 Dave Kingman	.20	.15	.06	63 Luis Tiant		.10	.07	.03
27 Jerry Koosman	.10	.07	.03	64 Joe Torre		.15	.10	.04
28 Mickey Lolich	.10	.07	.03	65 Mike Tyson		.07	.05	.02
29 Greg Luzinski	.15	.10	.04	66 Bob Watson		.07	.05	.02
30 Fred Lynn	.30	.25	.10	67 Wilbur Wood		.07	.05	.02
31 Bill Madlock	.10	.07	.03	68 Jimmy Wynn		.07	.05	.02
32 Carlos May	.07	.05	.02	69 Carl Yastrzemski		.40	.30	.12
33 John Mayberry	.10	.07	.03	70 Richie Zisk		.10	.07	.03
34 Bake McBride	.10	.07	.03					

1981 DONRUSS (605)

2 1/2" X 3 1/2"

ROLLIE FINGERS PITCHER

Donruss has launched itself into the baseball card field with a set containing 600 numbered cards and five unnumbered checklists. The cards are printed on extremely thin stock and more than one pose exists for several popular players. There are numerous name misspellings and incorrect pictures in the set, which may be corrected in a later printing, subsequent to the publication of this Price Guide.

	MINT	VG-E	F-G
COMPLETE SET	14.00	10.00	5.00
COMMON PLAYER	.03	.02	.01

#	Player	MINT	VG-E	F-G
1	Ozzie Smith	.03	.02	.01
2	Rollie Fingers	.08	.06	.02
3	Rick Wise	.05	.03	.01
4	Gene Richards	.03	.02	.01
5	Alan Trammel	.06	.04	.02
6	Tom Brookens	.03	.02	.01
7	Duffy Dyer	.03	.02	.01
8	Mark Fidrych	.06	.04	.02
9	Dave Rozema	.03	.02	.01
10	Ricky Peters	.03	.02	.01
11	Mike Schmidt	.25	.20	.08
12	Willie Stargell	.20	.15	.06
13	Tim Foli	.03	.02	.01
14	Manny Sanguillen	.03	.02	.01
15	Grant Jackson	.03	.02	.01
16	Eddie Solomon	.03	.02	.01
17	Omar Moreno	.10	.07	.03
18	Joe Morgan	.10	.07	.03
19	Rafael Landestoy	.03	.02	.01
20	Bruce Bochy	.03	.02	.01
21	Joe Sambito	.06	.04	.02
22	Manny Trillo	.05	.03	.01
23	Dave Smith	.03	.02	.01
24	Terry Puhl	.06	.04	.02
25	Bump Wills	.03	.02	.01
26	John Ellis	.03	.02	.01
27	Jim Kern	.03	.02	.01
28	Richie Zisk	.06	.04	.02
29	John Mayberry	.06	.04	.02
30	Bob Davis	.03	.02	.01
31	Jackson Todd	.03	.02	.01
32	Al Woods	.03	.02	.01
33	Steve Carlton	.20	.15	.06
34	Lee Mazzilli	.06	.04	.02
35	John Stearns	.03	.02	.01
36	Roy Jackson	.03	.02	.01
37	Mike Scott	.03	.02	.01
38	Lamar Johnson	.03	.02	.01
39	Kevin Bell	.03	.02	.01
40	Ed Farmer	.03	.02	.01
41	Ross Baumgarten	.03	.02	.01
42	Leo Sutherland	.03	.02	.01
43	Dan Meyer	.03	.02	.01
44	Ron Reed	.03	.02	.01
45	Mario Mendoza	.03	.02	.01
46	Rick Honeycutt	.03	.02	.01
47	Glen Abbott	.03	.02	.01
48	Leon Roberts	.03	.02	.01
49	Rod Carew	.25	.20	.08
50	Bert Campaneris	.05	.03	.01
51	Tom Donahue	.03	.02	.01
52	Dave Frost	.03	.02	.01
53	Ed Halicki	.03	.02	.01
54	Dan Ford	.03	.02	.01
55	Garry Maddox	.06	.04	.02
56	Steve Garvey	.25	.20	.08
57	Bill Russell	.03	.02	.01
58	Don Sutton	.15	.11	.05
59	Reggie Smith	.12	.08	.04
60	Rick Monday	.05	.03	.01
61	Ray Knight	.06	.04	.02
62	Johnny Bench	.25	.20	.08
63	Mario Soto	.03	.02	.01
64	Doug Bair	.03	.02	.01
65	George Foster	.15	.11	.05
66	Jeff Burroughs	.06	.04	.02
67	Keith Hernandez	.15	.11	.05
68	Tom Herr	.03	.02	.01
69	Bob Forsch	.03	.02	.01
70	John Fulgham	.03	.02	.01
71	Bobby Bonds	.08	.06	.02
72	Rennie Stennett	.03	.02	.01
73	Joe Strain	.03	.02	.01
74	Ed Whitson	.03	.02	.01
75	Tom Griffin	.03	.02	.01
76	Billy North	.03	.02	.01
77	Gene Garber	.03	.02	.01
78	Mike Hargrove	.03	.02	.01
79	Dave Rosello	.03	.02	.01
80	Ron Hassey	.03	.02	.01
81	Sid Monge	.03	.02	.01
82	Joe Charboneau	.08	.06	.02
83	Cecil Cooper	.10	.07	.03
84	Sal Bando	.03	.02	.01
85	Moose Haas	.03	.02	.01
86	Mike Caldwell	.05	.03	.01
87	Larry Hisle	.08	.06	.02
88	Luis Gomez	.03	.02	.01
89	Larry Parrish	.06	.04	.02
90	Gary Carter	.12	.08	.04
91	Bill Gullickson	.03	.02	.01
92	Fred Norman	.03	.02	.01
93	Tommy Hutton	.03	.02	.01
94	Carl Yastrzemski	.30	.25	.10
95	Glenn Hoffman	.03	.02	.01
96	Dennis Eckersley	.06	.04	.02
97	Tom Burgmeier	.03	.02	.01
98	Win Remmerswaal	.03	.02	.01
99	Bob Horner	.20	.15	.06
100	George Brett	.30	.25	.10
101	Dave Chalk	.03	.02	.01
102	Dennis Leonard	.06	.04	.02
103	Renie Martin	.03	.02	.01
104	Amos Otis	.06	.04	.02
105	Graig Nettles	.08	.06	.02
106	Eric Soderholm	.03	.02	.01
107	Tommy John	.12	.08	.04
108	Tom Underwood	.03	.02	.01
109	Lou Piniella	.06	.04	.02
110	Micky Klutts	.03	.02	.01
111	Bobby Murcer	.08	.06	.02
112	Eddie Murray	.10	.07	.03
113	Rick Dempsey	.03	.02	.01
114	Scott McGregor	.06	.04	.02
115	Ken Singleton	.10	.07	.03
116	Gary Roenicke	.03	.02	.01
117	Dave Revering	.06	.04	.02
118	Mike Norris	.15	.11	.05
119	Rickey Henderson	.15	.11	.05
120	Mike Heath	.03	.02	.01
121	Dave Cash	.03	.02	.01
122	Randy Jones	.06	.04	.02
123	Eric Rasmussen	.03	.02	.01
124	Jerry Mumphrey	.03	.02	.01
125	Richie Hebner	.05	.03	.01
126	Mark Wagner	.03	.02	.01
127	Jack Morris	.05	.03	.01
128	Dan Petry	.03	.02	.01
129	Bruce Robbins	.03	.02	.01
130	Champ Summers	.03	.02	.01
131	Pete Rose	.30	.25	.10
132	Willie Stargell	.20	.15	.06
133	Ed Ott	.03	.02	.01
134	Jim Bibby	.05	.03	.01
135	Bert Blyleven	.06	.04	.02
136	Dave Parker	.25	.20	.08
137	Bill Robinson	.03	.02	.01
138	Enos Cabell	.03	.02	.01

	MINT	VG-E	F-G			MINT	VG-E	F-G
139 Dave Bergman	.03	.02	.01	232 Rich Dauer		.03	.02	.01
140 J. R. Richard	.15	.11	.05	233 Dan Graham		.03	.02	.01
141 Ken Forsch	.03	.02	.01	234 Mike Flanagan		.08	.06	.02
142 Larry Bowa	.10	.07	.03	235 John Lowenstein		.03	.02	.01
143 Frank LaCorte	.03	.02	.01	236 Benny Ayala		.03	.02	.01
144 Dennis Walling	.03	.02	.01	237 Wayne Gross		.03	.02	.01
145 Buddy Bell	.08	.06	.02	238 Rick Langford		.05	.03	.01
146 Ferguson Jenkins	.08	.06	.02	239 Tony Armas		.08	.06	.02
147 Danny Darwin	.03	.02	.01	240 Bob Lacy		.03	.02	.01
148 John Grubb	.03	.02	.01	241 Gene Tenace		.05	.03	.01
149 Alfredo Griffin	.03	.02	.01	242 Bob Shirley		.03	.02	.01
150 Jerry Garvin	.03	.02	.01	243 Gary Lucas		.03	.02	.01
151 Paul Mirabella	.03	.02	.01	244 Jerry Turner		.03	.02	.01
152 Rick Bosetti	.03	.02	.01	245 John Wockenfuss		.03	.02	.01
153 Dick Ruthven	.03	.02	.01	246 Stan Papi		.03	.02	.01
154 Frank Taveras	.03	.02	.01	247 Milt Wilcox		.03	.02	.01
155 Craig Swan	.06	.04	.02	248 Dan Schatzeder		.03	.02	.01
156 Jeff Reardon	.03	.02	.01	249 Steve Kemp		.10	.07	.03
157 Steve Henderson	.06	.04	.02	250 Jim Lentine		.03	.02	.01
158 Jim Morrison	.03	.02	.01	251 Pete Rose		.30	.25	.10
159 Glenn Borgmann	.03	.02	.01	252 Bill Madlock		.06	.04	.02
160 Lamarr Hoyt	.03	.02	.01	253 Dale Berra		.03	.02	.01
161 Rich Wortham	.03	.02	.01	254 Kent Tekulve		.06	.04	.02
162 Thad Bosley	.03	.02	.01	255 Enrique Romo		.03	.02	.01
163 Julio Cruz	.03	.02	.01	256 Mike Easler		.03	.02	.01
164 Del Unser	.03	.02	.01	257 Chuck Tanner		.05	.03	.01
165 Jim Anderson	.03	.02	.01	258 Art Howe		.03	.02	.01
166 Jim Beattie	.03	.02	.01	259 Alan Ashby		.03	.02	.01
167 Shane Rawley	.03	.02	.01	260 Nolan Ryan		.20	.15	.06
168 Joe Simpson	.03	.02	.01	261 Vern Ruhle		.03	.02	.01
169 Rod Carew	.25	.20	.08	262 Bob Boone		.03	.02	.01
170 Fred Patek	.03	.02	.01	263 Cesar Cedeno		.15	.11	.05
171 Frank Tanana	.05	.03	.01	264 Jeff Leonard		.03	.02	.01
172 Alfredo Martinez	.03	.02	.01	265 Pat Putnam		.03	.02	.01
173 Chris Knapp	.03	.02	.01	266 Jon Matlack		.06	.04	.02
174 Joe Rudi	.05	.03	.01	267 Dave Rajsich		.03	.02	.01
175 Greg Luzinski	.10	.07	.03	268 Bill Sample		.03	.02	.01
176 Steve Garvey	.25	.20	.08	269 Damaso Garcia		.03	.02	.01
177 Joe Ferguson	.03	.02	.01	270 Tom Buskey		.03	.02	.01
178 Bob Welch	.03	.02	.01	271 Joey McLaughlin		.03	.02	.01
179 Dusty Baker	.10	.07	.03	272 Barry Bonnell		.03	.02	.01
180 Rudy Law	.03	.02	.01	273 Tug McGraw		.06	.04	.02
181 Dave Concepcion	.08	.06	.02	274 Mike Jorgensen		.03	.02	.01
182 Johnny Bench	.25	.20	.08	275 Pat Zachry		.03	.02	.01
183 Mike LaCoss	.03	.02	.01	276 Neil Allen		.03	.02	.01
184 Ken Griffey	.06	.04	.02	277 Joel Youngblood		.03	.02	.01
185 Dave Collins	.06	.04	.02	278 Greg Pryor		.03	.02	.01
186 Brian Asselstine	.03	.02	.01	279 Britt Burns		.03	.02	.01
187 Garry Templeton	.15	.11	.05	280 Rich Dotson		.03	.02	.01
188 Mike Phillips	.03	.02	.01	281 Chet Lemon		.06	.04	.02
189 Pete Vuckovich	.03	.02	.01	282 Rusty Kuntz		.03	.02	.01
190 John Urrea	.03	.02	.01	283 Ted Cox		.03	.02	.01
191 Tony Scott	.03	.02	.01	284 Sparky Lyle		.06	.04	.02
192 Darrell Evans	.03	.02	.01	285 Larry Cox		.03	.02	.01
193 Milt May	.03	.02	.01	286 Floyd Bannister		.03	.02	.01
194 Bob Knepper	.03	.02	.01	287 Byron McLaughlin		.03	.02	.01
195 Randy Moffitt	.03	.02	.01	288 Rodney Craig		.03	.02	.01
196 Larry Herndon	.03	.02	.01	289 Bobby Grich		.06	.04	.02
197 Rick Camp	.03	.02	.01	290 Dickie Thon		.03	.02	.01
198 Andre Thornton	.06	.04	.02	291 Mark Clear		.03	.02	.01
199 Tom Veryzer	.03	.02	.01	292 Dave Lemanczyk		.03	.02	.01
200 Gary Alexander	.03	.02	.01	293 Jason Thompson		.06	.04	.02
201 Rick Waits	.03	.02	.01	294 Rick Miller		.03	.02	.01
202 Rick Manning	.03	.02	.01	295 Lonnie Smith		.03	.02	.01
203 Paul Molitor	.15	.11	.05	296 Ron Cey		.06	.04	.02
204 Jim Gantner	.03	.02	.01	297 Steve Yeager		.03	.02	.01
205 Paul Mitchell	.03	.02	.01	298 Bobby Castillo		.03	.02	.01
206 Reggie Cleveland	.03	.02	.01	299 Manny Mota		.06	.04	.02
207 Sixto Lezcano	.06	.04	.02	300 Jay Johnstone		.03	.02	.01
208 Bruce Benedict	.03	.02	.01	301 Dan Driessen		.03	.02	.01
209 Rodney Scott	.03	.02	.01	302 Joe Nolan		.03	.02	.01
210 John Tamargo	.03	.02	.01	303 Paul Householder		.03	.02	.01
211 Bill Lee	.05	.03	.01	304 Harry Spilman		.03	.02	.01
212 Andre Dawson	.06	.04	.02	305 Cesar Geronimo		.03	.02	.01
213 Rowland Office	.03	.02	.01	306 Gary Matthews		.06	.04	.02
214 Carl Yastrzemski	.30	.25	.10	307 Ken Reitz		.03	.02	.01
215 Jerry Remy	.03	.02	.01	308 Ted Simmons		.12	.08	.04
216 Mike Torrez	.03	.02	.01	309 John Littlefield		.03	.02	.01
217 Skip Lockwood	.03	.02	.01	310 George Frazier		.03	.02	.01
218 Fred Lynn	.25	.20	.08	311 Dane Iorg		.03	.02	.01
219 Chris Chambliss	.06	.04	.02	312 Mike Ivie		.03	.02	.01
220 Willie Aikens	.06	.04	.02	313 Dennis Littlejohn		.03	.02	.01
221 John Wathan	.03	.02	.01	314 Gary Lavelle		.03	.02	.01
222 Dan Quisenberry	.08	.06	.02	315 Jack Clark		.08	.06	.02
223 Willie Wilson	.15	.11	.05	316 Jim Wohlford		.03	.02	.01
224 Clint Hurdle	.03	.02	.01	317 Rick Matula		.03	.02	.01
225 Bob Watson	.06	.04	.02	318 Toby Harrah		.03	.02	.01
226 Jim Spencer	.03	.02	.01	319 Dwane Kuiper		.03	.02	.01
227 Ron Guidry	.20	.15	.06	320 Len Barker		.05	.03	.01
228 Reggie Jackson	.25	.20	.08	321 Victor Cruz		.03	.02	.01
229 Oscar Gamble	.06	.04	.02	322 Dell Alston		.03	.02	.01
230 Jeff Cox	.03	.02	.01	323 Robin Yount		.08	.06	.02
231 Luis Tiant	.06	.04	.02	324 Charlie Moore		.03	.02	.01
						.03	.02	.01

		MINT	VG-E	F-G			MINT	VG-E	F-G
325	Lary Sorensen	.03	.02	.01	418	Rick Sutcliffe	.03	.02	.01
326	Gorman Thomas	.08	.06	.02	419	Derrel Thomas	.03	.02	.01
327	Bob Rodgers	.03	.02	.01	420	Tommy Lasorda	.06	.04	.02
328	Phil Niekro	.10	.07	.03	421	Charles Leibrandt	.03	.02	.01
329	Chris Speier	.03	.02	.01	422	Tom Seaver	.25	.20	.08
330	Steve Rodgers	.03	.02	.01	423	Ron Oester	.03	.02	.01
331	Woodie Fryman	.03	.02	.01	424	Junior Kennedy	.03	.02	.01
332	Warren Cromartie	.03	.02	.01	425	Tom Seaver	.25	.20	.08
333	Jerry White	.03	.02	.01	426	Bobby Cox	.03	.02	.01
334	Tony Perez	.10	.07	.03	427	Leon Durham	.03	.02	.01
335	Carlton Fisk	.15	.11	.05	428	Terry Kennedy	.03	.02	.01
336	Dick Drago	.03	.02	.01	429	Silvio Martinez	.03	.02	.01
337	Steve Renko	.03	.02	.01	430	George Hendrick	.08	.06	.02
338	Jim Rice	.25	.20	.08	431	Red Schoendienst	.06	.04	.02
339	Jerry Royster	.03	.02	.01	432	John LeMaster	.03	.02	.01
340	Frank White	.06	.04	.02	433	Vida Blue	.10	.07	.03
341	Jamie Quirk	.03	.02	.01	434	John Montefusco	.03	.02	.01
342	Paul Splittorff	.03	.02	.01	435	Terry Whitfield	.03	.02	.01
343	Marty Pattin	.03	.02	.01	436	Dave Bristol	.03	.02	.01
344	Pete LaCock	.03	.02	.01	437	Dale Murphy	.06	.04	.02
345	Willie Randolph	.06	.04	.02	438	Jerry Dybzinski	.03	.02	.01
346	Rick Cerone	.06	.04	.02	439	Jorge Orta	.03	.02	.01
347	Rich Gossage	.10	.07	.03	440	Wayne Garland	.03	.02	.01
348	Reggie Jackson	.25	.20	.08	441	Miguel Dilone	.05	.03	.01
349	Ruppert Jones	.03	.02	.01	442	Dave Garcia	.03	.02	.01
350	Dave McKay	.03	.02	.01	443	Don Money	.05	.03	.01
351	Yogi Berra	.20	.15	.06	444	Buck Martinez	.03	.02	.01
352	Doug Decinces	.03	.02	.01	445	Jerry Augustine	.03	.02	.01
353	Jim Palmer	.20	.15	.06	446	Ben Oglivie	.06	.04	.02
354	Tippy Martinez	.03	.02	.01	447	Jim Slaton	.03	.02	.01
355	Al Bumbry	.03	.02	.01	448	Doyle Alexander	.03	.02	.01
356	Earl Weaver	.06	.04	.02	449	Tony Bernazard	.03	.02	.01
357	Bob Picciolo	.03	.02	.01	450	Scott Sanderson	.03	.02	.01
358	Matt Keough	.03	.02	.01	451	Dave Palmer	.03	.02	.01
359	Dwayne Murphy	.08	.06	.02	452	Stan Bahnsen	.03	.02	.01
360	Brian Kingman	.03	.02	.01	453	Dick Williams	.05	.03	.01
361	Bill Fahey	.03	.02	.01	454	Rick Burleson	.08	.06	.02
362	Steve Mura	.03	.02	.01	455	Gary Allenson	.03	.02	.01
363	Dennis Kinney	.03	.02	.01	456	Bob Stanley	.03	.02	.01
364	Dave Winfield	.25	.20	.08	457	John Tudor	.03	.02	.01
365	Lou Whitaker	.06	.04	.02	458	Dwight Evans	.03	.02	.01
366	Lance Parrish	.06	.04	.02	459	Glenn Hubbard	.03	.02	.01
367	Tim Corcoran	.03	.02	.01	460	U. L. Washington	.03	.02	.01
368	Pat Underwood	.03	.02	.01	461	Larry Gura	.06	.04	.02
369	Al Cowens	.03	.02	.01	462	Rich Gale	.03	.02	.01
370	Sparky Anderson	.06	.04	.02	463	Hal McRae	.03	.02	.01
371	Pete Rose	.30	.25	.10	464	Jim Frey	.03	.02	.01
372	Phil Garner	.03	.02	.01	465	Bucky Dent	.06	.04	.02
373	Steve Nicosia	.03	.02	.01	466	Dennis Werth	.03	.02	.01
374	John Candelaria	.05	.03	.01	467	Ron Davis	.03	.02	.01
375	Don Robinson	.03	.02	.01	468	Reggie Jackson	.25	.20	.08
376	Lee Lacy	.03	.02	.01	469	Bobby Brown	.03	.02	.01
377	John Milner	.03	.02	.01	470	Mike Davis	.03	.02	.01
378	Craig Reynolds	.03	.02	.01	471	Gaylord Perry	.15	.11	.05
379	Luis Pujois	.03	.02	.01	472	Mark Belanger	.05	.03	.01
380	Joe Niekro	.05	.03	.01	473	Jim Palmer	.20	.15	.06
381	Joaquin Andujar	.03	.02	.01	474	Sammy Stewart	.03	.02	.01
382	Keith Moreland	.03	.02	.01	475	Tim Stoddard	.03	.02	.01
383	Jose Cruz	.05	.03	.01	476	Steve Stone	.10	.07	.03
384	Bill Virdon	.06	.04	.02	477	Jeff Newman	.03	.02	.01
385	Jim Sundberg	.06	.04	.02	478	Steve McCatty	.03	.02	.01
386	Doc Medich	.03	.02	.01	479	Billy Martin	.10	.07	.03
387	Al Oliver	.10	.07	.03	480	Mitchell Page	.05	.03	.01
388	Jim Norris	.03	.02	.01	481	Cy Young 1980	.05	.03	.01
389	Bob Bailor	.03	.02	.01	482	Bill Buckner	.08	.06	.02
390	Ernie Whitt	.03	.02	.01	483	Ivan DeJesus	.03	.02	.01
391	Otto Velez	.03	.02	.01	484	Cliff Johnson	.03	.02	.01
392	Roy Howell	.03	.02	.01	485	Lenny Randle	.03	.02	.01
393	Bob Walk	.03	.02	.01	486	Larry Milbourne	.03	.02	.01
394	Doug Flynn	.03	.02	.01	487	Roy Smalley	.06	.04	.02
395	Pete Falcone	.03	.02	.01	488	John Castino	.03	.02	.01
396	Tom Hausman	.03	.02	.01	489	Ron Jackson	.03	.02	.01
397	Elliott Maddox	.03	.02	.01	490	Dave Roberts	.03	.02	.01
398	Mike Squires	.03	.02	.01	491	M.V.P. AL 1980	:10	.07	.03
399	Marvis Foley	.03	.02	.01	492	Mike Cubbage	.03	.02	.01
400	Steve Trout	.03	.02	.01	493	Rob Wilfong	.03	.02	.01
401	Wayne Nordhagen	.03	.02	.01	494	Danny Goodwin	.03	.02	.01
402	Tony LaRussa	.03	.02	.01	495	Jose Morales	.03	.02	.01
403	Bruce Bochte	.05	.03	.01	496	Mickey Rivers	.08	.06	.02
404	Bake McBride	.05	.03	.01	497	Mike Edwards	.03	.02	.01
405	Jerry Narron	.03	.02	.01	498	Mike Sadek	.03	.02	.01
406	Rob Dressler	.03	.02	.01	499	Lenn Sakata	.03	.02	.01
407	Dave Heaverlo	.03	.02	.01	500	Gene Michael	.05	.03	.01
408	Tom Paciorek	.03	.02	.01	501	Dave Roberts	.03	.02	.01
409	Carney Lansford	.06	.04	.02	502	Steve Dillard	.03	.02	.01
410	Brian Downing	.05	.03	.01	503	Jim Essian	.03	.02	.01
411	Don Aase	.03	.02	.01	504	Rance Mulliniks	.03	.02	.01
412	Jim Barr	.03	.02	.01	505	Darrell Porter	.06	.04	.02
413	Don Baylor	.12	.08	.04	506	Joe Torre	.06	.04	.02
414	Jim Fregosi	.06	.04	.02	507	Terry Crowley	.03	.02	.01
415	Dallas Green	.06	.04	.02	508	Bill Travers	.03	.02	.01
416	Dave Lopes	.06	.04	.02	509	Nelson Norman	.03	.02	.01
417	Jerry Reuss	.06	.04	.02	510	Bob McClure	.03	.02	.01

	MINT	VG-E	F-G			MINT	VG-E	F-G
511 Steve Howe	.03	.02	.01		559 Tim Blackwell	.03	.02	.01
512 Dave Rader	.03	.02	.01		560 Bruce Sutter	.15	.11	.05
513 Mike Kelleher	.03	.02	.01		561 Rick Reuschel	.08	.06	.02
514 Kiko Garcia	.03	.02	.01		562 Lynn McGlothen	.03	.02	.01
515 Larry Biittner	.03	.02	.01		563 Bob Owchinko	.03	.02	.01
516 Willie Norwood	.03	.02	.01		564 John Verhoeven	.03	.02	.01
517 Bo Diaz	.03	.02	.01		565 Ken Landreaux	.06	.04	.02
518 Juan Beniquez	.03	.02	.01		566 Glen Adams	.03	.02	.01
519 Scot Thompson	.03	.02	.01		567 Hosken Powell	.03	.02	.01
520 Jim Tracy	.03	.02	.01		568 Dick Noles	.03	.02	.01
521 Carlos Lezcano	.03	.02	.01		569 Danny Ainge	.03	.02	.01
522 Joe Amalfitano	.03	.02	.01		570 Bobby Mattick	.03	.02	.01
523 Preston Hanna	.03	.02	.01		571 Joe LeFebvre	.03	.02	.01
425 Ray Burris	.03	.02	.01		572 Bobby Clark	.03	.02	.01
525 Broderick Perkins	.03	.02	.01		573 Dennis Lamp	.03	.02	.01
526 Mickey Hatcher	.03	.02	.01		574 Randy Lerch	.03	.02	.01
527 John Goryl	.03	.02	.01		575 Mookie Wilson	.03	.02	.01
528 Dick Davis	.03	.02	.01		576 Ron LeFlore	.08	.06	.02
529 Butch Wynegar	.03	.02	.01		577 Jim Dwyer	.03	.02	.01
530 Sal Butera	.03	.02	.01		578 Bill Castro	.03	.02	.01
531 Jerry Koosman	.05	.03	.01		579 Greg Minton	.03	.02	.01
532 Jeff Zahn	.03	.02	.01		580 Mark Littell	.03	.02	.01
533 Dennis Martinez	.03	.02	.01		581 Andy Hassler	.03	.02	.01
534 Gary Thomasson	.03	.02	.01		582 Dave Steib	.03	.02	.01
535 Steve Macko	.03	.02	.01		583 Ken Oberkfell	.03	.02	.01
536 Jim Kaat	.08	.06	.02		584 Larry Bradford	.03	.02	.01
537 Best Hitters	.05	.03	.01		585 Fred Stanley	.03	.02	.01
538 Tim Raines	.03	.02	.01		586 Bill Caudill	.03	.02	.01
539 Keith Smith	.03	.02	.01		587 Doug Capilla	.03	.02	.01
540 Ken Macha	.03	.02	.01		588 George Riley	.03	.02	.01
541 Burt Hooton	.06	.04	.02		589 Willie Hernandez	.03	.02	.01
542 Butch Hobson	.03	.02	.01		590 M.V.P. NL 1980	.10	.07	.03
543 Bill Stein	.03	.02	.01		591 Cy Young 1980	.10	.07	.03
544 Dave Stapleton	.03	.02	.01		592 Rick Sofield	.03	.02	.01
545 Bob Pate	.03	.02	.01		593 Bombo Rivera	.03	.02	.01
546 Doug Corbett	.03	.02	.01		594 Gary Ward	.03	.02	.01
547 Darrell Jackson	.03	.02	.01		595 Dave Edwards	.03	.02	.01
548 Pete Redfern	.03	.02	.01		596 Mike Proly	.03	.02	.01
549 Roger Erickson	.03	.02	.01		597 Tommy Boggs	.03	.02	.01
550 Al Hrabosky	.06	.04	.02		598 Greg Gross	.03	.02	.01
551 Dick Tidrow	.03	.02	.01		599 Elias Sosa	.03	.02	.01
552 Dave Ford	.03	.02	.01		600 Pat Kelly	.03	.02	.01
553 Dave Kingman	.10	.07	.03		Checklist 1	.03	.02	.01
554 Mike Vail	.03	.02	.01		Checklist 2	.03	.02	.01
555 Jerry Martin	.03	.02	.01		Checklist 3	.03	.02	.01
556 Jesus Figueroa	.03	.02	.01		Checklist 4	.03	.02	.01
557 Don Stanhouse	.03	.02	.01		Checklist 5	.03	.02	.01
558 Barry Foote	.03	.02	.01					

1941 DOUBLE PLAY (75) SEPIA   2 1/2" X 3 1/8"

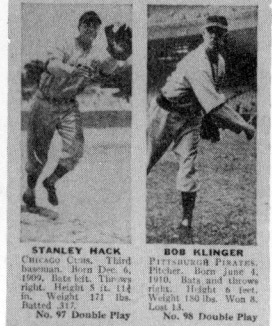

The 1941 Double Play set, R-330 (ACC), is a blank-back issue from Gum Products containing 75 two-player cards. Card nos. 81-100 are vertical action pictures of players issued elsewhere in the set. Cards cut in half have greatly reduced value.

	MINT	VG-E	F-G
COMPLETE SET	650.00	500.00	200.00
COMMON PAIRS (1-100)	6.50	5.00	2.50
COMMON PAIRS (101-150)	8.00	6.25	3.00
CUT HALVES	1.00	.75	.30

	MINT	VG-E	F-G
1-2 French-Page	6.50	5.00	2.50
3-4 Herman-Hack	7.50	5.75	2.50
5-6 Frey-Vander Meer	7.50	5.75	2.50
7-8 Derringer-Walters	7.50	5.75	2.50
9-10 McCormick-Werber	6.50	5.00	2.50
11-12 Ripple-Lombardi	7.50	5.75	2.50
13-14 Kampouris-Wyatt	6.50	5.00	2.50
15-16 Owen-Paul Waner	8.50	6.50	3.00
17-18 Lavagetto-Reiser	7.50	5.75	2.50
19-20 Wasdell-Camilli	6.50	5.00	2.50
21-22 Walker-Medwick	8.50	6.50	3.00
23-24 Reese-Higbe	11.00	8.00	3.50
25-26 Danning-Melton	6.50	5.00	2.50
27-28 Gumbert-Whitehead	6.50	5.00	2.50
29-30 Orengo-Moore	6.50	5.00	2.50
31-32 Ott-Young	11.00	8.00	3.50
33-34 Handley-Vaughn	7.50	5.75	2.50
35-36 Klinger-Brown	6.50	5.00	2.50
37-38 Moore-Mancuso	6.50	5.00	2.50
39-40 Mize-Slaughter	11.00	8.00	3.50
41-42 Cooney-Sisti	6.50	5.00	2.50
43-44 West-Rowell	6.50	5.00	2.50
45-46 Litwhiler-May	6.50	5.00	2.50
47-48 Hayes-Brancato	6.50	5.00	2.50
49-50 Johnson-Nagel	6.50	5.00	2.50
51-52 Newsom-Greenberg	10.00	7.00	3.00
53-54 McCoskey-Gehringer	10.00	7.00	3.00
55-56 Higgins-Bartell	6.50	5.00	2.50
57-58 Ted Williams-Tabor	45.00	34.00	15.00
59-60 Cronin-Foxx	24.00	18.00	8.50
61-62 Gomez-Rizzuto	16.00	12.00	5.50
63-64 J.DiMaggio-Keller	65.00	48.00	22.00
65-66 Rolfe-Dickey	12.00	8.75	4.00
67-68 Gordon-Ruffing	10.00	7.00	3.00
69-70 Tresh-Appling	8.50	6.50	3.00
71-72 Solters-Rigney	6.50	5.00	2.50
73-74 Meyer-Chapman	6.50	5.00	2.50

	MINT	VG-E	F-G
75-76 Travis-Case	6.50	5.00	2.50
77-78 Krakauskas-Feller	16.00	12.00	5.50
79-80 Keltner-Trosky	6.50	5.00	2.50
81-82 T.Williams-Cronin	55.00	42.00	19.00
83-84 Gordon-Keller	7.50	5.75	2.50
85-86 Greenberg-Ruffing	16.00	12.00	5.50
87-88 Trosky-Case	6.50	5.00	2.50
89-90 Ott-Whitehead	12.00	8.75	4.00
91-92 Danning-Gumbert	6.50	5.00	2.50
93-94 Young-Melton	6.50	5.00	2.50
95-96 Ripple-Walters	6.50	5.00	2.50
97-98 Jack-Klinger	6.50	5.00	2.50
99-100 Mize-Litwhiler	7.50	5.75	2.50
101-102 Dallesandro-Galan	8.00	6.25	3.00
103-104 Lee-Cavaretta	9.00	6.75	3.00
105-106 Grove-Doerr	12.00	8.75	4.00
107-108 Pytlak-D. DiMaggio	10.00	7.00	3.00
109-110 Priddy-Murphy	10.00	7.00	3.00
111-112 Henrich-Russo	10.00	7.00	3.00
113-114 Crosetti-Sturm	10.00	7.00	3.00
115-116 Goodman-McCormick	8.00	6.25	3.00
117-118 Joost-Koy	8.00	6.25	3.00
119-120 L. Waner - Majeski	10.00	7.00	3.00
121-122 Hassett-Moore	8.00	6.25	3.00
123-124 Etten-Rizzo	8.00	6.25	3.00
125-126 Chapman-Moses	8.00	6.25	3.00
127-128 Babich-Siebert	8.00	6.25	3.00
129-130 Potter-McCoy	8.00	6.25	3.00
131-132 Campbell-Boudreau	10.00	7.00	3.00
133-134 Hemsley-Harder	8.00	6.25	3.00
135-136 Walker-Heving	8.00	6.25	3.00
137-138 Rucker-Adams	8.00	6.25	3.00
139-140 Arnovich-Hubbell	12.00	8.75	4.00
141-142 Riggs-Durocher	10.00	7.00	3.00
143-144 Fitzsimmons-Vosmik	8.00	6.25	3.00
145-146 Crespi-Brown	8.00	6.25	3.00
147-148 Heffner-Clift	8.00	6.25	3.00
149-150 Garms-Fletcher	8.00	6.25	3.00

FC59 HONEY BOY ICE CREAM

1950 DRAKES (36)

2 1/2" X 2 1/2"

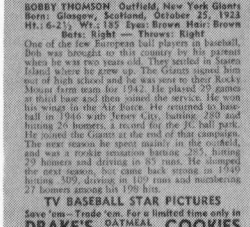

The 1950 Drake Cookies set contains 36 numbered black & white cards. The players are pictures inside a simulated television screen and the caption "TV Baseball Series" appears on the cards. The ACC designation is D358.

	MINT	VG-E	F-G
COMPLETE SET	1350.00	1050.00	475.00
COMMON PLAYER	35.00	27.00	13.00
1 Preacher Roe	40.00	30.00	13.00
2 Clint Hartung	35.00	27.00	13.00
3 Earl Torgeson	35.00	27.00	13.00
4 Lou Brissie	35.00	27.00	13.00
5 Duke Snider	90.00	70.00	30.00
6 Roy Campanella	100.00	70.00	30.00
7 Sheldon Jones	35.00	27.00	13.00
8 Whitey Lockman	35.00	27.00	13.00
9 Bobby Thomson	40.00	30.00	13.00
10 Dick Sisler	35.00	27.00	13.00
11 Gil Hodges	60.00	45.00	20.00
12 Eddie Waitkus	35.00	27.00	13.00
13 Bobby Kerr	35.00	27.00	13.00
14 Warren Spahn	60.00	45.00	20.00
15 Buddy Kerr	35.00	27.00	13.00
16 Sid Gordon	35.00	27.00	13.00
17 Willard Marshall	35.00	27.00	13.00
18 Carl Furillo	40.00	30.00	13.00
19 Peewee Reese	50.00	38.00	17.00
20 Alvin Dark	40.00	30.00	13.00
21 Del Ennis	35.00	27.00	13.00
22 Ed Stanky	40.00	30.00	13.00
23 Tom Henrich	40.00	30.00	13.00
24 Yogi Berra	70.00	50.00	23.00
25 Phil Rizzuto	55.00	42.00	19.00
26 Jerry Coleman	40.00	30.00	13.00
27 Joe Page	35.00	27.00	13.00
28 Allie Reynolds	40.00	30.00	13.00
29 Ray Scarborough	35.00	27.00	13.00
30 Birdie Tebbetts	35.00	27.00	13.00
31 Maurice McDermott	35.00	27.00	13.00
32 Johnny Pesky	35.00	27.00	13.00
33 Dom DiMaggio	45.00	34.00	15.00
34 Vern Stephens	35.00	27.00	13.00
35 Bob Elliott	35.00	27.00	13.00
36 Enos Slaughter	45.00	34.00	15.00

1966 EAST HILLS PIRATES (25)

3 1/4" X 4 1/4"

BOB CLEMENTE   (Outfielder)   #21

The 1966 East Hills Pirates set contains 25 full color, numbered (by uniform number) cards and features Pittsburgh Pirates only. The SCB designation is F 405.

	MINT	VG-E	F-G
COMPLETE SET	5.00	3.75	1.50
COMMON PLAYER	.16	.12	.04
3 Harry Walker	.16	.12	.04
7 Bob Bailey	.16	.12	.04
8 Willie Stargell	.80	.60	.25
9 Bill Mazeroski	.30	.25	.10
10 Jim Pagliaroni	.16	.12	.04
11 Jose Pagan	.16	.12	.04
12 Jerry May	.16	.12	.04
14 Gene Alley	.16	.12	.04
15 Manny Mota	.25	.20	.08
16 Andy Rodgers	.16	.12	.04
17 Donn Clendenon	.16	.12	.04
18 Matty Alou	.20	.15	.06

	MINT	VG-E	F-G
19 Pete Mikkelsen	.16	.12	.04
20 Jess Gonder	.16	.12	.04
21 Bob Clemente	1.50	1.10	.50
22 Woody Fryman	.16	.12	.04
24 Jerry Lynch	.16	.12	.04
25 Tommie Sisk	.16	.12	.04
26 Roy Face	.30	.25	.10
28 Steve Blass	.20	.15	.06
32 Vernon Law	.25	.20	.08
34 Al McBean	.16	.12	.04
39 Bob Veale	.16	.12	.04
43 Don Cardwell	.16	.12	.04
45 Gene Michael	.30	.25	.10

1954 ESSKAY (36)

2 1/4" X 3 1/2"

The 1954 Esskay Meats set contains 36 color, unnumbered cards featuring Baltimore Orioles only. The cards were issued in panels of two on boxes of Esskay hot dogs; consequently, many have grease stains on the cards and are quite difficult to obtain in mint condition. The 1954 Esskay set can be distinguished from the 1955 Esskay set supposedly by the white or off-white (the 1955 set) backs of the cards. The backs of the 1954 cards are also supposedly "waxed" to a greater degree than the 1955 cards. The ACC designation is F181.

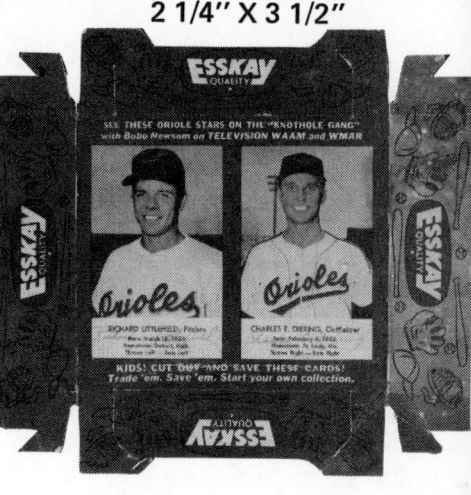

DARRELL JOHNSON, Catcher
Born August 25, 1927
Hometown: Richmond, Calif.
Throws Right — Bats Right

	MINT	VG-E	F-G
COMPLETE SET	2600.00	2000.00	800.00
COMMON PLAYER	85.00	65.00	15.00

		MINT	VG-E	F-G
1	Cal Abrams	85.00	65.00	15.00
2	Neil Berry	100.00	70.00	30.00
3	Michael Blyzka	85.00	65.00	15.00
4	Harry Brecheen	100.00	70.00	30.00
5	Gil Coan	85.00	65.00	15.00
6	Joe Coleman	85.00	65.00	15.00
7	Clint Courtney	100.00	70.00	30.00
8	Charles E. Diering	85.00	65.00	15.00
9	Jimmie Dykes	100.00	70.00	30.00
10	Frank Fanovich	85.00	65.00	15.00
11	Howard Fox	85.00	65.00	15.00
12	Jim Fridley	85.00	65.00	15.00
13	Chico Garcia	85.00	65.00	15.00
14	Jehosie Heard	85.00	65.00	15.00
15	Darrel Johnson	100.00	70.00	30.00
16	Robert D. Kennedy	100.00	70.00	30.00
17	Dick Kokos	85.00	65.00	15.00
18	Dave Koslo	85.00	65.00	15.00

		MINT	VG-E	F-G
19	Lou Kretlow	85.00	65.00	15.00
20	Richard D. Kryhoski	85.00	65.00	15.00
21	Robert Kuzava	85.00	65.00	15.00
22	Don Larsen	125.00	90.00	40.00
23	Don Lenhardt	85.00	65.00	15.00
24	Dick Littlefield	85.00	65.00	15.00
25	Sam Mele	85.00	65.00	15.00
26	John Lester Moss	85.00	65.00	15.00
27	Ray L. Murray	85.00	65.00	15.00
28	Bobo Newsom	100.00	70.00	30.00
29	Tom Oliver	85.00	65.00	15.00
30	Duane Pillette	85.00	65.00	15.00
31	Francis M. Skaff	85.00	65.00	15.00
32	Marlin Stuart	85.00	65.00	15.00
33	Robert L. Turley	125.00	90.00	40.00
34	Eddie Waitkus	85.00	65.00	15.00
35	Vic Wertz	100.00	70.00	30.00
36	Robert G. Young	85.00	65.00	15.00

1955 ESSKAY (27)

2 1/4" X 3 1/2"

The 1955 Esskay Meats set was issued in panels of two on boxes of Esskay hot dogs. This set of 27 full color, blank back, unnumbered cards features Baltimore Orioles only. Many of the players in the 1954 Esskay set were also issued in this set. The ACC designation is F181.

CHARLES E. DIERING, Outfielder
Born: February 5, 1923
Hometown: St. Louis, Mo.
Throws Right — Bats Right

	MINT	VG-E	F-G
COMPLETE SET	2200.00	1650.00	700.00
COMMON PLAYER	85.00	65.00	25.00

		MINT	VG-E	F-G
1	Cal Abrams	85.00	65.00	25.00
2	Robert Alexander	85.00	65.00	25.00
3	Harry Brecheen	100.00	70.00	30.00
4	Harry Byrd	85.00	65.00	25.00
5	Gil Coan	85.00	65.00	25.00
6	Joe Coleman	85.00	65.00	25.00
7	William Cox	100.00	70.00	30.00
8	Charles E. Diering	85.00	65.00	25.00
9	Walter Evers	100.00	70.00	30.00
10	Don Johnson	85.00	65.00	25.00
11	Robert D. Kennedy	100.00	70.00	30.00
12	Lou Kretlow	85.00	65.00	25.00
13	Robert Kuzava	85.00	65.00	25.00

		MINT	VG-E	F-G
14	Fred Marsh	85.00	65.00	25.00
15	Charles Maxwell	85.00	65.00	25.00
16	Jim McDonald	85.00	65.00	25.00
17	Bill Miller	85.00	65.00	25.00
18	Willie Miranda	100.00	70.00	30.00
19	Raymond L. Moore	85.00	65.00	25.00
20	John Lester Moss	85.00	65.00	25.00
21	Bobo Newsom	100.00	70.00	30.00
22	Duane Pillette	85.00	65.00	25.00
23	Harold W. Smith	85.00	65.00	25.00
24	Gus Triandos	110.00	80.00	35.00
25	Eddie Waitkus	85.00	65.00	25.00
26	Gene Woodling	110.00	80.00	35.00
27	Robert G. Young	85.00	65.00	25.00

1939-1946 SALUTATION (80) EXHIBITS

3 5/16" X 5 5/16"

This collection of 80 exhibit cards shares a common style: the "personal greeting" or "salutation". The specific greeting varies from card to card—"Yours truly, Best wishes, etc."—as does the location of the exhibit identification (lower left or lower right). Some players appear with different teams and there are occasional misspellings.

	MINT	VG-E	F-G
COMPLETE SET	800.00	600.00	250.00
COMMON PLAYER	1.50	1.10	.40
1 Luke Appling (LL)	3.00	2.25	1.00
Sincerely Yours			
2 Luke Appling (LR)	2.00	1.50	.60
Sincerely Yours			
3 Earl Averill	50.00	38.00	17.00
Very Best Wishes			
4 Charles "Red" Barrett	2.00	1.50	.60
Yours Truly			
5 Henry "Hank" Borowy	2.00	1.50	.60
Sincerely Yours			
6 Lou Boudreau	2.00	1.50	.60
Sincerely			
7 Adolf Camilli	8.00	6.00	2.50
Very Truly Yours			
8 Phil Cavaretta	1.50	1.10	.40
Cordially Yours			
9 Tony Cuccinello	10.00	7.00	3.00
Very Best Wishes			
10 Dizzy Dean	15.00	11.00	5.00
Sincerely			
11 Paul Derringer	2.00	1.50	.60
Yours Truly			
12 Bill Dickey (LR)	10.00	7.00	3.00
Cordially Yours			
13 Bill Dickey (LL)	12.00	8.75	4.00
Cordially Yours			
14 Joe DiMaggio	10.00	7.00	3.00
Cordially			
15 Bob Elliott	1.50	1.10	.40
Truly Yours			
16 Bob Feller	20.00	15.00	6.50
Best Wishes			
17 Bob Feller	6.00	4.50	2.00
Yours Truly			
18 Dave Ferriss	1.50	1.10	.40
Best of Luck			
19 Jimmy Foxx	25.00	18.50	8.75
Sincerely			
20 Lou Gehrig	100.00	70.00	30.00
Sincerely			
21 Charlie Gehringer	15.00	11.00	5.00
Yours Truly			
22 Vernon Gomez	30.00	22.50	10.50
Sincerely Yours			
23 Joe Gordon (Cleve)	10.00	7.00	3.00
Sincerely			
24 Joe Gordon (NY)	2.00	1.50	.60
Sincerely			
25 Hank Greenberg	6.00	4.50	2.50
Truly Yours			
26 Henry Greenberg	25.00	18.50	8.75
Very Truly Yours			
27 Robert Grove	20.00	15.00	6.50
Cordially Yours			

	MINT	VG-E	F-G
28 Gabby Hartnett	50.00	38.00	17.00
Cordially			
29 Buddy Hassett	5.00	3.75	1.75
Yours Truly			
30 Jeff Heath	6.00	4.50	2.00
Best Wishes			
31 Jeff Heath (Small Pic)	2.00	1.50	.60
Best Wishes			
32 Kirby Higbe	5.00	3.75	1.75
Sincerely			
33 Tommy Holmes	1.50	1.10	.40
Yours Truly			
34 Tommy Holmes	30.00	22.50	10.50
Sincerely Yours			
35 Carl Hubbell	12.00	8.75	4.00
Best Wishes			
36 Bob Johnson	5.00	3.75	1.75
Yours Truly			
37 Charles Keller	2.00	1.50	.60
Best Wishes			
38 Ken Keltner	8.00	6.00	2.50
Sincerly (sic)			
39 Chuck Klein	30.00	22.50	10.50
Yours Truly			
40 Mike Kreevich	25.00	18.50	8.75
Sincerely			
41 Joe Kuhel	5.00	3.75	1.75
Truly Yours			
42 Bill Lee	5.00	3.75	1.75
Cordially Yours			
43 Ernie Lombardi ((½B)	25.00	18.50	8.75
Cordially			
44 Ernie Lombardi	2.00	1.50	.60
Cordially Yours			
45 Marty Marion	1.50	1.10	.40
Best Wishes			
46 Merrill May	5.00	3.75	1.75
Best Wishes			
47 Frank McCormick (LL)	5.00	3.75	1.75
Sincerely			
48 Frank McCormick (LR)	2.00	1.50	.60
Sincerely			
49 George McQuinn (LL)	5.00	3.75	1.75
Yours Truly			
50 George McQuinn (LR)	4.00	3.00	1.40
Yours Truly			
51 Joe Medwick	10.00	7.00	3.00
Very Best Wishes			
52 Johnny Mize (LL)	7.00	5.25	2.50
Yours Truly			
53 Johnny Mize (LR)	3.00	2.25	1.00
Yours Truly			
54 Hugh Mulcahy	25.00	18.50	8.75
Cordially			
55 Hal Newhouser	2.00	1.50	.60
Best Wishes			

ST. LOUIS BASEBALL CARD STORE

4512 Hampton Avenue
(2 miles South of I-44
Take Hampton Avenue Exit)
**Hours: Friday   Noon - 8 P.M.
        Saturday 9 A.M. - 7 P.M.
Owner: Paul E. Marchant
Phone: 314/353-9611**

We carry a complete line of sport and non-sport cards — sets and single cards. Also hobby supplies, guides, and many other miscellaneous sports collectibles.

EXHIBIT SUPPLY CO. BASEBALL CARDS

1980 Exhibit   **1980 Hall of Fame**

Banks, Musial,   Cobb, DiMaggio, Mantle,
Gehrig, Maris, etc.   J. Robinson, Ruth, etc.

Each set consists of 32 postcard size cards issued by the original Exhibit Supply Co. which has issued cards sinced 1921. Price $5.00 per set or $9.00 for both. Wholesale prices available upon request.

**Exhibit Supply Co.
R. R. 4, Box 33
Charleston, Illinois 61920**

COLLECTORS CARDS

Send a self-addressed stamped envelope for a free list of hundreds of card sets available or send $1 for a large comprehensive price list containing sets, single cards (thousands of superstars) and miscellaneous items. We feature football cards, basketball cards, hockey cards and non-sport cards as well as baseball cards. Order from a dependable dealer in sport and non-sport cards for over 7 years — now with over 15 million cards in stock. Wholesale prices available upon request.

**Paul E. Marchant
R. R. 4, Box 33, Dept. PG
Charleston, Illinois 61920**

BASEBALL CARDS FOR SALE

1981 Topps Baseball Set (726)	$20.00
1980 Topps Baseball Set (726)	$20.00
1979 Topps Baseball Set (726)	$25.00
1978 Topps Baseball Set (726)	$30.00
1981 Fleer Baseball Set (660)	$18.00
1981 Donruss Baseball Set (605)	$16.00
1973 Kellogg Baseball Set (54)	$40.00
1977 Kellogg Baseball Set (57)	$15.00
1976 Crane Baseball (70)	$ 7.00
1977 Topps Baseball Strips of 3 Cards 5 Different Strips (15 cards)	$ 3.00
1978 Topps Baseball Sheets of 6 Cards 5 Different Sheets (30 cards)	$ 5.00

We reserve the right to change prices on 1978-80 Topps Sets if necessary.
Please add $1.50 shipping on orders less than $25.00.

**Paul E. Marchant
R. R. 4, Box 33, Dept BBPG
Charleston, Illinois 61920**

	MINT	VG-E	F-G
56 Louis (Buck) Newsom	2.00	1.50	.60
Sincerely			
57 Buck Newson (sic)	25.00	18.50	8.75
Very Best Wishes			
58 Mel Ott (LL)	12.00	8.75	4.00
Sincerely Yours			
59 Mel Ott (LR)	10.00	7.00	3.00
Sincerely Yours			
60 Andy Pafko	1.50	1.10	.40
Sincerely Yours			
61 Andy Pafko	1.50	1.10	.40
Yours Truly			
62 Claude Passeau	1.50	1.10	.40
Sincerely			
63 Howard Pollett (LL)	5.00	3.75	1.75
Best Wishes			
64 Howard Pollett (LR)	2.00	1.50	.60
Best Wishes			
65 Pete Reiser (LL)	25.00	18.50	8.75
Truly Yours			
66 Pete Reiser (LR)	2.00	1.50	.60
Truly Yours			
67 Johnny Rizzo	25.00	18.50	8.75
Sincerely Yours			
68 Glen Russell	25.00	18.50	8.75
Sincerely			

	MINT	VG-E	F-G
69 George Stirnweiss	1.50	1.10	.40
Yours Truly			
70 Cecil Travis	5.00	3.75	1.75
Best Wishes			
71 Paul Trout	1.50	1.10	.40
Truly Yours			
72 Johnny Vander Meer	10.00	7.00	3.00
Cordially Yours			
73 Arky Vaughn	6.00	4.50	2.00
Best Wishes			
74 Fred "Dixie" Walker	2.00	1.50	.60
"D" on Hat			
Yours Truly			
75 Fred "Dixie" Walker	10.00	7.00	3.00
Cap blanked out			
Yours Truly			
76 Bucky Walters	1.50	1.10	.40
Sincerely Yours			
77 Lon Warneke	5.00	3.75	1.75
Very Truly Yours			
78 Ted Williams (#9)	50.00	40.00	15.00
Sincerely			
79 Ted Williams	8.00	6.00	2.50
Sincerely Yours			
80 Rudy York	1.50	1.10	.40
Cordially			

1948 HALL OF FAME EXHIBITS (33)   3 5/16" X 5 5/16"

BASEBALL'S GREAT
HALL OF FAME

Greatest Drawing Card in baseball history. Holder of many home run and other batting records. 714 home runs in addition to 15 in World Series. Boston-New York-A.L.—Boston, N.L. 1915-1935.

This exhibit set, entitled "Baseball's Great Hall of Fame," consists of black & white photos on gray background. The pictures are framed on the sides by Greek columns and a short biography is printed at the bottom. The cards are blank back. Twenty-four of the cards were re-issued in 1974 on extremely white stock.

	MINT	VG-E	F-G
COMPLETE SET	135.00	100.00	40.00
COMMON PLAYER	2.00	1.50	.70

	MINT	VG-E	F-G
1 G. C. Alexander	3.00	2.25	1.00
2 Roger Bresnahan	2.00	1.50	.70
3 Frank Chance	2.00	1.50	.70
4 Jack Chesbro	2.00	1.50	.70
5 Fred Clarke	2.00	1.50	.70
6 Ty Cobb	5.00	4.00	2.00
7 Mickey Cochrane	2.00	1.50	.70
8 Eddie Collins	2.00	1.50	.70
9 Hugh Duffy	2.00	1.50	.70
10 Johnny Evers	2.00	1.50	.70
11 Frankie Frisch	2.00	1.50	.70
12 Lou Gehrig	5.00	4.00	2.00
13 Clark Griffith	2.00	1.50	.70
14 Robert "Lefty" Grove	2.50	2.00	1.00
15 Rogers Hornsby	3.00	2.50	1.00
16 Carl Hubbell	2.00	1.50	.70

	MINT	VG-E	F-G
17 Hughie Jennings	2.00	1.50	.70
18 Walter Johnson	3.50	2.50	1.20
19 Willie Keeler	3.00	2.25	1.00
20 Nap Lajoie	2.50	2.00	1.00
21 Connie Mack	2.50	2.00	1.00
22 Christy Mathewson	3.00	2.50	1.00
23 John McGraw	2.50	1.80	.80
24 Eddie Plank	2.50	1.80	.80
25A Babe Ruth(swinging)	6.00	4.50	2.00
25B Babe Ruth(bats in	50.00	38.00	17.00
front) 10 bats			
26 George Sisler	2.00	1.50	.70
27 Tris Speaker	3.00	2.25	1.00
28 Joe Tinker	2.00	1.50	.70
29 Rube Waddell	2.00	1.50	.70
30 Honus Wagner	3.00	2.50	1.00
31 Ed Walsh	2.00	1.50	.70
32 Cy Young	3.00	2.25	1.00

1947-1966 EXHIBITS (319)   3 3/8" X 5 5/16"

Orestes Minoso

This grouping encompasses a wide time span but displays a common design. The following players have been illegally reprinted in mass quantities on a thinner-than-original cardboard which is also characterized by a dark gray back: Aaron, Ford, Fox, Hodges, Elston Howard, Mantle, Mays, Musial, Newcombe, Reese, Spahn, and Ted Williams.

	MINT	VG-E	F-G
COMPLETE SET	400.00	300.00	125.00
COMMON PLAYER	.50	.40	.15

	MINT	VG-E	F-G
1 Hank Aaron	5.00	3.75	1.75
2A Joe Adcock(script)	1.00	.70	.30
2B Joe Adcock(sign.)	.50	.40	.15
3 Max Alvis	.50	.40	.15
4A Johnny Antonelli (Brave)	1.00	.70	.30
4B Johnny Antonelli (Giants)	1.00	.70	.30
5A Luis Aparicio(port.)	1.00	.70	.30
5B Luis Aparicio(batting)	5.00	3.75	1.75
6 Luke Appling	2.00	1.50	.60
7A Richie Ashburn (Phillies)	1.00	.70	.30
7B Richie Ashburn(Cubs)	1.50	1.10	.50
8 Bob Aspromonte	.50	.40	.15
9 Toby Atwell	1.00	.70	.30
10A Ed Bailey(Cinn. cap)	1.00	.70	.30
10B Ed Bailey(no cap)	1.00	.70	.30
11 Gene Baker	1.00	.70	.30
12A Ernie Banks(script)	5.00	3.75	1.75
12B Ernie Banks(sign.)	2.50	1.80	.30
12C Ernie Banks(port.)	2.00	1.50	.60
13 Steve Barber	.50	.40	.15
14 Earl Battey	.50	.40	.15
15 Matt Batts	1.00	.70	.30
16A Hank Bauer(NY cap)	1.00	.70	.30
16B Hank Bauer(plain cap)	2.00	1.50	.60
17 Frank Baumholtz	1.00	.70	.30
18 Gene Bearden	1.00	.70	.30
19 Joe Beggs	2.00	1.50	.60
20A Yogi Berra	4.00	3.00	1.50
20B Larry "Yogi" Berra	3.00	2.25	1.00
21 Steve Bilko	1.00	.70	.30
22A Ewell Blackwell (foot up)	1.50	1.10	.50
22B Ewell Blackwell(port.)	1.50	1.10	.50
23A Don Blasingame (St.L. cap)	.75	.55	.25
23B Don Blasingame (plain cap)	.75	.55	.25
24 Ken Boyer	1.00	.70	.30
25 Ralph Branca	1.00	.70	.30
26 Jackie Brandt	.50	.40	.15
27 Harry Brecheen	1.00	.70	.30
28 Tom Brewer	.50	.40	.15
29 Lou Brissie	1.00	.70	.30
30 Bill Bruton	.50	.40	.15
31A Lew Burdette (side view)	1.25	.90	.40
31B Lew Burdette(facing)	.75	.55	.25
32 Johnny Callison	.50	.40	.18
33 Roy Campanella	4.00	3.00	1.50

	MINT	VG-E	F-G
34A Chico Carrasquel (White Sox)	1.25	.90	.40
34B Chico Carrasquel (plain cap)	1.00	.70	.30
35 George Case	2.00	1.50	.60
36 Hugh Casey	1.00	.70	.30
37 Norm Cash	.75	.55	.25
38A Orlando Cepeda(port.)	1.00	.70	.30
38B Orlando Cepeda(batt.)	1.50	1.10	.50
39A Bob Cerv(A's uniform)	1.00	.70	.30
39B Bob Cerv(plain unif.)	.75	.55	.25
40 Dean Chance	.50	.40	.15
41 Spud Chandler	1.00	.70	.30
42 Tom Cheney	.50	.40	.15
43 Bubba Church	1.00	.70	.30
44 Roberto Clemente	4.00	3.00	1.40
45A Rocky Colavito(port.)	1.00	.70	.30
45B Rocky Colavito(batt.)	1.00	.70	.30
46 Choo-Choo Coleman	.50	.40	.15
47 Gordy Coleman	.50	.40	.15
48 Jerry Coleman	1.00	.70	.30
49 Mort Cooper	1.00	.70	.30
50 Walker Cooper (2)	1.25	.90	.40
51 Roger Craig	.50	.40	.15
52 Delmar Crandall	.50	.40	.15
53A Joe Cunningham(port.)	.50	.40	.15
53B Joe Cunningham (batting, Cards)	.50	.40	.15
54 Guy Curtright (sic)	1.50	1.10	.50
55 Bud Daley	.75	.55	.25
56A Alvin Dark (Boston cap)	1.50	1.10	.50
56B Alvin Dark(NY cap)	1.50	1.10	.50
56C Alvin Dark(Cubs)	1.00	.70	.30
57 Murray Dickson	1.00	.70	.30
58 Bob Dillinger	1.00	.70	.30
59 Dom DiMaggio	3.00	2.25	1.00
60 Joe Dobson	1.00	.70	.30
61 Larry Doby	1.00	.70	.30
62 Bobby Doerr	1.00	.70	.30
63A Dick Donovan(Brave, plain cap)	1.00	.70	.30
63B Dick Donovan (White Sox)	.50	.40	.15
64 Walter Dropo	1.00	.70	.30
65A Don Drysdale(port.)	2.00	1.50	.60
65B Don Drysdale(port.½)	3.00	2.25	1.00
66 Luke Easter	1.00	.70	.30
67 Bruce Edwards	1.00	.70	.30
68 Del Ennis	.50	.40	.15
69 Al Evans	1.00	.70	.30
70 Walter Evers	1.00	.70	.30

	MINT	VG-E	F-G
71A Ferris Fain(batting)	1.00	.70	.30
71B Ferris Fain(port.)	1.00	.70	.30
72 Dick Farrell	.50	.40	.15
73A Whitey Ford(no glove, throwing)	2.50	1.80	.80
73B Whitey Ford(port.)	5.00	3.75	1.75
73C Whitey Ford(glove on shoulder, throwing)	3.50	2.50	1.20
74 Dick Fowler	1.00	.70	.30
75 Nelson Fox	.75	.55	.25
76 Tito Francona	.50	.40	.15
77 Bob Friend	.50	.40	.15
78 Carl Furillo	1.50	1.10	.50
79 Augie Galan	1.00	.70	.30
80 Jim Gentile	.50	.40	.15
81 Tony Gonzalez	.50	.40	.15
82A Billy Goodman (W.S., 1952)	1.00	.70	.30
82B Billy Goodman(batt.)	.50	.40	.15
83 Ted Greengrass	1.00	.70	.30
84 Dick Groat	.50	.40	.15
85 Steve Gromek	1.00	.70	.30
86 Johnny Groth	1.00	.70	.30
87 Orval Grove	1.00	.70	.30
88A Frank Gustine (Pirates)	1.25	.90	.40
88B Frank Gustine(Cubs)	1.25	.90	.40
89 Berthold Haas	2.00	1.50	.60
90 Grady Hatton	1.00	.70	.30
91 Jim Hegan	1.00	.70	.30
92 Tom Henrich	2.00	1.50	.60
93 Ray Herbert	.50	.40	.15
94 Gene Hermanski	1.00	.70	.30
95 Whitey Herzog	.75	.55	.25
96 Kirby Higbe	1.00	.70	.30
97 Chuck Hinton	.50	.40	.15
98 Don Hoak	.50	.40	.15
99A Gil Hodges(Braves cap)	2.50	1.80	.80
99B Gil Hodges(LA cap)	3.00	2.25	1.00
100 Johnny Hopp	1.25	.90	.40
101 Elston Howard	1.00	.70	.30
102 Frank Howard	1.00	.70	.30
103 Ken Hubbs	.50	.40	.15
104 Tex Hughson	1.00	.70	.30
105 Fred Hutchinson	1.25	.90	.40
106 Monte Irvin	2.00	1.50	.60
107 Joey Jay	.50	.40	.15
108 Jackie Jensen	3.00	2.25	1.00
109 Sam Jethroe	1.00	.70	.30
110 Bill Johnson	1.00	.70	.30
111 Walter Judnich	1.00	.70	.30
112A Al Kaline(kneeling)	5.00	3.75	1.75
112B Al Kaline(port.)	3.00	2.25	1.00
113 George Kell	1.25	.90	.40
114 Charley Keller	1.25	.90	.40
115 Alex Kellner	1.00	.70	.30
116 Kenn Keltner	1.25	.90	.40
117A Harmon Killebrew(pin stripes, batting)	2.00	1.50	.60
117B Harmon Killebrew (portrait)	3.00	2.25	1.00
117C Harmon Killebrew (throwing)	2.50	1.80	.80
118 Ellis Kinder	1.00	.70	.30
119 Ralph Kiner	2.50	1.80	.80
120 Billy Klaus	.50	.40	.15
121A Ted Kluszewski(Reds)	2.00	1.50	.60
121B Ted Kluszewski (Pirates)	1.50	1.10	.50
121C Ted Kluszewski (plain uniform)	1.00	.70	.30
122 Don Kolloway	1.00	.70	.30
123 Jim Konstanty	1.50	1.10	.50
124 Sandy Koufax	4.00	3.00	1.50
125 Ed Kranepool	3.00	2.25	1.00
126A Tony Kubek(dark background)	2.00	1.50	.60
126B Tony Kubek(light background)	1.00	.70	.30
127A Harvey Kuenn(Detroit)	2.00	1.50	.60
127B Harvey Kuenn(plain uniform)	1.00	.70	.30
127C Harvey Kuenn(S.F.)	1.00	.70	.30
128 Kurowski	1.00	.70	.30
129 Eddie Lake	1.00	.70	.30
130 Jim Landis	.50	.40	.15
131 Don Larsen	1.50	1.10	.50

	MINT	VG-E	F-G
132A Bob Lemon(left arm not shown)	3.00	2.25	1.00
132B Bob Lemon(left arm extended)	3.00	2.25	1.00
133 Buddy Lewis	1.00	.70	.30
134 Johnny Lindell	5.00	3.75	1.75
135 Phil Linz	.50	.40	.15
136 Don Lock	.50	.40	.15
137 Whitey Lockman	1.00	.70	.30
138 Johnny Logan	.50	.40	.15
139A Dale Long(Pirates)	1.00	.70	.30
139B Dale Long(Cubs)	.50	.40	.15
140 Ed Lopat	1.50	1.10	.50
141A Harry Lowery	1.25	.90	.40
141B Harry Lowery(smaller)	1.25	.90	.40
142 Sam Maglie	1.00	.70	.30
143 Art Mahaffey	.50	.40	.15
144 Hank Majeski	1.00	.70	.30
145 Frank Malzone	.50	.40	.15
146A Mickey Mantle (batting to waist)	10.00	7.00	3.00
146B Mickey Mantle (batting full)	7.50	5.75	2.50
146C Mickey Mantle(port.)	12.50	9.00	4.00
147 Marty Marion	1.25	.90	.40
148 Roger Maris	2.50	1.80	.80
149 Willard Marshall	1.00	.70	.30
150A Eddie Mathews(script)	4.00	3.00	1.40
150B Eddie Mathews(sign.)	3.00	2.25	1.00
150C Ed Mathews	3.00	2.25	1.00
151 Ed Mayo	1.00	.70	.30
152A Willie Mays(N.Y.)	7.50	5.75	2.50
152B Willie Mays(S.F.)	5.00	3.75	1.75
153A Bill Mazeroski(port.)	1.00	.70	.30
153B Bill Mazeroski(batt.)	1.00	.70	.30
154 Ken McBride	.50	.40	.15
155A Barney McCaskey(sic)	3.00	2.25	1.00
155B Barney McCoskey	2.00	1.50	.60
156 Lindy McDaniel	.50	.40	.15
157 Gil McDougald	.75	.55	.25
158 Albert Mele	2.00	1.50	.60
159 Sam Mele	1.00	.70	.30
160A Orestes Minoso(W.S.)	1.00	.70	.30
160B Orestes Minoso(Cleve.)	1.50	1.10	.50
161 Dale Mitchell	1.00	.70	.30
162 Wally Moon	.50	.40	.15
163 Don Mueller	1.00	.70	.30
164A Stan Musial(3 bats, kneeling)	6.00	4.50	2.00
164B Stan Musial(batt.)	4.50	3.50	1.60
165 Charles Neal	.50	.40	.15
166A Don Newcombe(hands folded)	2.50	1.80	.80
166B Don Newcombe (Brooklyn cap)	1.50	1.10	.50
166C Don Newcombe (plain cap)	1.00	.70	.30
167 Hal Newhouser	1.00	.70	.30
168 Ron Northey	1.00	.70	.30
169 Bill O'Dell	.50	.40	.15
170 Andy Pafko	.50	.40	.15
171 Joe Page	3.00	2.25	1.00
172 Satchel Paige	4.50	3.50	1.60
173 Milt Pappas	.50	.40	.15
174 Camilo Pascual	.50	.40	.15
175 Albie Pearson	.50	.40	.15
176 Johnny Pesky	1.00	.70	.30
177 Gary Peters	.50	.40	.15
178 Dave Philley	1.00	.70	.30
179 Billy Pierce	.75	.55	.25
180 Jimmy Piersall	5.00	3.75	1.75
181 Vada Pinson	.75	.55	.25
182 Bob Porterfield	1.00	.70	.30
183 John "Boog" Powell	1.00	.70	.30
184 Vic Raschi	1.50	1.10	.50
185 Harold "Pee Wee" Reese	3.00	2.25	1.00
186 Del Rice	.50	.40	.15
187 Bobby Richardson	4.00	3.00	1.40
188 Phil Rizzuto	3.00	2.25	1.00
189A Robin Roberts(sign.)	2.00	1.50	.60
189B Robin Roberts(script)	4.00	3.00	1.50
190 Brooks Robinson	3.00	2.25	1.00
191A Eddie Robinson(port.)	1.00	.70	.30
191B Eddie Robinson(run.)	1.00	.70	.30
192 Floyd Robinson	.50	.40	.15
193 Frankie Robinson	3.00	2.25	1.00
194 Jackie Robinson	5.00	3.75	1.75
195 Preacher Roe	1.50	1.10	.50

EXHIBITS (CONTINUED)

	MINT	VG-E	F-G
196 Bob Rogers(sic)	.50	.40	.15
197 Richard Rollins	.50	.40	.15
198 Pete Runnels	1.00	.70	.30
199 John Sain	1.50	1.10	.50
200 Ron Santo	.75	.55	.25
201 Henry Sauer	1.25	.90	.40
202A Carl Sawatski	.50	.40	.15
(Milwaukee cap)			
202B Carl Sawatski	.50	.40	.15
(Philadelphia cap)			
202C Carl Sawatski	.50	.40	.15
(plain cap)			
203 Johnny Schmitz	1.00	.70	.15
204A Red Schoendeinst	1.50	1.10	.50
(one foot shown,			
catching)			
204B Red Schoendeinst	1.50	1.10	.50
(small C version			
of above, catch.)			
204C Red Schoendeinst	1.50	1.10	.50
(batting)			
205A Herb Score	1.50	1.10	.50
(Cleveland cap)			
205B Herb Score	.75	.55	.25
(plain cap)			
206 Andy Seminick	1.00	.70	.30
207 Rip Sewell	1.00	.70	.30
208 Norm Siebern	.50	.40	.15
209A Roy Sievers(Browns)	1.25	.90	.40
209B Roy Sievers	.75	.55	.25
(Senators)			
209C Roy Sievers	.75	.55	.25
(plain uniform)			
210 Curt Simmons	.50	.40	.15
211 Dick Sisler	1.00	.70	.30
212A Bill Skowron(N.Y.)	.75	.55	.25
212B Bill "Moose" Skowron	3.50	2.50	1.20
(White Sox)			
213 Enos Slaughter	2.00	1.50	.60
214A Duke Snider(Brrklyn)	4.00	3.00	1.50
214B Duke Snider(L.A.)	4.00	3.00	1.50
215A Warren Spahn	3.00	2.25	1.00
(Boston, ball)			
215B Warren Spahn(Milw.)	2.00	1.50	.60
216 Stanley Spence	1.00	.70	.30
217A Ed Stanky (arms up)	1.00	.70	.30
217B Ed Stanky (Giants)	1.00	.70	.30
218A Vern Stephens	1.00	.70	.30
(Browns)			

	MINT	VG-E	F-G
218B Vern Stephens	1.00	.70	.30
(Red Sox)			
219 Ed Stewart	1.00	.70	.30
220 Snuffy Stirnweiss	2.00	1.50	.60
221 George "Birdie"	1.00	.70	.30
Tebbetts			
222A Frankie Thomas	5.00	3.75	1.75
(batting)			
(Bob Skinner pict.)			
222B Frank Thomas(Cubs)	.50	.40	.15
223 Lee Thomas	.50	.40	.15
224 Bobby Thomson	1.00	.70	.30
225A Earl Torgeson(Braves)	1.00	.70	.30
225B Earl Torgeson	.50	.40	.15
(plain uniform)			
226 Gus Triandos	.50	.40	.15
227 Virgil Trucks	1.00	.70	.30
228 Johnny Vandermeer	2.00	1.50	.60
229 Emil Verban	1.00	.70	.30
230A Mickey Vernon	1.00	.70	.30
(throwing)			
230B Mickey Vernon	1.00	.70	.30
(batting)			
231 Bill Voiselle	2.00	1.50	.60
232 Leon Wagner	.50	.40	.15
233A Eddie Waitkus(Cub	3.00	2.25	1.00
uniform)			
233B Eddie Waitkus	1.00	.70	.30
(plain uniform)			
233C Eddie Waitkus	1.00	.70	.30
(Phillie uniform)			
234 Dick Wakefield	1.00	.70	.30
235 Harry Walker	1.00	.70	.30
236 Bucky Walters	1.00	.70	.30
237 Pete Ward	3.00	2.25	1.00
238 Skeeter Webb	1.00	.70	.30
239 Herman Wehmeier	1.00	.70	.30
240A Vic Wertz(Tigers)	1.00	.70	.30
240B Vic Wertz(Red Sox)	.50	.40	.15
241 Wally Westlake	1.00	.70	.30
242 Wes Westrum	1.00	.70	.30
243 Billy Williams	1.00	.70	.30
244 Maurice Wills	1.00	.70	.30
245 Gene Woodling	.50	.40	.15
246 Taffy Wright	1.00	.70	.30
247 Carl Yastrzemski	5.00	3.75	1.75
248 Al Zarilla	1.00	.70	.30
249 Gus Zernial	1.00	.70	.30

1948-1956 TEAM EXHIBITS (16)   3 3/8" X 5 5/16"

The cards found listed in this classification were not a separate issue from the individual player cards of the same period but have been assembled together in the Price Guide for emphasis. Each of these 1948-1956 Exhibit team cards was issued to honor the champions of the National and American Leagues, except for 1953, when none were printed. Reprints of these popular cards are known to exist.

	MINT	VG-E	F-G
COMPLETE SET	110.00	85.00	35.00
COMMON TEAM	5.00	4.00	1.00

	MINT	VG-E	F-G
1 1948 Boston Braves	8.00	6.00	2.50
2 1948 Cleveland Indians	8.00	6.00	2.50
3 1949 Brooklyn Dodgers	9.00	6.75	3.00
4 1949 New York Yankees	10.00	7.00	3.00
5 1950 Phila. Phillies	8.00	6.00	2.50
6 1950 New York Yankees	8.00	6.00	2.50
7 1951 New York Giants	7.00	5.25	2.50
8 1951 New York Yankees	8.00	6.00	2.50

	MINT	VG-E	F-G
9 1952 Brooklyn Dodgers	7.00	5.25	2.50
10 1952 New York Yankees	8.00	6.00	2.50
11 1954 New York Giants	6.00	4.50	2.00
12 1954 Cleveland Indians	5.00	4.00	1.00
13 1955 Brooklyn Dodgers	7.00	5.25	2.50
14 1955 New York Yankees	8.00	6.00	2.50
15 1956 Brooklyn Dodgers	7.00	5.25	2.50
16 1956 New York Yankees	8.00	6.00	2.50

1962 EXHIBIT STAT BACK (32)   3 5/16" X 5 5/16"

The 32-card sheet was a standard production feature of the Exhibit Card Company, although generally more than one sheet comprised a set. The 32 card set issued in 1962 thus amounted to one-half a normal printing, and it is differentiated from other current Exhibit issues by the inclusion of records, printed in black, on the reverse of each card.

MANTLE, MICKEY CHARLES, Outfielder, New York Yankees   Throws: Right
Born: Spavinaw, Oklahoma, October 20, 1931   Ht: 6'   Wt: 200   Bats: Both

YEAR	CLUB	LEA.	POS.	G	AB	R	H	2B	3B	HR	RBI	SB	AVG
1949	Independence	K om	SS	89	323	54	101	15	7	7	63	20	.313
1950	Joplin	W.A.	SS	137	519	141	199	30	12	26	136	22	.383
1951	Kansas City	A.A.	OF	40	166	32	60	9	3	11	50	5	.361
1951	New York	A.A	OF	96	341	61	91	11	5	13	65	8	.267
1952	New York	A.L.	OF-3B	142	549	94	171	37	7	23	87	4	.311
1953	New York	A.L.	OF-SS	127	461	105	136	24	3	21	92	8	.295
1954	New York	A.L.	OF-2B	146	543	129	163	17	12	27	102	5	.300
1955	New York	A.L.	OF-SS	147	517	121	158	25	11	37	99	8	.306
1956	New York	A.L.	OF	150	533	132	188	22	5	52	130	10	.353
1957	New York	A.L.	OF	144	474	121	173	28	6	34	94	16	.365
1958	New York	A.L.	OF	150	519	127	158	21	1	42	97	18	.304
1959	New York	A.L.	OF	144	541	104	154	23	4	31	75	21	.285
1960	New York	A.L.	OF	153	527	119	145	17	6	40	94	14	.275
1961	New York	A.L.	OF	153	514	132	163	16	6	54	128	12	.317
MAJOR LEAGUE TOTALS				1552	5519	1245	1700	241	66	374	1063	124	.308

	MINT	VG-E	F-G
COMPLETE SET	40.00	30.00	12.00
COMMON PLAYER	.50	.40	.15

	MINT	VG-E	F-G
1 Hank Aaron	5.00	3.75	1.75
2 Luis Aparicio	1.00	.70	.30
3 Ernie Banks	3.00	2.25	1.00
4 Larry "Yogi" Berra	3.50	2.50	1.20
5 Ken Boyer	1.00	.70	.30
6 Lew Burdette	.75	.55	.25
7 Norm Cash	.75	.55	.25
8 Orlando Cepeda	1.00	.70	.30
9 Roberto Clemente	4.00	3.00	1.40
10 Rocky Colavito	1.00	.70	.30
11 Ed "Whitey" Ford	3.00	2.25	1.00
12 Nelson Fox	1.00	.70	.30
13 Tito Francona	.50	.40	.15
14 Jim Gentile	.50	.40	.15
15 Dick Groat	.75	.55	.25
16 Don Hoak	.50	.40	.15

	MINT	VG-E	F-G
17 Al Kaline	3.00	2.25	1.00
18 Harmon Killebrew	2.00	1.50	.60
19 Sandy Koufax	4.00	3.00	1.40
20 Jim Landis	.50	.40	.15
21 Art Mahaffey	.50	.40	.15
22 Frank Malzone	.50	.40	.15
23 Mickey Mantle	6.00	4.50	2.00
24 Roger Maris	2.50	1.80	.80
25 Eddie Mathews	2.50	1.80	.80
26 Willie Mays	5.00	3.75	1.75
27 Wally Moon	.50	.40	.15
28 Stan Musial	5.00	3.75	1.75
29 Milt Pappas	.50	.40	.15
30 Vada Pinson	.75	.55	.25
31 Norm Siebern	.50	.40	.15
32 Warren Spahn	2.50	1.80	.80

JAYNE'S BASEBALL FOLDER

1963 EXHIBIT STAT BACK (64)   3 5/16" X 5 5/16"

This 1963 Exhibit issue features 64 cards with statistics printed in red on the backs.

YEAR	CLUB	LEA.	POS.	G	AB	R	H	2B	3B	HR	RBI	SB	AVG
1950	Trenton	Int. St.	O.F.	81	306	50	108	20	8	4	55	7	.353
1951	Minneapolis	A.A.	O.F.	35	149	38	71	18	3	8	30	5	.477
1951	New York	N.L.	O.F.	121	464	59	127	22	5	20	68	7	.274
1952	New York	N.L.	O.F.	34	127	17	30	2	4	4	23	4	.236
1952-3							(IN MILITARY SERVICE)						
1954	New York	N.L.	O.F.	151	565	119	195	33	13	41	110	8	.345
1955	New York	N.L.	O.F.	152	580	123	185	18	13	51	127	24	.319
1956	New York	N.L.	O.F.	152	578	101	171	27	8	36	84	40	.296
1957	New York	N.L.	O.F.	152	585	112	195	26	20	35	97	38	.333
1958	San Francisco	N.L.	O.F.	152	600	121	208	33	11	29	96	31	.347
1959	San Francisco	N.L.	O.F.	151	575	125	180	43	5	34	104	27	.313
1960	San Francisco	N.L.	O.F.	153	595	107	190	29	12	29	103	25	.319
1961	San Francisco	N.L.	O.F.	154	572	129	176	32	3	40	123	18	.308
1962	San Francisco	N.L.	OF	162	621	130	189	36	8	49	141	18	.304
MAJOR LEAGUE TOTALS				1534	5862	1143	1846	301	102	368	1076	240	.314

MAYS, WILLIE HOWARD, Jr., Outfielder, San Francisco Giants   Bats: Right
Born: Fairfield, Ala., May 6, 1931   Hr: 5'11"   Wt: 180   Throws: Right

	MINT	VG-E	F-G
COMPLETE SET	70.00	50.00	20.00
COMMON PLAYER	.50	.40	.15
1 Hank Aaron	5.00	3.75	1.75
2 Luis Aparicio	1.00	.70	.30
3 Bob Aspromonte	.50	.40	.15
4 Ernie Banks	3.00	2.25	1.00
5 Steve Barber	.50	.40	.15
6 Earl Battey	.50	.40	.15
7 Larry "Yogi" Berra	3.50	2.50	1.20
8 Ken Boyer	1.00	.70	.30
9 Lew Burdette	.75	.55	.25
10 Johnny Callison	.50	.40	.15
11 Norm Cash	.75	.55	.25
12 Orlando Cepeda	1.00	.70	.30
13 Dean Chance	.50	.40	.15
14 Tom Cheney	.50	.40	.15
15 Roberto Clemente	4.00	3.00	1.40
16 Rocky Colavito	1.00	.70	.30
17 Choo Choo Coleman	.50	.40	.15
18 Roger Craig	.75	.55	.25
19 Joe Cunningham	.50	.40	.15
20 Don Drysdale	2.00	1.50	.60
21 Dick Farrell	.50	.40	.15
22 Ed "Whitey" Ford	3.00	2.25	1.00
23 Nelson Fox	1.00	.70	.30
24 Tito Francona	.50	.40	.15
25 Jim Gentile	.50	.40	.15
26 Tony Gonzales	.50	.40	.15
27 Dick Groat	.75	.55	.25
28 Ray Herbert	.50	.40	.15
29 Chuck Hinton	.50	.40	.15
30 Don Hoak	.50	.40	.15
31 Frank Howard	1.00	.70	.30

	MINT	VG-E	F-G
32 Ken Hubbs	.75	.55	.25
33 Joey Jay	.50	.40	.15
34 Al Kaline	3.00	2.25	1.00
35 Harmon Killebrew	2.00	1.50	.60
36 Sandy Koufax	4.00	3.00	1.40
37 Harvey Kuenn	.75	.55	.25
38 Jim Landis	.50	.40	.14
39 Art Mahaffey	.50	.40	.15
40 Frank Malzone	.50	.40	.15
41 Mickey Mantle	6.00	4.50	2.00
42 Roger Maris	2.50	1.80	.80
43 Eddie Matthews	2.50	1.80	.80
44 Willie Mays	5.00	3.75	1.75
45 Bill Mazeroski	.75	.55	.25
46 Ken McBride	.50	.40	.15
47 Wally Moon	.50	.40	.15
48 Stan Musial	5.00	3.75	1.75
49 Charlie Neal	.50	.40	.15
50 Bill O'Dell	.50	.40	.15
51 Milt Pappas	.50	.40	.15
52 Camilo Pascual	.50	.40	.15
53 Jim Piersall	1.00	.70	.30
54 Vada Pinson	.75	.55	.25
55 Brooks Robinson	3.00	2.25	1.00
56 Frankie Robinson	2.50	1.80	.80
57 Pete Runnels	.50	.40	.15
58 Ron Santo	1.00	.70	.30
59 Norm Siebern	.50	.40	.15
60 Warren Spahn	2.50	1.80	.80
61 Lee Thomas	.50	.40	.15
62 Leon Wagner	.50	.40	.15
63 Billy Williams	1.00	.70	.30
64 Maurice Wills	1.00	.70	.30

ROGERS HORNSBY
2nd B.—St. Louis Nationals

A photograph or a member of either the American or National League will be found in every 5 cent tin package of our products. There are 80 to the set.

STANDARD
BISCUIT
COMPANY
San Francisco, Cal.

Sole Makers of
Paradise Sodas

D350-1 STANDARD BAKING

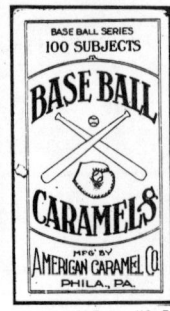

The 1908 E90-1 set contains 120 unnumbered cards. In order, the Mitchell-Cincinnati, Sweeney-Boston, Graham, Walsh, Stahl and Speaker cards are more difficult to obtain than other cards in the set. Several players exist in more than one pose. These cards are noted in the check-list.

	MINT	VG-E	F-G
COMPLETE SET	1350.00	1000.00	400.00
COMMON PLAYER	8.00	6.25	2.50
1 Bailey, William	8.00	6.25	2.50
2 Frank Baker	16.00	12.00	5.50
3 Barry, Jack	8.00	6.25	2.50
4 Bell, George	8.00	6.25	2.50
5 Bemis , Harry	16.00	12.00	5.50
6 Chief Bender	8.00	6.25	2.50
7 Bescher, Bob	8.00	6.25	2.50
8 Blankenship, Clifford	8.00	6.25	2.50
9 Bliss, John	8.00	6.25	2.50
10 Bradley, William J.	8.00	6.25	2.50
11 Bransfield-blue bkgd	10.00	7.00	3.00
12 Bransfield-pink bkgd	15.00	11.00	5.00
13 Roger Bresnahan	15.00	11.00	5.00
14 Bridwell, Al	8.00	6.25	2.50
15 Brown, Bost. NL	8.00	6.25	2.50
16 Brown, Chic. NL	25.00	18.50	8.75
17 Bush, Donie	8.00	6.25	2.50
18 Butler, John A.	10.00	7.00	3.00
19 Camnitz, Howie	8.00	6.25	2.50
20 Frank Chance	20.00	15.00	6.50
21 Chase, Hal	8.00	6.25	2.50
22 Clarke, Phi. NL	15.00	11.00	5.00
23 Clarke, Pit.	50.00	38.00	17.00
24 Clement, Wallace O.	15.00	11.00	5.00
25 "Ty" Cobb	80.00	60.00	25.00
26 Collins, Eddie	16.00	12.00	5.50
27 Corridon, Frank	8.00	6.25	2.50
28 Crawford, Sam	16.00	12.00	5.50
29 Criger, Lou	8.00	6.25	2.50
30 Davis, Harry "Jasper"	8.00	6.25	2.50
31 G. Davis, George	8.00	6.25	2.50
32 Demmitt, Ray	15.00	11.00	5.00
33 Mike Donlin	8.00	6.25	2.50
34 Donovan, Wild Bill	8.00	6.25	2.50
35 Dooin, Red	8.00	6.25	2.50
36 Dougherty, Patsy	8.00	6.25	2.50
37 Hugh Duffy	60.00	45.00	20.00
38 Dygert, Jimmy	8.00	6.25	2.50
39 Ellis, Rube	8.00	6.25	2.50
40 Engle, Clyde	8.00	6.25	2.50
41 Fromme, Art	15.00	11.00	5.00
42 Gibson-back view	25.00	18.50	8.75
43 Gibson-front view	8.00	6.25	2.50
44 Graham, George	80.00	60.00	25.00
45 Grant, Eddie	8.00	6.25	2.50
46 Gray, Dolly	8.00	6.25	2.50
47 Groom, Bob	8.00	6.25	2.50
48 Hall, Charles	8.00	6.25	2.50
49 Hartzell-green bkgd	8.00	6.25	2.50
50 Hartzell-pink bkgd	8.00	6.25	2.50
51 Heitmuller, William	8.00	6.25	2.50
52 Howell-follow through	8.00	6.25	2.50
53 Howell-windup	15.00	11.00	5.00
54 Irwin	8.00	6.25	2.50
55 Isbell, Frank	8.00	6.25	2.50
56 Jackson, Joe	40.00	30.00	13.00
57 Hugh Jennings	16.00	12.00	5.50
58 Jordan, Buck	8.00	6.25	2.50
59 Joss-portrait	18.00	13.50	6.00
60 Joss-horiz. pitching	35.00	26.00	12.00
61 Karger, Ed	30.00	22.50	10.50
62 Keeler-por. pink bkgd	20.00	15.00	6.50
63 Keeler-por. red bkgd	25.00	18.50	8.75
64 Keeler-horiz throwing	40.00	30.00	13.00
65 Knight, John	20.00	15.00	6.50
66 Krause, Harry	8.00	6.25	2.50
67 Lajoie, Napolean	25.00	18.50	8.75
68 Leach-batting	8.00	6.25	2.50
69 Leach-throwing	8.00	6.25	2.50
70 Leever, Sam	8.00	6.25	2.50

	MINT	VG-E	F-G
71 Lobert, Hans	20.00	15.00	6.50
72 Lumley, Harry	8.00	6.25	2.50
73 Rube Marquard	16.00	12.00	5.50
74 Christy Mathewson	35.00	26.00	12.00
75 McInnes, John "Stuffy"	8.00	6.25	2.50
76 McIntyre, Matty	8.00	6.25	2.50
77 McLean, Larry	20.00	15.00	6.50
78 McQuillan, George	8.00	6.25	2.50
79 Miller, John "Dots"	8.00	6.25	2.50
80 Mitchell, Cin.	175.00	125.00	60.00
81 Mitchell, N.Y., AL	8.00	6.25	2.50
82 Mullin, George	8.00	6.25	2.50
83 Oakes, Rebel	8.00	6.25	2.50
84 O'Connor, Patrick	8.00	6.25	2.50
85 O'Leary, Charley	8.00	6.25	2.50
86 Overall, Orval	20.00	15.00	6.50
87 Pastorius, Jim	8.00	6.25	2.50
88 Phelps, Ed	8.00	6.25	2.50
89 Eddie Plank	20.00	15.00	6.50
90 Richie, Lew	8.00	6.25	2.50
91 Schaefer, Germany	8.00	6.25	2.50
92 Schlitzer, Victor	20.00	15.00	6.50
93 Seigle	20.00	15.00	6.50
94 Shean, Dave	15.00	11.00	5.00
95 Sheckard, Jimmy	12.00	8.75	4.00
96 Tris Speaker	80.00	60.00	25.00
97 Stahl, Jake	50.00	38.00	17.00
98 Stanage, Oscar	8.00	6.25	2.50
99 Stone-green bkgd	8.00	6.25	2.50
100 Stone-sky bkgd	8.00	6.25	2.50
101 Stovall, George	8.00	6.25	2.50
102 Summers, Ed	8.00	6.25	2.50
103 Sweeney, Bos.	100.00	70.00	30.00
104 Sweeney, N.Y.	8.00	6.25	2.50
105 Tannehill-Chi. Amer.	8.00	6.25	2.50
106 Tannehill-Chi. Nat.	8.00	6.25	2.50
107 Tenney, Fred	8.00	6.25	2.50
108 Thomas-Phila. Amer.	8.00	6.25	2.50
109 Thomas-Boston Nat.	8.00	6.25	2.50
110 Joe Tinker	16.00	12.00	5.50
111 Unglaub, Bob	8.00	6.25	2.50
112 Upp, Jerry	15.00	11.00	5.00
113 Wagner-batting	35.00	26.00	12.00
114 Wagner-throwing	35.00	26.00	12.00
115 Wallace, Bobby	15.00	11.00	5.00
116 Walsh, Ed	80.00	60.00	25.00
117 Willis, Vic	8.00	6.25	2.50
118 Wiltse, Hooks	20.00	15.00	6.50
119 Young-Boston Amer.	20.00	15.00	6.50
120 Young-Cleveland	30.00	22.50	10.50

1910 E90—2 (11)

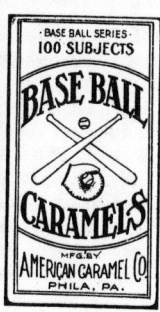

1 1/2" X 2 3/4"

The 1910 E90-2 American Caramels Baseball Star set contains 11 unnumbered cards featuring players from the 1909 Pittsburgh Pirates. The backs of these cards are exactly like the E90-1 cards; however, blue print is used for the names of the players and the teams on the fronts of the cards.

	MINT	VG-E	F-G
COMPLETE SET	225.00	160.00	70.00
COMMON PLAYER	18.00	13.50	6.00
1 Adams, Charles "Babe"	18.00	13.50	6.00
2 Clarke, Fred	30.00	22.50	10.50
3 Gibson, George	18.00	13.50	6.00
4 Hyatt, Ham	18.00	13.50	6.00

	MINT	VG-E	F-G
5 Leach, Tommy	18.00	13.50	6.00
6 Leever, Sam	18.00	13.50	6.00
7 Maddox, Nick	18.00	13.50	6.00
8 Miller, John "Dots"	18.00	13.50	6.00
9 Phillippe, Deacon	18.00	13.50	6.00
10 Wagner, Honus	80.00	60.00	25.00
11 Wilson, John "Chief"	18.00	13.50	6.00

1910 E90—3 (20)

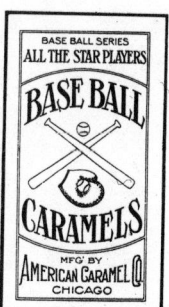

1 1/2" X 2 3/4"

The E90-3 American Caramels "All the Star Players" set contains 20 unnumbered cards featuring the Chicago White Sox and Chicago Cubs. The Cubs are listed in the checklist below with the prefix letter C while the White Sox are designated by the prefix letters WS. The backs are slightly different from E90-1 cards and the fronts differ in the use of the team nicknames.

	MINT	VG-E	F-G
COMPLETE SET	400.00	300.00	125.00
COMMON PLAYER	18.00	13.50	6.00
C1 Archer, Jimmy	18.00	13.50	6.00
C2 Brown, Mordecai	30.00	22.50	10.50
C3 Chance, Frank	40.00	30.00	13.00
C4 Cole, King	18.00	13.50	6.00
C5 Evers, Johnny	35.00	26.00	12.00
C6 Hoffman, Solly	18.00	13.50	6.00
C7 Overall, Orval	18.00	13.50	6.00
C8 Schulte, Frank	18.00	13.50	6.00
C9 Sheckard, Jimmy	18.00	13.50	6.00

	MINT	VG-E	F-G
C10 Steinfeldt, Harry	18.00	13.50	6.00
C11 Tinker, Joe	30.00	22.50	10.50
WS1 Blackburne, Lena	18.00	13.50	6.00
WS2 Dougherty, Patsy	18.00	13.50	6.00
WS3 Gandil, Chick	18.00	13.50	6.00
WS4 Hahn, Ed	18.00	13.50	6.00
WS5 Payne, Fred	20.00	15.00	6.50
WS6 Purtell, Billy	20.00	15.00	6.50
WS7 Smith, Frank "Nig"	18.00	13.50	6.00
WS8 Walsh, Ed	30.00	22.50	10.50
WS9 Zeider, Rollie	18.00	13.50	6.50

E270 COLGANS CHIPS

E91 BASE BALL CARAMELS (99)

1 1/2" X 2 3/4"

E91 encompasses three separate sets of color cards issued in 1908 and 1910. The 33 ballplayer drawings of the 1908 set were also used in the two 1910 sets. Eleven players were dropped and 11 added in set 2 (the first 1910 set), and all new players were added for set 3. Although there are 99 cards in E91, there are only 75 different players, so that, for example, there are two cards of Bender with identical fronts, but a different player is "named" in the same pose in set 3. Likewise, there can be three different players assigned to the same pose—one from each set. The set 1 checklist lists "Athletics" first; set 2 lists "Chicago" first; set 3 "Pittsburgh" first.

	MINT	VG-E	F-G
COMPLETE SET	600.00	450.00	200.00
COMMON PLAYER	6.00	4.50	2.00

	MINT	VG-E	F-G
1 Chief Bender	8.00	6.00	2.50
2 Roger Bresnahan	8.00	6.00	2.50
3 Al Bridwell	6.00	4.50	2.00
4 Mordecai Brown	8.00	6.00	2.50
5 Frank Chance	10.00	7.00	3.00
6 James Collins	8.00	6.00	2.50
7 Harry Davis	6.00	4.50	2.00
8 Art Devlin	6.00	4.50	2.00
9 Mike Donlin	6.00	4.50	2.00
10 Johnny Evers	8.00	6.00	2.50
11 Fred Hartzell	6.00	4.50	2.00
12 Johnny Kling	6.00	4.50	2.00
13 Christy Mathewson	12.00	8.75	4.00
14 Joe McGinnity	6.00	4.50	2.00
15 John McGraw	10.00	7.00	3.00
16 Danny Murphy	6.00	4.50	2.00
17 Simon Nichols	6.00	4.50	2.00
18 Rube Oldring	6.00	4.50	2.00
19 Orval Overall	6.00	4.50	2.00
20 Eddie Plank	10.00	7.00	3.00
21 Ed Reulbach	6.00	4.50	2.00
22 Jimmy Scheckard (sic)	6.00	4.50	2.00
23 Osee Schreckengost	6.00	4.50	2.00
24 Frank Schulte	6.00	4.50	2.00
25 Ralph Seybold	6.00	4.50	2.00
26 J. B. Seymore	6.00	4.50	2.00
27 Daniel Shay	6.00	4.50	2.00
28 James Slagle	6.00	4.50	2.00
29 Harry Steinfeldt	6.00	4.50	2.00
30 Luther Taylor	6.00	4.50	2.00
31 Fred Tenney	6.00	4.50	2.00
32 Joe Tinker	8.00	6.00	2.50
33 Rube Waddell	8.00	6.00	2.50
34 Jimmy Archer	6.00	4.50	2.00
35 J. Frank Baker	8.00	6.00	2.50
36 Jack Barry	6.00	4.50	2.00
37 Chief Bender	8.00	6.00	2.50
38 Al Bridwell	6.00	4.50	2.00
39 Mordecai Brown	8.00	6.00	2.50
40 Frank Chance	10.00	7.00	3.00
41 Eddie Collins	8.00	6.00	2.50
42 Harry Davis	6.00	4.50	2.00
43 Art Devlin	6.00	4.50	2.00
44 Mike Donlin	6.00	4.50	2.00
45 Larry Doyle	6.00	4.50	2.00
46 Johnny Evers	8.00	6.00	2.50
47 Bob Ganley	6.00	4.50	2.00
48 Fred Hartzell	6.00	4.50	2.00
49 Solly Hoffman	6.00	4.50	2.00
50 Harry Krause	6.00	4.50	2.00

	MINT	VG-E	F-G
51 Rube Marquard	8.00	6.00	2.50
52 Christy Mathewson	12.00	8.75	4.00
53 John McGraw	10.00	7.00	3.00
54 Chief Meyers	6.00	4.50	2.00
55 Danny Murphy	6.00	4.50	2.00
56 Red Murray	6.00	4.50	2.00
57 Orval Overall	6.00	4.50	2.00
58 Eddie Plank	10.00	7.00	3.00
59 Ed Reulbach	6.00	4.50	2.00
60 Jimmy Scheckard (sic)	6.00	4.50	2.00
61 Frank Schulte	6.00	4.50	2.00
62 J. B. Seymore	6.00	4.50	2.00
63 Harry Steinfeldt	6.00	4.50	2.00
64 Fred Tenney	6.00	4.50	2.00
65 Ira Thomas	6.00	4.50	2.00
66 Joe Tinker	8.00	6.00	2.50
67 Jap Barbeau	6.00	4.50	2.00
68 George Browne	6.00	4.50	2.00
69 Ed Carger	6.00	4.50	2.00
70 Robert Chech	6.00	4.50	2.00
71 Fred Clarke	8.00	6.00	2.50
72 Wid Conroy	6.00	4.50	2.00
73 Jim Delehanty	6.00	4.50	2.00
74 Jiggs Donahue	6.00	4.50	2.00
75 J. A. Donohue	6.00	4.50	2.00
76 George Gibson	6.00	4.50	2.00
77 Bob Groom	6.00	4.50	2.00
78 Harry Hooper	8.00	6.00	2.50
79 Tom Hughes	6.00	4.50	2.00
80 Walter Johnson	14.00	10.50	4.75
81 Tommy Leach	6.00	4.50	2.00
82 Sam Leever	6.00	4.50	2.00
83 Harry Lord	6.00	4.50	2.00
84 George McBride	6.00	4.50	2.00
85 Amby McConnell	6.00	4.50	2.00
86 Clyde Milan	6.00	4.50	2.00
87 J. B. Miller	6.00	4.50	2.00
88 Harry Niles	6.00	4.50	2.00
89 Deacon Phillippe	6.00	4.50	2.00
90 Tris Speaker	12.00	8.75	4.00
91 Jack Stahl	6.00	4.50	2.00
92 Allen Storke	6.00	4.50	2.00
93 Gabby Street	6.00	4.50	2.00
94 Bob Unglaub	6.00	4.50	2.00
95 C. Wagner	6.00	4.50	2.00
96 Hans Wagner	15.00	11.00	5.00
97 Vic Willis	6.00	4.50	2.00
98 Owen Wilson	6.00	4.50	2.00
99 Joe Wood	6.00	4.50	2.00

SOME VALUABLE CARDS from the collection of BARRY HALPER

1959 FLEER #68

1949 BOWMAN PAIGE

T206 COBB w/COBB BACK

1934 GOUDEY GEHRIG

1951 CURRENT A-S STANKY

1952 TOPPS MANTLE

1933 GOUDEY LAJOIE

1951 CURRENT
A-S ROBERTS

T206 MAGIE

T206 WAGNER

T206 PLANK

1951 CURRENT
A-S KONSTANTY

1954 BOWMAN WILLIAMS

1941 PLAY BALL DI MAGGIO

1953 TOPPS MAYS

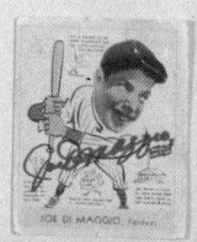

1938 GOUDEY DI MAGGIO

1951 BOWMAN MAYS

T207 LOUDERMILK

T207 MILLER CHI-NL

T207 LEWIS BOS-NL

R328 RUTH

WORLD SERIES PRESS PINS
1911-1938

WORLD SERIES PRESS PINS
1939-1962

39N Cinn

39A N.Y.

40N Cinn

40A Det

41N Bkln

41A N.Y.

42N St.L

42A N.Y.

43N St.L

43A N.Y.

44N St. L

44A St.L

45N Chi

45A Det

46N St. L

46A Bost

47N Bkln

47A N.Y.

48N Bost

48A Cleve

49N Bkln

49A N.Y.

50N Phil

50A N.Y.

51N N.Y.

51A N.Y.

52N Bkln

52A N.Y.

53N Bkln

53A N.Y.

54N N.Y.

54A Cleve

55N Bkln

55A N.Y.

56A N.Y.

57N Mil

57A N.Y.

58N Mil

58A N.Y.

59N L.A.

59A Chi

60N Pitt

60A N.Y.

61N Cinn

61A N.Y.

62N S.F.

62A N.Y.

ALL-STAR GAME PRESS PINS
1941-1980

41 Det

43 Phil

46 Bost

47 Chi

48 St.L

49 Bkln

46 Bost

50 Chi

51 Det

52 Phil

54 Cleve

55 Mil

56 Wash

57 St.L

58 Balt

59 L.A.

59 Pitt

60 N.Y.

60 K.C.

61 Bost

61 S.F.

62 Chi

62 Wash

63 Cleve

64 N.Y.

65 Minn

66 St.L

67 Calif

68 Hous

69 Wash

70 Cinn

71 Det

72 Atl

73 K.C.

74 Pitt

75 Mil

76 Phil

77 N.Y.

78 S.D.

79 Seat

80 L.A.

WRAPPERS
1933—1955

1933 GOUDEY

1934 GOUDEY

1936 GOUDEY

1938 GOUDEY

1941 GOUDEY

1933 DELONG

1933 SPORT KINGS

1934—36 DIAMOND STARS

1939 PLAY BALL

1940 PLAY BALL

1949 BOWMAN

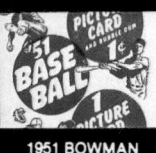

1951 BOWMAN

1952 BOWMAN

1953 BOWMAN B&W

1953 BOWMAN COLOR

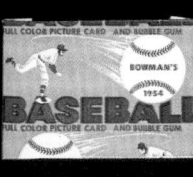

1954 BOWMAN

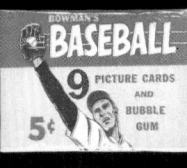

1955 BOWMAN

WRAPPERS
TOPPS 1951—1963
FLEER 1959-1963

1951 TOPPS REDBACK

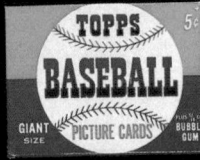

1952 TOPPS

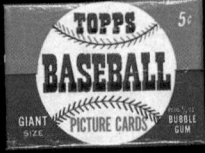

1953 TOPPS

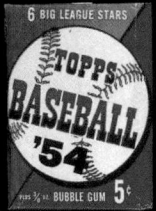

1954 TOPPS

1955 TOPPS

1955 TOPPS DOUBLEHEADER

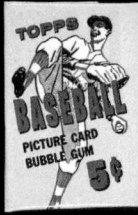

1956 TOPPS

1957 TOPPS

1958 TOPPS—5¢

1958 TOPPS—1¢

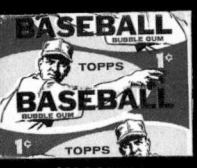

1959 TOPPS

1960 TOPPS

1961 TOPPS

1962 TOPPS

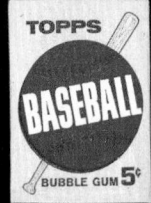

1963 TOPPS

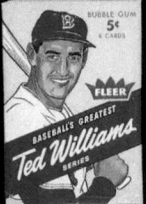

1959 FLEER

1960 FLEER

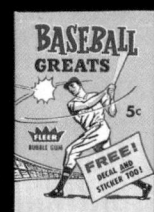

1961 FLEER

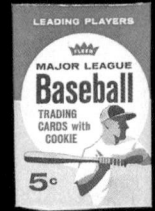

1963 FLEER

WRAPPERS
1964—1981 TOPPS
1981 DONRUSS & FLEER

1964 TOPPS

1965 TOPPS

1966 TOPPS

1967 TOPPS

1968 TOPPS

1969 TOPPS

1970 TOPPS

1971 TOPPS

1972 TOPPS

1973 TOPPS

1974 TOPPS

1975 TOPPS

1976 TOPPS

1977 TOPPS

1978 TOPPS

1979 TOPPS

1980 TOPPS

1981 TOPPS

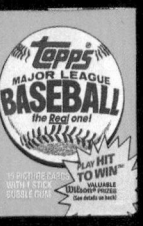

1981 DONRUSS

1981 FLEER

1930's EXHIBIT

1948 LEAF

W515

4-in-1 EXHIBIT

W517 ORIGINAL ART #20

R309-1

1935 GOUDEY

1933 SPORTS KINGS

1933 GOUDEY #144

1933 GOUDEY #181

1933 GOUDEY #149

1933 GOUDEY #53

V100

CARD FROM MOVIE

R328

1951 TOPPS
CONNIE MACK A-S

E92 50 BASE BALL PLAYERS (55)   1 1/2" X 2 3/4"

[...]re are 55 cards in this set [...]ed about 1910 by Dock-[...]n, Nadja, and Croft and [...]n. There are four known [...]rses, with the "Base Ball

Gum" (Dockman) back the most common, and the "Nadja" back the most difficult (Nadja backs with blue

printing on the obverse belong to E104). The set contains poses identical to those in E101, E102 and E105.

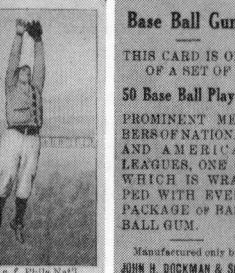
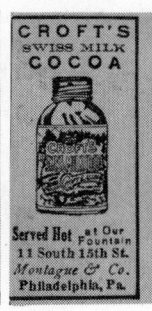

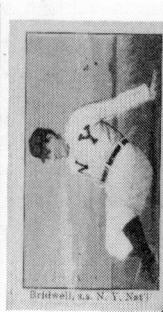

	MINT	VG-E	F-G
COMPLETE SET	925.00	700.00	300.00
COMMON PLAYER	8.00	6.25	3.00
1 Bill Bailey	75.00	55.00	24.00
2 Jack Barry	15.00	11.00	5.00
3 Harry Bemis	8.00	6.25	3.00
4A Chief Bender (striped cap)	30.00	22.50	10.50
4B Chief Bender (white cap)	Y5.00	11.00	5.00
5 Bill Bergen	8.00	6.25	3.00
6 Bob Bescher	8.00	6.25	3.00
7 Al Bridwell	8.00	6.25	3.00
8 Casey	8.00	6.25	3.00
9 Frank Chance	16.00	12.00	5.50
10 Hal Chase	8.00	6.25	3.00
11 Ty Cobb	100.00	70.00	30.00
12 Eddie Collins	50.00	38.0C	17.00
13 Sam Crawford	13.00	9.50	4.00
14 Harry Davis	8.00	6.25	3.00
15 Art Devlin	8.00	6.25	3.00
16 Wild Bill Donovan	15.00	11.00	5.00
17 Red Dooin	8.00	6.25	3.00
18 Mickey Doolan	8.00	6.25	3.00
19 Patsy Dougherty	8.00	6.25	3.00
20A Larry Doyle(batting)	10.00	7.00	3.00
20B Larry Doyle(throwing)	10.00	7.00	3.00
21 Johnny Evers	75.00	55.00	24.00
22 George Gibson	8.00	6.25	3.00
23 Topsy Hartsel	8.00	6.25	3.00
24 Fred Hartzell	75.00	55.00	24.00

	MINT	VG-E	F-G
25 Harry Howell	75.00	55.00	24.00
26 Fred Jacklitsch	15.00	11.00	5.00
27 Hugh Jennings	13.00	9.50	4.00
28 Red Kleinow	8.00	6.25	3.00
29 Otto Knabe	15.00	11.00	5.00
30 John Knight	15.00	11.00	5.00
31 Napoleon Lajoie	25.00	18.50	8.75
32 Hans Lobert	8.00	6.25	3.00
33 Sherry Magee	8.00	6.25	3.00
34 Christy Mathewson	30.00	22.50	10.50
35 John McGraw	22.00	17.00	8.00
36 Larry McLean	8.00	6.25	3.00
37A J.B. Miller(batting)	10.00	7.00	3.00
37B J.B. Miller(fielding)	15.00	11.00	5.00
38 Danny Murphy	8.00	6.25	3.00
39 Bill O'Hara	8.00	6.25	3.00
40 Germany Schaefer	8.00	6.25	3.00
41 Admiral Schlei	8.00	6.25	3.00
42 Boss Schmidt	8.00	6.25	3.00
43 Seigle	8.00	6.25	3.00
44 Dave Shean	8.00	6.25	3.00
45 Smith	8.00	6.25	3.00
46 George Stone	75.00	55.00	24.00
47 Joe Tinker	13.00	9.50	4.00
48A Honus Wagner(batting)	40.00	30.00	13.00
48B Honus Wagner(throw)	40.00	30.00	13.00
49 Bobby Wallace	75.00	55.00	24.00
50 Cy Young	22.00	17.00	8.00
51 Heinie Zimmerman	8.00	6.25	3.00

E93 BASE BALL STARS (30)   1 1/2" X 2 3/4"

The E93 set was distributed by Standard Caramel in 1910. It consists of black & white player photos which were tinted and placed against solid color backgrounds. A checklist, starting with "Ames," is printed in brown ink on the reverse. Some blank backs are known and all poses also appear in W555.

BASE BALL STARS
This card is one of a set of 30 stars from original photographs
1. AMES, New York National
2. BENDER, Phila. American
3. BROWN, Chicago National
4. CHANCE, Chicago National
5. COVELESKIE, Cincinnati Nat'l
6. CHASE, New York American
7. COBB, Detroit American
8. CLARKE, Pittsburg National
10. DELEHANTY, Detroit American
11. DONOVAN, Detroit American
12. DOOIN, Philadelphia National
13. EVERS, Chicago National
14. GIBSON, Pittsburg National
15. GRIFFITH, Cincinnati National
16. JENNINGS, Detroit American
17. JONES, Cleveland American
18. JOSS, Cleveland American
19. LAJOIE, Cleveland American
20. LEACH, Pittsburg National
21. MATHEWSON, N.Y. National
22. McGRAW, New York National
23. PHILLIPPI, Pittsburg National
24. PLANK, Philadelphia American
25. PASTORIOUS, Brooklyn Nat'l
26. TINKER, Chicago National
27. WADDELL, St. Louis American
28. WAGNER, Pittsburg National
29. WILTSE, New York National
30. CY. YOUNG, Cleveland Amer.
Manufactured only by
Standard Caramel Co., Lancaster, Pa.

	MINT	VG-E	F-G
COMPLETE SET	500.00	370.00	160.00
COMMON PLAYER	9.50	7.00	3.00
1 Red Ames	9.50	7.00	3.00
2 Chief Bender	14.00	10.50	4.75
3 Mordecai Brown	14.00	10.50	4.75
4 Frank Chance	18.00	13.50	6.00
5 Hal Chase	9.50	7.00	3.00
6 Ty Cobb	90.00	70.00	30.00
7 Eddie Collins	14.00	10.50	4.75
8 Stan Coveleskie	14.00	10.50	4.75
9 Fred Clarke	14.00	10.50	4.75
10 Delehanty	9.50	7.00	3.00
11 Wild Bill Donovan	9.50	7.00	3.00
12 Red Dooin	9.50	7.00	3.00
13 Johnny Evers	14.00	10.50	4.75
14 George Gibson	9.50	7.00	3.00
15 Clarke Griffith	14.00	10.50	4.75

	MINT	VG-E	F-G
16 Hugh Jennings	14.00	10.50	4.75
17 Jones	9.50	7.00	3.00
18 Addie Joss	18.00	13.50	6.00
19 Napoleon Lajoie	25.00	18.50	8.75
20 Tommy Leach	9.50	7.00	3.00
21 Christy Mathewson	30.00	22.50	10.50
22 John McGraw	22.00	17.00	8.00
23 Jim Pastorius	9.50	7.00	3.00
24 Deacon Phillippe	9.50	7.00	3.00
25 Eddie Plank	16.00	12.00	5.50
26 Joe Tinker	14.00	10.50	4.75
27 Rube Waddel	14.00	10.50	4.75
28 Honus Wagner	40.00	30.00	13.00
29 Hooks Wiltse	9.50	7.00	3.00
30 Cy Young	22.00	17.00	8.00

E94 STAR BASE BALL PLAYERS (30)   1 1/2" X 2 3/4"

This card is one of a set of Star Base Ball Players' Cards as follows:

MOORE, Philadelphia National
GRANT, Cincinnati National
MURRAY, New York National
BYRNE, Pittsburg National
CRAWFORD, Detroit American
AUSTIN, New York American
"JOE" LAKE, St. Louis National
LOBERT, Philadelphia National
MAGEE, Philadelphia National
"HUGH" JENNINGS, Det. American
DOOLAN, Philadelphia National
"OLD" CY YOUNG, Cleveland Amer.
"HARRY" DAVIS, Phila. American
McGRAW, New York National
"TY" COBB, Detroit American
"TOMMY" LEACH, Pittsburg Natl.
LORD, Chicago American
DOUGHERTY, New York American
LAJOIE, Cleveland American
DEVORE, New York American
CHANCE, Chicago National
CICOTTE, Boston American
BATES, Philadelphia National
"HANS" WAGNER, Pittsburg Nat.
SPEAKER, Boston American
KLEINOW, New York American
BESCHER, Cincinnati National
TURNER, Cleveland American
EVERS, Chicago National
DEVLIN, New York National

DOOLAN, Phila. Nat'l.

The E94 format, like that of E93, consists of tinted, black & white photos on solid color backgrounds (seven colors seen; each player seen in more than one color). Issued in 1911, cards from this set may be found with advertising overstamps covering the gray-print checklist on the back (begins with "Moore"). Some blank backs have been found, and the set is identical to M131.

	MINT	VG-E	F-G
COMPLETE SET	500.00	375.00	175.00
COMMON PLAYER	12.00	9.00	4.00

	MINT	VG-E	F-G
1 Jimmy Austin	12.00	9.00	4.00
2 Johnny Bates	12.00	9.00	4.00
3 Bob Bescher	12.00	9.00	4.00
4 Bobby Byrne	12.00	9.00	4.00
5 Frank Chance	35.00	26.00	12.00
6 Eddie Cicotte	12.00	9.00	4.00
7 Ty Cobb	100.00	70.00	30.00
8 Sam Crawford	20.00	15.00	6.50
9 Harry Davis	12.00	9.00	4.00
10 Art Devlin	12.00	9.00	4.00
11 Josh Devore	12.00	9.00	4.00
12 Mickey Doolan	12.00	9.00	4.00
13 Patsy Dougherty	12.00	9.00	4.00
14 Johnny Evers	20.00	15.00	6.50
15 Eddie Grant	12.00	9.00	4.00

	MINT	VG-E	F-G
16 Hugh Jennings	20.00	15.00	6.50
17 Red Kleinow	12.00	9.00	4.00
18 Napoleon Lajoie	35.00	26.00	12.00
19 Joe Lake	12.00	9.00	4.00
20 Tommy Leach	12.00	9.00	4.00
21 Hans Lobert	12.00	9.00	4.00
22 Harry Lord	12.00	9.00	4.00
23 Sherry Magee	12.00	9.00	4.00
24 John McGraw	30.00	22.50	10.50
25 Earl Moore	12.00	9.00	4.00
26 Red Murray	12.00	9.00	4.00
27 Tris Speaker	30.00	22.50	10.50
28 Terry Turner	12.00	9.00	4.00
29 Hans Wagner	50.00	38.00	17.00
30 Old Cy Young	35.00	26.00	12.00

E95 25 BALL PLAYERS (25)   1 1/2" X 2 3/4"

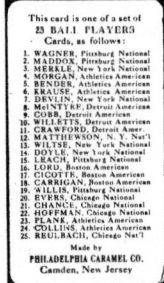

This card is one of a set of 25 BALL PLAYERS Cards, as follows:

1. WAGNER, Pittsburg National
2. MADDOX, Pittsburg National
3. MERKLE, New York National
4. MORGAN, Athletics American
5. BENDER, Athletics American
6. KRAUSE, Athletics American
7. DEVLIN, New York National
8. McINTYRE, Detroit American
9. COBB, Detroit American
10. WILLETTS, Detroit American
11. CRAWFORD, Detroit Amer.
12. MATTHEWSON, N.Y. Nat'l
13. WILTSE, New York National
14. DOYLE, New York National
15. LEACH, Pittsburg National
16. LORD, Boston American
17. CICOTTE, Boston American
18. CARRIGAN, Boston American
19. WILLIS, Pittsburg National
20. EVERS, Chicago National
21. CHANCE, Chicago National
22. HOFFMAN, Chicago National
23. PLANK, Athletics American
24. COLLINS, Athletics American
25. REULBACH, Chicago Nat'l

Made by
PHILADELPHIA CARAMEL CO.
Camden, New Jersey

WAGNER, PITTSBURG NAT'L

This set of color drawings was issued by the Philadelphia Caramel Company about 1909. The back is checklisted with its own numbering system (begins with 1. Wagner), but has been alpha-betized for convenience in this listing. Blank backs found in this set are probably cut from advertising panels and should not be considered as proof cards.

	MINT	VG-E	F-G
COMPLETE SET	330.00	250.00	110.00
COMMON PLAYER	8.00	6.00	2.50

	MINT	VG-E	F-G
1 Chief Bender	13.00	9.50	4.00
2 Bill Carrigan	8.00	6.00	2.50
3 Frank Chance	16.00	12.00	5.50
4 Eddie Cicotte	8.00	6.00	2.50
5 Ty Cobb	80.00	60.00	25.00
6 Eddie Collins	13.00	9.50	4.00
7 Sam Crawford	13.00	9.50	4.00
8 Art Devlin	8.00	6.00	2.50
9 Larry Doyle	8.00	6.00	2.50
10 Johnny Evers	13.00	9.50	4.00
11 Solly Hoffman	8.00	6.00	2.50
12 Harry Krause	8.00	6.00	2.50
13 Tommy Leach	8.00	6.00	2.50

	MINT	VG-E	F-G
14 Harry Lord	8.00	6.00	2.50
15 Nick Maddox	8.00	6.00	2.50
16 Christy Mathewson	30.00	22.50	10.50
17 Matty McIntyre	8.00	6.00	2.50
18 Fred Merkle	8.00	6.00	2.50
19 Harry (Cy) Morgan	8.00	6.00	2.50
20 Eddie Plank	16.00	12.00	5.50
21 Ed Reulbach	8.00	6.00	2.50
22 Honus Wagner	40.00	30.00	13.00
23 Ed Willett	8.00	6.00	2.50
24 Vic Willis	8.00	6.00	2.50
25 Hooks Wiltse	8.00	6.00	2.50

Watch the hobby papers and your local bookstores for the release later this year of the Sport Americana Baseball Memorabilia Price Guide. This book will contain prices and descriptions of baseball memorabilia other than the popular baseball card issues — yearbooks, baseball coins, programs, press pins, uniforms, statues, postcards, etc.

E96 30 BALL PLAYERS (30)　　　1 1/2" X 2 3/4"

 *(checklist card)*

This Card is one of a New Set of
30 BALL PLAYERS
1. DAVIS, Athletics
2. CONNIE MACK, Athletics
3. THOMAS, Athletics
4. BAKER, Phila. Natl.
5. DOOIN, Phila. Natl.
6. McQUILLAN, Phila. Natl.
7. KONETCHY, St. Louis Natl
8. KARGER, St. Louis Natl.
9. MOWRAY, St. Louis Natl.
10. MURRAY, St. Louis Natl.
11. LAJOIE, Cleveland
12. ROSSMAN, Cleveland
13. RUCKER, Brooklyn
14. JENNINGS, Detroit
15. DONOVAN, Detroit
16. DELAHANTY, Detroit
17. MULLIN, Detroit
18. ARRELANES, Boston Am
19. SPENCER, Boston Am.
20. KLING, Chicago
21. PFISTER, Chicago
22. BROWN, Chicago
23. TINKER, Chicago
24. CLARK, Pittsburg
25. GIBSON, Pittsburg
26. ADAMS, Pittsburg
27. AMES, N. Y. Natl.
28. MARQUARD, N. Y. Natl.
29. HERZOG, N. Y. Natl.
30. MYERS, N. Y. Natl.
Previous Series 25, making total issue 55 Cards
PHILADELPHIA CARAMEL CO.
Camden, N. J.

The red-printed backs in this set carry the statement "Previous Series 25, making total issue 55 cards," and for this reason it is often referred to as the second series of E95. Issued about 1912, the numbering of the original checklist (starts with 1. Davis) has been rearranged alphabetically below. Some blank backs are known.

	MINT	VG-E	F-G
COMPLETE SET	325.00	250.00	110.00
COMMON PLAYER	9.00	6.75	3.00

		MINT	VG-E	F-G			MINT	VG-E	F-G
1	Bert Adams	9.00	6.75	3.00	16	Ed Konetchy	9.00	6.75	3.00
2	Red Ames	9.00	6.75	3.00	17	Napoleon Lajoie	25.00	18.50	8.75
3	Arrelanes	9.00	6.75	3.00	18	Connie Mack	20.00	15.00	6.50
4	J. Frank Baker	14.00	10.50	4.75	19	Rube Marquard	14.00	10.50	4.75
5	Mordecai Brown	14.00	10.50	4.75	20	George McQuillan	9.00	6.75	3.00
6	Fred Clark (sic)	14.00	10.50	4.75	21	Chief Meyers	9.00	6.75	3.00
7	Harry Davis	9.00	6.75	3.00	22	Mike Mowrey	9.00	6.75	3.00
8	Jim Delehanty	9.00	6.75	3.00	23	George Mullin	9.00	6.75	3.00
9	Wild Bill Donovan	9.00	6.75	3.00	24	Red Murray	9.00	6.75	3.00
10	Red Dooin	9.00	6.75	3.00	25	Jack Pfeister	9.00	6.75	3.00
11	George Gibson	9.00	6.75	3.00	26	Claude Rossman	9.00	6.75	3.00
12	Buck Herzog	9.00	6.75	3.00	27	Nap Rucker	9.00	6.75	3.00
13	Hugh Jennings	14.00	10.50	4.75	28	Tubby Spencer	9.00	6.75	3.00
14	Ed Karger	9.00	6.75	3.00	29	Ira Thomas	9.00	6.75	3.00
15	Johnny Kling	9.00	6.75	3.00	30	Joe Tinker	14.00	10.50	4.75

E97 30 BALL PLAYERS (32)　　　1 1/2" X 2 3/4"

(checklist card)
This card is one of a set of
30 BALL PLAYERS
Cards, as follows :
AUSTIN, New York American
BRADLEY, Cleveland American
BIRMINGHAM, Cleveland American
BRANSFIELD, Philadelphia National
CARRIGAN, Boston American
CAMNITZ, Pittsburg National
DURHAM, New York National
DYGERT, Philadelphia American
DOOLAN, Philadelphia National
DEVORE, New York National
DAVIS, Philadelphia American
HEMPHILL, New York American
HINCHMAN, Cleveland American
HARTSEL, Philadelphia American
KROH, Chicago National
KLEINOW, New York National
KELLY, Boston National
KEELER, New York National
McINTYRE, Detroit American
McDONNELL, Boston American
MOORE, Philadelphia National
MULLIN, Detroit American
MURRAY, New York National
MEYERS, New York National
NICHOLS, Cleveland American
ROSSMAN, Detroit American
SULLIVAN, Chicago American
STEINFELDT, Chicago National
SCHLEI, New York National
CY. YOUNG, Cleveland American
C.A. BRIGGS CO., Lozenge Makers
Boston, Mass.

The C.A. Briggs Company distributed this set in 1909, and it is one of the most highly prized of caramel issues. The cards come in two distinct varieties: one group in color with a brown-print checklist on back; the other with identical player poses in black & white with blank backs. A comparison of team and name variations suggests that the black & white set pre-dates the color issue.

	MINT	VG-E	F-G
COMPLETE SET	850.00	650.00	300.00
COMMON PLAYER	22.00	17.00	8.00

		MINT	VG-E	F-G			MINT	VG-E	F-G
1	Jimmy Austin	22.00	17.00	8.00	17	Red Kleinow	22.00	17.00	8.00
2	Joe Birmingham	22.00	17.00	8.00	18	Rube Kroh	22.00	17.00	8.00
3	William J. Bradley	22.00	17.00	8.00	19	Amby McConnell	22.00	17.00	8.00
4	Kitty Bransfield	22.00	17.00	8.00	20	Matty McIntyre	22.00	17.00	8.00
5	Howie Camnitz	22.00	17.00	8.00	21	Chief Meyers	22.00	17.00	8.00
6	Bill Carrigan	22.00	17.00	8.00	22	Earl Moore	22.00	17.00	8.00
7	Harry Davis	22.00	17.00	8.00	23	George Mullin	22.00	17.00	8.00
8	Josh Devore	22.00	17.00	8.00	24	Red Murray	22.00	17.00	8.00
9	Mickey Doolan	22.00	17.00	8.00	25	Simon Nichols (sic)	22.00	17.00	8.00
10	Bull Durham	22.00	17.00	8.00	26	Claude Rossman	22.00	17.00	8.00
11	Jimmy Dygert	22.00	17.00	8.00	27	Admiral Schlei	22.00	17.00	8.00
12	Topsy Hartsel	22.00	17.00	8.00	28	Harry Steinfeldt	22.00	17.00	8.00
13	Charlie Hemphill	22.00	17.00	8.00	29A	W. J. Sullivan (Chi)	22.00	17.00	8.00
14	Bill Hinchman	22.00	17.00	8.00	29B	W. J. Sullivan(Boston)	100.00	70.00	30.00
15	Willie Keeler	50.00	38.00	17.00	30A	Cy Young (Boston)	100.00	70.00	30.00
16	Joseph J. Kelly (sic)	40.00	30.00	13.00	30B	Cy Young (Cleve.)	40.00	30.00	13.00

E98 30 BALL PLAYERS (30)   1 1/2" X 2 3/4"

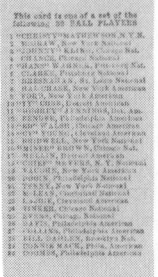

E98 is an anonymous set with more similarities to Standard Caramel issues than to Briggs. Most players are found in four different background colors and the brown-print checklist (starts with 1. "Christy" Mathewson) has been alphabetized below. The set was issued in 1910.

	MINT	VG-E	F-G
COMPLETE SET	600.00	450.00	200.00
COMMON PLAYER	15.00	11.00	5.00

	MINT	VG-E	F-G
1 Chief Bender	20.00	15.00	6.50
2 Roger Bresnahan	20.00	15.00	6.50
3 Al Bridwell	15.00	11.00	5.00
4 Miner Brown	20.00	15.00	6.50
5 Frank Chance	20.00	15.00	6.50
6 Hal Chase	15.00	11.00	5.00
7 Fred Clarke	20.00	15.00	6.50
8 Ty Cobb	100.00	70.00	30.00
9 Eddie Collins	20.00	15.00	6.50
10 Jack Coombs	15.00	11.00	5.00
11 Bill Dahlen	15.00	11.00	5.00
12 Harry Davis	15.00	11.00	5.00
13 Red Dooin	15.00	11.00	5.00
14 Johnny Evers	20.00	15.00	6.50
15 Russ Ford	15.00	11.00	5.00

	MINT	VG-E	F-G
16 Hughey Jennings	20.00	15.00	6.50
17 Johnny Kling	15.00	11.00	5.00
18 Napoleon Lajoie	50.00	38.00	17.00
19 Connie Mack	30.00	22.50	10.50
20 Christy Mathewson	50.00	38.00	17.00
21 John McGraw	25.00	18.50	8.75
22 Larry McLean	15.00	11.00	5.00
23 Chief Meyers	15.00	11.00	5.00
24 George Mullin	15.00	11.00	5.00
25 Fred Tenney	15.00	11.00	5.00
26 Joe Tinker	20.00	15.00	6.50
27 Hippo Vaughn	15.00	11.00	5.00
28 Hans Wagner	50.00	38.00	17.00
29 Ed Walsh	20.00	15.00	6.50
30 Cy Young	25.00	18.50	8.75

E101 50 BASE BALL PLAYERS (50)   1 1/2" X 2 3/4"

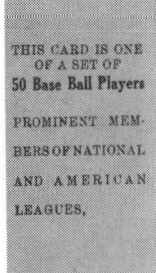

The "Prominent Members of National and American Leagues" portrayed in E101 are identical to the line drawings of E92 and E105. The set was distributed about 1910.

	MINT	VG-E	F-G
COMPLETE SET	650.00	500.00	200.00
COMMON PLAYER	11.00	8.25	4.00

	MINT	VG-E	F-G
1 Jack Barry	11.00	8.25	4.00
2 Harry Bemis	11.00	8.25	4.00
3 Chief Bender (2)	15.00	11.00	5.00
4 Bill Bergen	11.00	8.25	4.00
5 Bob Bescher	11.00	8.25	4.00
6 Al Bridwell	11.00	8.25	4.00
7 Doc Casey	11.00	8.25	4.00
8 Frank Chance	18.00	13.50	6.00
9 Hal Chase	11.00	8.25	4.00
10 Ty Cobb	100.00	70.00	30.00
11 Eddie Collins	15.00	11.00	5.00
12 Sam Crawford	15.00	11.00	5.00
13 Harry Davis	11.00	8.25	4.00
14 Art Devlin	11.00	8.25	4.00
15 Wild Bill Donovan	11.00	8.25	4.00
16 Red Dooin	11.00	8.25	4.00
17 Mickey Doolan	11.00	8.25	4.00
18 Patsy Dougherty	11.00	8.25	4.00
19A Larry Doyle(batting)	15.00	11.00	5.00
19B Larry Doyle(throw)	15.00	11.00	5.00
20 Johnny Evers	15.00	11.00	5.00
21 George Gibson	11.00	8.25	4.00
22 Topsy Harsel	11.00	8.25	4.00
23 Fred Jacklitsch	11.00	8.25	4.00

	MINT	VG-E	F-G
24 Hugh Jennings	15.00	11.00	5.00
25 Red Kleinow	11.00	8.25	4.00
26 Otto Knabe	11.00	8.25	4.00
27 John Knight	11.00	8.25	4.00
28 Napoleon Lajoie	30.00	22.50	10.50
29 Hans Lobert	11.00	8.25	4.00
30 Sherry Magee	11.00	8.25	4.00
31 Christy Mathewson	40.00	30.00	13.00
32 John McGraw	20.00	15.00	6.50
33 Larry McLean	11.00	8.25	4.00
34A J. B. Miller(batting)	15.00	11.00	5.00
34B J. B. Miller(field)	15.00	11.00	5.00
35 Danny Murphy	11.00	8.25	4.00
36 Bill O'Hara	11.00	8.25	4.00
37 Germany Schaefer	11.00	8.25	4.00
38 Admiral Schlei	11.00	8.25	4.00
39 Boss Schmidt	11.00	8.25	4.00
40 Seigle	11.00	8.25	4.00
41 Dave Shean	11.00	8.25	4.00
42 Smith	11.00	8.25	4.00
43 Joe Tinker	15.00	11.00	5.00
44A Honus Wagner(batting)	50.00	38.00	17.00
44B Honus Wagner(throw)	50.00	38.00	17.00
45 Cy Young	20.00	15.00	6.50
46 Heine Zimmerman	11.00	8.25	4.00

E102 TWENTY-FIVE BASE BALL (28) PLAYERS

1 1/2" X 2 3/4"

 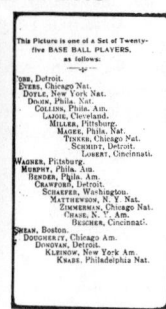

The player poses in E102 are identical to those in E92. The reverse of each card carries an angled checklist (begins with "Cobb, Detroit") printed in black. Smith is not listed, and two poses exist for both Doyle and Miller. The set was issued circa 1910.

	MINT	VG-E	F-G
COMPLETE SET	425.00	340.00	150.00
COMMON PLAYER	11.00	8.25	4.00
1 Chief Bender	15.00	11.00	5.00
2 Bob Bescher	11.00	8.25	4.00
3 Hal Chase	11.00	8.25	4.00
4 Ty Cobb	100.00	70.00	30.00
5 Eddie Collins	15.00	11.00	5.00
6 Sam Crawford	15.00	11.00	5.00
7 Wild Bill Donovan	11.00	8.25	4.00
8 Red Dooin	11.00	8.25	4.00
9 Patsy Dougherty	11.00	8.25	4.00
10A Larry Doyle(batting)	15.00	11.00	5.00
10B Larry Doyle(throwing)	15.00	11.00	5.00
11 Johnny Evers	15.00	11.00	5.00
12 Red Kleinow	11.00	8.25	4.00

	MINT	VG-E	F-G
13 Otto Knabe	11.00	8.25	4.00
14 Napoleon Lajoie	30.00	22.50	10.50
15 Hans Lobert	11.00	8.25	4.00
16 Sherry Magee	11.00	8.25	4.00
17 Christy Mathewson	40.00	30.00	13.00
18 J. B. Miller(2)	11.00	8.25	4.00
19 Danny Murphy	11.00	8.25	4.00
20 Germany Schaefer	11.00	8.25	4.00
21 Boss Schmidt	20.00	15.00	6.50
22 Dave Shean	11.00	8.25	4.00
23 Smith	11.00	8.25	4.00
24 Joe Tinker	15.00	11.00	5.00
25 Honus Wagner	50.00	38.00	17.00
26 Heinie Zimmerman	11.00	8.25	4.00

E103 WILLIAMS CARAMELS (30)

1 1/2" X 2 3/4"

E103 is distinctive for its black & white player portraits set onto a solid red background. Player names and teams are listed below each photo, with "Williams", the manufactirer's name, on the line below. Printed on thin cardboard, the blank-back Williams set was released to the public about 1910.

	MINT	VG-E	F-G
COMPLETE SET	925.00	700.00	300.00
COMMON PLAYER	25.00	20.00	8.00
1 Chief Bender	40.00	30.00	13.00
2 Roger Bresnahan	35.00	26.00	12.00
3 Mordecai Brown	40.00	30.00	13.00
4 Frank Chance	50.00	38.00	17.00
5 Hal Chase	25.00	20.00	8.00
6 Ty Cobb	150.00	110.00	50.00
7 Eddie Collins	40.00	30.00	13.00
8 Sam Crawford	35.00	26.00	12.00
9 Harry Davis	25.00	20.00	8.00
10 Art Devlin	25.00	20.00	8.00
11 Wild Bill Donovan	25.00	20.00	8.00
12 Red Dooin	25.00	20.00	8.00
13 Larry Doyle	25.00	20.00	8.00
14 John Ewing	25.00	20.00	8.00
15 George Gibson	25.00	20.00	8.00

	MINT	VG-E	F-G
16 Hugh Jennings	35.00	26.00	12.00
17 David Jones	25.00	20.00	8.00
18 Tim Jordon	25.00	20.00	8.00
19 Napoleon Lajoie	50.00	38.00	17.00
20 Tommy Leach	25.00	20.00	8.00
21 Harry Lord	25.00	20.00	8.00
22 Christy Mathewson	60.00	45.00	20.00
23 Larry McLean	25.00	20.00	8.00
24 George McQuillan	25.00	20.00	8.00
25 Jim Pastorious	25.00	20.00	8.00
26 Nap Rucker	25.00	20.00	8.00
27 Fred Tenney	25.00	20.00	8.00
28 Ira Thomas	25.00	20.00	8.00
29 Honus Wagner	75.00	55.00	24.00
30 Joe Wood	25.00	20.00	8.00

EDDIE COLLINS
SECOND BASE, CHICAGO AMERICANS

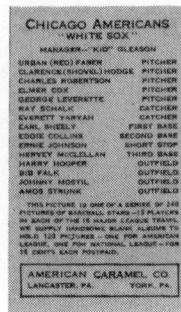

The 1922 E120 set was issued by American Caramels and contains 240 unnumbered cards which are numbered here alphabetically within team for convenience. This set is one of the most popular of the E card sets.

		MINT	VG-E	F-G
COMPLETE SET		2500.00	1700.00	750.00
COMMON PLAYER		8.50	6.50	3.00
1	Burns, George	8.50	6.50	3.00
2	J. Collins	8.50	6.50	3.00
3	Dugan, Joe	8.50	6.50	3.00
4	Harris	8.50	6.50	3.00
5	Karr, Ben	8.50	6.50	3.00
6	Leibold, Harry	8.50	6.50	3.00
7	Menosky, Michael	8.50	6.50	3.00
8	Myers	8.50	6.50	3.00
9	Pennock, Herb	15.00	11.00	5.00
10	Pittenger, Clarke	8.50	6.50	3.00
11	Pratt	8.50	6.50	3.00
12	Quinn, John	8.50	6.50	3.00
13	Ruel, Muddy	8.50	6.50	3.00
14	Elmer Smith	8.50	6.50	3.00
15	Walters, Alfred	8.50	6.50	3.00
16	E. Collins	15.00	11.00	5.00
17	Cox	8.50	6.50	3.00
18	Faber, Urban	15.00	11.00	5.00
19	Falk, Bibb	8.50	6.50	3.00
20	Hodge, Clarence	8.50	6.50	3.00
21	Harry Hooper	15.00	11.00	5.00
22	E. Johnson	8.50	6.50	3.00
23	Leverette, Horace	8.50	6.50	3.00
24	McClellan, Hervey	8.50	6.50	3.00
25	Mostil, Johnny	8.50	6.50	3.00
26	Robertson	8.50	6.50	3.00
27	Schalk, Ray	14.00	10.50	4.75
28	Sheely, Earl	8.50	6.50	3.00
29	Strunk, Amos	8.50	6.50	3.00
30	Yaryan, Clarence	8.50	6.50	3.00
31	Bagby, Jim	8.50	6.50	3.00
32	Coveleskie, Stan	14.00	10.50	4.75
33	Gardner, Harry	8.50	6.50	3.00
34	Graney, Jack	8.50	6.50	3.00
35	Jamieson, Charles	8.50	6.50	3.00
36	Mails, John	8.50	6.50	3.00
37	McInnis, Stuffy	8.50	6.50	3.00
38	Nunamaker, Leslie	8.50	6.50	3.00
39	O'Neill, Steve	8.50	6.50	3.00
40	Sewell	13.00	9.50	4.00
41	Sothoron, Allen	8.50	6.50	4.00
42	Speaker, Tris	30.00	22.50	10.50
43	Uhle, George	8.50	6.50	4.00
44	Wambsganss, Bill	8.50	6.50	4.00
45	Wood, Joe	8.50	6.50	4.00
46	Bassler, John	8.50	6.50	4.00
47	Blue, Lu	8.50	6.50	4.00
48	Cobb, Ty	100.00	70.00	30.00
49	Cole	8.50	6.50	4.00
50	Cutshaw, George	8.50	6.50	4.00
51	Dauss, George	8.50	6.50	4.00
52	Ehmke, Howard	8.50	6.50	4.00
53	Flagstead, Ira	8.50	6.50	4.00
54	Heilman, Harry	17.00	12.50	6.00
55	S. Johnson	8.50	6.50	4.00
56	B. Jones	8.50	6.50	4.00
57	Pillette, Herman	8.50	6.50	4.00

		MINT	VG-E	F-G
58	Rigney	8.50	6.50	3.00
59	Veach, Bob	8.50	6.50	3.00
60	Woodall, Charles	8.50	6.50	3.00
61	Baker, Home Run	15.00	11.00	5.00
62	Bush, Joe	8.50	6.50	3.00
63	Devormer, Albert	8.50	6.50	3.00
64	Hoyt, Waite	15.00	11.00	5.00
65	S. Jones,	8.50	6.50	3.00
66	Mays, Carl	8.50	6.50	3.00
67	McNally, Michael	8.50	6.50	3.00
68	B. Meusel	8.50	6.50	3.00
69	E. Miller	8.50	6.50	3.00
70	Pipp, Wally	10.00	7.00	3.00
71	Ruth, Babe	150.00	110.00	50.00
72	Schang, Wallie	8.50	6.50	3.00
73	Scott, Everett	8.50	6.50	3.00
74	Shawkey, Bob	8.50	6.50	3.00
75	Ward, Aaron	8.50	6.50	3.00
76	Calloway, Frank	8.50	6.50	3.00
77	Dykes, Jimmy	10.00	7.00	3.00
78	Fuhrman, Alfred	8.50	6.50	3.00
79	Galloway, Chick	8.50	6.50	3.00
80	Harris	8.50	6.50	3.00
81	Hasty, Robert	8.50	6.50	3.00
82	Hauser, Joe	8.50	6.50	3.00
83	D. Johnston	8.50	6.50	3.00
84	B. Miller	8.50	6.50	3.00
85	Moore	8.50	6.50	3.00
86	Naylor, Roleine	8.50	6.50	3.00
87	Perkins, Cy	8.50	6.50	3.00
88	Rommel, Ed	8.50	6.50	3.00
89	C. Walker	8.50	6.50	3.00
90	Welch	8.50	6.50	3.00
91	Bayne, William	8.50	6.50	3.00
92	P. Collins	8.50	6.50	3.00
93	Danforth, David	8.50	6.50	3.00
94	D. Davis	8.50	6.50	3.00
95	Ellerbe, Francis	8.50	6.50	3.00
96	Gerber, Walter	8.50	6.50	3.00
97	Jacobson	8.50	6.50	3.00
98	McManus, Marty	8.50	6.50	3.00
99	Severeid, Hank	8.50	6.50	3.00
100	Shocker, Urban	8.50	6.50	3.00
101	Shorten, Charles	8.50	6.50	3.00
102	Sisler, George	16.00	12.00	5.50
103	Tobin, John	8.50	6.50	3.00
104	Van Gilder	8.50	6.50	3.00
105	K. Williams	8.50	6.50	3.00
106	Courtney, Henry	8.50	6.50	3.00
107	Gharrity, Edward	8.50	6.50	3.00
108	Goslin, Goose	15.00	11.00	5.00
109	S. Harris	14.00	10.50	4.75
110	W. Johnson	60.00	45.00	20.00
111	Judge, Joe	8.50	6.50	3.00
112	Milan, Clyde	8.50	6.50	3.00
113	Mogridge, George	8.50	6.50	3.00
114	Peckinpaugh, Roger	8.50	6.50	3.00
115	Phillips	8.50	6.50	3.00
116	Picinich, Val	8.50	6.50	3.00
117	Rice, Sam	14.00	10.50	4.75

REMEMBER THE NATIONAL CONVENTION IS BEING HELD JULY 9 - 12, 1981, IN PLYMOUTH, MICHIGAN

E 120 (CONTINUED)

	MINT	VG-E	F-G
118 Shanks, Howard	8.50	6.50	3.00
119 Earl Smith	8.50	6.50	3.00
120 Zachary, Tom	8.50	6.50	3.00
121 Barbare, Walter	8.50	6.50	3.00
122 Boeckel, Norman	8.50	6.50	3.00
123 Cruise, Walton	8.50	6.50	3.00
124 Fillingim, Dana	8.50	6.50	3.00
125 Ford	8.50	6.50	3.00
126 Gowdy, Hank	8.50	6.50	3.00
127 Holke, Walter	8.50	6.50	3.00
128 Kopf, Larry	8.50	6.50	3.00
129 Marquard, Rube	15.00	11.00	5.00
130 McQuillan	8.50	6.50	3.00
131 Oeschger, Joe	8.50	6.50	3.00
132 O'Neil	8.50	6.50	3.00
133 Powell, Roy	8.50	6.50	3.00
134 Southworth, William H.	8.50	6.50	3.00
135 Watson	8.50	6.50	3.00
136 Cadore, Leon	8.50	6.50	3.00
137 Crane, Samuel	8.50	6.50	3.00
138 DeBerry, Hank	8.50	6.50	3.00
139 Griffith, Tom	8.50	6.50	3.00
140 Grimes, Burleigh	15.00	11.00	5.00
141 Hungling, Bernard	8.50	6.50	3.00
142 J. Johnston	8.50	6.50	3.00
143 Mamaux, Albert	8.50	6.50	3.00
144 Mitchell	8.50	6.50	3.00
145 Myers	8.50	6.50	3.00
146 Olson	8.50	6.50	3.00
147 Ruether, Walter	8.50	6.50	3.00
148 Schmandt	8.50	6.50	3.00
149 S. Smith	8.50	6.50	3.00
150 Wheat, Zach	15.00	11.00	5.00
151 Aldridge, Victor	8.50	6.50	3.00
152 Alexander, Grover C.	25.00	18.50	8.75
153 Barber, Tyrus	8.50	6.50	3.00
154 Callaghan	8.50	6.50	3.00
155 Cheeves, Virgil	8.50	6.50	3.00
156 Flack, Max	8.50	6.50	3.00
157 Grimes, Oscar	8.50	6.50	3.00
158 Hartnett, Gabby	15.00	11.00	5.00
159 Hollocher, Charles	8.50	6.50	3.00
160 P. Jones	8.50	6.50	3.00
161 Kelleher	8.50	6.50	3.00
162 Krug, Martin	8.50	6.50	3.00
163 H. Miller	8.50	6.50	3.00
164 O'Farrell, Bob	8.50	6.50	3.00
165 Statz, Arnold	8.50	6.50	3.00
166 Bohne	8.50	6.50	3.00
167 Burns	8.50	6.50	3.00
168 Caveney, James	8.50	6.50	3.00
169 Daubert, Jake	8.50	6.50	3.00
170 Donohue, Pete	8.50	6.50	3.00
171 Duncan, Pat	8.50	6.50	3.00
172 Gillespie	8.50	6.50	3.00
173 Hargrave	8.50	6.50	3.00
174 Luque, Dolph	8.50	6.50	3.00
175 Markle	8.50	6.50	3.00
176 Neale, A. E.	8.50	6.50	3.00
177 Pinelli, Ralph	8.50	6.50	3.00
178 Rixey, Eppa	14.00	10.50	4.75

	MINT	VG-E	F-G
179 Roush, Ed	15.00	11.00	5.00
180 Wingo, Ivy	8.50	6.50	3.00
181 Bancroft, Dave	14.00	10.50	4.75
182 Barnes, Jesse	8.50	6.50	3.00
183 Cunningham	8.50	6.50	3.00
184 Douglas	8.50	6.50	3.00
185 Frisch, Frank	22.00	16.50	7.50
186 Groh, Heine	8.50	6.50	3.00
187 Kelly, George	15.00	11.00	5.00
188 I. Meusel	8.50	6.50	3.00
189 Nehf, Art	8.50	6.50	3.00
190 Rawlings, John	8.50	6.50	3.00
191 Shinners, Ralph	8.50	6.50	3.00
192 Earl Smith	8.50	6.50	3.00
193 Snyder	8.50	6.50	3.00
194 Toney, Fred	8.50	6.50	3.00
195 Young, Pep	8.50	6.50	3.00
196 Betts, Walter	8.50	6.50	3.00
197 Fletcher	8.50	6.50	3.00
198 Henline, Walter	8.50	6.50	3.00
199 Hubbell, Carl	20.00	15.00	6.50
200 King, Lee	8.50	6.50	3.00
201 Leslie, Roy	8.50	6.50	3.00
202 Meadows, Henry	8.50	6.50	3.00
203 Parkinson, Frank	8.50	6.50	3.00
204 Peters	8.50	6.50	3.00
205 Rapp, Joseph	8.50	6.50	3.00
206 Ring, James	8.50	6.50	3.00
207 Snover, Colonel	8.50	6.50	3.00
208 Walker	8.50	6.50	3.00
209 C. Williams	8.50	6.50	3.00
210 Wrightstone, Russell	8.50	6.50	3.00
211 Adams, Babe	8.50	6.50	3.00
212 Barnhart, Clyde	8.50	6.50	3.00
213 Bigbee, Carlson	8.50	6.50	3.00
214 Carey, Max	15.00	11.00	5.00
215 Cooper, Wilbur	8.50	6.50	3.00
216 Glazner, Charles	8.50	6.50	3.00
217 Gooch	8.50	6.50	3.00
218 Grimm, Charlie	10.00	7.00	3.00
219 Hamilton, Earl	8.50	6.50	3.00
220 Maranville, Rabbit	14.00	10.50	4.75
221 Moran	8.50	6.50	3.00
222 Morrison, John	8.50	6.50	3.00
223 Schmidt, Walter	8.50	6.50	3.00
224 Tierney, James	8.50	6.50	3.00
225 Traynor, Pie	20.00	15.00	6.50
226 Ainsmith, Edward	8.50	6.50	3.00
227 Clemons	8.50	6.50	3.00
228 Doak, William	8.50	6.50	3.00
229 Fournier, John	8.50	6.50	3.00
230 Haines, Jesse	14.00	10.50	4.75
231 Heathcoate, Cliff	8.50	6.50	3.00
232 Hornsby, Rogers	50.00	38.00	17.00
233 Lavan, John	8.50	6.50	3.00
234 McHenry, Austin	8.50	6.50	3.00
235 Pertice	8.50	6.50	3.00
236 Schultz, Joe	8.50	6.50	3.00
237 Sherdel, William	8.50	6.50	3.00
238 J. Smith, Jack	8.50	6.50	3.00
239 Stock, Milt	8.50	6.50	3.00
240 Torporcer, George	8.50	6.50	3.00

99

E121 BASE BALL STARS (?) "SERIES OF 80"

2" X 3 1/2"

HUGH JENNINGS
Ass't Mgr.—New York Nationals

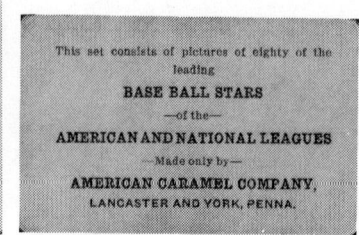

This set consists of pictures of eighty of the leading
BASE BALL STARS
—of the—
AMERICAN AND NATIONAL LEAGUES
—Made only by—
AMERICAN CARAMEL COMPANY,
LANCASTER AND YORK, PENNA.

The E121 sets contain many errors, misspellings and minor variations in titles and photos, which accounts for the difficulty in collecting the "entire" set. Many photos were taken from E135 and a fine screen is apparent on the cards. The American Caramel Co. marketed this black & white issue about 1922. Many localized advertising reverses have been found, and these cards more properly belong to the "W" classification than to E121.

	MINT	VG-E	F-G
COMPLETE SET	1400.00	1000.00	400.00
COMMON PLAYER	7.25	5.50	2.50
1 Grover C. Alexander (2)	25.00	18.00	8.00
2 Jim Bagby	7.25	5.50	2.50
3A Frank Baker	16.00	12.00	5.50
3B J. Franklin Baker	16.00	12.00	5.50
4A Dave Bancroft-dark cap	16.00	12.00	5.50
4B Dave Bancroft-light cap	16.00	12.00	5.00
5 Ping Bodie	7.25	5.50	2.50
6 George Burns	7.25	5.50	2.50
7 George J. Burns	7.25	5.50	2.50
8 Owen "Donie" Bush	7.25	5.50	2.50
9A Max Carey(ready to swing)	16.00	12.00	5.50
9B Max Carey(hands on hips)	16.00	12.00	5.50
10 Cecil Causey	7.25	5.50	2.50
11A Ty Cobb(catcher mitt, manager)	100.00	70.00	30.00
11B Ty Cobb(catcher mitt, Mgr.)	100.00	70.00	30.00
11C Ty Cobb(fielder mitt, Mgr.)	100.00	70.00	30.00
12 Eddie Collins	12.50	9.00	4.00
13 "Rip" Collins	7.25	5.50	2.50
14 Jake Daubert	7.25	5.50	2.50
15 George Dauss	7.25	5.50	2.50
16A Charles Deal(dark unf.)	10.00	7.00	3.00
16B Charles Deal(light unf.)	10.00	7.00	3.00
17 William Doak	7.25	5.50	2.50
18 Wild Bill Donovan	7.25	5.50	2.50
19A Johnny Evers(manager)	16.00	12.00	5.50
19B Johnny Evers(Mgr.)	16.00	12.00	5.50
20A Red Faber(dark unf.)	16.00	12.00	5.50
20B Red Faber(light unf.)	16.00	12.00	5.50
21 Eddie Foster	7.25	5.50	2.50
22 Frisch Frisch	15.00	11.00	5.00
23 W. L. Gardner	7.25	5.50	2.50
24 Kid Gleason	7.25	5.50	2.50
25 Mike Gonzales	7.25	5.50	2.50
26 Hank Gowdy	7.25	5.50	2.50
27 Jack Graney	7.25	5.50	2.50
28 Tom Griffith	7.25	5.50	2.50
29 Heine Groh	7.25	5.50	2.50
30 Harry Heilman	15.00	11.00	5.00
31 Walter Holke	7.25	5.50	2.50
32 Charlie Hollocher	7.25	5.50	2.50
33 Harry Hooper	12.50	9.00	4.00
34 Rogers Hornsby	40.00	30.00	13.00
35 Miller Huggins	12.50	9.00	4.00
36 Wm. C. Jacobson	7.25	5.50	2.50
37 Hugh Jennings	12.50	9.00	4.00
38A Walter Johnson(arms at chest)	50.00	38.00	17.00
38B Walter Johnson(throwing following thru)	50.00	38.00	17.00
39 James Johnston	7.25	5.50	2.50
40 Joe Judge	7.25	5.50	2.50
41 George Kelly	12.50	9.00	4.00
42 Dickie Kerr	7.25	5.50	2.50
43 P. J. Kilduff	7.25	5.50	2.50
44A Wm. Killefer	10.00	7.00	3.00
44B Wm. Killifer(sic)	10.00	7.00	3.00
45 John Lavan	7.25	5.50	2.50
46 Nemo Leibold	7.25	5.50	2.50
47 Duffy Lewis	7.25	5.50	2.50
48 Al Mamaux	7.25	5.50	2.50
49 Rabbit Maranville	12.50	9.00	4.00
50A Carl May(sic)	10.00	7.00	3.00
50B Carl Mays	10.00	7.00	3.00

	MINT	VG-E	F-G
51 John McGraw	16.00	12.00	5.50
52 Jack McInnis	7.25	5.50	2.50
53 Michael McNally	7.25	5.50	2.50
54 Bob Meusel	7.25	5.50	2.50
55 Irish Meusel	7.25	5.50	2.50
56 Clyde Milan	7.25	5.50	2.50
57 Elmer Miller	7.25	5.50	2.50
58 Otto Miller	7.25	5.50	2.50
59 Guy Morton	7.25	5.50	2.50
60 Eddie Murphy	7.25	5.50	2.50
61 Hy Myers	7.25	5.50	2.50
62 Art Nehf	7.25	5.50	2.50
63 Steve O'Neill	7.25	5.50	2.50
64A Roger Peckinbaugh(sic)	12.00	8.75	4.00
64B Roger Peckinbaugh	12.00	8.75	4.00
65 Percy	7.25	5.50	2.50
66 Jeff Pfeffer(Brooklyn)	7.25	5.50	2.50
67 Jeff Pfeffer(Cards)	7.25	5.50	2.50
68 Wally Pipp	10.00	7.00	3.00
69 Jack Quinn	7.25	5.50	2.50
70 John Rawlings	7.25	5.50	2.50
71 Sam Rice	12.50	9.00	4.00
72 Eppa Rixey	12.50	9.00	4.00
73 Bob Roth	7.25	5.50	2.50
74A Ed Rousch(LF)	16.00	12.00	5.00
74B Ed Rousch(CF)	16.00	12.00	5.00
75A Babe Ruth	125.00	90.00	40.00
75B "Babe" Ruth	125.00	90.00	40.00
75C George Ruth	125.00	90.00	40.00
76 "Bill" Ryan	7.25	5.50	2.50
77 Slim Sallee (2)	10.00	7.00	3.00
78 Ray Schalk	12.50	9.00	4.00
79 Wallie Schang	7.25	5.50	2.50
80A Ferd Schupp	10.00	7.00	3.00
80B Fred Schupp	10.00	7.00	3.00
81 Everett Scott	7.25	5.50	2.50
82 Hank Severeid	7.25	5.50	2.50
83 Bob Shawkey	7.25	5.50	2.50
84A Pat Shea	10.00	7.00	3.00
84B "Pat" Shea	10.00	7.00	3.00
85 George Sisler	16.00	12.00	5.50
86 J. Carlisle Smith	7.25	5.50	2.50
87 Frank Snyder	7.25	5.50	2.50
88A Tris Speaker(manager)	25.00	18.50	8.75
88B Tris Speaker(Mgr.)	25.00	18.50	8.75
89 Milt Stock	7.25	5.50	2.50
90 Amos Strunk	7.25	5.50	2.50
91 Zeb Terry	7.25	5.50	2.50
92 Chester Thomas	7.25	5.50	2.50
93A Fred Toney(throwing left foot up)	10.00	7.00	3.00
93B Fred Toney(side view)	10.00	7.00	3.00
94 George Tyler	7.25	5.50	2.50
95A Jim Vaughn(stripe unf.)	10.00	7.00	3.00
95B Jim Vaughn(plain unf.)	10.00	7.00	3.00
96 Bob Veach	7.25	5.50	2.50
97 Oscar Vitt	7.25	5.50	2.50
98 Bill Wambsganss	7.25	5.50	2.50
99 Aaron Ward	7.25	5.50	2.50
100 Zach Wheat	12.50	9.00	4.00
101 George Whitted	7.25	5.50	2.50
102 Fred Williams	7.25	5.50	2.50
103 Ivy Wingo	7.25	5.50	2.50
104 Joe Wood	10.00	7.00	3.00
105 Pep Young	7.25	5.50	2.50

E121 BASE BALL STARS (?)
"SERIES OF 120"

"BULLET JOE" BUSH
P.- New York Americans

This set consists of pictures of 120 of the leading

BASE BALL STARS

—of the—

AMERICAN AND NATIONAL LEAGUES

—Made only by—

AMERICAN CARAMEL COMPANY,

LANCASTER AND YORK, PENNA.

Many of the photos which appear in the "Series of 80" are duplicated in the so-called "Series of 120." As noted above, the variations in titling and photos have run the known number of cards past the original statement of length, and collectors should expect to encounter additions to both E121 lists in the future.

	MINT	VG-E	F-G
COMPLETE SET	1600.00	1250.00	550.00
COMMON PLAYER	7.25	5.50	2.50
1 Babe Adams	7.25	5.50	2.50
2 Grover C. Alexander	20.00	15.00	6.50
3 Jim Bagby	7.25	5.50	2.50
4 Dave Bancroft	12.50	9.00	4.00
5 Ty Barber	7.25	5.50	2.50
6A Carlson Bigbee	9.00	6.75	3.00
6B Carlson L. Bigbee	9.00	6.75	3.00
6C Bigbee, Corson L.	9.00	6.75	3.00
6D Bigbee, L.	9.00	6.75	3.00
7 Owen "Donie" Bush	7.25	5.50	2.50
8 Max Carey	12.50	9.00	4.00
9A Ty Cobb(batting)	100.00	70.00	30.00
9B Ty Cobb(throwing)	100.00	70.00	30.00
10 Eddie Collins	12.50	9.00	4.00
11 Wilbur Cooper	7.25	5.50	2.50
12 Stan Coveleskie	12.50	9.00	4.00
13 Dave Danforth	7.25	5.50	2.50
14 George Davis	7.25	5.50	2.50
15 "Dixie" Davis	7.25	5.50	2.50
16 Lou DeVormer	7.25	5.50	2.50
17 William Doak	7.25	5.50	2.50
18 Phil Douglas	7.25	5.50	2.50
19 Urban Faber	12.50	9.00	4.00
20 Bibb Falk	7.25	5.50	2.50
21 Wm. Fewster	7.25	5.50	2.50
22 Max Flack	7.25	5.50	2.50
23 Ira Flagstead	7.25	5.50	2.50
24 Eddie Foster	7.25	5.50	2.50
25 Frank Frisch	16.00	12.00	5.50
26 Larry Gardner	7.25	5.50	2.50
27 Alexander Gaston	7.25	5.50	2.50
28 Ed Gharrity	7.25	5.50	2.50
29 George Gibson	7.25	5.50	2.50
30 Charles Glazner	7.25	5.50	2.50
31 Kid Gleason	7.25	5.50	2.50
32 Hank Gowdy	7.25	5.50	2.50
33 John Graney	7.25	5.50	2.50
34 Tom Griffith	7.25	5.50	2.50
35 Charlie Grimm	8.00	6.00	2.50
36 Heine Groh	7.25	5.50	2.50
37 Jesse Haines	12.50	9.00	4.00
38 Harry Harper	7.25	5.50	2.50
39A Harry Heilman(sic)	16.00	12.00	5.50
39B Harry Heilmann	16.00	12.00	5.50
40 Clarence Hodge	7.25	5.50	2.50
41 Walter Holke	7.25	5.50	2.50
42 Charlie Hollocher	7.25	5.50	2.50
43 Harry Hooper	12.50	9.00	4.00
44 Rogers Hornsby	40.00	30.00	13.00
45 Waite Hoyt	12.50	9.00	4.00
46 Miller Huggins	12.50	9.00	4.00
47 Walter Johnson	50.00	38.00	17.00
48 Joe Judge	7.25	5.50	2.50
49 George Kelly	12.50	9.00	4.00
50 Dickie Kerr	7.25	5.50	2.50
51 P. J. Kilduff	7.25	5.50	2.50
52A Bill Killefer	10.00	7.00	3.00
52B Bill Killifer(sic)	10.00	7.00	3.00
53 John Lavan	7.25	5.50	2.50
54 Mails	7.25	5.50	2.50
55 Rabbit Maranville	12.50	9.00	4.00
56 Elwood Martin	7.25	5.50	2.50
57 Carl Mays	7.25	5.50	2.50
59 John McGraw	16.00	12.00	5.50
60 Jack McInnes	7.25	5.50	2.50
61 Bob Meusel	7.25	5.50	2.50
62 Irish Meusel	7.25	5.50	2.50
63 Clyde Milan	7.25	5.50	2.50

	MINT	VG-E	F-G
64 Elmer Miller	7.25	5.50	2.50
65 Otto Miller	7.25	5.50	2.50
66 Johnny Mostil	7.25	5.50	2.50
67 Eddie Mulligan	7.25	5.50	2.50
68A Hy Myers	10.00	7.00	3.00
68B "Hy" Myers	10.00	7.00	3.00
69 A. E. Neale	7.25	5.50	2.50
70 Art Nehf	7.25	5.50	2.50
71 Les Nunamaker	7.25	5.50	2.50
72 Joe Oeschger	7.25	5.50	2.50
73 Steve O'Neill	7.25	5.50	2.50
74 Wally Pipp	10.00	7.00	3.00
75 Derril Pratt	7.25	5.50	2.50
76A John Rawlings(2B)	10.00	7.00	3.00
76B John Rawlings(Util.)	10.00	7.00	3.00
77 Sam Rice	12.50	9.00	4.00
78 Eppa Rixey	12.50	9.00	4.00
79 Wilbert Robinson	12.50	9.00	4.00
80 Rogers	7.25	5.50	2.50
81A Ed Rommel	10.00	7.00	3.00
81B Ed Rounnel	20.00	15.00	6.50
82 Ed Rousch	12.50	9.00	4.00
83 Muddy Ruel	7.25	5.50	2.50
84 Walter Ruether	7.25	5.50	2.50
85A Babe Ruth(3 photos)	125.00	90.00	40.00
85B "Babe" Ruth(3 photos)	125.00	90.00	40.00
85C Babe Ruth(bird)	125.00	90.00	40.00
85D "Babe" Ruth(bird)	125.00	90.00	40.00
85E "Babe" Ruth(ball)	125.00	90.00	40.0C
86 Bill Ryan	7.25	5.50	2.50
87A Ray Schalk(bunting)	16.00	12.00	5.50
87B Ray Schalk(catching)	16.00	12.00	5.50
88 Walter Schang	7.25	5.50	2.50
89 Fred Schupp	7.25	5.50	2.50
90 Everett Scott	7.25	5.50	2.50
91 Joe Sewell	12.50	9.00	4.00
92 Bob Shawkey	7.25	5.50	2.50
93 Pat Shea	7.25	5.50	2.50
94 Earl Sheely	7.25	5.50	2.50
95 Urban Shocker	7.25	5.50	2.50
96A George Sisler(batting)	18.00	13.50	6.00
96B George Sisler(throw.)	18.00	13.50	6.00
97 Elmer Smith	7.25	5.50	2.50
98 J. Carlisle Smith	7.25	5.50	2.50
99 Frank Snyder	7.25	5.50	2.50
100 Bill Southworth	7.25	5.50	2.50
101 Tris Speaker(2)	25.00	18.50	8.75
102A Milton Stock	10.00	7.00	3.00
102B Milton J. Stock	10.00	7.00	3.00
103A Amos Strunk (CF)	10.00	7.00	3.00
103B Amos Strunk(OF)	10.00	7.00	3.00
104 Zeb Terry	7.25	5.50	2.50
105 Fred Toney	7.25	5.50	2.50
106 Specs Toporcer	7.25	5.50	2.50
107 Bob Veach	7.25	5.50	2.50
108 Oscar Vitt	7.25	5.50	2.50
109 Curtis Walker	7.25	5.50	2.50
110 Bill Wambsganss	7.25	5.50	2.50
111 Aaron Ward	7.25	5.50	2.50
112 Zach Wheat	12.50	9.00	4.00
113A George Whitted(Brk.)	10.00	7.00	3.00
113B George Whitted(Pitt.)	10.00	7.00	3.00
114 Fred Williams	7.25	5.50	2.50
115 Ivy Wingo	7.25	5.50	2.50
116 Pep Young	7.25	5.50	2.50

E135 BASEBALL'S HALL OF FAME (200)   2" X 3 1/4"

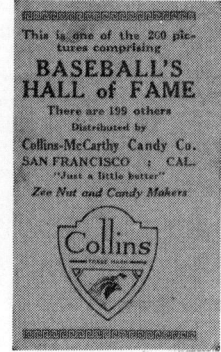

Collins-McCarthy, the West Coast manufacturer of Zee Nuts (E137), issued the Baseball's Hall of Fame set of 200 players in 1916. These black & white photos of current players were not only numbered but also listed alphabetically. The set is similar to D328, except that E135 is printed on thinner stock.

	MINT	VG-E	F-G
COMPLETE SET	2900.00	2200.00	900.00
COMMON PLAYER	13.00	10.00	4.00

#	Player	MINT	VG-E	F-G
1	Sam Agnew	13.00	10.00	4.00
2	Grover Alexander	25.00	18.50	3.75
3	W. E. Alexander	13.00	10.00	4.00
4	Leon Ames	13.00	10.00	4.00
5	Fred Anderson	13.00	10.00	4.00
6	Ed Appleton	13.00	10.00	4.00
7	Jimmy Archer	13.00	10.00	4.00
8	Jimmy Austin	13.00	10.00	4.00
9	Jim Bagby	13.00	10.00	4.00
10	H. D. Baird	13.00	10.00	4.00
11	J. Franklin Baker	20.00	15.00	6.50
12	Dave Bancroft	20.00	15.00	6.50
13	Jack Barry	13.00	10.00	4.00
14	Joe Benz	13.00	10.00	4.00
15	Al Betzel	13.00	10.00	4.00
16	Ping Bodie	13.00	10.00	4.00
17	Joe Boehling	13.00	10.00	4.00
18	Eddie Burns	13.00	10.00	4.00
19	George Burns(Detroit)	13.00	10.00	4.00
20	Geo. J. Burns(N.Y.)	13.00	10.00	4.00
21	Joe Bush	13.00	10.00	4.00
22	Owen Bush	13.00	10.00	4.00
23	Bobbie Byrne	13.00	10.00	4.00
24	Forrest Cady	13.00	10.00	4.00
25	Max Carey	20.00	15.00	6.50
26	Ray Chapman	13.00	10.00	4.00
27	Larry Cheney	13.00	10.00	4.00
28	Eddie Cicotte	13.00	10.00	4.00
29	Tom Clarke	13.00	10.00	4.00
30	Ty Cobb	100.00	70.00	30.00
31	Eddie Collins	20.00	15.00	6.50
32	"Shauno" Collins	13.00	10.00	4.00
33	Fred Coumbe	13.00	10.00	4.00
34	Harry Coveleskie	13.00	10.00	4.00
35	Gavvy Cravath	13.00	10.00	4.00
36	Sam Crawford	20.00	15.00	6.50
37	Geo. Cutshaw	13.00	10.00	4.00
38	Jack Daubert	13.00	10.00	4.00
39	Geo. Dauss	13.00	10.00	4.00
40	Charles Deal	13.00	10.00	4.00
41	Wheezer Dell	13.00	10.00	4.00
42	William Doak	13.00	10.00	4.00
43	Bill Donovan	13.00	10.00	4.00
44	Larry Doyle	13.00	10.00	4.00
45	Johnny Evers	20.00	15.00	6.50
46	Urban Faber	20.00	15.00	6.50
47	Hap Felsch	13.00	10.00	4.00
48	Bill Fischer	13.00	10.00	4.00
49	Ray Fisher	13.00	10.00	4.00
50	Art Fletcher	13.00	10.00	4.00
51	Eddie Foster	13.00	10.00	4.00
52	Jacques Fournier	13.00	10.00	4.00
53	Del Gainer	13.00	10.00	4.00
54	Bert Gallia	13.00	10.00	4.00
55	Chic Gandil	13.00	10.00	4.00
56	Larry Gardner	13.00	10.00	4.00
57	Joe Gedeon	13.00	10.00	4.00
58	Gus Getz	13.00	10.00	4.00
59	Frank Gilhooley	13.00	10.00	4.00
60	Wm. Gleason	13.00	10.00	4.00

#	Player	MINT	VG-E	F-G
61	M. A. Gonzales	13.00	10.00	4.00
62	Hank Gowdy	13.00	10.00	4.00
63	John Graney	13.00	10.00	4.00
64	Tom Griffith	13.00	10.00	4.00
65	Heinie Groh	13.00	10.00	4.00
66	Bob Groom	13.00	10.00	4.00
67	Louis Guisto	13.00	10.00	4.00
78	Earl Hamilton	13.00	10.00	4.00
69	Harry Harper	13.00	10.00	4.00
70	Grover Hartley	13.00	10.00	4.00
71	Harry Heilmann	20.00	15.00	6.50
72	Claude Hendrix	13.00	10.00	4.00
73	Olaf Henriksen	13.00	10.00	4.00
74	John Henry	13.00	10.00	4.00
75	Buck Herzog	13.00	10.00	4.00
76	Hugh High	13.00	10.00	4.00
77	Dick Hublitzell	13.00	10.00	4.00
78	Walter Holke	13.00	10.00	4.00
79	Harry Hooper	20.00	15.00	6.50
80	Rogers Hornsby	40.00	30.00	13.00
81	Ivan Howard	13.00	10.00	4.00
82	Joe Jackson	50.00	38.00	17.00
83	Harold Janvrin	13.00	10.00	4.00
84	William James	13.00	10.00	4.00
85	C. Jamieson	13.00	10.00	4.00
86	Hugh Jennings	20.00	15.00	6.50
87	Walter Johnson	60.00	45.00	20.00
88	James Johnston	13.00	10.00	4.00
89	Fielder Jones	13.00	10.00	4.00
90	Joe Judge	13.00	10.00	4.00
91	Hans Lobert	13.00	10.00	4.00
92	Benny Kauff	13.00	10.00	4.00
93	Wm. Killefer, Jr.	13.00	10.00	4.00
94	Ed Konetchy	13.00	10.00	4.00
95	John Lavan	13.00	10.00	4.00
96	Jimmy Lavender	13.00	10.00	4.00
97	Nemo Leibold	13.00	10.00	4.00
98	H. B. Leonard	13.00	10.00	4.00
99	Duffy Lewis	13.00	10.00	4.00
100	Tom Long	13.00	10.00	4.00
101	Wm. Louden	13.00	10.00	4.00
102	Fred Luderus	13.00	10.00	4.00
103	Lee Magee	13.00	10.00	4.00
104	Sherwood Magee	13.00	10.00	4.00
105	Al Mamaux	13.00	10.00	4.00
106	Leslie Mann	13.00	10.00	4.00
107	Rabbit Maranville	20.00	15.00	6.50
108	Rube Marquard	20.00	15.00	6.50
109	Armando Marsans	13.00	10.00	4.00
110	J. Erskine Mayer	13.00	10.00	4.00
111	George McBride	13.00	10.00	4.00
112	Lew McCarty	13.00	10.00	4.00
113	John J. McGraw	25.00	18.50	8.75
114	Jack McInnis	13.00	10.00	4.00
115	Lee Meadows	13.00	10.00	4.00
116	Fred Merkle	13.00	10.00	4.00
117	Chief Meyers	13.00	10.00	4.00
118	Clyde Milan	13.00	10.00	4.00
119	Otto Miller	13.00	10.00	4.00
120	Clarence Mitchell	13.00	10.00	4.00

	MINT	VG-E	F-G
121 Ray Morgan	13.00	10.00	4.00
122 Guy Morton	13.00	10.00	4.00
123 Mike Mowrey	13.00	10.00	4.00
124 Elmer Myers	13.00	10.00	4.00
125 Hy Myers	13.00	10.00	4.00
126 A. E. Neale	13.00	10.00	4.00
127 Arthur Nehf	13.00	10.00	4.00
128 J. A. Niehoff	13.00	10.00	4.00
129 Steve O'Neill	13.00	10.00	4.00
130 Dode Paskert	13.00	10.00	4.00
131 R. Peckinpaugh	13.00	10.00	4.00
132 Pol Perritt	13.00	10.00	4.00
133 Jeff Pfeffer	13.00	10.00	4.00
134 Walter Pipp	15.00	11.00	5.00
135 Derril Pratt	13.00	10.00	4.00
136 Bill Rariden	13.00	10.00	4.00
137 E. C. Rice	20.00	15.00	6.50
138 Wm. A. Ritter	13.00	10.00	4.00
139 Eppa Rixey, Jr.	20.00	15.00	6.50
140 Davey Robertson	13.00	10.00	4.00
141 Bob Roth	13.00	10.00	4.00
142 Ed Roush	20.00	15.00	6.50
143 Calrence Rowland	13.00	10.00	4.00
144 Dick Rudolph	13.00	10.00	4.00
145 William Rumler	13.00	10.00	4.00
146 Reb Russell	13.00	10.00	4.00
147 Babe Ruth	150.00	110.00	50.00
148 Vic Saier	13.00	10.00	4.00
149 Slim Sallee	13.00	10.00	4.00
150 Ray Schalk	20.00	15.00	6.50
151 Walter Schang	13.00	10.00	4.00
152 Frank Schulte	13.00	10.00	4.00
153 Ferd Schupp	13.00	10.00	4.00
154 Everett Scott	13.00	10.00	4.00
155 Hank Severeid	13.00	10.00	4.00
156 Howard Shanks	13.00	10.00	4.00
157 Bob Shawkey	13.00	10.00	4.00
158 Jas. Sheckard	13.00	10.00	4.00
159 Ernie Shore	13.00	13.00	4.00
160 C. H. Shorten	13.00	10.00	4.00
161 Burt Shotton	13.00	10.00	4.00
162 Geo. Sisler	20.00	15.00	6.50
163 Elmer Smith	13.00	10.00	4.00
164 J. Carlisle Smith	13.00	10.00	4.00
165 Fred Snodgrass	13.00	10.00	4.00
166 Tris Speaker	25.00	18.50	8.75
167 Oscar Stanage	13.03	10.00	4.00
168 Charles Stengel	30.00	22.50	10.50
169 Milton Stock	13.00	10.00	4.00
170 Amos Strunk	13.00	10.00	4.00
171 Zeb Terry	13.00	10.00	4.00
172 Jeff Tesreau	13.00	10.00	4.00
173 Chester Thomas	13.00	10.00	4.00
174 Fred Toney	13.00	10.00	4.00
175 Terry Turner	13.00	10.00	4.00
176 George Tyler	13.00	10.00	4.00
177 Jim Vaughn	13.00	10.00	4.00
178 Bob Veach	13.00	10.00	4.00
179 Oscar Vitt	13.00	10.00	4.00
180 Hans Wagner	50.00	38.00	17.00
181 Clarence Walker	13.00	10.00	4.00
182 Jim Walsh	13.00	10.00	4.00
183 Al Walters	13.00	10.00	4.00
184 W. Wambsganss	13.00	10.00	4.00
185 Buck Weaver	13.00	10.00	4.00
186 Carl Weilman	13.00	10.00	4.00
187 Zack Wheat	20.00	15.00	6.50
188 Geo. Whitted	13.00	10.00	4.00
189 Joe Wilhoit	13.00	10.00	4.00
190 Claude Williams(2)	13.00	10.00	4.00
191 Fred Williams	13.00	10.00	4.00
192 Art Wilson	13.00	10.00	4.00
193 Lawton Witt	13.00	10.00	4.00
194 Joe Wood	15.00	11.00	5.00
195 William Wortman	13.00	10.00	4.00
196 Steve Yerkes	13.00	10.00	4.00
197 Earl Yingling	13.00	10.00	4.00
198 Pep Young	13.00	10.00	4.00
199 Rollie Zeider	13.00	10.00	4.00
200 Heine Zimmerman	13.00	10.00	4.00

WHEATIES BOX

1941 — How Ted Hit .400

BASEBALL'S GREATEST
Ted Williams

#17

COLLECT
ALL 80

One week before the 1941 season ended, Ted was batting .406. The Yankees had clinched the pennant and the Red Sox were assured second place. Manager Joe Cronin told the "Splendid Splinter" to sit out the remaining games to protect his .406 mark. But Ted insisted on playing every day. His average slipped to .399 on the next to the last day of the season. Ted singled the first time up against the Philadelphia A's on the last day to go over .400 again. Instead of retiring from the game to protect his average, Ted played the entire double header and banged out 6 hits in 8 at bats.

The youthful Williams as he looked in 1941.

The 1959 Fleer set, also known as the Ted Williams set, portrays the life of Ted Williams. Card no. 68 is relatively scarce.

	MINT	VG-E	F-G
COMPLETE SET	75.00	60.00	24.00
COMMON CARDS	.35	.26	.11
1 The Early Years	.35	.26	.11
2 Ted's Idol - Babe Ruth	1.00	.70	.30
3 Practice Makes Perfect	.35	.26	.11
4 Learns Fine Points	.35	.26	.11
5 Ted's Fame Spreads	.35	.26	.11
6 Ted Turns Pro	.35	.26	.11
7 From Mound to Plate	.35	.26	.11
8 1937-First Full Season	.35	.26	.11
9 First Step to Majors	.35	.26	.11
10 Gunning as Pasttime	.35	.26	.11
11 First Spring Training	.35	.26	.11
12 Burning Up Minors	.35	.26	.11
13 1939-Shows Will Stay	.35	.26	.11
14 Outstanding Rookie 1939	.35	.26	.11
15 Licks Sophomore Jinx	.35	.26	.11
16 1941-Greatest Year	.35	.26	.11
17 How Ted Hit .400	.35	.26	.11
18 1941-All Star Hero	.35	.26	.11
19 Ted Wins Triple Crown	.35	.26	.11
20 On to Naval Training	.35	.26	.11
21 Honors for Williams	.35	.26	.11
22 1944-Ted Solos	.35	.26	.11
23 Williams Wins Wings	.35	.26	.11
24 1945-Sharpshooter	.35	.26	.11
25 1945-Ted Discharged	.35	.26	.11
26 Off to Flying Start	.35	.26	.11
27 July 9, 1946-One Man Show	.35	.26	.11
28 The Williams Shift	.35	.26	.11
29 Ted Hits for Cycle	.35	.26	.11
30 Beating Williams Shift	.35	.26	.11
31 Sox Lose Series	.35	.26	.11
32 Most Valuable Player	.35	.26	.11
33 Another Triple Crown	.35	.26	.11
34 Runs-Scored Record	.35	.26	.11
35 Sox Miss Pennant	.35	.26	.11
36 Banner Year for Ted	.35	.26	.11
37 1949-Sox Miss Again	.35	.26	.11
38 1949-Power Rampage	.35	.26	.11

	MINT	VG-E	F-G
39 1950-Great Start	.35	.26	.11
40 Ted Crashes into Wall	.35	.26	.11
41 1950-Ted Recovers	.35	.26	.11
42 Slowed by Injury	.35	.26	.11
43 Double Play Lead	.35	.26	.11
44 Back to Marines	.35	.26	.11
45 Farewell to Baseball?	.35	.26	.11
46 Ready for Combat	.35	.26	.11
47 Ted Crash Lands Jet	.35	.26	.11
48 1953-Ted Returns	.35	.26	.11
49 Smash Return	.35	.26	.11
50 1954-Spring Injury	.35	.26	.11
51 Ted is Patched Up	.35	.26	.11
52 1954-Ted's Comeback	.35	.26	.11
53 Comeback is Success	.35	.26	.11
54 Ted Hooks Big One	.35	.26	.11
55 Retirement "No Go"	.35	.26	.11
56 2,000th Hit	.35	.26	.11
57 400th Homer	.35	.26	.11
58 Williams Hits .388	.35	.26	.11
59 Hot September for Ted	.35	.26	.11
60 More Records for Ted	.35	.26	.11
61 1957-Outfielder Ted	.35	.26	.11
62 1958-6th Batting Title	.35	.26	.11
63 Ted's All-Star Record	.35	.26	.11
64 Daughter and Daddy	.35	.26	.11
65 August 30, 1958	.35	.26	.11
66 1958 Powerhouse	.35	.26	.11
67 Two Famous Fishermen	.35	.26	.11
68 Ted Signs for 1959	50.00	40.00	16.00
69 A Future Ted Williams?	.35	.26	.11
70 Williams and Thorpe	.60	.50	.20
71 Hitting Fund #1	.35	.26	.11
72 Hitting Fund #2	.35	.26	.11
73 Hitting Fund #3	.35	.26	.11
74 Here's How!	.35	.26	.11
75 Williams' Value to Sox	.35	.26	.11
76 "On Base" Record	.35	.26	.11
77 Ted Relaxes	.35	.26	.11
78 Honors for Williams	.35	.26	.11
79 Where Ted Stands	.35	.26	.11
80 Ted's Goals for 1959	.35	.26	.11

1959 FLEER

HONUS WAGNER

The 1960 Fleer set of Baseball Greats has no known Scarcities.

#62 BASEBALL GREATS
JOHN PETER WAGNER

(Honus)—Feb. 24, 1874 to Dec. 6, 1955

Shortstop—Pgh (NL)—1900-1917, batted right

One of the greatest right-handed hitters in the game's history. Wagner batted over .300 17 seasons in a row and established lifetime National League records for times at bat, hits, singles (2426), doubles and triples. Although he won eight batting titles, he is also considered one of the finest shortstops baseball has ever produced. Wagner was elected to the Hall of Fame in 1936.

MAJOR LEAGUE TOTALS

Games	A.B.	Hits	Ave.	RBI	2B	3B	HR
2785	10,427	3430	.329	xxx	651	252	101

WORLD SERIES TOTALS

15	52	14	.269	9	3	1	0

©F. H. Fleer   Printed in U.S.A.   World Wide Photo

	MINT	VG-E	F-G
COMPLETE SET	45.00	35.00	15.00
COMMON PLAYERS	.40	.30	.12
1 Napoleon Lajoie	1.50	.75	.25
2 Christopher Mathewson	1.00	.70	.30
3 George H. Ruth	4.00	3.00	1.40
4 Carl Hubbell	.60	.45	.20
5 Grover Alexander	.70	.50	.20
6 Walter P. Johnson	1.25	.90	.40
7 Charles A. Bender	.40	.30	.12
8 Roger P. Bresnahan	.40	.30	.12
9 Mordecai P. Brown	.40	.30	.12
10 Tristram Speaker	.60	.45	.20
11 Joseph Vaughan	.40	.30	.12
12 Zachariah Wheat	.40	.30	.12
13 George Sisler	.40	.30	.12
14 Connie Mack	.60	.45	.20
15 Clark C. Griffith	.40	.30	.12
16 Louis Boudreau	.60	.45	.20
17 Ernest Lombardi	.40	.30	.12
18 Henry Manush	.40	.30	.12
19 Martin Marion	.40	.30	.12
20 Edward Collins	.40	.30	.12
21 James Maranville	.40	.30	.12
22 Joseph Medwick	.40	.30	.12
23 Edward Barrow	.40	.30	.12
24 Gordon Cochrane	.60	.45	.20
25 James J. Collins	.40	.30	.12
26 Robert Feller	1.50	.75	.25
27 Lucius Appling	.60	.45	.20
28 Lou Gehrig	3.00	2.25	1.00
29 Charles Hartnett	.40	.30	.12
30 Charles Klein	.40	.30	.12
31 Anthony Lazzeri	.40	.30	.12
32 Aloysius Simmons	.40	.30	.12
33 Wilbert Robinson	.40	.30	.12
34 Edgar Rice	.40	.30	.12
35 Herbert Pennock	.40	.30	.12
36 Melvin Ott	.70	.50	.20
37 Frank O'Doul	.40	.30	.12
38 John Mize	.50	.40	.18
39 Edmund Miller	.40	.30	.12
40 Joseph Tinker	.40	.30	.12
41 John Baker	.40	.30	.12
42 Tyrus Cobb	3.00	2.25	1.00
43 Paul Derringer	.40	.30	.12
44 Adrian Anson	.40	.30	.12
45 James Bottomley	.40	.30	.12
46 Edward S. Plank	.50	.40	.18
47 Denton Young	.50	.40	.18
48 Hack Wilson	.40	.30	.12
49 Edward Walsh	.40	.30	.12
50 Frank Chance	.50	.40	.18
51 Arthur Vance	.40	.30	.12
52 William Terry	.60	.45	.20
53 James Foxx	1.50	.75	.25
54 Vernon Gomez	.60	.45	.20
55 Branch Rickey	.40	.30	.12
56 Raymond Schalk	.40	.30	.12
57 John Evers	.40	.30	.12
58 Charles Gehringer	.60	.45	.20
59 Burleigh Grimes	.50	.40	.18
60 Robert Grove	.80	.60	.25
61 George Waddell	.40	.30	.12
62 John Wagner	1.25	.90	.40
63 Charles Ruffing	.50	.40	.18
64 Kenesaw Landis	.40	.30	.12
65 Harry Heilmann	.40	.30	.12
66 John McGraw	.50	.40	.18
67 Hugh Jennings	.40	.30	.12
68 Harold Newhouser	.40	.30	.12
69 Waite Hoyt	.50	.40	.18
70 Louis Newsom	.40	.30	.12
71 Howard Averill	.50	.40	.18
72 Theodore Williams	2.50	1.80	.80
73 Warren Giles	.40	.30	.12
74 Ford Frick	.40	.30	.12
75 Hazen Cuyler	.40	.30	.12
76 Paul Waner	.50	.40	.18
77 Harold Traynor	.50	.40	.18
78 Lloyd Waner	.50	.40	.18
79 Ralph Kiner	.50	.40	.18

1960 FLEER

1961 FLEER

1963 FLEER

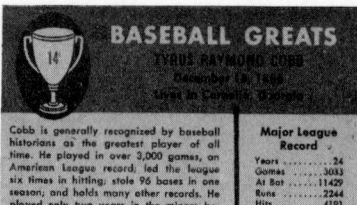

The 1961 Fleer set of Baseball Greats contains somewhat more difficult to obtain high numbers 89-154. Note the player-alphabetized card numbering, i.e. nos. 1-88 and nos. 89-154.

	MINT	VG-E	F-G			MINT	VG-E	F-G
COMPLETE SET	110.00	85.00	40.00	63 Johnny Mize		.70	.50	.20
COMMON PLAYERS (1-88)	.40	.30	.12	64 J. Mostil		.40	.30	.12
COMMON PLAYERS (89-154)	.75	.55	.25	65 A. Nehf		.40	.30	.12
				66 Hal Newhouser		.40	.30	.12
1 Baker, Cobb, Wheat	1.50	.75	.30	67 D. Newsom		.40	.30	.12
2 G. C. Alexander	.70	.50	.20	68 Mel Ott		.70	.50	.20
3 Nick Altrock	.40	.30	.12	69 Allie Reynolds		.40	.30	.12
4 Cap Anson	.40	.30	.12	70 Sam Rice		.40	.30	.12
5 Earl Averill	.50	.40	.18	71 Eppa Rixey		.40	.30	.12
6 Frank Baker	.40	.30	.12	72 Ed Roush		.40	.30	.12
7 D. Bancroft	.40	.30	.12	73 Schoolboy Rowe		.40	.30	.12
8 Chief Bender	.40	.30	.12	74 Red Ruffing		.50	.40	.18
9 Jim Bottomley	.40	.30	.12	75 Babe Ruth		4.00	3.00	1.40
10 Roger Bresnahan	.40	.30	.12	76 Joe Sewell		.40	.30	.12
11 Mordecai Brown	.40	.30	.12	77 Al Simmons		.40	.30	.12
12 Max Carey	.40	.30	.12	78 George Sisler		.40	.30	.12
13 Jack Chesbro	.40	.30	.12	79 Tris Speaker		.70	.50	.20
14 Ty Cobb	3.00	2.25	1.00	80 Fred Toney		.40	.30	.12
15 Mickey Cochrane	.50	.40	.18	81 Dazzy Vance		.40	.30	.12
16 Eddie Collins	.40	.30	.12	82 J. Vaughn		.40	.30	.12
17 Earle Combs	.40	.30	.12	83 E. Walsh		.40	.30	.12
18 Charles Comiskey	.40	.30	.12	84 Lloyd Waner		.40	.30	.12
19 Kiki Cuyler	.40	.30	.12	85 Paul Waner		.40	.30	.12
20 Paul Derringer	.40	.30	.12	86 Zack Wheat		.40	.30	.12
21 Howard Ehmke	.40	.30	.12	87 Hack Wilson		.40	.30	.12
22 W. Evans	.40	.30	.12	88 J. Wilson		.40	.30	.12
23 Johnny Evers	.40	.30	.12	89 Sisler and Traynor		1.00	.70	.30
24 Urban Faber	.40	.30	.12	90 B. Adams		.75	.55	.25
25 Bob Feller	1.50	.75	.30	91 D. Alexander		.75	.55	.25
26 W. Ferrell	.40	.30	.12	92 J. Bagby		.75	.55	.25
27 L. Fonseca	.40	.30	.12	93 O. Bluege		.75	.55	.25
28 Jimmy Foxx	1.50	.75	.30	94 Lou Boudreau		1.50	1.10	.50
29 Ford Frick	.40	.30	.12	95 Tom Bridges		.75	.55	.25
30 Frank Frisch	.50	.40	.18	96 D. Bush		.75	.55	.25
31 Lou Gehrig	3.00	2.25	1.00	97 Dolph Camilli		.75	.55	.25
32 Charlie Gehringer	.60	.45	.20	98 Frank Chance		1.00	.70	.30
33 Warren Giles	.40	.30	.12	99 J. Collins		.75	.55	.25
34 Lefty Gomez	.60	.45	.20	100 Stan Coveleskie		.75	.55	.25
35 Goose Goslin	.40	.30	.12	101 Hugh Critz		.75	.55	.25
36 Clark Griffith	.40	.30	.12	102 A. Crowder		.75	.55	.25
37 Burleigh Grimes	.50	.40	.18	103 Joe Dugan		.75	.55	.25
38 Lefty Grove	.80	.60	.25	104 B. Falk		.75	.55	.25
39 Chick Hafey	.40	.30	.12	105 R. Ferrell		.75	.55	.25
40 Jesse Haines	.40	.30	.12	106 A. Fletcher		.75	.55	.25
41 Gabby Hartnett	.40	.30	.12	107 D. Galehouse		.75	.55	.25
42 Harry Heilmann	.40	.30	.12	108 C. Galloway		.75	.55	.25
43 Rogers Hornsby	1.25	.90	.40	109 M. Haas		.75	.55	.25
44 Waite Hoyt	.50	.40	.18	110 Stan Hack		.75	.55	.25
45 Carl Hubbell	.60	.45	.20	111 B. Hadley		.75	.55	.25
46 Miller Huggins	.40	.30	.12	112 B. Hamilton		.75	.55	.25
47 Hugh Jennings	.40	.30	.12	113 J. Hauser		.75	.55	.25
48 B. Johnson	.40	.30	.12	114 Babe Herman		.75	.55	.25
49 Walter Johnson	1.25	.90	.40	115 Travis Jackson		.75	.55	.25
50 Ralph Kiner	.70	.50	.20	116 Eddie Joost		.75	.55	.25
51 Chuck Klein	.40	.30	.12	117 Addie Joss		.75	.55	.25
52 Johnny Kling	.40	.30	.12	118 Joe Judge		.75	.55	.25
53 K. M. Landis	.40	.30	.12	119 Joe Kuhel		.75	.55	.25
54 Tony Lazzeri	.40	.30	.12	120 Napoleon Lajoie		2.00	1.50	.60
55 Ernie Lombardi	.40	.30	.12	121 Dutch Leonard		.75	.55	.25
56 Dolf Luque	.40	.30	.12	122 Ted Lyons		1.00	.70	.30
57 Heine Manush	.40	.30	.12	123 Connie Mack		1.50	1.10	.50
58 Marty Marion	.40	.30	.12	124 Rabbit Maranville		.75	.55	.25
59 Christy Mathewson	1.00	.70	.30	125 Fred Marberry		.75	.55	.25
60 John McGraw	.50	.40	.18	126 Joe McGinnity		.75	.55	.25
61 Joe Medwick	.40	.30	.12	127 Oscar Melillo		.75	.55	.25
62 E. Miller	.40	.30	.12					

1961 FLEER (CONTINUED)

	MINT	VG-E	F-G			MINT	VG-E	F-G
128 Ray Mueller	.75	.55	.25	141 Billy Sullivan		.75	.55	.25
129 Kid Nichols	.75	.55	.25	142 Bill Terry		1.25	.90	.40
130 Lefty O'Doul	.75	.55	.25	143 Joe Tinker		1.00	.70	.30
131 Bob O'Farrell	.75	.55	.25	144 Pie Traynor		1.00	.70	.30
132 Roger Peckinpaugh	.75	.55	.25	145 Hal Trosky		.75	.55	.25
133 Herb Pennock	.75	.55	.25	146 George Uhle		.75	.55	.25
134 George Pipgras	.75	.55	.25	147 Johnny Vander Meer		.75	.55	.25
135 Eddie Plank	1.25	.90	.40	148 Arky Vaughan		.75	.55	.25
136 Ray Schalk	.75	.55	.25	149 Rube Waddell		.75	.55	.25
137 Hal Schumacher	.75	.55	.25	150 Honus Wagner		3.00	2.25	1.00
138 Luke Sewell	.75	.55	.25	151 Dixie Walker		.75	.55	.25
139 Bob Shawkey	.75	.55	.25	152 Ted Williams		4.00	3.00	1.40
140 Riggs Stephenson	.75	.55	.25	153 Cy Young		2.00	1.50	.60
				154 Ross Young		.75	.55	.25

1963 FLEER (66)   2 1/2" X 3 1/2"

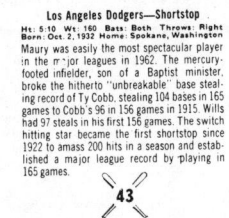

The 1963 Fleer set of current players contains an unnumbered checklist which is difficult to obtain. Card number 43 Wills and card number 46 Adcock are also difficult to obtain. The latter being the scarcest card in the set. The complete set price includes the checklist.

	MINT	VG-E	F-G			MINT	VG-E	F-G
COMPLETE SET	90.00	70.00	30.00	33 Gene Freese		.40	.30	.13
COMMON PLAYERS	.40	.30	.13	34 Vada Pinson		.80	.60	.25
				35 Bob Purkey		.40	.30	.13
1 Steve Barber	.60	.40	.15	36 Joe Amalfitano		.40	.30	.13
2 Ron Hansen	.40	.30	.13	37 Bob Aspromonte		.40	.30	.13
3 Milt Pappas	.50	.40	.18	38 Dick Farrell		.40	.30	.13
4 Brooks Robinson	4.00	3.00	1.40	39 Al Spangler		.40	.30	.13
5 Willie Mays	7.00	5.25	2.50	40 Tommy Davis		.80	.60	.25
6 Lou Clinton	.40	.30	.13	41 Don Drysdale		3.25	2.40	1.10
7 Bill Monbouquette	.40	.30	.13	42 Sandy Koufax		6.00	4.50	2.00
8 Carl Yastrzemski	6.00	4.50	2.00	43 Maury Wills		7.00	5.25	2.50
9 Ray Herbert	.40	.30	.13	44 Frank Bolling		.40	.30	.13
10 Jim Landis	.40	.30	.13	45 Warren Spahn		3.50	2.50	1.20
11 Dick Donovan	.40	.30	.13	*46 Joe Adcock*		25.00	18.50	8.75
12 Tito Francona	.40	.30	.13	47 Roger Craig		.50	.40	.18
13 Jerry Kindall	.40	.30	.13	48 Al Jackson		.40	.30	.13
14 Frank Lary	.40	.30	.13	49 Rod Kanehl		.40	.30	.13
15 Dick Howser	.50	.40	.18	50 Ruben Amaro		.40	.30	.13
16 Jerry Lumpe	.40	.30	.13	51 John Callison		.40	.30	.13
17 Norm Siebern	.40	.30	.13	52 Clay Dalrymple		.40	.30	.13
18 Don Lee	.40	.30	.13	53 Don Demeter		.40	.30	.13
19 Albie Pearson	.40	.30	.13	54 Art Mahaffey		.40	.30	.13
20 Bob Rodgers	.40	.30	.13	55 Smokey Burgess		.40	.30	.13
21 Leon Wagner	.40	.30	.13	56 Roberto Clemente		6.00	4.50	2.00
22 Jim Kaat	.80	.60	.25	57 Roy Face		.50	.40	.18
23 Vic Power	.40	.30	.13	58 Vernon Law		.50	.40	.18
24 Rich Rollins	.40	.30	.13	59 Bill Mazeroski		.60	.45	.20
25 Bobby Richardson	.80	.60	.25	60 Ken Boyer		.80	.60	.25
26 Ralph Terry	.40	.30	.13	61 Bob Gibson		2.50	1.80	.80
27 Tom Cheney	.40	.30	.13	62 Gene Oliver		.40	.30	.13
28 Chuck Cottier	.40	.30	.13	63 Bill White		.40	.30	.13
29 Jim Piersall	.80	.60	.25	64 Orlando Cepeda		1.00	.70	.30
30 Dave Stenhouse	.40	.30	.13	65 Jim Davenport		.40	.30	.13
31 Glen Hobbie	.40	.30	.13	66 Bill O'Dell		.40	.30	.13
32 Ron Santo	.80	.60	.25	*Checklist*		20.00	14.00	6.00

Attend a Sports Memorabilia Show or Convention in your area sometime this year. They are both interesting and enjoyable to all members of the family.

This issue of 660 cards marks Fleer's first entry into the current-player baseball card market since 1963. Players from the same team are conveniently listed together by number in the set. At publica-

tion time, a number of errors have been found in the initial Fleer press run. Two poses exist for eight different players, but each of the two poses has the same number on the back, although each pose is

assigned a different num according to the Fleer ch list cards. Thus, there are different poses of Amos and both are listed on back as number 32. No n ber 483, as listed for on the poses in the check exists. Other error cards two number 5, no num 640; two number 6, no n ber 660; two number 7, number 657; two number no number 665; two num 29, no number 551; number 79, no number (two number 216, no num 202; and the numbe "Triple Threat" card sho be number 645. These other discrepancies may corrected by Fleer in a l printing.

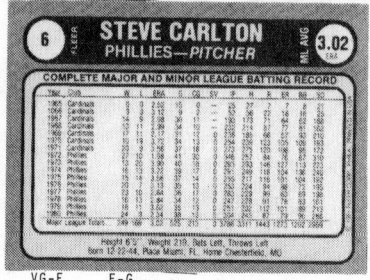

	MINT	VG-E	F-G			MINT	VG-E	F-G
COMPLETE SET	14.50	11.00	5.00	70	Rafael Landestoy	.03	.02	.01
COMMON PLAYER	.03	.02	.01	71	Dave Smith	.03	.02	.01
				72	Danny Heep	.03	.02	.01
1 Pete Rose	.30	.25	.10	73	Julio Gonzalez	.03	.02	.01
2 Larry Bowa	.10	.07	.03	74	Craig Reynolds	.03	.02	.01
3 Manny Trillo	.03	.02	.01	75	Gary Woods	.03	.02	.01
4 Bob Boone	.03	.02	.01	76	Dave Bergman	.03	.02	.01
5 Mike Schmidt	.25	.20	.08	77	Randy Niemann	.03	.02	.01
6 Steve Carlton	.20	.15	.06	78	Joe Morgan	.10	.07	.03
7 Tug McGraw	.06	.04	.02	79	Reggie Jackson	.25	.20	.08
8 Larry Christenson	.03	.02	.01	80	Bucky Dent	.06	.04	.02
9 Bake McBride	.05	.03	.01	81	Tommy John	.15	.11	.05
10 Greg Luzinski	.10	.07	.03	82	Luis Tiant	.06	.04	.02
11 Ron Reed	.03	.02	.01	83	Rick Cerone	.06	.04	.02
12 Dickie Noles	.03	.02	.01	84	Dick Howser	.03	.02	.01
13 Keith Moreland	.03	.02	.01	85	Lou Piniella	.06	.04	.02
14 Bob Walk	.03	.02	.01	86	Ron Davis	.03	.02	.01
15 Lonnie Smith	.03	.02	.01	87	Graig Nettles	.10	.07	.03
16 Dick Ruthven	.03	.02	.01	88	Ron Guidry	.20	.15	.06
17 Sparky Lyle	.06	.04	.02	89	Rich Gossage	.15	.11	.05
18 Greg Gross	.03	.02	.01	90	Rudy May	.06	.04	.02
19 Garry Maddox	.06	.04	.02	91	Gaylord Perry	.15	.11	.05
20 Nino Espinosa	.03	.02	.01	92	Eric Soderholm	.03	.02	.01
21 George Vukovich	.03	.02	.01	93	Bob Watson	.06	.04	.02
22 John Vukovich	.03	.02	.01	94	Bobby Murcer	.06	.04	.02
23 Ramon Aviles	.03	.02	.01	95	Bobby Brown	.03	.02	.01
24 Kevin Saucier	.03	.02	.01	96	Jim Spencer	.03	.02	.01
25 Randy Lerch	.03	.02	.01	97	Tom Underwood	.03	.02	.01
26 Del Unser	.03	.02	.01	98	Oscar Gamble	.06	.04	.02
27 Tim McCarver	.03	.02	.01	99	Johnny Oates	.03	.02	.01
28 George Brett	.30	.25	.10	100	Fred Stanley	.03	.02	.01
29 Willie Wilson	.15	.11	.05	101	Ruppert Jones	.03	.02	.01
30 Paul Splittorff	.03	.02	.01	102	Dennis Werth	.03	.02	.01
31 Dan Quisenberry	.06	.04	.02	103	Joe Lefebvre	.03	.02	.01
32 Amos Otis	.06	.04	.02	104	Brian Doyle	.03	.02	.01
33 Steve Busby	.03	.02	.01	105	Aurelio Rodriguez	.03	.02	.01
34 U. L. Washington	.03	.02	.01	106	Doug Bird	.03	.02	.01
35 Dave Chalk	.03	.02	.01	107	Mike Griffin	.03	.02	.01
36 Darrell Porter	.06	.04	.02	108	Tim Lollar	.03	.02	.01
37 Marty Pattin	.03	.02	.01	109	Willie Randolph	.06	.04	.02
38 Larry Gura	.06	.04	.02	110	Steve Garvey	.25	.20	.08
39 Renie Martin	.03	.02	.01	111	Reggie Smith	.15	.11	.05
40 Rich Gale	.03	.02	.01	112	Don Sutton	.15	.11	.05
41 Hal McRae	.03	.02	.01	113	Burt Hooton	.06	.04	.02
42 Dennis Leonard	.06	.04	.02	114	Davy Lopes	.06	.04	.02
43 Willie Aikens	.06	.04	.02	115	Dusty Baker	.10	.07	.03
44 Frank White	.06	.04	.02	116	Tom Lasorda	.06	.04	.02
45 Clint Hurdle	.03	.02	.01	117	Bill Russell	.03	.02	.01
46 John Wathan	.03	.02	.01	118	Jerry Reuss	.06	.04	.02
47 Pete La Cock	.03	.02	.01	119	Terry Forster	.06	.04	.02
48 Rance Mulliniks	.03	.02	.01	120	Robert Welch	.03	.02	.01
49 Jeff Twitty	.03	.02	.01	121	Don Stanhouse	.03	.02	.01
50 Jamie Quirk	.03	.02	.01	122	Rick Monday	.03	.02	.01
51 Art Howe	.03	.02	.01	123	Derrel Thomas	.03	.02	.01
52 Ken Forsch	.03	.02	.01	124	Joe Ferguson	.03	.02	.01
53 Vern Ruhle	.03	.02	.01	125	Rick Sutcliffe	.03	.02	.01
54 Joe Niekro	.05	.03	.01	126	Ron Cey	.06	.04	.02
55 Frank La Corte	.03	.02	.01	127	Dave Goltz	.03	.02	.01
56 J. R. Richard	.15	.11	.05	128	Jay Johnstone	.03	.02	.01
57 Nolan Ryan	.20	.15	.06	129	Steve Yeager	.03	.02	.01
58 Enos Cabell	.03	.02	.01	130	Gary Weiss	.03	.02	.01
59 Cesar Cedeno	.15	.11	.05	131	Mike Scioscia	.03	.02	.01
60 Jose Cruz	.06	.04	.02	132	Vic Davalillo	.03	.02	.01
61 Bill Virdon	.06	.04	.02	133	Doug Rau	.03	.02	.01
62 Terry Puhl	.06	.04	.02	134	Pepe Frias	.03	.02	.01
63 Joaquin Andujar	.03	.02	.01	135	Mickey Hatcher	.03	.02	.01
64 Alan Ashby	.03	.02	.01	136	Steve Howe	.03	.02	.01
65 Joe Sambito	.06	.04	.02	137	Robert Castillo	.03	.02	.01
66 Denny Walling	.03	.02	.01	138	Gary Thomasson	.03	.02	.01
67 Jeff Leonard	.03	.02	.01	139	Rudy Law	.03	.02	.01
68 Luis Pujols	.03	.02	.01	140	Fernand Valenzuela	.03	.02	.01
69 Bruce Bochy	.03	.02	.01	141	Manny Mota	.06	.04	.02

	MINT	VG-E	F-G			MINT	VG-E	F-G
142 Gary Carter	.10	.07	.03	235 Jim Dwyer		.03	.02	.01
143 Steve Rogers	.06	.04	.02	236 Dave Stapleton		.03	.02	.01
144 Warren Cromartie	.03	.02	.01	237 Glen Hoffman		.03	.02	.01
145 Andre Dawson	.06	.04	.02	238 Jerry Remy		.03	.02	.01
146 Larry Parrish	.06	.04	.02	239 Dick Drago		.03	.02	.01
147 Rowland Office	.03	.02	.01	240 Bill Campbell		.03	.02	.01
148 Ellis Valentine	.06	.04	.02	241 Tony Perez		.10	.07	.03
149 Dick Williams	.06	.04	.02	242 Phil Niekro		.10	.07	.03
150 Bill Gullickson	.03	.02	.01	243 Dale Murphy		.06	.04	.02
151 Elias Sosa	.03	.02	.01	244 Bob Horner		.20	.15	.06
152 John Tamargo	.03	.02	.01	245 Jeff Burroughs		.06	.04	.02
153 Chris Speier	.03	.02	.01	246 Rick Camp		.03	.02	.01
154 Ron LeFlore	.10	.07	.03	247 Bob Cox		.03	.02	.01
155 Rodney Scott	.03	.02	.01	248 Bruce Benedict		.03	.02	.01
156 Stan Bahnsen	.03	.02	.01	249 Gene Garber		.03	.02	.01
157 Bill Lee	.05	.03	.01	250 Jerry Royster		.03	.02	.01
158 Fred Norman	.03	.02	.01	251 Garry Matthews		.06	.04	.02
159 Woodie Fryman	.03	.02	.01	252 Chris Chambliss		.06	.04	.02
160 Dave Palmer	.03	.02	.01	253 Luis Gomez		.03	.02	.01
161 Jerry White	.03	.02	.01	254 Bill Nahorodny		.03	.02	.01
162 Roberto Ramos	.03	.02	.01	255 Doyle Alexander		.03	.02	.01
163 John D'Acquisto	.03	.02	.01	256 Brian Asselstine		.03	.02	.01
164 Tommy Hutton	.03	.02	.01	257 Biff Pocoroba		.03	.02	.01
165 Charlie Lea	.03	.02	.01	258 Mike Lum		.03	.02	.01
166 Scott Sanderson	.03	.02	.01	259 Charlie Spikes		.03	.02	.01
167 Ken Macha	.03	.02	.01	260 Glenn Hubbard		.03	.02	.01
168 Tony Bernazard	.03	.02	.01	261 Tommy Boggs		.03	.02	.01
169 Jim Palmer	.20	.15	.06	262 Al Hrabosky		.06	.04	.02
170 Steve Stone	.10	.07	.03	263 Rick Matula		.03	.02	.01
171 Mike Flanagan	.10	.07	.03	264 Preston Hanna		.03	.02	.01
172 Al Bumbry	.03	.02	.01	265 Larry Bradford		.03	.02	.01
173 Doug DeCinces	.03	.02	.01	266 Rafael Ramirez		.03	.02	.01
174 Scott McGregor	.06	.04	.02	267 Larry McWilliams		.03	.02	.01
175 Mark Belanger	.03	.02	.01	268 Rod Carew		.25	.20	.08
176 Tim Stoddard	.03	.02	.01	269 Bobby Grich		.06	.04	.02
177 Rick Dempsey	.03	.02	.01	270 Carney Lansford		.06	.04	.02
178 Earl Weaver	.06	.04	.02	271 Don Baylor		.15	.11	.05
179 Tippy Martinez	.03	.02	.01	272 Joe Rudi		.06	.04	.02
180 Dennis Martinez	.03	.02	.01	273 Dan Ford		.05	.03	.01
181 Sammy Stewart	.03	.02	.01	274 Jim Fregosi		.06	.04	.02
182 Rich Dauer	.03	.02	.01	275 Dave Frost		.03	.02	.01
183 Lee May	.03	.02	.01	276 Frank Tanana		.05	.03	.01
184 Eddie Murray	.10	.07	.03	277 Dickie Thon		.03	.02	.01
185 Benny Ayala	.03	.02	.01	278 Jason Thompson		.06	.04	.02
186 John Lowenstein	.03	.02	.01	279 Rick Miller		.03	.02	.01
187 Gary Roenicke	.03	.02	.01	280 Bert Campaneris		.05	.03	.01
188 Ken Singleton	.10	.07	.03	281 Tom Donohue		.03	.02	.01
189 Dan Graham	.03	.02	.01	282 Brian Downing		.05	.03	.01
190 Terry Crowley	.03	.02	.01	283 Fred Patek		.03	.02	.01
191 Kiko Garcia	.03	.02	.01	284 Bruce Kison		.03	.02	.01
192 Dave Ford	.03	.02	.01	285 Dave LaRoche		.03	.02	.01
193 Mark Corey	.03	.02	.01	286 Don Aase		.03	.02	.01
194 Lenn Sakata	.03	.02	.01	287 Jim Barr		.03	.02	.01
195 Doug DeCinces	.03	.02	.01	288 Alfredo Martinez		.03	.02	.01
196 Johnny Bench	.25	.20	.08	289 Larry Harlow		.03	.02	.01
197 Dave Concepcion	.08	.06	.02	290 Andy Hassler		.03	.02	.01
198 Ray Knight	.06	.04	.02	291 Dave Kingman		.10	.07	.03
199 Ken Griffey	.06	.04	.02	292 Bill Buckner		.06	.04	.02
200 Tom Seaver	.25	.20	.08	293 Rick Reuschel		.08	.06	.02
201 Dave Collins	.06	.04	.02	294 Bruce Sutter		.15	.11	.05
202 George Foster	.15	.11	.05	295 Jerry Martin		.03	.02	.01
203 Junior Kennedy	.03	.02	.01	296 Scot Thompson		.03	.02	.01
204 Frank Pastore	.03	.02	.01	297 Ivan De Jesus		.03	.02	.01
205 Dan Driessen	.03	.02	.01	298 Steve Dillard		.03	.02	.01
206 Hector Cruz	.03	.02	.01	299 Dick Tidrow		.03	.02	.01
207 Paul Moskau	.03	.02	.01	300 Randy Martz		.03	.02	.01
208 Charlie Leibrandt	.03	.02	.01	301 Lenny Randle		.03	.02	.01
209 Harry Spilman	.03	.02	.01	302 Lynn McGlothen		.03	.02	.01
210 Joe Price	.03	.02	.01	303 Cliff Johnson		.03	.02	.01
211 Tom Hume	.03	.02	.01	304 Tim Blackwell		.03	.02	.01
212 Joe Nolan	.03	.02	.01	305 Dennis Lamp		.03	.02	.01
213 Doug Bair	.03	.02	.01	306 Bill Caudill		.03	.02	.01
214 Mario Soto	.03	.02	.01	307 Carlos Lezcano		.03	.02	.01
215 Bill Bonham	.03	.02	.01	308 Jim Tracy		.03	.02	.01
216 George Foster	.15	.11	.05	309 Doug Capilla		.03	.02	.01
217 Paul Householder	.03	.02	.01	310 Willie Hernandez		.03	.02	.01
218 Ron Oester	.03	.02	.01	311 Mike Vail		.03	.02	.01
219 Sam Mejias	.03	.02	.01	312 Mike Krukow		.03	.02	.01
220 Sheldon Burnside	.03	.02	.01	313 Barry Foote		.03	.02	.01
221 Carl Yastrzemski	.30	.25	.10	314 Larry Biittner		.03	.02	.01
222 Jim Rice	.25	.20	.08	315 Mike Tyson		.03	.02	.01
223 Fred Lynn	.25	.20	.08	316 Lee Mazzilli		.08	.06	.02
224 Carlton Fisk	.15	.11	.05	317 John Stearns		.03	.02	.01
225 Rick Burleson	.10	.07	.03	318 Alex Trevino		.03	.02	.01
226 Dennis Eckersley	.06	.04	.02	319 Craig Swan		.06	.04	.02
227 Butch Hobson	.03	.02	.01	320 Frank Taveras		.03	.02	.01
228 Tom Burgmeier	.03	.02	.01	321 Steve Henderson		.06	.04	.02
229 Garry Hancock	.03	.02	.01	322 Neil Allen		.03	.02	.01
230 Don Zimmer	.06	.04	.02	323 Mark Bomback		.03	.02	.01
231 Steve Renko	.03	.02	.01	324 Mike Jorgensen		.03	.02	.01
232 Dwight Evans	.03	.02	.01	325 Joe Torre		.06	.04	.02
233 Mike Torrez	.05	.03	.01	325 Elliott Maddox		.03	.02	.01
234 Bob Stanley	.03	.02	.01	327 Pete Falcone		.03	.02	.01
				328 Ray Burris		.03	.02	.01

	MINT	FG-E	F-G			MINT	VG-E	F-G
329 Claudell Washington	.03	.02	.01	422 Al Woods		.03	.02	.01
330 Doug Flynn	.03	.02	.01	423 Garth Iorg		.03	.02	.01
331 Joel Youngblood	.03	.02	.01	424 Doug Ault		.03	.02	.01
332 Bill Almon	.03	.02	.01	425 Ken Schrom		.03	.02	.01
333 Tom Hausman	.03	.02	.01	426 Mike Willis		.03	.02	.01
334 Pat Zachry	.03	.02	.01	427 Steve Braun		.03	.02	.01
335 Jeff Reardon	.03	.02	.01	428 Bob Davis		.03	.02	.01
336 Wally Backman	.03	.02	.01	429 Jerry Garvin		.03	.02	.01
337 Dan Norman	.03	.02	.01	430 Alfredo Griffin		.03	.02	.01
338 Jerry Morales	.03	.02	.01	431 Bob Mattick		.03	.02	.01
339 Ed Farmer	.03	.02	.01	432 Vida Blue		.10	.07	.03
340 Bob Molinaro	.03	.02	.01	433 Jack Clark		.08	.06	.02
341 Todd Cruz	.03	.02	.01	434 Willie McCovey		.20	.15	.06
342 Britt Burns	.03	.02	.01	435 Mike Ivie		.03	.02	.01
343 Kevin Bell	.03	.02	.01	436 Darrell Evans		.03	.02	.01
344 Tony LaRussa	.03	.02	.01	437 Terry Whitfield		.03	.02	.01
345 Steve Trout	.03	.02	.01	438 Rennie Stennett		.03	.02	.01
346 Harold Baines	.03	.02	.01	439 John Montefusco		.03	.02	.01
347 Richard Wortham	.03	.02	.01	440 Jim Wohlford		.03	.02	.01
348 Wayne Nordhagen	.03	.02	.01	441 Bill North		.03	.02	.01
349 Mike Squires	.03	.02	.01	442 Milt May		.03	.02	.01
350 Lamar Johnson	.03	.02	.01	443 Max Venable		.03	.02	.01
351 Rickey Henderson	.15	.11	.05	444 Ed Whitson		.03	.02	.01
352 Francisco Barrios	.03	.02	.01	445 Al Holland		.03	.02	.01
353 Thad Bosley	.03	.02	.01	446 Randy Moffitt		.03	.02	.01
354 Chet Lemon	.06	.04	.02	447 Bob Knepper		.03	.02	.01
355 Bruce Kimm	.03	.02	.01	448 Gary Lavelle		.03	.02	.01
356 Richard Dotson	.03	.02	.01	449 Greg Minton		.03	.02	.01
357 Jim Morrison	.03	.02	.01	450 Johnnie LeMaster		.03	.02	.01
358 Mike Proly	.03	.02	.01	451 Larry Herndon		.03	.02	.01
359 Greg Pryor	.03	.02	.01	452 Rich Murray		.03	.02	.01
360 Dave Parker	.25	.20	.08	453 Joe Pettini		.03	.02	.01
361 Omar Moreno	.10	.07	.03	454 Allen Ripley		.03	.02	.01
362 Kent Tekulve	.06	.04	.02	455 Dennis Littlejohn		.03	.02	.01
363 Willie Stargell	.20	.15	.06	456 Tom Griffin		.03	.02	.01
364 Phil Garner	.03	.02	.01	457 Alan Hargesheimer		.03	.02	.01
365 Ed Ott	.03	.02	.01	458 Joe Strain		.03	.02	.01
366 Don Robinson	.03	.02	.01	459 Steve Kemp		.10	.07	.03
367 Chuck Tanner	.05	.03	.01	460 Sparky Anderson		.06	.04	.02
368 Jim Rooker	.03	.02	.01	461 Alan Trammell		.08	.06	.02
369 Dale Berra	.03	.02	.01	462 Mark Fidrych		.06	.04	.02
370 Jim Bibby	.05	.03	.01	463 Lou Whitaker		.06	.04	.02
371 Steve Nicosia	.03	.02	.01	464 Dave Rozema		.03	.02	.01
372 Mike Easler	.03	.02	.01	465 Milt Wilcox		.03	.02	.01
373 Bill Robinson	.03	.02	.01	466 Champ Summers		.03	.02	.01
374 Lee Lacy	.03	.02	.01	467 Lance Parrish		.06	.04	.02
375 John Candelaria	.05	.03	.01	468 Dan Petry		.03	.02	.01
376 Manny Sanguillen	.05	.03	.01	469 Pat Underwood		.03	.02	.01
377 Rick Rhoden	.03	.02	.01	470 Rick Peters		.03	.02	.01
378 Grant Jackson	.03	.02	.01	471 Al Cowens		.03	.02	.01
379 Tom Foli	.03	.02	.01	472 John Wockenfuss		.03	.02	.01
380 Rod Scurry	.03	.02	.01	473 Tom Brookens		.03	.02	.01
381 Bill Madlock	.06	.04	.02	474 Richie Hebner		.05	.03	.01
382 Kurt Bevacqua	.03	.02	.01	475 Jack Morris		.05	.03	.01
383 Bert Blyleven	.06	.04	.02	476 Jim Lentine		.03	.02	.01
384 Eddie Solomon	.03	.02	.01	477 Bruce Robbins		.03	.02	.01
385 Enrique Romo	.03	.02	.01	478 Mark Wagner		.03	.02	.01
386 John Milner	.03	.02	.01	479 Tim Corcoran		.03	.02	.01
387 Mike Hargrove	.03	.02	.01	480 Stan Papi		.03	.02	.01
388 Jorge Orta	.03	.02	.01	481 Kirk Gibson		.06	.04	.02
389 Toby Harrah	.03	.02	.01	482 Dan Schatzeder		.03	.02	.01
390 Tom Veryzer	.03	.02	.01	483 Aurelio Lopez		.03	.02	.01
391 Miguel Dilone	.05	.03	.01	484 Dave Winfield		.25	.20	.08
392 Dan Spillner	.03	.02	.01	485 Rollie Fingers		.10	.07	.03
393 Jack Brohamer	.03	.02	.01	486 Gene Richards		.03	.02	.01
394 Wayne Garland	.03	.02	.01	487 Randy Jones		.06	.04	.02
395 Sid Monge	.03	.02	.01	488 Ozzie Smith		.03	.02	.01
396 Rick Waits	.03	.02	.01	489 Gene Tenace		.05	.03	.01
397 Joe Charboneau	.08	.06	.02	490 Bill Fahey		.03	.02	.01
398 Gary Alexander	.03	.02	.01	491 John Curtis		.03	.02	.01
399 Jerry Dybzinski	.03	.02	.01	492 Dave Cash		.03	.02	.01
400 Mike Stanton	.03	.02	.01	493 Tim Flannery		.03	.02	.01
401 Mike Paxton	.03	.02	.01	494 Jerry Mumphrey		.03	.02	.01
402 Gary Gray	.03	.02	.01	495 Bob Shirley		.03	.02	.01
403 Rick Manning	.03	.02	.01	496 Steve Mura		.03	.02	.01
404 Bo Diaz	.03	.02	.01	497 Eric Rasmussen		.03	.02	.01
405 Ron Hassey	.03	.02	.01	498 Broderick Perkins		.03	.02	.01
406 Ross Grimsley	.03	.02	.01	499 Barry Evans		.03	.02	.01
407 Victor Cruz	.03	.02	.01	500 Chuck Baker		.03	.02	.01
408 Len Barker	.05	.03	.01	501 Luis Salazar		.03	.02	.01
409 Bob Bailor	.03	.02	.01	502 Gary Lucas		.03	.02	.01
410 Otto Velez	.03	.02	.01	503 Mike Armstrong		.03	.02	.01
411 Ernie Whitt	.03	.02	.01	504 Jerry Turner		.03	.02	.01
412 Jim Clancy	.03	.02	.01	505 Dennis Kinney		.03	.02	.01
413 Barry Bonnell	.03	.02	.01	506 Willie Montanez		.03	.02	.01
414 Dave Stieb	.03	.02	.01	507 Gorman Thomas		.10	.07	.03
415 Damaso Garcia	.03	.02	.01	508 Ben Oglivie		.06	.04	.02
416 John Mayberry	.06	.04	.02	509 Larry Hisle		.08	.06	.02
417 Roy Howell	.03	.02	.01	510 Sal Bando		.06	.04	.02
418 Dan Ainge	.03	.02	.01	511 Robin Yount		.06	.04	.02
419 Jesse Jefferson	.03	.02	.01	512 Mike Caldwell		.03	.02	.01
420 Joey McLaughlin	.03	.02	.01	513 Sixto Lezcano		.03	.02	.01
421 Lloyd Moseby	.03	.02	.01	514 Jerry Augustine		.03	.02	.01
				515 Paul Molitor		.08	.06	.02

	MINT	VG-E	F-G
516 Moose Haas	.03	.02	.01
517 Bill Castro	.03	.02	.01
518 Jim Slaton	.03	.02	.01
519 Lary Sorensen	.03	.02	.01
520 Bob McClure	.03	.02	.01
521 Charlie Moore	.03	.02	.01
522 Jim Gantner	.03	.02	.01
523 Reggie Cleveland	.03	.02	.01
524 Don Money	.05	.03	.01
525 Bill Travers	.03	.02	.01
526 Buck Martinez	.03	.02	.01
527 Dick Davis	.03	.02	.01
528 Ted Simmons	.10	.07	.03
529 Garry Templeton	.15	.11	.05
530 Ken Reitz	.03	.02	.01
531 Tony Scott	.03	.02	.01
532 Ken Oberkfell	.03	.02	.01
533 Bob Sykes	.03	.02	.01
534 Keith Smith	.03	.02	.01
535 John Littlefield	.03	.02	.01
536 Jim Kaat	.10	.07	.03
537 Bob Forsch	.03	.02	.01
538 Mike Phillips	.03	.02	.01
539 Terry Landrum	.03	.02	.01
540 Leon Durham	.03	.02	.01
541 Terry Kennedy	.03	.02	.01
542 George Hendrick	.08	.06	.02
543 Dane Iorg	.03	.02	.01
544 Mark Littell	.03	.02	.01
545 Keith Hernandez	.15	.11	.05
546 Silvio Martinez	.03	.02	.01
547 Pete Vuckovich	.03	.02	.01
548 Bobby Bonds	.10	.07	.03
549 Mike Ramsey	.03	.02	.01
550 Tom Herr	.03	.02	.01
551 Roy Smalley	.06	.04	.02
552 Jerry Koosman	.06	.04	.02
553 Ken Landreaux	.06	.04	.02
554 John Castino	.03	.02	.01
555 Doug Corbett	.03	.02	.01
556 Bombo Rivera	.03	.02	.01
557 Ron Jackson	.03	.02	.01
558 Butch Wynegar	.03	.02	.01
559 Hosken Powell	.03	.02	.01
560 Pete Redfern	.03	.02	.01
561 Roger Erickson	.03	.02	.01
562 Glenn Adams	.03	.02	.01
563 Rick Sofield	.03	.02	.01
564 Geoff Zahn	.03	.02	.01
565 Pete Mackanin	.03	.02	.01
566 Mike Cubbage	.03	.02	.01
567 Darrell Jackson	.03	.02	.01
568 Dave Edwards	.03	.02	.01
569 Rob Wilfong	.03	.02	.01
570 Sal Butera	.03	.02	.01
571 Jose Morales	.03	.02	.01
572 Rick Langford	.03	.02	.01
573 Mike Norris	.06	.04	.02
574 Rickey Henderson	.15	.11	.05
575 Tony Armas	.08	.06	.02
576 Dave Revering	.03	.02	.01
577 Jeff Newman	.03	.02	.01
578 Bob Lacey	.03	.02	.01
579 Brian Kingman	.03	.02	.01
580 Mitchell Page	.05	.03	.01
581 Billy Martin	.08	.06	.02
582 Rob Picciolo	.03	.02	.01
583 Mike Heath	.03	.02	.01
584 Mickey Klutts	.03	.02	.01
585 Orlando Gonzalez	.03	.02	.01
586 Mike Davis	.03	.02	.01
587 Wayne Gross	.03	.02	.01
588 Matt Keough	.03	.02	.01
589 Steve McCatty	.03	.02	.01
590 Dwayne Murphy	.10	.07	.03
591 Mario Guerrero	.03	.02	.01
592 Dave McKay	.03	.02	.01
593 Jim Essian	.03	.02	.01
594 Dave Heaverlo	.03	.02	.01
595 Maury Wills	.08	.06	.02
596 Juan Beniquez	.03	.02	.01
597 Rodney Craig	.03	.02	.01
598 Jim Anderson	.03	.02	.01
599 Floyd Bannister	.03	.02	.01
600 Bruce Bochte	.05	.03	.01
601 Julio Cruz	.03	.02	.01
602 Ted Cox	.03	.02	.01
603 Dan Meyer	.03	.02	.01
604 Larry Cox	.03	.02	.01
605 Bill Stein	.03	.02	.01
606 Steve Garvey	.25	.20	.08
607 Dave Roberts	.03	.02	.01
608 Leon Roberts	.03	.02	.01

	MINT	VG-E	F-G
609 Reggie Walton	.03	.02	.01
610 Dave Edler	.03	.02	.01
611 Larry Milbourne	.03	.02	.01
612 Kim Allen	.03	.02	.01
613 Mario Mendoza	.03	.02	.01
614 Tom Paciorek	.03	.02	.01
615 Glenn Abbott	.03	.02	.01
616 Joe Simpson	.03	.02	.01
617 Mickey Rivers	.08	.06	.02
618 Jim Kern	.03	.02	.01
619 Jim Sundberg	.06	.04	.02
620 Richie Zisk	.06	.04	.02
621 Jon Matlack	.05	.03	.01
622 Ferguson Jenkins	.08	.06	.02
623 Pat Corrales	.03	.02	.01
624 Ed Figueroa	.03	.02	.01
625 Buddy Bell	.06	.04	.02
626 Al Oliver	.10	.07	.03
627 Doc Medich	.03	.02	.01
628 Bump Wills	.05	.03	.01
629 Rusty Staub	.08	.06	.02
630 Pat Putnam	.03	.02	.01
631 John Grubb	.03	.02	.01
632 Danny Darwin	.03	.02	.01
633 Ken Clay	.03	.02	.01
634 Jim Norris	.03	.02	.01
635 John Butcher	.03	.02	.01
636 Dave Roberts	.03	.02	.01
637 Billy Sample	.03	.02	.01
638 Carl Yastrzemski	.30	.25	.10
639 Cecil Cooper	.10	.07	.03
640 Mike Schmidt '80 Homer King	.20	.15	.06
641 Phillies/Royals Checklist	.03	.02	.01
642 Astros/Yankees Checklist	.03	.02	.01
643 Expos/Dodgers Checklist	.03	.02	.01
644 Reds/Orioles Checklist	.03	.02	.01
645 Schmidt, Rose, Bowa Triple Threat	.10	.07	.03
646 Braves/Red Sox Checklist	.03	.02	.01
647 Cubs/Angels Checklist	.03	.02	.01
648 Mets/White Sox Checklsit	.03	.02	.01
649 Indians/Pirates Checklist	.03	.02	.01
650 Reggie Jackson "Mr. Baseball"	.20	.15	.06
651 Giants/Blue Jays Checklist	.03	.02	.01
652 Tigers/Padres Checklist	.03	.02	.01
653 Hal McRae "Double Threat"	.05	.03	.01
654 Brewers/Cardinals Checklist	.03	.02	.01
655 George Brett ".390 Average"	.20	.15	.06
656 Twins/Oakland A's Checklist	.03	.02	.01
657 Tug McGraw "Game Saver"	.06	.04	.02
658 Rangers/Mariners Checklist	.03	.02	.01
659 Team and Misc. Checklist	.13	.02	.01
660 Steve Carlton "Lefty....The Golden Arm"	.15	.11	.05

1981 FLEER STICKERS (128)　　　2 1/2" X 3 1/2"

GEORGE BRETT
ROYALS　　THIRD BASE

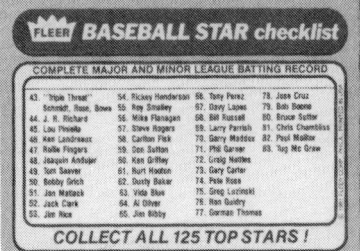

The 1981 Fleer Baseball Stickers set consists of 125 numbered cards with peelable, full color sticker fronts and three unnumbered checklist The backs of the numbere player cards are the same a the 1981 Fleer regular issu cards except for the number while the checklist cards hav sticker fronts of Jackso (1-42), Brett (43-83) an Schmidt (84-125). Becaus Fleer cards are printed i 132-card sheets, there speculation that there ma be four doubly printed card of which we have no informa tion at publication time.

	MINT	VG-E	F-G
COMPLETE SET	10.00	7.00	3.00
COMMON PLAYER	.05	.03	.01
1 Steve Garvey	.40	.30	.12
2 Ron LeFlore	.10	.07	.03
3 Ron Cey	.10	.07	.03
4 Dave Revering	.05	.03	.01
5 Tony Armas	.08	.06	.02
6 Mike Norris	.08	.06	.02
7 Steve Kemp	.10	.07	.03
8 Bruce Bochte	.05	.03	.01
9 Mike Schmidt	.40	.30	.12
10 Scott McGregor	.08	.06	.02
11 Buddy Bell	.08	.06	.02
12 Carney Lansford	.08	.06	.02
13 Carl Yastrzemski	.50	.35	.15
14 Ben Oglivie	.08	.06	.02
15 Willie Stargell	.30	.25	.10
16 Cecil Cooper	.10	.07	.03
17 Gene Richards	.05	.03	.01
18 Jim Kern	.05	.03	.01
19 Jerry Koosman	.05	.03	.01
20 Larry Bowa	.10	.07	.03
21 Kent Tekulve	.05	.03	.01
22 Dan Driessen	.05	.03	.01
23 Phil Niekro	.10	.07	.03
24 Dan Quisenberry	.10	.07	.03
25 Dave Winfield	.40	.30	.12
26 Dave Parker	.40	.30	.12
27 Rick Langford	.05	.03	.01
28 Amos Otis	.08	.06	.02
29 Bill Buckner	.08	.06	.02
30 Al Bumbry	.05	.03	.01
31 Bake McBride	.08	.06	.02
32 Mickey Rivers	.08	.06	.02
33 Rick Burleson	.08	.06	.02
34 Dennis Eckersley	.08	.06	.02
35 Cesar Cedeno	.10	.07	.03
36 Enos Cabell	.05	.03	.01
37 Johnny Bench	.40	.30	.12
38 Robin Yount	.08	.06	.02
39 Mark Belanger	.05	.03	.01
40 Rod Carew	.40	.30	.12
41 George Foster	.25	.20	.08
42 Lee Mazzilli	.08	.06	.02
43 "Triple Threat" Schmidt, Rose, Bowa	.25	.20	.08
44 J. R. Richard	.15	.11	.05
45 Lou Piniella	.08	.06	.02
46 Ken Landreaux	.05	.03	.01
47 Rollie Fingers	.08	.06	.02
48 Joaquin Andujar	.05	.03	.01
49 Tom Seaver	.40	.30	.12
50 Bobby Grich	.05	.03	.01
51 Jon Matlack	.05	.03	.01
52 Jack Clark	.10	.07	.03
53 Jim Rice	.40	.30	.12
54 Rickey Henderson	.10	.07	.03
55 Roy Smalley	.05	.03	.01
56 Mike Flanagan	.08	.06	.02
57 Steve Rogers	.08	.06	.02
58 Carlton Fisk	.20	.15	.06
59 Don Sutton	.12	.08	.04
60 Ken Griffey	.08	.06	.02
61 Burt Hooton	.08	.06	.02
62 Dusty Baker	.08	.06	.02

	MINT	VG-E	F-G
63 Vida Blue	.12	.08	.04
64 Al Oliver	.12	.08	.04
65 Jim Bibby	.05	.03	.01
66 Tony Perez	.10	.07	.03
67 Davy Lopes	.08	.06	.02
68 Bill Russell	.05	.03	.01
69 Larry Parrish	.08	.06	.02
70 Garry Maddox	.08	.06	.02
71 Phil Garner	.05	.03	.01
72 Graig Nettles	.10	.07	.03
73 Gary Carter	.15	.11	.05
74 Pete Rose	.50	.35	.15
75 Greg Luzinski	.10	.07	.03
76 Ron Guidry	.15	.11	.05
77 Gorman Thomas	.12	.03	.04
78 Jose Cruz	.05	.03	.01
79 Bob Boone	.08	.06	.02
80 Bruce Sutter	.15	.11	.05
81 Chris Chambliss	.08	.06	.02
82 Paul Molitor	.12	.08	.04
83 Tug McGraw	.05	.03	.01
84 Ferguson Jenkins	.10	.07	.03
85 Steve Carlton	.30	.25	.10
86 Miguel Dilone	.05	.03	.01
87 Reggie Smith	.10	.07	.03
88 Rick Cerone	.08	.06	.02
89 Alan Trammell	.08	.06	.02
90 Doug DeCinces	.05	.03	.01
91 Sparky Lyle	.08	.06	.02
92 Warren Cromartie	.05	.03	.01
93 Rick Reuschel	.10	.07	.03
94 Larry Hisle	.08	.06	.02
95 Paul Splittorff	.05	.03	.01
96 Manny Trillo	.05	.03	.01
97 Frank White	.08	.06	.02
98 Fred Lynn	.40	.30	.12
99 Bob Horner	.25	.20	.08
100 Omar Moreno	.08	.06	.02
101 Dave Concepcion	.08	.06	.02
102 Larry Gura	.08	.06	.02
103 Ken Singleton	.10	.07	.03
104 Steve Stone	.08	.06	.02
105 Richie Zisk	.08	.06	.02
106 Willie Wilson	.15	.11	.05
107 Willie Randolph	.08	.06	.02
108 Nolan Ryan	.25	.20	.08
109 Joe Morgan	.15	.11	.05
110 Bucky Dent	.08	.06	.02
111 Dave Kingman	.12	.08	.04
112 John Castino	.05	.03	.01
113 Joe Rudi	.05	.03	.01
114 Ed Farmer	.05	.03	.01
115 Reggie Jackson	.40	.30	.12
116 George Brett	.50	.35	.15
117 Eddie Murray	.15	.11	.05
118 Rich Gossage	.10	.07	.03
119 Dale Murphy	.08	.06	.02
120 Ted Simmons	.15	.11	.05
121 Tommy John	.15	.11	.05
122 Don Baylor	.12	.08	.04
123 Andre Dawson	.10	.07	.03
124 Jim Palmer	.30	.25	.10
125 Garry Templeton	.20	.15	.06
Checklist 1 - Jackson	.20	.15	.06
Checklist 2 - Brett	.20	.15	.06
Checklist 3 - Schmidt	.20	.15	.06

1928 FRO—JOY (6)   2 1/16" X 4"

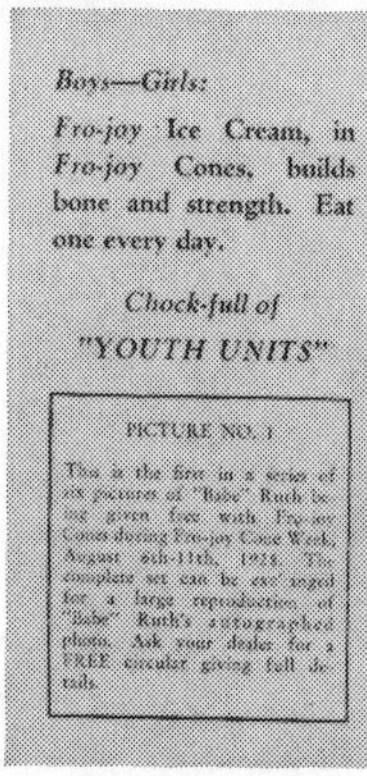

George Herman ("Babe") Ruth

"The Sultan of Swat" who holds the world's record for home-run hits in a single season with 60 circuit clouts during the regular playing season of 1927, topped by 3 more against Pittsburgh during the World's Series game last year.

The Fro-joy set of 1928 was designed to exploit the advertising potential of the mighty Babe Ruth. Six black & white cards explained specific baseball techniques while the reverse advertising extolled the virtues of Fro-joy ice cream and ice cream cones.

	MINT	VG-E	F-G
COMPLETE SET	500.00	450.00	200.00
COMMON CARDS	80.00	60.00	25.00
1 George Herman (Babe) Ruth	80.00	60.00	25.00
2 Look out, Mr. Pitcher!	80.00	60.00	25.00
3 Bang! The Babe lines one out!	150.00	110.00	50.00
4 When the Babe comes	150.00	110.00	50.00
5 Babe Ruth's Grip!	80.00	60.00	25.00
6 Ruth is a crack fielder	80.00	60.00	25.00

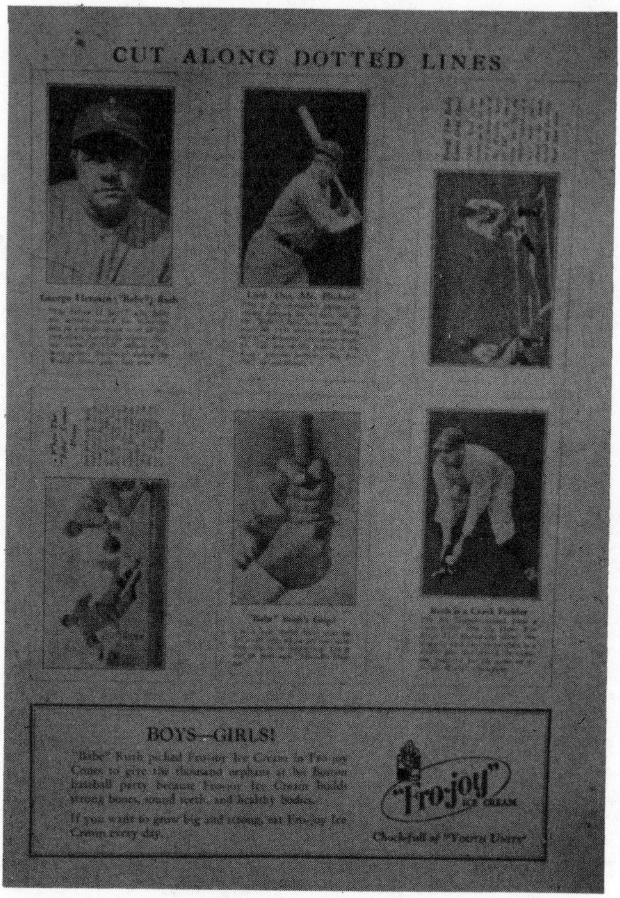

1954 GLENDALE (28)　　　　2 5/8" X 3 3/4"

HAROLD J. ERICKSON, Pitcher　　Ht. 6 ft. 3 in.　Wt. 200
Born in Portland, Ore., July 17, 1919　　　B. and T.—Right

Year	Club	League	G	IP	W	L	Pct.	H	R	ER	BB	Ave.
1947	Syracuse	Int.	27	56	2	1	667	62	42	31	30	26	4.98
1948	Syracuse	Int.	29	54	3	3	790	60	42	37	29	23	6.17
1949	Quebec	Can.-Amer.	38	252	21	8	778	207	96	64	208	61	3.79
1950	Quebec	Can.-Amer.	31	238	20	7	741	207	79	53	88	240	
1951	Dallas	Texas	39	209	12	10	545	124	76	57	82	65	2.46
1952	Dallas*	Texas	37	224	20	14	588	222	98	79	124	76	2.60

*Acquired from Dallas Club in exchange for infielder Ben Taylor, Dec. 19, 1952.
The big right hander had a record of 20 won and 11 lost with Dallas last season.

FIRST PRIZE: Trip for 2 to WORLD SERIES
Save and collect these cards. Mail them, all at one time, not later than Sept. 15, to "Glendale," Box No. 651, Detroit 31, Michigan. 3 FIRST PRIZES and 150 other valuable prizes for most cards sent in.

Glendale PREMIUM QUALITY MEATS

HAL ERICKSON

The 1954 Glendale Meats [set] of 28 full color, unnumb[ered] cards features Detroit Ti[gers] only. There are several sc[arce] cards in this set; they ar[e in] order of scarcity, Houtten[man,] Ginsberg, Hoeft, Gray, W[ight] and Jordan. The ACC desi[gna-] tion is F151.

	MINT	VG-E	F-G
COMPLETE SET	2200.00	1650.00	700.00
COMMON PLAYER	60.00	45.00	20.00

	MINT	VG-E	F-G			MINT	VG-E	F-G
1 Matt Batts	60.00	45.00	20.00	15 Bill Hoeft		125.00	90.00	40.00
2 Johnny Bucha	60.00	45.00	20.00	16 Art Houtteman		800.00	575.00	250.00
3 Frank Carswell	60.00	45.00	20.00	17 Milt Jordan		80.00	60.00	25.00
4 Jim Delsing	60.00	45.00	20.00	18 Harvey Kueen		80.00	60.00	25.00
5 Walt Dropo	60.00	45.00	20.00	19 Don Lund		60.00	45.00	20.00
6 Hal Erickson	60.00	45.00	20.00	20 Dave Madison		60.00	45.00	20.00
7 Paul Foytack	60.00	45.00	20.00	21 Dick Marlowe		60.00	45.00	20.00
8 Owen Friend	60.00	45.00	20.00	22 Pat Mullin		60.00	45.00	20.00
9 Ned Garver	60.00	45.00	20.00	23 Bob Nieman		60.00	45.00	20.00
10 Joe Ginsberg	200.00	140.00	60.00	24 Johnny Pesky		65.00	48.00	22.00
11 Ted Gray	80.00	60.00	25.00	25 Jerry Priddy		60.00	45.00	20.00
12 Fred Hatfield	60.00	45.00	20.00	26 Steve Souchock		60.00	45.00	20.00
13 Ray Herbert	60.00	45.00	20.00	27 Russ Sullivan		60.00	45.00	20.00
14 Bill Hitchcock	60.00	45.00	20.00	28 Bill Wight		80.00	60.00	25.00

1961 GOLDEN PRESS (33)　　　　2 1/2" X 3 1/2"

9 Joseph Paul DiMaggio
"Joltin' Joe"　"The Yankee Clipper"
1936-1951 New York AL

Joe DiMaggio was one of the best center fielders ever to play in the major leagues. As a fielder, he covered the vast center field of Yankee Stadium with ease, making even the most difficult plays look easy. In 1941, DiMaggio hit safely in 56 consecutive games—a major league record. He led the American League in batting in 1939 and 1940, in home runs in 1937 and 1948, and in runs batted in in 1941 and 1948. He appeared in ten World Series, setting many Series records.

Lifetime Record 13 yrs.

G	AB	R	H	HR	RBI	SB	PCT
1736	6821	1390	2214	361	1537	30	.325

Elected to Hall of Fame 1955

JOE DI MAGGIO
outfield

The 1961 Golden Press set of 33 full color cards features members of Baseball's Hall of Fame. The cards came in a booklet with perforations for punching the cards out of the book. The SCB designation is W524. The price for the full book is 50% higher than the complete set price listed.

	MINT	VG-E	F-G
COMPLETE SET	20.00	15.00	6.00
COMMON PLAYER	.40	.32	.14

	MINT	VG-E	F-G		MINT	VG-E	F-G
1 Mel Ott	.60	.45	.20	16 Lou Gehrig	2.50	1.80	.80
2 Grover C. Alexander	.60	.45	.20	17 Lefty Grove	.80	.60	.25
3 Babe Ruth	3.00	2.25	1.00	18 Chief Bender	.40	.32	.14
4 Hank Greenberg	.60	.45	.20	19 Frankie Frisch	.60	.45	.20
5 Bill Terry	.60	.45	.20	20 Al Simmons	.50	.40	.18
6 Carl Hubbell	.60	.45	.20	21 Home Run Baker	.40	.32	.14
7 Rogers Hornsby	1.00	.70	.30	22 Jimmy Foxx	1.00	.70	.30
8 Dizzy Dean	2.00	1.50	.60	23 John McGraw	.50	.40	.18
9 Joe DiMaggio	2.50	1.80	.80	24 Christy Mathewson	.80	.60	.25
10 Charlie Gehringer	.50	.40	.18	25 Ty Cobb	2.50	1.80	.80
11 Gabby Hartnett	.40	.32	.14	26 Dazzy Vance	.40	.32	.14
12 Mickey Cochrane	.40	.32	.14	27 Bill Dickey	.60	.45	.20
13 George Sisler	.40	.32	.14	28 Eddie Collins	.40	.32	.14
14 Joe Cronin	.40	.32	.14	29 Walter Johnson	1.00	.70	.30
15 Pie Traynor	.50	.40	.18	30 Tris Speaker	.50	.40	.18
				31 Nap Lajoie	.60	.45	.20
				32 Honus Wagner	1.00	.70	.30
				33 Cy Young	.60	.45	.20

1933 GOUDEY (240)

2 3/8″ X 2 7/8″

— No. 181 —
GEORGE HERMAN (BABE) RUTH
NEW YORK YANKEES
One of the keenest students of baseball, New York Yankees Home Run Star. He is also one of the hardest men to pitch to in the game. Box men say you can fool him on a certain ball once, but the next time he gets it, he is apt to hit it out of the park.
Before starring as a home run hitter, was rated as one of the best pitchers in the American League. Born in Baltimore, Md., Feb. 7, 1894, Ruth is a left hander, 6 feet 2 inches tall and weighs 210 pounds.

This is one of a series of 240 Baseball Stars

BIG LEAGUE
CHEWING GUM
GOUDEY GUM CO.   BOSTON
Made by the originators of
INDIAN GUM

The 1933 Goudey set, also known as R-391 (ACC), was Goudey's first issue. The four Babe Ruth cards and the two Lou Gehrig cards in the set are extremely popular with collectors. Card number 106, Napoleon (Larry) Lajoie, is quite rare as it was not printed in 1933 but printed on a very limited basis with the 1934 Goudey set. The complete set price below does not include the Lajoie card.

	MINT	VG-E	F-G
COMPLETE SET	2600.00	1800.00	800.00
COMMON PLAYER	8.00	5.50	2.50
1 Benny Bengough	50.00	13.00	4.00
2 Dazzy Vance	15.00	11.00	5.00
3 Hugh Critz	8.00	5.50	2.50
4 Heine Schuble	8.00	5.50	2.50
5 Babe Herman	9.00	6.75	3.00
6 Jimmy Dykes	9.00	6.75	3.00
7 Ted Lyons	15.00	11.00	5.00
8 Roy Johnson	8.00	5.50	2.50
9 Dave Harris	8.00	5.50	2.50
10 Glenn Myatt	8.00	5.50	2.50
11 Billy Rogell	8.00	5.50	2.50
12 George Pipgras	8.00	5.50	2.50
13 Lafayette Thompson	8.00	5.50	2.50
14 Henry Johnson	8.00	5.50	2.50
15 Victor Sorrell	8.00	5.50	2.50
16 George Blaeholder	8.00	5.50	2.50
17 Watson Clark	8.00	5.50	2.50
18 Muddy Ruel	8.00	5.50	2.50
19 Bill Dickey	30.00	22.50	10.50
20 Bill Terry (T)	21.00	15.50	7.00
21 Phil Collins	8.00	5.50	2.50
22 Pie Traynor	19.00	14.50	6.50
23 Kiki Cuyler	15.00	11.00	5.00
24 Horace Ford	8.00	5.50	2.50
25 Paul Waner	17.00	12.50	6.00
26 Chalmer Cissell	8.00	5.50	2.50
27 George Connally	8.00	5.50	2.50
28 Dick Bartell	8.00	5.50	2.50
29 Jimmy Foxx	50.00	38.00	17.00
30 Frank Hogan	8.00	5.50	2.50
31 Tony Lazzeri	10.00	7.00	3.00
32 Bud Clancy	8.00	5.50	2.50
33 Ralph Kress	8.00	5.50	2.50
34 Bob O'Farrell	8.00	5.50	2.50
35 Al Simmons	18.00	13.50	6.00
36 Tommy Thevenow	8.00	5.50	2.50
37 Jimmy Wilson	8.00	5.50	2.50
38 Fred Bickell	8.00	5.50	2.50
39 Mark Koenig	8.00	5.50	2.50
40 Taylor Douthit	8.00	5.50	2.50
41 Gus Mancuso	8.00	5.50	2.50
42 Eddie Collins	16.00	12.00	5.50
43 Lew Fonseca	8.00	5.50	2.50
44 Jim Bottomley	15.00	11.00	5.00
45 Larry Benton	8.00	5.50	2.50
46 Ethan Allen	8.00	5.50	2.50
47 Heine Manush (B)	15.00	11.00	5.00
48 Marty McManus	8.00	5.50	2.50
49 Frank Frisch	20.00	15.00	6.50
50 Ed Brandt	8.00	5.50	2.50
51 Charlie Grimm	9.00	6.75	3.00
52 Andy Cohen	8.00	5.50	2.50
53 Babe Ruth (3/4 B)	275.00	200.00	80.00
54 Ray Kremer	8.00	5.50	2.50
55 Pat Malone	8.00	5.50	2.50
56 Charlie Ruffing	15.00	11.00	5.00
57 Earl Clark	8.00	5.50	2.50
58 Lefty O'Doul	9.00	6.75	3.00
59 Bing Miller	8.00	5.50	2.50
60 Waite Hoyt	15.00	11.00	5.00
61 Max Bishop	8.00	5.50	2.50
62 Pepper Martin	10.00	7.00	3.00
63 Joe Cronin (B)	17.00	12.50	6.00
64 Burleigh Grimes	15.00	11.00	5.00
65 Milt Gaston	8.00	5.50	2.50
66 George Grantham	8.00	5.50	2.50
67 Guy Bush	8.00	5.50	2.50
68 Horace Lisenbee	8.00	5.50	2.50
69 Randy Moore	8.00	5.50	2.50
70 Floyd (Pete) Scott	8.00	5.50	2.50
71 Robert J. Burke	8.00	5.50	2.50
72 Owen Carroll	8.00	5.50	2.50
73 Jess Haines	15.00	11.00	5.00
74 Eppa Rixey	15.00	11.00	5.00
75 Willie Kamm	8.00	5.50	2.50
76 Mickey Cochrane	21.00	15.50	7.00
77 Adam Comorosky	8.00	5.50	2.50
78 Jack Quinn	8.00	5.50	2.50
79 Red Faber	15.00	11.00	5.00
80 Clyde Manion	8.00	5.50	2.50
81 Sam Jones	8.00	5.50	2.50
82 Dibrell Williams	8.00	5.50	2.50
83 Pete Jablonowski	8.00	5.50	2.50
84 Glenn Spencer	8.00	5.50	2.50
85 Heine Sand	8.00	5.50	2.50
86 Phil Todt	8.00	5.50	2.50
87 Frank O'Rourke	8.00	5.50	2.50
88 Russell Rollings	8.00	5.50	2.50
89 Tris Speaker	25.00	18.50	8.75
90 Jess Petty	8.00	5.50	2.50
91 Tom Zachary	8.00	5.50	2.50
92 Lou Gehrig	160.00	120.00	60.00
93 John Welch	8.00	5.50	2.50
94 Bill Walker	8.00	5.50	2.50
95 Alvin Crowder	8.00	5.50	2.50
96 Willis Hudlin	8.00	5.50	2.50
97 Joe Morrissey	8.00	5.50	2.50
98 Walter Berger	8.00	5.50	2.50
99 Tony Cuccinello	8.00	5.50	2.50
100 George Uhle	8.00	5.50	2.50
101 Richard Coffman	8.00	5.50	2.50
102 Travis Jackson	8.00	5.50	2.50
103 Earl Combs	15.00	11.00	5.00
104 Fred Marberry	8.00	5.50	2.50
105 Bernie Friberg	8.00	5.50	2.50
106 Napoleon Lajoie	6000.00	4500.00	2000.00
107 Heine Manush (1/2)	15.00	11.00	5.00
108 Joe Kuhel	8.00	5.50	2.50
109 Joe Cronin	17.00	12.50	6.00
110 Goose Goslin	15.00	11.00	5.00
111 Monte Weaver	8.00	5.50	2.50
112 Fred Schulte	8.00	5.50	2.50
113 Oswald Bluege	8.00	5.50	2.50
114 Luke Sewell	9.00	6.75	3.00
115 Cliff Heathcote	8.00	5.50	2.50
116 Eddie Morgan	8.00	5.50	2.50
117 Rabbit Maranville	15.00	11.00	5.00
118 Val Picinich	8.00	5.50	2.50
119 Rogers Hornsby (F)	45.00	34.00	15.00
120 Carl Reynolds	8.00	5.50	2.50
121 Walter Stewart	8.00	5.50	2.50
122 Alvin Crowder	8.00	5.50	2.50
123 Jack Russell	8.00	5.50	2.50
124 Earl Whitehill	8.00	5.50	2.50
125 Bill Terry	21.00	15.50	7.00

	MINT	VG-E	F-G
126 Joe Moore	8.00	5.50	2.50
127 Mel Ott	30.00	22.50	10.50
128 Chuck Klein	15.00	11.00	5.00
129 Hal Schumacher (P)	8.00	5.50	2.50
130 Fred Fitzsimmons	8.00	5.50	2.50
131 Fred Frankhouse	8.00	5.50	2.50
132 Jim Elliott	8.00	5.50	2.50
133 Fred Lindstrom	15.00	11.00	5.00
134 Sam Rice	15.00	11.00	5.00
135 Woody English	8.00	5.50	2.50
136 Flint Rhem	8.00	5.50	2.50
137 Fred (Red) Lucas	8.00	5.50	2.50
138 Herb Pennock	15.00	11.00	5.00
139 Ben Cantwell	8.00	5.50	2.50
140 Bump Hadley	8.00	5.50	2.50
141 Ray Benge	8.00	5.50	2.50
142 Paul Richards	9.00	6.75	3.00
143 Glenn Wright	8.00	5.50	2.50
144 Babe Ruth (B)	250.00	175.00	80.00
145 George Walberg	8.00	5.50	2.50
146 Walter Stewart (P)	8.00	5.50	2.50
147 Leo Durocher	12.00	8.75	4.00
148 Eddie Farrell	8.00	5.50	2.50
149 Babe Ruth (3/4 B/red)	275.00	200.00	90.00
150 Ray Kolp	8.00	5.50	2.50
151 Jake Flowers	8.00	5.50	2.50
152 Zack Taylor	8.00	5.50	2.50
153 Buddy Myer	8.00	5.50	2.50
154 Jimmy Foxx	50.00	38.00	17.00
155 Joe Judge	8.00	5.50	2.50
156 Danny MacFayden	8.00	5.50	2.50
157 Sam Byrd	8.00	5.50	2.50
158 Moe Berg	9.00	6.75	3.00
159 Oswald Bluege	8.00	5.50	2.50
160 Lou Gehrig	160.00	120.00	60.00
161 Al Spohrer	8.00	5.50	2.50
162 Leo Mangum	8.00	5.50	2.50
163 Luke Sewell	9.00	6.75	3.00
164 Lloyd Waner	15.00	11.00	5.00
165 Joe Sewell	15.00	11.00	5.00
166 Sam West	8.00	5.50	2.50
167 Jack Russell	8.00	5.50	2.50
168 Goose Goslin	15.00	11.00	5.00
169 Al Thomas	8.00	5.50	2.50
170 Harry McCurdy	8.00	5.50	2.50
171 Charlie Jamieson	8.00	5.50	2.50
172 Billy Hargrave	8.00	5.50	2.50
173 Roscoe Holm	8.00	5.50	2.50
174 Warren (Curly) Ogden	8.00	5.50	2.50
175 Dan Howley	8.00	5.50	2.50
176 John Ogden	8.00	5.50	2.50
177 Walter French	8.00	5.50	2.50
178 Jackie Warner	8.00	5.50	2.50
179 Fred Leach	8.00	5.50	2.50
180 Eddie Moore	8.00	5.50	2.50
181 Babe Ruth	275.00	200.00	90.00
182 Andy High	8.00	5.50	2.50

	MINT	VG-E	F-G
183 George Walberg	8.00	5.50	2.50
184 Charley Berry	8.00	5.50	2.50
185 Bob Smith	8.00	5.50	2.50
186 John Schulte	8.00	5.50	2.50
187 Heine Manush	15.00	11.00	5.00
188 Rogers Hornsby	45.00	34.00	15.00
189 Joe Cronin	17.00	12.50	6.00
190 Fred Schulte	8.00	5.50	2.50
191 Ben Chapman	8.00	5.50	2.50
192 Walter Brown	8.00	5.50	2.50
193 Lynford Lary	8.00	5.50	2.50
194 Earl Averill	15.00	11.00	5.00
195 Evan Swanson	8.00	5.50	2.50
196 Leroy Mahaffey	8.00	5.50	2.50
197 Rick Ferrell	8.00	5.50	2.50
198 Jack Burns	8.00	5.50	2.50
199 Tom Bridges	8.00	5.50	2.50
200 Bill Hallahan	8.00	5.50	2.50
201 Ernie Orsatti	8.00	5.50	2.50
202 Gabby Hartnett	15.00	11.00	5.00
203 Lon Warneke	8.00	5.50	2.50
204 Riggs Stephenson	9.00	6.75	3.00
205 Heine Meine	8.00	5.50	2.50
206 Gus Suhr	8.00	5.50	2.50
207 Mel Ott (B)	30.00	22.50	10.50
208 Bernie James	8.00	5.50	2.50
209 Adolfo Luque	8.00	5.50	2.50
210 Virgil Davis	8.00	5.50	2.50
211 Hack Wilson	15.00	11.00	5.00
212 Billy Urbanski	8.00	5.50	2.50
213 Earl Adams	8.00	5.50	2.50
214 John Kerr	8.00	5.50	2.50
215 Russ Van Atta	8.00	5.50	2.50
216 Vernon Gomez	30.00	22.50	10.50
217 Frank Crosetti	10.00	7.00	3.00
218 Wes Ferrell	9.00	6.75	3.00
219 Mule Haas	8.00	5.50	2.50
220 Lefty Grove	35.00	26.00	12.00
221 Dale Alexander	8.00	5.50	2.50
222 Charley Gehringer	21.00	15.50	7.00
223 Dizzy Dean	85.00	65.00	30.00
224 Frank Demaree	8.00	5.50	2.50
225 Bill Jurges	8.00	5.50	2.50
226 Charley Root	8.00	5.50	2.50
227 Bill Herman	15.00	11.00	5.00
228 Tony Piet	8.00	5.50	2.50
229 Floyd Vaughn	9.00	6.75	3.00
230 Carl Hubbell (P)	25.00	18.60	8.75
231 Joe Moore (F)	8.00	5.50	2.50
232 Lefty O'Doul	9.00	6.75	3.00
233 Johnny Vergez	8.00	5.50	2.50
234 Carl Hubbell	25.00	18.50	8.75
235 Fred Fitzsimmons	8.00	5.50	2.50
236 George Davis	8.00	5.50	2.50
237 Gus Mancuso	8.00	5.50	2.50
238 Hugh Critz	8.00	5.50	2.50
239 Leroy Parmelee	8.00	5.50	2.50
240 Hal Schumacher	10.00	7.00	3.00

1934 GOUDEY (96) 2 3/8" X 2 7/8"

— No. 2 — 1934 Series —

GORDON (MICKEY) COCHRANE

MANAGER, DETROIT TIGERS

"Mickey Cochrane rates as the best batting catcher in the American League and in 1933 rolled up an average of .322. He's a great hitter, a shrewd ball player and a good catcher. In 1928 he won the title of most valuable player in the American League. Last season he made 104 runs out of 138 hits in 130 games. At the end of the 1933 season he was traded by the Philadelphia Athletics to Detroit and signed to manage the Tigers.

"Mickey Cochrane was born in Bridgewater, Mass., played football at Boston University, and started minor league baseball in 1923. He was purchased from Portland, Ore., in 1924 by Connie Mack for $50,000, and stayed with the Athletics from 1925 to the end of 1933 when he went to Detroit. He is 5 feet, 10½ inches tall and weighs around 180 pounds."

This is one of the 1934 Series of pictures of Big League Baseball Stars. Collect the entire series.

BIG LEAGUE

CHEWING GUM

GOUDEY GUM CO. BOSTON

Made by the originators of **INDIAN GUM**

The 1934 Goudey is also known as R-320 (ACC). Cards nos. 1—72 are common compared to the last 24 numbers. The 1934 Goudey issue is less plentiful than the 1933 Goudey issue. Most of the cards in the set contain a blue "Lou Gehrig Say's" endorsement on the face; however, 12 of the high numbers contain a red "Chuck Klein Say's" endorsement.

	MINT	VG-E	F-G
COMPLETE SET	1600.00	1200.00	500.00
COMMON PLAYER (1-48)	8.00	5.50	2.50
COMMON PLAYER (49-72)	10.00	7.00	3.00
COMMON PLAYER (73-96)	32.00	25.00	10.00
1 Jimmy Foxx	80.00	40.00	15.00
2 Mickey Cochrane	20.00	15.00	6.50
3 Charlie Grimm	9.50	7.00	3.00
4 Woody English	8.00	5.50	2.50
5 Ed Brandt	8.00	5.50	2.50

	MINT	VG-E	F-G
6 Dizzy Dean	80.00	60.00	25.00
7 Leo Durocher	11.00	8.00	3.50
8 Tony Piet	8.00	5.00	2.50
9 Ben Chapman	8.00	5.00	2.50
10 Chuck Klein	14.00	10.50	4.75
11 Paul Waner	16.00	12.00	5.50
12 Carl Hubbell	22.00	16.50	7.50
13 Frank Frisch	22.00	16.50	7.50
14 Willie Kamm	8.00	5.50	2.50

	MINT	VG-E	F-G
15 Alvin Crowder	8.00	5.50	2.50
16 Joe Kuhel	8.00	5.50	2.50
17 Hugh Critz	8.00	5.50	2.50
18 Heinie Manush	14.00	10.50	4.75
19 Lefty Grove	25.00	18.50	8.75
20 Frank Hogan	8.00	5.50	2.50
21 Bill Terry	20.00	15.00	6.50
22 Arkie Vaughan	10.00	7.00	3.00
23 Charlie Gehringer	18.00	13.50	6.00
24 Ray Benge	8.00	5.50	2.50
25 Roger Cramer	8.00	5.50	2.50
26 Gerald Walker	8.00	5.50	2.50
27 Luke Appling	14.00	10.50	4.75
28 Ed Coleman	8.00	5.50	2.50
29 Larry French	8.00	5.50	2.50
30 Julius Solters	8.00	5.50	2.50
31 Buck Jordan	8.00	5.50	2.50
32 Blondy Ryan	8.00	5.50	2.50
33 Frank Hurst	8.00	5.50	2.50
34 Chick Hafey	14.00	10.50	4.75
35 Ernie Lombardi	11.00	8.00	3.50
36 Walter Betts	8.00	5.50	2.50
37 Lou Gehrig	160.00	120.00	60.00
38 Oral Hildebrand	8.00	5.50	2.50
39 Fred Walker	8.00	5.50	2.50
40 John Stone	8.00	5.50	2.50
41 George Earnshaw	8.00	5.50	2.50
42 John Allen	8.00	5.50	2.50
43 Dick Porter	8.00	5.50	2.50
44 Tom Bridges	8.00	5.50	2.50
45 Oscar Melillo	8.00	5.50	2.50
46 Joe Stripp	8.00	5.50	2.50
47 John Frederick	8.00	5.50	2.50
48 Tex Carleton	8.00	5.50	2.50
49 Sam Leslie	10.00	7.00	3.00
50 Walter Beck	10.00	7.00	3.00
51 Rip Collins	10.00	7.00	3.00
52 Herman Bell	10.00	7.00	3.00
53 George Watkins	10.00	7.00	3.00
54 Wesley Schulmerich	10.00	7.00	3.00
55 Ed Holley	10.00	7.00	3.00
56 Mark Koenig	10.00	7.00	3.00
57 Bill Swift	10.00	7.00	3.00
58 Earl Grace	10.00	7.00	3.00
59 Joe Mowry	10.00	7.00	3.00
60 Lynn Nelson	10.00	7.00	3.00
61 Lou Gehrig	210.00	160.00	75.00
62 Hank Greenberg	22.00	16.50	7.50
63 Minter Hayes	10.00	7.00	3.00
64 Frank Grube	10.00	7.00	3.00
65 Cliff Bolton	10.00	7.00	3.00
66 Mel Harder	10.00	7.00	3.00
67 Bob Weiland	10.00	7.00	3.00
68 Bob Johnson	10.00	7.00	3.00
69 John Marcum	10.00	7.00	3.00
70 Pete Fox	10.00	7.00	3.00
71 Lyle Tinning	10.00	7.00	3.00
72 Arndt Jorgens	10.00	7.00	3.00
73 Ed Wells	32.00	25.00	10.00
74 Bob Boken	32.00	25.00	10.00
75 Bill Werber	32.00	25.00	10.00
76 Hal Trosky	32.00	25.00	10.00
77 Joe Vosmik	32.00	25.00	10.00
78 Pinky Higgins	32.00	25.00	10.00
79 Ed Durham	32.00	25.00	10.00
80 Marty McManus	32.00	25.00	10.00
81 Bob Brown	32.00	25.00	10.00
82 Bill Hallahan	32.00	25.00	10.00
83 Jim Mooney	32.00	25.00	10.00
84 Paul Derringer	40.00	30.00	13.00
85 Adam Comorosky	32.00	25.00	10.00
86 Lloyd Johnson	32.00	25.00	10.00
87 George Darrow	32.00	25.00	10.00
88 Homer Peel	32.00	25.00	10.00
89 Linus Frey	32.00	25.00	10.00
90 Ki-Ki Cuyler	60.00	45.00	20.00
91 Dolph Camilli	32.00	25.00	10.00
92 Steve Larkin	32.00	25.00	10.00
93 Fred Ostermueller	32.00	25.00	10.00
94 Red Rolfe	40.00	30.00	13.00
95 Myril Hoag	32.00	25.00	10.00
96 James DeShong	40.00	30.00	13.00

1935 GOUDEY (36)

2 3/8" X 2 7/8"

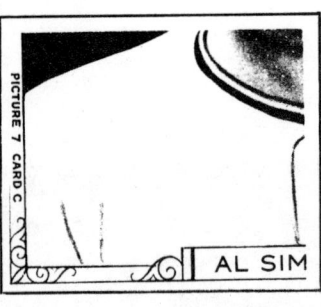

The 1935 Goudey set is sometimes called the "Goudey Puzzle Set", the "Goudey 4-in-1's", or R-321 (ACC). There are 36 different card fronts but 114 different front-back combinations. The card number in the checklist refers to the back puzzle number, and the backs can be arranged to form a puzzle picturing a player or team. The "(b)" in the checklist refers to a card with a blue border, as most cards have a red border. The set price below includes only the 36 different fronts, making no distinction as to which backs are present. The cards with an asterisk in the checklist below are more difficult to obtain. The following is the list of the puzzle "backs" 1. Detroit Tigers, 2. Chuck Klein, 3. Frankie Frisch, 4. Mickey Cochrane, 5. Joe Cronin, 6. Jimmy Foxx, 7. Al Simmons, 8. Cleveland Indians and 9. Washington Senators.

	MINT	VG-E	F-G
COMPLETE SET	450.00	330.00	150.00
COMMON CARDS	10.25	7.25	3.50
1-A Frisch, Dean, Orsatti, Carleton	15.00	11.00	5.00
1-B Mahaffey, Foxx, Williams, Higgins	15.00	11.00	5.00
1-C Manush, Lary, Weaver, Hadley	10.25	7.25	3.50
1-D Cochrane, Gehringer, Bridges, Rogell	12.00	8.75	4.00
1-E P. Waner, Bush, Hoyt, L. Waner	12.00	8.75	4.00
1-E Wilson, Allen, Jonnard, Brickell*	20.00	15.00	6.50
1-F Grimes, Klein, Cuyler, English	12.00	8.75	4.00
1-F West, Melillo, Blaeholder, Coffman*	20.00	15.00	6.50
1-G Leslie, Frey, Stripp, Clark	10.25	7.25	3.50
1-G Cronin, Reynolds, Bishop, Cissel*	20.00	15.00	6.50
1-H Piet, Comorosky, Bottomley, Adams	10.25	7.25	3.50
1-H Schuble, Marberry, Goslin, Crowder*	20.00	15.00	6.50
1-I Earnshaw, Dykes, L. Sewell, Appling	10.25	7.25	3.50
1-J Ruth, McManus, Brandt, Maranville	90.00	70.00	30.00
1-J Ruel, Simmons, Kamm, Cochrane*	20.00	15.00	6.50
1-K Terry, Schumacher, Mancuso, Jackson	10.25	7.25	3.50
1-K Hudlin, Myatt, Comorosky, Bottomley*	20.00	15.00	6.50
1-L Kamm, Hildebrand, Averill, Trosky	10.25	7.25	3.50
2-A Frisch, Dean, Orsatti, Carleton	15.00	11.00	5.00
2-A(b) Critz, Bartell, Ott, Mancuso*	20.00	15.00	6.50
2-B Mahaffey, Foxx, Williams, Higgins	15.00	11.00	5.00
2-B(b) Traynor, Lucas, Thevenow, Wright*	20.00	15.00	6.50

2-C Manush, Lary, Weaver, Hadley	10.25	7.25	3.50
2-C(b) Berry, Burke, Kress, Vance*	20.00	15.00	6.50
2-D Cochrane, Gehringer, Bridges, Rogell	12.00	8.75	4.00
2-D(b) Ruffing, Malone, Lazzeri, Dickey*	20.00	15.00	6.50
2-E Kamm, Hildebrand, Averill, Trosky	10.25	7.25	3.50
2-E(b) Moore, Hogan, Frankhouse, Brandt*	20.00	15.00	6.50
2-F Earnshaw, Dykes, L. Sewell, Appling	10.25	7.25	3.50
2-F(b) Martin, O'Farrell, Byrd, MacFayden*	20.00	15.00	6.50
3-A Ruth, McManus, Brandt, Maranville	90.00	70.00	30.00
3-A Ruel, Simmons, Kamm, Cochrane *	20.00	15.00	6.50
3-B Terry, Schumacher, Mancuso, Jackson*	10.25	7.25	3.50
3-B Hudlin, Myatt, Comorosky, Bottomley *	20.00	15.00	6.50
3-C P. Waner, Bush, Hoyt, L. Waner	12.00	8.75	4.00
3-C Wilson, Allen, Jonnard, Brickell *	20.00	15.00	6.50
3-D Grimes, Klein, Cuyler, English	12.00	8.75	4.00
3-D West, Melillo, Blaeholder, Coffman *	20.00	15.00	6.50
3-E Leslie, Frey, Stripp, Clark	10.25	7.25	3.50
3-E Cronin, Reynolds, Bishop, Cissell*	20.00	15.00	6.50
3-F Piet, Comorosky, Bottomley, Adams	10.25	7.25	3.50
3-F Schuble, Marberry, Goslin, Crowder *	20.00	15.00	6.50
4-A Ruth, McManus, Brandt, Maranville*	125.00	90.00	40.00
4-A(b) Critz, Bartell, Ott, Mancuso	11.00	8.00	3.50
4-B Terry, Schumacher, Mancuso, Jackson*	20.00	15.00	6.50
4-B(b) Traynor, Lucas, Thevenow, Wright	10.25	7.25	3.50
4-C P. Waner, Bush, Hoyt, L. Waner*	20.00	15.00	6.50
4-C(b) Berry, Burke, Kress, Vance	10.25	7.25	3.50
4-D Ruffing, Malone, Lazzeri, Dickey	20.00	15.00	6.50
4-D Grimes, Klein, Cuyler, English*	12.00	8.75	4.00
4-E Leslie, Frey, Stripp, Clark*	20.00	15.00	6.50
4-E(b) Moore, Hogan, Frankhouse, Brandt	10.25	7.25	3.50
4-F Piet, Comorosky, Bottomley, Adams*	20.00	15.00	6.50
4-F(b) Martin, O'Farrell, Byrd, MacFayden	10.25	7.25	3.50
5-A Ruel, Simmons, Kamm, Cochrane	12.00	8.75	4.00
5-A Ruth, McManus, Brandt, Maranville *	150.00	110.00	50.00
5-B Hudlin, Myatt, Comorosky, Bottomley	10.25	7.25	3.50
5-B Terry, Schumacher, Mancuso, Jackson *	20.00	15.00	6.50
5-C P. Waner, Bush, Hoyt, L. Waner	12.00	8.75	4.00
5-C Wilson, Allen, Jonnard, Brickell *	20.00	15.00	6.50
5-D West, Melillo, Blaeholder, Coffman	10.25	7.25	3.50
5-D Grimes, Klein, Cuyler, English *	20.00	15.00	6.50
5-E Leslie, Frey, Stripp, Clark	10.25	7.25	3.50
5-E Cronin, Reynolds, Bishop, Cissell *	20.00	15.00	6.50
5-F Schuble, Marberry, Goslin, Crowder	10.25	7.25	3.50
5-F Piet, Comorosky, Bottomley, Adams *	20.00	15.00	6.50
6-A Ruel, Simmons, Kamm, Cochrane	12.00	8.75	4.00
6-A Frisch, Dean, Orsatti, Carleton *	30.00	22.50	10.50
6-B Hudlin, Myatt, Comorosky, Bottomley	10.25	7.25	3.50
6-B Mahaffey, Foxx, Williams, Higgins *	30.00	22.50	10.50
6-C Manush, Lary, Weaver, Hadley *	10.25	7.25	3.50
6-C Wilson, Allen, Jonnard, Brickell	20.00	15.00	6.50
6-D West, Melillo, Blaeholder, Coffman *	10.25	7.25	3.50
6-D Cochrane, Gehringer, Bridges, Rogell *	25.00	18.50	8.75
6-E Cronin, Reynolds, Bishop, Cissell	10.25	7.25	3.50
6-E Kamm, Hildebrand, Averill, Trosky *	20.00	15.00	6.50
6-F Schuble, Marberry, Goslin, Crowder	10.25	7.25	3.50
6-F Earnshaw, Dykes, L. Sewell, Appling*	20.00	15.00	6.50
7-A Frisch, Dean, Orsatti, Carleton*	30.00	22.50	10.50
7-A(b) Critz, Bartell, Ott, Mancuso	11.00	8.00	3.50
7-B Mahaffey, Foxx, Williams, Higgins *	30.00	22.50	10.50
7-B(b) Traynor, Lucas, Thevenow, Wright	10.25	7.25	3.50
7-C Manush, Lary, Weaver, Hadley*	20.00	15.00	6.50
7-C(b) Berry, Burke, Kress, Vance	10.25	7.25	3.50
7-D Cochrane, Gehringer, Bridges, Rogell*	25.00	18.50	8.75
7-D(b) Ruffing, Malone, Lazzeri, Dickey	12.00	8.75	4.00
7-E Kamm, Hildebrand, Averill, Trosky*	20.00	15.00	6.50
7-E(b) Moore, Hogan, Frankhouse, Brandt	10.25	7.25	3.50
7-F Earnshaw, Dykes, L. Sewell, Appling*	20.00	15.00	6.50
7-F(b) Martin, O'Farrell, Byrd, MacFayden	10.25	7.25	3.50
8-A Koenig, Fitzsimmons, Benge, Zachary	10.25	7.25	3.50
8-B Hayes, Lyons, Haas, Bonura	10.25	7.25	3.50
8-C Burns, Hemsley, Grube, Weiland	10.25	7.25	3.50
8-D Campbell, Meyers, Goodman, Kampouris	10.25	7.25	3.50
8-E DeShong, Allen, Rolfe, Walker	10.25	7.25	3.50
8-F Fox, Greenberg, Walker, Rowe	10.25	7.25	3.50
8-G Werber, R. Ferrell, W. Ferrell, Ostermueller	11.00	8.00	3.50
8-H Kuhel, Whitehill, Meyer, Stone	10.25	7.25	3.50
8-I Vosmik, Knickerbocker, Harder, Stewart	10.25	7.25	3.50
8-J Johnson, Coleman, Marcum, Cramer	10.25	7.25	3.50
8-K Herman, Suhr, Padden, Blanton	10.25	7.25	3.50
8-L Spohrer, Rhem, Cantwell, Benton	10.25	7.25	3.50
9-A Koenig, Fitzsimmons, Benge, Zachary	10.25	7.25	3.50
9-B Hayes, Lyons, Haas, Bonura	10.25	7.25	3.50
9-C Burns, Hemsley, Grube, Weiland	10.25	7.25	3.50
9-D Campbell, Meyers, Goodman, Kampouris	10.25	7.25	3.50
9-E DeShong, Allen, Rolfe, Walker	10.25	7.25	3.50
9-F Fox, Greenberg, Walker, Rowe	10.25	7.25	3.50
9-G Werber, R. Ferrell, W. Ferrell, Ostermueller	11.00	8.00	3.50
9-H Kuhel, Whitehill, Meyer, Stone	10.25	7.25	3.50
9-I Vosmik, Knickerbocker, Harder, Stewart	10.25	7.25	3.50
9-J Johnson, Coleman, Marcum, Cramer	10.25	7.25	3.50
9-K Herman, Suhr, Padden, Blanton	10.25	7.25	3.50
9-L Spohrer, Rhem, Cantwell, Benton	10.25	7.25	3.50

T215 RED SUN

T213 COUPON

1936 GOUDEY (25) B&W ### 2 3/8" X 2 7/8"

OUT!!

High infield fly—taken
by the 3rd baseman.
Runners hold bases.

James (Jimmie) Dykes — after 14
great seasons with the Athletics, he
was traded to the White Sox in 1933,
and was appointed manager early in
1934. He's doing a fine job. Dykes is
also a noted after dinner speaker.

base.
ЯƎTAS znur уnA
ТЕR SAFE!
-ТАВ .llad eht delbmut ohw
namesab drと of hsams eniⅬ

¡¡¡RORRƎ

The 1936 Goudey set is also
known as the "Goudey
Game Back Set", the
"Goudey Black & White
Set", or R-322 (ACC). There
are 25 different fronts but
perhaps as many as 200 different front-back combinations.

	MINT	VG-E	F-G
COMPLETE SET	250.00	175.00	75.00
COMMON PLAYER	9.00	6.50	3.00
1 Wally Berger	9.00	6.50	3.00
2 Zeke Bonura	9.00	6.50	3.00
3 Frenchie Bordagaray	9.00	6.50	3.00
4 Bill Brubaker	9.00	6.50	3.00
5 Dolph Camilli	9.00	6.50	3.00
6 Clyde Castleman	9.00	6.50	3.00
7 Mickey Cochrane	15.00	11.00	5.00
8 Joe Coscarart	9.00	6.50	3.00
9 Frank Crosetti	10.00	7.00	3.00
10 Kiki Cuyler	12.00	8.75	4.00
11 Paul Derringer	10.00	7.00	3.00

	MINT	VG-E	F-G
12 Jimmy Dykes	10.00	7.00	3.00
13 Rich Ferrell	9.00	6.50	3.00
14 Lefty Gomez	18.00	13.50	6.00
15 Hank Greenberg	16.00	12.00	5.50
16 Bucky Harris	12.00	8.75	4.00
17 Rollie Hemsley	9.00	6.50	3.00
18 Pinky Higgins	9.00	6.50	3.00
19 Oral Hildebrand	9.00	6.50	3.00
20 Chuck Klein	12.00	8.75	4.00
21 Pepper Martin	10.00	7.00	3.00
22 Bobo Newsom	10.00	7.00	3.00
23 Paul Waner	12.00	8.75	4.00
24 Bill Werber	9.00	6.50	3.00
25 Joe Vosmik	9.00	6.50	3.00

1938 GOUDEY (48) ### 2 3/8" X 2 7/8"

The 1938 Goudey set is commonly referred to as the
"Heads-Up Set", or R-323
(ACC). These very popular
but difficult to obtain cards
came in two series of the
same 24 players. The first
series nos. 241-264 is distinguished from the second series
nos. 265-288 in that the second contains etched cartoons
and comments surrounding
the player picture. Althou
the set starts with no. 24
it is not a continuation
the 1933 Goudey set, but
separate set in its own righ

— No. 264 —
ROBERT "BOB" FELLER

Born Van Meter, Iowa Nov. 3, 1918
Bats Right Throws Right
Height 5' 11¼" Weight 180 lbs.
Position PITCHER
"Bob" began his professional baseball career with
the Cleveland Club in 1936. He entered the majors
in 1936 with the Cleveland Indians with which
team he is now playing.
His two year major league record is as follows:
Games .... 10 Innings Pitched .. 211
Won .... 14 Lost 10
Strike outs ...... 229 Bases on Balls .. 153
Hits .... 165 Pct. Games Won .583

This is one of a series of 288 Baseball Stars

BIG LEAGUE
CHEWING GUM
GOUDEY GUM CO.   BOSTON
Made by the originator of
INDIAN GUM

	MINT	VG-E	F-G
COMPLETE SET	2400.00	1800.00	700.00
COMMON PLAYER (241-264)	32.00	25.00	10.00
COMMON PLAYER (265-288)	40.00	30.00	12.00
241 Charlie Gehringer	65.00	48.00	22.00
242 Pete Fox	32.00	25.00	10.00
243 Joe Kuhel	32.00	25.00	10.00
244 Frank Demaree	32.00	25.00	10.00
245 Frank Pytlak	32.00	25.00	10.00
246 Ernie Lombardi	40.00	30.00	12.00
247 Joe Vosmik	32.00	25.00	10.00
248 Dick Bartell	32.00	25.00	10.00
249 Jimmie Foxx	120.00	85.00	40.00
250 Joe DiMaggio	275.00	200.00	80.00
251 Bump Hadley	32.00	25.00	10.00
252 Zeke Bonura	32.00	25.00	10.00
253 Hank Greenberg	70.00	50.00	23.00
254 Van Lingle Mungo	32.00	25.00	10.00
255 Moose Solters	32.00	25.00	10.00
256 Vernon Kennedy	32.00	25.00	10.00
257 Al Lopez	40.00	30.00	12.00
258 Bobby Doerr	32.00	25.00	10.00
259 Billy Werber	32.00	25.00	10.00
260 Rudy York	32.00	25.00	10.00
261 Rip Radcliff	32.00	25.00	10.00
262 Joe Medwick	65.00	48.00	22.00
263 Mickey Owen	32.00	25.00	10.00

	MINT	VG-E	F-G
264 Bob Feller	120.00	85.00	40.00
265 Charlie Gehringer	75.00	55.00	24.00
266 Pete Fox	40.00	30.00	12.00
267 Joe Kuhel	40.00	30.00	12.00
268 Frank Demaree	40.00	30.00	12.00
269 Frank Pytlak	40.00	30.00	12.00
270 Ernie Lombardi	45.00	34.00	15.00
271 Joe Vosmik	40.00	30.00	12.00
272 Dick Bartell	40.00	30.00	12.00
273 Jimmie Foxx	150.00	110.00	50.00
274 Joe DiMaggio	350.00	250.00	100.00
275 Bump Hadley	40.00	30.00	12.00
276 Zeke Bonura	40.00	30.00	12.00
277 Hank Greenberg	80.00	60.00	25.00
278 Van Lingle Mungo	40.00	30.00	12.00
279 Moose Solters	40.00	30.00	12.00
280 Vernon Kennedy	40.00	30.00	12.00
281 Al Lopez	45.00	34.00	15.00
282 Bobby Doerr	40.00	30.00	12.00
283 Billy Werber	40.00	30.00	12.00
284 Rudy York	40.00	30.00	12.00
285 Rip Radcliff	40.00	30.00	12.00
286 Joe Medwick	75.00	55.00	24.00
287 Mickey Owen	40.00	30.00	12.00
288 Bob Feller	150.00	110.00	50.00

1937 R325 GOUDEY (24)   2 3/8" X 2 7/8"

The 1937 "Knot Hole League Game" was another of the many innovative marketing ideas of the Goudey Gum Company. Advertised as a series of 100 game cards promising "exciting" baseball action, the set actually was limited to the 24 cards listed below.

	MINT	VG-E	F-G
COMPLETE SET	90.00	70.00	30.00
COMMON CARD	4.00	3.00	1.40

	MINT	VG-E	F-G
1 Double-Foul	4.00	3.00	1.40
2 Steals Home-Strike	4.00	3.00	1.40
3 Ball-Out	4.00	3.00	1.40
4 Strike-Ball	4.00	3.00	1.40
5 Strike-Wild Pitch	4.00	3.00	1.40
6 Ball-Out	4.00	3.00	1.40
7 Bunt-Scratch Hit- Stolen Base	4.00	3.00	1.40
8 Hit By Pitched Ball-Out	4.00	3.00	1.40
9 Foul-Ball	4.00	3.00	1.40
10 Foul-Double!!	4.00	3.00	1.40
11 Out-Ball	4.00	3.00	1.40
12 Foul-Force Out	4.00	3.00	1.40

	MINT	VG-E	F-G
13 Out-Single	4.00	3.00	1.40
14 Strike-Ball	4.00	3.00	1.40
15 Foul Tip-Strike!	4.00	3.00	1.40
16 Unknown	4.00	3.00	1.40
17 Ball-Out	4.00	3.00	1.40
18 Out!!-Error!!!	4.00	3.00	1.40
19 Strike-Foul	4.00	3.00	1.40
20 Double Play-Out	4.00	3.00	1.40
21 !!Home Run!!-Ball	5.00	3.75	1.75
22 Out-Strike	4.00	3.00	1.40
23 Ball-Out	4.00	3.00	1.40
24 Strike-Ball	4.00	3.00	1.40

1937 R326 GOUDEY "FLIP MOVIES" (26)   2" X 3"

The 26 "Flip Movies" which comprise this set are a miniature version of the popular penny arcade features of the period. Each movie comes in two parts, clearly labeled, and there are several cover colors as well as incorrect photos known to exist.

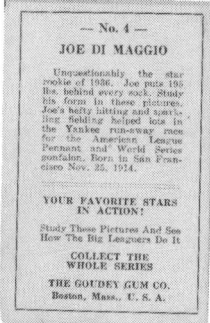
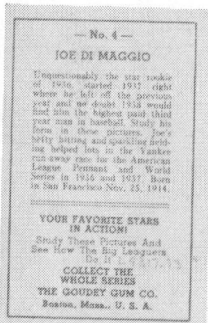

	MINT	VG-E	F-G
COMPLETE SET	500.00	375.00	175.00
COMMON PLAYER	17.00	12.50	6.00

	MINT	VG-E	F-G
1A John Irving Burns- Poles Two Bagger	17.00	12.50	6.00
1B John Irving Burns- Poles Two Bagger	17.00	12.50	6.00
2A Joe Vosmik-Triples	17.00	12.50	6.00
2B Joe Vosmik-Triples	17.00	12.50	6.00
3A Mel Ott	30.00	22.50	10.50
3B Mel Ott	30.00	22.50	10.50
4A Joe DiMaggio-Socks A Sizzling Long Drive	60.00	45.00	20.00
4B Joe DiMaggio-Socks A Sizzling Long Drive	60.00	45.00	20.00
5A Wally Moses-Leans Against A Fast Ball	17.00	12.50	6.00
5B Wally Moses-Leans Against A Fast Ball	17.00	12.50	6.00
6A Van Lingle Mungo- Tosses Fire-Ball	17.00	12.50	6.00
6B Van Lingle Mungo- Tosses Fire-Ball	17.00	12.50	6.00
7A Luke Appling-Gets Set For Double Play	20.00	15.00	6.50
7B Luke Appling-Gets Set For Double Play	20.00	15.00	6.50

	MINT	VG-E	F-G
8A Bob Feller	40.00	30.00	13.00
8B Bob Feller	40.00	30.00	13.00
9A Paul Derringer-Demon- strates A Sharp Curve	17.00	12.50	6.00
9B Paul Derringer-Demon- strates A Sharp Curve	17.00	12.50	6.00
10A Paul Waner-Big Poison Smacks A Triple	25.00	18.50	8.75
10B Paul Waner-Big Poison Smacks A Triple	25.00	18.50	8.75
11A Joe Medwick-Bats Hard Grounder	25.00	18.50	8.75
11B Joe Medwick-Bats Hard Grounder	25.00	18.50	8.75
12A James Emory Foxx- Smacks A Homer	40.00	30.00	13.00
12B James Emory Foxx- Smacks A Homer	40.00	30.00	13.00
13A Wally Berger-Puts One In The Bleachers	17.00	12.50	6.00
13B Wally Berger-Puts One In The Bleachers	17.00	12.50	6.00

1941 GOUDEY (33)   2 3/8" X 2 7/8"

The 1941 Goudey set or "Goudey Blank Backs", or R-324 (ACC), includes 33 different players, each printed with four different colored backgrounds—red, blue, green, or yellow. Cards are sometimes seen without numbers. This unattractive set was unevenly distributed and nos. 21—25 are scarcer than the others.

	MINT	VG-E	F-G
COMPLETE SET	800.00	525.00	225.00
COMMON PLAYER	20.00	15.00	6.00
1 Hugh Mulcahy	20.00	15.00	6.00
2 Harland Clift	20.00	15.00	6.00
3 Louis Chiozza	20.00	15.00	6.00
4 Warren Rosar	20.00	15.00	6.00
5 George McQuinn	20.00	15.00	6.00
6 Emerson Dickman	20.00	15.00	6.00
7 Wayne Ambler	20.00	15.00	6.00
8 Bob Muncrief	20.00	15.00	6.00
9 Bill Dietrich	20.00	15.00	6.00
10 Taft Wright	20.00	15.00	6.00
11 Don Heffner	20.00	15.00	6.00
12 Fritz Ostermueller	20.00	15.00	6.00
13 Frank Hayes	20.00	15.00	6.00
14 John Kramer	20.00	15.00	6.00
15 Dario Lodigiani	20.00	15.00	6.00

	MINT	VG-E	F-G
16 George Case	20.00	15.00	6.00
17 Vito Tamulis	20.00	15.00	6.00
18 Whitlow Wyatt	20.00	15.00	6.00
19 Bill Posedel	20.00	15.00	6.00
20 Carl Hubbell	40.00	30.00	13.00
21 Harold Warstler	35.00	26.00	12.00
22 Joe Sullivan	100.00	70.00	30.00
23 Norman Young	35.00	26.00	12.00
24 Stanley Andrews	50.00	38.00	17.00
25 Morris Arnovich	35.00	26.00	12.00
26 Elbert Fletcher	20.00	15.00	6.00
27 Bill Crough	20.00	15.00	6.00
28 Al Todd	20.00	15.00	6.00
29 Debs Garms	20.00	15.00	6.00
30 Jim Tobin	20.00	15.00	6.00
31 Chester Ross	20.00	15.00	6.00
32 George Coffman	20.00	15.00	6.00
33 Mel Ott	50.00	38.00	17.00

1955 ROBERT F. GOULD (28)   2 1/2" X 3 1/2"

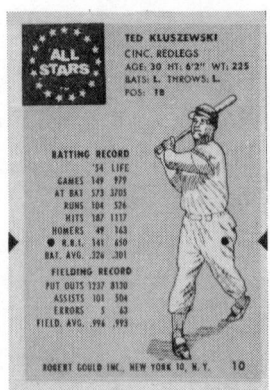

The 1955 Robert F. Gould set of 28 black and white on green, numbered cards were toy store cardboard holders for small plastic statues. The statues were attached to the card by a rubber band through two holes on the side of the card. The ACC designation is W605.

	MINT	VG-E	F-G
COMPLETE SET	360.00	270.00	120.00
COMMON PLAYER	12.00	9.00	4.00
1 Willie Mays	125.00	90.00	40.00
2 Guz Zernial	12.00	9.00	4.00
3 Al "Red" Schoendienst	15.00	11.00	5.00
4 Chico Carrasquel	12.00	9.00	4.00
5 Jim Hegan	12.00	9.00	4.00
6 Curt Simmons	12.00	9.00	4.00
7 Bob Porterfield	12.00	9.00	4.00
8 Jim Busby	12.00	9.00	4.00
9 Don Mueller	12.00	9.00	4.00
10 Ted Kluszewski	15.00	11.00	5.00
11 Ray Boone	12.00	9.00	4.00
12 Smokey Burgess	12.00	9.00	4.00
13 Bob Rush	12.00	9.00	4.00
14 Early Wynn	17.00	12.50	6.00

	MINT	VG-E	F-G
15 Bill Bruton	12.00	9.00	4.00
16 Gus Bell	12.00	9.00	4.00
17 Jim Finigan	12.00	9.00	4.00
18 Gran Hamner	12.00	9.00	4.00
19 Hank Thompson	12.00	9.00	4.00
20 Joe Coleman	12.00	9.00	4.00
21 Don Newcombe	15.00	11.00	5.00
22 Richie Ashburn	15.00	11.00	5.00
23 Bobby Thomson	15.00	11.00	5.00
24 Sid Gordon	12.00	9.00	4.00
25 Gerry Coleman	12.00	9.00	4.00
26 Ernie Banks	40.00	30.00	13.00
27 Billy Pierce	15.00	11.00	5.00
28 Mel Parnell	12.00	9.00	4.00

123

1958 HIRES (66)

2 5/16'' X 3 1/2''
2 5/16'' X 7''

BOB FRIEND
PITCHER—PITTSBURGH PIRATES

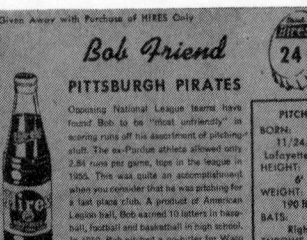

Given Away with Purchase of HIRES Only

Bob Friend
PITTSBURGH PIRATES

Opposing National League teams have found Bob to be "most unfriendly" in scoring runs off his assortment of pitching stuff. The ex-Purdue athlete allowed only 2.84 runs per game, tops in the league in 1955. This was quite an accomplishment when you consider that he was pitching for a last place club. A product of American Legion ball, Bob earned 10 letters in baseball, football and basketball in high school. In 1950, Bob pitched a no-hitter for Waco (Big State League) in his first season in organized baseball.

PITCHER
BORN: 11/24/30 Lafayette, Ind.
HEIGHT: 6'
WEIGHT: 190 lbs.
BATS: Right
THROWS: Right

The 1958 Hires Root beer set of 66 numbered, color cards was issued with detachable coupons as inserts with Hires Root Beer cartons. Cards with the coupon still intact are worth 25% higher than the prices listed below.

	MINT	VG-E	F-G
COMPLETE SET	275.00	200.00	80.00
COMMON PLAYER	3.00	2.25	1.00
10 Richie Ashburn	4.00	2.25	1.00
11 Chico Carrasquel	3.00	2.25	1.00
12 Dave Philley	3.00	2.25	1.00
13 Don Newcombe	5.00	3.75	1.75
14 Wally Post	3.00	2.25	1.00
15 Rip Repulski	3.00	2.25	1.00
16 Chico Fernandez	3.00	2.25	1.00
17 Larry Doby	5.00	3.75	1.75
18 Hector Brown	3.00	2.25	1.00
19 Danny O'Connell	3.00	2.25	1.00
20 Granny Hamner	3.00	2.25	1.00
21 Dick Groat	4.00	2.25	1.00
22 Ray Narleski	3.00	2.25	1.00
23 Pee Wee Reese	7.50	5.75	2.50
24 Bob Friend	3.00	2.25	1.00
25 Willie Mays	60.00	45.00	20.00
26 Bob Nieman	3.00	2.25	1.00
27 Frank Thomas	3.00	2.25	1.00
28 Curt Simmons	3.00	2.25	1.00
29 Stan Lopata	3.00	2.25	1.00
30 Bob Skinner	3.00	2.25	1.00
31 Ron Kline	3.00	2.25	1.00
32 Willie Miranda	3.00	2.25	1.00
33 Bob Avila	3.00	2.25	1.00
34 Clem Labine	3.00	2.25	1.00
35 Ray Jablonski	3.00	2.25	1.00
36 Bill Mazeroski	5.00	3.75	1.75
37 Billy Gardner	3.00	2.25	1.00
38 Pete Runnels	3.00	2.25	1.00
39 Jack Sanford	3.00	2.25	1.00
40 Dave Sisler	3.00	2.25	1.00
41 Don Zimmer	4.00	3.00	1.40

	MINT	VG-E	F-G
42 Johnny Podres	4.00	3.00	1.40
43 Dick Farrell	3.00	2.25	1.00
44 Hank Aaron	50.00	38.00	17.00
45 Bill Virdon	5.00	3.75	1.75
46 Bobby Thomson	5.00	3.75	1.75
47 Willard Nixon	3.00	2.25	1.00
48 Billy Loes	3.00	2.25	1.00
49 Hank Sauer	4.00	3.00	1.40
50 Johnny Antonelli	4.00	3.00	1.40
51 Daryl Spencer	3.00	2.25	1.00
52 Ken Lehman	3.00	2.25	1.00
53 Sammy White	3.00	2.25	1.00
54 Charley Neal	3.00	2.25	1.00
55 Don Drysdale	10.00	7.00	3.00
56 Jackie Jensen	5.00	3.75	1.75
57 Ray Katt	3.00	2.25	1.00
58 Frank Sullivan	3.00	2.25	1.00
59 Roy Face	4.00	3.00	1.40
60 Willie Jones	3.00	2.25	1.00
61 Duke Snider	20.00	15.00	6.50
62 Whitey Lockman	3.00	2.25	1.00
63 Gino Cimoli	3.00	2.25	1.00
64 Marv Grissom	3.00	2.25	1.00
65 Gene Baker	3.00	2.25	1.00
66 George Zuverink	3.00	2.25	1.00
67 Ted Kluszewski	5.00	3.75	1.75
68 Jim Busby	3.00	2.25	1.00
69 Not Issued	xxx	xxx	xxx
70 Curt Barclay	3.00	2.25	1.00
71 Hank Foiles	3.00	2.25	1.00
72 Gene Stephens	3.00	2.25	1.00
73 Al Worthington	3.00	2.25	1.00
74 Al Walker	3.00	2.25	1.00
75 Bob Boyd	3.00	2.25	1.00
76 Al Pilarcik	3.00	2.25	1.00

1958 HIRES TEST SET (8)

2 5/16'' X 3 1/2''
2 5/16'' X 7''

Bob Friend
PITCHER—PITTSBURGH PIRATES

Bob Friend
Pittsburgh Pirates

Opposing National League teams have found Bob to be "most unfriendly" in scoring runs off his assortment of pitching stuff. The ex-Purdue athlete allowed only 2.84 runs per game, tops in the league in 1955. This was quite an accomplishment when you consider that he was pitching for a last place club. A product of American Legion ball, Bob earned 10 letters in baseball, football and basketball in high school. In 1950, Bob pitched a no-hitter for Waco (Big State League) in his first season in organized baseball.

PITCHER
Born: 11/24/30 Lafayette, Ind.
Height: 6'
Weight: 190 lbs.
Bats: Right
Throws: Right

The 1958 Hires Root Beer test set contains eight unnumbered, color cards. The cards contain a detachable coupon just as the regular Hires issue does. Cards were issued on a very limited basis in select cities. Cards with the coupon still intact are worth more than the prices in the checklist below.

	MINT	VG-E	F-G
COMPLETE SET	450.00	350.00	150.00
COMMON PLAYER	50.00	38.00	17.00
1 Johnny Antonelli	50.00	38.00	17.00
2 Jim Busby	60.00	45.00	20.00
3 Chico Fernandez	50.00	38.00	17.00

	MINT	VG-E	F-G
4 Bob Friend	50.00	38.00	17.00
5 Vern Law	50.00	38.00	17.00
6 Stan Lopata	50.00	38.00	17.00
7 Willie Mays	150.00	110.00	50.00
8 Al Pilarcik	60.00	45.00	20.00

1947 W571 (48)
1947 HOMOGENIZED BOND (48)

2 1/4" X 3 1/2"
2 1/4" X 3 1/2"

The 1947 W571/D305 Homogenized Bread are sets of 48 unnumbered cards containing 44 baseball players and four boxers. The W571 set exists in two styles. Style one is identical to the D305 set except for the back printing while style two has perforated edges and movie stars depicted on the backs. The second style of W571 cards contains only 13 cards.

	MINT	VG-E	F-G			MINT	VG-E	F-G
COMPLETE SET	200.00	150.00	65.00	24 Edwin Joost		3.25	2.50	1.20
COMMON PLAYER	3.25	2.50	1.20	25 Charlie Keller		4.00	3.00	1.40
				26 Ken Keltner		3.25	2.50	1.20
1 Rex Barney	3.25	2.50	1.20	27 Buddy Kerr		3.25	2.50	1.20
2 Larry Berra	9.99	6.75	3.00	28 Ralph Kiner		6.00	4.50	2.00
3 Ewell Blackwell	3.25	2.50	1.20	29 Jake LaNotta		4.00	3.00	1.40
4 Lou Boudreau	6.00	4.50	2.00	30 John Lindell		3.25	2.50	1.20
5 Ralph Branca	3.25	2.50	1.20	31 Whitey Lockman		3.25	2.50	1.20
6 Harry Brecheen	3.25	2.50	1.20	32 Joe Louis		7.50	5.75	2.50
7 Primo Carnera	2.00	1.50	.60	33 Willard Marshall		3.25	2.50	1.20
8 Marcel Cerdan	2.00	1.50	.60	34 Johnny Mize		6.00	4.50	2.00
9 Dom DiMaggio	5.00	3.75	1.75	35 Stan Musial		18.00	13.50	6.00
10 Joe DiMaggio	25.00	18.50	8.75	36 Andy Pafko		3.25	2.50	1.20
11 Bobbie Doerr	4.00	3.00	1.40	37 Johnny Pesky		3.25	2.50	1.20
12 Bruce Edwards	3.25	2.50	1.20	38 "Pee Wee" Reese		6.00	4.50	2.00
13 Bob Elliott	3.25	2.50	1.20	39 Phil Rizzuto		6.00	4.50	2.00
14 Del Ennis	3.25	2.50	1.20	40 Aaron Robinson		3.25	2.50	1.20
15 Bob Feller	9.00	6.75	3.00	41 Jackie Robinson		18.00	13.50	6.00
16 Carl Furillo	4.00	3.00	1.40	42 John Sain		5.00	3.75	1.75
17 Joe Gordon	3.25	2.50	1.20	43 Enos Slaughter		5.00	3.75	1.75
18 Sid Gordon	3.25	2.50	1.20	44 Vern Stephens		3.25	2.50	1.20
19 Joe Hatten	3.25	2.50	1.20	45 George Tebbetts		3.25	2.50	1.20
20 Gil Hodges	6.00	4.50	2.00	46 Bob Thomson		5.00	3.75	1.75
21 Tommy Holmes	4.00	3.00	1.40	47 Johnny VanderMeer		5.00	3.75	1.75
22 Larry Jansen	3.25	2.50	1.20	48 Ted Williams		20.00	15.00	6.50
23 Sheldon Jones	3.25	2.50	1.20					

1953 HUNTERS (26)

2 1/4" X 3 1/2"

HARVEY HADDIX, Pitcher
Born September 18, 1925, at Midway, Ohio
THROWS LEFT — BATS LEFT

MICHAEL CLARK, Pitcher
Born February 12, 1922, at Camden, N. J.
THROWS RIGHT — BATS RIGHT

The 1953 Hunter's Wieners set of 26 full color, blank backed unnumbered cards feature St. Louis Cardinal players only. The cards have red borders and were issued in panels of two on hot dog packages. The ACC designation is F-153-1.

	MINT	VG-E	F-G			MINT	VG-E	F-G
COMPLETE SET	1200.00	900.00	400.00	13 Larry Miggins		45.00	35.00	15.00
COMMON PLAYER	45.00	35.00	15.00	14 Stuart Miller		45.00	35.00	15.00
				15 Wilmer Mizell		45.00	35.00	15.00
1 Steve Bilko	45.00	35.00	15.00	16 Stan Musial		250.00	175.00	80.00
2 Alpha Brazle	45.00	35.00	15.00	17 Joe Presko		45.00	35.00	15.00
3 Cloyd Boyer	45.00	35.00	15.00	18 Del Rice		45.00	35.00	15.00
4 Cliff Chambers	45.00	35.00	15.00	19 Hal Rice		45.00	35.00	15.00
5 Mike Clark	45.00	35.00	15.00	20 Willard Schmidt		45.00	35.00	15.00
6 Jack Crimian	45.00	35.00	15.00	21 Al Schoendienst		75.00	55.00	24.00
7 Les Fusselman	45.00	35.00	15.00	22 Dick Sisler		45.00	35.00	15.00
8 Harvey Haddix	50.00	38.00	17.00	23 Enos Slaughter		90.00	70.00	30.00
7 Solly Hemus	45.00	35.00	15.00	24 Gerry Staley		45.00	35.00	15.00
10 Ray Jablonski	45.00	35.00	15.00	25 Ed Stanky		50.00	45.00	20.00
11 Will Johnson	45.00	35.00	15.00	26 John Yuhas		45.00	35.00	15.00
12 Harry Lowrey	45.00	35.00	15.00					

1954 HUNTERS (30)

WHAT'S MY NAME?
WHAT'S MY RECORD?

The 1954 Hunter's Wieners set of 30 full color, blank backed, unnumbered cards feature St. Louis Cardinals only. They were issued in pairs on the backs of hot dog packages as in 1953. The poses are the same as in the 1953 set; however, there are captions which read "What's My Name" on picture cards and "What's My Record" on statistical cards. The ACC designation is F153-2.

	MINT	VG-E	F-G		MINT	VG-E	F-G
COMPLETE SET	1400.00	1100.00	500.00	15 Tom Poholsky	50.00	38.00	17.00
COMMON PLAYER	50.00	38.00	17.00	16 Bill Posedel	50.00	38.00	17.00
				17 Joe Presko	50.00	38.00	17.00
1 Tom Alston	50.00	38.00	17.00	18 Vic Raschi	65.00	48.00	22.00
2 Steve Bilko	50.00	38.00	17.00	19 Dick Rand	50.00	38.00	17.00
3 Alpha Brazle	50.00	38.00	17.00	20 Rip Repulski	50.00	38.00	17.00
4 Tom Burgess	50.00	38.00	17.00	21 Del Rice	50.00	38.00	17.00
5 Cot Deal	50.00	38.00	17.00	22 John Riddle	50.00	38.00	17.00
6 Alex Grammas	50.00	38.00	17.00	23 Mike Ryba	50.00	38.00	17.00
7 Harvey Haddix	55.00	42.00	19.00	24 Al Schoendienst	75.00	55.00	24.00
8 Solly Hemus	50.00	38.00	17.00	25 Dick Schofield	50.00	38.00	17.00
9 Ray Jablonski	50.00	38.00	17.00	26 Enos Slaughter	95.00	70.00	30.00
10 Royce Lint	50.00	38.00	17.00	27 Gerry Staley	50.00	38.00	17.00
11 Harry Lowrey	50.00	38.00	17.00	28 Ed Stanky	60.00	45.00	20.00
12 Memo Luna	50.00	38.00	17.00	29 Ed Yuhas	50.00	38.00	17.00
13 Stu Miller	50.00	38.00	17.00	30 Sal Yvars	50.00	38.00	17.00
14 Stan Musial	275.00	200.00	90.00				

1955 HUNTERS (30)

TRADING CARDS
Cut out, Trade and Save

GORDON BASSETT JONES
Born April 2, 1930, at Portland, Oregon
Throws right, bats right.
Height: 6   Weight: 190

The 1955 Hunter's Wieners set of 30 full color, blank-back, unnumbered cards features St. Louis Cardinals only. This year presented a different format from the previous two years in that there are two pictures on the front of each card, one full figure shot and a close-up bust shot. The ACC designation is F153-3.

	MINT	VG-E	F-G		MINT	VG-E	F-G
COMPLETE SET	1500.00	1250.00	600.00	15 Stan Musial	300.00	225.00	100.00
COMMON PLAYER	55.00	43.00	20.00	16 Tom Poholsky	55.00	43.00	20.00
				17 Bill Posedel	55.00	43.00	20.00
1 Tom Alston	55.00	43.00	20.00	18 Vic Raschi	70.00	50.00	23.00
2 Ken Boyer	90.00	70.00	30.00	19 Rip Repulski	55.00	43.00	20.00
3 Harry Elliott	55.00	43.00	20.00	20 Del Rice	55.00	43.00	20.00
4 Jack Faszholz	55.00	43.00	20.00	21 John Riddle	55.00	43.00	20.00
5 Joe Frazier	55.00	43.00	20.00	22 Bill Sarni	55.00	43.00	20.00
6 Alex Grammas	55.00	43.00	20.00	23 Albert Schoendienst	80.00	60.00	25.00
7 Harvey Haddix	60.00	45.00	20.00	24 Dick Schofield	55.00	43.00	20.00
8 Solly Hemus	55.00	43.00	20.00	25 Frank Smith	55.00	43.00	20.00
9 Larry Jackson	55.00	43.00	20.00	26 Ed Stanky	65.00	48.00	22.00
10 Tony Jacobs	75.00	55.00	24.00	27 Bob Tiefenauer	55.00	43.00	20.00
11 Gordon Jones	55.00	43.00	20.00	28 Bill Virdon	90.00	70.00	30.00
12 Paul LaPalme	55.00	43.00	20.00	29 Fred Walker	55.00	43.00	20.00
13 Brooks Lawrence	55.00	43.00	20.00	30 Floyd Woolridge	55.00	43.00	20.00
14 Wally Moon	60.00	45.00	20.00				

1975 HOSTESS (150)

2 1/4″ X 3 1/4″
3 1/4″ X 7 1/4″

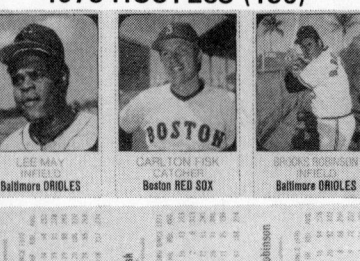

LEE MAY
INFIE
Baltimore ORIOLES

CARLTON FISK
CATCHE
Boston RED SOX

BROOKS ROBINSON
INFIE
Baltimore ORIOLES

The 1975 Hostess set contains 150 color cards which were issued in panels of three cards each on the backs of family-sized packages of Hostess cakes. Card number 125, Madlock, was listed correctly as an infielder and incorrectly as a pitcher. Number 11, Hooten, and number 89, Radar, are spelled two different ways. Some panels are more scarce than others as they were issued only on the backs of less popular Hostess products. These scarcer panels are shown with asterisks in the checklist.

HANK AARON
OF 2/5/34 6 TR BR

MILTON BRADLEY

	AS INDIVIDUALS			AS PANELS		
	MINT	VG-E	F-G	MINT	VG-E	F-G
COMPLETE SET	30.00	21.00	8.00	80.00	60.00	25.00
COMMON PANEL	xxx	xxx	xxx	.95	.75	.30
COMMON PLAYER	.16	.11	.04	xxx	xxx	xxx
Bob Tolan	.16	.11	.04			
2 Cookie Rojas	.16	.11	.04	.95	.75	.30
3 Darrel Evans	.16	.11	.04			
4 Sal Bando	.20	.15	.06			
5 Joe Morgan	.30	.25	.10	.95	.75	.30
6 Mickey Lolich	.20	.15	.06			
7 Don Sutton	.30	.25	.10			
8 Bill Melton	.16	.11	.04	.95	.75	.30
9 Tim Foli	.16	.11	.04			
0 Joe Lahoud	.16	.11	.04			
A Bert Hooten (sic)	.80	.60	.25	2.00	1.50	.60
B Burt Hooton	.80	.60	.25	2.00	1.50	.60
2 Paul Blair	.16	.11	.04			
3 Jim Barr	.16	.11	.04			
4 Toby Harrah	.16	.11	.04	.95	.75	.30
5 John Milner	.16	.11	.04			
6 Ken Holtzman	.16	.11	.04			
7 Cesar Cedeno	.30	.25	.10	.95	.75	.30
8 Dwight Evans	.16	.11	.04			
9 Willie McCovey	.40	.30	.13			
0 Tony Oliva	.25	.20	.08	1.25	.90	.40
1 Manny Sanguillen	.16	.11	.04			
2 Mickey Rivers	.16	.11	.04			
3 Lou Brock	.50	.40	.18	1.25	.90	.40
4 Graig Nettles	.30	.25	.10			
5 Jim Wynn	.16	.11	.04			
6 George Scott	.16	.11	.04	.95	.75	.30
7 Greg Luzinski	.30	.25	.10			
8 Bert Campaneris	.16	.11	.04			
9 Pete Rose	.80	.60	.25	1.50	1.10	.50
0 Buddy Bell	.25	.20	.08			
1 Gary Matthews	.20	.15	.06			
2 Freddie Patek	.16	.11	.04	.95	.75	.30
3 Mike Lum	.16	.11	.04			
4 Ellie Rodriguez	.16	.11	.04			
5 Milt May (Lee May pic)	.50	.40	.18	.95	.75	.30
6 Willie Horton	.16	.11	.04			
7 Dave Winfield	.50	.40	.18			
8 Tom Grieve	.16	.11	.04	.95	.75	.30
9 Barry Foote	.16	.11	.04			
0 Joe Rudi	.20	.15	.06			
1 Bake McBride	.20	.15	.06	.95	.75	.30
2 Mike Cuellar	.16	.11	.04			
3 Garry Maddox	.20	.15	.06			
4 Carlos May	.16	.11	.04	.95	.75	.30
5 Bud Harrelson	.16	.11	.04			
6 Dave Chalk	.16	.11	.04			
7 Dave Concepcion	.25	.20	.08	1.25	.90	.40
8 Carl Yastrzemski	.70	.50	.20			
9 Steve Garvey	.60	.45	.20			
0 Amos Otis	.30	.25	.10	1.25	.90	.40
1 Rick Reuschel	.25	.20	.08			
2 Rollie Fingers	.25	.20	.08			
3 Bob Watson	.20	.15	.06	.95	.75	.30
4 John Ellis	.16	.11	.04			
5 Bob Bailey	.16	.11	.04			
6 Rod Carew	.60	.45	.20	1.25	.90	.40
7 Rich Hebner	.60	.45	.20			
8 Nolan Ryan	.60	.45	.20			
9 Reggie Smith	.30	.25	.10	1.25	.90	.40
0 Joe Coleman	.16	.11	.04			
1 Ron Cey	.25	.20	.08			
2 Darrell Porter	.20	.15	.06	1.25	.90	.40
3 Steve Carlton	.40	.30	.13			

	MINT	VG-F	F-G	MINT	VG-E	F-G
64 Gene Tenace	.16	.11	.04			
65 Jose Cardenal	.16	.11	.04	.95	.75	.30
66 Bill Lee	.16	.11	.04			
67 Dave Lopes	.20	.15	.06			
68 Wilbur Wood	.16	.11	.04	.95	.75	.30
69 Steve Renko	.16	.11	.04			
70 Joe Torre	.30	.25	.10			
71 Ted Sizemore	.16	.11	.04	.95	.75	.30
72 Bobby Grich	.20	.15	.06			
73 Chris Speier	.16	.11	.04			
74 Bert Blyleven	.20	.15	.06	1.25	.90	.40
75 Tom Seaver	.60	.45	.20			
76 Nate Colbert	.16	.11	.04			
77 Don Kessinger	.20	.15	.06	.95	.75	.30
78 George Medich	.16	.11	.04			
79 Andy Messersmith*	.20	.15	.06			
80 Robin Yount*	.25	.20	.08	4.00	3.00	1.40
81 Al Oliver*	.30	.25	.10			
82 Bill Singer*	.16	.11	.04			
83 Johnny Bench*	1.00	.70	.30	5.00	3.75	1.75
84 Gaylord Perry*	.80	.60	.25			
85 Dave Kingman*	.80	.60	.25			
86 Ed Herrmann*	.16	.11	.04	4.00	3.00	1.40
87 Ralph Garr*	.16	.11	.04			
88 Reggie Jackson*	1.00	.70	.30			
89A Doug Radar*	.80	.60	.25	4.00	3.00	1.40
89B Doug Rader*	1.50	1.10	.50	10.00	7.00	3.00
90 Elliott Maddox*	.16	.11	.04			
91 Bill Russell*	.16	.11	.04			
92 John Mayberry*	.20	.15	.06	4.00	3.00	1.40
93 Dave Cash*	.16	.11	.04			
94 Jeff Burroughs*	.25	.20	.08			
95 Ted Simmons*	.60	.45	.20	4.00	3.00	1.40
96 Joe Decker*	.16	.11	.04			
97 Bill Buckner*	.30	.25	.10			
98 Bobby Darwin*	.16	.11	.04	3.00	2.25	1.00
99 Phil Niekro*	.40	.30	.13			
100 Jim Sundberg	.25	.20	.08			
101 Greg Gross	.16	.11	.04	.95	.75	.30
102 Luis Tiant	.25	.20	.08			
103 Glenn Beckert	.16	.11	.04			
104 Hal McRae	.16	.11	.04	.95	.75	.30
105 Mike Jorgensen	.16	.11	.04			
106 Mike Hargrove	.16	.11	.04			
107 Don Gullett	.16	.11	.04	.95	.75	.30
108 Tito Fuentes	.16	.11	.04			
109 John Grubb	.16	.11	.04			
110 Jim Kaat	.30	.25	.10	.95	.75	.30
111 Felix Millan	.16	.11	.04			
112 Don Money	.20	.15	.06			
113 Rick Monday	.20	.15	.06	.95	.75	.30
114 Dick Bosman	.16	.11	.04			
115 Roger Metzger	.16	.11	.04			
116 Fergie Jenkins	.30	.25	.10	.95	.75	.30
117 Dusty Baker	.20	.15	.06			
118 Billy Champion*	.16	.11	.04			
119 Bob Gibson*	.80	.60	.25	3.00	2.25	1.30
120 Bill Freehan*	.25	.20	.08			
121 Cesar Geronimo	.16	.11	.04			
122 Jorge Orta	.16	.11	.04	.95	.75	.30
123 Cleon Jones	.16	.11	.04			
124 Steve Busby	.16	.11	.04			
125A Bill Madlock(correct)	.60	.45	.20	2.00	1.50	.60
125B Bill Madlock(error)	.60	.45	.20	2.00	1.50	.60
126 Jim Palmer	.60	.45	.20			
127 Tony Perez	.25	.20	.08			
128 Larry Hisle	.20	.15	.06	.95	.75	.30
129 Rusty Staub	.25	.20	.08			
130 Hank Aaron*	1.25	.90	.40			
131 Rennie Stennett*	.16	.11	.04	4.00	3.00	1.40
132 Rico Petrocelli*	.25	.20	.08			
133 Mike Schmidt	.60	.45	.20			
134 Sparky Lyle	.25	.20	.08	1.50	1.10	.50
135 Willie Stargell	.50	.40	.18			
136 Ken Henderson	.16	.11	.04			
137 Willie Montanez	.16	.11	.04	1.25	.90	.40
138 Thurman Munson	.60	.45	.20			
139 Richie Zisk	.20	.15	.06			
140 George Hendrick	.30	.25	.10	.95	.75	.30
141 Bobby Murcer	.20	.15	.06			
142 Lee May	.20	.15	.06			
143 Carlton Fisk	.30	.25	.10	1.25	.90	.40
144 Brooks Robinson	.60	.45	.20			
145 Bobby Bonds	.25	.20	.08			
146 Gary Sutherland	.16	.11	.04	.95	.75	.30
147 Oscar Gamble	.20	.15	.06			
148 Jim Hunter	.30	.25	.10			
149 Tug McGraw	.20	.15	.06	.95	.75	.30
150 Dave McNally	.20	.15	.06			

Roberto Clemente
Outfielder
No. 21 KDKA GROUP W

H830-1 KDKA PIRATES

1975 HOSTESS TWINKIE (60)   2 1/4" X 3 1/4"

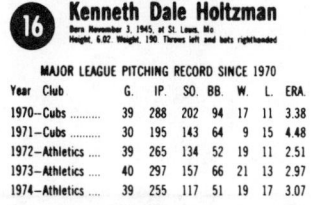

The 1975 Hostess Twinkie set was issued on a limited basis in the far west part of the country. Sixty cards were issued in the set. The set contains the same numbers as the regular set to No. 36; however, the set is skip-numbered after No. 36. The cards were backs for 25 cent Twinkies packs.

	MINT	VG-E	F-G
COMPLETE SET	33.00	27.00	12.00
COMMON PLAYER	.45	.35	.15

	MINT	VG-E	F-G			MINT	VG-E	F-G
1 Bob Tolan	.45	.35	.15	31 Gary Matthews	.55	.40	.18
2 Cookie Rojas	.45	.35	.15	32 Freddie Patek	.45	.35	.15
3 Darrell Evans	.45	.35	.15	33 Mike Lum	.45	.35	.15
4 Sal Bando	.55	.40	.18	34 Ellie Rodriguez	.45	.35	.15
5 Joe Morgan	.75	.55	.25	35 Milt May (Lee May pic)	.75	.55	.25
6 Mickey Lolich	.55	.40	.18	36 Willie Horton	.55	.40	.18
7 Don Sutton	.75	.55	.25	40 Joe Rudi	.55	.40	.18
8 Bill Melton	.45	.35	.15	43 Garry Maddox	.55	.40	.18
9 Tim Foli	.45	.35	.15	46 Dave Chalk	.45	.35	.15
10 Joe Lahoud	.45	.35	.15	49 Steve Garvey	1.00	.70	.30
11 Bert Hooten (sic)	.75	.55	.25	52 Rollie Fingers	.55	.40	.18
12 Paul Blair	.45	.35	.15	58 Nolan Ryan	.80	.60	.25
13 Jim Barr	.45	.35	.15	61 Ron Cey	.55	.40	.18
14 Toby Harrah	.45	.35	.15	64 Gene Tenace	.45	.35	.15
15 John Milner	.45	.35	.15	65 Jose Cardenal	.45	.35	.15
16 Ken Holtzman	.45	.35	.15	67 Dave Lopes	.55	.40	.18
17 Cesar Cedeno	.65	.50	.20	68 Wilbur Wood	.45	.35	.15
18 Dwight Evans	.45	.35	.15	73 Chris Speier	.45	.35	.15
19 Willie McCovey	.80	.60	.25	77 Don Kessinger	.45	.35	.15
20 Tony Oliva	.65	.50	.20	79 Andy Messersmith	.55	.40	.18
21 Manny Sanguillen	.45	.35	.15	80 Robin Yount	.65	.50	.20
22 Mickey Rivers	.55	.40	.18	82 Bill Singer	.45	.35	.15
23 Lou Brock	1.00	.70	.30	103 Glenn Beckert	.45	.35	.15
24 Graig Nettles	.65	.50	.20	110 Jim Kaat	.65	.50	.20
25 Jim Wynn	.45	.35	.15	112 Don Money	.45	.35	.15
26 George Scott	.45	.35	.15	113 Rick Monday	.45	.35	.15
27 Greg Luzinski	.65	.50	.20	122 Jorge Orta	.45	.35	.15
28 Bert Campaneris	.45	.35	.15	125 Bill Madlock	.45	.35	.15
29 Pete Rose	1.50	1.10	.50	130 Hank Aaron	1.50	1.10	.50
30 Buddy Bell	.65	.50	.20	136 Ken Henderson	.45	.35	.15

1976 HOSTESS (150)   2 1/4" X 3 1/4"
3 1/4" X 7 1/4"

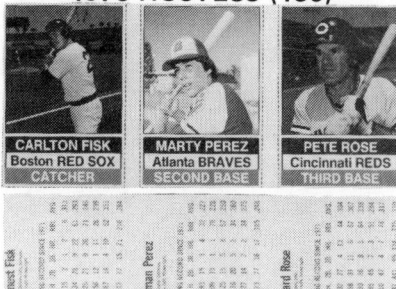

The 1976 Hostess set contains 150 color, numbered cards issued in panels of three cards each on family-sized packages of Hostess cakes. Scarcer panels are listed in the checklist below with asterisks.

	AS INDIVIDUALS			AS PANELS		
	MINT	VG-E	F-G	MINT	VG-E	F-G
COMPLETE SET	30.00	21.00	8.00	70.00	53.00	24.00
COMMON PLAYER	.16	.11	.04	xxxxx	xxx	xxx
COMMON PANEL	xxx	xxx	xxx	.95	.75	.30
1 Fred Lynn	.80	.60	.25			
2 Joe Morgan	.30	.25	.10	1.50	1.10	.50
3 Phil Niekro	.30	.25	.10			

1976 HOSTESS (CONTINUED)

	MINT	VG-E	F-G	MINT	VG-E	F-G
4 Gaylord Perry	.40	.30	.13			
5 Bob Watson	.20	.15	.06	.95	.75	.30
6 Bill Freehan	.20	.15	.06			
7 Lou Brock	.80	.60	.25			
8 Al Fitzmorris	.16	.11	.04	1.25	.90	.40
9 Rennie Stennett	.16	.11	.04			
10 Tony Oliva	.30	.25	.10			
11 Robin Yount	.25	.20	.08	.95	.75	.30
12 Rick Manning	.16	.11	.04			
13 Bobby Grich	.20	.15	.06			
14 Terry Forster	.20	.15	.06	.95	.75	.30
15 Dave Kingman	.40	.30	.13			
16 Thurman Munson	.60	.45	.20			
17 Rick Reuschel	.25	.20	.08	1.25	.90	.40
18 Bobby Bonds	.25	.20	.08			
19 Steve Garvey	.60	.45	.20			
20 Vida Blue	.30	.25	.10	1.25	.90	.40
21 Dave Rader	.16	.11	.04			
22 Johnny Bench	.80	.60	.25			
23 Luis Tiant	.25	.20	.08	1.25	.90	.40
24 Darrell Evans	.16	.11	.04			
25 Larry Dierker	.16	.11	.04			
26 Willie Horton	.20	.15	.06	.95	.75	.30
27 John Ellis	.16	.11	.04			
28 Al Cowens	.16	.11	.04			
29 Jerry Reuss	.25	.20	.08	.95	.75	.30
30 Reggie Smith	.30	.25	.10			
31 Bobby Darwin*	.16	.11	.04			
32 Fritz Peterson*	.16	.11	.04	2.00	1.50	.60
33 Rod Carew*	1.00	.70	.30			
34 Carlos May*	.16	.11	.04			
35 Tom Seaver*	1.00	.70	.30	3.00	2.25	1.00
36 Brooks Robinson*	1.00	.70	.30			
37 Jose Cardenal	.16	.11	.04			
38 Ron Blomberg	.16	.11	.04	.95	.75	.30
39 Leroy Stanton	.16	.11	.04			
40 Dave Cash	.16	.11	.04			
41 John Montefusco	.16	.11	.04	.95	.75	.30
42 Bob Tolan	.16	.11	.04			
43 Carl Morton	.16	.11	.04			
44 Rick Burleson	.30	.25	.10	.95	.75	.30
45 Don Gullett	.16	.11	.04			
46 Vern Ruhle	.16	.11	.04			
47 Cesar Cedeno	.30	.25	.10	.95	.75	.30
48 Tody Harrah	.16	.11	.04			
49 Willie Stargell	.40	.30	.13			
50 Al Hrabosky	.20	.15	.06	1.25	.90	.40
51 Amos Otis	.25	.20	.08			
52 Bud Harrelson	.16	.11	.04			
53 Jim Hughes	.16	.11	.04	.95	.75	.30
54 George Scott	.16	.11	.04			
55 Mike Vail*	.16	.11	.04			
56 Jim Palmer*	1.00	.70	.30	2.50	1.80	.80
57 Jorge Orta*	.16	.11	.04			
58 Chris Chambliss*	.25	.20	.08			
59 Dave Chalk*	.16	.11	.04	2.00	1.50	.60
60 Ray Burris*	.16	.11	.04			
61 Bert Campaneris*	.25	.20	.08			
62 Gary Carter*	.60	.45	.20	2.00	1.50	.60
63 Ron Cey*	.30	.25	.10			
64 Carlton Fisk*	.50	.40	.18			
65 Marty Perez*	.50	.40	.18	4.00	3.00	1.40
66 Pete Rose*	1.25	.90	.40			
67 Roger Metzger*	.16	.11	.04			
68 Jim Sundberg*	.16	.11	.04	2.00	1.50	.60
69 Ron LeFlore*	.30	.25	.10			
70 Ted Sizemore*	.16	.11	.04			
71 Steve Busby*	.16	.11	.04	2.00	1.50	.60
72 Manny Sanguillen*	.16	.11	.04			
73 Larry Hisle*	.25	.20	.08			
74 Pete Broberg*	.16	.11	.04	2.00	1.50	.60
75 Boog Powell*	.30	.25	.10			
76 Ken Singleton*	.40	.30	.13			
77 Rich Gossage*	.40	.30	.13	2.00	1.50	.60
78 Jerry Grote*	.16	.11	.04			
79 Nolan Ryan*	1.00	.70	.30			
80 Rick Monday*	.30	.25	.10	2.50	1.80	.80
81 Graig Nettles*	.30	.25	.10			
82 Chris Speier	.16	.11	.04			
83 Dave Winfield	.60	.45	.20	1.50	1.10	.50
84 Mike Schmidt	.60	.45	.20			
85 Buzz Capra	.16	.11	.04			
86 Tony Perez	.30	.25	.10	.95	.75	.30
87 Dwight Evans	.16	.11	.04			
88 Mike Hargrove	.16	:11	.04			
89 Joe Coleman	.16	.11	.04	.95	.75	.30
90 Greg Gross	.16	.11	.04			
91 John Mayberry	.25	.20	.08			
92 John Candelaria	.20	.15	.06	.95	.75	.30
93 Bake McBride	.20	.15	.06			

19th CENTURY SPALDIN

		MINT	VG-E	F-G	MINT	VG-E	F-G
94	Hank Aaron	1.00	.70	.30			
95	Buddy Bell	.25	.20	.08	1.50	1.10	.50
96	Steve Braun	.16	.11	.04			
97	Jon Matlack	.20	.15	.06			
98	Lee May	.16	.11	.04	.95	.75	.30
99	Wilbur Wood	.16	.11	.04			
100	Bill Madlock	.16	.11	.04			
101	Frank Tanana	.25	.20	.08	.95	.75	.30
102	Mickey Rivers	.20	.15	.06			
103	Mike Ivie	.16	.11	.04			
104	Rollie Fingers	.25	.20	.08	.95	.75	.30
105	Dave Lopes	.25	.20	.08			
106	George Foster	.40	.30	.13			
107	Denny Doyle	.16	.11	.04	.95	.75	.30
108	Earl Williams	.16	.11	.04			
109	Tom Veryzer	.16	.11	.04			
110	J.R. Richard	.50	.40	.18	1.25	.90	.40
111	Jeff Burroughs	.20	.15	.06			
112	Al Oliver	.30	.25	.10			
113	Ted Simmons	.40	.30	.13	1.50	1.10	.50
114	George Brett	1.00	.70	.30			
115	Frank Duffy	.16	.11	.04			
116	Bert Byleven	.25	.20	.08	.95	.75	.30
117	Darrell Porter	.25	.20	.08			
118	Don Baylor	.30	.25	.10			
119	Bucky Dent	.20	.15	.06	.95	.75	.30
120	Felix Millan	.16	.11	.04			
121	Mike Cuellar	.16	.11	.04			
122	Gene Tenace	.16	.11	.04	.95	.75	.30
123	Bobby Murcer	.20	.15	.06			
124	Willie McCovey	.40	.30	.13			
125	Greg Luzinski	.30	.25	.10	1.25	.90	.40
126	Larry Parrish	.30	.25	.10			
127	Jim Rice	.80	.60	.25			
128	Dave Concepcion	.25	.20	.08	1.50	1.10	.50
129	Jim Wynn	.16	.11	.04			
130	Tom Grieve	.16	.11	.04			
131	Mike Cosgrove	.16	.11	.04	.95	.75	.30
132	Dan Meyer	.16	.11	.04			
133	Dave Parker	.80	.60	.25			
134	Don Kessinger	.16	.11	.04	1.25	.90	.40
135	Hal McRae	.16	.11	.04			
136	Don Money	.20	.15	.06			
137	Dennis Eckersley	.20	.15	.06	.95	.75	.30
138	Fergie Jenkins	.25	.20	.08			
139	Mike Torrez	.20	.15	.06			
140	Jerry Morales	.16	.11	.04	.95	.75	.30
141	Jim Hunter	.30	.25	.10			
142	Gary Matthews	.20	.15	.06			
143	Randy Jones	.20	.15	.06	.95	.75	.30
144	Mike Jorgensen	.16	.11	.04			
145	Larry Bowa	.30	.25	.10			
146	Reggie Jackson	.80	.60	.25	1.50	1.10	.50
147	Steve Yeager	.16	.11	.04			
148	Dave May	.16	.11	.04			
149	Carl Yastrzemski	.80	.60	.25	1.50	1.10	.50
150	Cesar Geronimo	.16	.11	.04			

1976 HOSTESS TWINKIE (60) 2 1/4" X 3 1/4"

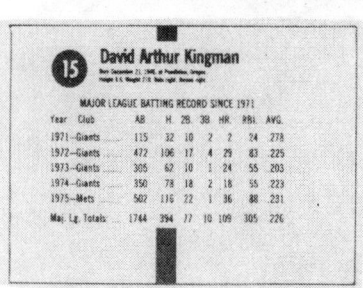

The 1976 Hostess Twinkies set contains the first 60 cards of the 1976 Hostess set. These cards were issued as backs on 25-cent Twinkie packages as in the 1975 Twinkies set.

		MINT	VG-E	F-G
	COMPLETE SET	33.00	27.00	12.00
	COMMON PLAYER	.40	.30	.12
1	Fred Lynn	1.00	.70	.30
2	Joe Morgan	.60	.45	.20
3	Phil Niekro	.60	.45	.20
4	Gaylord Perry	.70	.50	.20
5	Bob Watson	.50	.40	.18
6	Bill Freehan	.50	.40	.18
7	Lou Brock	.80	.60	.25
8	Al Fitzmorris	.40	.30	.12
9	Rennie Stennett	.40	.30	.12
10	Tony Oliva	.60	.45	.20
11	Robin Yount	.60	.45	.20
12	Rick Manning	.40	.30	.12
13	Bobby Grich	.50	.40	.18
14	Terry Forster	.50	.40	.18
15	Dave Kingman	.80	.60	.25
16	Thurman Munson	1.00	.70	.30
17	Rick Reuschel	.60	.45	.20
18	Bobby Bonds	.60	.45	.20
19	Steve Garvey	1.00	.70	.30
20	Vida Blue	.60	.45	.20
21	Dave Rader	.40	.30	.12

		MINT	VG-E	F-G
22	Johnny Bench	1.00	.70	.30
23	Luis Tiant	.50	.40	.18
24	Darrell Evans	.40	.30	.12
25	Larry Dierker	.40	.30	.12
26	Willie Horton	.50	.40	.18
27	John Ellis	.40	.30	.12
28	Al Cowens	.40	.30	.12
29	Jerry Reuss	.50	.40	.18
30	Reggie Smith	.60	.45	.20
31	Bobby Darwin	.40	.30	.12
32	Fritz Peterson	.40	.30	.12
33	Rod Carew	1.00	.70	.30
34	Carlos May	.40	.30	.12
35	Tom Seaver	1.00	.70	.30
36	Brooks Robinson	1.00	.70	.30
37	Jose Cardenal	.40	.30	.12

		MINT	VG-E	F-G
38	Ron Blomberg	.40	.30	.12
39	Leroy Stanton	.40	.30	.12
40	Dave Cash	.40	.30	.12
41	John Montefusco	.40	.30	.12
42	Bob Tolan	.40	.30	.12
43	Carl Morton	.40	.30	.12
44	Rick Burleson	.60	.45	.20
45	Don Gullett	.40	.30	.12
46	Vern Ruhle	.40	.30	.12
47	Cesar Cedeno	.60	.45	.20
48	Toby Harrah	.40	.30	.12
49	Willie Stargell	.80	.60	.25
50	Al Hrabosky	.50	.40	.18
51	Amos Otis	.50	.40	.18
52	Bud Harrelson	.40	.30	.12
53	Jim Hughes	.40	.30	.12
54	George Scott	.40	.30	.12
55	Mike Vail	.40	.30	.12
56	Jim Palmer	1.00	.70	.30
57	Jorge Orta	.40	.30	.12
58	Chris Chambliss	.50	.40	.18
59	Dave Chalk	.40	.30	.12
60	Ray Burris	.40	.30	.12

1977 HOSTESS (150)

BILL STEIN
Seattle MARINERS
SECOND BASE

ROLLIE FINGERS
San Diego PADRES
PITCHER

BRIAN DOWNING
Chicago WHITE SOX
CATCHER

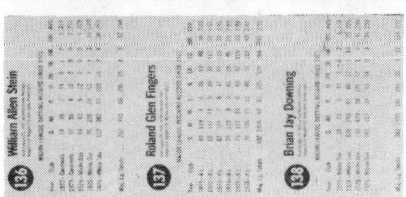

2 1/4" X 3 1/4"
3 1/4" X 7 1/4"

The 1977 Hostess set contains 150 color, numbered cards issued in panels of three cards each with Hostess family-sized cake products. Scarcer panels are listed in the checklist with asterisks.

		AS INDIVIDUALS			AS PANELS		
		MINT	VG-E	F-G	MINT	VG-E	F-G
	COMPLETE SET	30.00	21.00	8.00	65.00	50.00	20.00
	COMMON PLAYER	.16	.11	.04	xxxxx	xxx	xxx
	COMMON PANEL	xxx	xxx	xxx	.95	.75	.30
1	Jim Palmer	.60	.45	.20			
2	Joe Morgan	.30	.25	.10	2.00	1.50	.60
3	Reggie Jackson	.80	.60	.25			
4	Carl Yastrzemski	.80	.60	.25			
5	Thurman Munson	.80	.60	.25	2.50	1.80	.80
6	Johnny Bench	.80	.60	.25			
7	Tom Seaver	.60	.45	.20			
8	Pete Rose	.80	.60	.25	2.00	1.50	.60
9	Rod Carew	.60	.45	.20			
10	Luis Tiant	.25	.20	.08			
11	Phil Garner	.16	.11	.04	.95	.75	.30
12	Sixto Lezcano	.20	.15	.06			
13	Mike Torrez	.20	.15	.06			
14	Dave Lopes	.20	.15	.06	.95	.75	.30
15	Doug DeCinces	.16	.11	.04			
16	Jim Spencer	.16	.11	.04			
17	Hal McRae	.16	.11	.04	.95	.75	.30
18	Mike Hargrove	.16	.11	.04			
19	Willie Montanez*	.25	.20	.08			
20	Roger Metzger*	.16	.11	.04	2.50	1.80	.80
21	Dwight Evans*	.16	.11	.04			
22	Steve Rogers*	.40	.30	.13			
23	Jim Rice*	1.00	.70	.30	3.00	2.25	1.00
24	Pete Falcone*	.16	.11	.04			
25	Greg Luzinski*	.50	.40	.18			
26	Randy Jones*	.50	.40	.18	2.50	1.80	.80
27	Willie Stargell*	1.00	.70	.30			

	MINT	VG-E	F-G	MINT	VG-E	F-G
28 John Hiller*	.16	.11	.04			
29 Bobby Murcer*	.25	.20	.08	2.00	1.50	.60
30 Rick Monday*	.25	.20	.08			
31 John Montefusco*	.16	.11	.04			
32 Lou Brock*	1.00	.70	.30	2.50	1.80	.80
33 Bill North*	.16	.11	.04			
34 Robin Yount*	.40	.30	.13			
35 Steve Garvey*	1.00	.70	.30	3.00	2.25	1.00
36 George Brett*	1.25	.90	.40			
37 Toby Harrah*	.20	.15	.06			
38 Jerry Royster*	.16	.11	.04	2.00	1.50	.60
39 Bob Watson*	.20	.15	.06			
40 George Foster	.40	.30	.13			
41 Gary Carter	.30	.25	.10	1.25	.90	.40
42 John Denny	.16	.11	.04			
43 Mike Schmidt	.60	.45	.20			
44 Dave Winfield	.60	.45	.20	1.50	1.10	.50
45 Al Oliver	.30	.25	.10			
46 Mark Fidrych	.25	.20	.08			
47 Larry Herndon	.16	.11	.04	.95	.75	.30
48 Dave Goltz	.16	.11	.04			
49 Jerry Morales	.16	.11	.04			
50 Ron LeFlore	.30	.25	.10	1.25	.90	.40
51 Fred Lynn	.80	.60	.25			
52 Vida Blue	.30	.25	.10			
53 Rick Manning	.16	.11	.04	.95	.75	.30
54 Bill Buckner	.30	.25	.10			
55 Lee May	.16	.11	.04			
56 John Mayberry	.20	.15	.06	.95	.75	.30
57 Darrel Chaney	.16	.11	.04			
58 Cesar Cedeno	.30	.25	.10			
59 Ken Griffey	.30	.25	.10	.95	.75	.30
60 Dave Kingman	.40	.30	.13			
61 Ted Simmons	.40	.30	.13			
62 Larry Bowa	.25	.20	.08	.95	.75	.30
63 Frank Tanana	.25	.20	.08			
64 Jason Thompson	.20	.15	.06			
65 Ken Brett	.16	.11	.04	.95	.75	.30
66 Roy Smalley	.20	.15	.06			
67 Ray Burris	.16	.11	.04			
68 Rick Burleson	.30	.25	.10	.95	.75	.30
69 Buddy Bell	.30	.25	.10			
70 Don Sutton	.30	.25	.10			
71 Mark Belanger	.16	.11	.04	.95	.75	.30
72 Dennis Leonard	.20	.15	.06			
73 Gaylord Perry	.40	.30	.13			
74 Dick Ruthven	.16	.11	.04	.95	.75	.30
75 Jose Cruz	.16	.11	.04			
76 Cesar Geronimo	.16	.11	.04			
77 Jerry Koosman	.20	.15	.06	.95	.75	.30
78 Garry Templeton	.40	.30	.13			
79 Jim Hunter	.30	.25	.10			
80 John Candelaria	.16	.11	.04	1.25	.90	.40
81 Nolan Ryan	.60	.45	.20			
82 Rusty Staub	.25	.20	.08			
83 Jim Barr	.16	.11	.04	.95	.75	.30
84 Butch Wynegar	.16	.11	.04			
85 Jose Cardenal	.16	.11	.04			
86 Claudell Washington	.16	.11	.04	.95	.75	.30
87 Bill Travers	.16	.11	.04			
88 Rick Waits	.16	.11	.04			
89 Ron Cey	.25	.20	.08	.95	.75	.30
90 Al Bumbry	.16	.11	.04			
91 Bucky Dent	.25	.20	.08			
92 Amos Otis	.25	.20	.08	.95	.75	.30
93 Tom Grieve	.16	.11	.04			
94 Enos Cabell	.16	.11	.04			
95 Dave Concepcion	.25	.20	.08	.95	.75	.30
96 Felix Millan	.16	.11	.04			
97 Bake McBride	.20	.15	.06			
98 Chris Chambliss	.20	.15	.06	.95	.75	.30
99 Butch Metzger	.16	.11	.04			
100 Rennie Stennett	.16	.11	.04			
101 Dave Roberts	.16	.11	.04	.95	.75	.30
102 Lyman Bostock	.30	.25	.10			
103 Rick Reuschel	.30	.25	.10			
104 Carlton Fisk	.35	.27	.12	.95	.75	.30
105 Jim Slaton	.16	.11	.04			
106 Dennis Eckersley	.20	.15	.06			
107 Ken Singleton	.25	.20	.08	.95	.75	.30
108 Ralph Garr	.16	.11	.04			
109 Freddie Patek*	.16	.11	.04			
110 Jim Sundberg*	.30	.25	.10	2.00	1.50	.60
111 Phil Niekro*	.40	.30	.13			
112 J. R. Richard*	.80	.60	.25			
113 Gary Nolan*	.16	.11	.04	2.00	1.50	.60
114 Jon Matlack*	.25	.20	.08			
115 Keith Hernandez*	.80	.60	.25			
116 Graig Nettles*	.40	.30	.13	2.50	1.80	.80
117 Steve Carlton*	.80	.60	.25			

BF2 PENNANT

	MINT	VG-E	F-G	MINT	VG-E	F-G
118 Bill Madlock*	.30	.25	.10			
119 Jerry Reuss*	.30	.25	.10	2.00	1.50	.60
120 Aurelio Rodriguez*	.16	.11	.04			
121 Dan Ford*	.16	.11	.04			
122 Ray Fosse*	.16	.11	.04	2.00	1.50	.60
123 George Hendrick*	.40	.30	.13			
124 Alan Ashby	.16	.11	.04			
125 Joe Lis	.16	.11	.04	.95	.75	.30
126 Sal Bando	.25	.20	.08			
127 Richie Zisk	.25	.20	.08			
128 Rich Gossage	.40	.30	.13	1.25	.90	.40
129 Don Baylor	.30	.25	.10			
130 Dave McKay	.16	.11	.04			
131 Bob Grich	.20	.15	.06	.95	.75	.30
132 Dave Pagan	.16	.11	.04			
133 Dave Cash	.16	.11	.04			
134 Steve Braun	.16	.11	.04	.95	.75	.30
135 Dan Meyer	.16	.11	.04			
136 Bill Stein	.16	.11	.04			
137 Rollie Fingers	.30	.25	.10	.95	.75	.30
138 Brian Downing	.20	.15	.06			
139 Bill Singer	.16	.11	.04			
140 Doyle Alexander	.16	.11	.04	.95	.75	.30
141 Gene Tenace	.16	.11	.04			
142 Gary Matthews	.20	.15	.06			
143 Don Gullett	.16	.11	.04	.95	.75	.30
144 Wayne Garland	.16	.11	.04			
145 Pete Broberg	.16	.11	.04			
146 Joe Rudi	.20	.15	.06	.95	.75	.30
147 Glenn Abbott	.16	.11	.04			
148 George Scott	.16	.11	.04			
149 Bert Campaneris	.16	.11	.04	.95	.75	.30
150 Andy Messersmith	.20	.15	.06			

1978 HOSTESS (150)

2 1/4" X 3 1/4"
3 1/4" X 7 1/4"

TOMMY JOHN — LOS ANGELES DODGERS
GREG LUZINSKI — PHILADELPHIA PHILLIES
ENOS CABELL — HOUSTON ASTROS

Thomas Edward John
Gregory Michael Luzinski
Enos Milton Cabell

The 1978 Hostess set contains 150 full color, numbered cards issued in panels of three cards each on family packages of Hostess cake products. Scarcer panels are listed in the checklist with astericks. The 1978 Hostesss panels are somewhat more difficult to obtain than Hostess panels of other years.

	AS INDIVIDUALS			AS PANELS		
	MINT	VG-E	F-G	MINT	VG-E	F-G
COMPLETE SET	30.00	21.00	8.00	70.00	53.00	24.00
COMMON PANEL	xxx	xxx	xxx	1.10	.85	.35
COMMON PLAYER	.16	.11	.04	xxxx	xxx	xxx
1 Butch Hobson	.16	.11	.04			
2 George Foster	.40	.30	.13	1.10	.85	.35
3 Bob Forsch	.16	.11	.04			
4 Tony Perez	.25	.20	.08			
5 Bruce Sutter	.40	.30	.13	1.10	.85	.35
6 Hal McRae	.16	.11	.04			
7 Tommy John	.30	.25	.10			
8 Greg Luzinski	.16	.11	.04	1.25	.90	.40
9 Enos Cabell	.16	.11	.04			
10 Dout DeCinces	.16	.11	.04			
11 Willie Stargell	.40	.30	.13	1.25	.90	.40
12 Ed Halicki	.16	.11	.04			

		MINT	VG-E	F-G	MINT	VG-E	F-G
13	Hisle, Larry	.20	.15	.06			
14	Slaton, Jim	.16	.11	.04	1.10	.85	.35
15	Bell, Buddy	.30	.25	.10			
16	Williams, Earl	.16	.11	.04			
17	Abbott, Glenn	.16	.11	.04	1.10	.85	.35
18	Ford, Dan	.16	.11	.04			
19	Matthews, Gary	.20	.15	.06			
20	Soderholm, Eric	.16	.11	.04	1.10	.85	.35
21	Wills, Bump	.20	.15	.06			
22	Hernandez, Keith	.60	.45	.20			
23	Cash, Dave	.16	.11	.04	1.10	.85	.35
24	Scott, George	.16	.11	.04			
25	Guidry, Ron	.60	.45	.20			
26	Kingman, Dave	.40	.30	.13	2.50	1.80	.80
27	Brett, George	1.00	.70	.30			
28	Watson, Bob*	.20	.15	.06			
29	Boone, Bob*	.20	.15	.06	1.50	1.10	.50
30	Smith, Reggie*	.25	.20	.08			
31	Murray, Eddie*	.25	.20	.08			
32	Lavelle, Gary*	.16	.11	.04	2.50	1.80	.80
33	Stennett, Rennie*	.16	.11	.04			
34	Kuiper, Duane*	.16	.11	.04			
35	Lezcano, Sixto*	.20	.15	.06	2.50	1.80	.80
36	Rozema, Dave*	.16	.11	.04			
37	Wynegar, Butch*	.16	.11	.04			
38	Page, Mitchell*	.16	.11	.04	1.50	1.10	.50
39	Stein*	.16	.11	.04			
40	Maddox, Elliott	.16	.11	.04			
41	Hargrove, Mike	.16	.11	.04	1.10	.85	.35
42	Bonds, Bobby	.25	.20	.08			
43	Templeton, Garry	.40	.30	.13			
44	Bench, Johnny	.60	.45	.20	2.50	1.80	.80
45	Rice, Jim	.60	.45	.20			
46	Buckner, Bill	.30	.25	.10			
47	Jackson, Reggie	.60	.45	.20	1.50	1.10	.50
48	Patek, Freddie	.16	.11	.04			
49	Carlton, Steve	.40	.30	.13			
50	Cedeno, Cesar	.30	.25	.10	1.25	.90	.40
51	Yeager, Steve	.16	.11	.04			
52	Garner, Phil	.16	.11	.04			
53	May, Lee	.16	.11	.04	1.10	.85	.35
54	Evans, Darrell	.16	.11	.04			
55	Kemp, Steve	.25	.20	.08			
56	Baker, Dusty	.25	.20	.08	1.10	.85	.35
57	Fosse, Ray	.16	.11	.04			
58	Sanguillen, Manny	.16	.11	.04			
59	Johnson, Tom	.16	.11	.04	1.10	.85	.35
60	Stanton, Lee	.16	.11	.04			
61	Burroughs, Jeff	.20	.15	.06			
62	Grich, Bobby	.20	.15	.06	1.10	.85	.35
63	Winfield, Dave	.60	.45	.20			
64	Driessen, Dan	.16	.11	.04			
65	Simmons, Ted	.40	.30	.13	1.10	.85	.35
66	Remy, Jerry	.16	.11	.04			
67	Cowens, Al	.16	.11	.04			
68	Lyle, Sparky	.25	.20	.08	1.10	.85	.35
69	Trillo, Manny	.16	.11	.04			
70	Sutton, Don	.40	.30	.13			
71	Bowa, Larry	.25	.20	.08	1.10	.85	.35
72	Cruz, Jose	.25	.20	.08			
73	McCovey, Willie	.50	.40	.18			
74	Blyleven, Bert	.20	.15	.06	1.50	1.10	.50
75	Singleton, Ken	.25	.20	.08			
76	North, Bill	.16	.11	.04			
77	Thompson, Jason	.16	.11	.04	1.10	.85	.35
78	Eckersley	.20	.15	.06			
79	Sundberg	.25	.20	.08			
80	Koosman	.20	.15	.06	1.10	.85	.35
81	Bochte, Bruce	.16	.11	.04			
82	Hendrick, George	.25	.20	.08			
83	Ryan, Nolan	.50	.40	.18	1.25	.90	.40
84	Howell, Roy	.16	.11	.04			
85	Metzger	.16	.11	.04			
86	Medich, Doe	.16	.11	.04	1.10	.85	.35
87	Morgan, Joe	.30	.25	.10			
88	Leonard, Dennis	.25	.20	.08			
89	Randolph, Willie	.25	.20	.08	1.10	.85	.35
90	Murcer, Bobby	.20	.15	.06			
91	Manning, Rick	.16	.11	.04			
92	Richard, J. R.	.50	.40	.18	1.10	.85	.35
93	Cey, Ron	.25	.20	.08			
94	Bando, Sal	.20	.15	.06			
95	LeFlore, Ron	.25	.20	.08	1.10	.85	.35
96	Goltz, Dave	.16	.11	.04			
97	Meyer, Dan	.16	.11	.04			
98	Chambliss, Chris	.20	.15	.06	1.10	.85	.35
99	Pocoroba, Biff	.16	.11	.04			
100	Gamble, Oscar	.20	.15	.06			
101	Tanana, Frank	.20	.15	.06	1.10	.85	.35
102	Randle, Len	.16	.11	.04			
103	Hutton, Tommy	.16	.11	.04			
104	Candelaria, John	.16	.11	.04	1.10	.85	.35
105	Orta, George	.16	.11	.04			

1978 HOSTESS (CONTINUED)

	MINT	VG-E	F-G	MINT	VG-E	F-G
106 Reitz, Ken	.16	.11	.04			
107 Campbell, Bill	.16	.11	.04	1.10	.85	.35
108 Concepcion, Dave	.25	.20	.08			
109 Ferguson, Joe	.16	.11	.04			
110 Rivers, Mickey	.20	.15	.06	1.10	.85	.35
111 Splittorff	.20	.15	.06			
112 Lopes	.20	.15	.06			
113 Schmidt	.80	.60	.25	1.50	1.10	.50
114 Rudi	.20	.15	.06			
115 May, Milt	.16	.11	.04			
116 Palmer, Jim	.80	.60	.25	1.25	.90	.40
117 Madlock	.20	.15	.06			
118 Smalley	.20	.15	.06			
119 Cooper, Cecil	.30	.25	.10	1.10	.85	.35
120 Langford, Rick	.16	.11	.04			
121 Jones, Ruppert	.20	.15	.06			
122 Niekro, Phil	.30	.25	.10	1.10	.85	.35
123 Harrah, Toby	.16	.11	.04			
124 Lemon, Chet	.20	.15	.06			
125 Tenace, Gene	.16	.11	.04	1.10	.85	.35
126 Henderson, Steve	.20	.15	.06			
127 Torrez	.20	.15	.06			
128 Rose, Pete	1.00	.70	.30	1.50	1.10	.50
129 Denny, John	.16	.11	.04			
130 Porter, Darrel	.25	.20	.08			
131 Reuschel, Rick	.25	.20	.08	1.10	.85	.35
132 Nettles, Graig	.25	.20	.08			
133 Maddox, Garry	.20	.15	.06			
134 Flanagan, Mike	.25	.20	.08	1.25	.90	.40
135 Parker, Dave	.60	.45	.20			
136 Whitfield, Terry	.16	.11	.04			
137 Garland, Wayne	.16	.11	.04	1.10	.85	.35
138 Yount	.25	.20	.08			
139 Perry, Gaylord	.40	.30	.13			
140 Carew	.60	.45	.20	1.50	1.10	.50
141 Gross, Greg	.16	.11	.04			
142 Bonnell, Barry	.16	.11	.04			
143 Montanez	.16	.11	.04	1.10	.85	.35
144 Fingers	.30	.25	.10			
145 Bostock, Lyman	.30	.25	.10			
146 Carter, Gary	.40	.30	.13	1.10	.85	.35
147 Blomberg, Ron	.16	.11	.04			
148 Bailor, Bob	.16	.11	.04			
149 Seaver, Tom	.80	.60	.25	1.50	1.10	.50
150 Munson, Thurman	.80	.60	.25			

1979 HOSTESS (150)

3 1/4" X 7 1/4"

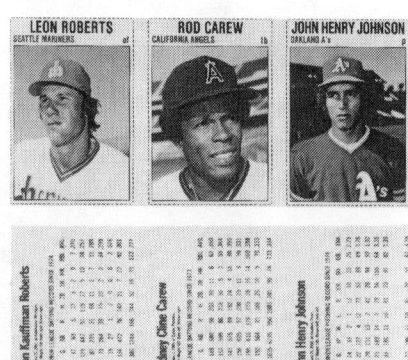

The 1979 Hostess set contains 150 full color, numbered cards issued in panels of three cards each on the backs of family-sized Hostess cake products. Scarcer panels are listed in the checklist below with asterisks.

	AS INDIVIDUALS			AS PANELS		
	MINT	VG-E	F-G	MINT	VG-E	F-G
COMPLETE SET	30.00	21.00	8.00	65.00	50.00	20.00
COMMON PANEL	xxx	xxx	xxx	.95	.75	.30
COMMON PLAYER	.16	.11	.04	xxx	xxx	xxx
1 Denny, John	.16	.11	.04			
2 Rice, Jim	.80	.60	.25	1.25	.90	.40
3 Bair, Doug	.16	.11	.04			
4 Porter, Darrell	.25	.20	.08			
5 Grimsley, Ross	.16	.11	.04	.95	.75	.30
6 Murcer, Bobby	.20	.15	.06			

	MINT	VG-E	F-G	MINT	VG-E	F-G
7 Mazzilli	.30	.25	.10			
8 Garvey	.60	.45	.20	2.00	1.50	.60
9 Schmidt	.60	.45	.20			
10 Whitfield, Terry	.16	.11	.04			
11 J. Palmer	.60	.45	.20	1.25	.90	.40
12 Moreno, Omar	.20	.15	.06			
13 Kuiper	.16	.11	.04			
14 Caldwell, Mike	.20	.15	.06	.95	.75	.30
15 Kemp	.20	.15	.06			
16 Goltz	.20	.15	.06			
17 Page, Mitchell	.16	.11	.04	.95	.75	.30
18 Stein, Bill	.16	.11	.04			
19 Tenace, Gene	.16	.11	.04			
20 Burroughs, Jeff	.20	.15	.06	.95	.75	.30
21 Barrios, Francisco	.16	.11	.04			
22 Torrez	.20	.15	.06			
23 Reitz, Ken	.16	.11	.04	.95	.75	.30
24 Carter, Gary	.30	.25	.10			
25 Hrabosky	.20	.15	.06			
26 Munson	.60	.45	.20	1.25	.90	.40
27 Buckner	.30	.25	.10			
28 Cey*	.20	.15	.06			
29 Richard, J. R.*	.50	.40	.18	2.50	1.80	.80
30 Luzinski*	.30	.25	.10			
31 Ott, Ed*	.16	.11	.04			
32 D. Martinez*	.16	.11	.04	2.00	1.50	.60
33 D. Evans (SF)*	.16	.11	.04			
34 LeFlore	.25	.20	.08			
35 Waits, Rick	.16	.11	.04	.95	.75	.30
36 Cooper, Cecil	.30	.25	.10			
37 L. Roberts	.16	.11	.04			
38 Carew	.60	.45	.20	1.25	.90	.40
39 J. Johnson	.16	.11	.04			
40 C. Lemon	.20	.15	.06			
41 Swan, Craig	.20	.15	.06	.95	.75	.30
42 Matthews, Gary	.20	.15	.06			
43 L. Johnson	.16	.11	.04			
44 Simmons, Ted	.40	.30	.13	.95	.75	.30
45 Griffey	.20	.15	.06			
46 Patek	.16	.11	.04			
47 Tanana	.20	.15	.06	.95	.75	.30
48 Gossage	.30	.25	.10			
49 Hooten, Burt	.20	.15	.06			
50 E. Valentine	.20	.15	.06	.95	.75	.30
51 K. Forsch	.16	.11	.04			
52 Knepper, Bob	.16	.11	.04			
53 Parker, Dave	.60	.45	.20	1.25	.90	.40
54 DeCinces	.16	.11	.04			
55 Yount	.30	.25	.10			
56 Staub	.25	.20	.08	.95	.75	.30
57 G. Alexander	.16	.11	.04			
58 J. Cruz (Sea)	.16	.11	.04			
59 Keough, Matt	.16	.11	.04	.95	.75	.30
60 Smalley	.20	.15	.06			
61 J. Morgan	.30	.25	.10			
62 P. Niekro	.30	.25	.10	1.25	.90	.40
63 Baylor, Don	.30	.25	.10			
64 D. Evans (Bos)	.16	.11	.04			
65 Seaver, Tom	.60	.45	.20	1.25	.90	.40
66 Hendrick, George	.30	.25	.10			
67 R. Reuschel, Rick	.30	.25	.10			
68 G. Brett	.80	.60	.25	1.50	1.10	.50
69 Pinella, Lou	.20	.15	.06			
70 Cabell	.16	.11	.04			
71 Carlton	.60	.45	.20	1.25	.90	.40
72 R. Smith	.30	.25	.10			
73 Dempsey, Rick*	.16	.11	.04			
74 Blue*	.50	.40	.18	2.00	1.50	.60
75 Garner, Phil*	.16	.11	.04			
76 Manning, Rick*	.16	.11	.04			
77 Fidrych*	.30	.25	.10	2.00	1.50	.60
78 Guerrero, Mario	.16	.11	.04			
79 Stinson*	.16	.11	.04			
80 Oliver*	.40	.30	.13	2.00	1.50	.60
81 Flynn, Doug	.16	.11	.04			
82 Mayberry	.20	.15	.06			
83 Perry, Gaylord	.40	.30	.13	.95	.75	.30
84 Rudi	.20	.15	.06			
85 Concepcion	.25	.20	.08			
86 Candelaria	.20	.15	.06	.95	.75	.30
87 Vuckovich, Pete	.16	.11	.04			
88 DeJesus, Ivan	.16	.11	.04			
89 Guidry, Ron	.60	.45	.20	1.25	.90	.40
90 McRae, Hal	.16	.11	.04			
91 Cedeno	.30	.25	.10			
92 Sutton	.30	.25	.10	.95	.75	.30
93 Thornton, Andre	.20	.15	.06			
94 Erickson, Roger	.16	.11	.04			
95 Hisle	.20	.15	.06	.95	.75	.30
96 Thompson, Jason	.20	.15	.06			
97 Sundberg	.25	.20	.08			
98 Horner, Bob	.50	.40	.18	.95	.75	.30
99 R. Jones	.20	.15	.06			

1930's MATCHBOOK COVER

137

	MINT	VG-E	F-G	MINT	VG-E	F-G
100 Montanez, Willie	.16	.11	.04			
101 Ryan, Nolan	.50	.40	.18	1.25	.90	.40
102 O. Smith	.20	.15	.06			
103 Soderholm	.16	.11	.04			
104 Stargell, Willie	.50	.40	.18	1.25	.90	.40
105 Bailor, Bob	.16	.11	.04			
106 Fisk, Carlton	.30	.25	.10			
107 Foster, George	.40	.30	.13	1.50	1.10	.50
108 K. Hernandez	.50	.40	.18			
109 Leonard, Dennis	.20	.15	.06			
110 Nettles	.20	.15	.06	.95	.75	.30
111 J. Cruz (Hou)	.20	.15	.06			
112 Bobby Grich	.20	.15	.06			
113 Boone	.16	.11	.04	.95	.75	.30
114 Lopes	.20	.15	.06			
115 Murray, Eddie	.30	.25	.10			
116 Clark, Jack	.30	.25	.10	1.25	.90	.40
117 Whitaker, Lou	.20	.15	.06			
118 Dilone	.16	.11	.04			
119 Bando	.20	.15	.06	1.25	.90	.40
120 R. Jackson	.60	.45	.20			
121 Murphy, Dale	.16	.11	.04			
122 Matlack	.20	.15	.06	.95	.75	.30
123 Bochte	.16	.11	.04			
124 Stearns	.20	.15	.06			
125 Winfield, Dave	.50	.40	.18	.95	.75	.30
126 Orta	.16	.11	.04			
127 Templeton, Gary	.40	.30	.13			
128 Bench, John	.70	.50	.20	1.25	.90	.40
129 Hobson, Butch	.16	.11	.04			
130 Sutter	.40	.30	.13			
131 Dent	.20	.15	.06	.95	.75	.30
132 Otis	.20	.15	.06			
133 Blyleven	.20	.15	.06			
134 Bowa	.25	.20	.08	.95	.75	.30
135 Singleton, Ken	.25	.20	.08			
136 Lezcano	.20	.15	.06			
137 Howell, Roy	.16	.11	.04	.95	.75	.30
138 Madlock, Bill	.20	.15	.06			
139 Revering	.16	.11	.04			
140 Zisk, Richie	.20	.15	.06	.95	.75	.30
141 Wynegar, Butch	.16	.11	.04			
142 Ashby	.16	.11	.04			
143 Lyle, Sparky	.20	.15	.06	1.50	1.10	.50
144 Rose, Pete	.80	.60	.25			
145 Eckersley	.20	.15	.06			
146 D. Kingman	.40	.30	.13	.95	.75	.30
147 Bell, Buddy	.30	.25	.10			
148 Hargrove	.16	.11	.04			
149 Koosman	.20	.15	.06	.95	.75	.30
150 Harrah	.20	.15	.06			

BRIGGS PANEL

1962 JELLO (200)   2 1/2" X 3 1/2"

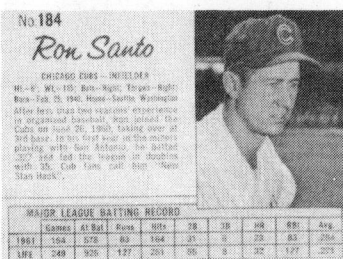

The 1962 Jello set is considered by many to be a test issue and has the same checklist as the 1962 Post set. While the cards feature the same numbers and players as the 1962 Post Cereal set, the scarcities and cards difficult to obtain are by no means the same. Cards Nos. 29, 82, and 176 were not issued. The Jellow set can be distinguished from the Post set because it does not have the Post oval in the lower right portion of the player biography. The SCB designation is F229-1.

	MINI	VG-E	F-G
COMPLETE SET	1000.00	700.00	300.00
COMMON PLAYER	4.75	3.50	1.50

		MINT	VG-E	F-G
1 Bill Skowron	10.00	7.00	3.00
2 Bobby Richardson	10.00	7.00	3.00
3 Cletis Boyer	4.75	3.50	1.50
4 Tony Kubek	6.00	4.50	2.00
5 Mickey Mantle	80.00	60.00	25.00
6 Roger Maris	10.00	7.00	3.00
7 Yogi Berra	12.00	8.75	4.00
8 Elston Howard	6.00	4.50	2.00
9 Whitey Ford	10.00	7.00	3.00
10 Ralph Terry	4.75	3.50	1.50
11 John Blanchard	4.75	3.50	1.50
12 Luis Arroyo	4.75	3.50	1.50
13 Bill Stafford	4.75	3.50	1.50
14 Norm Cash	6.00	4.50	2.00
15 Jake Wood	4.75	3.50	1.50
16 Steve Boros	4.75	3.50	1.50
17 Chico Fernandez	4.75	3.50	1.50
18 Bill Bruton	4.75	3.50	1.50
19 Ken Aspromonte	4.75	3.50	1.50
20 Al Kaline	12.00	8.75	4.00
21 Dick Brown	4.75	3.50	1.50
22 Frank Lary	4.75	3.50	1.50
23 Don Mossi	4.75	3.50	1.50
24 Phil Regan	4.75	3.50	1.50
25 Charley Maxwell	4.75	3.50	1.50
26 Jim Bunning	6.00	4.50	3.00
27 Jim Gentile	4.75	3.50	1.50
28 Marv Breeding	4.75	3.50	1.50
29 not issued	xxx	xxx	xxx
30 Ron Hansen	4.75	3.50	1.50
31 Jackie Brandt	4.75	3.50	1.50
32 Dick Williams	6.00	4.50	2.00
33 Gus Triandos	4.75	3.50	1.50
34 Milt Pappas	4.75	3.50	1.50
35 Hoyt Wilhelm	6.00	4.50	2.00
36 Chuck Estrada	4.75	3.50	1.50
37 Vic Power	4.75	3.50	1.50
38 Johnny Temple	4.75	3.50	1.50
39 Bubba Phillips	4.75	3.50	1.50
40 Tito Francona	4.75	3.50	1.50
41 Willie Kirkland	4.75	3.50	1.50
42 John Romano	4.75	3.50	1.50
43 Jim Perry	4.75	3.50	1.50
44 Woodie Held	4.75	3.50	1.50
45 Chuck Essegian	4.75	3.50	1.50
46 Roy Sievers	4.75	3.50	1.50
47 Nellie Fox	6.00	4.50	2.00
48 Al Smith	4.75	3.50	1.50
49 Luis Aparicio	6.00	4.50	2.00
50 Jim Landis	4.75	3.50	1.50
51 Minnie Minoso	6.00	4.50	2.00
52 Andy Carey	4.75	3.50	1.50
53 Sherman Lollar	4.75	3.50	1.50
54 Bil Pierce	6.00	4.50	2.00
55 Early Wynn	7.00	5.25	2.50
56 Chuck Schilling	4.75	3.50	1.50
57 Pete Runnels	4.75	3.50	1.50
58 Frank Malzone	4.75	3.50	1.50
59 Don Buddin	4.75	3.50	1.50
60 Gary Geiger	4.75	3.50	1.50
61 Carl Yastrzemski	30.00	22.50	10.50
62 Jackie Jensen	6.00	4.50	2.00
63 Jim Pagliaroni	10.00	7.00	3.00
64 Don Schwall	4.75	3.50	1.50
65 Dale Long	4.75	3.50	1.50
66 Chuck Cottier	4.75	3.50	1.50
67 Billy Klaus	4.75	3.50	1.50
68 Coot Veal	4.75	3.50	1.50
69 Marty Keough	10.00	7.00	3.00
70 Willie Tasby	10.00	7.00	3.00
71 Gene Woodling	4.75	3.50	1.50
72 Gene Green	4.75	3.50	1.50
73 Dick Donovan	4.75	3.50	1.50
74 Steve Bilko	4.75	3.50	1.50
75 Rocky Bridges	4.75	3.50	1.50
76 Eddie Yost	4.75	3.50	1.50
77 Leon Wagner	4.75	3.50	1.50
78 Albie Pearson	4.75	3.50	1.50
79 Ken Hunt	4.75	3.50	1.50
80 Earl Averill	4.75	3.50	1.50
81 Ryne Duren	4.75	3.50	1.50
82 not issued	xxx	xxx	xxx
83 Bob Allison	4.75	3.50	1.50
84 Billy Martin	6.00	4.50	2.00
85 Harmon Killebrew	8.00	6.00	2.50
86 Zoilo Versalles	4.75	3.50	1.50
87 Lenny Green	4.75	3.50	1.50
88 Bill Tuttle	4.75	3.50	1.50
89 Jim Lemon	4.75	3.50	1.50
90 Earl Battey	4.75	3.50	1.50
91 Camilo Pascual	4.75	3.50	1.50
92 Norm Sieburn	4.75	3.50	1.50
93 Jerry Lumpe	4.75	3.50	1.50
94 Dick Howser	4.75	3.50	1.50
95 Gene Stephens	10.00	7.00	3.00
96 Leo Posada	4.75	3.50	1.50
97 Joe Pignatano	4.75	3.50	1.50
98 Jim Archer	4.75	3.50	1.50
99 Haywood Sullivan	4.75	3.50	1.50
100 Art Ditmar	4.75	3.50	1.50
101 Gil Hodges	10.00	7.00	3.00
102 Charlie Neal	4.75	3.50	1.50
103 Daryl Spencer	4.75	3.50	1.50
104 Maury Wills	6.00	4.50	2.00
105 Tommy Davis	6.00	4.50	2.00
106 Willie Davis	4.75	3.50	1.50
107 John Roseboro	10.00	7.00	3.00
108 John Podres	4.75	3.50	1.50
109 Sandy Koufax	12.00	8.75	4.00
110 Don Drysdale	8.00	6.00	2.50
111 Larry Sherry	4.75	3.50	1.50
112 Jim Gilliam	6.00	4.50	2.00
113 Norm Larker	4.75	3.50	1.50
114 Duke Snider	12.00	8.75	4.00
115 Stan Williams	4.75	3.50	1.50
116 Gordy Coleman	12.00	8.75	4.00
117 Don Blasingame	4.75	3.50	1.50
118 Gene Freese	10.00	7.00	3.00
119 Ed Kasko	4.75	3.50	1.50
120 Gus Bell	4.75	3.50	1.50

	MINT	VG-E	F-G			MINT	VG-E	F-G
121 Vada Pinson	6.00	4.50	2.00		161 Carl Warwick	4.75	3.50	1.50
122 Frank Robinson	10.00	7.00	3.00		162 Carl Sawatski	4.75	3.50	1.50
123 Bob Purkey	4.75	3.50	1.50		163 Lindy McDaniel	4.75	3.50	1.50
124 Joey Jay	4.75	3.50	1.50		164 Ernie Broglio	4.75	3.50	1.50
125 Jim Brosnan	4.75	3.50	1.50		165 Larry Jackson	4.75	3.50	1.50
126 Jim O'Toole	4.75	3.50	1.50		166 Curt Flood	4.75	3.50	1.50
127 Jerry Lynch	4.75	3.50	1.50		167 Curt Simmons	10.00	7.00	3.00
128 Wally Post	4.75	3.50	1.50		168 Alex Grammas	4.75	3.50	1.50
129 Ken Hunt	4.75	3.50	1.50		169 Dick Stuart	4.75	3.50	1.50
130 Jerry Zimmerman	4.75	3.50	1.50		170 Bill Mazeroski	10.00	7.00	3.00
131 Willie McCovey	10.00	7.00	3.00		171 Don Hoak	4.75	3.50	1.50
132 Jose Pagan	4.75	3.50	1.50		172 Dick Groat	6.00	4.50	2.00
133 Felipe Alou	4.75	3.50	1.50		173 Roberto Clemente	25.00	18.50	8.75
134 Jim Davenport	4.75	3.50	1.50		174 Bob Skinner	4.75	3.50	1.50
135 Harvey Kuenn	6.00	4.50	2.00		175 Bill Virdon	6.00	4.50	2.00
136 Orlando Cepeda	8.00	6.00	2.50		176 not issued	xxx	xxx	xxx
137 Ed Bailey	4.75	3.50	1.50		177 Elroy Face	4.75	3.50	1.50
138 Sam Jones	4.75	3.50	1.50		178 Bob Friend	4.75	3.50	1.50
139 Mike McCormick	4.75	3.50	1.50		179 Vernon Law	4.75	3.50	1.50
140 Juan Marichal	8.00	6.00	2.50		180 Harvey Haddix	10.00	7.00	3.00
141 Jack Sanford	4.75	3.50	1.50		181 Hal Smith	4.75	3.50	1.50
142 Willie Mays	40.00	30.00	13.00		182 Ed Bouchee	4.75	3.50	1.50
143 Stu Miller	4.75	3.50	1.50		183 Don Zimmer	6.00	4.50	2.00
144 Joe Amalfitano	4.75	3.50	1.50		184 Ron Santo	6.00	4.50	2.00
145 Joe Adcock	4.75	3.50	1.50		185 Andre Rodgers	4.75	3.50	1.50
146 Frank Bolling	4.75	3.50	1.50		186 Richie Ashburn	6.00	4.50	2.00
147 Ed Mathews	9.00	6.75	3.00		187 George Altman	4.75	3.50	1.50
148 Roy McMillan	4.75	3.50	1.50		188 Ernie Banks	15.00	11.00	5.00
149 Hank Aaron	40.00	30.00	13.00		189 Sam Taylor	4.75	3.50	1.50
150 Gino Cimoli	4.75	3.50	1.50		190 Don Elston	4.75	3.50	1.50
151 Frank Thomas	4.75	3.50	1.50		191 Jerry Kindall	4.75	3.50	1.50
152 Joe Torre	6.00	4.50	2.00		192 Pancho Herrera	4.75	3.50	1.50
153 Lew Burdette	6.00	4.50	2.00		193 Tony Taylor	4.75	3.50	1.50
154 Bob Buhl	4.75	3.50	1.50		194 Ruben Amaro	4.75	3.50	1.50
155 Carlton Willey	4.75	3.50	1.50		195 Don Demeter	4.75	3.50	1.50
156 Lee Maye	4.75	3.50	1.50		196 Bobby Gene Smith	4.75	3.50	1.50
157 Al Spangler	10.00	7.00	3.00		197 Clay Dalrymple	4.75	3.50	1.50
158 Bill White	4.75	3.50	1.50		198 Robin Roberts	8.00	6.00	2.50
159 Ken Boyer	6.00	4.50	2.00		199 Art Mahaffey	4.75	3.50	1.50
160 Joe Cunningham	4.75	3.50	1.50		200 John Buzhardt	4.75	3.50	1.50

1963 JELLO (200)

2 1/2" X 3 1/2"

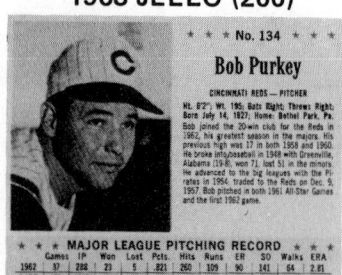

The 1963 Jello set of 200 cards features the same players and numbers as the 1963 Post Cereal set. The scarcities, however, are not the same for the Jello set as for the Post set. The Post and Jello cards of this year are quite difficult to distinguish from one another; however, the Jello card is slightly smaller and features smaller print. The cards with an asterisk came on the relatively unpopular 6 oz. boxes and are more difficult to obtain.

	MINT	VG-E	F-G
COMPLETE SET	675.00	500.00	200.00
COMMON PLAYER	.75	.60	.25
COMMON PLAYER (*)	7.50	6.00	2.50

	MINT	VG-E	F-G			MINT	VG-E	F-G
1 Vic Power	.75	.60	.25		21 John Blanchard*	7.50	6.00	2.50
2 Bernie Allen*	7.50	6.00	2.50		22 Bill Stafford*	7.50	6.00	2.50
3 Zoilo Versalles*	7.50	6.00	2.50		23 Tom Tresh	.75	.60	.25
4 Rich Rollins	.75	.60	.25		24 Steve Bilko	.75	.60	.25
5 Harmon Killebrew	3.00	2.25	1.00		25 Bill Moran	.75	.60	.25
6 Lenny Green*	7.50	6.00	2.50		26 Joe Koppe	.75	.60	.25
7 Bob Allison	.75	.60	.25		27 Felix Torres	.75	.60	.25
8 Earl Battey*	7.50	6.00	2.50		28 Leon Wagner	.75	.60	.25
9 Camilo Pascual	.75	.60	.25		29 Albie Pearson	.75	.60	.25
10 Jim Kaat*	9.00	6.75	3.00		30 Lee Thomas	.75	.60	.25
11 Jack Kralick	.75	.60	.25		31 Bob Rodgers*	7.50	6.00	2.50
12 Bill Skowron*	7.50	6.00	2.50		32 Dean Chance	.75	.60	.25
13 Bobby Richardson	1.00	.70	.30		33 Ken McBride*	7.50	6.00	2.50
14 Cletis Boyer	.75	.60	.25		34 George Thomas*	7.50	6.00	2.50
15 Mickey Mantle	50.00	38.00	17.00		35 Joe Cunningham*	7.50	6.00	2.50
16 Roger Maris	10.00	7.00	3.00		36 Nelson Fox	1.25	.90	.40
17 Yogi Berra	7.50	5.75	2.50		37 Luis Aparicio	1.25	.90	.40
18 Elston Howard*	9.00	6.75	3.00		38 Al Smith	.75	.60	.25
19 Whitey Ford	5.00	3.75	1.75		39 Floyd Robinson	.75	.60	.25
20 Ralph Terry	.75	.60	.25		40 Jim Landis	.75	.60	.25

REMEMBER THE NATIONAL CONVENTION IS BEING HELD JULY 9 - 12, 1981, IN PLYMOUTH, MICHIGAN

		MINT	VG-E	F-G			MINT	VG-E	F-G
41	Charlie Maxwell	.75	.60	.25	121	Sandy Koufax	15.00	11.00	5.00
42	Sherman Lollar	.75	.60	.25	122	Stan Williams*	7.50	6.00	2.50
43	Early Wynn	3.00	2.25	1.00	123	Don Drysdale	5.00	3.75	1.75
44	Juan Pizarro*	7.50	6.00	2.50	124	Daryl Spencer	.75	.60	.25
45	Ray Herbert*	7.50	6.00	2.50	125	Gordy Coleman	.75	.60	.25
46	Norm Cash	1.00	.70	.30	126	Don Blasingame*	7.50	6.00	2.50
47	Steve Boros*	7.50	6.00	2.50	127	Leo Cardenas	.75	.60	.25
48	Dick McAuliffe	.75	.60	.25	128	Eddie Kasko*	7.50	6.00	2.50
49	Bill Bruton*	7.50	6.00	2.50	129	Jerry Lynch	.75	.60	.25
50	Rocky Colavito	1.25	.90	.40	130	Vada Pinson	1.00	.70	.30
51	Al Kaline	6.00	4.50	2.00	131	Frank Robinson	6.00	4.50	2.00
52	Dick Brown*	7.50	6.00	2.50	132	John Edwards*	7.50	6.00	2.50
53	Jim Bunning	1.00	.70	.30	133	Joey Jay	.75	.60	.25
54	Hank Aguirre	.75	.60	.25	134	Bob Purkey	.75	.60	.25
55	Frank Lary*	7.50	6.00	2.50	135	Marty Keough*	7.50	6.00	2.50
56	Don Mossi*	7.50	6.00	2.50	136	Jim O'Toole*	7:50	6.00	2.50
57	Jim Gentile	.75	.60	.25	137	Dick Stuart	.75	.60	.25
58	Jackie Brandt	.75	.60	.25	138	Bill Mazeroski	1.00	.70	.30
59	Brooks Robinson	6.00	4.50	2.00	139	Dick Groat	1.00	.70	.30
60	Ron Hanson	.75	.60	.25	140	Don Hoak	.75	.60	.25
61	Jerry Adair*	7.50	6.00	2.50	141	Bob Skinner	.75	.60	.25
62	John Powell	1.00	.70	.30	142	Bill Virdon	1.50	1.10	.50
63	Russ Snyder*	7.50	6.00	2.50	143	Roberto Clemente	15.00	11.00	5.00
64	Steve Barber	.75	.60	.25	144	Smokey Burgess	.75	.60	.25
65	Milt Pappas*	7.50	6.00	2.50	145	Bob Friend	.75	.60	.25
66	Robin Roberts	3.00	2.25	1.00	146	Al McBean*	7.50	6.00	2.50
67	Tito Francona	.75	.60	.25	147	Elroy Face	1.00	.70	.30
68	Jerry Kindall*	7.50	6.00	2.50	148	Joe Adcock	1.00	.70	.30
69	Woody Held	.75	.60	.25	149	Frank Bolling	.75	.60	.25
70	Bubba Phillips	.75	.60	.25	150	Roy McMillan	.75	.60	.25
71	Chuck Essegian	.75	.60	.25	151	Eddie Mathews	5.00	3.75	1.75
72	Willie Kirkland*	7.50	6.00	2.50	152	Hank Aaron	30.00	22.50	10.50
73	Al Luplow	.75	.60	.25	153	Del Crandall*	7.50	6.00	2.50
74	Ty Cline*	7.50	6.00	2.50	154	Bob Shaw	.75	.60	.25
75	Dick Donovan	.75	.60	.25	155	Lew Burdette	1.00	.70	.30
76	John Romano	.75	.60	.25	156	Joe Torre*	9.00	6.75	3.00
77	Pete Runnels	.75	.60	.25	157	Tony Cloninger *	7.50	6.00	2.50
78	Ed Bressoud*	7.50	6.00	2.50	158	Bill White	.75	.60	.25
79	Frank Malzone	.75	.60	.25	159	Julian Javier*	7.50	6.00	2.50
80	Carl Yastrzemski	20.00	15.00	6.50	160	Ken Boyer	1.25	.90	.40
81	Gary Geiger	.75	.60	.25	161	Julio Gotay *	7.50	6.00	2.50
82	Lou Clinton*	7.50	6.00	2.50	162	Curt Flood	1.00	.70	.30
83	Earl Wilson	.75	.60	.25	163	Charlie James*	7.50	6.00	2.50
84	Bill Monbouquette	.75	.60	.25	164	Gene Oliver *	7.50	6.00	2.50
85	Norm Sieburn	.75	.60	.25	165	Ernie Broglio	.75	.60	.25
86	Jerry Lumpe	.75	.60	.25	166	Bob Gibson*	20.00	15.00	6.50
87	Manny Jimenez	.75	.60	.25	167	Lindy McDaniel*	7.50	6.00	2.50
88	Gino Cimoli	.75	.60	.25	168	Ray Washburn	.75	.60	.25
89	Ed Charles*	7.50	6.00	2.50	169	Ernie Banks	8.00	6.00	2.50
90	Ed Rakow	.75	.60	.25	170	Ron Santo	1.00	.70	.30
91	Bob DelGreco	7.50	6.00	2.50	171	George Altman	.75	.60	.25
92	Haywood Sullivan*	7.50	6.00	2.50	172	Billy Williams*	12.00	8.75	4.00
93	Chuck Hinton	.75	.60	.25	173	Andre Rodgers*	7.50	6.00	2.50
94	Ken Retzer*	7.50	6.00	2.50	174	Ken Hubbs	1.00	.70	.30
95	Harry Bright*	7.50	6.00	2.50	175	Don Landrum*	7.50	6.00	2.50
96	Bob Johnson	.75	.60	.25	176	Dick Bertell*	7.50	6.00	2.50
97	Dave Stenhouse*	7.50	6.00	2.50	177	Roy Sievers	.75	.60	.25
98	Chuck Cottier	.75	.60	.25	178	Tony Taylor*	7.50	6.00	2.50
99	Tom Cheney	.75	.60	.25	179	John Callison	.75	.60	.25
100	Claude Osteen*	7.50	6.00	2.50	180	Don Demeter	.75	.60	.25
101	Orlando Cepeda	1.50	1.10	.50	181	Tony Gonzalez *	7.50	6.00	2.50
102	Charley Hiller*	7.50	6.00	2.50	182	Wes Covington*	7.50	6.00	2.50
103	Jose Pagan*	7.50	6.00	2.50	183	Art Mahaffey	.75	.60	.25
104	Jim Davenport	.75	.60	.25	184	Clay Dalrymple	.75	.60	.25
105	Harvey Kuenn	1.00	.70	.30	185	Al Spangler	.75	.60	.25
106	Willie Mays	30.00	22.50	10.50	186	Roman Mejias	.75	.60	.25
107	Felipe Alou	1.00	.70	.30	187	Bob Aspromonte *	20.00	15.00	6.50
108	Tom Haller	.75	.60	.25	188	Norm Larker	.75	.60	.25
109	Juan Marichal	1.50	1.10	.50	189	Johnny Temple	.75	.60	.25
110	Jack Sanford	.75	.60	.25	190	Carl Warwick*	7.50	6.00	2.50
111	Bill O'Dell	.75	.60	.25	191	Bob Lillis*	7.50	6.00	2.50
112	Willie McCovey *	20.00	15.00	6.50	192	Dick Farrell*	7.50	6.00	2.50
113	Lee Walls*	7.50	6.00	2.50	193	Gil Hodges	4.00	3.00	1.40
114	Jim Gilliam*	10.00	7.00	3.00	194	Marv Throneberry	.75	.60	.25
115	Maury Wills	1.25	.90	.40	195	Charlie Neal*	7.50	6.00	2.50
116	Ron Fairly	1.00	.70	.30	196	Frank Thomas	.75	.60	.25
117	Tommy Davis	1.00	.70	.30	197	Richie Ashburn	1.25	.90	.40
118	Duke Snider	6.00	4.50	2.00	198	Felix Mantilla*	7.50	6.00	2.50
119	Willie Davis	.75	.60	.25	199	Rod Kanehl*	7.50	6.00	2.50
120	John Roseboro	.75	.60	.25	200	Roger Craig*	7.50	6.00	2.50

Watch the hobby papers and your local bookstores for the release later this year of the Sport Americana Baseball Memorabilia Price Guide. This book will contain prices and descriptions of baseball memorabilia other than the popular baseball card issues — yearbooks, baseball coins, programs, press pins, uniforms, statues, postcards, etc.

1953 JOHNSTON COOKIES (25)   2 9/16" X 3 5/16"

WARREN SPAHN

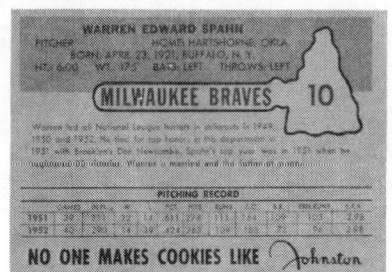

The 1953 Johnston's Cook set of 25 numbered ca features Milwaukee Bra players only. This set is most plentiful of the th Johnston's Cookies sets no known scarcities exist. ACC designation is D356-1

	MINT	VG-E	F-G
COMPLETE SET	110.00	75.00	35.00
COMMON PLAYER	4.00	3.00	1.40

	MINT	VG-E	F-G			MINT	VG-E	F-G
1 Charlie Grimm	4.00	3.00	1.40	14 Walker Cooper		4.00	3.00	1.40
2 John Antonelli	5.00	3.75	1.75	15 Del Crandall		5.00	3.75	1.75
3 Vern Bickford	4.00	3.00	1.40	16 Ebba St. Clair		4.00	3.00	1.40
4 Bob Buhl	4.00	3.00	1.40	17 Joe Adcock		5.00	3.75	1.75
5 Lew Burdette	6.50	5.00	2.25	18 George Crowe		4.00	3.00	1.40
6 Dave Cole	4.00	3.00	1.40	19 Jack Dittmer		4.00	3.00	1.40
7 Ernie Johnson	4.00	3.00	1.40	20 Johnny Logan		4.00	3.00	1.40
8 Dave Jolly	4.00	3.00	1.40	21 Ed Mathews		15.00	11.00	5.00
9 Don Liddle	4.00	3.00	1.40	22 Bill Bruton		4.00	3.00	1.40
10 Warren Spahn	15.00	11.00	5.00	23 Sid Gordon		4.00	3.00	1.40
11 Max Surkont	4.00	3.00	1.40	24 Andy Pafko		4.00	3.00	1.40
12 Jim Wilson	4.00	3.00	1.40	25 Jim Pendleton		4.00	3.00	1.40
13 Sibbi Sisti	4.00	3.00	1.40					

1954 JOHNSTON COOKIES (35)   2" X 3 7/8"

ED MATHEWS

The 1954 Johnston's Cookie set of 35 cards are numbere by the player's uniform num ber, with the exception of th Lacks and the Taylor card which are unnumbered. Th Bobby Thomson card wa withdrawn early in the yea after his injury; hence, it quite scarce. The ACC des ignation is D356-2.

	MINT	VG-E	F-G
COMPLETE SET	200.00	90.00	80.00
COMMON PLAYER	5.00	3.65	1.75

	MINT	VG-E	F-G			MINT	VG-E	F-G
1 Del Crandall	6.00	4.50	2.00	16 Chet Nichols		5.00	3.65	1.75
3 Jim Pendleton	5.00	3.65	1.75	17 Dave Jolly		5.00	3.65	1.75
4 Danny O'Connell	5.00	3.65	1.75	19 Jim Wilson		5.00	3.65	1.75
5 Hank Aaron	85.00	65.00	30.00	20 Ray Crone		5.00	3.65	1.75
6 Jack Dittmer	5.00	3.65	1.75	21 Warren Spahn		16.00	12.00	5.50
9 Joe Adcock	6.00	4.50	2.00	22 Gene Conley		5.00	3.65	1.75
10 Bob Buhl	5.00	3.65	1.75	23 Johnny Logan		5.00	3.65	1.75
11 Phil Paine	5.00	3.65	1.75	24 Charlie White		5.00	3.65	1.75
12 Ben Johnson	5.00	3.65	1.75	27 George Metkovich		5.00	3.65	1.75
13 Sibbi Sisti	5.00	3.65	1.75	28 Johnny Cooney		5.00	3.65	1.75
15 Charles Gorin	5.00	3.65	1.75	29 Paul Burris		5.00	3.65	1.75
				31 Bucky Walters		5.00	3.65	1.75
				32 Ernie Johnson		5.00	3.65	1.75
				33 Lou Burdette		9.00	6.75	3.00

PLASTIC SHEETS 16¢ EACH IN LOTS OF 100

S4-4 POCKET - POSTCARDS
S8-8 POCKET - 1952-56 TOPPS 53-55 BOWMAN
S9-9 POCKET - TOPPS - 1957 TO PRESENT
S12-12 POCKET - 1948-50 BOWMAN
S16-16 POCKET CIGARETTE CARDS T206
SM9-9 POCKET - 1951-52 BOWMAN

WE ARE VERY PLEASED TO MIX AND MATCH SIZES.

P35-6 POCKET 3½ x 3½ PHOTOS
P45-4 POCKET 3½ x 5" PHOTOS
P57-2 POCKET 5 x 7 PHOTOS
P81   8 x 10 POCKET
S1   MAGAZINE SIZE (YEARBOOK)

OUR PRICE-------$16.00 PER HUNDRED OF ANY SIZE OR COMBINATION OF SIZES TO MAKE A TOTAL OF 100. ALL ORDERS SHIPPED UPS FREIGHT COLLECT, IF POSTAGE OF $1.75 PER 100 SHEETS IS NOT INCLUDED WITH ORDER. STATES WEST OF THE MISSISSIPPI RIVER, ADD AN ADDITIONAL $1.00 PER 100 SHEETS. ALL INQUIRIES MUST INCLUDE SASE. WE HAVE ONE OF THE LARGEST INVENTORIES OF SPORTS AND NON-SPORTS CARDS AVAILABLE. SEND US YOUR WANT LISTS OF CARDS, SETS, PUBLICATIONS, ETC. CHECKS REQUIRE 2 WEEKS TO CLEAR FOR SHIPMENT. MONEY ORDERS ALLOW US TO SHIP WITHIN THREE DAYS. WE WILL SHIP C.O.D. WE ACCEPT MASTER CHARGE AND VISA.

"FREE"- RUTH, MANTLE, AND MUNSON CARDS PLUS OUR CATALOG FOR 25¢.

100 T.C.M.A. BABE RUTH BASEBALL CARDS - $6.00 PPD.
100 TOPPS N.Y. YANKEES, N.Y. METS, OR BOSTON RED SOX BASEBALL CARDS, VG-MINT, 1967 TO 1976 - $10.00 PPD.
STARTER LOTS - 1 TOPPS BASEBALL CARD FROM EACH YEAR, 1955 TO 1975, VG-MINT - $5.00 PPD.
500 ASSORTED TOPPS BASEBALL CARDS (OUR CHOICE), GOOD TO MINT - $5.00 PPD.

T.C.M.A. BASEBALL IMMORTAL SINGLES (IN COLOR) MANTLE, MAYS, MATHEWS, SNIDER, FORD, H. WILSON, W. GILES - 50¢ each plus 15¢ stamp   ALL 7 FOR $2.00

DICK AND CHARLIE'S SPORTS

K SIKES   CHARLIE SACHELI

TEL. (413) 736-8178

P. O. Box 3092 G, 19 LOCUST STREET
SPRINGFIELD, MASS. 01101
PRICES SUBJECT TO CHANGE WITHOUT NOTICE.

SUPER STAR SET

45 Card Set of All Superstars

Attractive 3-color set with clear black and white photos with yellow and blue border.

- NO commons
- NO stiffs
- NO benchwarmers
- NO has-beens
- NO have-nots
- NO reprint set

4 different poses of
- Mickey Mantle
- Willie Mays
- Hank Aaron
- Ted Williams
- Joe Dimaggio
- Babe Ruth
- Lou Gehrig
- Sandy Koufax
- Bob Clemente

Eight special combination star cards and a special Thurman Munson memorial card

MICKEY MANTLE

WHOLESALE PRICE LIST

rster Set of 45 cards 25 sets @ $2.00/set = $50.00 plus postage
50 sets @ $1.50/set = $75.00 plus postage
100 sets for $100.00 ppd
Sample set for 50¢ and S.A.S.E

Thurman Munson Memorial Cards $13.50 ppd
Thurman Munson Memorial Cards $21.50 ppd
Thurman Munson Memorial Cards $41.50 ppd

Mickey Mantle Cards (two different poses) $13.50 ppd
Mickey Mantle Cards (two different poses) $21.50 ppd
Mickey Mantle Cards (two different poses) $41.50 ppd

Special Combination Star Cards (our choice) $21.50 ppd
Special Combination Star Cards (our choice) $31.50 ppd
Cards of any other player (two different poses) $21.50 ppd
Cards of any other player (four different poses) $31.50 ppd

Munson Memorial Cards & 50 Mantle Cards (two different poses) $13.50 ppd
Munson Memorial Cards & 100 Mantle Cards (two different poses) $21.50 ppd
Munson Memorial Cards & 250 Mantle Cards (two different poses) $41.50 ppd

Order Now!!

1 set **$3.50** Postpaid

4 sets **$10.00** Postpaid

ORDER YOUR 1981 SETS NOW! shipped as soon as we receive them!

TOPPS
DONRUSS $20.00 Per Set Postpaid
FLEERS   **FREE** SUPER STARS SET WITH EACH SET

SPECIAL!!! ALL 3 SETS WITH 4 SUPERSTAR SETS **$50.00**

rder From — Dick and Charlie's Sports P.O. Box 3092 G Springfield, Mass. 01101

VOL. III

- More Pages & Checklists
- More Illustrations
- Condition and Grading Explained
- Wrappers - A New Collectable w/Prices
- Where To Sell and Buy
- Each Set Priced To Tell Card Price As Well As Set Price

**7.00 + 1.00
1ST. CLASS**

Order From:

REBEL PEDDLER
P.O. Box 3092 G (19 Locust Street)
Springfield, Mass. 01101
24 Hour Phone 413-736-8178
Store Hrs: 9:30-5:30 Mon. -Sat.

1981 NON SPORTS CARDS OVER 1000 SETS

$700

PRICE GUIDE and CHECK LIST
by **RICHARD and MARK SIKES**

ADVENTURE and TOPICAL CARDS

OVER 200 ILLUSTRATIONS

Buying and Selling All Items of Nostalgia

Comics
Bubble Gum Cards — Sports and Non-Sports
Radio Premiums
Movie Posters and Related Paper, Movie Magazines
Sports Items
Pulp Magazines
Playboys

Advertising Items
Political Items
Old Toys, Games and Dolls
Old Magazines
World War II Collectables
War Posters

Check with us on anything in the paper collectable area.

143

1954 JOHNSTON COOKIES (CONT.)

		MINT	VG-E	F-G			MINT	VG-E	F-G
34	Bob Thomson	65.00	48.00	22.00	42	Sam Calderone	5.00	3.65	1.75
35	Bob Keely	5.00	3.65	1.75	47	Joey Jay	5.00	3.65	1.75
38	Bill Bruton	5.00	3.65	1.75	48	Andy Pafko	5.00	3.65	1.75
40	Charlie Grimm	5.00	3.65	1.75		Dr. Charles Leaks	5.00	3.65	1.75
41	Eddie Mathews	16.00	12.00	5.50		Joseph F. Taylor	5.00	3.65	1.75

1955 JOHNSTON COOKIES (35)   2 3/4" X 4"

JOE ADCOCK

The 1955 Johnston's Cookies set of 35 are numbered according to the player's uniform numbers, except the Lacks, Lewis and Taylor cards. The set features Milwaukee Braves players only. ... cards were issued in ... or panels of six cards and... available from the com... by sending five cents a... cookie wrapper. The de... tion next to the player's ... in the checklist indicate... panel on which the p... appears. Note the ... appears on both panel 2 a... Cards are worth 30%... than the listed prices ... complete panel is still i... The ACC designation is ... 3.

	MINT	VG-E	F-G		MINT	VG-E	F-G
COMPLETE SET	400.00	300.00	110.00	23 Johnny Logan (P4)	10.00	7.00	3.50
COMMON PLAYER	10.00	7.00	3.50	24 Charlie White (P2)	10.00	7.00	3.50
				28 Johnny Cooney (P4)	10.00	7.00	3.50
1 Del Crandall (P1)	11.00	8.00	3.50	30 Roy Smalley (P3)	10.00	7.00	3.50
3 Jim Pendleton (P3)	10.00	7.00	3.50	31 Bucky Walters (P6)	10.00	7.00	3.50
4 Danny O'Connell (P1)	10.00	7.00	3.50	32 Ernie Johnson (P5)	10.00	7.00	3.50
6 Jack Dittmer (P6)	10.00	7.00	3.50	33 Lew Burdette (P1)	13.00	9.50	4.00
9 Joe Adcock (P2)	11.00	8.00	3.50	34 Bobby Thomson (P6)	15.00	11.00	5.00
10 Bob Buhl (P6)	10.00	7.00	3.50	35 Bob Keely (P1)	10.00	7.00	3.50
11 Phil Paine (P5)	10.00	7.00	3.50	38 Bill Bruton (P4)	10.00	7.00	3.50
12 Ray Crone (P5)	10.00	7.00	3.50	39 George Crowe (P3)	10.00	7.00	3.50
15 Charlie Gorin (P1)	10.00	7.00	3.50	40 Charlie Grimm (P6)	11.00	8.00	3.50
16 Dave Jolly (P4)	10.00	7.00	3.50	41 Eddie Mathews (P5)	20.00	15.00	6.50
17 Chet Nichols (P2)	10.00	7.00	3.50	44 Hank Aaron (P1)	100.00	70.00	30.00
18 Chuck Tanner (P5)	12.00	8.75	4.00	47 Joey Jay (P2)	10.00	7.00	3.50
19 Jim Wilson (P6)	10.00	7.00	3.50	48 Andy Pafko (P2, P4)	10.00	7.00	3.50
20 Dave Koslo (P4)	10.00	7.00	3.50	Dr. Charles Leaks (P2)	10.00	7.00	3.50
21 Warren Spahn (P3)	20.00	15.00	6.50	Duffy Lewis (P5)	10.00	7.00	3.50
22 Gene Conley (P3)	10.00	7.00	3.50	Joe Taylor (P3)	10.00	7.00	3.50

THEY NEVER MADE IT......UNTIL NOW!!!

1955 KAHN'S (6)

Compliments of Kahn's Wieners
"THE WIENER THE WORLD AWAITED"

The 1955 Kahn's Wieners set contains six cards and is of very limited distribution. The cards were given away at an amusement park. The set portrays the players in street clothes rather than in uniform. All Kahn's sets from 1955 through 1963 are black and white and contain a 1/2" tab. Cards with the tab still intact are worth approximately 15% more than cards without the tab. Cincinnati Redlegs players only are featured.

	MINT	VG-E	F-G
COMPLETE SET	800.00	600.00	250.00
COMMON PLAYER	125.00	90.00	40.00
1 Gus Bell	250.00	175.00	70.00
2 Ted Kluszewski	150.00	110.00	50.00
3 Roy McMillan	125.00	90.00	40.00

	MINT	VG-E	F-G
4 Joe Nuxhall	150.00	110.00	50.00
5 Wally Post	125.00	90.00	40.00
6 Johnny Temple	125.00	90.00	40.00

1956 KAHN'S (15)

Compliments of Kahn's Wieners
"THE WIENER THE WORLD AWAITED"

The 1956 Kahn's set of 15 was the first set to be issued with Kahn's meat products. The cards are blank-back. The set is distinguished by the old style, short sleeve shirts on the players and the existence of backgrounds (Kahn's cards of later years utilize a blank background). Cards which have the tab still intact are worth approximately 15% more than cards without the tab. Cincinnati Redlegs players only are featured.

	MINT	VG-E	F-G
COMPLETE SET	340.00	265.00	125.00
COMMON PLAYER	22.00	16.50	7.50
Ed Bailey	22.00	16.50	7.50
Gus Bell	22.00	16.50	7.50
Joe Black	22.00	16.50	7.50
Smoky Burgess	22.00	16.50	7.50
Art Fowler	22.00	16.50	7.50
Hershel Freeman	22.00	16.50	7.50
Ray Jablonski	22.00	16.50	7.50

	MINT	VG-E	F-G
John Klippstein	22.00	16.50	7.50
Ted Kluszewski	40.00	30.00	13.00
Brooks Lawrence	22.00	16.50	7.50
Roy McMillan	22.00	16.50	7.50
Joe Nuxhall	22.00	16.50	7.50
Wally Post	22.00	16.50	7.50
Frank Robinson	50.00	38.00	17.00
Johnny Temple	22.00	16.50	7.50

1957 KAHN'S (29)   3 1/4" X 4"

Compliments of Kahn's Wieners
"THE WIENER THE WORLD AWAITED"

The 1957 Kahn's Wieners set contains 29 black & white, blank backed, unnumbered cards. The set features the Cincinnati Redlegs and Pittsburgh Pirates only. The cards feature a light background. The Groat card exists with a "Richard Groat" autograph and also exists with the printed name "Dick Groat" on the card. The ACC designation is F155-3.

	MINT	VG-E	F-G
COMPLETE SET	500.00	375.00	180.00
COMMON PLAYER	18.00	13.50	6.00
1 Tom Acker	18.00	13.50	6.00
2 Ed Bailey	18.00	13.50	6.00
3 Gus Bell	18.00	13.50	6.00
4 Smoky Burgess	18.00	13.50	6.00
5 Robert Clemente	80.00	60.00	25.00
6 George Crowe	18.00	13.50	6.00
7 Elroy Face	20.00	15.00	6.50
8 Hershel Freeman	18.00	13.50	6.00
9 Bob Friend	18.00	13.50	6.00
10 Dick Groat	20.00	15.00	6.50
11 Richard Groat	40.00	30.00	13.00
12 Don Gross	18.00	13.50	6.00
13 Warren Hacker	18.00	13.50	6.00
14 Don Hoak	18.00	13.50	6.00

	MINT	VG-E	F-G
15 Hal Jeffcoat	18.00	13.50	6.00
16 Ron Kline	18.00	13.50	6.00
17 John Klippstein	18.00	13.50	6.00
18 Ted Kluszewski	30.00	22.50	10.50
19 Brooks Lawrence	18.00	13.50	6.00
20 Dale Long	18.00	13.50	6.00
21 Bill Mazeroski	20.00	15.00	6.50
22 Roy McMillan	18.00	13.50	6.00
23 Joe Nuxhall	20.00	15.00	6.50
24 Wally Post	18.00	13.50	6.00
25 Frank Robinson	50.00	38.00	17.00
26 John Temple	18.00	13.50	6.00
27 Frank Thomas	18.00	13.50	6.00
28 Bob Thurman	18.00	13.50	6.00
29 Lee Walls	18.00	13.50	6.00

1958 KAHN'S (29)   3 1/4" X 4"

Compliments of Kahn's Wieners
"THE WIENER THE WORLD AWAITED"

MY GREATEST THRILL IN BASEBALL
By ROBERTO CLEMENTE

In 1955, my first year in the majors, I got a little homesick. So I arranged for my family to come from Puerto Rico and spend the weekend in New York, since I was going to be there with the Pittsburgh Pirates playing against the Dodgers. I didn't get in the game until the seventh, when I went in as a pinch.

As I walked to the plate, I could see my mother in the stands, watching me in a big league game for the first time. I think she said a prayer to help me get a hit. We needed one pretty badly because we were two runs behind. Well, I tripled with two men on base, tying the game up. I'll always remember the expression of happiness on my mother's face.

The 1958 Kahn's Wieners set of 29 unnumbered, black & white cards features Cincinnati Redlegs, Philadelphia Phillies and Pittsburgh Pirates. The backs present a story for each player entitled "My Greatest Thrill in Baseball". A method of distinguishing 1958 Kahn's from 1959 Kahn's Wieners is the word Wieners on the front of the 1958 but not on the front of the 1959 cards.

	MINT	VG-E	F-G
COMPLETE SET	500.00	375.00	180.00
COMMON PLAYER	18.00	13.50	6.00
1 Ed Bailey	18.00	13.50	6.00
2 Gene Baker	18.00	13.50	6.00
3 Gus Bell	18.00	13.50	6.00
4 Smoky Burgess	18.00	13.50	6.00
5 Roberto Clemente	80.00	60.00	25.00
6 George Crowe	18.00	13.50	6.00
7 Elroy Face	20.00	15.00	6.50
8 Hank Foiles	18.00	13.50	6.00
9 Dee Fondy	18.00	13.50	6.00
10 Bob Friend	18.00	13.50	6.00
11 Dick Groat	20.00	15.00	6.50
12 Harvey Haddix	18.00	13.50	6.00
13 Don Hoak	18.00	13.50	6.00

	MINT	VG-E	F-G
14 Hal Jeffcoat	18.00	13.50	6.00
15 Ron Kline	18.00	13.50	6.00
16 Ted Kluszewski	30.00	22.50	10.50
17 Vernon Law	20.00	15.00	6.50
18 Brooks Lawrence	18.00	13.50	6.00
19 Bill Mazeroski	20.00	15.00	6.50
20 Roy McMillan	18.00	13.50	6.00
21 Joe Nuxhall	20.00	15.00	6.50
22 Wally Post	18.00	13.50	6.00
23 John Powers	18.00	13.50	6.00
24 Bob Purkey	18.00	13.50	6.00
25 Charlie Rabe	30.00	22.50	10.50
26 Frank Robinson	50.00	38.00	17.00
27 Bob Skinner	18.00	13.50	6.00
28 Johnny Temple	18.00	13.50	6.00
29 Frank Thomas	40.00	30.00	13.00

1959 KAHN'S (38)

Compliments of Kahn's
"THE WIENER THE WORLD AWAITED"

THE TOUGHEST PLAY I HAD TO MAKE
by BILLY MARTIN

"I shall never forget the world series of 1952 between the Yankees and the Dodgers. In the seventh inning of the seventh game, we were leading the Dodgers and seemed assured of another world's championship. The Dodgers loaded the bases with two out and Jackie Robinson came to bat against Bob Kuzava. Robinson hit a high infield pop fly for what looked like a routine play for first baseman Joe Collins. Suddenly he lost the ball in the sun. I came racing from deep second base, all the way between first and home and on the dead run caught the ball for the third out to give us victory."

The 1959 Kahn's set of 38 cards features Cincinnati, Cleveland and Pittsburgh players. The backs feature stories entitled "The Toughest Play I Have to Make," or "The Toughest Batter I Have to Face." The Brodowski card is very scarce while Haddix, Held and McLish are quite difficult to obtain.

	MINT	VG-E	F-G
COMPLETE SET	700.00	500.00	200.00
COMMON PLAYER	15.00	11.00	5.00
1 Ed Bailey	15.00	11.00	5.00
2 Gary Bell	15.00	11.00	5.00
3 Gus Bell	15.00	11.00	5.00
4 Dick Brodowski	200.00	150.00	65.00
5 Smoky Burgess	15.00	11.00	5.00
6 Roberto Clemente	60.00	45.00	20.00
7 Rocky Colavito	30.00	22.50	10.50
8 Elroy Face	20.00	15.00	6.50
9 Bob Friend	15.00	11.00	5.00
10 Joe Gordon	15.00	11.00	5.00
11 Jim Grant	15.00	11.00	5.00
12 Dick Groat	20.00	15.00	5.00
13 Harvey Haddix(blank)	100.00	70.00	30.00
14 Woodie Held	100.00	70.00	30.00
15 Don Hoak	15.00	11.00	5.00
16 Ron Kline	15.00	11.00	5.00
17 Ted Kluszewski	25.00	18.50	8.75
18 Vernon Law	15.00	11.00	5.00

	MINT	VG-E	F-G
19 Jerry Lynch	15.00	11.00	5.00
20 Billy Martin	30.00	22.50	10.50
21 Bill Mazeroski	20.00	15.00	6.50
22 Cal McLish	100.00	70.00	30.00
23 Roy McMillan	15.00	11.00	5.00
24 Minnie Minoso	25.00	18.50	8.75
25 Rus Nixon	15.00	11.00	5.00
26 Joe Nuxhall	20.00	15.00	6.50
27 Jim Perry	20.00	15.00	6.50
28 Vada Pinson	25.00	18.50	8.75
29 Vic Power	15.00	11.00	5.00
30 Bob Purkey	15.00	11.00	5.00
31 Frank Robinson	40.00	30.00	13.00
32 Herb Score	20.00	15.00	6.50
33 Bob Skinner	15.00	11.00	5.00
34 George Strickland	15.00	11.00	5.00
35 Dick Stuart	15.00	11.00	5.00
36 Johnny Temple	15.00	11.00	5.00
37 Frank Thomas	15.00	11.00	5.00
38 George Witt	15.00	11.00	5.00

1960 KAHN'S (42)

Compliments of Kahn's
"THE WIENER THE WORLD AWAITED"

CLEVELAND INDIANS...HERBERT JUDE SCORE, Pitcher

Residence: Rocky River, Ohio
BORN: June 7, 1933
at Rosedale, N.Y.

Bats and Throws Left
Height - 6' 2"
Weight - 185 lbs.

YEAR	CLUB	WON	LOST	EARN RUN AVERAGE
1952	INDIANAPOLIS	2	6	5.23
1953	READING	7	3	4.68
1954	INDIANAPOLIS	22	5	2.62
1955	CLEVELAND	16	10	2.85
1956	CLEVELAND	20	9	2.53
1957	CLEVELAND	2	1	2.00
1958	CLEVELAND	2	3	3.95
1959	CLEVELAND	9	11	4.70
A. L. TOTALS		49	34	3.16

SELECTED FOR ALL-STAR GAME IN 1955 BUT DID NOT PLAY. PITCHED ONE INNING IN ALL-STAR GAME IN 1956, STRUCK OUT ONE BATTER, WALKED ONE, HAD NO EARNED RUN AVERAGE.

The 1960 Kahn's set of 42 cards features players of the Chicago Cubs, Chicago White Sox, Cincinnati, Cleveland, Pittsburgh, and St. Louis. The backs give vital player information and records through the 1959 season. Kline appears with either St. Louis or Pittsburgh. Kuenn also appears with a blank back, which is scarce.

	MINT	VG-E	F-G
COMPLETE SET	500.00	375.00	170.00
COMMON PLAYER	12.50	9.00	4.00
1 Ed Bailey	12.50	9.00	4.00
2 Gary Bell	12.50	9.00	4.00
3 Gus Bell	12.50	9.00	4.00
4 Smoky Burgess	12.50	9.00	4.00
5 Gino Cimoli	12.50	9.00	4.00
6 Roberto Clemente	60.00	45.00	20.00
7 Roy Face	15.00	11.00	5.00
8 Tito Francona	12.50	9.00	4.00
9 Bob Friend	12.50	9.00	4.00
10 Jim Grant	12.50	9.00	4.00

	MINT	VG-E	F-G
11 Dick Groat	15.00	11.00	5.00
12 Harvey Haddix	12.50	9.00	4.00
13 Woodie Held	12.50	9.00	4.00
14 Bill Henry	12.50	9.00	4.00
15 Don Hoak	12.50	9.00	4.00
16 Jay Hook	12.50	9.00	4.00
17 Eddie Kasko	12.50	9.00	4.00
18 Ron Kline*	20.00	15.00	6.50
19 Ted Kluszewski	20.00	15.00	6.50
20 Harvey Kuenn (blank)	100.00	70.00	30.00
21 Vernon Law	15.00	11.00	5.00
22 Brooks Lawrence	12.50	9.00	4.00
23 Jerry Lynch	12.50	9.00	4.00

1960 KAHN'S (CONTINUED)

	MINT	VG-E	F-G
24 Billy Martin	30.00	22.50	10.50
25 Bill Mazeroski	15.00	11.00	5.00
26 Cal McLish	12.50	9.00	4.00
27 Roy McMillan	12.50	9.00	4.00
28 Don Newcombe	15.00	11.00	5.00
29 Russ Nixon	12.50	9.00	4.00
30 Joe Nuxhall	15.00	11.00	5.00
31 Jim O'Toole	12.50	9.00	4.00
32 Jim Perry	12.50	9.00	4.00

	MINT	VG-E	F-G
33 Vada Pinson	15.00	11.00	5.00
34 Vic Power	12.50	9.00	4.00
35 Bob Purkey	12.50	9.00	4.00
36 Frank Robinson	40.00	30.00	13.00
37 Herb Score	15.00	11.00	5.00
38 Bob Skinner	12.50	9.00	4.00
39 Dick Stuart	12.50	9.00	4.00
40 Johnny Temple	12.50	9.00	4.00
41 Frank Thomas	12.50	9.00	4.00
42 Lee Walls	12.50	9.00	4.00

1961 KAHN'S (43) 3 1/4" X 4"

PIRATES

DICK GROAT,
Infielder Bats and Throws Right
Born November 4, 1930 Height – 6'
at Swissvale, Pennsylvania Weight – 180 lbs.
Ancestry, German – Married
Obtained – Farm System

Team Captain. Led NL Shortstops in double plays, 1958.
Won 1960 National League Batting Championship. Tied
Modern League Record for most hits in a game – 6. Voted
NL "Most Valuable Player", 1960.

YEAR	CLUB	LEAGUE	BATTING AVERAGE	FIELDING AVERAGE	HOME RUNS
1952	PITTSBURGH	NL	.284	.952	1
1953-54	(IN MILITARY SERVICE)				
1955	PITTSBURGH	NL	.267	.961	4
1956	PITTSBURGH	NL	.273	.956	0
1957	PITTSBURGH	NL	.315	.957	7
1958	PITTSBURGH	NL	.300	.975	3
1959	PITTSBURGH	NL	.275	.984	5
1960	PITTSBURGH	NL	.325	.956	2

Member of World Champs – 1960
All Star: 1959, 1960

Compliments of Kahn's
"THE WIENER THE WORLD AWAITED"

The 1961 Kahn's Wieners set of 43 black and white, unnumbered cards features players from Cincinnati, Cleveland and Pittsburgh. This year was the first year Kahn's made complete sets available to the public. The backs give vital player information and year by year career statistics through 1960. The ACC designation is F155-7.

	MINT	VG-E	F-G
COMPLETE SET	250.00	175.00	80.00
COMMON PLAYER	6.00	4.50	2.00
1 John Antonelli	6.00	4.50	2.00
2 Ed Bailey	6.00	4.50	2.00
3 Gary Bell	6.00	4.50	2.00
4 Gus Bell	6.00	4.50	2.00
5 Jim Brosnan	6.00	4.50	2.00
6 Smoky Burgess	6.00	4.50	2.00
7 Gino Cimoli	6.00	4.50	2.00
8 Roberto Clemente	50.00	38.00	17.00
9 Gordie Coleman	6.00	4.50	2.00
10 Jimmy Dykes	6.00	4.50	2.00
11 Roy Face	7.00	5.25	2.50
12 Tito Francona	6.00	4.50	2.00
13 Gene Freese	6.00	4.50	2.00
14 Bob Friend	6.00	4.50	2.00
15 Jim Grant	6.00	4.50	2.00
16 Dick Groat	7.00	5.25	2.50
17 Harvey Haddix	6.00	4.50	2.00
18 Woodie Held	6.00	4.50	2.00
19 Don Hoak	6.00	4.50	2.00
20 Jay Hook	6.00	4.50	2.00

	MINT	VG-E	F-G
21 Joey Jay	6.00	4.50	2.00
22 Eddie Kasko	6.00	4.50	2.00
23 Willie Kirkland	6.00	4.50	2.00
24 Vernon Law	7.00	5.25	2.50
25 Jerry Lynch	6.00	4.50	2.00
26 Jim Maloney	7.00	5.25	2.50
27 Bill Mazeroski	7.00	5.25	2.50
28 Wilmer Mizell	6.00	4.50	2.50
29 Rocky Nelson	6.00	4.50	2.50
30 Jim U'Toole	6.00	4.50	2.50
31 Jim Perry	6.00	4.50	2.50
32 Bubba Phillips	6.00	4.50	2.50
33 Vada Pinson	8.00	6.00	2.50
34 Wally Post	6.00	4.50	2.00
35 Vic Power	6.00	4.50	2.00
36 Bob Purkey	6.00	4.50	2.00
37 Frank Robinson	30.00	22.50	10.50
38 John Romano	6.00	4.50	2.00
39 Dick Schofield	6.00	4.50	2.00
40 Bob Skinner	6.00	4.50	2.00
41 Hal Smith	6.00	4.50	2.00
42 Dick Stuart	6.00	4.50	2.00
43 Johnny Temple	6.00	4.50	2.00

1962 KAHN'S (38) 3 1/4" X 4"

REDS

VADA PINSON
Outfielder Bats and Throws Left
Born August 11, 1938 Height – 5'11"
Ancestry, Negro – Married Weight – 174 lbs.
Obtained – Farm System

1960 – Led League in doubles with 37. Tied Major League record, 1960, 803 hits as runner. Led both in 5 categories last season including batting, and League sacrifices in doubles. 2nd N.L. Batting.

YEAR	CLUB	LEAGUE	BATTING AVERAGE	FIELDING AVERAGE	HOME RUNS
1956	WAUSAU	NORTH	.278	.980	3
1957	VISALIA	CAL	.367	.958	20
1958	SEATTLE	PCL	.343	.964	11
	CINCINNATI	NL	.273	1.000	1
1959	CINCINNATI	NL	.316	.988	20
1960	CINCINNATI	NL	.287	.991	20
1961	CINCINNATI	NL	.343	.976	16

All Star Game: 1959, 1960

Member of National League Champions – 1961

Compliments of Kahn's
"THE WIENER THE WORLD AWAITED"

The 1962 Kahn's Wieners set of 41 black and white, unnumbered cards features Cincinnati, Cleveland, Minnesota and Pittsburgh players. Card Nos. 1 Bell, 33 Power, and 34 Purkey exist in two different forms. These variations are listed in the checklist. The backs of the cards contain career information. The ACC designation is F155-8.

	MINT	VG-E	F-G
COMPLETE SET	400.00	300.00	140.00
COMMON PLAYER	5.00	3.75	1.75
1a Gary Bell with fat man	60.00	45.00	20.00
1b Gary Bell (no fat man)	15.00	11.00	5.00

	MINT	VG-E	F-G
2 Jim Brosnan	5.00	3.75	1.75
3 Smoky Burgess	5.00	3.75	1.75
4 Chico Cardenas	5.00	3.75	1.75
5 Roberto Clemente	50.00	38.00	17.00
6 Ty Cline	5.00	3.75	1.75

	MINT	VG-E	F-G
7 Gordon Coleman	5.00	3.75	1.75
8 Dick Donovan	10.00	7.00	3.00
9 John Edwards	5.00	3.75	1.75
10 Tito Francona	5.00	3.75	1.75
11 Gene Freese	5.00	3.75	1.75
12 Bob Friend	5.00	3.75	1.75
13 Joe Gibbon	40.00	30.00	13.00
14 Jim Grant	5.00	3.75	1.75
15 Dick Groat	6.00	4.50	2.00
16 Harvey Haddix	5.00	3.75	1.75
17 Woodie Held	5.00	3.75	1.75
18 Bill Henry	5.00	3.75	1.75
19 Don Hoak	5.00	3.75	1.75
20 Ken Hunt	5.00	3.75	1.75
21 Joey Jay	5.00	3.75	1.75
22 Eddie Kasko	5.00	3.75	1.75

	MINT	VG-E	F-G
23 Willie Kirkland	5.00	3.75	1.75
24 Barry Latman	5.00	3.75	1.75
25 Jerry Lynch	5.00	3.75	1.75
26 Jim Maloney	6.00	4.50	2.00
27 Bill Mazeroski	6.00	4.50	2.00
28 Jim O'Toole	5.00	3.75	1.75
29 Jim Perry	5.00	3.75	1.75
30 Bubba Phillips	5.00	3.75	1.75
31 Vada Pinson	6.00	4.50	2.00
32 Wally Post	5.00	3.75	1.75
33a Vic Power (Indians)	15.00	11.00	5.00
33b Vic Power (Twins)	60.00	45.00	20.00
34a Bob Purkey (with auto)	15.00	11.00	5.00
34b Bob Purkey (no auto)	150.00	110.00	50.00
35 Frank Robinson	30.00	22.50	10.50
36 John Romano	5.00	3.75	1.75
37 Dick Stuart	5.00	3.75	1.75
38 Bill Virdon	10.00	7.00	3.00

1962 KAHN'S ATLANTA (24)   3 1/4" X 4"

Compliments of Kahn's
"THE WIENER THE WORLD AWAITED"

The 1962 Kahn's Wieners Atlanta set features 24 un-numbered, black and white cards of the Atlanta Crackers of the International League. The backs contain player statistical information as well as instructions on how to obtain free tickets. The ACC designation is F155-9.

	MINT	VG-E	F-G
COMPLETE SET	110.00	85.00	40.00
COMMON PLAYER	5.00	3.75	1.75
1 Jim Beauchamp	5.00	3.75	1.75
2 Gerry Buchek	5.00	3.75	1.75
3 Bob Burda	5.00	3.75	1.75
4 Dick Dietz	5.00	3.75	1.75
5 Bob Duliba	5.00	3.75	1.75
6 Harry Fanok	5.00	3.75	1.75
7 Phil Gagliano	5.00	3.75	1.75
8 John Glenn	5.00	3.75	1.75
9 Leroy Gregory	5.00	3.75	1.75
10 Dick Hughes	5.00	3.75	1.75

	MINT	VG-E	F-G
11 Johnny Kucks	5.00	3.75	1.75
12 Johnny Lewis	5.00	3.75	1.75
13 Tim McCarver	7.50	5.75	2.50
14 Bob Milliken	5.00	3.75	1.75
15 Joe Morgan	5.00	3.75	1.75
16 Ron Plaza	5.00	3.75	1.75
17 Bob Sandowski	5.00	3.75	1.75
18 Jim Saul	5.00	3.75	1.75
19 Willard Schmidt	5.00	3.75	1.75
20 Joe Schultz	5.00	3.75	1.75
21 Mike Shannon	6.00	4.50	2.00
22 Paul Toth	5.00	3.75	1.75
23 Lou Vickery	5.00	3.75	1.75
24 Fred Whitfield	5.00	3.75	1.75

1963 KAHN'S (30)   3 1/4" X 4"

Compliments of Kahn's
"THE WIENER THE WORLD AWAITED"

The 1963 Kahn's Wieners set of 30 black and white, unnumbered cards features players from Cincinnati, Cleveland, St. Louis, Pittsburgh and the N.Y. Yankees. The cards feature a white border around the picture of the player. The backs contain career information. The ACC designation is F155-10.

	MINT	VG-E	F-G
COMPLETE SET	150.00	115.00	55.00
COMMON PLAYER	4.50	3.50	1.60
1 Bob Bailey	4.50	3.50	1.60
2 Don Blasingame	4.50	3.50	1.60
3 Clete Boyer	4.50	3.50	1.60
4 Smoky Burgess	4.50	3.50	1.60
5 Chico Cardenas	4.50	3.50	1.60
6 Roberto Clemente	40.00	30.00	13.00
7 Donn Clendenon	4.50	3.50	1.60

	MINT	VG-E	F-G
8 Gordon Coleman	4.50	3.50	1.60
9 John Edwards	4.50	3.50	1.60
10 Gene Freese	4.50	3.50	1.60
11 Bob Friend	4.50	3.50	1.60
12 Joe Gibbon	4.50	3.50	1.60
13 Dick Groat	6.00	4.50	2.00
14 Harvey Haddix	4.50	3.50	1.60
15 Elston Howard	7.50	5.75	2.50
16 Joey Jay	4.50	3.50	1.60
17 Eddie Kasko	4.50	3.50	1.60

	MINT	VG-E	F-G			MINT	VG-E	F-G
18 Tony Kubek	7.50	5.75	2.50	24 Vada Pinson		6.00	4.50	2.00
19 Jerry Lynch	4.50	3.50	1.60	25 Bob Purkey		4.50	3.50	1.60
20 Jim Maloney	6.00	4.50	2.00	26 Bobby Richardson		6.00	4.50	2.00
21 Bill Mazeroski	6.00	4.50	2.00	27 Frank Robinson		25.00	18.50	8.75
22 Joe Nuxhall	6.00	4.50	2.00	28 Bill Stafford		4.50	3.50	1.60
23 Jim O'Toole	4.50	3.50	1.60	29 Ralph Terry		4.50	3.50	1.60
				30 Bill Virdon		10.00	7.00	3.00

1964 KAHN'S (31)   3" X 3 1/2"

The 1964 Kahn's set marks the beginning of the full color cards and the elimination of the tabs which existed on previous Kahn's cards. The set of 31 unnumbered cards contains player information through the 1963 season on the backs. The set features Cincinnati, Cleveland and Pittsburgh players.

	MINT	VG-E	F-G			MINT	VG-E	F-G
COMPLETE SET	125.00	90.00	40.00					
COMMON PLAYER	4.00	3.00	1.40	15 Jerry Lynch		4.00	3.00	1.40
				16 Jim Maloney		5.00	3.75	1.75
1 Max Alvis	4.00	3.00	1.40	17 Bill Mazeroski		5.00	3.75	1.75
2 Bob Bailey	4.00	3.00	1.40	18 Alvin McBean		4.00	3.00	1.40
3 Chico Cardenas	4.00	3.00	1.40	19 Joe Nuxhall		4.50	3.50	1.60
4 Roberto Clemente	30.00	22.50	10.50	20 Jim Pagliaroni		4.00	3.00	1.40
5 Donn Clendenon	4.00	3.00	1.40	21 Vada Pinson		5.00	3.75	1.75
6 Vic Davalillo	4.00	3.00	1.40	22 Bob Purkey		4.00	3.00	1.40
7 Dick Donovan	4.00	3.00	1.40	23 Pedro Ramos		4.00	3.00	1.40
8 John Edwards	4.00	3.00	1.40	24 Frank Robinson		20.00	15.00	6.50
9 Bob Friend	4.00	3.00	1.40	25 John Romano		4.00	3.00	1.40
10 Jim Grant	4.00	3.00	1.40	26 Pete Rose		30.00	22.50	10.50
11 Tommy Harper	4.00	3.00	1.40	27 John Tsitouris		4.00	3.00	1.40
12 Woodie Held	4.00	3.00	1.40	28 Bob Veale		4.00	3.00	1.40
13 Joey Jay	4.00	3.00	1.40	29 Bill Virdon		8.00	6.00	2.50
14 Jack Kralick	4.00	3.00	1.40	30 Leon Wagner		4.00	3.00	1.40
				31 Fred Whitfield		4.00	3.00	1.40

1965 KAHN'S (45)   3" X 3 1/2"

The 1965 Kahn's set contains 45 full color, unnumbered cards. The set features Cincinnati, Cleveland, Pittsburgh and Milwaukee players. Backs contain statistical information through the 1964 season.

	MINT	VG-E	F-G			MINT	VG-E	F-G
COMPLETE SET	150.00	115.00	50.00	15 Tommy Harper		3.50	2.50	1.20
COMMON PLAYER	3.50	2.50	1.20	16 Chuck Hinton		3.50	2.50	1.20
				17 Dick Howser		5.00	3.75	1.75
1 Henry Aaron	25.00	18.50	8.75	18 Joey Jay		3.50	2.50	1.20
2 Max Alvis	3.50	2.50	1.20	19 Deron Johnson		3.50	2.50	1.20
3 Joe Azcue	3.50	2.50	1.20	20 Jack Kralick		3.50	2.50	1.20
4 Bob Bailey	3.50	2.50	1.20	21 Denver Lemaster		3.50	2.50	1.20
5 Frank Bolling	3.50	2.50	1.20	22 Jerry Lynch		3.50	2.50	1.20
6 Chico Cardenas	3.50	2.50	1.20	23 Jim Maloney		5.00	3.75	1.75
7 Rico Carty	5.00	3.75	1.75	24 Lee Maye		3.50	2.50	1.20
8 Donn Clendenon	3.50	2.50	1.20	25 Bill Mazeroski		5.00	3.75	1.75
9 Tony Cloninger	3.50	2.50	1.20	26 Alvin McBean		3.50	2.50	1.20
10 Gordon Coleman	3.50	2.50	1.20	27 Bill McCool		3.50	2.50	1.20
11 Vic Davalillo	3.50	2.50	1.20	28 Sam McDowell		5.00	3.75	1.75
12 John Edwards	3.50	2.50	1.20	29 Don McMahon		3.50	2.50	1.20
13 Sammy Ellis	3.50	2.50	1.20	30 Denis Menke		3.50	2.50	1.20
14 Bob Friend	3.50	2.50	1.20	31 Joe Nuxhall		5.00	3.75	1.75

1965 KAHN'S (CONTINUED)

	MINT	VG-E	F-G
32 Gene Oliver	3.50	2.50	1.20
33 Jim O'Toole	3.50	2.50	1.20
34 Jim Pagliaroni	3.50	2.50	1.20
35 Vada Pinson	5.00	3.75	1.75
36 Frank Robinson	16.00	12.00	5.50
37 Pete Rose	25.00	18.50	8.75

	MINT	VG-E	F-G
38 Willie Stargell	15.00	11.00	5.00
39 Ralph Terry	3.50	2.50	1.20
40 Luis Tiant	5.00	3.75	1.75
41 Joe Torre	7.50	5.75	2.50
42 John Tsitouris	3.50	2.50	1.20
43 Bob Veale	3.50	2.50	1.20
44 Bill Virdon	7.50	5.75	2.50
45 Leon Wagner	3.50	2.50	1.20

1966 KAHN'S (32)

2 13/16" X 4"

HENRY AARON

1966 Kahn's full color, un-numbered set of 32 cards features players from Atlanta, Cincinnati, Cleveland and Pittsburgh. The set is identified by yellow and white vertical stripes and the name Kahn's written in red across a red rose at the top. The cards contain a 1 5/16" ad in the form of a tab. Cards with the ad are worth 15% more than cards without the ad.

	MINT	VG-E	F-G
COMPLETE SET	140.00	110.00	50.00
COMMON PLAYER	3.50	2.50	1.20
1 Henry Aaron - portrait - no windbreaker under Jersey	20.00	15.00	6.50
2 Felipe Alou - Braves - full pose batting (swing) screen in bkground	4.00	3.00	1.40
3 Max Alvis - Indians - full pose kneeling w/bat - no patch on jersey	3.50	2.50	1.20
4 Bob Bailey	3.50	2.50	1.20
5 Wade Blasingame	3.50	2.50	1.20
6 Frank Bolling	3.50	2.50	1.20
7 Chico Cardenas - Reds - fielding - feet at base	3.50	2.50	1.20
8 Roberto Clemente	20.00	15.00	6.50
9 Tony Cloninger - Brave - pitching - foulpole in background	3.50	2.50	1.20
10 Vic Davalillo	3.50	2.50	1.20
11 John Edwards - Reds - catching	3.50	2.50	1.20
12 Sam Ellis - Reds - White hat	3.50	2.50	1.20
13 Pedro Gonzalez	3.50	2.50	1.20
14 Tommy Harper - Reds - arm cocked to throw	3.50	2.50	1.20
15 Deron Johnson - Reds - batting - batting cage in bkground	3.50	2.50	1.20
16 Mack Jones	3.50	2.50	1.20

	MINT	VG-E	F-G
17 Denver Lemaster	3.50	2.50	1.20
18 Jim Maloney- Reds- pitching-white hat	4.50	3.50	1.60
19 Bill Mazeroski - Pirates-throwing	5.00	3.75	1.75
20 Bill McCool-Reds-white hat-both hands down	3.50	2.50	1.20
21 Sam McDowell-Indians kneeling	4.50	3.50	1.60
22 Denis Menke-Braves- white windbreaker under jersey	3.50	2.50	1.20
23 Joe Nuxhall	4.50	3.50	1.60
24 Jim Pagliaroni-Pirate catching	3.50	2.50	1.20
25 Milt Pappas	4.50	3.50	1.60
26 Vada Pinson-Reds- fielding ball on ground	5.00	3.75	1.75
27 Pete Rose-Reds-with glove	20.00	15.00	6.50
28 Sonny Siebert-Indians- pitching-signature at feet	3.50	2.50	1.20
29 Willie Stargell-Pirate batting-clouds in sky	14.00	10.50	4.75
30 Joe Torre-Braves- catching-hand on mask	6.00	4.50	2.00
31 Bob Veale-Pirates-hands at knees w/glasses	3.50	2.50	1.20
32 Fred Whitfield	3.50	2.50	1.20

1967 KAHN'S (41)

2 13/16" X 4"

The 1967 Kahn's set of 41 full color, unnumbered cards is almost identical in style to the 1966 issue. Different meat products had different background colors (yellow and white stripes, red and white stripes, etc.). The set features players from Atlanta, Cincinnati, Cleveland, New York Mets and Pittsburgh. Cards with the ads (see 1966 set) are worth 15% more than cards without the ads.

	MINT	VG-E	F-G
COMPLETE SET	150.00	115.00	50.00
COMMON PLAYER	3.25	2.40	1.10
1 Henry Aaron-Braves-pose-batting(swing) glove,ball,hat on grd	20.00	15.00	6.50
2 Gene Alley-Pirates-port	3.25	2.40	1.10
3 Felipe Alou-Braves-full pose bat on shoulder	4.00	3.00	1.40
4 Matty Alou-Pirates-port w/bat signed Matio Rojas Alou	3.25	2.40	1.10
5 Max Alvis-Indians-fielding hands on knees	3.25	2.40	1.10
6 Ken Boyer	5.00	3.75	1.75
7 Chico Cardenas-Reds-fielding-hand on knee	3.25	2.40	1.10
8 Rico Carty	4.00	3.00	1.40
9 Tony Cloninger-Braves-pitching-no foulpole in background	3.25	2.40	1.10
10 Tommy Davis	4.00	3.00	1.40
11 John Edwards-Reds-kneeling w/bat	3.25	2.40	1.10
12 Sam Ellis-Reds-all red hat	3.25	2.40	1.10
13 Jack Fisher	3.25	2.40	1.10
14 Steve Hargan-Indians-pitching-blue sky (no clouds)	3.25	2.40	1.10
15 Tommy Harper-Reds-fielding-glove on grn	3.25	2.40	1.10
16 Tommy Helms	3.25	2.40	1.10
17 Deron Johnson-Reds-batting-blue sky	3.25	2.40	1.10
18 Ken Johnson	3.25	2.40	1.10
19 Cleon Jones	3.25	2.40	1.10
20 Ed Kranepool	3.25	2.40	1.10

	MINT	VG-E	F-G
21 Jim Maloney-Reds-red hat-pitching follow thru delivery	4.00	3.00	1.40
22 Lee May-Reds-hands on knee	3.25	2.40	1.10
23 Bill Mazeroski-Pirate portrait	5.00	3.75	1.75
24 Bill McCool-Reds-red hat-left hand out	3.25	2.40	1.10
25 Sam McDowell-Indians-pitching-left hand under glove	4.00	3.00	1.40
26 Denis Menke-Braves-blue sleeves	3.25	2.40	1.10
27 Jim Pagliaroni-Pirates catching-no chest protector	3.25	2.40	1.10
28 Don Pavletich	3.25	2.40	1.10
29 Tony Perez-Reds-throw	5.00	3.75	1.75
30 Vada Pinson-Reds-ready to throw	4.00	3.00	1.40
31 Dennis Ribant	3.25	2.40	1.10
32 Pete Rose-Reds-batting	20.00	15.00	6.50
33 Art Shamsky-Reds	3.25	2.40	1.10
34 Bob Shaw	3.25	2.40	1.10
35 Sonny Siebert-Indians-pitching-signature at knees	3.25	2.40	1.10
36 Willie Stargell-Pirate batting-no clouds	14.00	10.50	4.75
37 Joe Torre-Braves-catching-mask on grnd	6.00	4.50	2.00
38 Bob Veale-Pirates-port hands not showing	3.25	2.40	1.10
39 Leon Wagner-Indians-fielding	3.25	2.40	1.10
40 Fred Whitfield	3.25	2.40	1.10
41 Woody Woodward	3.25	2.40	1.10

1968 KAHN'S (12) (38)

2 13/16" X 3 1/4"
2 13/16" X 3 7/8"

The 1968 Kahn's set of 50 full color blanked backed unnumbered cards features players from Atlanta, Chicago Cubs, Chicago White Sox, Cincinnati, Cleveland, Detroit, New York Mets and Pittsburgh. Two sizes of cards exist. The smaller cards of the two sizes, listed with the letter A in the checklist, are 2 13/16 X 3 1/4 with the ad tab and 2 13/16" X 1 7/8" without the ad tab. In the small sized set of 12, Maloney exists with either yellow or yellow and green stripes at the

top of the card. The larger cards of the two sizes is 2 13/16" X 3 7/8" with the ad tab and 2 13/16" X 2 11/16" without the ad tab. This large card set of 38 contains five cards which exist in two variations. The large set is listed with the letter B on the checklist. The variations in this large set have either yellow or red stripes at the top of the cards, with Maloney being an exception. Maloney has either a yellow stripe or a "Blue Mountain ad" at the top.

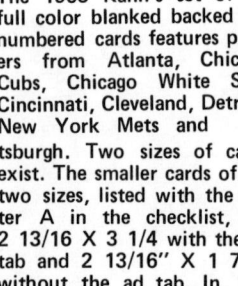

	MINT	VG-E	F-G
COMPLETE SET	140.00	105.00	45.00
COMMON PLAYER	2.75	2.00	.90
A 1 Hank Aaron	17.00	12.50	6.00
A 2 Gene Alley	2.75	2.00	.90
A 3 Max Alvis	2.75	2.00	.90
A 4 Clete Boyer	2.75	2.00	.90

	MINT	VG-E	F-G
A 6 Bill Freehan	3.00	2.25	1.00
A 7 Jim Maloney (2)	3.50	2.50	1.20
A 8 Lee May	2.75	2.00	.90
A 9 Bill Mazeroski	4.00	3.00	1.40
A10 Vada Pinson	3.50	2.50	1.20
A11 Joe Torre	5.00	3.75	1.75
A12 Bob Veale	2.75	2.00	.90

	MINT	VG-E	F-G
B 1 Hank Aaron-Braves- full pose batting (bat cocked)	17.00	12.50	6.00
B 2 Tommy Agee	2.75	2.00	.90
B 3 Gene Alley- Pirates- fielding full pose	2.75	2.00	.90
B 4 Felipe Alou-Braves- full pose batting (swing) player in background	3.00	2.25	1.00
B 5 Matty Alou-Pirates- portrait w/bat "Matio Alou" (2)	3.00	2.25	1.00
B 6 Max Alvis-Indians- fielding, glove on ground	2.75	2.00	.90
B 7 Gerry Arrigo-Reds- pitching-follow thru delivery	2.75	2.00	.90
B 8 John Bench	17.00	12.50	6.00
B 9 Clete Boyer	2.75	2.00	.90
B10 Larry Brown	2.75	2.00	.90
B11 Leo Cardenas-Reds- leaping in the air	2.75	2.00	.90
B12 Bill Freehan	3.00	2.25	1.00
B13 Steve Hargan-Indians- pitching-clouds in background	2.75	2.00	.90
B14 Joel Horlen-White Sox portrait	2.75	2.00	.90
B15 Tony Horton-Indians- portrait-signed Anthony	3.00	2.25	1.00
B16 Willie Horton	3.00	2.25	1.00
B17 Ferguson Jenkins	4.00	3.00	1.40
B18 Deron Johnson-Brave	2.75	2.00	.90
B19 Mack Jones-Reds	2.75	2.00	.90

	MINT	VG-E	F-G
B20 Bob Lee	2.75	2.00	.90
B21 Jim Maloney-Reds-Red hat-pitching hands up (2)	3.50	2.50	1.20
B22 Lee May-Reds-batting	2.75	2.00	.90
B23 Bill Mazeroski-Pirate fielding hands in front of body	4.00	3.00	1.40
B24 Dick McAuliffe	2.75	2.00	.90
B25 Bill McCool-Reds-Red hat-left hand down	2.75	2.00	.90
B26 Sam McDowell-Indians- pitching-left hand over head (2)	3.50	2.50	1.20
B27 Tony Perez-Reds- fielding ball in glove (2)	5.00	3.75	1.75
B28 Gary Peters-White Sox portrait	2.75	2.00	.90
B29 Vada Pinson-Reds- batting	3.50	2.50	1.20
B30 Chico Ruiz	2.75	2.00	.90
B31 Ron Santo-Cubs-bat follow thru (2)	3.50	2.50	1.20
B32 Art Shamsky- Mets	2.75	2.00	.90
B33 Luis Tiant-Indians hands over head	3.50	2.50	1.20
B34 Joe Torre-Braves- batting	5.00	3.75	1.75
B35 Bob Veale-Pirates- hands chest high	2.75	2.00	.90
B36 Leon Wagner-Indians- batting	2.75	2.00	.90
B37 Billy Williams-Cubs- bat behind back	5.00	3.75	1.75
B38 Earl Wilson	2.75	2.00	.90

1969 KAHN'S (3)
(22)

2 13/16" X 3 1/4"
2 13/16" X 3 15/16"

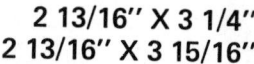

The 1969 Kahn's Wieners set of 25 full color, unnumbered cards features players from Atlanta, Chicago Cubs, Chicago White Sox, Cincinnati, Cleveland, Pittsburgh and St. Louis. The set contains three small cards (see 1968 description) and 22 large cards (see 1968 description). The small cards have the letter A in the checklist while the large cards have the letter B in the checklist. Four of the larger cards exist in two variations (red or yellow color stripes at the top of the card). These variations are identified in the checklist below.

	MINT	VG-E	F-G
COMPLETE SET	80.00	60.00	25.00
COMMON PLAYER	2.50	1.75	.80
A 1 Hank Aaron-portrait	15.00	11.00	5.00
A 2 Jim Maloney-pitching	3.00	2.25	1.00
A 3 Tony Perez-glove on	5.00	3.75	1.75
B 1 Hank Aaron	15.00	11.00	5.00
B 2 Matty Alou-batting	2.50	1.75	.80
B 3 Max Alvis-'69 patch	2.50	1.75	.80
B 4 Gerry Arrigo-leg-up	2.50	1.75	.80
B 5 Steve Blass	2.50	1.75	.80
B 6 Clay Carroll	2.50	1.75	.80
B 7 Tony Cloninger-Reds	2.50	1.75	.80
B 8 George Culver	2.50	1.75	.80

	MINT	VG-E	F-G
B 9 Joel Horlen-pitching	2.50	1.75	.80
B10 Tony Horton-batting	3.00	2.25	1.00
B11 Alex Johnson	2.50	1.75	.80
B12 Jim Maloney	3.00	2.25	1.00
B13 Lee May-foot on bag(2)	2.50	1.75	.80
B14 Bill Mazeroski-hands on knees (2)	3.50	2.50	1.20
B15 Sam McDowell-leg-up(2)	3.00	2.25	1.00
B16 Tony Perez	5.00	3.75	1.75
B17 Gary Peters-pitching	2.50	1.75	.80
B18 Ron Santo-emblem (2)	3.50	2.50	1.20
B19 Luis Tiant-glv. at knee	3.50	2.50	1.20
B20 Joe Torre-Cardinals	5.00	3.75	1.75
B21 Bob Veale-hands at knees-no glasses	2.50	1.75	.80
B22 Billy Williams-bat behind head	5.00	3.75	1.75

Attend a Sports Memorabilia Show or Convention in your area sometime this year. They are both interesting and enjoyable to all members of the family.

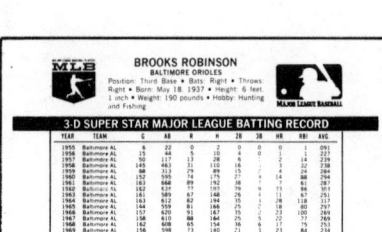

The 1970 Kellogg set was Kellogg's first venture into the baseball card producing field. The cards could be obtained in packages of cereal. There is reason to believe that the second series nos. 16–30 are somewhat more difficult to obtain than the other series. The cards, called 3-D cards, give the impression of being three dimensional.

	MINT	VG-E	F-G
COMPLETE SET	42.00	30.00	12.00
COMMON PLAYER	.35	.26	.10
COMMON PLAYER (16-30)	.55	.40	.15

	MINT	VG-E	F-G
1 Ed Kranepool	.35	.26	.10
2 Pete Rose	1.75	1.25	.55
3 Cleon Jones	.35	.26	.10
4 Willie McCovey	1.00	.70	.30
5 Mel Stottlemyre	.35	.26	.10
6 Frank Howard	.50	.40	.18
7 Tom Seaver	1.25	.90	.40
8 Don Sutton	.50	.40	.18
9 Jim Wynn	.35	.26	.10
10 Jim Maloney	.35	.26	.10
11 Tommie Agee	.35	.26	.10
12 Willie Mays	1.75	1.25	.55
13 Juan Marichal	.60	.45	.20
14 Dave McNally	.35	.26	.10
15 Frank Robinson	1.00	.70	.30
16 Carlos May	.55	.40	.15
17 Bill Singer	.55	.40	.15
18 Rick Reichardt	.55	.40	.15
19 Boog Powell	.60	.45	.20
20 Gaylord Perry	1.00	.70	.30
21 Brooks Robinson	1.75	1.25	.55
22 Luis Aparicio	.80	.60	.25
23 Joel Horlen	.55	.40	.15
24 Mike Epstein	.55	.40	.15
25 Tom Haller	.55	.40	.15
26 Willie Crawford	.55	.40	.15
27 Roberto Clemente	1.75	1.25	.55
28 Matty Alou	.55	.40	.15
29 Willie Stargell	1.25	.90	.40
30 Tim Cullen	.55	.40	.15
31 Randy Hundley	.35	.26	.10
32 Reggie Jackson	1.25	.90	.40
33 Rich Allen	.50	.40	.18
34 Tim McCarver	.35	.26	.10
35 Ray Culp	.35	.26	.10
36 Jim Fregosi	.50	.40	.18

	MINT	VG-E	F-G
37 Billy Williams	.50	.40	.18
38 Johnny Odom	.35	.26	.10
39 Bert Campaneris	.35	.26	.10
40 Ernie Banks	1.25	.90	.40
41 Chris Short	.35	.26	.10
42 Ron Santo	.50	.40	.18
43 Glenn Beckert	.35	.26	.10
44 Lou Brock	1.25	.90	.40
45 Larry Hisle	.50	.40	.18
46 Reggie Smith	.60	.45	.20
47 Rod Carew	1.25	.90	.40
48 Curt Flood	.50	.40	.18
49 Jim Lonborg	.50	.40	.18
50 Sam McDowell	.50	.40	.18
51 Sal Bando	.50	.40	.18
52 Al Kaline	1.25	.90	.40
53 Gary Nolan	.35	.26	.10
54 Rico Petrocelli	.50	.40	.18
55 Ollie Brown	.35	.26	.10
56 Luis Tiant	.50	.40	.18
57 Bill Freehan	.40	.30	.13
58 Johnny Bench	1.25	.90	.40
59 Joe Pepitone	.50	.40	.18
60 Bobby Murcer	.50	.40	.18
61 Harmon Killebrew	.80	.60	.25
62 Don Wilson	.35	.26	.10
63 Tony Oliva	.60	.45	.20
64 Jim Perry	.40	.30	.13
65 Mickey Lolich	.50	.40	.18
66 Jose Laboy	.35	.26	.10
67 Dean Chance	.35	.26	.10
68 Bud Harrelson	.35	.26	.10
69 Willie Horton	.35	.26	.10
70 Wally Bunker	.35	.26	.10
71 Bob Gibson	1.00	.70	.30
72 Joe Morgan	.60	.45	.20
73 Denny McLain	.50	.40	.18
74 Tommy Harper	.35	.26	.10
75 Don Mincher	.35	.26	.10

W530

1971 KELLOGG (75)

2 1/4" X 3 1/2"

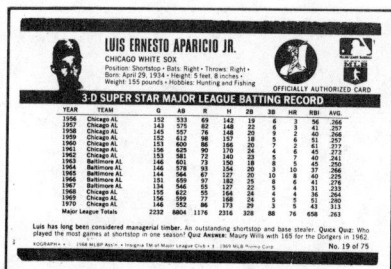

The 1971 Kellogg set is the scarcest of all the Kellogg issues. It is the only issue that has neither been offered as a complete set from the company nor found its way in larger supplies into the hands of dealers. The set gives the impression of being three dimensional.

	MINT	VG-E	F-G
MPLETE SET	150.00	110.00	45.00
MMON PLAYER	1.75	1.25	.45
Wayne Simpson	1.75	1.25	.45
Tom Seaver	6.00	4.50	2.00
Jim Perry	1.75	1.25	.45
Bob Robertson	1.75	1.25	.45
Roberto Clemente	6.50	5.00	2.25
Gaylord Perry	4.50	3.50	1.60
Felipe Alou	1.75	1.25	.45
Denis Menke	1.75	1.25	.45
Don Kessinger	1.75	1.25	.45
Willie Mays	7.00	5.25	2.50
Jim Hickman	1.75	1.25	.45
Tony Oliva	2.50	1.80	.80
Manny Sanguillen	1.75	1.25	.45
Frank Howard	2.50	1.80	.80
Frank Robinson	5.00	3.75	1.75
Willie Davis	1.75	1.25	.45
Lou Brock	5.50	4.25	2.00
Cesar Tovar	1.75	1.25	.45
Luis Aparicio	2.50	1.80	.80
Boog Powell	2.00	1.50	.60
Dick Selma	1.75	1.25	.45
Danny Walton	1.75	1.25	.45
Carl Morton	1.75	1.25	.45
Sonny Siebert	1.75	1.25	.45
Jim Merritt	1.75	1.25	.45
Jose Cardenal	1.75	1.25	.45

	MINT	VG-E	F-G
27 Don Mincher	1.75	1.25	.45
28 Clyde Wright	1.75	1.25	.45
29 Les Cain	1.75	1.25	.45
30 Danny Cater	1.75	1.25	.45
31 Don Sutton	2.50	1.80	.80
32 Chuck Dobson	1.75	1.25	.45
33 Willie McCovey	4.50	3.50	1.60
34 Mike Epstein	1.75	1.25	.45
35 Paul Blair	1.75	1.25	.45
36 Gary Nolan	1.75	1.25	.45
37 Sam McDowell	2.00	1.50	.60
38 Amos Otis	2.00	1.50	.60
39 Ray Fosse	1.75	1.25	.45
40 Mel Stottlemyre	1.75	1.25	.45
41 Clarence Gaston	1.75	1.25	.45
42 Dick Dietz	1.75	1.25	.45
43 Roy White	1.75	1.25	.45
44 Al Kaline	5.00	3.75	1.75
45 Carlos May	1.75	1.25	.45
46 Tommie Agee	1.75	1.25	.45
47 Tommy Harper	1.75	1.25	.45
48 Larry Dierker	1.75	1.25	.45
49 Mike Cuellar	1.75	1.25	.45
50 Ernie Banks	5.00	3.75	1.75
51 Bob Gibson	4.00	3.00	1.40
52 Reggie Smith	2.50	1.80	.80
53 Matty Alou	1.75	1.25	.45
54 Alex Johnson	1.75	1.25	.45
55 Harmon Killebrew	4.00	3.00	1.40

1971 KELLOGG (CONTINUED)

	MINT	VG-E	F-G
56 Bill Grabarkewitz	1.75	1.25	.45
57 Richie Allen	2.50	1.80	.80
58 Tony Perez	2.50	1.80	.80
59 Dave McNally	2.00	1.50	.60
60 Jim Palmer	5.00	3.75	1.75
61 Billy Williams	3.00	2.25	1.00
62 Joe Torre	3.00	2.25	1.00
63 Jim Northrup	1.75	1.25	.45
64 Jim Fregosi	3.00	2.50	1.00

	MINT	VG-E	F-G
65 Pete Rose	6.50	5.00	2.25
66 Bud Harrelson	1.75	1.25	.45
67 Tony Taylor	1.75	1.25	.45
68 Willie Stargell	4.50	3.50	1.60
69 Tony Horton	2.00	1.50	.60
70 Claude Osteen	1.75	1.25	.45
71 Glenn Beckert	1.75	1.25	.45
72 Nate Colbert	1.75	1.25	.45
73 Rick Monday	2.00	1.50	.60
74 Tommy John	3.00	2.25	1.00
75 Chris Short	1.75	1.25	.45

1972 KELLOGG (54)   2 1/8" X 3 1/4"

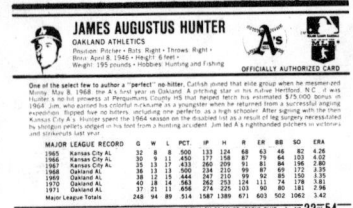

The 1972 Kellogg set saw a reduction in both the size of the card and the number in the set. The set gives the impression of being three dimensional.

	MINT	VG-E	F-G
COMPLETE SET	25.00	20.00	7.00
COMMON PLAYER	.32	.25	.10
1 Tom Seaver	1.50	1.10	.50
2 Amos Otis	.50	.40	.18
3 Willie Davis	.32	.25	.10
4 Wilbur Wood	.32	.25	.10
5 Bill Parsons	.32	.25	.10
6 Pete Rose	2.50	1.80	.80
7 Willie McCovey	1.00	.70	.30
8 Ferguson Jenkins	.50	.40	.18
9 Vida Blue	.80	.60	.25
10 Joe Torre	.80	.60	.25
11 Merv Rettenmund	.32	.25	.10
12 Bill Melton	.32	.25	.10
13 Jim Palmer	1.25	.90	.40
14 Doug Rader	.32	.25	.10
15 Dave Roberts	.32	.25	.10
16 Bobby Murcer	.50	.40	.18
17 Wes Parker	.32	.25	.10
18 Joe Coleman	.32	.25	.10
19 Manny Sanguillen	.32	.25	.10
20 Reggie Jackson	1.25	.90	.40
21 Ralph Garr	.32	.25	.10
22 Jim Hunter	.80	.60	.25
23 Rick Wise	.32	.25	.10
24 Glenn Beckert	.32	.25	.10
25 Tony Oliva	.60	.45	.20

	MINT	VG-E	F-G
26 Bob Gibson	1.00	.70	.30
27 Mike Cuellar	.32	.25	.10
28 Chris Speier	.32	.25	.10
29 Dave McNally	.32	.25	.10
30 Leo Cardenas	.32	.25	.10
31 Bill Freehan	.32	.25	.10
32 Bud Harrelson	.32	.25	.10
33 Sam McDowell	.32	.25	.10
34 Claude Osteen	.32	.25	.10
35 Reggie Smith	.50	.40	.18
36 Sonny Siebert	.32	.25	.10
37 Lee May	.32	.25	.10
38 Mickey Lolich	.50	.40	.18
39 Cookie Rojas	.32	.25	.10
40 Dick Drago	.32	.25	.10
41 Nate Colbert	.32	.25	.10
42 Andy Messersmith	.40	.30	.13
43 Dave Johnson	.32	.25	.10
44 Steve Blass	.32	.25	.10
45 Bob Robertson	.32	.25	.10
46 Billy Williams	.60	.45	.20
47 Juan Marichal	.60	.45	.20
48 Lou Brock	1.25	.90	.40
49 Roberto Clemente	2.00	1.50	.60
50 Mel Stottlemyre	.32	.25	.10
51 Don Wilson	.32	.25	.10
52 Sal Bando	.50	.40	.18
53 Willie Stargell	1.25	.90	.40
54 Willie Mays	2.50	1.80	.80

BASEBALL BUBBLE GUM

1979 TOPPS CARTOON

1980 BURGER KING Pitch, hit & run set
33 of the leading pitchers, hitters and runners . $12.50
1979 TOPPS COMIC SET (33) in 3 uncut strips with
11 per strip $12.75
1977 BURGER CHEF SET (216) $12.50
1981 TOPPS TEAM SET (your choice) $3.00
1981 FLEER TEAM SET (your choice) $3.00
1981 DONRUSS TEAM SET (choice)............$3.00

KELLOGG 3-D SETS
BASEBALL SETS

1973 2-D SET (54) $40.00
1974 3-D SET (54) $14.50
1976 3-D SET (57) $12.50
1976 3-D SET-3 (54) $6.50
1977 3-D SET (57) $10.00

FOOTBALL SETS

1970 3-D SET (60) $10.00

THE BASEBALL CARD SHOP

DEPT. PG3

9272 Cincinnati-Columbus Rd.
Cincinnati, Ohio 45241

Thousands of Stars & Individual Cards Listed
24 page pricelist for 75¢.

Orders over $10.00 PPD. Under $10.00 must add $1.00 for postage & handling.

1972 KELLOGG ATG (15)   2 1/4" X 3 1/2"

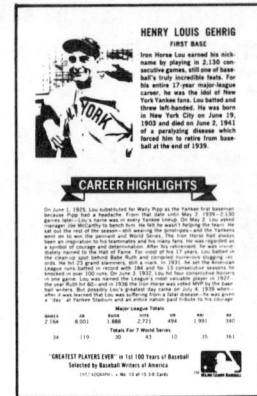

The 1972 ALL-Time Greats 3-D set was issued with Kellogg's Danish Go-Rounds. The set is a reissue of a 1970 set issued by Rold Gold Pretzels to commemorate baseball's first 100 years.

	MINT	VG-E	F-G
COMPLETE SET	7.00	5.00	2.00
COMMON PLAYER	.32	.25	.10
1 Walter Johnson	.50	.40	.18
2 Rogers Hornsby	.50	.40	.18
3 John McGraw	.40	.30	.12
4 Mickey Cochrane	.40	.30	.12
5 George Sisler	.32	.25	.10
6 Babe Ruth	1.50	1.10	.50

	MINT	VG-E	F-G
7 Lefty Grove	.32	.25	.10
8 Pie Traynor	.32	.25	.10
9 Honus Wagner	.50	.40	.18
10 Eddie Collins	.32	.25	.10
11 Tris Speaker	.40	.30	.12
12 Cy Young	.40	.30	.12
13 Lou Gehrig	1.00	.70	.30
14 Babe Ruth	1.50	1.10	.50
15 Ty Cobb	1.00	.70	.30

1973 KELLOGG 2-D (54)   2 1/4" X 3 1/2"

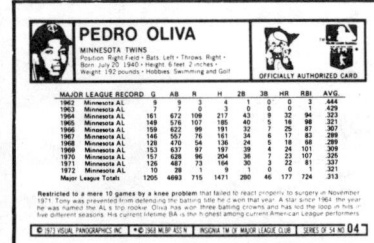

The 1973 Kellogg set is the only non 3-D set by Kellogg. The complete set could be obtained from the company through a box top redemption procedure. The card size is slightly larger than the previous year.

	MINT	VG-E	F-G
COMPLETE SET	45.00	35.00	15.00
COMMON PLAYER	.50	.35	.15
1 Amos Otis	.65	.50	.20
2 Ellie Rodriguez	.50	.35	.15
3 Mickey Lolich	.65	.50	.20
4 Tony Oliva	.80	.60	.25
5 Don Sutton	.80	.60	.25
6 Pete Rose	1.75	1.25	.55
7 Steve Carlton	1.00	.70	.30
8 Bobby Bonds	.60	.45	.20
9 Wilbur Wood	.50	.35	.15
10 Billy Williams	.60	.45	.20
11 Steve Blass	.50	.35	.15
12 Jon Matlack	.60	.45	.20
13 Cesar Cedeno	.65	.50	.20
14 Bob Gibson	1.00	.70	.30
15 Sparky Lyle	.60	.45	.20
16 Nolan Ryan	1.00	.70	.30
17 Jim Palmer	1.25	.90	.40
18 Ray Fosse	.50	.35	.15
19 Bobby Murcer	.60	.45	.20
20 Jim Hunter	.80	.60	.25
21 Tom McCraw	.50	.35	.15
22 Reggie Jackson	1.25	.90	.40
23 Bill Stoneman	.50	.35	.15
24 Lou Piniella	.50	.35	.15
25 Willie Stargell	1.00	.70	.30

	MINT	VG-E	F-G
26 Dick Allen	.60	.45	.20
27 Carlton Fisk	.80	.60	.25
28 Ferguson Jenkins	.60	.45	.20
29 Phil Niekro	.65	.50	.20
30 Gary Nolan	.50	.35	.15
31 Joe Torre	.65	.50	.20
32 Bobby Tolan	.50	.35	.15
33 Nate Colbert	.50	.35	.15
34 Joe Morgan	.80	.60	.25
35 Bert Blyleven	.65	.50	.20
36 Joe Rudi	.50	.35	.15
37 Ralph Garr	.50	.35	.15
38 Gaylord Perry	.80	.60	.25
39 Bobby Grich	.60	.45	.20
40 Lou Brock	1.00	.70	.30
41 Pete Broberg	.50	.35	.15
42 Manny Sanguillen	.50	.35	.15
43 Willie Davis	.50	.35	.15
44 Dave Kingman	.80	.60	.25
45 Carlos May	.50	.35	.15
46 Tom Seaver	1.25	.90	.40
47 Mike Cuellar	.50	.35	.15
48 Joe Coleman	.50	.35	.15
49 Claude Osteen	.50	.35	.15
50 Steve Kline	.50	.35	.15
51 Rod Carew	1.25	.90	.40
52 Al Kaline	1.25	.90	.40
53 Larry Dierker	.50	.35	.15
54 Ron Santo	.65	.50	.20

1974 KELLOGG (54)

2 1/8" X 3 1/4"

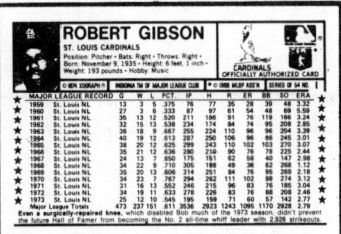

In 1974 Kellogg returned to its 3-D format, which it has continued to the present. It also returned to the smaller sized card. Complete sets could be obtained from the company through a box top offer.

	MINT	VG-E	F-G
COMPLETE SET	12.00	9.00	4.00
COMMON PLAYER	.18	.13	.05
1 Bob Gibson	.60	.45	.20
2 Rick Monday	.18	.13	.05
3 Joe Coleman	.18	.13	.05
4 Bert Campaneris	.18	.13	.05
5 Carlton Fisk	.40	.30	.13
6 Jim Palmer	1.00	.70	.30
7 Ron Santo	.30	.25	.10
8 Nolan Ryan	.80	.60	.25
9 Greg Luzinski	.30	.25	.10
10 Buddy Bell	.30	.25	.10
11 Bob Watson	.30	.25	.10
12 Bill Singer	.18	.13	.05
13 Dave May	.18	.13	.05
14 Jim Brewer	.18	.13	.05
15 Manny Sanguillen	.18	.13	.05
16 Jeff Burroughs	.30	.25	.10
17 Amos Otis	.30	.25	.10
18 Ed Goodson	.18	.13	.05
19 Nate Colbert	.18	.13	.05
20 Reggie Jackson	1.00	.70	.30
21 Ted Simmons	.50	.40	.18
22 Bobby Murcer	.30	.25	.10
23 Willie Horton	.18	.13	.05
24 Orlando Cepeda	.40	.30	.13
25 Ron Hunt	.18	.13	.05

	MINT	VG-E	F-G
26 Wayne Twitchell	.18	.13	.05
27 Ron Fairly	.18	.13	.05
28 Johnny Bench	1.00	.70	.30
29 John Mayberry	.30	.25	.10
30 Rod Carew	1.00	.70	.30
31 Ken Holtzman	.18	.13	.05
32 Billy Williams	.40	.30	.13
33 Dick Allen	.40	.30	.13
34 Wilbur Wood	.18	.13	.05
35 Danny Thompson	.18	.13	.05
36 Joe Morgan	.50	.40	.18
37 Willie Stargell	.80	.60	.25
38 Pete Rose	1.00	.70	.30
39 Bobby Bonds	.30	.25	.10
40 Chris Speier	.18	.13	.05
41 Sparky Lyle	.30	.25	.10
42 Cookie Rojas	.18	.13	.05
43 Tommy Davis	.18	.13	.05
44 Jim Hunter	.50	.40	.18
45 Willie Davis	.18	.13	.05
46 Bert Blyleven	.30	.25	.10
47 Pat Kelly	.18	.13	.05
48 Ken Singleton	.30	.25	.10
49 Manny Mota	.25	.20	.08
50 Dave Johnson	.18	.13	.05
51 Sal Bando	.25	.20	.08
52 Tom Seaver	1.00	.70	.30
53 Felix Millan	.18	.13	.05
54 Ron Blomberg	.18	.13	.05

1975 KELLOGG (57)

2 1/8" X 3 1/4"

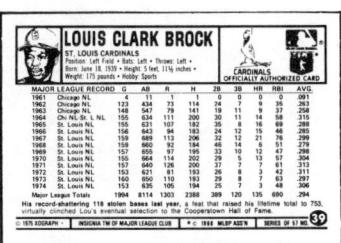

The 1975 Kellogg 3-D set could be obtained by card in cereal boxes or as a set from a box top offer from the company. Card no. 44 Jim Hunter exists with the A's emblem or the Yankee's emblem on the back of the card.

	MINT	VG-E	F-G
COMPLETE SET	11.00	8.00	3.00
COMMON PLAYER	.16	.12	.05
1 Roy White	.16	.12	.05

	MINT	VG-E	F-G
2 Ross Grimsley	.16	.12	.05
3 Reggie Smith	.30	.25	.10
4 Bob Grich	.20	.15	.06
5 Greg Gross	.16	.12	.05

	MINT	VG-E	F-G
6 Bob Watson	.25	.20	.08
7 Johnny Bench	.80	.60	.25
8 Jeff Burroughs	.25	.20	.08
9 Elliott Maddox	.16	.12	.05
10 Jon Matlack	.16	.12	.05
11 Pete Rose	1.00	.70	.30
12 Lee Stanton	.16	.12	.05
13 Bake McBride	.20	.15	.06
14 Jorge Orta	.16	.12	.05
15 Al Oliver	.30	.25	.10
16 John Briggs	.16	.12	.05
17 Steve Garvey	.80	.60	.25
18 Brooks Robinson	.80	.60	.25
19 John Hiller	.16	.12	.05
20 Lynn McGlothen	.16	.12	.05
21 Cleon Jones	.16	.12	.05
22 Fergie Jenkins	.25	.20	.08
23 Bill North	.16	.12	.05
24 Steve Busby	.16	.12	.05
25 Richie Zisk	.20	.15	.06
26 Nolan Ryan	.80	.60	.25
27 Joe Morgan	.50	.40	.18
28 Joe Rudi	.16	.12	.05
29 Jose Cardenal	.16	.12	.05
30 Andy Messersmith	.20	.15	.06

	MINT	VG-E	F-G
31 Willie Montanez	.16	.12	.05
32 Bill Buckner	.25	.20	.08
33 Rod Carew	.80	.60	.25
34 Lou Piniella	.25	.20	.08
35 Ralph Garr	.16	.12	.05
36 Mike Marshall	.16	.12	.05
37 Garry Maddox	.20	.15	.06
38 Dwight Evans	.16	.12	.05
39 Lou Brock	.70	.50	.20
40 Ken Singleton	.25	.20	.08
41 Steve Braun	.16	.12	.05
42 Rich Allen	.25	.20	.08
43 John Grubb	.16	.12	.05
44 Jim Hunter (2)	.60	.45	.20
45 Gaylord Perry	.60	.45	.20
46 Geo. Hendrick	.25	.20	.08
47 Sparky Lyle	.25	.20	.08
48 Dave Cash	.16	.12	.05
49 Luis Tiant	.25	.20	.08
50 Cesar Geronimo	.16	.12	.05
51 Carl Yastrzemski	.80	.60	.25
52 Ken Brett	.16	.12	.05
53 Hal McRae	.16	.12	.05
54 Reggie Jackson	.80	.60	.25
55 Rollie Fingers	.25	.20	.08
56 Mike Schmidt	.60	.45	.20
57 Richie Hebner	.16	.12	.05

1976 KELLOGG (57) 2 1/8" X 3 1/4"

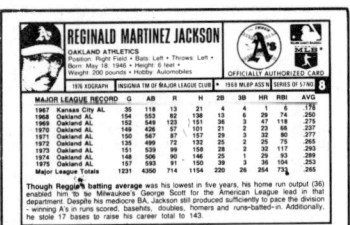

The 1976 Kellogg 3-D set could be obtained by card in cereal boxes or as a set from a box top offer from the company. Card no. 6 Clay Carroll exists with the Reds emblem or the White Sox emblem on the back.

	MINT	VG-E	F-G
COMPLETE SET	10.00	7.00	3.00
COMMON PLAYER	.15	.11	.05
1 Steve Hargan	.75	.55	.25
2 C. Washington	.75	.55	.25
3 Don Gullett	.75	.55	.25
4 Randy Jones	.20	.15	.06
5 Jim Hunter	.40	.30	.13
6 Clay Carroll (2)	.20	.15	.06
7 Joe Rudi	.15	.11	.05
8 Reggie Jackson	.60	.45	.20
9 Felix Millan	.15	.11	.05
10 Jim Rice	.60	.45	.20
11 Bert Blyleven	.20	.15	.06
12 Ken Singleton	.20	.15	.06
13 Don Sutton	.30	.25	.10
14 Joe Morgan	.40	.30	.13
15 Dave Parker	.60	.45	.20
16 Dave Cash	.15	.11	.05
17 Ron LeFlore	.25	.20	.08
18 Greg Luzinski	.25	.20	.08
19 Den. Eckersley	.20	.15	.06
20 Bill Madlock	.15	.11	.05
21 George Scott	.15	.11	.05
22 Willie Stargell	.60	.45	.20
23 Al Hrabosky	.20	.15	.06
24 Carl Yastrzemski	.80	.60	.25
25 Jim Kaat	.20	.15	.06
26 Marty Perez	.15	.11	.05
27 Bob Watson	.20	.15	.06

	MINT	VG-E	F-G
28 Eric Soderholm	.15	.11	.05
29 Bill Lee	.15	.11	.05
30 Frank Tanana	.20	.15	.06
31 Fred Lynn	.60	.45	.20
32 Tom Seaver	.60	.45	.20
33 Steve Busby	.15	.11	.05
34 Gary Carter	.30	.25	.10
35 Rick Wise	.15	.11	.05
36 Johnny Bench	.60	.45	.20
37 Jim Palmer	.60	.45	.20
38 Bobby Murcer	.20	.15	.06
39 Von Joshua	.15	.11	.05
40 Lou Brock	.60	.45	.20
41 Mickey Rivers (2)	.20	.15	.06
42 Manny Sanguillen	.15	.11	.05
43 Jerry Reuss	.20	.15	.06
44 Ken Griffey	.20	.15	.06
45 Jorge Orta	.15	.11	.05
46 John Mayberry	.20	.15	.06
47 Vida Blue (2)	.50	.40	.18
48 Rod Carew	.50	.40	.18
49 Jon Matlack	.15	.11	.05
50 Boog Powell	.20	.15	.06
51 Mike Hargrove	.15	.11	.05
52 Paul Lindblad	.15	.11	.05
53 Thurman Munson	.60	.45	.20
54 Steve Garvey	.60	.45	.20
55 Pete Rose	.80	.60	.25
56 Greg Gross	.15	.11	.05
57 Ted Simmons	.50	.40	.18

REMEMBER THE NATIONAL CONVENTION IS BEING HELD JULY 9 - 12, 1981, IN PLYMOUTH, MICHIGAN

1977 KELLOGG (57)　　　　　　2 1/8" X 3 1/4"

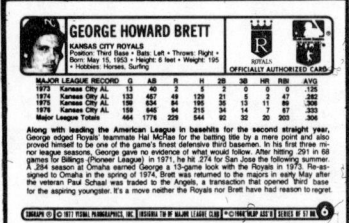

The 1977 Kellogg 3-D set could be obtained by card from cereal boxes or as a set from a box top offer from the company.

	MINT	VG-E	F-G
COMPLETE SET	9.00	6.50	3.00
COMMON PLAYER	.14	.10	.04
1 George Foster	.30	.25	.10
2 B. Campaneris	.14	.10	.04
3 Fergie Jenkins	.20	.15	.06
4 Dock Ellis	.14	.10	.04
5 John Montefusco	.14	.10	.04
6 George Brett	.50	.40	.18
7 John Candelaria	.14	.10	.04
8 Fred Norman	.14	.10	.04
9 Bill Travers	.14	.10	.04
10 Hal McRae	.14	.10	.04
11 Doug Rau	.14	.10	.04
12 Greg Luzinski	.20	.15	.06
13 Ralph Garr	.14	.10	.04
14 Steve Garvey	.40	.30	.13
15 Rick Manning	.14	.10	.04
16 Lyman Bostock	.30	.25	.10
17 Randy Jones	.20	.15	.06
18 Ron Cey	.20	.15	.06
19 Dave Parker	.40	.30	.13
20 Pete Rose	.50	.40	.18
21 Wayne Garland	.14	.10	.04
22 Bill North	.14	.10	.04
23 Thurman Munson	.50	.40	.18
24 Tom Poquette	.14	.10	.04
25 Ron LeFlore	.20	.15	.06
26 Mark Fidrych	.20	.15	.06
27 Sixto Lezcano	.20	.15	.06

	MINT	VG-E	F-G
28 Dave Winfield	.40	.30	.13
29 Jerry Koosman	.20	.15	.06
30 Mike Hargrove	.14	.10	.04
31 Willie Montanez	.14	.10	.04
32 Don Stanhouse	.20	.15	.06
33 Jay Johnstone	.14	.10	.04
34 Bake McBride	.20	.15	.06
35 Dave Kingman	.30	.25	.10
36 Fred Patek	.14	.10	.04
37 Garry Maddox	.20	.15	.06
38 Ken Reitz	.14	.10	.04
39 Bobby Grich	.20	.15	.06
40 Cesar Geronimo	.14	.10	.04
41 Jim Lonborg	.20	.15	.06
42 Ed Figueroa	.14	.10	.04
43 Bill Madlock	.14	.10	.04
44 Jerry Remy	.14	.10	.04
45 Frank Tanana	.20	.15	.06
46 Al Oliver	.25	.20	.08
47 Charlie Hough	.14	.10	.04
48 Lou Piniella	.20	.15	.06
49 Ken Griffey	.20	.15	.06
50 Jose Cruz	.20	.15	.06
51 Rollie Fingers	.20	.15	.06
52 Chris Chambliss	.20	.15	.06
53 Rod Carew	.40	.30	.13
54 Andy Messersmith	.20	.15	.06
55 Mickey Rivers	.20	.15	.06
56 Butch Wynegar	.14	.10	.04
57 Steve Carlton	.30	.25	.10

1978 KELLOGG (57)　　　　　　2 1/8" X 3 1/4"

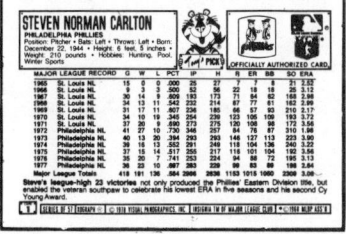

The 1978 Kellogg 3-D set could be obtained by card from cereal boxes or as a set from a box top offer from the company.

	MINT	VG-E	F-G
COMPLETE SET	8.00	6.00	2.50
COMMON PLAYERS	.12	.08	.03
1 Carlton, Steve	.30	.25	.10
2 Dent, Bucky	.15	.11	.05
3 Schmidt, Mike	.30	.25	.10
4 Griffey, Ken	.15	.11	.05
5 Cowens, Al	.12	.08	.03
6 Brett, George	.40	.30	.13

	MINT	VG-E	F-G
7 Brock, Lou	.30	.25	.10
8 Gossage, Rich	.20	.15	.06
9 Johnson	.12	.08	.03
10 Foster, George	.20	.15	.06
11 Winfield, Dave	.30	.25	.10
12 Meyer, Dan	.12	.08	.03
13 Chambliss, Chris	.15	.11	.05
14 Dade, Paul	.12	.08	.03
15 Burroughs, Jeff	.15	.11	.05

1978 KELLOGGS (CONTINUED)

		MINT	VG-E	F-G
16	Cruz,Jose	.15	.11	.05
17	Rivers, Mickey	.15	.11	.05
18	Candelaria, John	.12	.08	.03
19	Valentine, Ellis	.15	.11	.05
20	McRae, Hal	.12	.08	.03
21	Rozema, Dave	.12	.08	.03
22	Randle, Lenny	.12	.08	.03
23	McCovey, Willie	.25	.20	.08
24	Cey, Ron	.15	.11	.05
25	Murray,Eddie	.20	.15	.06
26	Bowa, Larry	.15	.11	.05
27	Seaver,Tom	.30	.25	.10
28	Maddox, Garry	.15	.11	.05
29	Carew, Rod	.30	.25	.10
30	Munson, Thurman	.40	.30	.13
31	Templeton, Gary	.25	.20	.08
32	Soderholm, Eric	.12	.08	.03
33	Luzinski, Greg	.15	.11	.05
34	Smith, Reggie	.15	.11	.05
35	Goltz,Dave	.12	.08	.03

		MINT	VG-E	F-G
36	John,Tommy	.20	.15	.06
37	Garr, Ralph	.12	.08	.03
38	Bannister, Alan	.12	.08	.03
39	Bailor, Bob	.12	.08	.03
40	Jackson, Reggie	.30	.25	.10
41	Cooper, Cecil	.20	.15	.06
42	Hooton, Burt	.15	.11	.05
43	Lyle, Sparky	.15	.11	.05
44	Ontiveros, Steve	.12	.08	.03
45	Reuschel, Rick	.15	.11	.05
46	Bostock, Lyman	.15	.11	.05
47	Page, Mitchell	.12	.08	.03
48	Sutter, Bruce	.25	.20	.08
49	Rice, Jim	.30	.25	.10
50	Forsch, Ken	.12	.08	.03
51	Ryan, Nolan	.25	.20	.08
52	Parker, Dave	.25	.20	.08
53	Blyleven, Bert	.15	.11	.05
54	Tanana, Frank	.15	.11	.05
55	Singleton, Ken	.15	.11	.05
56	Hargrove, Mike	.12	.08	.03
57	Sutton, Don	.20	.15	.06

1979 KELLOGG (60)   1 15/16" X 3 1/4"

The 1979 Kellogg's set con-tains 60 three-dimensional appearing cards quite similar to other recent Kellogg's issues. This set contains the most number of cards since Kellogg's 1971 issue, and the actual size of the card has been reduced slightly from the previous year.

	MINT	VG-E	F-G
COMPLETE SET	6.50	5.00	2.00
COMMON PLAYER	.09	.07	.03

		MINT	VG-E	F-G
1	Bruce Sutter	.25	.20	.08
2	Ted Simmons	.20	.15	.06
3	Ross Grimsley	.09	.07	.03
4	Wayne Nordhagen	.09	.07	.03
5	Jim Palmer	.25	.20	.08
6	John Johnson	.09	.07	.03
7	Jason Thompson	.09	.07	.03
8	Pat Zachry	.09	.07	.03
9	Dennis Eckersley	.15	.11	.05
10	Paul Splittorff	.09	.07	.03
11	Ron Guidry	.25	.20	.08
12	Jeff Burroughs	.15	.11	.05
13	Rod Carew	.25	.20	.08
14	Buddy Bell	.15	.11	.05
15	Jim Rice	.25	.20	.08
16	Garry Maddox	.15	.11	.05
17	Willie McCovey	.20	.15	.06
18	Steve Carlton	.25	.20	.08
19	J.R. Richard	.25	.20	.08
20	Paul Molitor	.15	.11	.05
21	Dave Parker	.20	.15	.06
22	Pete Rose	.30	.25	.10
23	Vida Blue	.15	.11	.05
24	Richie Zisk	.15	.11	.05
25	Darrell Porter	.15	.11	.05
26	Dan Driessen	.09	.07	.03
27	Jeff Zahn	.09	.07	.03
28	Phil Niekro	.15	.11	.05
29	Tom Seaver	.25	.20	.08
30	Fred Lynn	.25	.20	.08

		MINT	VG-E	F-G
31	Bill Bonham	.09	.07	.03
32	George Foster	.20	.15	.06
33	Terry Puhl	.15	.11	.05
34	John Candelaria	.09	.07	.03
35	Bob Knepper	.09	.07	.03
36	Fred Patek	.09	.07	.03
37	Chris Chambliss	.09	.07	.03
38	Bob Forsch	.09	.07	.03
39	Ken Griffey	.15	.11	.05
40	Jack Clark	.15	.11	.05
41	Dwight Evans	.09	.07	.03
42	Lee Mazzilli	.15	.11	.05
43	Mario Guerrero	.09	.07	.03
44	Larry Bowa	.15	.11	.05
45	Carl Yastrzemski	.25	.20	.08
46	Reggie Jackson	.25	.20	.08
47	Rick Reuschel	.15	.11	.05
48	Mike Flanagan	.15	.11	.05
49	Gaylord Perry	.20	.15	.06
50	George Brett	.30	.25	.10
51	C. Reynolds	.09	.07	.03
52	Dave Lopes	.15	.11	.05
53	Bill Almon	.09	.07	.03
54	Roy Howell	.09	.07	.03
55	Frank Tanana	.15	.11	.05
56	Doug Rau	.09	.07	.03
57	Rick Monday	.09	.07	.03
58	Jon Matlack	.09	.07	.03
59	Ron Jackson	.09	.07	.03
60	Jim Sundberg	.15	.11	.05

Attend a Sports Memorabilia Show or Convention in your area sometime this year. They are both interesting and enjoyable to all members of the family.

The 1980 Kellogg's 3-D set contains 60 cards quite similar to, but smaller than, the other recent Kellogg's issues. Sets could be obtained card by card from cereal boxes or as a set from a box top offer from the company.

	MINT	VG-E	F-G
COMPLETE SET	5.00	3.50	1.50
COMMON PLAYER	.06	.04	.02

		MINT	VG-E	F-G
1	Ross Grimsley	.06	.04	.02
2	Mike Schmidt	.25	.20	.08
3	Mike Flanagan	.10	.07	.03
4	Ron Guidry	.15	.11	.05
5	Bert Blyleven	.10	.07	.03
6	Dave Kingman	.10	.07	.03
7	Jeff Newman	.06	.04	.02
8	Steve Rogers	.10	.07	.03
9	George Brett	.30	.25	.10
10	Bruce Sutter	.20	.15	.06
11	Gorman Thomas	.15	.11	.05
12	Darrell Porter	.10	.07	.03
13	Roy Smalley	.10	.07	.03
14	Steve Carlton	.20	.15	.06
15	Jim Palmer	.20	.15	.06
16	Bob Bailor	.06	.04	.02
17	Jason Thompson	.06	.04	.02
18	Graig Nettles	.10	.07	.03
19	Ron Cey	.10	.07	.03
20	Nolan Ryan	.20	.15	.06
21	Ellis Valentine	.10	.07	.03
22	Larry Hisle	.10	.07	.03
23	Dave Parker	.20	.15	.06
24	Eddie Murray	.15	.11	.05
25	Willie Stargell	.15	.11	.05
26	Reggie Jackson	.25	.20	.08
27	Carl Yastrzemski	.25	.20	.08
28	Andre Thorton	.06	.04	.02
29	Dave Lopes	.06	.04	.02
30	Ken Singleton	.10	.07	.03
31	Steve Garvey	.20	.15	.06
32	Dave Winfield	.20	.15	.06
33	Steve Kemp	.10	.07	.03
34	Claudell Washington	.06	.04	.02
35	Pete Rose	.25	.20	.08
36	Cesar Cedeno	.15	.11	.05
37	John Stearns	.06	.04	.02
38	Lee Mazzilli	.10	.07	.03
39	Larry Bowa	.10	.07	.03
40	Fred Lynn	.20	.15	.06
41	Carlton Fisk	.15	.11	.05
42	Vida Blue	.15	.11	.05
43	Keith Hernandez	.20	.15	.06
44	Ted Simmons	.15	.11	.05
45	Chet Lemon	.10	.07	.03
46	Jim Rice	.20	.15	.06
47	Ferguson Jenkins	.10	.07	.03
48	Gary Matthews	.10	.07	.03
49	Tom Seaver	.20	.15	.06
50	George Foster	.15	.11	.05
51	Phil Niekro	.10	.07	.03
52	Johnny Bench	.20	.15	.06
53	Buddy Bell	.10	.07	.03
54	Lance Parrish	.10	.07	.03
55	Joaquin Andujar	.06	.04	.02
56	Don Baylor	.10	.07	.03
57	Jack Clark	.10	.07	.03
58	J.R. Richard	.20	.15	.06
59	Bruce Bochte	.06	.04	.02
60	Rod Carew	.20	.15	.06

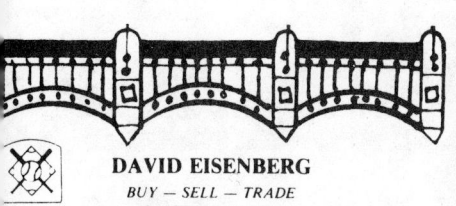

1960 LAKE TO LAKE (28)　　　2 1/2" X 3 1/4"

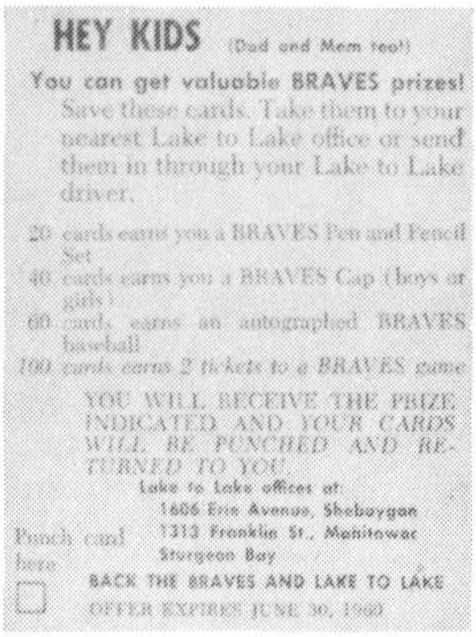

BOB BUHL
Pitcher

The 1960 Lake to Lake set of 28 unnumbered, blue tinted cards features Milwaukee Braves players only. The cards were issued on milk cartons by Lake to Lake Dairy. Most cards have staple holes in the upper right corner. The backs are in red and give details and prizes associated with the card promotion. Cards with staple holes can be considered very good to excellent at best The ACC designation is F102-1.

	MINT	VG-E	F-G
COMPLETE SET	320.00	200.00	80.00
COMMON PLAYER	3.75	2.50	1.20

	MINT	VG-E	F-G		MINT	VG-E	F-G
Hank Aaron	100.00	70.00	30.00	Lee Maye	3.75	2.50	1.20
Joe Adcock	6.00	4.50	2.10	Don McMahon	3.75	2.50	1.20
Ray Boone	60.00	45.00	20.00	George Myatt	3.75	2.50	1.20
Bill Bruton	150.00	100.00	40.00	Andy Pafko	3.75	2.50	1.20
Bob Buhl	3.75	2.50	1.20	Juan Pizzarro	3.75	2.50	1.20
Lew Burdette	6.00	4.50	2.10	Mel Roach	3.75	2.50	1.20
Chuck Cottier	3.75	2.50	1.20	Bob Rush	3.75	2.50	1.20
Wes Covington	3.75	2.50	1.20	Bob Scheffing	3.75	2.50	1.20
Del Crandall	5.00	3.75	1.75	Red Schoendienst	7.50	5.75	2.60
Chuck Dressen	5.00	3.75	1.75	Warren Spahn	15.00	11.00	5.00
Bob Giggie	3.75	2.50	1.20	Al Spangler	3.75	2.50	1.20
Joey Jay	3.75	2.50	1.20	Frank Torre	3.75	2.50	1.20
Johnny Logan	3.75	2.50	1.20	Carlton Willey	3.75	2.50	1.20
Felix Mantilla	3.75	2.50	1.20	Whit Wyatt	5.00	3.75	1.75

1953 BOWMAN COLOR UNCUT SHEET

1---JOE DI MAGGIO (JOLTIN' JOE)
Outfielder—N. Y. Yankees
Age—34   Bats—right
Ht.—6' 1"   Throws—right
Home—New York Wgt.—195 lbs.
Smashed out 39 home runs (tops) and 190 hits for .320 average last season. Has lifetime bat mark of .330. Topped American league in hitting in 1939 (.381) and 1940 (.352). Holds Major league record for hitting safely in 56 consecutive games—from May 15 through June 16, 1941—finally being stopped by Al Smith and Jim Bagby of Cleveland.

ALL-STAR BASEBALL GUM
Collect this series of Diamond Greats
Decorate your room with colorful felt pennants of your favorite teams. Send 5 All-Star Baseball Wrappers and 10¢ for big 12" x 6" pennant of any team in the American league or the National league.
Send Wrappers and Coin to
LEAF GUM CO., Box 5967 CHICAGO 80, ILL.
Copyright 1948

The 1948-49 Leaf set is the first modern era card set in color (althogh rather poor color). The set is skip-numbered from number 1-168. While 49 of the cards are relatively common, the other 49 are rare. The rare Leafs are indicated by italics on the checklist below.

	MINT	VG-E	F-G
COMPLETE SET	4200.00	3300.00	1400.00
COMMON NUMBERS	6.00	4.50	2.00
RARE NUMBERS(ITALICS)	65.00	45.00	20.00
1 Joe DiMaggio	120.00	85.00	40.00
3 Babe Ruth	120.00	85.00	40.00
4 Stan Musial	60.00	45.00	20.00
5 Trucks	65.00	45.00	20.00
8 Satchel Paige	325.00	250.00	100.00
10 Trout	6.00	4.50	2.00
11 Phil Rizzuto	16.00	12.00	5.50
13 C. Michaels	65.00	45.00	20.00
14 Billy Johnson	6.00	4.50	2.00
17 Frank Overmire	6.00	4.50	2.00
19 Wyrostek	65.00	45.00	20.00
20 Hank Sauer	70.00	50.00	23.00
22 Evans	6.00	4.50	2.00
26 Sam Chapman	6.00	4.50	2.00
27 Mickey Harris	6.00	4.50	2.00
28 Jim Hegan	6.00	4.50	2.00
29 Elmer Valo	6.00	4.50	2.00
30 Billy Goodman	65.00	45.00	20.00
31 Brissie	6.00	4.50	2.00
32 Warren Spahn	20.00	15.00	6.50
33 Peanuts Lowery	65.00	45.00	23.00
36 Al Zarilla	65.00	45.00	20.00
38 Ted Kluszewski	10.00	7.00	3.00
39 Ewell Blackwell	7.00	5.25	2.50
42 K. Peterson	6.00	4.50	2.00
43 E. Stevens	65.00	45.00	20.00
45 Ken Keltner	65.00	45.00	20.00
46 Johnny Mize	14.00	10.50	4.75
47 Vico	6.00	4.50	2.00
48 Schmitz	65.00	45.00	23.00
49 Del Ennis	7.00	5.25	2.50
50 Wakefield	6.00	4.50	2.00
51 Al Dark	75.00	55.00	24.00
53 Johnny Vander Meer	10.00	7.00	3.00
54 Adams	65.00	45.00	20.00
55 Tommy Henrich	80.00	60.00	25.00
56 Jansen	6.00	4.50	2.00
57 McCall	6.00	4.50	2.00
59 Luke Appling	14.00	10.50	4.75
61 Early	6.00	4.50	2.00
62 Eddie Joost	65.00	45.00	20.00
63 McCoskey	65.00	45.00	20.00
65 R. Elliott	5.00	4.50	2.00
66 Grove	65.00	45.00	20.00
68 Miller	65.00	45.00	20.00
70 Honus Wagner	40.00	30.00	13.00
72 H. Edwards	6.00	4.50	2.00
73 Pat Seerey	6.00	4.50	2.00

	MINT	VG-E	F-G
75 Dom DiMaggio	90.00	70.00	30.00
76 Ted Williams	85.00	65.00	30.00
77 Roy Smalley	6.00	4.50	2.00
78 Hoot Evers	65.00	45.00	20.00
79 Jackie Robinson	60.00	45.00	20.00
81 Whitey Kurowski	65.00	45.00	20.00
82 Johnny Lindell	6.00	4.50	2.00
83 Bobby Doerr	7.00	5.25	2.50
84 Sid Hudson	6.00	4.50	2.00
85 Dave Philley	65.00	45.00	20.00
86 Ralph Weigel	6.00	4.50	2.00
88 Frank Gustine	65.00	45.00	20.00
91 Ralph Kiner	16.00	12.00	5.50
93 Bob Feller	250.00	185.00	87.50
95 George Stirnweiss	6.00	4.50	2.50
97 Marty Marion	9.00	6.75	3.00
98 Hal Newhouser	75.00	55.00	24.00
102A Gene Hermansk	40.00	30.00	13.00
102B Gene Hermanski	7.00	5.25	2.50
104 Eddie Stewart	65.00	45.00	20.00
106 Lou Boudreau	15.00	11.00	5.00
108 Matt Batts	65.00	45.00	20.00
111 Jerry Priddy	6.00	4.50	2.00
113 Dutch Leonard	65.00	45.00	20.00
117 Joe Gordon	6.00	4.50	2.00
120 George Kell	75.00	55.00	24.00
121 Johnny Pesky	70.00	50.00	23.00
123 Cliff Fannin	65.00	45.00	20.00
125 Andy Pafko	6.00	4.50	2.00
127 Enos Slaughter	120.00	85.00	40.00
128 Buddy Rosar	6.00	4.50	2.00
129 Kirby Higbe	65.00	45.00	20.00
131 Sid Gordon	65.00	45.00	20.00
133 Tommy Holmes	70.00	50.00	23.00
136A Aberson-full sleeve	7.00	5.25	2.50
136B Aberson-short sleeve	20.00	15.00	6.50
137 Harry Walker	70.00	50.00	23.00
138 Larry Doby	80.00	60.00	25.00
139 Johnny Hopp	7.00	5.25	2.50
142 Danny Murtaugh	70.00	50.00	23.00
143 Dick Sisler	65.00	45.00	20.00
144 Bob Dillinger	65.00	45.00	20.00
146 Pete Reiser	70.00	50.00	23.00
149 Hank Majeski	65.00	45.00	20.00
153 Floyd Baker	65.00	45.00	20.00
158 Harry Brecheen	70.00	50.00	23.00
159 Mizell Platt	6.00	4.50	2.00
160 Bob Scheffing	65.00	45.00	20.00
161 Vern Stephens	65.00	45.00	20.00
163 Fred Hutchinson	75.00	55.00	24.00
165 Dale Mitchell	65.00	45.00	20.00
168 Phil Cavaretta	70.00	50.00	23.00

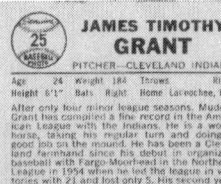

LEAF VARIATIONS

1960 LEAF (144) B&W   2 1/2" X 3 1/2"

The 1960 Leaf set was issued with marbles by Sports Novelties, Inc. Leaf Gum helped in the distribution; therefore, this set is considered a Leaf issue. Card numbers 73-144 are somewhat more difficult to obtain, while number 25 with a Jim Grant front and back is the scarcest card of the issue. Two poses exist for the four cards listed with an asterisk.

	MINT	VG-E	F-G
COMPLETE SET	250.00	190.00	80.00
COMMON PLAYER (1-72)	.40	.30	.12
COMMON PLAYER (73-144)	3.00	2.25	1.00
1 Luis Aparicio	1.00	.60	.25
2 Woodson Held	.40	.30	.12
3 Frank Lary	.40	.30	.12
4 Camilo Pascual	.40	.30	.12
5 Juan Herrera	.40	.30	.12
6 Felipe Alou	.50	.35	.15
7 Benjamin Daniels	.40	.30	.12
8 Roger Craig	.40	.30	.12
9 Edward Kasko	.40	.30	.12
10 Robert Anton Grim	.40	.30	.12
11 James Busby	.40	.30	.12
12 Kenton Boyer	.80	.60	.25
13 Robert Boyd	.40	.30	.12
14 Samuel Jones	.40	.30	.12
15 Lawrence Jackson	.40	.30	.12
16 Elroy Face	.50	.35	.15
17 Walter Moryn*	.40	.30	.12
18 James Gilliam	.80	.60	.25
19 Donald Newcombe	.80	.60	.25
20 Glen Hobbie	.40	.30	.12
21 Pedro Ramos	.40	.30	.12
22 Rinold Duren	.50	.35	.15
23 Joseph Jay*	.40	.30	.12
24 Louis Berberet	.40	.30	.12

	MINT	VG-E	F-G
25a Jim Grant (correct)	30.00	21.00	9.00
25b Jim Grant (error)	15.00	11.00	5.00
26 Thomas Borland	.40	.30	.12
27 Brooks Robinson	4.00	3.00	1.40
28 Jerry Adair	.40	.30	.12
29 Ronald Jackson	.40	.30	.12
30 George Strickland	.40	.30	.12
31 Everett L. Bridges	.40	.30	.12
32 William Tuttle	.40	.30	.12
33 Kenneth Hunt	.40	.30	.12
34 Harold Griggs	.40	.30	.12
35 James Coates*	.40	.30	.12
36 Brooks Lawrence	.50	.35	.15
37 Edwin Snider	4.00	3.00	1.40
38 Albert Spangler	.40	.30	.12
39 James Owens	.40	.30	.12
40 William Virdon	.80	.60	.25
41 Ernest Broglio	.40	.30	.12
42 Andre Rodgers	.40	.30	.12
43 Julio Becquer	.40	.30	.12
44 Antonio Taylor	.40	.30	.12
45 Gerald Lynch	.40	.30	.12
46 Cletis Boyer	.40	.30	.12
47 Jerry Lumpe	.40	.30	.12
48 Charles Maxwell	.40	.30	.12
49 James Perry	.50	.35	.15
50 Daniel McDevitt	.40	.30	.12
51 Juan Pizarro	.40	.30	.12
52 Dallas Green	.80	.60	.25

1960 LEAF (CONTINUED)

	MINT	VG-E	F-G			MINT	VG-E	F-G
53 Robert Friend	.50	.35	.15	98 Willie Jones		3.00	2.25	1.00
54 Jack Sanford	.40	.30	.12	99 Marshall Renfroe		3.00	2.25	1.00
55 Manuel Rivera	.40	.30	.12	100 Willie Tasby		3.00	2.25	1.00
56 Theodore Wills	.40	.30	.12	101 Irv Noren		3.00	2.25	1.00
57 Milton Pappas	.50	.35	.15	102 Russ Snyder		3.00	2.25	1.00
58 Harold Smith	.40	.30	.12	103 Bob Turley		4.00	3.00	1.40
59 Roberto Avila	.40	.30	.12	104 Jim Woods		3.00	2.25	1.00
60 Clement Labine	.40	.30	.12	105 Ronnie Kline		3.00	2.25	1.00
61 Norman Rehm	.40	.30	.12	106 Steve Bilko		3.00	2.25	1.00
62 John Gabler	.40	.30	.12	107 Elmer Valo		3.00	2.25	1.00
63 John Tsitouris	.40	.30	.12	108 Tom McAvoy		3.00	2.25	1.00
64 David Sisler	.40	.30	.12	109 Stan Williams		3.00	2.25	1.00
65 Victor Power	.40	.30	.12	110 Earl Averill		3.00	2.25	1.00
66 Earl Battey	.40	.30	.12	111 Lee Walls		3.00	2.25	1.00
67 Robert Purkey	.40	.30	.12	112 Paul Richards		4.00	3.00	1.40
68 Myron Drabowsky	.40	.30	.12	113 Ed Sadowski		3.00	2.25	1.00
69 James Wilhelm	.80	.60	.25	114 Stover McIlwain		3.00	2.25	1.00
60 Humberto Robinson	.40	.30	.12	115 Chuck Tanner		4.00	3.00	1.40
71 Dorrel Herzog	.80	.60	.25	116 Lou Klimchock		3.00	2.25	1.00
72 Richard Donovan*	.40	.30	.12	117 Neil Chrisley		3.00	2.25	1.00
73 Gordon Jones	3.00	2.25	1.00	118 John Callison		3.00	2.25	1.00
74 Joe Hicks	3.00	2.25	1.00	119 Hal Smith		3.00	2.25	1.00
75 Ray Culp	3.00	2.25	1.00	120 Carl Sawatski		3.00	2.25	1.00
76 Dick Drott	3.00	2.25	1.00	121 Frank Leja		3.00	2.25	1.00
77 Bob Duliba	3.00	2.25	1.00	122 Earl Torgeson		3.00	2.25	1.00
78 Art Ditmar	3.00	2.25	1.00	123 Art Schult		3.00	2.25	1.00
79 Steve Korcheck	3.00	2.25	1.00	124 Jim Brosnan		3.00	2.25	1.00
80 Henry Mason	3.00	2.25	1.00	125 George Anderson		6.00	4.50	2.00
81 Harry Simpson	3.00	2.25	1.00	126 Joe Pignatano		3.00	2.25	1.00
82 Gene Green	3.00	2.25	1.00	127 Rocky Nelson		3.00	2.25	1.00
83 Bob Shaw	3.00	2.25	1.00	128 Orlando Cepeda		6.00	4.50	2.00
84 Howard Reed	3.00	2.25	1.00	129 Daryl Spencer		3.00	2.25	1.00
85 Dick Stigman	3.00	2.25	1.00	130 Ralph Lumenti		3.00	2.25	1.00
86 Rip Repulski	3.00	2.25	1.00	131 Sam Taylor		3.00	2.25	1.00
87 Seth Morehead	3.00	2.25	1.00	132 Harry Brecheen		3.00	2.25	1.00
88 Camilo Carreon	3.00	2.25	1.00	133 Johnny Groth		3.00	2.25	1.00
89 John Blanchard	3.00	2.25	1.00	134 Wayne Terwilliger		3.00	2.25	1.00
90 Billy Hoeft	3.00	2.25	1.00	135 Kent Hadley		3.00	2.25	1.00
91 Fred Hopke	3.00	2.25	1.00	136 Faye Throneberry		3.00	2.25	1.00
92 Joe Martin	3.00	2.25	1.00	137 Jack Meyer		3.00	2.25	1.00
93 Wally Shannon	3.00	2.25	1.00	138 Chuck Cottier		3.00	2.25	1.00
94 Two Hal Smith's	5.00	3.75	1.75	139 Joe DeMaestri		3.00	2.25	1.00
95 Al Schroll	3.00	2.25	1.00	140 Gene Freese		3.00	2.25	1.00
96 John Kucks	3.00	2.25	1.00	141 Curt Flood		4.00	3.00	1.40
97 Tom Morgan	3.00	2.25	1.00	142 Gino Cimoli		3.00	2.25	1.00
				143 Clay Dalrymple		3.00	2.25	1.00
				144 Jim Bunning		5.00	3.75	1.75

1949 LUMMIS PEANUT BUTTER (12)　　　3 1/4" X 4 1/4"

The 1949 Lummis set is a set of 12 black & white, unnumbered action poses of Philadelphia Phillies. The "cards" are actually stickers and were distributed by Lummis Peanut Butter and Sealtest Dairy Products, with the former considered more difficult to obtain than the latter. The ACC designation is F343.

	MINT	VG-E	F-G			MINT	VG-E	F-G
COMPLETE SET	700.00	500.00	250.00	6 Russ Meyer		55.00	40.00	20.00
COMMON PLAYER	55.00	40.00	20.00	7 Bill Nicholson		55.00	40.00	20.00
				8 Robin Roberts		100.00	80.00	40.00
1 Rich Ashburn	75.00	60.00	25.00	9 Schoolboy Rowe		60.00	45.00	20.00
2 Hank Borowy	55.00	40.00	20.00	10 Andy Seminick		55.00	40.00	20.00
3 Del Ennis	55.00	40.00	20.00	11 Curt Simmons		55.00	40.00	20.00
4 Granny Hamner	55.00	40.00	20.00	12 Ed Waitkus		55.00	40.00	20.00
5 Puddinhead Jones	55.00	40.30	20.00					

The 1971 Milk Duds set c
tains 32 American Lea
cards and 37 National Lea
cards. The cards are se
toned on a tan backgrou
and were issued on the ba
of five-cent boxes of M
Duds candy. The pri
listed in the checklist are
complete boxes. Cards
from boxes are 1 13/16"
2 5/8" and are worth appr
imately one-half of the lis
price.

	MINT	VG-E	F-G
COMPLETE SET	100.00	70.00	30.00
COMMON (FULL BOX)	1.00	.70	.30
COMMON (CUT)	.40	.30	.13

	MINT	VG-E	F-G
AL 1 Luis Aparicio	1.50	1.10	.50
AL 2 Stan Bahnsen	1.00	.70	.30
AL 3 Danny Cater	1.00	.70	.30
AL 4 Ray Culp	1.00	.70	.30
AL 5 Ray Fosse	1.00	.70	.30
AL 6 Bill Freehan	1.00	.70	.30
AL 7 Jim Fregosi	1.50	1.10	.50
AL 8 Tommy Harper	1.00	.70	.30
AL 9 Frank Howard	1.50	1.10	.50
AL10 Jim Hunter	2.00	1.50	.60
AL11 Tommy John	2.00	1.50	.60
AL12 Alex Johnson	1.00	.70	.30
AL13 Dave Johnson	1.00	.70	.30
AL14 Harmon Killebrew	3.00	2.25	1.00
AL15 Sam McDowell	1.00	.70	.30
AL16 Dave McNally	1.00	.70	.30
AL17 Bill Melton	1.00	.70	.30
AL18 Andy Messersmith	1.00	.70	.30
AL19 Thurman Munson	7.00	5.25	2.50
AL20 Tony Oliva	2.00	1.50	.60
AL21 Jim Palmer	4.00	3.00	1.40
AL22 Jim Perry	1.00	.70	.30
AL23 Fritz Peterson	1.00	.70	.30
AL24 Rico Petrocelli	1.00	.70	.30
AL25 Boog Powell	1.00	.70	.30
AL26 Brooks Robinson	5.00	3.75	1.75
AL27 Frank Robinson	4.00	3.00	1.40
AL28 George Scott	1.00	.70	.30
AL29 Reggie Smith	1.50	1.10	.50
AL30 Mel Stottlemyer	1.50	1.10	.50
AL31 Cesar Tovar	1.00	.70	.30
AL32 Roy White	1.00	.70	.30
NL 1 Hank Aaron	8.00	6.00	2.50
NL 2 Ernie Banks	6.00	4.50	2.00
NL 3 Glenn Beckert	1.00	.70	.30

	MINT	VG-E	F-G
NL 4 Johnny Bench	7.00	5.25	2.50
NL 5 Lou Brock	5.00	3.75	1.75
NL 6 Rico Carty	1.50	1.10	.50
NL 7 Orlando Cepeda	2.00	1.50	.60
NL 8 Roberto Clemente	7.00	5.25	2.50
NL 9 Willie Davis	1.00	.70	.30
NL10 Dick Dietz	1.00	.70	.30
NL11 Bob Gibson	2.50	1.80	.80
NL12 Bil Grabarkewitz	1.00	.70	.30
NL13 Bud Harrelson	1.00	.70	.30
NL14 Jim Hickman	1.00	.70	.30
NL15 Ken Holtzman	1.00	.70	.30
NL16 Randy Hundley	1.00	.70	.30
NL17 Fergie Jenkins	1.50	1.10	.50
NL18 Don Kessinger	1.00	.70	.30
NL19 Willie Mays	8.00	6.00	2.50
NL20 Willie McCovey	5.00	3.75	1.75
NL21 Dennis Menke	1.00	.70	.30
NL22 Jim Merritt	1.00	.70	.30
NL23 Felix Millan	1.00	.70	.30
NL24 Claude Osteen	1.50	1.10	.50
NL25 Milt Pappas	1.00	.70	.30
NL26 Tony Perez	2.00	1.50	.60
NL27 Gaylord Perry	2.50	1.80	.80
NL28 Pete Rose	8.00	6.00	2.50
NL29 Manny Sanguillen	1.00	.70	.30
NL30 Ron Santo	1.50	1.10	.50
NL31 Tom Seaver	5.00	3.75	1.75
NL32 Wayne Simpson	1.00	.70	.30
NL33 Rusty Staub	1.50	1.10	.50
NL34 Bobby Tolan	1.00	.70	.30
NL35 Joe Torre	2.00	1.50	.60
NL36 Luke Walker	1.00	.70	.30
NL37 Billy Williams	2.00	1.50	.60

1933 GEORGE C. MILLER (32)　　　2 1/2" X 3"

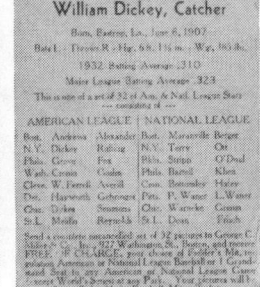

The 1933 George C. Miller Company set of 32 unnumbered, color cards is one of the most difficult R card sets to complete. The Andrews card is supposedly more scarce than the other cards in the set. The ACC designation is R300. For your viewing enjoyment an uncut proof sheet of 16 is pictured below.

	MINT	VG-E	F-G
COMPLETE SET	4000.00	3000.00	1200.00
COMMON PLAYER	125.00	90.00	40.00

	MINT	VG-E	F-G
Dale Alexander	125.00	90.00	40.00
Ivy Andrews	250.00	175.00	75.00
Earl Averill	150.00	110.00	50.00
Dick Bartell	125.00	90.00	40.00
Wally Berger	125.00	90.00	40.00
Jim Bottomley	150.00	110.00	50.00
Joe Cronin	175.00	125.00	60.00
Dizzy Dean	300.00	225.00	100.00
Bill Dickey	225.00	160.00	10.00
Jimmy Dykes	125.00	90.00	40.00
Wes Ferrell	125.00	90.00	40.00
Jimmy Foxx	300.00	225.00	100.00
Frank Frisch	175.00	125.00	60.00
Charlie Gehringer	175.00	125.00	60.00
Goose Goslin	150.00	110.00	50.00
Charlie Grimm	125.00	90.00	40.00

	MINT	VG-E	F-G
Lefty Grove	225.00	160.00	70.00
Chick Hafey	150.00	110.00	50.00
Ray Hayworth	125.00	90.00	40.00
Chuck Klein	150.00	110.00	50.00
Rabbit Maranville	150.00	110.00	50.00
Oscar Melillo	125.00	90.00	40.00
Lefty O'Doul	125.00	90.00	40.00
Mel Ott	200.00	150.00	75.00
Carl Reynolds	125.00	90.00	40.00
Red Ruffing	150.00	110.00	50.00
Al Simmons	175.00	125.00	60.00
Joe Stripp	125.00	90.00	40.00
Bill Terry	175.00	125.00	60.00
Lloyd Waner	150.00	110.00	50.00
Paul Waner	150.00	110.00	50.00
Lon Warneke	125.00	90.00	40.00

R300 UNCUT PROOF SHEET

1959 MORRELL (12)   2 1/2" X 3 1/2"

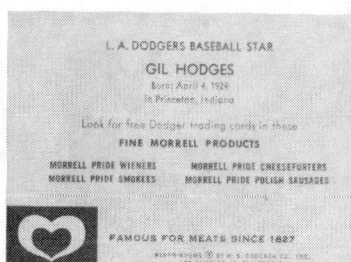

The 1959 Morrell Meats set
12 full color, unnumber
cards features Los Ange
Dodger players only. T
Morrell Meats logo is on t
backs of the cards. The Cle
Labine card actually feature
picture of Stan Williams a
the Norm Larker card actual
features a picture of J
Pignatano. The ACC desig
tion is F172-1.

	MINT	VG-E	F-G
COMPLETE SET	400.00	300.00	140.00
COMMON PLAYER	30.00	24.00	11.00
1 Don Drysdale	50.00	38.00	17.00
2 Carl Furillo	35.00	26.00	12.00
3 Jim Gilliam	35.00	26.00	12.00
4 Gil Hodges	40.00	30.00	13.00
5 Sandy Koufax	60.00	45.00	20.00
6 Clem Labine	30.00	24.00	11.00

	MINT	VG-E	F-G
7 Norm Larker	30.00	24.00	11.00
8 Charlie Neal	30.00	24.00	11.00
9 Johnny Podres	30.00	24.00	11.00
10 John Roseboro	30.00	24.00	11.00
11 Duke Snider	50.00	38.00	17.00
12 Don Zimmer	35.00	26.00	12.00

1960 MORRELL (12)   2 1/2" X 3 1/2"

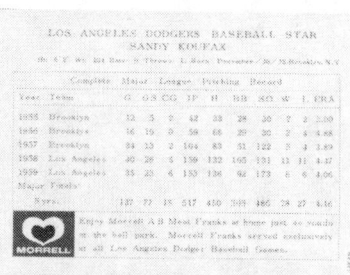

The 1960 Morrell Meats set of
12 full color, unnumbered
cards is similar in format to
the 1959 Morrell set but can
be distinguished from the 1959
set by a red heart which
appears in the Morrell logo on
the back. The Furillo, Hodges,
and Snider cards have limited
distribution and are hence
more scarce. The ACC designation is F172-2.

	MINT	VG-E	F-G
COMPLETE SET	190.00	140.00	60.00
COMMON PLAYER	8.00	6.00	2.50
1 Walt Alston	8.00	6.00	2.50
2 Roger Craig	8.00	6.00	2.50
3 Don Drysdale	16.00	12.00	5.50
4 Carl Furillo	40.00	30.00	13.00
5 Gil Hodges	50.00	38.00	17.00
6 Sandy Koufax	20.00	15.00	6.50

	MINT	VG-E	F-G
7 Wally Moon	8.00	6.00	2.50
8 Charlie Neal	8.00	6.00	2.50
9 Johnny Podres	8.00	6.00	2.50
10 John Roseboro	8.00	6.00	2.50
11 Larry Sherry	8.00	6.00	2.50
12 Duke Snider	60.00	45.00	20.00

1961 MORRELL (6)

2 1/4" X 3 1/4"

The 1961 Morrell Meats set of six full color, unnumbered cards features Los Angeles Dodger players only and contains statistical information on the backs of the cards in brown print. The ACC designation is F172-3.

	MINT	VG-E	F-G
COMPLETE SET	65.00	48.00	20.00
COMMON PLAYER	10.00	7.00	3.00

	MINT	VG-E	F-G			MINT	VG-E	F-G
1 Tommy Davis	11.00	8.00	3.50	4 Sandy Koufax		20.00	15.00	6.50
2 Don Drysdale	16.00	12.00	5.50	5 Norm Larker		10.00	7.00	3.00
3 Frank Howard	12.00	8.75	4.00	6 Maury Wills		14.00	10.50	4.75

1952 MOTHERS COOKIES (64)

2 3/16" X 3 1/2"

The 1952 Mothers Cookies set includes 64 numbered cards. Pacific Coast League players only are featured. The cards were issued in bags of Mothers Cookies. Card No. 29, Peterson, and card no. 43, Erautt, are reportedly scarce, and to a lesser degree, cards numbered 11, 16, and 37 are difficult to obtain. The ACC designation is D357-1.

	MINT	VG-E	F-G
COMPLETE SET	650.00	470.00	200.00
COMMON PLAYER	9.00	6.75	3.00

	MINT	VG-E	F-G			MINT	VG-E	F-G
1 Johnny Lindell	10.00	7.00	3.00	33 Sam Chapman		9.00	6.75	3.00
2 Jim Davis	9.00	6.75	3.00	34 John Ragni		9.00	6.75	3.00
3 Al Gettle	9.00	6.75	3.00	35 Dick Cole		9.00	6.75	3.00
4 Chuck Connors	60.00	45.00	20.00	36 Tom Saffel		9.00	6.75	3.00
5 Joe Grace	9.00	6.75	3.00	37 Roy Welmaker		25.00	18.50	8.75
6 Eddie Basinski	9.00	6.75	3.00	38 Lou Stringer		9.00	6.75	3.00
7 Gene Handley	9.00	6.75	3.00	39 Chuck Stevens		9.00	6.75	3.00
8 Walt Judnich	9.00	6.75	3.00	40 Artie Wilson		9.00	6.75	3.00
9 Jim Marshall	9.00	6.75	3.00	41 Charlie Schanz		9.00	6.75	3.00
10 Max West	9.00	6.75	3.00	42 Al Lyons		9.00	6.75	3.00
11 Bill MacCawley	16.00	12.00	5.50	43 Joe Erautt		75.00	55.00	24.00
12 Moreno Pieretti	9.00	6.75	3.00	44 Clarence Maddern		9.00	6.75	3.00
13 Fred Haney	10.00	7.00	3.00	45 Gene Baker		9.00	6.75	3.00
14 Earl Johnson	9.00	6.75	3.00	46 Tom Heath		9.00	6.75	3.00
15 Dave Dahle	9.00	6.75	3.00	47 Al Lien		9.00	6.75	3.00
16 Bob Talbot	16.00	12.00	5.50	48 Bill Reeder		9.00	6.75	3.00
17 Smokey Singleton	9.00	6.75	3.00	49 Bob Thurman		9.00	6.75	3.00
18 Frank Austin	9.00	6.75	3.00	50 Ray Orteig		9.00	6.75	3.00
19 Joe Gordon	10.00	7.00	3.00	51 Joe Brovia		9.00	6.75	3.00
20 Joe Marty	9.00	6.75	3.00	52 Jim Russell		9.00	6.75	3.00
21 Bob Gillespie	9.00	6.75	3.00	53 Fred Sanford		9.00	6.75	3.00
22 Red Embree	9.00	6.75	3.00	54 Jim Gladd		9.00	6.75	3.00
23 Lefty Olsen	9.00	6.75	3.00	55 Clay Hopper		9.00	6.75	3.00
24 Whitey Wietelmann	9.00	6.75	3.00	56 Bill Glynn		9.00	6.75	3.00
25 Frank O'Doul	12.00	8.75	4.00	57 Mike McCormick		9.00	6.75	3.00
26 Memo Luna	9.00	6.75	3.00	58 Richie Myers		9.00	6.75	3.00
27 John Davis	9.00	6.75	3.00	59 Vinnie Smith		9.00	6.75	3.00
28 Dick Faber	9.00	6.75	3.00	60 Stan Hack		12.00	8.75	4.00
29 Buddy Peterson	75.00	55.00	24.00	61 Bob Spicer		9.00	6.75	3.00
30 Hank Schenz	9.00	6.75	3.00	62 Jack Hollis		9.00	6.75	3.00
31 Tookie Gilbert	9.00	6.75	3.00	63 Ed Chandler		9.00	6.75	3.00
32 Mel Oll	35.00	26.00	12.00	64 Bill Moisan		9.00	6.75	3.00

1953 MOTHERS COOKIES (63) 2 3/16" X 3 1/2"

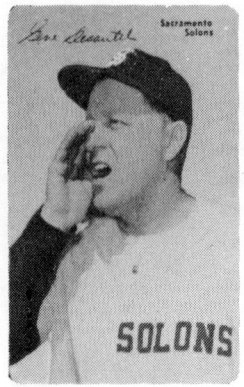

The 1953 Mothers Cookies set of 63 cards features Pacific Coast League players only. The cards are numbered and the corners of the cards are rounded. The cards can be distinguished from the 1952 set by an ad for a "trading card album" on the reverse. The higher numbered cards are reportedly more plentiful than the lower numbered cards. These plentiful 11 cards are numbers 45, 50, 51, 53, 54, 57-61, and 63; they carry an asterisk in the checklist below. The ACC designation is D357-2.

	MINT	VG-E	F-G
COMPLETE SET	210.00	155.00	70.00
COMMON PLAYER	3.75	2.75	1.25

	MINT	VG-E	F-G
1 Lee Winters	3.75	2.75	1.25
2 Joe Ostrowski	3.75	2.75	1.25
3 Willie Ramsdell	3.75	2.75	1.25
4 Bobby Bragan	6.00	4.50	2.00
5 Fletcher Robbe	3.75	2.75	1.25
6 Aaron Robinson	3.75	2.75	1.25
7 Augie Galan	3.75	2.75	1.25
8 Buddy Peterson	3.75	2.75	1.25
9 Frank O'Doul	7.00	5.25	2.50
10 Walt Poceday	3.75	2.75	1.25
11 Nine Tornay	3.75	2.75	1.25
12 Jim Moran	3.75	2.75	1.25
13 George Schmees	3.75	2.75	1.25
14 Al Widmar	3.75	2.75	1.25
15 Richie Myers	3.75	2.75	1.25
16 Bill Howerton	3.75	2.75	1.25
17 Chuck Stevens	3.75	2.75	1.25
18 Joe Brovia	3.75	2.75	1.25
19 Max West	3.75	2.75	1.25
20 Eddie Malone	3.75	2.75	1.25
21 Gene Handley	3.75	2.75	1.25
22 William D. McCawley	3.75	2.75	1.25
23 Bill Sweeney	3.75	2.75	1.25
24 Tom Alston	3.75	2.75	1.25
25 George Vico	3.75	2.75	1.25
26 Hank Arft	3.75	2.75	1.25
27 Al Benton	3.75	2.75	1.25
28 "Pete" Milne	3.75	2.75	1.25
29 Jim Gladd	3.75	2.75	1.25
30 Earl Rapp	3.75	2.75	1.25
31 Ray Orteig	3.75	2.75	1.25
32 Eddie Basinski	3.75	2.75	1.25

	MINT	VG-E	F-G
33 Reno Cheso	3.75	2.75	1.25
34 Clarence Maddern	3.75	2.75	1.25
35 Marino Pieretti	3.75	2.75	1.25
36 Bill Raimondi	3.75	2.75	1.25
37 Frank Kelleher	3.75	2.75	1.25
38 George Bamberger	6.00	4.50	2.00
39 Dick Smith	3.75	2.75	1.25
40 Charley Schanz	3.75	2.75	1.25
41 John Van Cuyk	3.75	2.75	1.25
42 Lloyd Hittle	3.75	2.75	1.25
43 Tommy Heath	3.75	2.75	1.25
44 Frank Kalin	3.75	2.75	1.25
45 Jack Tobin	3.00	2.25	1.00
46 Jim Davis	3.75	2.75	1.25
47 Claude Christy	3.75	2.75	1.25
48 Elvin Tappe	3.75	2.75	1.25
49 Stan Hack	6.00	4.50	2.00
50 Fred Richards	3.00	2.25	1.00
51 Clay Hopper	3.00	2.25	1.00
52 Roy Welmaker	3.75	2.75	1.25
53 Red Adams	3.00	2.25	1.00
54 Piper Davis	3.00	2.25	1.00
55 Spider Jorgensen	3.75	2.75	1.25
56 Lee Walls	3.75	2.75	1.25
57 Jack Phillips	3.00	2.25	1.00
58 Red Lynn	3.00	2.25	1.00
59 Eddie Robinson	3.00	2.25	1.00
60 Gene Desautels	3.00	2.25	1.00
61 Bob Dillinger	3.00	2.25	1.00
62 Al Federoff	3.75	2.75	1.25
63 Bill Boemler	3.00	2.25	1.00

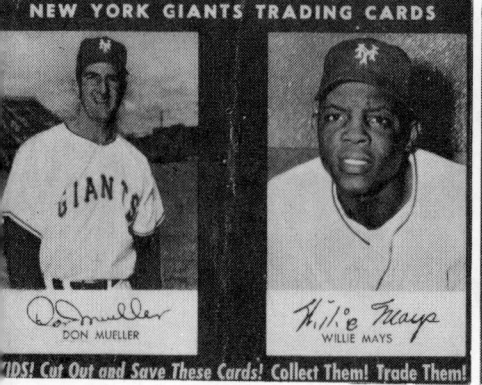

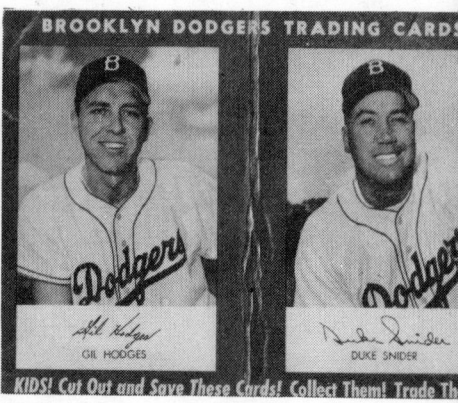

BRIGGS — UNCUT PANELS

1916 M101-4 SPORTING NEWS (200)   1 5/8" X 3"

J. CARLISLE SMITH
3rd B.—Boston Braves
163

Issued in 1916 as a premium offer, the M101-4 set features black & white photos of current ballplayers. Each card is numbered and the reverse carries Sporting News advertising. The fronts are the same as D329, H801-9, and the unclassified Famous & Barr set.

THE SPORTING NEWS
"THE BASEBALL PAPER of the WORLD"

FIVE CENTS THE COPY
PUBLISHED WEEKLY the YEAR 'ROUND

SAMPLE COPY FREE ON REQUEST
C. C. SPINK & SON : ST. LOUIS, MO.

	MINT	VG-E	F-G			MINT	VG-E	F-G
COMPLETE SET	1800.00	1300.00	600.00					
COMMON PLAYER	8.00	6.50	3.00					
1 Babe Adams	8.00	6.50	3.00	61 Eddie Foster	8.00	6.50	3.00
2 Sam Agnew	8.00	6.50	3.00	62 Jacques Fournier	8.00	6.50	3.00
3 Eddie Ainsmith	8.00	6.50	3.00	63 Del Gainer	8.00	6.50	3.00
4 Grover Alexander	20.00	15.00	7.00	64 Chick Gandil	8.00	6.50	3.00
5 Leon Ames	8.00	6.50	3.00	65 Larry Gardner	8.00	6.50	3.00
6 Jimmy Archer	8.00	6.50	3.00	66 Joe Gedeon	8.00	6.50	3.00
7 Jimmy Austin	8.00	6.50	3.00	67 Gus Getz	8.00	6.50	3.00
8 H. D. Baird	8.00	6.50	3.00	68 George Gibson	8.00	6.50	3.00
9 Frank Baker	13.50	10.00	4.00	69 Wilbur Good	8.00	6.50	3.00
10 Dave Bancroft	13.50	10.00	4.00	70 Hank Gowdy	8.00	6.50	3.00
11 Jack Barry	8.00	6.50	3.00	71 Jack Graney	8.00	6.50	3.00
12 Zinn Beck	8.00	6.50	3.00	72 Clark Griffith	13.50	10.00	4.00
13 Chief Bender	13.50	10.00	4.00	73 Tommy Griffith	8.00	6.50	3.00
14 Joe Benz	8.00	6.50	3.00	74 Heinie Groh	8.00	6.50	3.00
15 Bob Bescher	8.00	6.50	3.00	75 Earl Hamilton	8.00	6.50	3.00
16 Al Betzel	8.00	6.50	3.00	76 Bob Harmon	8.00	6.50	3.00
17 Mordecai Brown	13.50	10.00	4.00	77 Roy Hartzell	8.00	6.50	3.00
18 Eddie Burns	8.00	6.50	3.00	78 Claude Hendrix	8.00	6.50	3.00
19 George Burns	8.00	6.50	3.00	79 Olaf Henriksen	8.00	6.50	3.00
20 George J. Burns	8.00	6.50	3.00	80 John Henry	8.00	6.50	3.00
21 Joe Bush	8.00	6.50	3.00	81 Buck Herzog	8.00	6.50	3.00
22 Donie Bush	8.00	6.50	3.00	82 Hugh High	8.00	6.50	3.00
23 Art Butler	8.00	6.50	3.00	83 Dick Hoblitzel	8.00	6.50	3.00
24 Bobbie Byrne	8.00	6.50	3.00	84 Harry Hooper	13.50	10.00	4.00
25 Forrest Cady	8.00	6.50	3.00	85 Ivan Howard	8.00	6.50	3.00
26 Jim Callahan	8.00	6.50	3.00	86 Miller Huggins	13.50	10.00	4.00
27 Ray Caldwell	8.00	6.50	3.00	87 Joe Jackson	30.00	24.00	10.00
28 Max Carey	13.50	10.00	4.00	88 William James	8.00	6.50	3.00
29 George Chalmers	8.00	6.50	3.00	89 Harold Janvrin	8.00	6.50	3.00
30 Ray Chapman	8.00	6.50	3.00	90 Hughie Jennings	17.50	13.00	6.00
31 Larry Cheney	8.00	6.50	3.00	91 Walter Johnson	40.00	30.00	12.00
32 Ed Cicotte	8.00	6.50	3.00	92 Fielder Jones	8.00	6.50	3.00
33 Tommy Clarke	8.00	6.50	3.00	93 Joe Judge	8.00	6.50	3.00
34 Eddie Collins	13.50	10.00	4.00	94 Benny Kauff	8.00	6.50	3.00
35 Shano Collins	8.00	6.50	3.00	95 Bill Killifer	8.00	6.50	3.00
36 Charles Comiskey	13.50	10.00	4.00	96 Ed Konetchy	8.00	6.50	3.00
37 Joe Connolly	8.00	6.50	3.00	97 Nap Lajoie	30.00	24.00	10.00
38 Ty Cobb	80.00	60.00	25.00	98 Jack Lapp	8.00	6.50	3.00
39 Harry Covaleskie	8.00	6.50	3.00	99 John Lavan	8.00	6.50	3.00
40 Gabby Cravath	8.00	6.50	3.00	100 Jimmy Lavender	8.00	6.50	3.00
41 Sam Crawford	13.50	10.00	4.00	101 Nemo Leibold	8.00	6.50	3.00
42 Jean Dale	8.00	6.50	3.00	102 Hub Leonard	8.00	6.50	3.00
43 Jake Daubert	8.00	6.50	3.00	103 Duffy Lewis	8.00	6.50	3.00
44 Charles Deal	8.00	6.50	3.00	104 Hans Lobert	8.00	6.50	3.00
45 Frank Demaree	8.00	6.50	3.00	105 Tom Long	8.00	6.50	3.00
46 Josh Devore	8.00	6.50	3.00	106 Fred Luderus	8.00	6.50	3.00
47 William Doak	8.00	6.50	3.00	107 Connie Mack	25.00	20.00	8.00
48 Bill Donovan	8.00	6.50	3.00	108 Lee Magee	8.00	6.50	3.00
49 Red Dooin	8.00	6.50	3.00	109 Sherry Magee	8.00	6.50	3.00
50 Mike Doolan	8.00	6.50	3.00	110 Al Mamaux	8.00	6.50	3.00
51 Larry Doyle	8.00	6.50	3.00	111 Leslie Mann	8.00	6.50	3.00
52 Jean Dubuc	8.00	6.50	3.00	112 Rabbit Maranville	13.50	10.00	4.00
53 Oscar J. Dugey	8.00	6.50	3.00	113 Rube Marquard	13.50	10.00	4.00
54 John Evers	15.00	12.00	5.00	114 J. E. Mayer	8.00	6.50	3.00
55 Red Faber	13.50	10.00	4.00	115 George McBride	8.00	6.50	3.00
56 Happy Felsch	8.00	6.50	3.00	116 John McGraw	20.00	15.00	6.00
57 Bill Fischer	8.00	6.50	3.00	117 Jack McInnis	8.00	6.50	3.00
58 Ray Fisher	8.00	6.50	3.00	118 Fred Merkle	8.00	6.50	3.00
59 Max Flack	8.00	6.50	3.00	119 Chief Meyers	8.00	6.50	3.00
60 Art Fletcher	8.00	6.50	3.00	120 Clyde Milan	8.00	6.50	3.00

	MINT	VG-E	F-G		MINT	VG-E	F-G
121 John Miller	8.00	6.50	3.00	161 Bob Shawkey	8.00	6.50	3.00
122 Otto Miller	8.00	6.50	3.00	162 Ernie Shore	8.00	6.50	3.00
123 Willie Mitchell	8.00	6.50	3.00	163 Bert Shotton	8.00	6.50	3.00
124 Fred Mollwitz	8.00	6.50	3.00	164 George Sisler	17.50	13.00	6.00
125 Pat Moran	8.00	6.50	3.00	165 J. C. Smith	8.00	6.50	3.00
126 Ray Morgan	8.00	6.50	3.00	166 Fred Snodgrass	8.00	6.50	3.00
127 George Moriarty	8.00	6.50	3.00	167 George Stallings	8.00	6.50	3.00
128 Guy Morton	8.00	6.50	3.00	168 Oscar Stanage	8.00	6.50	3.00
129 Mike Mowrey	8.00	6.50	3.00	169 Charles Stengel	30.00	24.00	10.00
130 Eddie Murphy	8.00	6.50	3.00	170 Milton Stock	8.00	6.50	3.00
131 Hy Myers	8.00	6.50	3.00	171 Amos Strunk	8.00	6.50	3.00
132 Bert Niehoff	8.00	6.50	3.00	172 Billy Sullivan	8.00	6.50	3.00
133 Rube Oldring	8.00	6.50	3.00	173 Jeff Tesreau	8.00	6.50	3.00
134 Oliver O'Mara	8.00	6.50	3.00	174 Joe Tinker	15.00	12.00	5.00
135 Steve O'Neill	8.00	6.50	3.00	175 Fred Toney	8.00	6.50	3.00
136 Dode Paskert	8.00	6.50	3.00	176 Terry Turner	8.00	6.50	3.00
137 R. Peckinpaugh	9.00	7.00	3.00	177 George Tyler	8.00	6.50	3.00
138 Walter Pipp	10.00	7.50	3.50	178 Jim Vaughn	8.00	6.50	3.00
139 Del Pratt	8.00	6.50	3.00	179 Bobby Veach	8.00	6.50	3.00
140 Pat Ragan	8.00	6.50	3.00	180 James Viox	8.00	6.50	3.00
141 Bill Rariden	8.00	6.50	3.00	181 Oscar Vitt	8.00	6.50	3.00
142 Eppa Rixey	13.50	10.00	4.00	182 Honus Wagner	40.00	30.00	12.00
143 Davey Robertson	8.00	6.50	3.00	183 Clarence Walker	8.00	6.50	3.00
144 Wilbert Robinson	13.50	10.00	4.00	184 Ed Walsh	13.50	10.00	4.00
145 Bob Roth	8.00	6.50	3.00	185 Bill Wambsganss	8.00	6.50	3.00
146 Eddie Roush	13.50	10.00	4.00	186 Buck Weaver	8.00	6.50	3.00
147 Clarence Rowland	8.00	6.50	3.00	187 Carl Weilman	8.00	6.50	3.00
148 Nap Rucker	8.00	6.50	3.00	188 Zack Wheat	13.50	10.00	4.00
149 Dick Rudolph	8.00	6.50	3.00	189 George Whitted	8.00	6.50	3.00
150 Reb Russell	8.00	6.50	3.00	190 Fred Williams	8.00	6.50	3.00
151 Babe Ruth	100.00	70.00	30.00	191 Arthur Wilson	8.00	6.50	3.00
152 Vic Saier	8.00	6.50	3.00	192 J. O. Wilson	8.00	6.50	3.00
153 Slim Sallee	8.00	6.50	3.00	193 Ivy Wingo	8.00	6.50	3.00
154 Ray Schalk	13.50	10.00	4.00	194 Meldon Wolfgang	8.00	6.50	3.00
155 Wally Schang	8.00	6.50	3.00	195 Joe Wood	10.00	7.50	3.50
156 Frank Schulte	8.00	6.50	3.00	196 Steve Yerkes	8.00	6.50	3.00
157 Everett Scott	8.00	6.50	3.00	197 Pep Young	8.00	6.50	3.00
158 Jim Scott	8.00	6.50	3.00	198 Rollie Zeider	8.00	6.50	3.00
159 Tom Seaton	8.00	6.50	3.00	199 Heine Zimmerman	8.00	6.50	3.00
160 Howard Shanks	8.00	6.50	3.00	200 Dutch Zwilling	8.00	6.50	3.00

M101-2 SPORTING NEWS SUPPLEMENT OFFER

1916 M101-5 SPORTING NEWS (200)   1 5/8" X 3"

"MEL" WOLFGANG
P.—Chicago White Sox
195

The 1916 M101-5 series of 200 black & white, numbered baseball cards is essentially an updated version of M101-4. The set was offered as a marketing promotion by C.C. Spink & Son, publishers of The Sporting News ("The Baseball Paper of the World").

		MINT	VG-E	F-G			MINT	VG-E	F-G
	COMPLETE SET	1700.00	1200.00	600.00	61	Art Fletcher	7.50	6.00	3.00
	COMMON PLAYER	7.50	6.00	3.00	62	Eddie Foster	7.50	6.00	3.00
					63	Jacques Fournier	7.50	6.00	3.00
1	Babe Adams	7.50	6.00	3.00	64	Del Gainer	7.50	6.00	3.00
2	Sam Agnew	7.50	6.00	3.00	65	Larry Gardner	7.50	6.00	3.00
3	Ed Ainsmith	7.50	6.00	3.00	66	Joe Gedeon	7.50	6.00	3.00
4	Grover Alexander	20.00	15.00	7.00	67	Gus Getz	7.50	6.00	3.00
5	Leon Ames	7.50	6.00	3.00	68	George Gibson	7.50	6.00	3.00
6	Jimmy Archer	7.50	6.00	3.00	69	Wilbur Good	7.50	6.00	3.00
7	Jimmy Austin	7.50	6.00	3.00	70	Hank Gowdy	7.50	6.00	3.00
8	Frank Baker	13.50	10.00	4.00	71	Jack Graney	7.50	6.00	3.00
9	Dave Bancroft	13.50	10.00	4.00	72	Tommy Griffith	7.50	6.00	3.00
10	Jack Barry	7.50	6.00	3.00	73	Heinie Groh	7.50	6.00	3.00
11	Zinn Beck	7.50	6.00	3.00	74	Earl Hamilton	7.50	6.00	3.00
12	Luke Boone	7.50	6.00	3.00	75	Unknown	xxxx	xxxx	xxxx
13	Joe Benz	7.50	6.00	3.00	76	Roy Hartzell	7.50	6.00	3.00
14	Bob Bescher	7.50	6.00	3.00	77	Claude Hendrix	7.50	6.00	3.00
15	Al Betzel	7.50	6.00	3.00	78	Olaf Henriksen	7.50	6.00	3.00
16	Roger Bresnahan	13.50	10.00	4.00	79	John Henry	7.50	6.00	3.00
17	Eddie Burns	7.50	6.00	3.00	80	Buck Herzog	7.50	6.00	3.00
18	G. J. Burns	7.50	6.00	3.00	81	Hugh High	7.50	6.00	3.00
19	Joe Bush	7.50	6.00	3.00	82	Dick Hoblitzell	7.50	6.00	3.00
20	Owen Bush	7.50	6.00	3.00	83	Harry Hooper	13.50	10.00	4.00
21	Art Butler	7.50	6.00	3.00	84	Ivan Howard	7.50	6.00	3.00
22	Bobby Byrne	7.50	6.00	3.00	85	Miller Huggins	13.50	10.00	4.00
23	Mordecai Brown	13.50	10.00	4.00	86	Joe Jackson	25.00	20.00	8.00
24	Jimmy Callahan	7.50	6.00	3.00	87	William James	7.50	6.00	3.00
25	Ray Caldwell	7.50	6.00	3.00	88	Harold Janvrin	7.50	6.00	3.00
26	Max Carey	13.50	10.00	4.00	89	Hughie Jennings	13.50	10.00	4.00
27	George Chalmers	7.50	6.00	3.00	90	Walter Johnson	30.00	25.00	10.00
28	Frank Chance	17.50	13.00	6.00	91	Fielder Jones	7.50	6.00	3.00
29	Ray Chapman	7.50	6.00	3.00	92	Benny Kauff	7.50	6.00	3.00
30	Larry Cheney	7.50	6.00	3.00	93	Bill Killefer	7.50	6.00	3.00
31	Ed Cicotte	7.50	6.00	3.00	94	Ed Konetchy	7.50	6.00	3.00
32	Tommy Clarke	7.50	6.00	3.00	95	Unknown	xxxx	xxxx	xxxx
33	Unknown	xxxx	xxxx	xxxx	96	Jack Lapp	7.50	6.00	3.00
34	Shano Collins	7.50	6.00	3.00	97	John Lavan	7.50	6.00	3.00
35	Charles Comiskey	13.50	10.00	4.00	98	Jimmy Lavender	7.50	6.00	3.00
36	Joe Connolly	7.50	6.00	3.00	99	Nemo Leibold	7.50	6.00	3.00
37	L. Cook	7.50	6.00	3.00	100	Hub Leonard	7.50	6.00	3.00
38	Jack Coombs	7.50	6.00	3.00	101	Duffy Lewis	7.50	6.00	3.00
39	Costello	7.50	6.00	3.00	102	Hans Lobert	7.50	6.00	3.00
40	Harry Covaleskie	7.50	6.00	3.00	103	Tom Long	7.50	6.00	3.00
41	Gavvy Cravath	7.50	6.00	3.00	104	Fred Luderus	7.50	6.00	3.00
42	Sam Crawford	13.50	10.00	4.00	105	Connie Mack	17.50	13.00	6.00
43	Jean Dale	7.50	6.00	3.00	106	Lee Magee	7.50	6.00	3.00
44	Jake Daubert	7.50	6.00	3.00	107	Al Mamaux	7.50	6.00	3.00
45	G. A. Davis, Jr.	7.50	6.00	3.00	108	Leslie Mann	7.50	6.00	3.00
46	Charles Deal	7.50	6.00	3.00	109	Rabbit Maranville	13.50	10.00	4.00
47	Frank Demaree	7.50	6.00	3.00	110	Rube Marquard	13.50	10.00	4.00
48	Bill Doak	7.50	6.00	3.00	111	Armando Marsans	7.50	6.00	3.00
49	Bill Donovan	7.50	6.00	3.00	112	J. E. Mayer	7.50	6.00	3.00
50	Red Dooin	7.50	6.00	3.00	113	George McBride	7.50	6.00	3.00
51	Mike Doolan	7.50	6.00	3.00	114	John McGraw	17.50	13.00	6.00
52	Larry Doyle	7.50	6.00	3.00	115	Jack McInnis	7.50	6.00	3.00
53	Jean Dubuc	7.50	6.00	3.00	116	Fred Merkle	7.50	6.00	3.00
54	Oscar Dugey	7.50	6.00	3.00	117	Chief Meyers	7.50	6.00	3.00
55	John Evers	15.00	12.00	5.00	118	Clyde Milan	7.50	6.00	3.00
56	Red Faber	13.50	10.00	4.00	119	Otto Miller	7.50	6.00	3.00
57	Happy Felsch	7.50	6.00	3.00	120	Willie Mitchell	7.50	6.00	3.00
58	Bill Fischer	7.50	6.00	3.00	121	Fred Mollwitz	7.50	6.00	3.00
59	Ray Fisher	7.50	6.00	3.00	122	J. H. Moran	7.50	6.00	3.00
60	Max Flack	7.50	6.00	3.00	123	Pat Moran	7.50	6.00	3.00

M101-5 (CONTINUED)

	MINT	VG-E	F-G			MINT	VG-E	F-G
124 Ray Morgan	7.50	6.00	3.00	162 Howard Shanks		7.50	6.00	3.00
125 George Moriarty	7.50	6.00	3.00	163 Bob Shawkey		7.50	6.00	3.00
126 Guy Morton	7.50	6.00	3.00	164 Ernie Shore		7.50	6.00	3.00
127 Eddie Murphy	7.50	6.00	3.00	165 Bert Shotton		7.50	6.00	3.00
128 Jack Murray	7.50	6.00	3.00	166 George Sisler		17.50	13.00	6.00
129 Hy Myers	7.50	6.00	3.00	167 J. C. Smith		7.50	6.00	3.00
130 Bert Niehoff	7.50	6.00	3.00	168 Fred Snodgrass		7.50	6.00	3.00
131 Les Nunamaker	7.50	6.00	3.00	169 George Stallings		7.50	6.00	3.00
132 Rube Oldring	7.50	6.00	3.00	170 Oscar Stanage		7.50	6.00	3.00
133 Oliver O'Mara	7.50	6.00	3.00	171 Charles Stengel		25.00	20.00	8.00
134 Steve O'Neill	7.50	6.00	3.00	172 Milton Stock		7.50	6.00	3.00
135 Dode Paskert	7.50	6.00	3.00	173 Amos Strunk		7.50	6.00	3.00
136 R. Peckinpaugh	7.50	6.00	3.00	174 Billy Sullivan		7.50	6.00	3.00
137 E. J. Pfeffer	7.50	6.00	3.00	175 Jeff Tesreau		7.50	6.00	3.00
138 G. Pierce	7.50	6.00	3.00	176 Jim Thorpe		60.00	50.00	20.00
139 Walter Pipp	9.00	7.00	3.00	177 Joe Tinker		15.00	12.00	5.00
140 Del Pratt	7.50	6.00	3.00	178 Fred Toney		7.50	6.00	3.00
141 Bill Rariden	7.50	6.00	3.00	179 Terry Turner		7.50	6.00	3.00
142 Eppa Rixey	13.50	10.00	4.00	180 Jim Vaughn		7.50	6.00	3.00
143 Davey Robertson	7.50	6.00	3.00	181 Bobby Veach		7.50	6.00	3.00
144 Wilbert Robinson	13.50	10.00	4.00	182 James Viox		7.50	6.00	3.00
145 Bob Roth	7.50	6.00	3.00	183 Oscar Vitt		7.50	6.00	3.00
146 Ed Roush	13.50	10.00	4.00	184 Honus Wagner		30.00	25.00	10.00
147 Clarence Rowland	7.50	6.00	3.00	185 Clarence Walker		7.50	6.00	3.00
148 Nap Rucker	7.50	6.00	3.00	186 Zack Wheat		13.50	10.00	4.00
149 Dick Rudolph	7.50	6.00	3.00	187 Ed Walsh		13.50	10.00	4.00
150 Reb Russell	7.50	6.00	3.00	188 Buck Weaver		7.50	6.00	3.00
151 Babe Ruth	100.00	70.00	30.00	189 Carl Weilman		7.50	6.00	3.00
152 Vic Saier	7.50	6.00	3.00	190 George Whitted		7.50	6.00	3.00
153 Slim Sallee	7.50	6.00	3.00	191 Fred Williams		7.50	6.00	3.00
154 'Germany' Schaefer	7.50	6.00	3.00	192 Arthur Wilson		7.50	6.00	3.00
155 Ray Schalk	13.50	10.00	4.00	193 J. O. Wilson		7.50	6.00	3.00
156 Wally Schang	7.50	6.00	3.00	194 Ivy Wingo		7.50	6.00	3.00
157 Chas. Schmidt	7.50	6.00	3.00	195 Meldon Wolfgang		7.50	6.00	3.00
158 Frank Schulte	7.50	6.00	3.00	196 Joe Wood		7.50	6.00	3.00
159 Jim Scott	7.50	6.00	3.00	197 Steve Yerkes		7.50	6.00	3.00
160 Everett Scott	7.50	6.00	3.00	198 Unknown		xxxx	xxxx	xxxx
161 Tom Seaton	7.50	6.00	3.00	199 Heinie Zimmerman		7.50	6.00	3.00
				200 Dutch Zwilling		7.50	6.00	3.00

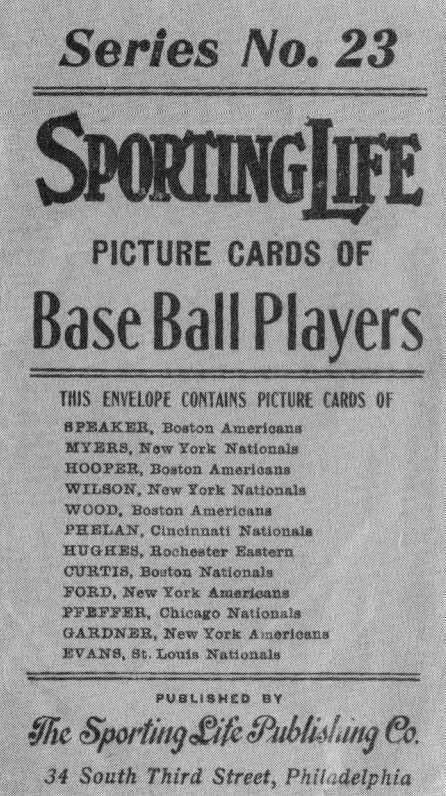

M116 ENVELOPE

1911 M116 SPORTING LIFE (288)

1 1/2" X 2 5/8"

 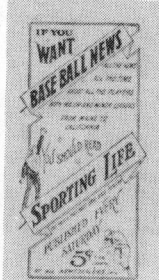 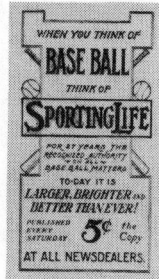

This Sporting Life set of 288 cards was offered as a premium to the publication's subscribers in 1911. Each of the 24 series of 12 cards came in an envelope printed with a list of the players within. Cards marked with an asterisk are also found with a special blue background and are worth double the listed price. McConnell appears with both Boston, A.L. (common) and Chicago White Sox (scarce); McQuillan appears with Phillies (common) and Cincinnati (scarce).

	MINT	VG-E	F-G		MINT	VG-E	F-G
COMPLETE SET	3600.00	2800.00	1200.00	61 T. Jones	12.50	9.00	4.00
COMMON PLAYER	12.50	9.00	4.00	62 Lathers	12.50	9.00	4.00
				63 McIntyre	12.50	9.00	4.00
1 Arellanes	12.50	9.00	4.00	64 Moriarty	12.50	9.00	4.00
2 Carrigan	12.50	9.00	4.00	65 Mullin	12.50	9.00	4.00
3 Cicotte	12.50	9.00	4.00	66 Pernell	12.50	9.00	4.00
4 Ray Collins	12.50	9.00	4.00	67 O'Leary	12.50	9.00	4.00
5 Donahue	12.50	9.00	4.00	68 Schmidt	12.50	9.00	4.00
6 Donovan	12.50	9.00	4.00	69 Stanage	12.50	9.00	4.00
7 Engle	12.50	9.00	4.00	70 Stroud	12.50	9.00	4.00
8 L. Gardner	12.50	9.00	4.00	71 Summers	12.50	9.00	4.00
9 Hall	12.50	9.00	4.00	72 Willett	12.50	9.00	4.00
10 Hooper, Harry	20.00	15.00	6.50	73 Works	12.50	9.00	4.00
11 Karger	12.50	9.00	4.00	74 Austin	12.50	9.00	4.00
12 Harry Lord*	12.50	9.00	4.00	75 Chase*	12.50	9.00	4.00
13 Madden	12.50	9.00	4.00	76 Cree	12.50	9.00	4.00
14 McConnell(2)	12.50	9.00	4.00	77 Criger	12.50	9.00	4.00
15 Speaker	25.00	18.50	8.75	78 Ford	12.50	9.00	4.00
16 Stahl	12.50	9.00	4.00	79 Gardner	12.50	9.00	4.00
17 Thoney	12.50	9.00	4.00	80 Knight	12.50	9.00	4.00
18 Wagner, Heine	12.50	9.00	4.00	81 LaPorte	12.50	9.00	4.00
19 Wood	12.50	9.00	4.00	82 Stallings	12.50	9.00	4.00
20 Blackburn	12.50	9.00	4.00	83 Sweeney	12.50	9.00	4.00
21 Block	12.50	9.00	4.00	84 Wolter	12.50	9.00	4.00
22 Dougherty	12.50	9.00	4.00	85 Atkins	12.50	9.00	4.00
23 Hugh Duffy	20.00	15.00	6.50	86 Baker	20.00	15.00	6.50
24 Hahn	12.50	9.00	4.00	87 Barry	12.50	9.00	4.00
25 Parent	12.50	9.00	4.00	88 Bender*	20.00	15.00	6.50
26 Payne	12.50	9.00	4.00	89 E. Collins*	20.00	15.00	6.50
27 Purtell	12.50	9.00	4.00	90 Coombs	12.50	9.00	4.00
28 Meloan	12.50	9.00	4.00	91 H. Davis*	12.50	9.00	4.00
29 Scott	12.50	9.00	4.00	92 Dygert	12.50	9.00	4.00
30 F. Smith	12.50	9.00	4.00	93 Heitmuller	12.50	9.00	4.00
31 Sullivan	12.50	9.00	4.00	94 Hartsel	12.50	9.00	4.00
32 Tannehill	12.50	9.00	4.00	95 Krause	12.50	9.00	4.00
33 Walsh, Ed	20.00	15.00	6.50	96 Lapp	12.50	9.00	4.00
34 White	12.50	9.00	4.00	97 Livingstone	12.50	9.00	4.00
35 I. Young	12.50	9.00	4.00	98 Connie Mack	25.00	18.50	8.75
36 Zwilling	12.50	9.00	4.00	99 McInnes	12.50	9.00	4.00
37 Bemis	12.50	9.00	4.00	100 Morgan	12.50	9.00	4.00
38 Berger	12.50	9.00	4.00	101 Murphy	12.50	9.00	4.00
39 Birmingham	12.50	9.00	4.00	102 Oldring	12.50	9.00	4.00
40 Bradley	12.50	9.00	4.00	103 Plank, Eddie	25.00	18.50	8.75
41 Clarke	12.50	9.00	4.00	104 Strunk	12.50	9.00	4.00
42 Falkenberg	12.50	9.00	4.00	105 Thomas*	12.50	9.00	4.00
43 Flick, Elmer	20.00	15.00	6.50	106 Bailey	12.50	9.00	4.00
44 Joss. Addie	25.00	18.50	8.75	107 Criss	12.50	9.00	4.00
45 Lajoie*	30.00	22.50	10.50	108 Graham	12.50	9.00	4.00
46 Linke	12.50	9.00	4.00	109 Hartzell	12.50	9.00	4.00
47 B. Lord	12.50	9.00	4.00	110 Hoffman	12.50	9.00	4.00
48 McGuire	12.50	9.00	4.00	111 Howell	12.50	9.00	4.00
49 Niles	12.50	9.00	4.00	112 Lake	12.50	9.00	4.00
50 Stovall	12.50	9.00	4.00	113 O'Conner	12.50	9.00	4.00
51 Turner	12.50	9.00	4.00	114 Pelty	12.50	9.00	4.00
52 Cy Young	30.00	22.50	10.50	115 Powell	12.50	9.00	4.00
53 Beckendorf	12.50	9.00	4.00	116 Schweitzer	12.50	9.00	4.00
54 Bush	12.50	9.00	4.00	117 Stephens	12.50	9.00	4.00
55 Ty Cobb*	100.00	70.00	30.00	118 Stone	12.50	9.00	4.00
56 Crawford*	20.00	15.00	6.50	119 Waddell	25.00	18.50	8.75
57 Jas. Delehanty	12.50	9.00	4.00	120 Wallace	20.00	15.00	6.50
58 W. Donovan*	12.50	9.00	4.00	121 Conroy	12.50	9.00	4.00
59 Jennings*	20.00	15.00	6.50	122 Elberfeld	12.50	9.00	4.00
60 D. Jones	12.50	9.00	4.00	123 Foster	12.50	9.00	4.00

		MINT	VG-E	F-G			MINT	VG-E	F-G
124	Gessler	12.50	9.00	4.00	206	Crandall	12.50	9.00	4.00
125	Johnson	50.00	38.00	17.00	207	Devlin	12.50	9.00	4.00
126	Killifer	12.50	9.00	4.00	208	Devore	12.50	9.00	4.00
127	McAleer	12.50	9.00	4.00	209	Doyle*	12.50	9.00	4.00
128	McBride	12.50	9.00	4.00	210	Fletcher	12.50	9.00	4.00
129	Milan	12.50	9.00	4.00	211	Mathewson, Christy	40.00	30.00	13.00
130	Miller	12.50	9.00	4.00	212	McGraw, John	30.00	22.50	10.50
131	Reisling	12.50	9.00	4.00	213	Merkle	12.50	9.00	4.00
132	Schaefer	12.50	9.00	4.00	214	Murray	12.50	9.00	4.00
133	Street	12.50	9.00	4.00	215	Myers	12.50	9.00	4.00
134	Unglaub	12.50	9.00	4.00	216	Raymond	12.50	9.00	4.00
135	Beck	12.50	9.00	4.00	217	Schlei	12.50	9.00	4.00
136	Brown	12.50	9.00	4.00	218	Seymour	12.50	9.00	4.00
137	Curtis	12.50	9.00	4.00	219	Shafer	12.50	9.00	4.00
138	Ferguson	12.50	9.00	4.00	220	Snodgrass	12.50	9.00	4.00
139	Frock	12.50	9.00	4.00	221	Tenney*	12.50	9.00	4.00
140	Graham	12.50	9.00	4.00	222	Wilson	12.50	9.00	4.00
141	Herzog	12.50	9.00	4.00	223	G. Wiltse	12.50	9.00	4.00
142	Lake	12.50	9.00	4.00	224	Bates	12.50	9.00	4.00
143	Sharpe	12.50	9.00	4.00	225	Bransfeld	12.50	9.00	4.00
144	Shean	12.50	9.00	4.00	226	Dooin*	12.50	9.00	4.00
145	C. Smith	12.50	9.00	4.00	227	Doolan	12.50	9.00	4.00
146	H. Smith	12.50	9.00	4.00	228	Ewing	12.50	9.00	4.00
147	Sweeney	12.50	9.00	4.00	229	Foxen	12.50	9.00	4.00
148	Barger	12.50	9.00	4.00	230	Grant	12.50	9.00	4.00
149	Bell	12.50	9.00	4.00	231	Jacklitsch	12.50	9.00	4.00
150	Bergen	12.50	9.00	4.00	232	Knabe	12.50	9.00	4.00
151	Burch	12.50	9.00	4.00	233	Magee	12.50	9.00	4.00
152	Dahlen	12.50	9.00	4.00	234	McQuillan* (2)	12.50	9.00	4.00
153	Davidson	12.50	9.00	4.00	235	Moore	12.50	9.00	4.00
154	Dessau	12.50	9.00	4.00	236	Moran	12.50	9.00	4.00
155	Erwin	12.50	9.00	4.00	237	Moren	12.50	9.00	4.00
156	Hummel	12.50	9.00	4.00	238	Paskert	12.50	9.00	4.00
157	Hunter	12.50	9.00	4.00	239	Schettler	12.50	9.00	4.00
158	Jordan*	12.50	9.00	4.00	240	Sparks	12.50	9.00	4.00
159	Lennox	12.50	9.00	4.00	241	Titus	12.50	9.00	4.00
160	McElveen	12.50	9.00	4.00	242	Walsh (2)	12.50	9.00	4.00
161	McMillan	12.50	9.00	4.00	243	Abbaticchio	12.50	9.00	4.00
162	Rucker	12.50	9.00	4.00	244	Adams	12.50	9.00	4.00
163	Scanlon	12.50	9.00	4.00	245	Byrne	12.50	9.00	4.00
164	Wilhelm	12.50	9.00	4.00	246	Camnitz	12.50	9.00	4.00
165	Archer	12.50	9.00	4.00	247	Campbell	12.50	9.00	4.00
166	Beaumont	12.50	9.00	4.00	248	Clarke	20.00	15.00	6.50
167	M. Brown*	20.00	15.00	6.50	249	Flynn	12.50	9.00	4.00
168	Chance*	25.00	18.50	8.75	250	Gibson*	12.50	9.00	4.00
169	Evers	20.00	15.00	6.50	251	Hyatt	12.50	9.00	4.00
170	Hofman	12.50	9.00	4.00	252	Leach*	12.50	9.00	4.00
171	Kane	12.50	9.00	4.00	253	Leever	12.50	9.00	4.00
172	Kling	12.50	9.00	4.00	254	Leifield	12.50	9.00	4.00
173	Kroh	12.50	9.00	4.00	255	Maddox	12.50	9.00	4.00
174	McIntire	12.50	9.00	4.00	256	Miller	12.50	9.00	4.00
175	Needham	12.50	9.00	4.00	257	O'Conner	12.50	9.00	4.00
176	Overall	12.50	9.00	4.00	258	Phillipe	12.50	9.00	4.00
177	Pfeffer	12.50	9.00	4.00	259	Simon	12.50	9.00	4.00
178	Pfiester	12.50	9.00	4.00	260	Hans Wagner*	50.00	38.00	17.00
179	Reulbach	12.50	9.00	4.00	261	Wilson	12.50	9.00	4.00
180	L. Richie	12.50	9.00	4.00	262	Bliss	12.50	9.00	4.00
181	Schulte	12.50	9.00	4.00	263	Bresnahan, Roger	20.00	15.00	6.50
182	Sheckard	12.50	9.00	4.00	264	Bachman	12.50	9.00	4.00
183	Steinfeldt	12.50	9.00	4.00	265	Corridon	12.50	9.00	4.00
184	Tinker	20.00	15.00	6.50	266	Demmitt	12.50	9.00	4.00
185	Zimmerman	12.50	9.00	4.00	267	Ellis	12.50	9.00	4.00
186	Beebe	12.50	9.00	4.00	268	Evans	12.50	9.00	4.00
187	Boscher	12.50	9.00	4.00	269	Harmon	12.50	9.00	4.00
188	Charles	12.50	9.00	4.00	270	Huggins	20.00	15.00	6.50
189	Clarke	12.50	9.00	4.00	271	Hulswitt	12.50	9.00	4.00
190	Downey	12.50	9.00	4.00	272	Konetchy	12.50	9.00	4.00
191	Doyle	12.50	9.00	4.00	273	Lush	12.50	9.00	4.00
192	Eagan	12.50	9.00	4.00	274	Mattern	12.50	9.00	4.00
193	Fromme	12.50	9.00	4.00	275	Mowery	12.50	9.00	4.00
194	Gaspar	12.50	9.00	4.00	276	Oakes	12.50	9.00	4.00
195	Griffith	20.00	15.00	6.50	277	Phelps	12.50	9.00	4.00
196	Hoblitzel	12.50	9.00	4.00	278	Sallee	12.50	9.00	4.00
197	Lobert	12.50	9.00	4.00	279	Willis	12.50	9.00	4.00
198	McLean	12.50	9.00	4.00	280	Coveleskie	40.00	30.00	13.00
199	Mitchell	12.50	9.00	4.00	281	Foster	25.00	18.50	8.75
200	Phelan	12.50	9.00	4.00	282	Frill	25.00	18.50	8.75
201	Rowan	12.50	9.00	4.00	283	Hughes	25.00	18.50	8.75
202	Space	12.50	9.00	4.00	284	Krueger	25.00	18.50	8.75
203	Suggs	12.50	9.00	4.00	285	Mitchell	25.00	18.50	8.75
204	Ames	12.50	9.00	4.00	286	O'Hara	25.00	18.50	8.75
205	Bridwell	12.50	9.00	4.00	287	Perring	25.00	18.50	8.75
					288	Ray	25.00	18.50	8.75

1969 NABISCO TEAM FLAKES (24)

1 15/16″ X 3″
1 3/4″ X 2 15/16″

Frank Robinson — OF
Baltimore Orioles

Frank Robinson — OF
Baltimore Orioles

The 1969 Nabisco Team Flakes set of 24 full color, blank backed, unnumbered cards was issued in three different panels of eight cards each. These cards are identified by a yellow border and the lack of a team insignia. The cards exist in two sizes (1 15/16″ X 3″ and 1 3/4″ X 2 15/16″) distinguished by the widths of the yellow border. The SCB designation is F275-34.

	MINT	VG-E	F-G
COMPLETE SET	175.00	125.00	50.00
COMMON PLAYER	4.00	3.00	1.40
1 Hank Aaron	20.00	15.00	6.50
2 Richie Allen	5.00	3.75	1.75
3 Lou Brock	15.00	11.00	5.00
4 Paul Casanova	4.00	3.00	1.40
5 Roberto Clemente	18.00	13.50	6.00
6 Al Ferrara	4.00	3.00	1.40
7 Bill Freehan	5.00	3.75	1.75
8 Jim Fregosi	6.00	4.50	2.00
9 Bob Gibson	10.00	7.00	3.00
10 Tony Horton	6.00	4.50	2.00
11 Tommy John	6.00	4.50	2.00
12 Al Kaline	15.00	11.00	5.00

	MINT	VG-E	F-G
13 Jim Lonborg	4.00	3.00	1.40
14 Juan Marichal	6.00	4.50	2.00
15 Willie Mays	20.00	15.00	6.50
16 Rick Monday	4.00	3.00	1.40
17 Tony Oliva	6.00	4.50	2.00
18 Brooks Robinson	15.00	11.00	5.00
19 Frank Robinson	12.00	8.75	4.00
20 Pete Rose	20.00	15.00	6.50
21 Ron Santo	5.00	3.75	1.75
22 Tom Seaver	15.00	11.00	5.00
23 Rusty Staub	6.00	4.50	2.00
24 Mel Stottlemyre	4.00	3.00	1.40

1952 NUM NUM (20)

3 1/2″ X 4 1/2″

#10—Al Rosen

Born in Spartanburg, South Carolina, March 1, 1925. Bats and throws right handed. Height: 5'11". Weight: 185 lbs. Black hair and blue eyes. Jewish ancestry. Single. Winter home: Miami Beach, Florida.

A graduate of University of Miami, he starred in basketball and football as well as baseball . . . also was once Florida State middleweight boxing champion . . . spends off season as good will ambassador for nationally known brewery . . . plays golf as often as possible . . . one of most aggressive ball players, he's also considered one of keenest students of the game . . . earned host of minor league honors before reaching majors . . . chosen Rookie of the Year by SPORT Magazine in 1950, but was ineligible for other similar awards . . . is excellent speaker and has great future in radio and television . . . played against his present manager as member of Kansas City club in 1948 . . . first American League rookie to lead circuit in homers since 1915, he also set all-time record for right handed Cleveland batter.

The 1952 Num Num Potato Chips issue features 20 black and white, numbered cards of the Cleveland Indians. Cards came with and without coupons (tabs). The cards were issued without coupons directly by the Cleveland baseball club. When the complete set was obtained the tabs were cut off and exchanged for an autographed baseball. Card No. 16, Kennedy, is rather scarce. Cards with the tabs still intact are worth approximately 20% more than the values listed below. The ACC designation is F337-2.

—Al Rosen   Save these tabs. When you have completed the entire set (pictures 1 to 20) return the set of 20 to NUM NUM Foods, and you will get an official American League Baseball—autographed by your favorite Cleveland player. (Cut tab along the dotted line.) OFFER EXPIRES SEPTEMBER 14, 1952.

NUM NUM FOODS, INC., 4180 Lorain, Cleveland 13, Ohio
Gentlemen: I am enclosing a complete set of tabs (1 to 20).
Send official league ball autographed by.....................
(insert name of player)
NAME.....................
ADDRESS.....................
CITY.....................

	MINT	VG-E	F-G
COMPLETE SET	350.00	260.00	120.00
COMMON PLAYER	13.00	10.00	4.50
Lou Brissie	13.00	10.00	4.50
Jim Hegan	13.00	10.00	4.50
Birdie Tebbetts	13.00	10.00	4.50
Bob Lemon	30.00	22.50	10.50
Bob Feller	40.00	30.00	13.00
Early Wynn	30.00	22.50	10.50
Mike Garcia	13.00	10.00	4.50
Steve Gromek	13.00	10.00	4.50
Bob Chakales	13.00	10.00	4.50
Al Rosen	30.00	22.50	10.50

	MINT	VG-E	F-G
11 Dick Rozek	13.00	10.00	4.50
12 Luke Easter	15.00	11.00	5.00
13 Ray Boone	13.00	10.00	4.50
14 Bobby Avila	13.00	10.00	4.50
15 Dale Mitchell	13.00	10.00	4.50
16 Bob Kennedy	150.00	110.00	50.00
17 Harry Simpson	13.00	10.00	4.50
18 Larry Doby	25.00	18.50	8.75
19 Sam Jones	13.00	10.00	4.50
20 Al Lopez	25.00	18.50	8.75

The authors have often been asked "Who has the best baseball card collection in the country?" Such a question is all but impossible to answer. Does one mean "Who has the most cards?" —certainly there are many dealers with millions of cards. Does one mean "Who has the most different cards?" —low quality (condition) cards, collector issues and other non-legitimate issue cards, and pseudo-cards (proof cards, blank-back cards, wrong back cards, reprints) could quite easily increase the sheer number of cards in anyone's collection. Does one mean "Who has the most valuable collection?", "the collection in the best condition?", "the oldest collection?" The question itself is too broad to answer. Beginning with this issue, the Price Guide will focus on a prominent collector each year, and present how this collector enjoys his hobby.

Barry Halper is a successful New Jersey businessman and partner in the Halper Bros. Paper Company of Elizabeth, NJ. His sports-related activities include being a partner in the New York Yankees Baseball Club. While he has been a baseball fan all his life and a collector since he was eight years old, his serious baseball memorabilia interest began but seven years ago. We emphasize memorabilia rather than the more narrow area of baseball cards, as cards are but a part of Barry's collection. Like many of us under the day-to-day turmoil of our occupations, Barry has found the hobby therapeutic and a panacea for daily tensions.

Certainly a nominee for the nebulous title of owner of best collection, Barry has done much more than just accumulate baseball memorabilia. He has designed and built a striking memorial to the history of baseball in the lower level of his own home. His card collection is priceless and numbers, among others, the page of highly valuable and scarce individual cards presented on one of the color pages of this book. A devout Yankee fan and ardent admirer of Babe Ruth and Lou Gehrig, he has many scrapbooks and albums on both men, each containing many unique and historically-significant items. The page of Ruth cards in the color section are from Barry's collection. His Ruth collection contains the Babe's first numbered uniform (1929) and his last uniform, a 1938 Dodger outfit which Babe wore as a coach. Other Yankee uniforms include those of Joe DiMaggio, Mickey Mantle, Casey Stengel and Yogi Berra.

His world series press-pin (see color insert) and all-star press-pin collection is comparable to any in the country, as he has almost every legitimate press pin issued. A complete run of black World Series and All-Star game bats, a complete run of baseball Hartland statues, colorful advertising pieces from the turn of the century through modern times, and many one-of-a-kind baseball antiques are features of the Halper collection. Yet for all the items in his collection, the most impressive and striking aspect of the Halper household is the way in which these items, —whether large or small, valuable or inexpensive; whether a piece of history or merely a piece of curiosity— are displayed. Rather than attempt to describe the appearance in words, the next several pages provide a visual idea of how one man, Barry Halper, chooses to enjoy his hobby.

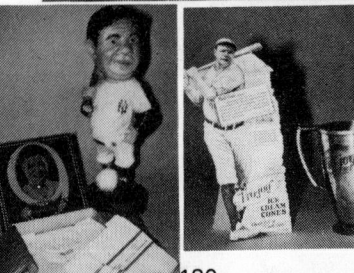

CLOCKWISE FROM ABOVE— (1) BARRY LEAVING ROOM WEARING OVERCOAT ONCE OWNED BY BABE RUTH. (2) RUTH'S UNIFORM, DUFFLE BAG, GLOVE, TWO OF HIS BATS AND FIVE BALLS AUTOGRAPHED BY THE BABE. (3) BARRY AND WIFE SHARON FLANK LIFE-SIZE WAX FIGURE OF RUTH OB-TAINED FROM MADAM TOU... MUSEUM IN LONDON. (4) ...JOY ICE CREAM AD FEAT... RUTH AND A FRO—JOY C... BOX OF BABE RUTH UNDE... AND CERAMIC STATUE P... TO LOOK LIKE RUTH.

RS. HALPER RECLINING ON
LOVE SEAT.

GEHRIG MEMORABILIA INCLUDING
LOU'S LAST GLOVE, AUTO-
GRAPHED BALL, BASEBALL CARDS
AND OFFICIAL COMMUNICATIONS
CONCERNING GEHRIG.

RACK OF BLACK WORLD SERIES
AND ALL-STAR BATS, ASSORTED
GLOVES AND UNIFORMS.

CIRCA 1910 TY COBB CUT PLUG
TOBACCO TIN AND 1930'S BABE
RUTH INSTRUCTIONAL FLIP BOOK.

BARRY AND SHARON WITH ORIGI-
NAL CONDITION BALLY BAMBINO
PIN BALL MACHINE.

CONTAINING HARTLAND
S, AND BALLS AUTO-
D BY PLAYERS DEPICTED
TUES. CASE IS LINED WITH
URF.

THE HALPER FAMILY—STEVE,
BARRY, SHARON (MRS. HALPER)
HOLDING JASON, AND MARNIE
(KNEELING). THE BABE RUTH
PLAZA SIGN ON THE PATIO WALL
WAS ORIGINALLY PART OF
YANKEE STADIUM BEFORE ITS
RENOVATION.

BARRY POURING OVER DRAWERS
CONTAINING PLASTIC SHEETS
FILLED WITH BASEBALL CARDS.

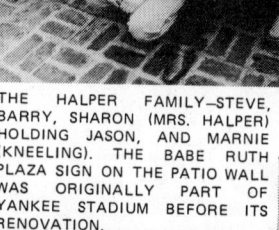

CIRCA 1951 PHOTO OF JOE D. AND
TED WILLIAMS FLANKING AN UN-
KNOWN YOUNGSTER.

LEFT: BARRY AND SON STEVE
HAM IT UP WITH THEIR FAVOR-
ITE LITERATURE.

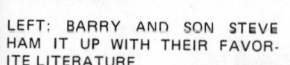

CASE CONTAINING BLACK WORLD
SERIES BATS. OTHER WORLD
SERIES BATS PICTURED ABOVE.

1960 NU-CARD BASEBALL HI-LITES (72) 3 1/4″ X 5 3/8″

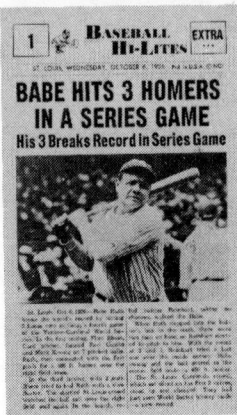

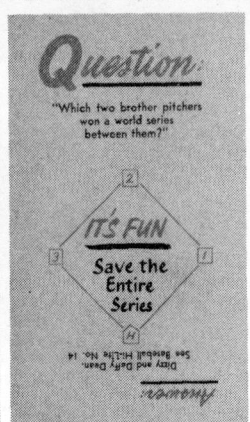

In 1960, the Nu-Card Company introduced its Baseball Hi-Lites set of 72 newspaper style cards. Each card singled out an individual baseball achievement with a picture and story. The reverses contain a baseball quiz. Cards 1-18 are more valuable if found printed totally in black on the front. They are copyrighted CVC as opposed to the NCI designation on red-and-black printed fronts.

	MINT	VG-E	F-G
COMPLETE SET	110.00	80.00	35.00
COMMON PLAYER	1.00	.75	.30
1 Babe Hits 3 Homers In A Series Game	6.00	4.50	2.00
2 Podres Pitching Wins Series	1.00	.75	.30
3 Bevans Pitches No Hitter, Almost	1.00	.75	.30
4 Box Score Devised By Reporter	1.00	.75	.30
5 VanderMeer Pitches 2 No Hitters	1.00	.75	.30
6 Indians Take Bums	1.00	.75	.30
7 Dimag Comes Thru	5.00	3.75	1.75
8 Mathewson Pitches 3 World Series Shutouts	2.00	1.50	.60
9 Haddix Pitches 12 Perfect Innings	1.00	.75	.30
10 Thomson's Homer Sinks Dodgers	2.00	1.50	.60
11 Hubbell Strikes Out 5 A.L. Stars	1.00	.75	.30
12 Pickoff Ends Series	1.00	.75	.30
13 Cards Take Series From Yanks	1.00	.75	.30
14 Dizzy and Daffy Dean Win Series	3.00	2.25	1.00
15 Owen Drops 3rd Strike	2.00	1.50	.60
16 Ruth Calls His Shot	6.00	4.50	2.00
17 Merkle Pulls Boner	1.00	.75	.30
18 Larsen Hurls Perfect World Series Game	2.00	1.50	.60
19 Bean Ball Ends Career of Mickey Cochrane	2.00	1.50	.60
20 Banks Belts 47 Homers Earns M.V.P. Award	3.00	2.25	1.00
21 Stan Musial Hits 5 Homers in 1 Day	3.00	2.25	1.00
22 Mickey Mantle Hits Longest Homer	5.00	3.75	1.75
23 Sievers Captures Home Run Title	1.00	.75	.30
24 Gehrig Consecutive Game Record Ends At 2,130 Games	5.00	3.75	1.75
25 Red Schoendienst Key Player in Braves Pennant Victory	1.00	.75	.30
26 Midget Pinch-Hits for St. Louis Browns	2.00	1.50	.60
27 Willie Mays Makes Greatest Catch	4.00	3.00	1.40
28 Homer by Yogi Berra Puts Yanks in 1st Place	2.00	1.50	.60
29 Campy National League Most Valuable Player	3.00	2.25	1.00
30 Bob Turley Hurls Yanks To World Series Championship	1.00	.75	.30
31 Dodgers Take Series From Sox in Six	1.00	.75	.30
32 Furillo Hero as Dodgers Beat Chicago in 3rd World Series Game	1.00	.75	.30
33 Adcock Gets 4 Homers, & A Double In 1 Game	1.00	.75	.30
34 Dickey Chosen All Star Catcher	2.00	1.50	.60
35 Burdette Beats Yanks in 3 Series Games	1.00	.75	.30
36 Umpires Clear White Sox Bench	1.00	.75	.30
37 Reese Honored As Greatest Dodger S.S.	2.00	1.50	.60
38 Joe DiMaggio Hits in 56 Straight Games	5.00	3.75	1.75
39 Ted Williams Hits .406 For Season	4.00	3.00	1.40
40 Walter Johnson Pitches 56 Straight	3.00	2.25	1.00
41 Hodges Hits 4 Home Runs In Nite Game	2.00	1.50	.60
42 Greenberg Returns to Tigers From Army	1.00	.75	.30
43 Ty Cobb Named Best Player Of All Time	4.00	3.00	1.40
44 Robin Roberts Wins 28 Games	1.00	.75	.30
45 Rizzuto's 2 Runs Save 1st Place	2.00	1.50	.60
46 Tigers Beat Out Senators For Pennant	1.00	.75	.30
47 Babe Ruth Hits 60th Home Run	6.00	4.50	2.00
48 Cy Young Honored	1.00	.75	.30
49 Killebrew Starts Spring Training	2.00	1.50	.60
50 Mantle Hits Longest Homer at Stadium	5.00	3.75	1.75
51 Braves Take Pennant	1.00	.75	.30
52 Ted Williams Hero Of All Star Game	4.00	3.00	1.40
53 Robinson Saves Dodgers For Playoff Series	3.00	2.25	1.00
54 Snodgrass Muffs Fly	1.00	.75	.30
55 Snider Belts 2 Homers Ties Homer Record	2.00	1.50	.60
56 Giants Win 26 Straight	1.00	.75	.30
57 Ted Kluszewski Stars In 1st Series Win	1.00	.75	.30
58 Ott Walks 5 Times In Single Game	2.00	1.50	.60
59 Harvey Kuenn Takes A.L. Batting Title	1.00	.75	.30
60 Bob Feller Hurls 3rd No-Hitter of Career	3.00	2.25	1.00
61 Yanks Champs Again!	1.00	.75	.30
62 Aaron's Bat Beats Yankees in Series	3.00	2.25	1.00
63 Warren Spahn Beats Yanks In World Series	2.00	1.50	.60
64 Ump's Wrong Call Helps Dodgers Beat Yanks	1.00	.75	.30
65 Kaline Hits 3 Homers, 2 In Same Inning	2.00	1.50	.60
66 Bob Allison Named A.L. Rookie of Year	1.00	.75	.30
67 McCovey Blasts Way Into Giant Lineup	2.00	1.50	.60
68 Colavito Hits Four Homers in One Game	2.00	1.50	.60
69 Erskine Sets Strike Out Record in World Series	1.00	.75	.30
70 Sal Maglie Pitches No-Hit Game	1.00	.75	.30
71 Early Wynn Victory Crushes Yanks	2.00	1.50	.60
72 Nellie Fox American League's M.V.P.	1.00	.75	.30

1961 NU-CARD BASEBALL SCOOPS (80) 2 1/2" X 3 1/2"

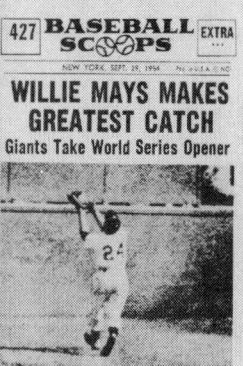

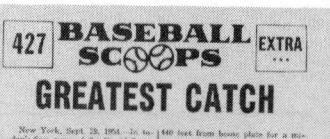

This series of 80 cards depicts great moments in the history of individual ballplayers. Each card is designed as a miniature newspaper front-page, complete with data and picture. Both the number (401-480) and title are printed in red on the obverse, and the "story" is found on the back. An album was issued to hold the set.

	MINT	VG-E	F-G
COMPLETE SET	80.00	60.00	25.00
COMMON PLAYER	.50	.40	.15

	MINT	VG-E	F-G			MINT	VG-E	F-G
1 Jim Gentile	.50	.40	.15	441 Gil Hodges		1.00	.70	.30
2 Spahn No-hitter	1.50	1.10	.50	442 Hank Greenberg		1.00	.70	.30
3 Bill Mazeroski	.50	.40	.15	443 Ty Cobb		3.00	2.25	1.00
4 Mays 3 triples	3.00	2.25	1.00	444 Robin Roberts		1.00	.70	.30
5 Woodie Held	.50	.40	.15	445 Phil Rizzuto		1.00	.70	.30
6 Vern Law	.50	.40	.15	446 Hal Newhouser		.50	.40	.15
7 Pete Runnels	.50	.40	.15	447 Ruth 60th Homer		4.00	3.00	1.40
8 Burdette No-hitter	.50	.40	.15	448 Cy Young		1.50	1.10	.50
9 Dick Stuart	.50	.40	.15	449 Harmon Killebrew		1.00	.70	.30
10 Don Cardwell	.50	.40	.15	450 Longest Homer(Mantle)		3.00	2.25	1.00
11 Camilo Pascual	.50	.40	.15	451 Braves Take Pennant		.50	.40	.15
12 Ed Mathews	1.50	1.10	.50	452 Williams All-Star Hero		3.00	2.25	1.00
13 Dick Groat	.50	.40	.15	453 Yogi Berra		2.00	1.50	.60
14 Gene Autry	1.50	1.10	.50	454 Fred Snodgrass		.50	.40	.15
15 Bobby Richardson	.50	.40	.15	455 Ruth 3 Homers		3.00	2.25	1.00
16 Roger Maris	1.50	1.10	.50	456 Giants 26 Game Streak		.50	.40	.15
17 Fred Merkle	.50	.40	.15	457 Ted Kluszewski		.75	.55	.25
18 Don Larson	.50	.40	.15	458 Mel Ott		1.50	1.10	.50
19 Mickey Cochrane	1.00	.70	.30	459 Harvey Kuenn		.50	.40	.15
20 Ernie Banks	2.00	1.50	.60	460 Bob Feller		2.00	1.50	.60
21 Stan Musial	3.00	2.25	1.00	461 Casey Stengel		2.00	1.50	.60
22 Mantle(longest homer)	3.00	2.25	1.00	462 Hank Aaron		3.00	2.25	1.00
23 Roy Sievers	.50	.40	.15	463 Spahn Beats Yanks		1.00	.70	.30
24 Lou Gehrig	3.50	2.50	1.20	464 Ump's Wrong Call		.50	.40	.15
25 Red Schoendienst	.75	.55	.25	465 Al Kaline		2.00	1.50	.60
26 Eddie Gaedel	1.00	.70	.30	466 Bob Allison		.50	.40	.15
27 Mays (greatest catch)	3.00	2.25	1.00	467 DiMaggio 4 Homers		3.00	2.25	1.00
28 Jackie Robinson	2.50	1.80	.80	468 Rocky Colavito		1.00	.70	.30
29 Roy Campanella	2.50	1.80	.80	469 Carl Erskine		.75	.55	.25
30 Bob Turley	.50	.40	.15	470 Sal Maglie		.50	.40	.15
31 Larry Sherry	.50	.40	.15	471 Early Wynn		1.00	.70	.30
32 Carl Furillo	.50	.40	.15	472 Nellie Fox		.75	.55	.25
33 Joe Adcock	.50	.40	.15	473 Marty Marion		.50	.40	.15
34 Bill Dickey	1.00	.70	.30	474 Johnny Podres		.50	.40	.15
35 Burdette 3 wins	.50	.40	.15	475 Mickey Owen		.75	.55	.25
36 Umpire Clears Bench	.50	.40	.15	476 Dean Brothers		2.00	1.50	.60
37 Pee Wee Reese	1.00	.70	.30	477 Christy Mathewson		2.00	1.50	.60
38 DiMaggio 56 games	3.00	2.25	1.00	478 Harvey Haddix		.50	.40	.15
39 Williams Hits .406	3.00	2.25	1.00	479 Carl Hubbell		1.00	.70	.30
40 Walter Johnson	2.00	1.50	.60	480 Bobby Thomson		1.00	.70	.30

D322 TIP TOP PIRATES

1954 N.Y. JOURNAL AMERICAN (59)   2" X 4"

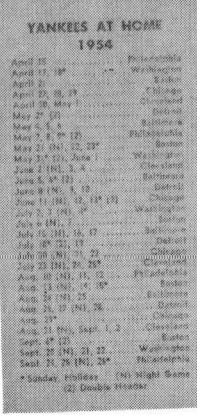

The 1954 NY Journal American set contains 59 black and white, unnumbered cards issued in the New York Daily News. The top portion of the card contains the player's picture while the bottom part contains instructions and a serial number for a weekly contest drawing. The set features Dodgers, Giants, and yankees only. The Palica card is considered the scarcest card in the set. The ACC designation is M127.

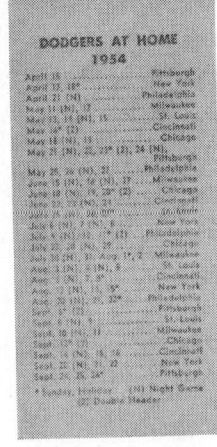

	MINT	VG-E	F-G
COMPLETE SET	675.00	500.00	200.00
COMMON PLAYER	5.50	4.25	2.00

	MINT	VG-E	F-G
BD 1 Joe Black	6.50	5.00	2.25
BD 2 Roy Campanella	35.00	26.00	12.00
BD 3 Billy Cox	5.50	4.25	2.00
BD 4 Carl Erskine	7.50	5.75	2.50
BD 5 Carl Furillo	7.50	5.75	2.50
BD 6 Junior Gilliam	9.00	6.75	3.00
BD 7 Gil Hodges	18.00	13.50	6.00
BD 8 Jim Hughes	5.50	4.25	2.00
BD 9 Clem Labine	5.50	4.25	2.00
BD10 Billy Loes	5.50	4.25	2.00
BD11 Russ Meyer	5.50	4.25	2.00
BD12 Don Newcombe	9.00	6.75	3.00
BD13 Ervin Palica	40.00	30.00	13.00
BD14 PeeWee Reese	13.00	9.50	4.00
BD15 Jackie Robinson	45.00	34.00	15.00
BD16 Preacher Roe	7.50	5.75	2.50
BD17 George Shuba	5.50	4.25	2.00
BD18 Duke Snider	35.00	26.00	12.00
BD19 Dick Williams	7.50	5.75	2.50
NYG 1 John Antonelli	6.50	5.00	2.25
NYG 2 Alvin Dark	6.50	5.00	2.25
NYG 3 Marv Grissom	5.50	4.25	2.00
NYG 4 Ruben Gomez	5.50	4.25	2.00
NYG 5 Jim Hearn	5.50	4.25	2.00
NYG 6 Bobby Hofman	5.50	4.25	2.00
NYG 7 Monte Irvin	13.00	9.50	4.00
NYG 8 Larry Jansen	5.50	4.25	2.00
NYG 9 Ray Katt	5.50	4.25	2.00
NYG10 Don Liddle	5.50	4.25	2.00
NYG11 Whitey Lockman	5.50	4.25	2.00

	MINT	VG-E	F-G
NYG12 Sal Maglie	6.50	5.00	2.25
NYG13 Willie Mays	120.00	85.00	40.00
NYG14 Don Mueller	5.50	4.25	2.00
NYG15 Dusty Rhodes	5.50	4.25	2.00
NYG16 Hank Thompson	5.50	4.25	2.00
NYG17 Wes Westrum	5.50	4.25	2.00
NYG18 Hoyt Wilhelm	9.00	6.75	3.00
NYG19 Davey Williams	5.50	4.25	2.00
NYG20 Al Worthington	5.50	4.25	2.00
NYY 1 Hank Bauer	7.50	5.75	2.50
NYY 2 Yogi Berra	35.00	26.00	12.00
NYY 3 Harry Byrd	5.50	4.25	2.00
NYY 4 Andy Carey	5.50	4.25	2.00
NYY 5 Jerry Coleman	6.50	5.00	2.25
NYY 6 Joe Collins	5.50	4.25	2.00
NYY 7 Whitey Ford	18.00	13.50	6.00
NYY 8 Steve Kraly	5.50	4.25	2.00
NYY 9 Bob Kuzava	5.50	4.25	2.00
NYY10 Frank Leja	5.50	4.25	2.00
NYY11 Ed Lopat	7.50	5.75	2.50
NYY12 Mickey Mantle	150.00	110.00	50.00
NYY13 Gil McDougald	7.50	5.75	2.50
NYY14 Bill Miller	5.50	4.25	2.00
NYY15 Tom Morgan	5.50	4.25	2.00
NYY16 Irv Noren	5.50	4.25	2.00
NYY17 Allie Reynolds	9.00	6.75	3.00
NYY18 Phil Rizzuto	15.00	11.00	5.00
NYY19 Ed Robinson	6.50	5.00	2.25
NYY20 Gene Woodling	6.50	5.00	2.25

1962 PEPSI TULSA OILERS (24)

2 1/2″ X 3 1/2″
5 1/2″ X 7″

CHARLES DALLAN MAXVILL, Infielder . . . Born February 18, 1939 at Granite City, Ill. . . . Makes his home there . . . Graduated Granite City High, 1957 . . . Played baseball . . . Attended Washington University (St. Louis, Mo.), 3½ years . . . Played baseball . . . Signed for the St. Louis Cardinals by Joe Monahan.

YEAR	CLUB	LEAGUE	G	AB	H	HR	RBI	PCT.
1960	Winnipeg	Northern	74	276	71	9	48	257
61	Charleston	A.A.	88	253	58	1	19	229
61	Winnipeg	Northern	50	193	46	3	22	238

Issued by Pepsi-Cola to spotlight the Tulsa Oilers, this set is distinguished by a two-card panel attached to a ring tab. An interesting feature of this issue is the two batboy cards, numbers 21 and 23. The SCB designation is F230-1.

	MINT	VG-E	F-G
MPLETE SET	30.00	24.00	10.00
MMON PLAYER	1.50	1.20	.50
Bob Blaylock	1.50	1.20	.50
Bud Bloomfield	1.50	1.20	.50
Dick Hughes	1.50	1.20	.50
Gary Kolb	1.50	1.20	.50
Chris Krug	1.50	1.20	.50
Hank Kuhlmann	1.50	1.20	.50
"Whitey" Kurowski	2.00	1.50	.70
Johnny Joe Lewis	1.50	1.20	.50
Elmer Lindsey	1.50	1.20	.50
Jeoff Long	1.50	1.20	.50
"Pepper" Martin	3.00	2.25	1.00

	MINT	VG-E	F-G
12 Jerry Marx	1.50	1.20	.50
13 Weldon Maudin	1.50	1.20	.50
14 Dal Maxvill	2.50	2.00	1.00
15 Bill McNamee	1.50	1.20	.50
16 Joe Patterson	1.50	1.20	.50
17 Gordon Richardson	1.50	1.20	.50
18 Daryl Robertson	1.50	1.20	.50
19 Tom Schwaner	1.50	1.20	.50
20 Joe Shipley	1.50	1.20	.50
21 Jon Smith (bat boy)	1.50	1.20	.50
22 Clint Stark	1.50	1.20	.50
23 Terry Tucker (bat boy)	1.50	1.20	.50
24 Bill Wakefield	1.50	1.20	.50

1963 PEPSI TULSA OILERS (24)

2 1/2″ X 3 1/2″
5″ X 7″

These sepia-tone cards are unnumbered as in the previous year, and show Tulsa Oilers only. The reverse is printed in black with a short biography and statistics of the player, plus contest rules on the ring tab. The SCB designation is F230-2.

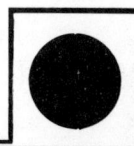

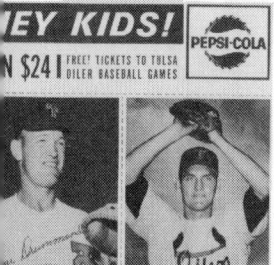

	MINT	VG-E	F-G
LETE SET	25.00	20.00	8.00
ON PLAYER	1.25	1.00	.40
ennis Aust	1.25	1.00	.40
im Beauchamp	1.25	1.00	.40
ud Bloomfield	1.25	1.00	.40
elix DeLeon	1.25	1.00	.40
on Dennis	1.25	1.00	.40
amar Drummonds	1.25	1.00	.40
om Hilgendorf	1.25	1.00	.40
ary Kolb	1.25	1.00	.40
nris Krug	1.25	1.00	.40
Bee" Lindsey	1.25	1.00	.40
ay Majtyka	1.25	1.00	.40

	MINT	VG-E	F-G
12 "Pepper" Martin	2.00	1.50	.70
13 Jerry Marx	1.25	1.00	.40
14 "Hunkey" Mauldin	1.25	1.00	.40
15 Joe Patterson	1.25	1.00	.40
16 Grover Resinger	1.25	1.00	.40
17 Gordon Richardson	1.25	1.00	.40
18 Jon Smith (bat boy)	1.25	1.00	.40
19 Chuck Taylor	1.25	1.00	.40
20 Terry Tucker (bat boy)	1.25	1.00	.40
21 Lou Vickery	1.25	1.00	.40
22 Bill Wakefield	1.25	1.00	.40
23 Harry Watts	1.25	1.00	.40
24 Jerry Wild	1.25	1.00	.40

1963 PEPSI COLT 45's (16)

2 3/8" X 3 11/16"
2 3/8" X 9 1/8"

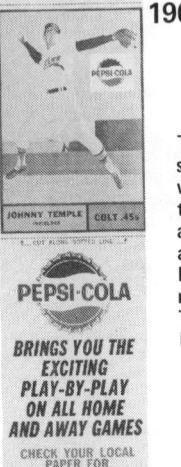

The 1963 Pepsi carton insert set consists of 16 black & white cards with a removable tab containing a schedule and ad material. Lillis and Temple are considered difficult, while Bateman and Warwick were never publically distributed. The SCB designation is F230-3.

	MINT	VG-E	F-G
COMPLETE SET	450.00	330.00	165.00
COMMON PLAYER	2.00	1.50	.70
1 Bob Aspromonte	2.00	1.50	.70
2 John Bateman*	400.00	300.00	150.00
3 Bob Bruce	2.00	1.50	.70
4 Jim Campbell	2.00	1.50	.70
5 Dick Farrell	2.00	1.50	.70
6 Ernie Fazio	2.00	1.50	.70
7 Carroll Hardy	2.00	1.50	.70

	MINT	VG-E	F-G
8 J. C. Hartman	2.00	1.50	.70
9 Ken Johnson	2.00	1.50	.70
10 Bob Lillis	10.00	7.50	3.50
11 Don McMahon	2.00	1.50	.70
12 Pete Runnels	2.00	1.50	.70
13 Al Spangler	2.00	1.50	.70
14 Rusty Staub	5.00	4.00	2.00
15 Johnny Temple	10.00	7.50	3.50
16 Carl Warwick*	40.00	30.00	15.00

1966 PEPSI TULSA OILERS (24)

2 1/2" X 3 1/4"
5 1/2" X 6 11/16"

The set consists of 24 sepia-tone, unnumbered cards of the Tulsa Oilers, similar to previous issues but on thinner stock. There are 16 different two-card panels in the complete panel set, resulting in eight players having two cards each. The SCB designation is F230-5.

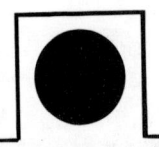

	MINT	VG-E	F-G
COMPLETE SET	25.00	20.00	8.00
COMMON PLAYER	1.25	1.00	.40
1 Florian Ackley	1.25	1.00	.40
2 Dennis Aust	1.25	1.00	.40
3 Elio Chacon(2)	1.25	1.00	.40
4 James Cosman	1.25	1.00	.40
5 Mack Creager	1.25	1.00	.40
6 Robert Dews(2)	1.25	1.00	.40
7 Harold Gilson	1.25	1.00	.40
8 Larry Jaster	1.25	1.00	.40
9 Alex Johnson	2.00	1.50	.70
10 George Kernek(2)	1.25	1.00	.40
11 Jose Laboy	1.25	1.00	.40

	MINT	VG-E	F-G
12 Richard LeMay	1.25	1.00	.40
13 Charles Metro	1.25	1.00	.40
14 David Pavlesic	1.25	1.00	.40
15 Robert Pfeil(2)	1.25	1.00	.40
16 Ronald Piche	1.25	1.00	.40
17 Robert Radovich	1.25	1.00	.40
18 David Ricketts(2)	1.25	1.00	.40
19 Theodore Savage(2)	1.25	1.00	.40
20 George Schultz	1.25	1.00	.40
21 Edward Spiezio(2)	1.25	1.00	.40
22 Clint Stark	1.25	1.00	.40
23 Robert Tolan	2.00	1.50	.70
24 Walter Williams(2)	1.25	1.00	.40

1977 PEPSI—COLA DISCS (72)

3 3/8″ X 3 3/8″
4 13/16″ X 9 1/8″

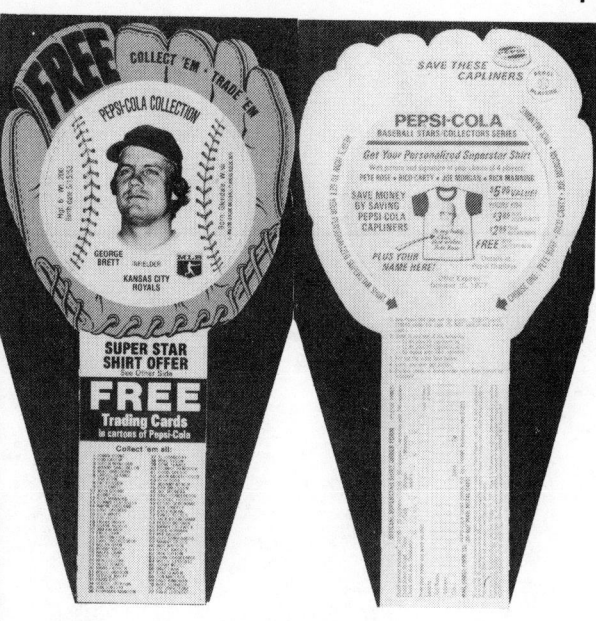

This set of 72 baseball-player discs was issued in cartons of Pepsi-Cola. It featured an attractively designed format with the detachable disc sitting in the palm of a baseball glove and a checklist on the insert tab. Although the checklist is numbered the individual cards are not, and the Jackson and Schmidt cards are found with either blue, purple, orange or green trim. Produced in Ohio, the set features 15 cards each from the Reds and the Indians.

	MINT	VG-E	F-G
COMPLETE SET	7.00	5.00	2.00
COMMON PLAYER	.07	.05	.02

	MINT	VG-E	F-G			MINT	VG-E	F-G
1 Robin Yount	.07	.05	.02	37 Al Hrabosky		.10	.07	.03
2 Rod Carew	.25	.20	.08	38 Mike Tyson		.07	.05	.02
3 Butch Wynegar	.07	.05	.02	39 Gene Tenace		.07	.05	.02
4 Manny Sanguillen	.07	.05	.02	40 George Hendrick		.10	.07	.03
5 Mike Hargrove	.07	.05	.02	41 Chris Speier		.07	.05	.02
6 Larvel Blanks	.07	.05	.02	42 John Montefusco		.07	.05	.02
7 Jim Kern	.07	.05	.02	43 Pete Rose		.30	.25	.10
8 Pat Dobson	.07	.05	.02	44 Johnny Bench		.30	.25	.10
9 Rico Carty	.07	.05	.02	45 Dan Driessen		.07	.05	.02
0 John Grubb	.07	.05	.02	46 Joe Morgan		.10	.07	.03
1 Buddy Bell	.10	.07	.03	47 Dave Concepcion		.07	.05	.02
2 Rick Manning	.07	.05	.02	48 George Foster		.15	.11	.05
3 Dennis Eckersley	.10	.07	.03	49 Cesar Geronimo		.07	.05	.02
4 Wayne Garland	.07	.05	.02	50 Ken Griffey		.10	.07	.03
5 Dave LaRoche	.07	.05	.02	51 Gary Nolan		.07	.05	.02
6 Rick Waits	.07	.05	.02	52 Santo Alcala		.07	.05	.02
7 Ray Fosse	.07	.05	.02	53 Jack Billingham		.07	.05	.02
8 Frank Duffy	.07	.05	.02	54 Pedro Borbon		.07	.05	.02
9 Duane Kuiper	.07	.05	.02	55 Rawly Eastwick		.07	.05	.02
0 Jim Palmer	.25	.20	.08	56 Fred Norman		.07	.05	.02
1 Fred Lynn	.30	.25	.10	57 Pat Zachry		.07	.05	.02
2 Carlton Fisk	.15	.11	.05	58 Jeff Burroughs		.10	.07	.03
3 Carl Yastrzemski	.30	.25	.10	59 Manny Trillo		.07	.05	.02
4 Nolan Ryan	.25	.20	.08	60 Bob Watson		.07	.05	.02
6 Bobby Grich	.07	.05	.02	61 Steve Garvey		.25	.20	.08
7 Ralph Garr	.07	.05	.02	62 Don Sutton		.15	.11	.05
7 Richie Zisk	.10	.07	.03	63 Joh Candelaria		.07	.05	.02
8 Ron FeFlore	.10	.07	.03	64 Willie Stargell		.25	.20	.08
9 Rusty Staub	.10	.07	.03	65 Jerry Reuss		.10	.07	.03
0 Mark Fidrych	.10	.07	.03	66 Dave Cash		.07	.05	.02
1 Willie Horton	.07	.05	.02	67 Tom Seaver		.25	.20	.08
2 George Brett	.30	.25	.10	68 Jon Matlack		.10	.07	.03
3 Amos Otis	.07	.05	.02	69 Dave Kingman		.15	.11	.05
4 Reggie Jackson (4)	.30	.25	.10	70 Mike Schmidt (4)		.30	.25	.10
5 Don Gullett	.07	.05	.02	71 Jay Johnstone		.07	.05	.02
6 Thurman Munson	.30	.25	.10	72 Greg Luzinski		.15	.11	.05

Attend a Sports Memorabilia Show or Convention in your area sometime this year. They are both interesting and enjoyable to all members of the family.

1961 PETER'S MEATS (26)　　　　　3 1/2" X 4 5/8"

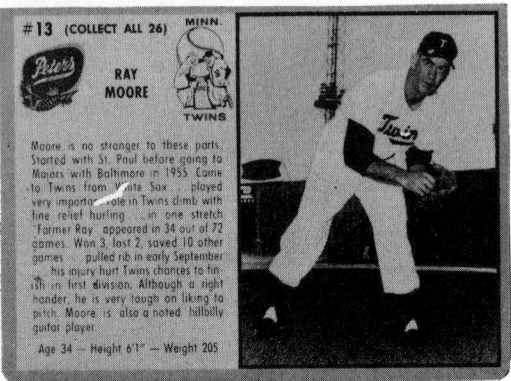

The 1961 Peter's Meats set of 26 full color, numbered cards features Minnesota Twins players only. The cards were issued as an outside wrapping on various Peter's Meats products. The cards are blank backed and coated heavily with wax. Complete boxes are sometimes available and are worth approximately 10% more than the prices listed below. The ACC designation is F173.

	MINT	VG-E	F-G		MINT	VG-E	F-G
COMPLETE SET	100.00	75.00	30.00	12 Elmer Valo	4.00	3.00	1.40
COMMON PLAYER	4.00	3.00	1.40	13 Ray Moore	4.00	3.00	1.40
				14 Billy Gardner	4.00	3.00	1.40
1 Zoilo Versalles	6.00	4.50	2.00	15 Lenny Green	4.00	3.00	1.40
2 Ed Lopat	8.00	6.00	2.50	16 Sam Mele	4.00	3.00	1.40
3 Pedro Ramos	4.00	3.00	1.40	17 Jim Lemon	4.00	3.00	1.40
4 Charles "Chuck" Stobbs	4.00	3.00	1.40	18 Harmon Killebrew	25.00	18.50	8.75
				19 Paul Giel	4.00	3.00	1.40
5 Don Mincher	4.00	3.00	1.40	20 Reno Bertoia	4.00	3.00	1.40
6 Jack Kralick	4.00	3.00	1.40	21 Clyde McCulloch	4.00	3.00	1.40
7 Jim Kaat	8.00	6.00	2.50	22 Earl Battey	4.00	3.00	1.40
8 Hal Naragon	4.00	3.00	1.40	23 Camilo Pascual	6.00	4.50	2.00
9 Don Lee	4.00	3.00	1.40	24 Dan Dobbek	4.00	3.00	1.40
10 Cookie Lavagetto	6.00	4.50	2.00	25 Jose Valdivielso	4.00	3.00	1.40
11 Pete Whisenant	4.00	3.00	1.40	26 Billy Consolo	4.00	3.00	1.40

1939 PLAY BALL-AMERICA (162) B&W 2 1/2" X 3 1/8"

The 1939 Play Ball set Gum, Inc., listed as R-3 (ACC), is a relatively un tractive black & white which includes three differe types of backs; 1) name ALL CAPITAL LETTERS Name in Initial Caps or 3) free sample card ad ov printed in red. Card no.1 was not issued and card n 116—162 are more diffic to obtain.

	MINT	VG-E	F-G		MINT	VG-E	F-G
COMPLETE SET	1200.00	900.00	400.00	13 Luke Hamlin	3.00	2.50	1.00
COMMON PLAYER (1-115)	3.00	2.50	1.00	14 Jim Tabor	3.00	2.50	1.00
COMMON PLAYER (116-162)	11.00	8.00	3.50	15 Paul Derringer	5.00	3.75	1.75
				16 John Peacock	3.00	2.50	1.00
1 Jake Powell	12.00	5.00	1.50	17 Emerson Dickman	3.00	2.50	1.00
2 Lee Grissom	3.00	2.50	1.00	18 Harry Danning	3.00	2.50	1.00
3 Red Ruffing	13.00	9.50	4.00	19 Paul Dean	6.00	4.50	2.00
4 Eldon Auker	3.00	2.50	1.00	20 Joe Heving	3.00	2.50	1.00
5 Luke Sewell	4.00	3.00	1.40	21 Dutch Leonard	3.00	2.50	1.00
6 Leo Durocher	7.50	5.75	2.50	22 Bucky Walters	4.00	3.00	1.40
7 Bob Doerr	4.00	3.00	1.40	23 Burgess Whitehead	3.00	2.50	1.00
8 Henry Pippen	3.00	2.50	1.00	24 Richard Coffman	3.00	2.50	1.00
9 James Tobin	3.00	2.50	1.00	25 George Selkirk	4.00	3.00	1.40
10 James DeShong	3.00	2.50	1.00	26 Joe DiMaggio	150.00	110.00	50.00
11 Johnny Rizzo	3.00	2.50	1.00	27 Fred Ostermueller	3.00	2.50	1.00
12 Hershel Martin	3.00	2.50	1.00	28 Sylvester Johnson	3.00	2.50	1.00

1939 PLAY BALL (CONTINUED)

	MINT	VG-E	F-G
29 John (Jack) Wilson	3.00	2.50	1.00
30 Bill Dickey	22.00	16.50	7.50
31 Sam West	3.00	2.50	1.00
32 Bob Seeds	3.00	2.50	1.00
33 Del Young	3.00	2.50	1.00
34 Frank Demaree	3.00	2.50	1.00
35 Bill Jurges	3.00	2.50	1.00
36 Frank McCormick	3.00	2.50	1.00
37 Virgil Davis	3.00	2.50	1.00
38 Billy Myers	3.00	2.50	1.00
39 Rick Ferrell	3.00	2.50	1.00
40 James Bagby, Jr.	3.00	2.50	1.00
41 Lon Warneke	3.00	2.50	1.00
42 Arndt Jorgens	3.00	2.50	1.00
43 Melo Almada	3.00	2.50	1.00
44 Don Heffner	3.00	2.50	1.00
45 Merrill May	3.00	2.50	1.00
46 Morris Arnovich	3.00	2.50	1.00
47 Buddy Lewis	3.00	2.50	1.00
48 Lefty Gomez	15.00	11.00	5.00
49 Eddie Miller	3.00	2.50	1.00
50 Charlie Gehringer	15.00	11.00	5.00
51 Mel Ott	22.00	16.50	7.50
52 Tommy Henrich	6.00	4.50	2.00
53 Carl Hubbell	18.00	13.50	6.00
54 Harry Gumpert	3.00	2.50	1.00
55 Arky Vaughan	6.00	4.50	2.00
56 Hank Greenberg	18.00	13.50	6.00
57 Buddy Hassett	3.00	2.50	1.00
58 Lou Chiozza	3.00	2.50	1.00
59 Ken Chase	3.00	2.50	1.00
60 Schoolboy Rowe	6.00	4.50	2.00
61 Tony Cuccinello	3.00	2.50	1.00
62 Tom Carey	3.00	2.50	1.00
63 Emmett Mueller	3.00	2.50	1.00
64 Wally Moses	4.00	3.00	1.40
65 Harry Craft	3.00	2.50	1.00
66 Jimmy Ripple	3.00	2.50	1.00
67 Ed Joost	3.00	2.50	1.00
68 Fred Sington	3.00	2.50	1.00
69 Elbie Fletcher	3.00	2.50	1.00
70 Fred Frankhouse	3.00	2.50	1.00
71 Monte Pearson	3.00	2.50	1.00
72 Debs Garms	3.00	2.50	1.00
73 Hal Schumacher	3.00	2.50	1.00
74 Cookie Lavagetto	3.00	2.50	1.00
75 Stan Bordagaray	3.00	2.50	1.00
76 Goody Rosen	3.00	2.50	1.00
77 Lew Riggs	3.00	2.50	1.00
78 Julius Solters	3.00	2.50	1.00
79 Jo-Jo Moore	3.00	2.50	1.00
80 Pete Fox	3.00	2.50	1.00
81 Babe Dahlgren	3.00	2.50	1.00
82 Chuck Klein	13.00	9.50	4.00
83 Gus Suhr	3.00	2.50	1.00
84 Skeeter Newsom	3.00	2.50	1.00
85 Johnny Cooney	3.00	2.50	1.00
86 Dolph Camilli	3.00	2.50	1.00
87 Milburn Schoffner	3.00	2.50	1.00
88 Charlie Keller	6.00	4.50	2.00
89 Lloyd Waner	14.00	10.50	4.75
90 Robert Klinger	3.00	2.50	1.00
91 John Knott	3.00	2.50	1.00
92 Ted Williams	100.00	70.00	30.00
93 Charles Gelbert	3.00	2.50	1.00
94 Heinie Manush	13.00	9.50	4.00

	MINT	VG-E	F-G
95 Whit Wyatt	3.00	2.50	1.00
96 Babe Phelps	3.00	2.50	1.00
97 Bob Johnson	3.00	2.50	1.00
98 Pinky Whitney	3.00	2.50	1.00
99 Wally Berger	3.00	2.50	1.00
100 Charles Myer	3.00	2.50	1.00
101 Roger Cramer	3.00	2.50	1.00
102 Lem Young	3.00	2.50	1.00
103 Moe Berg	3.00	2.50	1.00
104 Tom Bridges	3.00	2.50	1.00
105 Rabbit McNair	3.00	2.50	1.00
106 Dolly Stark	3.00	2.50	1.00
107 Joe Vosmik	3.00	2.50	1.00
108 Frank Hayes	3.00	2.50	1.00
109 Myril Hoag	3.00	2.50	1.00
110 Fred Fitzsimmons	3.00	2.50	1.00
111 Van Lingle Mungo	4.00	3.00	1.40
112 Paul Waner	14.00	10.50	4.75
113 Al Schacht	3.00	2.50	1.00
114 Cecil Travis	3.00	2.50	1.00
115 Ralph Kress	3.00	2.50	1.00
116 Gene Desautels	11.00	8.00	3.50
117 Wayne Ambler	11.00	8.00	3.50
118 Lynn Nelson	11.00	8.00	3.50
119 Willard Hershberger	12.00	9.00	4.00
120 Rabbit Warstler	11.00	8.00	3.50
121 Bill Posedel	11.00	8.00	3.50
122 George McQuinn	11.00	8.00	3.50
123 Roy T. Davis	11.00	8.00	3.50
124 Walter Brown	11.00	8.00	3.50
125 Cliff Melton	11.00	8.00	3.50
126 Not issued	xxxxx	xxxx	xxxx
127 Gil Brack	11.00	8.00	3.50
128 Joe Bowman	11.00	8.00	3.50
129 Bill Swift	11.00	8.00	3.50
130 Bill Brubaker	11.00	8.00	3.50
131 Mort Cooper	11.00	8.00	3.50
132 Jim Brown	11.00	8.00	3.50
133 Lynn Myers	11.00	8.00	3.50
134 Tot Presnell	11.00	8.00	3.50
135 Mickey Owen	12.00	8.75	4.00
136 Roy Bell	11.00	8.00	3.50
137 Pete Appleton	11.00	8.00	3.50
138 George Case	11.00	8.00	3.50
139 Vito Tamulis	11.00	8.00	3.50
140 Ray Hayworth	11.00	8.00	3.50
141 Pete Coscarart	11.00	8.00	3.50
142 Ira Hutchinson	11.00	8.00	3.50
143 Earl Averill	30.00	22.50	10.50
144 Zeke Bonura	11.00	8.00	3.50
145 Mul Mulcahy	11.00	8.00	3.50
146 Tom Sunkel	11.00	8.00	3.50
147 George Coffman	11.00	8.00	3.50
148 Bill Trotter	11.00	8.00	3.50
149 Max West	11.00	8.00	3.50
150 James Walkup	11.00	8.00	3.50
151 Hugh Casey	11.00	8.00	3.50
152 Roy Weatherly	11.00	8.00	3.50
153 Paul Trout	11.00	8.00	3.50
154 Johnny Hudson	11.00	8.00	3.50
155 Jimmy Outlaw	11.00	8.00	3.50
156 Ray Berres	11.00	8.00	3.50
157 Don Padgett	11.00	8.00	3.50
158 Bud Thomas	11.00	8.00	3.50
159 Red Evans	11.00	8.00	3.50
160 Gene Moore	11.00	8.00	3.50
161 Lonnie Frey	11.00	8.00	3.50
162 Whitey Moore	12.50	8.00	3.50

N508 WOMEN BASEBALL PLAYERS

N321
"CALIFORNIA LEAGUE"

N135 TALK OF THE DIAMOND

179. GEORGE HAROLD SISLER

Former Major League Star
Elected Hall of Fame, 1938

Born. Manchester, O.   March 24, 1893
Bats: Left   Threw: Left
Height: 5' 10½"   Weight: 170 lbs.

When they want to praise a first-baseman, they say "He might be another Sisler." George Sisler was without a doubt one of the greatest players ever to hold down the initial sack. He was a picture fielder, making sensational, difficult plays look easy and, as a hitter, his lifetime average of .341 over 16 seasons talks for itself. There was nothing he couldn't do on a ball field. He won the American League batting crowns in 1920 and 1922 with averages of .407 and .420 respectively; he set a record for hits in a season with 257 in 1920 and batted safely in 41 consecutive games in 1922 for another league mark. Today, Sisler keeps his hand in baseball as Chairman of the National Semi-Pro Baseball Congress.

PLAY BALL

A pictorial news record of America's favorite sport. Save these cards . . . know all about the game and its prominent players. New pictures every year.

© 1940.   GUM, INC., Phila., Pa. ···········

The 1940 Play Ball set, R-335 (ACC), is a black & white set of 240 cards containing an abundance of Hall of Famers. Card nos. 181—240 were printed in lesser quantities, hence they are scarcer than the lower numbers.

	MINT	VG-E	F-G			MINT	VG-E	F-G
COMPLETE SET	1500.00	1200.00	500.00	60 John Cooney		3.50	2.75	1.25
COMMON PLAYER (1-180)	3.50	2.75	1.25	61 "Tony" Cuccinello		3.50	2.75	1.25
COMMON PLAYER (181-240)	10.00	7.25	3.25	62 "Buddy" Hassett		3.50	2.75	1.25
				63 "Pete" Coscarart		3.50	2.75	1.25
1 Joe DiMaggio	225.00	125.00	50.00	64 "Van" Mungo		6.00	4.50	2.00
2 "Art" Jorgens	3.50	2.75	1.25	65 "Fitz" Fitzsimmons		3.50	2.75	1.25
3 "Babe" Dahlgren	3.50	2.75	1.25	66 "Babe" Phelps		3.50	2.75	1.25
4 "Tommy" Henrich	8.00	6.00	2.50	67 "Whit" Wyatt		3.50	2.75	1.25
5 "Monte" Pearson	3.50	2.75	1.25	68 "Dolph" Camilli		3.50	2.75	1.25
6 " Lefty" Gomez	16.00	12.00	5.50	69 "Cookie" Lavagetto		3.50	2.75	1.25
7 "Bill" Dickey	26.00	19.00	9.00	70 "Hot Potato" Hamlin		3.50	2.75	1.25
8 "Twinkletoes" Selkirk	5.00	3.75	1.75	71 "Mel" Almada		3.50	2.75	1.25
9 "Charley" Keller	7.00	5.25	2.50	72 "Chuck" Dressen		5.00	3.75	1.75
10 "Red" Ruffing	15.00	11.00	5.00	73 Bucky Walters		5.00	3.75	1.75
11 "Jake" Powell	3.50	2.75	1.25	74 "Duke" Derringer		7.00	5.25	2.50
12 "Johnny" Schulte	3.50	2.75	1.25	75 "Buck" McCormick		5.00	3.75	1.75
13 "Jack" Knott	3.50	2.75	1.25	76 "Lonny" Frey		3.50	2.75	1.25
14 "Rabbit" McNair	3.50	2.75	1.25	77 "Bill" Hershberger		5.00	3.75	1.75
15 George Case	3.50	2.75	1.25	78 "Lew" Riggs		3.50	2.75	1.25
16 Cecil Travis	3.50	2.75	1.25	79 "Wildfire" Craft		3.50	2.75	1.25
17 "Buddy" Myer	3.50	2.75	1.25	80 "Billy" Myers		3.50	2.75	1.25
18 "Charley" Gelbert	3.50	2.75	1.25	81 "Wally" Berger		3.50	2.75	1.25
19 "Ken" Chase	3.50	2.75	1.25	82 "Hank" Gowdy		3.50	2.75	1.25
20 "Buddy" Lewis	3.50	2.75	1.25	83 "Clif" Melton		3.50	2.75	1.25
21 "Rick" Ferrell	3.50	2.75	1.25	84 "Jo-Jo" Moore		3.50	2.75	1.25
22 "Sammy" West	3.50	2.75	1.25	85 "Hal" Schumacher		3.50	2.75	1.25
23 "Dutch" Leonard	3.50	2.75	1.25	86 Harry Gumbert		3.50	2.75	1.25
24 Frank Hayes	3.50	2.75	1.25	87 Carl Hubbell		20.00	15.00	6.50
25 Bob Johnson	3.50	2.75	1.25	88 "Mel" Ott		25.00	18.50	8.75
26 "Wally" Moses	3.50	2.75	1.25	89 "Bill" Jurges		3.50	2.75	1.25
27 "Ted" Williams	120.00	90.00	40.00	90 Frank Demaree		3.50	2.75	1.25
28 "Gene" Desautels	3.50	2.75	1.25	91 "Suitcase" Seeds		3.50	2.75	1.25
29 "Doc" Cramer	3.50	2.75	1.25	92 "Whitey" Whitehead		3.50	2.75	1.25
30 "Moe" Berg	3.50	2.75	1.25	93 Harry Danning		3.50	2.75	1.25
31 "Jack" Wilson	3.50	2.75	1.25	94 "Gus" Suhr		3.50	2.75	1.25
32 "Jim" Bagby	3.50	2.75	1.25	95 "Mul" Mulcahy		3.50	2.75	1.25
33 Fritz Ostermueller	3.50	2.75	1.25	96 "Heinie" Mueller		3.50	2.75	1.25
34 John Peacock	3.50	2.75	1.25	97 "Morry" Arnovich		3.50	2.75	1.25
35 "Joe" Heving	3.50	2.75	1.25	98 "Pinky" May		3.50	2.75	1.25
36 "Jim" Tabor	3.50	2.75	1.25	99 "Syl" Johnson		3.50	2.75	1.25
37 Emerson Dickman	3.50	2.75	1.25	100 "Hersh" Martin		3.50	2.75	1.25
38 "Bobby" Doerr	5.00	3.75	1.75	101 "Del" Young		3.50	2.75	1.25
39 "Tom" Carey	3.50	2.75	1.25	102 "Chuck" Klein		14.00	10.50	4.75
40 "Hank" Greenberg	20.00	15.00	6.50	103 "Elbie" Fletcher		3.50	2.75	1.25
41 Charley Gehringer	16.00	12.00	5.50	104 "Big Poison" Waner		18.00	13.50	6.00
42 "Bud" Thomas	3.50	2.75	1.25	105 "Little Poison" Waner		15.00	11.00	5.00
43 Pete Fox	3.50	2.75	1.25	106 "Pep" Young		3.50	2.75	1.25
44 "Dizzy" Trout	3.50	2.75	1.25	107 "Arky" Vaughan		7.00	5.25	2.50
45 "Red" Kress	3.50	2.75	1.25	108 "Johnny" Rizzo		3.50	2.75	1.25
46 Earl Averill	15.00	11.00	5.00	109 "Don" Padgett		3.50	2.75	1.25
47 "Ol'Os" Vitt	3.50	2.75	1.25	110 "Tom" Sunkel		3.50	2.75	1.25
48 "Luke" Sewell	6.00	4.50	2.00	111 "Mickey" Owen		5.00	3.75	1.75
49 "Stormy" Weatherly	3.50	2.75	1.25	112 "Jimmy" Brown		3.50	2.75	1.25
50 "Hal" Trosky	3.50	2.75	1.25	113 "Mort" Cooper		3.50	2.75	1.25
51 "Don" Heffner	3.50	2.75	1.25	114 "Lon" Warneke		3.50	2.75	1.25
52 Myril Hoag	3.50	2.75	1.25	115 "Mike" Gonzales		3.50	2.75	1.25
53 "Mac" McQuinn	3.50	2.75	1.25	116 "Al" Schacht		5.00	3.75	1.75
54 "Bill" Trotter	3.50	2.75	1.25	117 "Dolly" Stark		4.00	3.00	1.25
55 "Slick" Coffman	3.50	2.75	1.25	118 "Schoolboy" Hoyt		15.00	11.00	5.00
56 "Eddie" Miller	3.50	2.75	1.25	119 "Ol' Pete" Alexander		22.00	16.50	7.50
57 Max West	3.50	2.75	1.25	120 Walter Johnson		25.00	18.50	8.75
58 "Bill" Posedel	3.50	2.75	1.25	121 Atley Donald		3.50	2.75	1.25
59 "Rabbit" Warstler	3.50	2.75	1.25	122 "Sandy" Sundra		3.50	2.75	1.25

1940 PLAY BALL (CONTINUED)

	MINT	VG-E	F-G
123 "Hildy" Hildebrand	3.50	2.75	1.25
124 "Colonel" Combs	14.00	10.50	4.75
125 "Art" Fletcher	3.50	2.75	1.25
126 "Jake" Solters	3.50	2.75	1.25
127 "Muddy" Ruel	3.50	2.75	1.25
128 "Pete" Appleton	3.50	2.75	1.25
129 Bucky Harris	13.00	9.50	4.00
130 "Deerfoot" Milan	3.50	2.75	1.25
131 "Zeke" Bonura	3.50	2.75	1.25
132 Connie Mack	17.00	12.50	6.00
133 "Jimmie" Foxx	30.00	22.50	10.50
134 "Joe" Cronin	18.00	13.50	6.00
135 "Line Drive" Nelson	3.50	2.75	1.25
136 "Cotton" Pippen	3.50	2.75	1.25
137 "Bing" Miller	3.50	2.75	1.25
138 "Beau" Bell	3.50	2.75	1.25
139 Elden Auker	3.50	2.75	1.25
140 "Dick" Coffman	3.50	2.75	1.25
141 "Highpockets" Kelly	14.00	10.50	4.75
142 "Casey" Stengel	22.00	16.50	7.50
143 "Gene" Moore	3.50	2.75	1.25
144 "Joe" Vosmik	3.50	2.75	1.25
145 "Vito" Tamulis	3.50	2.75	1.25
146 "Tot" Pressnell	3.50	2.75	1.25
147 "Johnny" Hudson	3.50	2.75	1.25
148 Hugh Casey	3.50	2.75	1.25
149 "Pinky" Shoffner	3.50	2.75	1.25
150 "Whitey" Moore	3.50	2.75	1.25
151 Edwin Joost	3.50	2.75	1.25
152 "Jimmy" Wilson	3.50	2.75	1.25
153 "Bill" McKechnie	10.00	7.00	3.00
154 "Jumbo" Brown	3.50	2.75	1.25
155 "Ray" Hayworth	3.50	2.75	1.25
156 "Daffy" Dean	7.00	5.25	2.50
157 "Lou" Chiozza	3.50	2.75	1.25
158 "Stonewall" Jackson	3.50	2.75	1.25
159 "Pancho" Snyder	3.50	2.75	1.25
160 "Hans" Lobert	3.50	2.75	1.25
161 Debs Garms	3.50	2.75	1.25
162 "Joe" Bowman	3.50	2.75	1.25
163 "Spud" Davis	3.50	2.75	1.25
164 "Ray" Berres	3.50	2.75	1.25
165 "Bob" Klinger	3.50	2.75	1.25
166 "Bill" Brubaker	3.50	2.75	1.25
167 Frankie Frisch	18.00	13.50	6.00
168 "Honus" Wagner	25.00	18.50	8.75
169 "Gabby" Street	3.50	2.75	1.25
170 "Tris" Speaker	22.00	16.50	7.50
171 Harry Heilmann	18.00	13.50	6.00
172 "Chief" Bender	15.00	11.00	5.00
173 "Larry" Lajoie	25.00	18.50	8.75
174 "Johnny" Evers	15.00	11.00	5.00
175 "Christy" Mathewson	25.00	18.50	8.75
176 "Heinie" Manush	14.00	10.50	4.75
177 "Homerun" Baker	15.00	11.00	5.00
178 Max Carey	14.00	10.50	4.75
179 George Sisler	18.00	13.50	6.00
180 "Mickey" Cochrane	21.00	15.50	7.00

	MINT	VG-E	F-G
181 "Spud" Chandler	10.00	7.25	3.25
182 "Knick" Knickerbocker	10.00	7.25	3.25
183 Marvin Breuer	10.00	7.25	3.25
184 "Mule" Haas	10.00	7.25	3.25
185 "Joe" Kuhel	10.00	7.25	3.25
186 Taft Wright	10.00	7.25	3.25
187 "Jimmy" Dykes	12.00	8.75	4.00
188 "Joe" Krakauskas	10.00	7.25	3.25
189 "Jim" Bloodworth	10.00	7.25	3.25
190 "Charley" Berry	10.00	7.25	3.25
191 John Babich	10.00	7.25	3.25
192 "Dick" Siebert	10.00	7.25	3.25
193 "Chubby" Dean	10.00	7.25	3.25
194 "Sam" Chapman	10.00	7.25	3.25
195 "Dee" Miles	10.00	7.25	3.25
196 "Noony" Nonnenkamp	10.00	7.25	3.25
197 "Lou" Finney	10.00	7.25	3.25
198 "Denny" Galehouse	10.00	7.25	3.25
199 "Pinky" Higgins	10.00	7.25	3.25
200 "Soup" Campbell	10.00	7.25	3.25
201 Barney McCosky	10.00	7.25	3.25
202 "Al" Milnar	10.00	7.25	3.25
203 "Bad News" Hale	10.00	7.25	3.25
204 Harry Eisenstat	10.00	7.25	3.25
205 "Rollie" Hemsley	10.00	7.25	3.25
206 "Chet" Laabs	10.00	7.25	3.25
207 "Gus" Mancuso	10.00	7.25	3.25
208 Lee Gamble	10.00	7.25	3.25
209 "Hy" Vandenberg	10.00	7.25	3.25
210 "Bill" Lohrman	10.00	7.25	3.25
211 "Pop" Joiner	10.00	7.25	3.25
212 "Babe" Young	10.00	7.25	3.25
213 John Rucker	10.00	7.25	3.25
214 "Ken" O'Dea	10.00	7.25	3.25
215 "Johnnie" McCarthy	10.00	7.25	3.25
216 "Joe" Marty	10.00	7.25	3.25
217 Walter Beck	10.00	7.25	3.25
218 "Wally" Millies	10.00	7.25	3.25
219 "Russ" Bauers	10.00	7.25	3.25
220 Mace Brown	10.00	7.25	3.25
221 Lee Handley	10.00	7.25	3.25
222 "Max" Butcher	10.00	7.25	3.25
223 Hugh Jennings	21.00	15.50	7.00
224 "Pie" Traynor	30.00	22.50	10.50
225 "Shoeless Joe" Jackson	50.00	38.00	17.00
226 Harry Hooper	21.00	15.50	7.00
227 "Pop" Haines	21.00	15.50	7.00
228 "Charley" Grimm	12.00	8.75	4.00
229 Buck Herzog	10.00	7.25	3.25
230 "Red" Faber	21.00	15.50	7.00
231 "Dolf" Luque	10.00	7.25	3.25
232 "Goose" Goslin	21.00	15.50	7.00
233 "Moose" Earnshaw	12.00	8.75	4.00
234 Frank "Husk" Chance	25.00	18.50	8.75
235 John J. McGraw	25.00	18.50	8.75
236 Jim Bottomley	21.00	15.50	7.00
237 "Wee Willie" Keeler	30.00	22.50	10.50
238 Tony Lazzeri	17.00	12.50	6.00
239 George Uhle	10.00	7.25	3.25
240 "Bill" Atwood	16.00	12.00	5.00

T227 SERIES OF CHAMPIONS

1941 PLAY BALL HALL OF FAME (72) 2 1/2" X 3 1/8"

"TED" WILLIAMS

14. THEODORE SAMUEL WILLIAMS

Outfielder   Boston Red Sox

Born: San Diego, Cal.   October 30, 1918
Height: 6' 3"   Bats: Left   Throws: Right   Weight: 175 lbs.

Ted Williams proved last year that he was no flash-in-the-pan as one of the outstanding rookies of 1939. He batted a powerful .344, brought in 113 runs and led the league in runs scored for the Boston Red Sox with 134. His drives included 23 home runs, 14 triples and 43 two-base hits, with a total of 193 safe blows. He also improved his fielding percentage by 15 points. An enthusiastic ball player who would rather wield a bat than eat. Williams looms as one of the great hitters of modern times.

PLAY BALL
Sports Hall of Fame
Also ask for BLONY Super Bubble Gum, "the sweet that lasts longer."
© 1941   GUM, INC., Phila., Pa.   PRINTED IN U.S.A.

The 1941 Play Ball set, R-336 (ACC), is Gum, Inc.'s only color set. Card nos. 49–72 are slightly more difficult to obtain. A parallel paper issue is also known to exist.

	MINT	VG-E	F-G
COMPLETE SET	1100.00	800.00	350.00
COMMON PLAYER (1-48)	7.00	5.50	2.50
COMMON PLAYER (49-72)	9.00	6.75	3.00
1 Eddie Miller	20.00	8.00	3.00
2 Max West	7.00	5.50	2.50
3 Bucky Walters	7.00	5.50	2.50
4 Paul Derringer	9.00	6.75	3.00
5 Buck McCormick	7.00	5.50	2.50
6 Carl Hubbell	25.00	18.50	8.75
7 Harry Danning	7.00	5.50	2.50
8 Mel Ott	30.00	22.50	10.50
9 "Pinky" May	7.00	5.50	2.50
10 Arkie Vaughn	10.00	7.00	3.00
11 Debs Garms	7.00	5.50	2.50
12 Jimmy Brown	7.00	5.50	2.50
13 Jimmy Foxx	35.00	26.00	12.00
14 Ted Williams	160.00	120.00	55.00
15 Joe Cronin	22.00	16.50	7.50
16 Hal Trosky	7.00	5.50	2.50
17 Roy Weatherly	7.00	5.50	2.50
18 Hank Greenberg	25.00	18.50	8.75
19 Charlie Gehringer	20.00	15.00	6.50
20 "Red" Ruffing	18.00	13.50	6.00
21 Charlie Keller	10.00	7.00	3.00
22 "Indian Bob" Johnson	7.00	5.50	2.50
23 George McQuinn	7.00	5.50	2.50
24 "Dutch" Leonard	7.00	5.50	2.50
25 Gene Moore	7.00	5.50	2.50
26 Harry Gumpert	7.00	5.50	2.50
27 "Babe" Young	7.00	5.50	2.50
28 Joe Marty	7.00	5.50	2.50
29 Jack Wilson	7.00	5.50	2.50
30 Lou Finney	7.00	5.50	2.50
31 Joe Kuhel	7.00	5.50	2.50
32 Taft Wright	7.00	5.50	2.50
33 Al Milnar	7.00	5.50	2.50
34 Rollie Hemsley	7.00	5.50	2.50
35 "Pinky" Higgins	7.00	5.00	2.50
36 Barney McCosky	7.00	5.00	2.50
37 Bruce Campbell	7.00	5.00	2.50
38 Atley Donald	7.00	5.00	2.50
39 Tom Henrich	12.00	8.75	4.00
40 John Babich	7.00	5.00	2.50
41 "Pinky" Hayes	7.00	5.00	2.50
42 Wally Moses	7.00	5.00	2.50
43 Al Brancato	7.00	5.00	2.50
44 Sam Chapman	7.00	5.00	2.50
45 Eldon Auker	7.00	5.00	2.50
46 Sid Hudson	7.00	5.00	2.50
47 "Buddy" Lewis	7.00	5.00	2.50
48 Cecil Travis	7.00	5.00	2.50
49 Babe Dahlgren	9.00	6.75	3.00
50 Johnny Cooney	9.00	6.75	3.00
51 Dolph Camilli	9.00	6.75	3.00
52 Kirby Higbe	9.00	6.75	3.00
53 Luke Hamlin	9.00	6.75	3.00
54 Pee Wee Reese	35.00	26.00	12.00
55 Whit Wyatt	9.00	6.75	3.00
56 Johnny VanderMeer	12.00	8.75	4.00
57 Moe Arnovich	9.00	6.75	4.00
58 Frank Demaree	9.00	6.75	4.00
59 Bill Jurges	9.00	6.75	4.00
60 Chuck Klein	16.00	12.00	5.50
61 Vince DiMaggio	16.00	12.00	5.50
62 Elbie Fletcher	9.00	6.75	4.00
63 Dom DiMaggio	16.00	12.50	5.50
64 Bobby Doerr	10.00	7.00	3.00
65 Tommy Bridges	9.00	6.75	4.00
66 Harland Clift	9.00	6.75	4.00
67 Walt Judnich	9.00	6.75	4.00
68 John Knott	9.00	6.75	4.00
69 George Case	9.00	6.75	4.00
70 Bill Dickey	40.00	30.00	13.00
71 Joe DiMaggio	350.00	250.00	100.00
72 "Lefty" Gomez	40.00	27.00	12.00

1941 PLAY BALL PAPER ISSUE

192

I BUY & SELL
Baseball Cards
and COMIC BOOKS

Kovacs Baseball Card Store

DEPT. PG3

16108 Detroit Avenue
Lakewood, Ohio 44107
216-221-5400

The 1960 Post Cereal Sports Stars set contains nine un-numbered cards portraying popular athletes. These large cards were issued as the entire back panel of Post Grape Nuts

MICKEY MANTLE
New York Yankees

	MINT	VG-E	F-G
COMPLETE SET	1300.00	950.00	400.00
COMMON PLAYER (BASEBALL)	125.00	100.00	40.00
Bob Cousy	65.00	48.00	22.00
Don Drysdale	125.00	100.00	40.00
Frank Gifford	90.00	70.00	30.00
Al Kaline	200.00	150.00	65.00
Harmon Killebrew	125.00	100.00	40.00
Ed Mathews	175.00	125.00	60.00
Mickey Mantle	700.00	500.00	200.00
Bob Pettit	65.00	48.00	22.00
John Unitas	90.00	70.00	30.00

The 1961 Post set is Post Cereal's first major set. Cards were available from two sources—the backs of cereal boxes or directly from the company. Many variations exist as the two sources generated cards with slightly different colors as well as textual differences. Twins players came designated as Minnesota (A) on boxes and Minneapolis (B) from the company. Because of this uneven distribution, several cards are relatively difficult to obtain: the nine most difficult cards are (in order) nos. 23, 163, 183, 94, 70, 135, 10, 73, and 113.

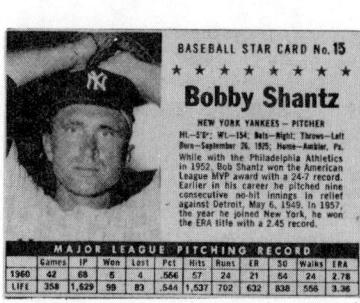

	MINT	VG-E	F-G
COMPLETE SET	350.00	250.00	100.00
COMMON PLAYER	.40	.30	.12

	MINT	VG-E	F-G
1 Yogi Berra	7.00	5.25	2.50
2 Elston Howard	.65	.50	.20
3 Bill Skowron	.60	.45	.20
4 Mickey Mantle	13.00	9.50	4.00
5 Bob Turley	2.00	1.50	.60
6 Whitey Ford	3.00	2.25	1.00
7 Roger Maris	3.00	2.25	1.00
8 Bobby Richardson	.50	.40	.18
9 Tony Kubek	.60	.45	.20
10 Gil McDougald	10.00	7.00	3.00
11 Cletis Boyer	.40	.30	.12
12 Hector Lopez	.40	.30	.12
13 Bob Cerv	.40	.30	.12
14 Ryne Duren	.40	.30	.12
15 Bobby Shantz	.40	.30	.12
16 Art Ditmar	.40	.30	.12
17 Jim Coates	.40	.30	.12
18 John Blanchard	.40	.30	.12
19 Luis Aparicio	.60	.45	.20
20 Nelson Fox	1.00	.70	.30
21 Bill Pierce	.60	.45	.20
22 Early Wynn	3.50	2.50	1.20
23 Bob Shaw	50.00	38.00	17.00
24 Al Smith	.40	.30	.12
25 Minnie Minoso	.75	.55	.25
26 Roy Sievers	.40	.30	.12
27 Jim Landis	.40	.30	.12
28 Sherman Lollar	.40	.30	.12
29 Gerry Staley	.40	.30	.12
30A Gene Freese (W.S.)	.40	.30	.12
30B Gene Freese (Reds)	.75	.55	.25
31 Ted Kluszewski	.75	.55	.25
32 Turk Lown	.40	.30	.12
33 Jim Rivera	.40	.30	.12
34 Frank Baumann	.40	.30	.12
35 Al Kaline	3.50	2.50	1.20
36 Rocky Colavito	.75	.55	.25
37 Charley Maxwell	.40	.30	.12
38 Frank Lary	.40	.30	.12
39 Jim Bunning	.60	.45	.20
40 Norm Cash	.50	.40	.18
41A Frank Bolling (Tigers)	.40	.30	.12
41B Frank Bolling (Braves)	.75	.55	.25
42 Don Mossi	.40	.30	.12
43 Lou Berberet	.40	.30	.12
44 Dave Sisler	.40	.30	.12
45 Ed Yost	.40	.30	.12
46 Pete Burnside	.40	.30	.12
47 Pete Runnels	.40	.30	.12
48 Frank Malzone	.40	.30	.12
49 Vic Wertz	.40	.30	.12
50 Tom Brewer	.40	.30	.12
51A Willie Tasby	.40	.30	.12
51B Willie Tasby (Sold)	.75	.55	.25
52 Russ Nixon	.40	.30	.12
53 Don Buddin	.40	.30	.12
54 Bill Monbouquette	.40	.30	.12
55A Frank Sullivan (R.S.)	.40	.30	.12
55B Frank Sullivan (Phils)	.75	.55	.25

	MINT	VG-E	F-G
56 Haywood Sullivan	.50	.40	.18
57A Harvey Kuenn (Indians)	.50	.40	.18
57B Harvey Kuenn (Giants)	1.00	.70	.30
58 Gary Bell	.40	.30	.12
59 Jim Perry	.50	.40	.18
60 Jim Grant	.40	.30	.12
61 Johnny Temple	.40	.30	.12
62 Paul Foytack	.40	.30	.12
63 Vic Power	.40	.30	.12
64 Tito Francona	.40	.30	.12
65A Ken Aspromonte	.40	.30	.12
65B Ken Aspromonte (Sold)	.75	.55	.25
66 Bob Wilson	.40	.30	.12
67 John Romano	.40	.30	.12
68 Jim Gentile	.40	.30	.12
69 Gus Triandos	.40	.30	.12
70 Gene Woodling	13.00	9.50	4.00
71 Milt Pappas	.40	.30	.12
72 Ron Hansen	.40	.30	.12
73 Chuck Estrada	10.00	7.00	3.00
74 Steve Barber	.40	.30	.12
75 Brooks Robinson	3.50	2.50	1.20
76 Jackie Brandt	.40	.30	.12
77 Marv Breeding	.40	.30	.12
78 Hal Brown	.40	.30	.12
79 Billy Klaus	.40	.30	.12
80 Hoyt Wilhelm	.75	.55	.25
81 Jerry Lumpe	.40	.30	.12
82 Norm Siebern	.40	.30	.12
83 Bud Daley	.40	.30	.12
84 Bill Tuttle	.40	.30	.12
85 Marv Throneberry	.40	.30	.12
86 Dick Williams	.50	.40	.18
87 Ray Herbert	.40	.30	.12
88 Whitey Herzog	.50	.40	.18
89A Ken Hamlin	.40	.30	.12
89B Ken Hamlin (Sold)	.75	.55	.25
90 Hank Bauer	.50	.40	.08
91A Bob Allison	1.00	.70	.30
91B Bob Allison	.50	.40	.18
92A Harmon Killebrew	5.00	3.74	1.75
92B Harmon Killebrew	2.50	1.80	.80
93A Jim Lemon	.80	.60	.25
93B Jim Lemon	.40	.30	.12
94A Chuck Stobbs	has not been verified		
94B Chuck Stobbs	18.00	13.50	6.00
95A Reno Bertoia	.80	.60	.25
95B Reno Bertoia	.40	.30	.12
96A Billy Gardner	.80	.60	.25
96B Billy Gardner	.40	.30	.12
97A Earl Battey	.80	.60	.25
97B Earl Battey	.40	.30	.12
98A Pedro Ramos	.80	.60	.25
98B Pedro Ramos	.40	.30	.12
99A Camilo Pascual	.00	.60	.25
99B Camilo Pascual	.40	.30	.12
100A Billy Consolo	.80	.60	.25
100B Billy Consolo	.40	.30	.12
101 Warren Spahn	3.50	2.50	1.20

1961 POST (CONTINUED)

	MINT	VG-E	F-G
102 Lew Burdette	.75	.55	.25
103 Bob Buhl	.40	.30	.12
104 Joe Adcock	.50	.40	.18
105 John Logan	.40	.30	.12
106 Ed Mathews	6.50	5.00	2.25
107 Hank Aaron	10.00	7.00	3.00
108 Wes Covington	.40	.30	.12
109A Bill Bruton (Braves)	.40	.30	.12
109B Bill Bruton (Tigers)	.80	.60	.25
110 Del Crandall	.40	.30	.12
111 Red Schoendienst	.50	.40	.18
112 Juan Pizarro	.40	.30	.12
113 Chuck Cottier	9.00	6.75	3.00
114 Al Spangler	.40	.30	.12
115 Dick Farrell	.40	.30	.12
116 Jim Owens	.40	.30	.12
117 Robin Roberts	2.50	1.80	.80
118 Tony Taylor	.40	.30	.12
119 Lee Walls	.40	.30	.12
120 Tony Curry	.40	.30	.12
121 Pancho Herrera	.40	.30	.12
122 Ken Walters	.40	.30	.12
123 John Callison	.40	.30	.12
124A Gene Conley (Phils)	.40	.30	.12
124B Gene Conley (R.S.)	.80	.60	.25
125 Bob Friend	.40	.30	.12
126 Vernon Law	.40	.30	.12
127 Dick Stuart	.40	.30	.12
128 Bill Mazeroski	.50	.40	.18
129 Dick Groat	.50	.40	.18
130 Don Hoak	.40	.30	.12
131 Bob Skinner	.40	.30	.12
132 Bob Clemente	7.00	5.25	2.50
133 Roy Face	.40	.30	.12
134 Harvey Haddix	.40	.30	.12
135 Bill Virdon	12.00	8.75	4.00
136 Gino Cimoli	.40	.30	.12
137 Rocky Nelson	.40	.30	.12
138 Smoky Burgess	.40	.30	.12
139 Hal Smith	.40	.30	.12
140 Wilmer Mizell	.40	.30	.12
141 Mike McCormick	.40	.30	.12
142A John Antonelli(S.F.)	.50	.40	.18
142B John Antonelli(Cle.)	1.00	.70	.30
143 Sam Jones	.40	.30	.12
144 Orlando Cepeda	1.00	.70	.30
145 Willie Mays	11.00	8.00	3.50
146A Willie Kirkland(S.F.)	.40	.30	.12
146A Willie Kirkland(Cle.)	.80	.60	.25
147 Willie McCovey	2.50	1.80	.80
148 Don Blasingame	.40	.30	.12
149 Jim Davenport	.40	.30	.12
150 Hobie Landrith	.40	.30	.12

	MINT	VG-E	F-
151 Bob Schmidt	.40	.30	.1
152 Ed Bressoud	.40	.30	.1
153A Andre Rodgers	.40	.30	.1
153B Andre Rodgers(Traded)	.80	.60	.2
154 Jack Sanford	.40	.30	.1
155 Billy O'Dell	.40	.30	.1
156 Norm Larker	.40	.30	.1
157 Charlie Neal	.40	.30	.1
158 Jim Gilliam	1.00	.30	.1
159 Wally Moon	.40	.30	.1
160 Don Drysdale	2.50	1.80	.80
161 Larry Sherry	.40	.30	.1
162 Stan Williams	4.00	3.00	1.40
163 Mel Roach	35.00	26.00	12.00
164 Maury Wills	1.00	.70	.30
165 Tom Davis	.50	.40	.18
166 John Roseboro	.40	.30	.1
167 Duke Snider	2.50	1.80	.80
168 Gil Hodges	2.50	1.80	.80
169 John Podres	.50	.40	.18
170 Ed Roebuck	.40	.30	.1
171 Ken Boyer	.75	.55	.2
172 Joe Cunningham	.40	.30	.1
173 Daryl Spencer	.40	.30	.1
174 Larry Jackson	.40	.30	.1
175 Lindy McDaniel	.40	.30	.1
176 Bill White	.40	.30	.1
177 Alex Grammas	.40	.30	.1
178 Curt Flood	.40	.30	.1
179 Ernie Broglio	.40	.30	.1
180 Hal Smith	.40	.30	.1
181 Vada Pinson	.60	.45	.20
182 Frank Robinson	3.50	2.50	1.20
183 Roy McMillan	30.00	22.50	10.50
184 Bob Purkey	.40	.30	.1
185 Ed Kasko	.40	.30	.1
186 Gus Bell	.40	.30	.1
187 Jerry Lynch	.40	.30	.1
188 Ed Bailey	.40	.30	.1
189 Jim O'Toole	.40	.30	.1
190A Billy Martin	.75	.55	.2
190B Billy Martin (Sold)	1.50	1.10	.50
191 Ernie Banks	4.00	3.00	1.40
192 Richie Ashburn	.75	.55	.25
193 Frank Thomas	.40	.30	.1
194 Don Cardwell	.40	.30	.1
195 George Altman	.40	.30	.1
196 Ron Santo	.60	.45	.20
197 Glen Hobbie	.40	.30	.1
198 Sam Taylor	.40	.30	.1
199 Jerry Kindall	.40	.30	.1
200 Don Elston	.40	.30	.1

1962 POST CEREAL (200)   2 1/2" X 3 1/2"

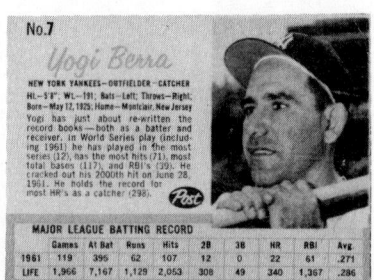

No.7
Yogi Berra

NEW YORK YANKEES—OUTFIELDER—CATCHER
Ht.—5'8", Wt.—191, Bats—Left, Throws—Right,
Born—May 12, 1925, Home—Montclair, New Jersey
Yogi has just about re-written the record books—both as a batter and receiver. He played in the most series (17), has the most hits (71), most total bases (117), and RBI's (39). He cracked out his 2000th hit on June 28, 1961. He holds the record for most HR's as a catcher (298).

MAJOR LEAGUE BATTING RECORD

	Games	At Bat	Runs	Hits	2B	3B	HR	RBI	Avg
1961	119	395	62	107	12	0	22	61	.271
LIFE	1,966	7,167	1,129	2,053	308	49	340	1,387	.286

The 1962 Post set is the easiest of the Post sets to complete. Still, there are numerous relative scarcities—the key cards being 140, 116, 92, 101, 131 and 55. Although the numbers are the same, the 1962 Jello and the 1962 Post Canadian sets are considered separate issues. Mantle and Maris ad cards are listed in the checklist as they were distributed through a promotion with national magazines.

	MINT	VG-E	F-G
COMPLETE SET	250.00	185.00	80.00
COMMON PLAYER	.35	.25	.10
1 Bill Skowron	.60	.45	.20
2 Bobby Richardson	.50	.40	.18
3 Cletis Boyer	.35	.25	.10
4 Tony Kubek	.60	.45	.20
5A Mickey Mantle	12.00	8.75	4.00
5B Mickey Mantle (ad)	12.00	8.75	4.00
6A Roger Maris	3.50	2.50	1.20
6B Roger Maris (ad)	3.50	2.50	1.20
7 Yogi Berra	4.50	3.50	1.60
8 Elston Howard	.60	.45	.20
9 Whitey Ford	3.00	2.25	1.00
10 Ralph Terry	.35	.25	.10
11 John Blanchard	.35	.25	.10
12 Luis Arroyo	.35	.25	.10
13 Bill Stafford	.35	.25	.10
14 Norm Cash	.50	.40	.18
15 Jake Wood	.35	.25	.10
16 Steve Boros	.35	.25	.10
17 Chico Fernandez	.35	.25	.10
18 Bill Bruton	.35	.25	.10

	MINT	VG-E	F-G
19 Rocky Colavito	.60	.45	.20
20 Al Kaline	3.50	2.50	1.20
21 Dick Brown	.35	.25	.10
22 Frank Lary	.35	.25	.10
23 Don Mossi	.35	.25	.10
24 Phil Regan	.35	.25	.10
25 Charley Maxwell	.35	.25	.10
26 Jim Bunning	.60	.45	.20
27 Jim Gentile	.35	.25	.10
28 Marv Breeding	.35	.25	.10
29 Brooks Robinson	3.50	2.50	1.20
30 Ron Hansen	.35	.25	.10
31 Jackie Brandt	.35	.25	.10
32 Dick Williams	.50	.40	.18
33 Gus Triandos	.35	.25	.10
34 Milt Pappas	.35	.25	.10
35 Hoyt Wilhelm	.75	.55	.25
36 Chuck Estrada	.35	.25	.10
37 Vic Power	.35	.25	.10
38 Johnny Temple	.35	.25	.10

	MINT	VG-E	F-G
39 Bubba Phillips	.35	.25	.10
40 Tito Francona	.35	.25	.10
41 Willie Kirkland	.35	.25	.10
42 John Romano	.35	.25	.10
43 Jim Perry	.50	.40	.18
44 Woodie Held	.35	.25	.10
45 Chuck Essegian	.35	.25	.10
46 Roy Sievers	.35	.25	.10
47 Nellie Fox	1.00	.70	.30
48 Al Smith	.35	.25	.10
49 Luis Aparicio	.75	.55	.25
50 Jim Landis	.35	.25	.10
51 Minnie Minoso	.75	.55	.25
52 Andy Carey	.35	.25	.10
53 Sherman Lollar	.35	.25	.10
54 Bill Pierce	.60	.45	.20
55 Early Wynn	12.50	9.00	4.00
56 Chuck Schilling	.35	.25	.10
57 Pete Runnels	.35	.25	.10
58 Frank Malzone	.35	.25	.10
59 Don Buddin	.35	.25	.10
60 Gary Geiger	.35	.25	.10
61 Carl Yastrzemski	6.00	4.50	2.00
62 Jackie Jensen	.50	.40	.18
63 Jim Pagliaroni	.35	.25	.10
64 Don Schwall	.35	.25	.10
65 Dale Long	.35	.25	.10
66 Chuck Cottier	.35	.25	.10
67 Billy Klaus	.35	.25	.10
68 Coot Veal	.35	.25	.10
69 Marty Keough	8.00	6.00	2.50
70 Willie Tasby	.35	.25	.10
71 Gene Woodling	.35	.25	.10
72 Gene Green	.35	.25	.10
73 Dick Donovan	.35	.25	.10
74 Steve Bilko	.35	.25	.10
75 Rocky Bridges	.35	.25	.10
76 Eddie Yost	.35	.26	.10
77 Leon Wagner	.35	.25	.10
78 Albie Pearson	.35	.25	.10
79 Ken Hunt	.35	.25	.10
80 Earl Averill	.35	.25	.10
81 Ryne Duren	.35	.25	.10
82 Ted Kluszewski	.75	.55	.25
83 Bob Allison	6.00	4.50	2.00
84 Billy Martin	1.00	.70	.30
85 Harmon Killebrew	2.50	1.80	.80
86 Zoilo Versalles	.35	.25	.10
87 Lenny Green	.35	.25	.10
88 Bill Tuttle	.35	.25	.10
89 Jim Lemon	.35	.25	.10
90 Earl Battey	.35	.25	.10
91 Camilo Pascual	.35	.25	.10
92 Norm Sieburn	15.00	11.00	5.00
93 Jerry Lumpe	.35	.25	.10
94 Dick Howser	.50	.40	.18
95 Gene Stephens	.35	.25	.10
96 Leo Posada	.35	.25	.10
97 Joe Pignatano	.35	.25	.10
98 Jim Archer	.35	.25	.10
99 Haywood Sullivan	.50	.40	.18
100 Art Ditmar	.35	.25	.10
101 Gil Hodges	20.00	15.00	6.50
102 Charlie Neal	.35	.25	.10
103 Daryl Spencer	7.00	5.25	2.50
104 Maury Wills	1.50	1.10	.50
105 Tommy Davis	.50	.40	.18
106 Willie Davis	.35	.25	.10
107 John Roseboro	.35	.25	.10
108 John Podres	.50	.40	.18
109 Sandy Koufax	6.00	4.50	2.00
110 Don Drysdale	2.50	1.80	.80
111 Larry Sherry	.35	.25	.10
112 Jim Gilliam	.75	.55	.25
113 Norm Larker	7.00	5.25	2.50
114 Duke Snider	3.00	2.25	1.00
115 Stan Williams	.35	.25	.10
116 Gordy Coleman	21.00	15.50	7.00
117 Don Blasingame	.35	.25	.10
118 Gene Freese	.35	.25	.10
119 Ed Kasko	.35	.25	.10

	MINT	VG-E	F-G
120 Gus Bell	.35	.25	.10
121 Vada Pinson	.60	.45	.20
122 Frank Robinson	3.00	2.25	1.00
123 Bob Purkey	.35	.25	.10
124 Joey Jay	.35	.25	.10
125 Jim Brosnan	7.00	5.25	2.50
126 Jim O'Toole	.35	.25	.10
127 Jerry Lynch	9.00	6.75	3.00
128 Wally Post	.35	.25	.10
129 Ken Hunt	.35	.25	.10
130 Jerry Zimmerman	.35	.25	.10
131 Willie McCovey	20.00	15.00	6.50
132 Jose Pagan	.35	.25	.10
133 Felipe Alou	.35	.25	.10
134 Jim Davenport	.35	.25	.10
135 Harvey Kuenn	.50	.40	.18
136 Orlando Cepeda	1.00	.70	.30
137 Ed Bailey	.35	.25	.10
138 Sam Jones	.35	.25	.10
139 Mike McCormick	.35	.25	.10
140 Juan Marichal	32.00	24.00	11.00
141 Jack Sanford	.35	.25	.10
142 Willie Mays	12.00	8.75	4.00
143 Stu Miller	1.50	1.10	.50
144 Joe Amalfitano	6.00	4.50	2.00
145 Joe Adcock	.35	.25	.10
146 Frank Bolling	.35	.25	.10
147 Ed Mathews	2.50	1.80	.80
148 Roy McMillan	.35	.25	.10
149 Hank Aaron	9.00	6.75	3.00
150 Gino Cimoli	.35	.25	.10
151 Frank Thomas	.35	.25	.10
152 Joe Torre	.75	.55	.25
153 Lew Burdette	.50	.40	.18
154 Bob Buhl	.35	.25	.10
155 Carlton Willey	.35	.25	.10
156 Lee Maye	.35	.25	.10
157 Al Spangler	.35	.25	.10
158 Bill White	6.00	4.50	2.00
159 Ken Boyer	.75	.55	.25
160 Joe Cunningham	.35	.25	.10
161 Carl Warwick	.35	.25	.10
162 Carl Sawatski	.35	.25	.10
163 Lindy McDaniel	.35	.25	.10
164 Ernie Broglio	.35	.25	.10
165 Larry Jackson	.35	.25	.10
166 Curt Flood	.50	.40	.18
167 Curt Simmons	.35	.25	.10
168 Alex Grammas	.35	.25	.10
169 Dick Stuart	.50	.40	.18
170 Bill Mazeroski	.35	.25	.10
171 Don Hoak	.50	.40	.18
172 Dick Groat	6.00	4.50	2.00
173 Roberto Clemente	.35	.25	.10
174 Bob Skinner	.75	.55	.25
175 Bill Virdon	.35	.25	.10
176 Smokey Burgess	.35	.25	.10
177 Elroy Face	.35	.25	.10
178 Bob Friend	.35	.25	.10
179 Vernon Law	.35	.25	.10
180 Harvey Haddix	.35	.25	.10
181 Hal Smith	.35	.25	.10
182 Ed Bouchee	.50	.40	.18
183 Don Zimmer	.60	.45	.20
184 Ron Santo	.35	.25	.10
185 Andre Rodgers	.75	.55	.25
186 Richie Ashburn	.35	.25	.10
187 George Altman	4.00	3.00	1.40
188 Ernie Banks	.35	.25	.10
189 Sam Taylor	.35	.25	.10
190 Don Elston	.35	.25	.10
191 Jerry Kindall	.35	.25	.10
192 Pancho Herrera	.35	.25	.10
193 Tony Taylor	.35	.25	.10
194 Ruben Amaro	.35	.25	.10
195 Don Demeter	.35	.25	.10
196 Bobby Gene Smith	.35	.25	.10
197 Clay Dalrymple	2.50	1.80	.80
198 Robin Roberts	.35	.25	.10
199 Art Mahaffey	.35	.25	.10
200 John Buzhardt	.35	.25	.10

1963 POST CEREAL (200) 2 1/2" X 3 1/2"

The 1963 Post set is an extremely difficult set to complete. There are numerous cards of various scarcities.

The most difficult cards, listed in order of known scarcity, are 187, 61, 128, 15, 80, 16, 196, 87, 119, 152 and 162.

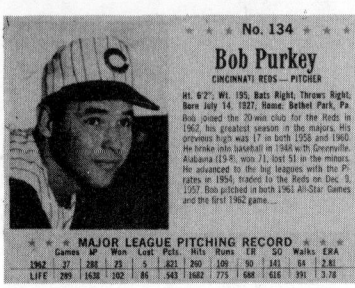

The 1963 Post cards are easily confused with the 1963 Jello cards as the Jello cards are identical to the Post cards except that the Jello cards are ¼" narrower.

	MINT	VG-E	F-G
COMPLETE SET	1000.00	700.00	300.00
COMMON PLAYER	.40	.30	.12
1 Vic Power	.40	.30	.12
2 Bernie Allen	.40	.30	.12
3 Zoilo Versalles	.40	.30	.12
4 Rich Rollins	.40	.30	.12
5 Harmon Killebrew	3.00	2.25	1.00
6 Lenny Green	20.00	15.00	6.50
7 Bob Allison	.40	.30	.12
8 Earl Battey	.40	.30	.12
9 Camilo Pascual	.40	.30	.12
10 Jim Kaat	.60	.45	.20
11 Jack Kralick	.40	.30	.12
12 Bill Skowron	.50	.40	.18
13 Bobby Richardson	.50	.40	.18
14 Cletis Boyer	.40	.30	.12
15 Mickey Mantle	125.00	90.00	40.00
16 Roger Maris	40.00	30.00	13.00
17 Yogi Berra	4.50	3.50	1.60
18 Elston Howard	.75	.55	.25
19 Whitey Ford	4.00	3.00	1.40
20 Ralph Terry	.40	.30	.12
21 John Blanchard	.40	.30	.12
22 Bill Stafford	.40	.30	.12
23 Tom Tresh	.40	.30	.12
24 Steve Bilko	.40	.30	.12
25 Bill Moran	.40	.30	.12
26 Joe Koppe	.40	.30	.12
27 Felix Torres	.40	.30	.12
28 Leon Wagner	.40	.30	.12
29 Albie Pearson	.40	.30	.12
30 Lee Thomas	20.00	15.00	6.50
31 Bob Rodgers	.40	.30	.12
32 Dean Chance	.40	.30	.12
33 Ken McBride	.40	.30	.12
34 George Thomas	.40	.30	.12
35 Joe Cunningham	.40	.30	.12
36 Nelson Fox	1.00	.70	.30
37 Luis Aparicio	.80	.60	.25
38 Al Smith	16.00	12.00	5.50
39 Floyd Robinson	25.00	18.50	8.75
40 Jim Landis	.40	.30	.12
41 Charlie Maxwell	.40	.30	.12
42 Sherman Lollar	.40	.30	.12
43 Early Wynn	2.50	1.80	.80
44 Juan Pizarro	.40	.30	.12
45 Ray Herbert	.40	.30	.12
46 Norm Cash	.50	.40	.18
47 Steve Boros	.40	.30	.12
48 Dick McAuliffe	10.00	7.00	3.00
49 Bill Bruton	.40	.30	.12
50 Rocky Colavito	.75	.55	.25
51 Al Kaline	3.50	2.50	1.20
52 Dick Brown	.40	.30	.12
53 Jim Bunning	30.00	22.50	10.50
54 Hank Aguirre	.40	.30	.12
55 Frank Lary	.40	.30	.12
56 Don Mossi	.40	.30	.12
57 Jim Gentile	.40	.30	.12
58 Jackie Brandt	.40	.30	.12
59 Brooks Robinson	3.50	2.50	1.20
60 Ron Hansen	.40	.30	.12
61 Jerry Adair	90.00	70.00	30.00
62 John Powell	.75	.55	.25
63 Russ Snyder	.40	.30	.12
64 Steve Barber	.40	.30	.12
65 Milt Pappas	.50	.40	.18
66 Robin Roberts	2.50	1.80	.80
67 Tito Francona	.40	.30	.12
68 Jerry Kindall	.40	.30	.12
69 Woody Held	.40	.30	.12
70 Bubba Phillips	6.00	4.50	2.00
71 Chuck Essegian	.40	.30	.12
72 Willie Kirkland	.40	.30	.12
73 Al Luplow	3.00	2.25	1.00
74 Ty Cline	.40	.30	.12
75 Dick Donovan	.40	.30	.12
76 John Romano	.40	.30	.12
77 Pete Runnels	.40	.30	.12
78 Ed Bressoud	.40	.30	.12
79 Frank Malzone	.40	.30	.12
80 Carl Yastrzemski	100.00	70.00	30.00
81 Gary Geiger	.40	.30	.12
82 Lou Clinton	.40	.30	.12
83 Earl Wilson	.40	.30	.12
84 Bill Monbouquette	.40	.30	.12
85 Norm Sieburn	.40	.30	.12
86 Jerry Lumpe	25.00	18.50	8.75
87 Manny Jimenez	35.00	26.00	12.00
88 Gino Cimoli	.40	.30	.12
89 Ed Charles	.40	.30	.12
90 Ed Rakow	.40	.30	.12
91 Bob DelGreco	.40	.30	.12
92 Haywood Sullivan	.50	.40	.18
93 Chuck Hinton	.40	.30	.12
94 Ken Retzer	.40	.30	.12
95 Harry Bright	.40	.30	.12
96 Bob Johnson	.40	.30	.12
97 Dave Stenhouse	.40	.30	.12
98 Chuck Cottier	12.00	8.75	4.00
99 Tom Cheney	.40	.30	.12
100 Claude Osteen	6.00	4.50	2.00
101 Orlando Cepeda	1.00	.70	.30
102 Charley Hiller	.40	.30	.12
103 Jose Pagan	.40	.30	.12
104 Jim Davenport	.40	.30	.12
105 Harvey Kuenn	.50	.40	.18
106 Willie Mays	9.00	6.75	3.00
107 Felipe Alou	.50	.40	.18
108 Tom Haller	20.00	15.00	6.50
109 Juan Marichal	1.25	.90	.40
110 Jack Sanford	.40	.30	.12
111 Bill O'Dell	.40	.30	.12
112 Willie McCovey	2.00	1.50	.60
113 Lee Walls	.40	.30	.12
114 Jim Gilliam	.75	.55	.25
115 Maury Wills	1.00	.70	.30
116 Ron Fairly	.50	.40	.18
117 Tommy Davis	.50	.40	.18
118 Duke Snider	3.00	2.25	1.00
119 Willie Davis	35.00	26.00	12.00
120 John Roseboro	.40	.30	.12
121 Sandy Koufax	6.00	4.50	2.00
122 Stan Williams	.40	.30	.12
123 Don Drysdale	2.00	1.50	.60
124 Daryl Spencer	.40	.30	.12
125 Gordy Coleman	.40	.30	.12

	MINT	VG-E	F-G
126 Don Blasingame	.40	.30	.12
127 Leo Cardenas	.40	.30	.12
128 Eddie Kasko	90.00	70.00	30.00
129 Jerry Lynch	.40	.30	.12
130 Vada Pinson	.60	.45	.20
131 Frank Robinson	3.00	2.25	1.00
132 John Edwards	.40	.30	.12
133 Joey Jay	.40	.30	.12
134 Bob Purkey	.40	.30	.12
135 Marty Keough	12.00	8.75	4.00
136 Jim O'Toole	.40	.30	.12
137 Dick Stuart	.40	.30	.12
138 Bill Mazeroski	.50	.40	.18
139 Dick Groat	.50	.40	.18
140 Don Hoak	10.00	7.00	3.00
141 Bob Skinner	5.00	3.75	1.75
142 Bill Virdon	.75	.55	.25
143 Roberto Clemente	6.50	5.00	2.25
144 Smokey Burgess	.40	.30	.12
145 Bob Friend	.40	.30	.12
146 Al McBean	.40	.30	.12
147 Elroy Face	.40	.30	.12
148 Joe Adcock	.40	.30	.12
149 Frank Bolling	.40	.30	.12
150 Roy McMillan	.40	.30	.12
151 Eddie Mathews	6.00	4.50	2.00
152 Hank Aaron	35.00	26.00	12.00
153 Del Crandall	10.00	7.00	3.00
154 Bob Shaw	.40	.30	.12
155 Lew Burdette	.60	.45	.20
156 Joe Torre	.60	.45	.20
157 Tony Cloninger	.40	.30	.12
158 Bill White	.40	.30	.12
159 Julian Javier	.40	.30	.12
160 Ken Boyer	.75	.55	.25
161 Julio Gotay	.40	.30	.12
162 Curt Flood	35.00	26.00	12.00

	MINT	VG-E	F-G
163 Charlie James	.40	.30	.12
164 Gene Oliver	.40	.30	.12
165 Ernie Broglio	.40	.30	.12
166 Bob Gibson	2.50	1.80	.80
167 Lindy McDaniel	.40	.30	.12
168 Ray Washburn	.40	.30	.12
169 Ernie Banks	3.50	2.50	1.20
170 Ron Santo	.60	.45	.20
171 George Altman	.40	.30	.12
172 Billy Williams	25.00	18.50	8.75
173 Andre Rodgers	4.00	3.00	1.40
174 Ken Hubbs	10.00	7.00	3.00
175 Don Landrum	.40	.30	.12
176 Dick Bertell	12.00	8.75	4.00
177 Roy Sievers	.40	.30	.12
178 Tony Taylor	.40	.30	.12
179 John Callison	.40	.30	.12
180 Don Demeter	.40	.30	.12
181 Tony Gonzalez	.40	.30	.12
182 Wes Covington	6.00	4.50	2.00
183 Art Mahaffey	.40	.30	.12
184 Clay Dalrymple	.40	.30	.12
185 Al Spangler	.40	.30	.12
186 Roman Mejias	.40	.30	.12
187 Bob Aspromonte	100.00	70.00	30.00
188 Norm Larker	12.00	8.75	4.00
189 Johnny Temple	.40	.30	.12
190 Carl Warwick	.40	.30	.12
191 Bob Lillis	.40	.30	.12
192 Dick Farrell	.40	.30	.12
193 Gil Hodges	2.50	1.80	.80
194 Marv Throneberry	.50	.40	.18
195 Charlie Neal	6.00	4.50	2.00
196 Frank Thomas	60.00	45.00	20.00
197 Richie Ashburn	3.00	2.25	1.00
198 Felix Mantilla	.40	.30	.12
199 Rod Kanehl	3.00	2.25	1.00
200 Roger Craig	.50	.40	.18

1954 RED HEART (33)　　　　2 5/8" X 3 3/4"

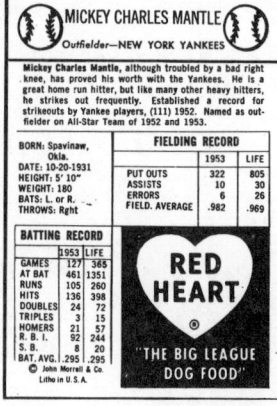

The 1954 Red Heart set is a popular 33 card set issued with Red Heart Dog Food. The set contains three groups of eleven cards which can be distinguished by their background color -red, green, or blue. Cards with red backgrounds are somewhat more difficult to obtain than the cards of the other two colors.

	MINT	VG-E	F-G
COMPLETE SET	290.00	215.00	100.00
COMMON PLAYER	6.50	5.00	2.25
Richie Ashburn(red)	8.50	6.50	3.00
Frank Baumholtz(red)	7.50	5.75	2.50
Gus Bell	6.50	5.00	2.25
Billy Cox	6.50	5.00	2.25
Alvin Dark	7.50	5.75	2.50
Carl Erskine(red)	8.50	6.50	3.00
Ferris Fain	6.50	5.00	2.25
Dee Fondy	6.50	5.00	2.25
Nelson Fox	8.00	6.00	2.50
Jim Gilliam	8.00	6.00	2.50
Jim Hegan(red)	7.50	5.75	2.50
George Kell	7.50	5.75	2.50
Ralph Kiner(red)	12.50	9.00	4.00
Ted Kluszewski (red)	9.00	6.75	3.00
Harvey Kuenn	7.50	5.75	2.50

	MINT	VG-E	F-G
Bob Lemon(red)	12.50	9.00	4.00
Sherman Lollar	6.50	5.00	2.25
Mickey Mantle	45.00	34.00	15.00
Billy Martin	11.00	8.00	3.50
Gil McDougald(red)	7.50	5.75	2.50
Roy McMillan	6.50	5.00	2.25
Minnie Minoso	7.50	5.75	2.50
Stan Musial(red)	50.00	38.00	17.00
Billy Pierce	7.50	5.75	2.50
Al Rosen(red)	11.00	8.00	3.50
Hank Sauer	7.50	3.75	2.50
Red Schoendienst(red)	8.50	6.50	3.00
Enos Slaughter	8.50	6.50	3.00
Duke Snider	16.00	12.00	5.50
Warren Spahn	12.50	9.00	4.00
Sammy White	6.50	5.00	2.25
Eddie Yost	6.50	5.00	2.25
Gus Zernial	6.50	5.00	2.25

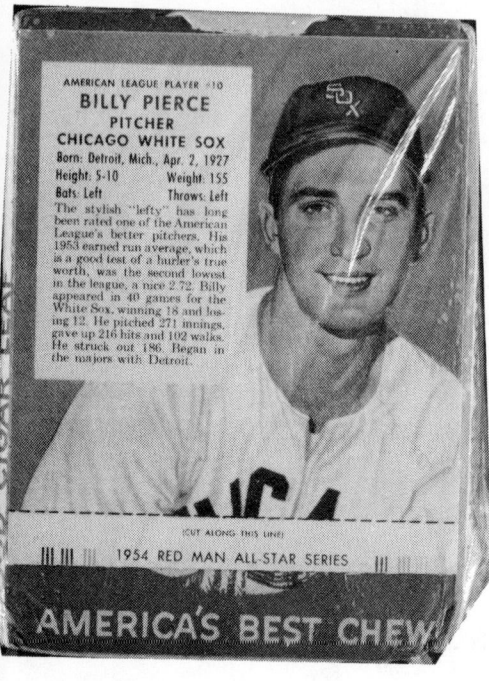

RED MAN UNOPENED PACKAGE

1952 RED MAN (52)

3 1/2" X 4"

RED MAN'S DOUBLE-HEADER FOR BASEBALL FANS!

(1) 52 Full-Color Picture Cards of Red Man's All-Star Major League Baseball Players

(2) *FREE OF EXTRA COST*—Big League Style Baseball Cap! (see details below)

Look at the other side of this card. You'll find a full-color picture and story of one of the 52 famous stars on the Red Man Big League teams — 25 top players in the American League and 25 in the National League — all selected by Editor J. G. Taylor Spink of baseball's bible, "The Sporting News," plus the 1951 World Series Managers, Casey Stengel of the Yankees and Leo Durocher of the Giants. Save these pictures — trade duplicates with your friends. These prints are found only in packages of famous...

RED MAN CHEWING TOBACCO

And that's not all. You can get the special Red Man bonus — a BIG LEAGUE style baseball cap at NO EXTRA COST to you! Just cut off and save the valuable stub below. When you have collected 50 of these stubs, mail them to Red Man, Box 68, Toledo 6, Ohio. YOU WILL RECEIVE A BASEBALL CAP WITH THE INSIGNIA OF ANY MAJOR LEAGUE TEAM THAT YOU CHOOSE. Be sure to state your name and address, the name of your favorite Major League Baseball team and your cap size (small, medium or large). This offer expires March 31, 1953.

These Baseball Cards are for Red Man "Chewers" and Their Boys

- - - - - - - - - - (CUT ALONG THIS LINE) - - - - - - - - - -
SAVE THIS VALUABLE STUB FOR YOUR
RED MAN BIG LEAGUE STYLE BASEBALL CAP

The 1952 Red Man issue was the first nationally available tobacco issue since the T cards of the teens. This 52 card set contains 26 top players from each league. Cards that have the tab (coupon) attached are generally worth 25% more than cards with the tab removed. Card numbers are located on the tabs.

	MINT	VG-E	F-G
COMPLETE SET	190.00	140.00	70.00
COMMON PLAYER	2.40	1.90	.85
AL 1 Casey Stengel	10.00	7.00	3.00
AL 2 Roberto Avila	2.40	1.90	.85
AL 3 Yogi Berra	12.00	8.75	4.00
AL 4 Gil Coan	2.40	1.90	.85
AL 5 Dom DiMaggio	5.00	3.75	1.75
AL 6 Larry Doby	4.00	3.00	1.40
AL 7 Ferris Fain	2.40	1.90	.85
AL 8 Bob Feller	12.00	8.75	4.00
AL 9 Nelson Fox	4.00	3.00	1.75
AL10 Johnny Groth	2.40	1.90	.85
AL11 Jim Hegan	2.40	1.90	.85
AL12 Eddie Joost	2.40	1.90	.85
AL13 George Kell	3.00	2.25	1.00
AL14 Gil McDougald	3.00	2.25	1.00
AL15 Minnie Minoso	4.00	3.00	1.40
AL16 Billy Pierce	3.00	2.25	1.00
AL17 Bob Porterfield	2.40	1.90	.85
AL18 Eddie Robinson	2.40	1.90	.85
AL19 Saul Rogovin	2.40	1.90	.85
AL20 Bobby Shantz	4.00	3.00	1.75
AL21 Vern Stephens	2.40	1.90	.85
AL22 Vic Wertz	2.40	1.90	.85
AL23 Ted Williams	30.00	22.50	10.50
AL24 Early Wynn	6.00	4.50	2.00

	MINT	VG-E	F-G
AL25 Eddie Yost	2.40	1.90	.85
AL26 Gus Zernial	2.40	1.90	.85
NL 1 Leo Durocher	6.00	4.50	2.00
NL 2 Richie Ashburn	4.00	3.00	1.40
NL 3 Ewell Blackwell	3.00	2.25	1.00
NL 4 Cliff Chambers	2.40	1.90	.85
NL 5 Murray Dickson	2.40	1.90	.85
NL 6 Sid Gordon	2.40	1.90	.85
NL 7 Granny Hamner	2.40	1.90	.85
NL 8 Jim Hearn	2.40	1.90	.85
NL 9 Monte Irvin	5.00	3.75	1.75
NL10 Larry Jansen	2.40	1.90	.85
NL11 Willie Jones	2.40	1.90	.85
NL12 Ralph Kiner	6.00	4.50	2.00
NL13 Whitey Lockman	2.40	1.90	.85
NL14 Sal Maglie	3.00	2.25	1.00
NL15 Willie Mays	30.00	22.50	10.50
NL16 Stan Musial	30.00	22.50	10.50
NL17 Pee Wee Reese	6.00	4.50	2.00
NL18 Robin Roberts	6.00	4.50	2.00
NL19 Al Schoendienst	3.00	2.25	1.00
NL20 Enos Slaughter	5.00	3.75	1.75
NL21 Duke Snider	12.00	8.75	4.00
NL22 Warren Spahn	7.00	5.25	2.50
NL23 Ed Stanky	3.00	2.25	1.00
NL24 Bobby Thomson	4.00	3.00	1.40
NL25 Earl Torgeson	2.40	1.90	.85
NL26 Wes Westrum	2.40	1.90	.85

1953 RED MAN (52)   3 1/2" X 4"

The 1953 Red Man Set contains 26 National League stars and 26 American League stars. Card numbers are located both on the write-up of the player and on the tab. Cards that have the tab (coupon) attached are generally worth 25% more than cards with the tab removed.

AMERICAN LEAGUE PLAYER #10
PHIL RIZZUTO
SHORTSTOP
NEW YORK YANKEES
Born: New York, N. Y., Sep. 25, '18
Height: 5-6   Weight: 160
Bats: Right   Throws: Right
Little Phil found out after the 1952 season that he was suffering from an ulcer. However, in spite of it he appeared in 152 games for the Yankees, batted .254, had 24 doubles, 10 triples and 2 homers among his 147 hits, and he batted in 43 runs. He's a fast man—his nickname is Scooter—and he's one of the best bunters in the business.

1953 AMERICAN LEAGUE SERIES
PHIL RIZZUTO—PLAYER #10

NEW FOR '53—RED MAN'S FAMOUS EXTRAS FOR BASEBALL FANS!
52 Full-Color Picture Cards of Red Man's All-Star Major League Baseball Players
PLUS A Big League Style Baseball Cap—FREE OF EXTRA COST! (see below)
On the other side of this card is a full-color picture and story of one of the 52 famous Red Man All-Stars—25 top players from the American League and 25 from the National—all personally selected by Editor J. G. Taylor Spink of "The Sporting News," plus 1952 World Series managers. Collect these pictures—trade with your friends. Remember, they come only in packages of famous

RED MAN CHEWING TOBACCO

And here's the special Red Man bonus—a BIG LEAGUE style baseball cap at NO EXTRA COST to you! Just cut off and save the stub below. When you have 50 stubs, mail them to Red Man, Box 68, Toledo 6, Ohio. YOU WILL RECEIVE A BASEBALL CAP WITH THE INSIGNIA OF YOUR FAVORITE MAJOR LEAGUE TEAM. Be sure to print your name and address, the name of your favorite major league team, and your cap size (small, medium, or large). This offer expires May 31, 1954.
Red Man "Chewers"—start a collection for your boys
(CUT ALONG THIS LINE)
SAVE THIS VALUABLE STUB FOR YOUR
RED MAN BIG LEAGUE STYLE BASEBALL CAP

	MINT	VG-E	F-G
COMPLETE SET	175.00	135.00	65.00
COMMON PLAYER	2.30	1.80	.80
AL 1 Casey Stengel	10.00	7.00	3.00
AL 2 Hank Bauer	4.00	3.00	1.40

	MINT	VG-E	F-G
AL 3 Yogi Berra	12.00	8.75	4.00
AL 4 Walt Dropo	2.30	1.80	.80
AL 5 Nelson Fox	4.00	3.00	1.40
AL 6 Jackie Jensen	3.00	2.25	1.00
AL 7 Eddie Joost	2.30	1.80	.80

	MINT	VG-E	F-G
AL 8 George Kell	3.00	2.25	1.00
AL 9 Dale Mitchell	2.30	1.80	.80
AL10 Phil Rizzuto	7.00	5.25	2.50
AL11 Eddie Robinson	2.30	1.80	.80
AL12 Gene Woodling	2.30	1.80	.80
AL13 Gus Zernial	2.30	1.80	.80
AL14 Early Wynn	6.00	4.50	2.00
AL15 Joe Dobson	2.30	1.80	.80
AL16 Billy Pierce	3.00	2.25	1.00
AL17 Bob Lemon	6.00	4.50	2.00
AL18 Johnny Mize	5.00	3.75	1.75
AL19 Bob Porterfield	2.30	1.80	.80
AL20 Bobby Shantz	3.00	2.25	1.00
AL21 Mickey Vernon	3.00	2.25	1.00
AL22 Dom DiMaggio	5.00	3.75	1.75
AL23 Gil McDougald	3.00	2.25	1.00
AL24 Al Rosen	5.00	3.75	1.75
AL25 Mel Parnell	2.30	1.80	.80
AL26 Bobby Avila	2.30	1.80	.80
NL 1 Charlie Dressen	2.30	1.80	.80
NL 2 Bobby Adams	2.30	1.80	.80
NL 3 Richie Ashburn	4.00	3.00	1.40

	MINT	VG-E	F-G
NL 4 Joe Black	3.00	2.25	1.00
NL 5 Roy Campanella	16.00	12.00	5.50
NL 6 Ted Kluszewski	4.00	3.00	1.40
NL 7 Whitey Lockman	3.00	2.25	1.00
NL 8 Sal Maglie	3.00	2.25	1.00
NL 9 Andy Pafko	2.30	1.80	.80
NL10 Pee Wee Reese	6.00	4.50	2.00
NL11 Robin Roberts	6.00	4.50	2.00
NL12 Al Schoendienst	3.00	2.25	1.00
NL13 Enos Slaughter	5.00	3.75	1.75
NL14 Duke Snider	12.00	8.75	4.00
NL15 Ralph Kiner	6.00	4.50	2.00
NL16 Hank Sauer	3.00	2.25	1.00
NL17 Del Ennis	2.30	1.80	.80
NL18 Granny Hamner	2.30	1.80	.80
NL19 Warren Spahn	7.00	5.25	2.50
NL20 Wes Westrum	2.30	1.80	.80
NL21 Hoyt Wilhelm	4.00	3.00	1.40
NL22 Murray Dickson	2.30	1.80	.80
NL23 Warren Hacker	2.30	1.80	.80
NL24 Gerry Staley	2.30	1.80	.80
NL25 Bobby Thomson	4.00	3.00	1.40
NL26 Stan Musial	30.00	22.50	10.50

1954 RED MAN (50)   3 1/2" X 4"

The 1954 Red Man set witnessed a reduction to 25 players from each league. Kell, Mele and Philley are known to exist with two different teams. Card no. 19 of the National League exists as Slaughter and as Bell. Card numbers are on the write-ups of the players. Cards that have the tab (coupon) attached are generally worth 25% more than cards with the tab removed.

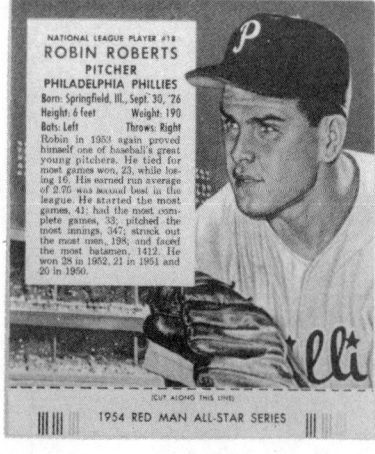

NATIONAL LEAGUE PLAYER #18
ROBIN ROBERTS
PITCHER
PHILADELPHIA PHILLIES
1954 RED MAN ALL-STAR SERIES

	MINT	VG-E	F-G
COMPLETE SET	210.00	155.00	7.00
COMMON PLAYERS	2.20	1.70	.80
AL 1 Bobby Avila	2.20	1.70	.80
AL 2 Jim Busby	2.20	1.70	.80
AL 3 Nelson Fox	4.00	3.00	1.40
AL 4a George Kell (Bos.)	5.00	3.75	1.75
AL 4b George Kell (Chi.)	16.00	12.00	5.50
AL 5 Sherman Lollar	2.20	1.70	.80
AL 6a Sam Mele (Balt.)	3.00	2.25	1.00
AL 6b Sam Mele (Chi.)	15.00	11.00	5.00
AL 7 Minnie Minoso	4.00	3.00	1.40
AL 8 Mel Parnell	2.20	1.70	.80
AL 9a Dave Philley (Cle.)	3.00	2.25	1.00
AL 9b Dave Philley (Phil)	15.00	11.00	5.00
AL10 Billy Pierce	3.00	2.25	1.00
AL11 Jim Piersall	4.00	3.00	1.40
AL12 Al Rosen	5.00	3.75	1.75
AL13 Mickey Vernon	3.00	2.25	1.00
AL14 Sammy White	2.20	1.70	.80
AL15 Gene Woodling	2.20	1.70	.80
AL16 Whitey Ford	7.50	5.75	2.50
AL17 Phil Rizzuto	6.50	5.00	2.25
AL18 Bob Porterfield	2.20	1.70	.80
AL19 Chico Carrasquel	2.20	1.70	.80
AL20 Yogi Berra	12.00	8.75	4.00
AL21 Bob Lemon	6.00	4.50	2.00
AL22 Ferris Fain	2.20	1.70	.80

	MINT	VG-G	F-G
AL23 Hank Bauer	3.50	2.50	1.20
AL24 Jim Delsing	2.20	1.70	.80
AL25 Gil McDougald	3.00	2.25	1.00
NL 1 Richie Ashburn	3.50	2.50	1.20
NL 2 Billy Cox	2.20	1.70	.80
NL 3 Del Crandall	2.20	1.70	.80
NL 4 Carl Erskine	3.00	2.25	1.00
NL 5 Monte Irvin	4.50	3.50	1.60
NL 6 Ted Kluszewski	3.50	2.50	1.20
NL 7 Don Mueller	2.20	1.70	.80
NL 8 Andy Pafko	2.20	1.70	.80
NL 9 Del Rice	2.20	1.70	.80
NL10 Al Schoendienst	3.00	2.25	1.00
NL11 Warren Spahn	6.50	5.00	2.25
NL12 Curt Simmons	2.20	1.70	.80
NL13 Roy Campanella	14.00	10.50	4.75
NL14 Jim Gilliam	4.00	3.00	1.40
NL15 Pee Wee Reese	5.50	4.25	2.00
NL16 Duke Snider	11.00	8.00	3.50
NL17 Rip Repulski	2.20	1.70	.80
NL18 Robin Roberts	5.50	4.25	2.00
NL19a Enos Slaughter	7.50	5.75	2.50
NL19b Gus Bell	15.00	11.00	5.00
NL20 Johnny Logan	2.20	1.70	.80
NL21 John Antonelli	2.20	1.70	.80
NL22 Gil Hodges	6.00	4.50	2.00
NL23 Eddie Mathews	6.00	4.50	2.00
NL24 Lew Burdette	3.00	2.25	1.00
NL25 Willie Mays	30.00	22.50	10.50

1955 RED MAN (50)

3 1/2" X 4"

The 1955 Red Man set contains 25 players from each league. Card numbers are on the write-ups of the players.

Cards that have the tab (coupon) attached are generally worth 25% more than cards with the tab removed.

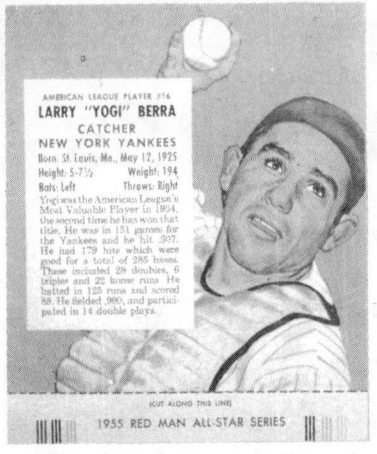

FREE * FOR YOU OR YOUR BOY **RED MAN BIG LEAGUE STYLE BASEBALL CAP**

PLUS 50 Beautiful Full-Color Pictures of the **RED MAN'S 1955 Major League All Stars**

On the other side of this card is a full-color picture and story of one of the 50 famous Red Man All-Stars—25 top players from the American League and 25 from the National—all personally selected by Editor J. G. Taylor Spink of "The Sporting News". Collect these pictures — trade with your friends. Remember, they come only in packages of famous

RED MAN CHEWING TOBACCO

* And here's the special Red Man bonus — a BIG LEAGUE style baseball cap FREE! Just cut off and save the stub below. When you have 50 stubs, mail them to Red Man, Box 68, Toledo 6, Ohio. YOU WILL RECEIVE A BASEBALL CAP WITH THE INSIGNIA OF YOUR FAVORITE MAJOR LEAGUE TEAM. Be sure to print your name and address, the name of your favorite major league team, and your cap size (small, medium, or large). This offer expires April 15, 1956.

Red Man "Chewers"— start a collection for your boys

- - - - - - - - - - - - - (CUT ALONG THIS LINE) - - - - - - - - - - - - -
SAVE THIS VALUABLE STUB FOR YOUR
RED MAN BIG LEAGUE STYLE BASEBALL CAP

	MINT	VG-E	F-G			MINT	VG-E	F-G
COMPLETE SET	175.00	130.00	60.00	AL24	Minnie Minoso	3.50	2.50	1.20
COMMON PLAYERS	2.20	1.70	.80	AL25	Sandy Consuegra	2.20	1.70	.80
				NL 1	Richie Ashburn	3.00	2.25	1.00
AL 1 Ray Boone	2.20	1.70	.80	NL 2	Del Crandall	2.20	1.70	.80
AL 2 Jim Busby	2.20	1.70	.80	NL 3	Gil Hodges	6.00	4.50	2.00
AL 3 Whitey Ford	7.00	5.25	2.50	NL 4	Brooks Lawrence	2.20	1.70	.80
AL 4 Nelson Fox	4.00	3.00	1.40	NL 5	Johnny Logan	2.20	1.70	.80
AL 5 Bob Grim	2.20	1.70	.80	NL 6	Sal Maglie	3.00	2.25	1.00
AL 6 Jack Harshman	2.20	1.70	.80	NL 7	Willie Mays	30.00	22.50	10.50
AL 7 Jim Hegan	2.20	1.70	.80	NL 8	Don Mueller	2.20	1.70	.80
AL 8 Bob Lemon	6.00	4.50	2.00	NL 9	Bill Sarni	2.20	1.70	.80
AL 9 Irv Noren	2.20	1.70	.80	NL10	Warren Spahn	6.50	5.00	2.25
AL10 Bob Porterfield	2.20	1.70	.80	NL11	Hank Thompson	2.20	1.70	.80
AL11 Al Rosen	5.00	3.75	1.75	NL12	Hoyt Wilhelm	4.00	3.00	1.40
AL12 Mickey Vernon	3.00	2.25	1.00	NL13	John Antonelli	2.20	1.70	.80
AL13 Vic Wertz	2.20	1.70	.80	NL14	Carl Erskine	3.00	2.25	1.00
AL14 Early Wynn	6.00	4.50	2.00	NL15	Granny Hamner	2.20	1.70	.80
AL15 Bobby Avila	2.20	1.70	.80	NL16	Ted Kluszewski	3.50	2.50	1.20
AL16 Yogi Berra	11.00	8.00	3.50	NL17	Pee Wee Reese	5.00	3.75	1.75
AL17 Joe Coleman	2.20	1.70	.80	NL18	Al Schoendienst	3.00	2.25	1.00
AL18 Larry Doby	3.50	2.50	1.20	NL19	Duke Snider	11.00	8.00	3.50
AL19 Jackie Jensen	3.00	2.25	1.10	NL20	Frank Thomas	2.20	1.70	.80
AL20 Pete Runnels	2.20	1.70	.80	NL21	Ray Jablonski	2.20	1.70	.80
AL21 Jim Piersall	3.50	2.50	1.20	NL22	Dusty Rhodes	2.20	1.70	.80
AL22 Hank Bauer	3.00	2.25	1.00	NL23	Gus Bell	2.20	1.70	.80
AL23 Chico Carrasquel	2.20	1.70	.80	NL24	Curt Simmons	2.20	1.70	.80
				NL25	Marv Grissom	2.20	1.70	.80

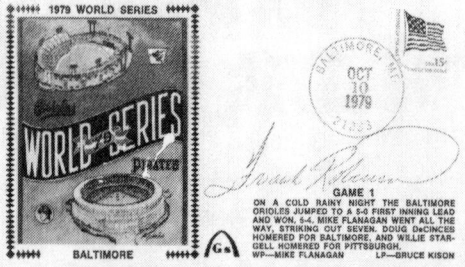

AUTOGRAPHS — F. ROBINSON ENVELOPE

1946 REMAR BREAD (23)　　　　2" X 3"

Hard-hitting CHAS. METRO, 25, joined Oaks in '45. Played in majors with Detroit Tigers, Philadelphia Athletics. Learned baseball on Pennsylvania sandlots. Boyhood idol: Babe Ruth; present-day favorite: Roger Cramer. Likes to bird hunt; enjoys all sports.

CHARLIE METRO
Oaks Outfielder　11

Listen to baseball play by play with "Bud" Foster KROW, 960 on your dial

Get the FOUR HOURS FRESHER winner....
REMAR BREAD

The 1946 Remar Bread set of 23 black and white cards was issued one player per week in stores carrying Remar Bread. The cards are distinguished by a "red loaf" of Remar Bread on the backs of the cards. The first few cards issued are unnumbered and the balance, beginning with number five, are numbered. Raimondi was the first card issued and is quite scarce. A 1945 Oakland Oaks team card might also be considered part of this set. This card is quite scarce. The set features Oakland Oaks players only. The ACC designation is D317-1.

	MINT	VG-E	F-G
COMPLETE SET	210.00	150.00	70.00
COMMON PLAYER	8.25	6.25	3.00

		MINT	VG-E	F-G
5	Herschel Martin	8.25	6.25	3.00
6	Bill Hart	8.25	6.25	3.00
7	Chuck Gassaway	8.25	6.25	3.00
8	Wally Westlake	8.25	6.25	3.00
9	Ora Burnett	8.25	6.25	3.00
10	Casey Stengel	30.00	22.50	10.50
11	Charles Metro	8.25	6.25	3.00
12	Tom Hafey	8.25	6.25	3.00
13	Tony Sabol	8.25	6.25	3.00
14	Ed Kearse	16.00	12.00	5.50
15	Bud Foster	8.25	6.25	3.00
16	Johnny Price	7.50	5.75	2.50

		MINT	VG-E	F-G
17	Gene Bearden	7.50	5.75	2.50
18	Floyd Speer	7.50	5.75	2.50
19	Bryan Stephens	7.50	5.75	2.50
20	Rinaldo Ardizola	8.25	6.25	3.00
21	Ralph Buxton	8.25	6.25	3.00
22	Ambrose Palica	8.25	6.25	3.00
	Brooks Holder	10.00	7.00	3.00
	Henry Pippen	10.00	7.00	3.00
	Bill Raimondi	35.00	26.00	12.00
	Les Scarsella	10.00	7.00	3.00
	Glen Stewart	10.00	7.00	3.00

1947 REMAR BREAD (25)　　　　2" X 3"

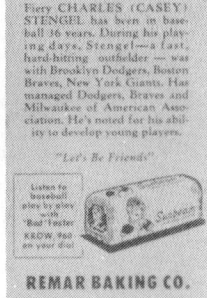

Fiery CHARLES (CASEY) STENGEL has been in baseball 36 years. During his playing days, Stengel—a fast, hard-hitting outfielder — was with Brooklyn Dodgers, Boston Braves, New York Giants. Has managed Dodgers, Braves and Milwaukee of American Association. He's noted for his ability to develop young players.

"Let's Be Friends"

CHARLES (Casey) STENGEL
Oaks Manager　8

Listen to baseball play by play with "Bud" Foster KROW, 960 on your dial

REMAR BAKING CO.

The 1947 Remar Bread set of 25 black & white, numbered cards features Oakland Oaks players only. Many cards are identical to the 1946 issue on the front except for the numbering. These cards are listed with an asterisk in the checklist. The backs are distinguishable from the 1946 issue by a "blue loaf" of Remar Bread. The backs are printed in blue and include player biographies and an ad for the Oakland Oaks radio station. The cards are on very thin stock. The ACC designation is D317-2.

	MINT	VG-E	F-G
COMPLETE SET	170.00	125.00	60.00
COMMON PLAYER	6.00	4.50	2.00

		MINT	VG-E	F-G
1	Bill Raimondi*	6.75	5.00	2.25
2	Les Scarsella*	6.75	5.00	2.25
3	Brooks Holder*	6.75	5.00	2.25
4	Chuck Gassaway*	6.75	5.00	2.25
5	Ora Burnett*	6.75	5.00	2.25
6	Ralph Buxton*	6.75	5.00	2.25
7	Ed Kearse*	6.75	5.00	2.25
8	Casey Stengel*	30.00	22.50	10.50
9	Bud Foster, Announcer*	6.75	5.00	2.25
10	Ambrose Palica*	6.00	4.50	2.00
11	Tom Hafey*	6.00	4.50	2.00
12	Herschel Martin*	6.00	4.50	2.00
13	Henry Pippen*	6.00	4.50	2.00

		MINT	VG-E	F-G
14	Floyd Speer*	6.00	4.50	2.00
15	Tony Sabol*	6.00	4.50	2.00
16	Will Hasey	6.00	4.50	2.00
17	Ray Hamrick	6.00	4.50	2.00
18	Maurice Van Robays	6.00	4.50	2.00
19	Dario Lodigiani	6.00	4.50	2.00
20	Mel Duezabou	6.00	4.50	2.00
21	Damon Hayes	6.00	4.50	2.00
22	Gene Lillard	6.00	4.50	2.00
23	Al Wilkie	6.00	4.50	2.00
24	Tony Soriano	6.00	4.50	2.00
25	Glenn Crawford	6.00	4.50	2.00

1949 REMAR BREAD (32)

2" X 3"

BILLY MARTIN
Oaks Infielder

REMAR BAKING CO.

The 1949 Remar Bread set of 32 black & white, unnumbered cards features Oakland Oaks players only. There is a white outside border around the photos and the "Oaks" name is found on the jersey. The backs, in blue print on white, give vital statistics, 1948 records, and show a Sunbeam bread loaf. The ACC designation is D317-4.

	MINT	VG-E	F-G
COMPLETE SET	120.00	85.00	40.00
COMMON PLAYER	2.50	1.80	.80
1 Ralph Buxton	2.50	1.80	.80
2 Mario Candini	10.00	7.00	3.00
3 Rex Cecil	10.00	7.00	3.00
4 Lloyd Christopher	2.50	1.80	.80
5 Mel Duezabou	2.50	1.80	.80
6 Chuck Dressen	4.00	3.00	1.40
7 Bud Foster	2.50	1.80	.80
8 Clarence Gassaway	2.50	1.80	.80
9 Ray Hamrick	2.50	1.80	.80
10 Jack Jensen	6.50	5.00	2.25
11 Earl Jones	2.50	1.80	.80
12 George Kelly	7.50	5.75	2.50
13 Frank Kerr	12.00	8.75	4.00
14 Dick Kryhoski	10.00	7.00	3.00
15 Cookie Lavagetto	4.00	3.00	1.40

	MINT	VG-E	F-G
16 Dario Lodigiani	2.50	1.80	.80
17 Billy Martin	16.00	12.00	5.50
18 George Metkovich	2.50	1.80	.80
19 Frank Nelson	2.50	1.80	.80
20 Don Padgett	2.50	1.80	.80
21 Alonzo Perry	8.00	6.00	2.50
22 Bill Raimondi	2.50	1.80	.80
23 Earl Rapp	2.50	1.80	.80
24 Ed Samcoff	2.50	1.80	.80
25 Les Scarsella	2.50	1.80	.80
26 Forest Thompson	8.00	6.00	2.50
27 Earl Toolson	8.00	6.00	2.50
28 Louis Tost	8.00	6.00	2.50
29 Maurice Van Robays	2.50	1.80	.80
30 Jim Wallace	2.50	1.80	.80
31 Artie Wilson	4.00	3.00	1.40
32 Parnell Woods	15.00	11.00	5.00

1950 REMAR BREAD (27)

2" X 3"

AUGIE GALAN
Oaks Outfielder

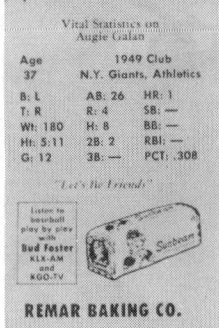

REMAR BAKING CO.

The 1950 Remar Bread set of 27 black and white, unnumbered cards features Oakland Oaks players only. The format is identical to the 1949 set except that the backs include 1949 records. The ACC designation is D317-5.

	MINT	VG-E	F-G
COMPLETE SET	65.00	48.00	20.00
COMMON PLAYER	2.25	1.75	.80
1 George Bamberger	3.00	2.25	1.00
2 Hank Behrman	2.25	1.75	.80
3 Lloyd Christopher	2.25	1.75	.80
4 Chuck Dressen	3.00	2.25	1.00
5 Mel Duezabou	2.25	1.75	.80
6 Augie Galan	2.25	1.75	.80
7 Clarence Gassaway	2.25	1.75	.80
8 Allen Gettel	2.25	1.75	.80
9 Ernie Groth	4.00	3.00	1.40
10 Ray Hamrick	2.25	1.75	.80
11 Earl Harrist	2.25	1.75	.80
12 Billy Herman	8.00	6.00	2.50

	MINT	VG-E	F-G
13 Bob Hofman	2.25	1.75	.80
14 George Kelly	8.00	6.00	2.50
15 Cookie Lavagetto	3.00	2.25	1.00
16 Eddie Malone	2.25	1.75	.80
17 George Metkovich	2.25	1.75	.80
18 Frank Nelson	2.25	1.75	.80
19 Rafael (Ray) Noble	2.25	1.75	.80
20 Don Padgett	2.25	1.75	.80
21 Earl Rapp	2.25	1.75	.80
22 Clyde Shoun	2.25	1.75	.80
23 Forest Thompson	2.25	1.75	.80
24 Louis Tost	2.25	1.75	.80
25 Dick Wakefield	5.00	3.75	1.75
26 Artie Wilson	2.25	1.75	.80
27 Roy Zimmerman	2.25	1.75	.80

1955 RODEO (47)

2 1/2" X 3 1/2"

Elmer Valo

The 1955 Rodeo Meats set contains 47 color unnumbered cards. The backs of the cards contain a scrapbook offer. The Grimes and Kryhoski cards listed in the scrapbook album never appeared in the set. The ACC designation is F152.

	MINT	VG-E	F-G
COMPLETE SET	1800.00	1350.00	625.00
COMMON PLAYER	35.00	25.00	10.00
1 Joe Astroth	35.00	25.00	10.00
2 Harold Bevan	45.00	34.00	15.00
3 Charles Bishop	45.00	34.00	15.00
4 Don Bollweg	45.00	34.00	15.00
5 Lou Boudreau	60.00	45.00	20.00
6 Cloyd Boyer(salmon)	35.00	25.00	10.00
7 Cloyd Boyer(light blue)	45.00	34.00	15.00
8 Ed Burtschy	45.00	34.00	15.00
9 Art Ceccarelli	35.00	25.00	10.00
10 Joe DeMaestri(yellow)	45.00	34.00	15.00
11 Joe DeMaestri(green)	35.00	25.00	10.00
12 Art Ditmar	35.00	25.00	10.00
13 John Dixon	45.00	34.00	15.00
14 Jim Finigan	35.00	25.00	10.00
15 Marion Fricano	45.00	34.00	15.00
16 Tom Gorman	35.00	25.00	10.00
17 John Gray	45.00	34.00	15.00
18 Ray Herbert	35.00	25.00	10.00
19 Forest "Spook" Jacobs	60.00	45.00	20.00
20 Alex Kellner	35.00	25.00	10.00
21 Harry Kraft	35.00	25.00	10.00
22 Jack Littrell	35.00	25.00	10.00
23 Hector Lopez	35.00	25.00	10.00

	MINT	VG-E	F-G
24 Oscar Melillo	35.00	25.00	10.00
25 Arnold Portocarrero (purple)	45.00	34.00	15.00
26 Arnold Portocarrero (gray)	35.00	25.00	10.00
27 Vic Power(yellow)	35.00	25.00	10.00
28 Vic Power(pink)	45.00	34.00	15.00
29 Vic Raschi	40.00	30.00	13.00
30 Bill Renna(lavender)	35.00	25.00	10.00
31 Bill Renna(dark pink)	45.00	34.00	15.00
32 Al Robertson	45.00	34.00	15.00
33 Johnny Sain	40.00	30.00	13.00
34 Bobby Shantz	40.00	30.00	13.00
35 Bobby Schantz (misspelling)	50.00	38.00	17.00
36 Wilmer Shantz(orange)	45.00	34.00	15.00
37 Wilmer Shantz(lav.)	35.00	26.00	12.00
38 Harry Simpson	35.00	25.00	10.00
39 Enos Slaughter	50.00	38.00	17.00
40 Lou Sleator	35.00	25.00	10.00
41 George Susce	45.00	34.00	15.00
42 Bob Trice	45.00	34.00	15.00
43 Elmer Valo(yellow)	45.00	34.00	15.00
44 Elmer Valo(greensky)	35.00	25.00	10.00
45 Bill Wilson(yellow)	45.00	34.00	15.00
46 Bill Wilson(lavender) (sky)	35.00	25.00	10.00
47 Gus Zernial	35.00	25.00	10.00

1956 RODEO (13)

2 1/2" X 3 1/2"

Vic Power

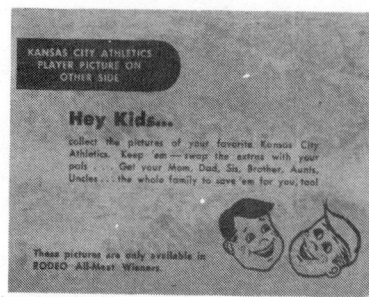

The 1956 Rodeo Meats set contains 13 color unnumbered cards issued with Rodeo Meats products. The cards from this set can be distinguished from the 1955 cards by the absence of the scrapbook offer on the backs of the cards. The ACC designation is F152.

	MINT	VG-E	F-G
COMPLETE SET	525.00	410.00	175.00
COMMON PLAYER	37.00	27.00	11.00
1 Joe Astroth	37.00	27.00	11.00
2 Lou Boudreau	75.00	55.00	24.00
3 Joe DeMaestri	37.00	27.00	11.00
4 Art Ditmar	37.00	27.00	11.00
5 Jim Finigan	37.00	27.00	11.00

	MINT	VG-E	F-G
6 Hector Lopez	37.00	27.00	11.00
7 Vic Power	37.00	27.00	11.00
8 Bobby Shantz	45.00	34.00	15.00
9 Wilmer Shantz	50.00	38.00	17.00
10 Harry Simpson	37.00	27.00	11.00
11 Enos Slaughter	60.00	45.00	20.00
12 Elmer Valo	37.00	27.00	11.00
13 Gus Zernial	37.00	27.00	11.00

ROYAL STARS OF BASEBALL No. 2

"PEE WEE" REESE

Harold (also "Little Colonel") Reese has been a Brooklyn Dodger since 1940, excepting 3 years in the Navy. Born in Ekron, Ky., July 23, 1919, Pee Wee is 5' 10", weighs 168, hits and throws right-handed.

Pee Wee's 1949 fielding averaged .977, tops for National League shortstops. He scored 132 runs to lead the league. Reese has played in 3 World's Series and on 4 All-Star teams.

Send for a Plastic Album to Hold Your Royal Stars Collection!

Eight clear envelopes, bound with colorful cover, displays 16 photographs. Mail 15¢ and 3 Royal Desserts package fronts to Royal, Box 89, New York 46, N.Y.

Pee Wee Reese

This FREE Card Starts Your ROYAL STARS Collection!

Look on the other side of this card for a signed photo and short life story of "Pee Wee" Reese. You will find other photos and histories of many more famous Movie and Baseball Stars on the package backs of Royal Puddings and Royal Gelatin Desserts. Use this card to start your exciting collection of ROYAL STARS of Baseball and Movies!

P-4075   10/51 PRINTED IN U.S.A.

This set of 24 black and numbered cards has a re[d] across the top which ca[n] set "Royal Stars of Base[ball]. These cards were issued [on] backs of Royal Pudding[s] ages in 1949 and 1951. two years are distingui[shed] best by biography ch[anges.] Card nos. 6, 7, 8, 14, 1[9,] 21 all appear with changes. The ACC de[signa-] tion is F219-1.

	MINT	VG-E	F-G
COMPLETE SET	350.00	250.00	120.00
COMMON PLAYER	13.00	9.00	4.50
1 Stan Musial	60.00	45.00	20.00
2 PeeWee Reese	20.00	15.00	6.50
3 George Kell	15.00	11.00	5.00
4 Dom DiMaggio	20.00	15.00	6.50
5 Warren Spahn	20.00	15.00	6.50
6 Andy Pafko	13.00	9.00	4.50
7 Andy Seminick	13.00	9.00	4.50
8 Lou Brissie	13.00	9.00	4.50
9 Ewell Blackwell	13.00	9.00	4.50
10 Bobby Thomson	15.00	11.00	5.00
11 Phil Rizzuto	20.00	15.00	6.50

	MINT	VG-E	F-G
12 Tommy Henrich	15.00	11.00	5.00
13 Joe Gordon	14.00	10.50	4.75
14 Ray Scarborough	13.00	9.00	4.50
15 Stan Rojek	13.00	9.00	4.50
16 Luke Appling	15.00	11.00	5.00
17 Willard Marshall	13.00	9.00	4.50
18 Alvin Dark	14.00	10.50	4.75
19 Dick Sisler	13.00	9.00	4.50
20 Johnny Ostrowski	13.00	9.00	4.50
21 Virgil Trucks	13.00	9.00	4.50
22 Eddie Robinson	14.00	10.50	4.75
23 Nanny Fernandez	13.00	9.00	4.50
24 Ferris Fain	14.00	10.50	4.75

1952 ROYAL (16)   5" X 7"

The 1952 Royal Desserts set features 16 black and white, unnumbered cards with facsimile autographed portraits. The designation "To a Royal Fan" appears on the cards. The ACC designation is F-219-6.

	MINT	VG-E	F-G
COMPLETE SET	200.00	140.00	60.00
COMMON PLAYER	11.00	8.00	3.50
1 Ewell Blackwell	12.00	8.75	4.00
2 Leland V. Brissie, Jr.	11.00	8.00	3.50
3 Alvin Dark	12.00	8.75	4.00
4 Dom DiMaggio	15.00	11.00	5.00
5 Ferris Fain	12.00	8.75	4.00
6 George Kell	12.00	8.75	4.00

	MINT	VG-E	F-G
7 Stan Musial	60.00	45.00	20.00
8 Andy Pafko	11.00	8.00	3.50
9 Pee Wee Reese	18.00	13.50	6.00
10 Phil Rizzuto	18.00	13.50	6.00
11 Eddie Robinson	12.00	8.75	4.00
12 Ray Scarborough	11.00	8.00	3.50
13 Andy Seminick	11.00	8.00	3.50
14 Dick Sisler	11.00	8.00	3.50
15 Warren Spahn	18.00	13.50	6.00
16 Bobby Thomson	15.00	11.00	5.00

1943 R302-1 MP & CO. (24)

2 11/16" X 2 1/4"

The MP & Co. issue of 1943 distinguishes itself by the absence of quality in the set. Rough drawings of players are combined with poor coloration to form an unattractive card. Player names are placed within a baseball on the obverse — often the only way of identifying the individual.

	MINT	VG-E	F-G
COMPLETE SET	100.00	70.00	30.00
COMMON PLAYER	3.00	2.25	1.00

	MINT	VG-E	F-G		MINT	VG-E	F-G
1 Ernie Bonham	3.00	2.25	1.00	13 Stan Hack	3.00	2.25	1.00
2 Lou Boudreau	5.00	3.75	1.75	14 Tom Henrich	4.00	3.00	1.40
3 Dolph Camilli	3.00	2.25	1.00	15 Carl Hubbell	5.00	3.75	1.75
4 Mort Cooper	3.00	2.25	1.00	16 Joe Medwick	5.00	3.75	1.75
5 Walker Cooper	3.00	2.25	1.00	17 John Mize	4.00	3.00	1.40
6 Joe Cronin	4.00	3.00	1.40	18 Lou Novikoff	3.00	2.25	1.00
7 Hank Danning	3.00	2.25	1.00	19 Mel Ott	8.00	6.00	2.50
8 Bill Dickey	8.00	6.00	2.50	20 Pee Wee Reese	6.00	4.50	2.00
9 Joe DiMaggio	15.00	11.00	5.00	21 Pete Reiser	4.00	3.00	1.40
10 Bob Feller	10.00	7.00	3.00	22 Charlie Ruffing	5.00	3.75	1.75
11 Jimmy Foxx	10.00	7.00	3.00	23 Johnny Vandermeer	4.00	3.00	1.40
12 Hank Greenberg	7.00	5.25	2.50	24 Ted Williams	12.00	8.75	4.00

1949 R302-2 MP & CO. (24)

2 11/16" X 2 1/4"

The 1949 rendition of MP & Co., was basically a re-issue of the 1943 set with different players and numbers on the back. The card fronts are even more washed out than the previous set. Card numbers 104, 118, and 120 are unknown and may be related to the two unnumbered cards found in the set. The ACC also lists the set as W523.

	MINT	VG-E	F-G
COMPLETE SET	85.00	60.00	25.00
COMMON PLAYER	2.50	1.75	.75

	MINT	VG-E	F-G		MINT	VG-E	F-G
100 Lou Boudreau	5.00	3.75	1.75	113 Hank Sauer	3.00	2.25	1.00
101 Ted Williams	12.00	8.75	4.00	114 Gil Coan	2.50	1.75	.75
102 Buddy Kerr	2.50	1.75	.75	115 Eddie Joost	2.50	1.75	.75
103 Bob Feller	10.00	7.00	3.00	116 Alvin Dark	3.00	2.25	1.00
104 unknown	xxx	xxx	xxx	117 Larry Berra	10.00	7.00	3.00
105 Joe DiMaggio	15.00	11.00	5.00	118 unknown	xxx	xxx	xxx
106 Pee Wee Reese	6.00	4.50	2.00	119 Bob Lemon	5.00	3.75	1.75
107 Ferris Fain	3.00	2.25	1.00	120 unknown	xxx	xxx	xxx
108 Andy Pafko	2.50	1.75	.75	121 Johnny Pesky	2.50	1.75	.75
109 Del Ennis	2.50	1.75	.75	122 Johnny Sain	4.00	3.00	1.40
110 Ralph Kiner	5.00	3.75	1.75	123 Hoot Evers	2.50	1.75	.75
111 Nippy Jones	2.50	1.75	.75	124 Larry Doby	4.00	3.00	1.40
112 Del Rice	2.50	1.75	.75	Tom Henrich	4.00	3.00	1.40
				Al Kozar	2.50	1.75	.75

1933 R309-1 GOUDEY PREMIUM (4)   5 1/2" X 8 15/16"

The most ambitious premium issue of the Goudey Gum Company was the R309—1 set of 1933. Printed on heavy cardboard, the black & white picture was embellished with a gold, frame-like border and a back stand.

	MINT	VG-E	F-G
COMPLETE SET	400.00	300.00	140.00
COMMON CARD	100.00	75.00	30.00
American League All-Stars of 1933	100.00	75.00	30.00
National League All-Stars of 1933	100.00	75.00	3C.u0
World's Champions of 1933	100.00	75.00	30.00
George Herman (Babe) Ruth	150.00	125.00	60.00

1933 R309-2 GOUDEY PREMIUM (18)   5 1/2" X 9"

The cards in the R309—2 Goudey premium set are unnumbered, glossy black & white photos on thin paper stock. The ballplayer is identified by his name rendered in longhand in the "wide pen" style of later Goudey issues. This written name is not a facsimile autograph.

	MINT	VG-E	F-G
COMPLETE SET	200.00	140.00	60.00
COMMON PLAYER	10.00	7.00	3.00
1 Boston Red Sox	12.00	8.75	4.00
2 Cleveland Indians	10.00	7.00	3.00
3 Washington Senators	10.00	7.00	3.00
4 Elden Auker	10.00	7.00	3.00
5 Johnny Babich	10.00	7.00	3.00
6 Dick Bartell	10.00	7.00	3.00
7 Lester Rowland Bell	10.00	7.00	3.00
8 Wally Berger	10.00	7.00	3.00
9 Mickey Cochrane	20.00	15.00	6.50

	MINT	VG-E	F-G
10 Ervin Fox	10.00	7.00	3.00
11 Vernon Gomez	20.00	15.00	6.50
12 Leon "Goose" Goslin	15.00	11.00	5.00
13 Hank Greenberg	20.00	15.00	6.50
14 Oscar Melillo	10.00	7.00	3.00
15 Mel Ott	20.00	15.00	6.50
16 Schoolboy Rowe	12.00	8.75	4.00
17 Vito Tamulis	10.00	7.00	3.00
18 Gerald Walker	10.00	7.00	3.00

1936 R311 LEATHER SURFACE (15)   6″ X 8″

1936 R311 GLOSSY SURFACE (28)   6″ X 8″

Harold "Pie" Traynor

The 1936 R311 set of Portraits and Team Baseball Photos exist in two different forms. Fifteen leather-like or uneven surface cards comprise the first type. Twenty-eight glossy surface, sepia or black and white cards comprise the second type. The Boston Red Sox team exists with or without a sky above the building at the right of the card. Scarcities include Pepper Martin, Harder, Rowe, and the Dodgers, Pirates, Braves, and Columbus team cards.

	MINT	VG-E	F-G
COMPLETE SET	530.00	400.00	180.00
COMMON PLAYER(LEATHERY)	16.00	12.00	5.00
COMMON PLAYER (GLOSSY)	8.00	6.00	2.50
L 1 Paul Derringer	16.00	12.00	5.00
L 2 Wes Ferrell	16.00	12.00	5.00
L 3 Jimmy Foxx	40.00	30.00	13.00
L 4 Charlie Gehringer	25.00	18.50	8.75
L 5 Mel Harder	16.00	12.00	5.00
L 6 Gabby Hartnett	21.00	15.50	7.00
L 7 Rogers Hornsby	35.00	26.00	12.00
L 8 Connie Mack	30.00	22.50	10.50
L 9 Van Mungo	16.00	12.00	5.00
L10 Steve O'Neill	16.00	12.00	5.00
L11 Charles Ruffing	25.00	18.50	8.75
L12 DiMaggio-Crosetti-Lazzeri	40.00	30.00	13.00
L13 Arky Vaughn-Honus Wagner	30.00	22.50	10.50
L14 American League Pennant Winners-1935	16.00	12.00	5.00
L15 National League Pennant Winners-1935	16.00	12.00	5.00
G 1 Earl Averill	10.00	7.00	3.00
G 2 James L. "Jim" Bottomley	10.00	7.00	3.00
G 3 Gordon S. "Mickey" Cochrane	12.00	8.75	4.00
G 4 Joe Cronin	12.00	8.75	4.00
G 5 Jerome "Dizzy" Dean	20.00	15.00	6.50
G 6 Jimmy Dykes	8.00	6.00	2.50
G 7 Jimmy Foxx	18.00	13.50	6.00
G 8 Frankie Frisch	12.00	8.75	4.00
G 9 Henry "Hank" Greenberg	12.00	8.75	4.00

	MINT	VG-E	F-G
G10 Mel Harder	9.00	6.75	3.00
G11 Ken Keltner	8.00	6.00	2.50
G12 Pepper Martin	9.00	6.75	3.00
G13 Lynwood "Schoolboy" Rowe	9.00	6.75	3.00
G14 William "Bill" Terry	12.00	8.75	4.00
G15 Harold "Pie" Traynor	12.00	8.75	4.00
G16 American League All Stars-1935	8.00	6.00	2.50
G17 American League Pennant Winners-1934 (Detroit Tigers)	8.00	6.00	2.50
G18 Boston Braves-1935	12.00	8.75	4.00
G19 Boston Red Sox(2)	9.00	6.75	3.00
G20 Brooklyn Dodgers-1935	12.50	10.00	4.00
G21 Chicago White Sox-1935	8.00	6.00	2.50
G22 Columbus Red Birds-1934 Pennant Winners of American Assoc.	10.00	7.00	3.00
G23 National League All Stars-1935	8.00	6.00	2.50
G24 National League Champions-1935 (Chicago Cubs)	8.00	6.00	2.50
G25 New York Yankees-1935	9.00	6.75	3.00
G26 Pittsburgh Pirates-1935	10.00	8.00	3.50
G27 St. Louis Browns-1935	8.00	6.00	2.50
G28 The World Champions 1934 (St. Louis Cards)	8.00	6.00	2.50

The 1936 R312 Baseball Photos set contains 25 color tinted, single player cards, listed with the letter A in the checklist; 14 multiple player cards, listed with the letter B in the checklist; 6 action cards with handwritten signatures, listed with the letter C in the checklist; and 5 action cards with printed titles, listed with the letter D in the checklist. The Allen card is reportedly more difficult to obtain than other cards in the set.

	MINT	VG-E	F-G
COMPLETE SET	425.00	325.00	150.00
COMMON CARDS	7.50	5.75	2.50
A 1 John Thomas Allen	12.00	8.75	4.00
A 2 Cy Blanton	7.50	5.75	2.50
A 3 Mace Brown	7.50	5.75	2.50
A 4 Dolph Camilli	7.50	5.75	2.50
A 5 Gordon Cochrane	12.00	8.75	4.00
A 6 "Rip" Collins	7.50	5.75	2.50
A 7 Ki Ki Cuyler	10.00	7.00	3.00
A 8 Bill Dickey	16.00	12.00	5.50
A 9 Joe DiMaggio	60.00	45.00	20.00
A10 "Chas." Dressen	7.50	5.75	2.50
A11 Benny Frey	7.50	5.75	2.50
A12 Hank Greenberg	12.00	8.75	4.00
A13 Mel Harder	7.50	5.75	2.50
A14 Rogers Hornsby	20.00	15.00	6.50
A15 Ernie Lombardi	9.00	6.75	3.00
A16 Pepper Martin	9.00	6.75	3.00
A17 "Johnny" Mize	10.00	7.00	3.00
A18 Van L. Mungo	7.50	5.75	2.50
A19 Bud Parmalee	7.50	5.75	2.50
A20 Chas. Ruffing	10.00	7.00	3.00
A21 Eugene Schott	7.50	5.75	2.50
A22 Casey Stengel	20.00	15.00	6.50
A23 Bill Sullivan	7.50	5.75	2.50
A24 Bill Swift	7.50	5.75	2.50
A25 Ralph Winegarner	7.50	5.75	2.50
B 1 Ollie Bejma-Rolly Hemsley	7.50	5.75	2.50
B 2 Cliff Bolton-Earl Whitehill	7.50	5.75	2.50
B 3 Bordagaray-Earnshaw	7.50	5.75	2.50
B 4 Cavaretta, Herman, Jurges, Hack	9.00	6.75	3.00
B 5 Pete Fox-"Jo Jo" White-Goose Goslin	8.00	6.00	2.50
B 6 Galan, Herman, Lindstrom, Hartnett, 5 others	9.00	6.75	3.00
B 7 Harris-Cronin	10.00	7.00	3.00
B 8 Hartnett-Warnecke (sp.)	9.00	6.75	3.00
B 9 Hoag-Gomez	9.00	6.75	3.00

	MINT	VG-E	F-G
B10 Allen Lothoron-Rogers Hornsby	10.00	7.00	3.00
B11 Mack-Grove	20.00	15.00	6.50
B12 Taylor-Speaker-Cuyler	10.00	7.00	3.00
B13 Walker-Haas-Kreevich	7.50	5.75	2.50
B14 Paul and Lloyd Waner, and "Big Jim" Weaver	10.00	7.00	3.00
C 1 Altrock-Schacht, Clowning on the Diamond	9.00	6.75	3.00
C 2 Bell(St. Louis) Out At First "Zeke" Bonura first baseman	7.50	5.75	2.50
C 3 Jim Collins(Safe) and Stan Hack	7.50	5.75	2.50
C 4 Jimmie Foxx batting, Luke Sewell catching	10.00	7.00	3.00
C 5 Lopez Traps Two Cubs on Third Base	9.00	6.75	3.00
C 6 "Pie" Traynor-Augie Galan	9.00	6.75	3.00
D 1 Alvin Crowder, after victory in the World Series	7.50	5.75	2.50
D 2 Floyd Vaughn, present Pirate Short Stop, and Coach Hans Wagner	10.00	7.00	3.00
D 3 Gabby Hartnett crossing home plate after hitting homer...	9.00	6.75	3.00
D 4 Kids flock around Schoolboy Rowe, as he leaves Cubs park...	7.50	5.75	2.50
D 5 Van Atta, St. Louis pitcher, out at plat - Ferrell, Boston, catching	7.50	5.75	2.50

Most serious collectors subscribe to at least one of the hobby papers. Read the ads in this Guide for The Trader Speaks (for advanced collectors), Sports Collectors Digest, and Baseball Hobby News to determine which one or more appeal to you.

1936 R313 NATIONAL CHICLE (120) 3 1/4" X 5 3/8"
FINE PEN PREMIUMS

The 1936 Fine Pen Premiums were issued anonymously by the National Chicle Company. The cards are blank backed, unnumbered and are among those premiums that could be obtained directly from a retail outlet rather than through the mail only. Three types of cards exist. Cards portraying but one player are listed with the letter A in the checklist; cards which portray several players are listed with a B in the checklist; and cards which feature action poses are listed with a C in the checklist. The ACC designation is R 313.

	MINT	VG-E	F-G
COMPLETE SET	400.00	300.00	130.00
COMMON CARDS (A)	2.25	1.65	.75
COMMON CARDS (B)	2.75	2.00	.90
COMMON CARDS (C)	4.00	3.00	1.40
A1 Mels Almada	2.25	1.65	.75
A2 Paul Andrews	2.25	1.65	.75
A3 Elden Auker	2.25	1.65	.75
A4 Earl Averill	4.00	3.00	1.40
A5 Jim Becher	2.25	1.65	.75
A6 Moe Berg	2.75	2.00	.90
A7 Walter Berger	2.25	1.65	.75
A8 Charles Berry	2.25	1.65	.75
A9 Ralph Birkhofer	2.25	1.65	.75
A10 "Cy" Blanton	2.25	1.65	.75
A11 O. Bluege	2.25	1.65	.75
A12 Cliff Bolton	2.25	1.65	.75
A13 Zeke Bonura	2.25	1.65	.75
A14 Thos. Bridges	2.25	1.65	.75
A15 Sam Byrd	2.25	1.65	.75
A16 Dolph Camilli	2.25	1.65	.75
A17 Bruce Campbell	2.25	1.65	.75
A18 Walter "Kit" Carson	2.25	1.65	.75
A19 Ben Chapman	2.25	1.65	.75
A20 "Rip" Collins	2.25	1.65	.75
A21 Joe Cronin	6.00	4.50	2.00
A22 Frank Crosetti	3.00	2.25	1.00
A23 Paul Derringer	2.75	2.00	.90
A24 Bill Dietrich	2.25	1.65	.75
A25 Carl Doyle	2.25	1.65	.75
A26 Pete Fox	2.25	1.65	.75
A27 Frankie Frisch	6.00	4.50	2.00
A28 Martin Galatzer	2.25	1.65	.75
A29 Chas. Gehringer	6.00	4.50	2.00
A30 Charley Gelbert	2.25	1.65	.75
A31 Jose Gomez	2.25	1.65	.75
A32 Leon Goslin	4.00	3.00	1.40
A33 Hank Gowdy	2.25	1.65	.75
A34 "Hank" Greenberg	6.00	4.50	2.00
A35 "Lefty" Grove	7.00	5.25	2.50
A36 Stan Hack	2.75	2.00	.90
A37 Odell Hale	2.25	1.65	.75
A38 Wild Bill Hallahan	2.25	1.65	.75
A39 Mel Harder	2.25	1.65	.75
A40 Stanley Bucky Harris	4.00	3.00	1.40
A41 Frank Higgins	2.25	1.65	.75
A42 Oral C. Hildebrand	2.25	1.65	.75
A43 Myril Hoag	2.25	1.65	.75
A44 Rogers Hornsby	8.00	6.00	2.05
A45 Waite Hoyt	4.00	3.00	1.40
A46 Willis G. Hudlin(2)	2.25	1.65	.75
A47 "Woody" Jensen (2)	2.25	1.65	.75
A48 Wm. Knickerbocker	2.25	1.65	.75
A49 Joseph Kuhel	2.25	1.65	.75
A50 Cookie Lavagetto	2.25	1.65	.75

	MINT	VG-E	F-G
A51 Thornton Lee	2.25	1.65	.75
A52 Red Lucas	2.25	1.65	.75
A53 Pepper Martin	3.00	2.25	1.00
A54 Joe Medwick	5.00	3.75	1.75
A55 Oscar Melillo	2.25	1.65	.75
A56 "Buddy" Meyer	2.25	1.65	.75
A57 Wallace Moses	2.25	1.65	.75
A58 V. Mungo	2.75	2.00	.90
A59 Lamar Newsom	2.25	1.65	.75
A60 Lewis "Buck" Newsom	2.75	2.00	.90
A61 Steve O'Neill	2.25	1.65	.75
A62 Tommie Paden	2.25	1.65	.75
A63 E. Babe Phillips	2.25	1.65	.75
A64 Bill Rogell	2.25	1.65	.75
A65 Lynn "Schoolboy" Rowe	3.00	2.25	1.00
A66 Al Simmons	5.00	3.75	1.75
A67 Leon "Moose" Solters	2.25	1.65	.75
A68 Casey Stengel	8.00	6.00	2.50
A69 Bill Swift	2.25	1.65	.75
A70 Cecil Travis	2.25	1.65	.75
A71 "Pie" Traynor	5.00	3.75	1.75
A72 Wm. Urbansky	2.25	1.65	.75
A73 Arky Vaughn	3.00	2.25	1.00
A74 Joe Vosmik	2.25	1.65	.75
A75 Honus Wagner	12.00	8.75	4.00
A76 Rube Walberg	2.25	1.65	.75
A77 Bill Walker	2.25	1.65	.75
A78 Gerald Walker	2.25	1.65	.75
A79 Bill Werber	2.25	1.65	.75
A80 Sam West	2.25	1.65	.75
A81 Pinkey Whitney	2.25	1.65	.75
A82 Vernon Whitshire	2.25	1.65	.75
A83 "Pep" Young	2.25	1.65	.75
B1 Babe and his babes	2.75	2.00	.90
B2 Stan Bordagaray-Geo. Earnshaw	2.75	2.00	.90
B3 James Bucher-John Babich	2.75	2.00	.90
B4 Ben Chapman-Bill Werber	2.75	2.00	.90
B5 Chicago White Sox 1936	4.00	3.00	1.50
B6 Fence Busters	2.75	2.00	.90
B7 Fox-Simmons-Cochrane	8.00	6.00	2.50
B8 "Gabby" and "Kiki"	7.00	5.25	2.50
B9 Gomez-Ruffing	7.00	5.25	2.50
B10 Harnett-Warneke	4.00	3.00	1.40
B11 Diamonds Daddies-Mack, McGraw	8.00	6.00	2.50
B12 Capt. Bill Myer-Mgr. Chas Dressen	2.75	2.00	.90
B13 P & L Waner - Big Jim Weaver	6.00	4.50	2.00

R313 (CONTINUED)

	MINT	VG-E	F-G
B14 Wes-Rick (Ferrells)	2.75	2.00	.90
C1 Altrock-Schacht	4.00	3.00	1.40
C2 Big Bosses Clash - Dykes safe	4.00	3.00	1.40
C3 Bottomley tagging Gelbert	4.00	3.00	1.40
C4 Camilli catches Jurgens off first	4.00	3.00	1.40
C5 CCS Radcliffe safe Harnett catching	4.50	3.50	1.60
C6 CCS Sewell blocks runner at plate	4.00	3.00	1.40
C7 CCS Washington safe	4.00	3.00	1.40
C8 Joe DiMaggio slams it,Erickson catch	15.00	11.00	5.00
C9 Double Play-McQuinn to Stine	4.00	3.00	1.40
C10 Dykes catches Cross-etti between 2nd and 3rd	4.50	3.50	1.60
C11 Glenn uses football play at plate	4.00	3.00	1.40

	MINT	VG-E	F-G
C12 Greenberg doubles Dickey catching	7.00	5.25	2.50
C13 Hassett makes the out	4.00	3.00	1.40
C14 Lombardi says "Ugh"	4.50	3.50	1.60
C15 McQuinn gets his man	4.00	3.00	1.40
C16 Randy Moore hurt stealing second	4.00	3.00	1.40
C17 T.Moore out at plate Wilson catching	4.00	3.00	1.40
C18 Sewell waits for ball while Clift scores	4.00	3.00	1.40
C19 Talking it over	4.00	3.00	1.40
C20 There she goes! CCS	4.00	3.00	1.40
C21 Ump says "No," Cleveland vs. Detroit	4.00	3.00	1.40
C22 L. Waner at bat, Gabby Hartnett behind plate	6.00	4.50	2.00
C23 World Series, 1935, Goslin out at first	6.00	4.50	2.00

1936 GOUDEY WIDE PEN (137) PREMIUMS
1936 GOUDEY WIDE PEN (41) CANADIAN PREMIUMS

3 1/4" X 5 1/2"
3 1/4 X 5 1/2"

The 1936 Wide Pen Premiums were issued by the Goudey Gum Company. These black & white, unnumbered cards could be obtained directly from a retail outlet rather than through the mail only. Four types of this card exist. Type A contains cards, mainly individual players, with "Litho USA" in the bottom border. Type B does not have the "Litho USA" marking and comes both with and without a border. Type C cards are American players on creamy paper stock with medium thickness signatures and no "Litho USA" markings. Type D consists of Canadian players from Montreal (M) or Toronto (T) on creamy stock paper with non-glossy photos. The ACC designation is R314.

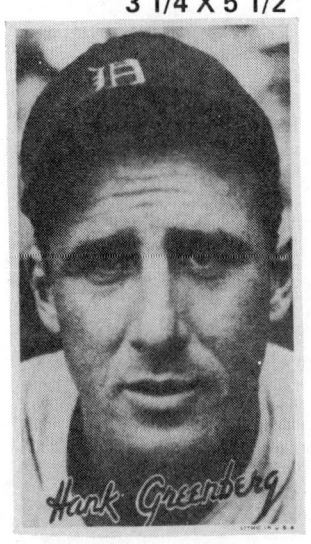

	MINT	VG-E	F-G
COMPLETE SET	850.00	650.00	250.00
COMMON CARD (A)	2.25	1.65	.75
COMMON CARD (B)	5.00	3.75	1.50
COMMON CARD (C)	5.00	3.75	1.50
COMMON CARD (D)	12.50	9.00	4.00
A1 Ethan Allen	2.25	1.65	.75
A2 Earl Averill	4.00	3.00	1.40
A3 Dick Bartell(hor)	2.25	1.65	.75
A4 Dick Bartell(port)	8.00	6.00	2.50
A5 Walter Berger	2.25	1.65	.75
A6 Geo. Blaeholder	2.25	1.65	.75
A7 "Cy" Blanton(port)	2.25	1.65	.75
A8 "Cliff" Bolton	2.25	1.65	.75
A9 Stan Bordagaray	2.25	1.65	.75
A10 Tommy Bridges(port)	2.25	1.65	.75
A11 Bill Brubaker	2.25	1.65	.75
A12 Sam Byrd	2.25	1.65	.75
A13 Dolph Camilli	2.25	1.65	.75
A14 Clydell Castleman(th)	2.25	1.65	.75
A15 Clydell Castleman(po)	2.25	1.65	.75
A16 Phil Cavaretta(hor)	2.75	2.00	.90
A17 "Mickey" Cochrane	6.00	4.50	2.00
A18 Earl Coombs(hor)	8.00	6.00	2.50
A19 Joe Coscarart	2.25	1.65	.75
A20 Joe Cronin	6.00	4.50	2.00
A21 Frank Crosetti	3.00	2.25	1.00
A22 Tony Cuccinello	2.25	1.65	.75
A23 "Kiki" Cuyler	4.00	3.00	1.40
A24 Curt Davis	2.25	1.65	.75
A25 Virgil Davis(hor)	2.25	1.65	.75
A26 Paul Derringer	2.75	2.00	.90

	MINT	VG-E	F-G
A27 "Bill" Dickey	7.00	5.25	2.50
A28 Jimmy Dykes(kneel)	2.75	2.00	.90
A29 "Rick" Ferrell(hor)	2.25	1.65	.75
A30 Wes Ferrell	2.25	1.65	.75
A31 Lou Finney	2.25	1.65	.75
A32 Ervin "Pete" Fox(port)	2.25	1.65	.75
A33 Tony Freitas	2.25	1.65	.75
A34 Lonnie Frey	2.25	1.65	.75
A35 Frankie Frisch	6.00	4.50	2.00
A36 "Augie" Galan(port)	2.25	1.65	.75
A37 Charles Gehringer	6.00	4.50	2.00
A38 Charlie Gelbert	2.25	1.65	.75
A39 "Lefty" Gomez	6.00	4.50	2.00
A40 "Goose" Goslin	4.00	3.00	1.40
A41 Earl Grace	2.25	1.65	.75
A42 Hank Greenberg(port)	6.00	4.50	2.00
A43 "Mule" Haas	2.25	1.65	.75
A44 Odell Hale	2.25	1.65	.75
A45 Bill Hallahan	2.25	1.65	.75
A46 "Mel" Harder	2.25	1.65	.75
A47 "Bucky" Harris	4.00	3.00	1.40
A48 "Gabby" Hartnett	20.00	15.00	6.50
A49 Ray Hayworth	2.25	1.65	.75
A50 Rolly Hemsley	2.25	1.65	.75
A51 Babe Herman	2.75	2.00	.90
A52 Frank Higgins(port)	2.25	1.65	.75
A53 Oral Hildebrand	2.25	1.65	.75
A54 Myril Hoag	2.25	1.65	.75
A55 Waite Hoyt	8.00	6.00	2.50
A56 Woody Jensen	2.25	1.65	.75
A57 Bob Johnson	2.25	1.65	.75

	MINT	VG-E	F-G
A58 "Buck" Jordan	2.25	1.65	.75
A59 Alex Kampouris	2.25	1.65	.75
A60 "Chuck" Klein	4.00	3.00	1.40
A61 Joe Kuhel	2.25	1.65	.75
A62 Lyn Lary	2.25	1.65	.75
A63 Harry Lavagetto	2.25	1.65	.75
A64 Sam Leslie	2.25	1.65	.75
A65 Freddie Lindstrom	3.50	2.50	1.20
A66 Lombardi (hor.)	3.00	2.25	1.00
A67 "Al" Lopez (hor.)	5.00	3.75	1.75
A68 Dan MacFayden	2.25	1.65	.75
A69 John Marcum	2.25	1.65	.75
A70 "Pepper" Martin	2.75	2.00	.90
A71 Eric McNair	2.25	1.65	.75
A72 "Ducky" Medwick	4.00	3.00	1.40
A73 Gene Moore	2.25	1.65	.75
A74 Randy Moore	2.25	1.65	.75
A75 Terry Moore	2.25	1.65	.75
A76 Edward Moriarty	2.25	1.65	.75
A77 "Wally" Moses(port)	2.25	1.65	.75
A78 "Buddy" Myer	2.25	1.65	.75
A79 "Buck" Newsom	2.25	1.65	.75
A80 Fred Ostermueller	2.25	1.65	.75
A81 Marvin Owen	2.25	1.65	.75
A82 Tommy Padden	2.25	1.65	.75
A83 Ray Pepper	2.25	1.65	.75
A84 Tony Piet	2.25	1.65	.75
A85 "Rabbit"Pytlak(hor)	2.25	1.65	.75
A86 "Rip" Radcliff	2.25	1.65	.75
A87 Bobby Reis	2.25	1.65	.75
A88 "Lew" Riggs	2.25	1.65	.75
A89 Bill Rogell	2.25	1.65	.75
A90 "Red" Rolfe	2.25	1.65	.75
A91 Schoolboy" Rowe(port)	2.75	2.00	.90
A92 Al Schacht	2.25	1.65	.75
A93 "Luke" Sewell	2.25	1.65	.75
A94 Al Simmons(port)	5.00	3.75	1.75
A95 John Stone	2.25	1.65	.75
A96 Gus Suhr	2.25	1.65	.75
A97 Joe Sullivan	2.25	1.65	.75
A98 Bill Swift	2.25	1.65	.75
A99 Vito Tamulis	2.25	1.65	.75
A00 Dan Taylor	2.25	1.65	.75
A01 Cecil Travis	2.25	1.65	.75
A02 Hal Troskey(port)	2.25	1.65	.75
A03 "Bill"Urbanski	2.25	1.65	.75
A04 Russ Van Atta	2.25	1.65	.75
A05 "Arky" Vaughn	2.75	2.00	.90
A06 Gerald Walker	2.25	1.65	.75
A07 "Buck" Walters	2.25	1.65	.75
A08 Lloyd Waner	5.00	3.75	1.75
A09 Paul Waner	5.00	3.75	1.75
A10 "Lon" Warneke	2.25	1.65	.75
A11 Warstler	2.25	1.65	.75
A12 Bill Werber	2.25	1.65	.75
A13 "Jo-Jo" White	2.25	1.65	.75
A14 Burgess Whitehead	2.25	1.65	.75
A15 John Whitehead(port)	2.25	1.65	.75
A16 Whitlow Wyatt	2.25	1.65	.75
A17 Ben Chapman-Bill Werber	3.00	2.25	1.00
A18 DiMaggio-McCarthy	25.00	18.50	8.75
A19 "Wes + Rick" Ferrell	5.00	3.75	1.75
A20 Frank Pytlak-Steve O'Neil	3.00	2.25	1.00
B1 Mel Almada	5.00	3.75	1.50
B2 Lucius Appling(port)	8.00	6.00	2.50
B3 Henry Bonura(port)	5.00	3.75	1.50
B4 Ben Chapman-Bill Werber	5.00	3.75	1.50
B5 Herman Clifton	5.00	3.75	1.50
B6 Roger "Doc" Cramer	5.00	3.75	1.50
B7 Joe Cronin	8.00	6.00	2.50
B8 Jimmy Dykes	5.00	3.75	1.50
B9 Ervin "Pete" Fox	5.00	3.75	1.50
B10 Jimmy Foxx	15.00	11.00	5.00
B11 Hank Greenberg	10.00	7.00	3.00
B12 Oral Hildebrand	5.00	3.75	1.50
B13 Alex Hooks(hor)	5.00	3.75	1.50
B14 Willis Hudlin	5.00	3.75	1.50
B15 Bill Knickerbocker	5.00	3.75	1.50
B16 Heinie Manush	8.00	6.00	2.50
B17 Steve O'Neill	5.00	3.75	1.50
B18 Marvin Owen	5.00	3.75	1.50
B19 Al Simmons	10.00	7.00	3.00
B20 Lem "Moose" Solters	5.00	3.75	1.50
B21 Hal Troskey	5.00	3.75	1.50
B22 Joe Vosmik(port)	5.00	3.75	1.50
B23 Joe Vosmik(batting)	5.00	3.75	1.50
B24 Earl Whitehill	5.00	3.75	1.50
B1 "Luke" Appling(batting)	8.00	6.00	2.50
B2 Earl Averill	8.00	6.00	2.50
B3 "Cy" Blanton	5.00	3.75	1.50
B4 "Zeke" Bonura(batting)	5.00	3.75	1.50
B5 Tom Bridges(port)	5.00	3.75	1.50
B6 "Joe" DiMaggio	40.00	30.00	13.00

	MINT	VG-E	F-G
C7 "Bobby" Doerr	5.00	3.75	1.50
C8 Jimmy Dykes(hor)	5.00	3.75	1.50
C9 "Bob" Feller	15.00	11.00	5.00
C10 "Elbie" Fletcher	5.00	3.75	1.50
C11 Pete Fox(batting)	5.00	3.75	1.50
C12 "Gus" Galan(batting)	5.00	3.75	1.50
C13 Charles Gehringer	10.00	7.00	3.00
C14 Hank Greenberg	10.00	7.00	3.00
C15 Mel Harder	5.00	3.75	1.50
C16 "Gabby" Hartnett	8.00	6.00	2.50
C17 "Pinky" Higgins	5.00	3.75	1.50
C18 Carl Hubbell	10.00	7.00	3.00
C19 "Wally" Moses(batting)	5.00	3.75	1.50
C20 Lou Newsom	5.00	3.75	1.50
C21 "Schoolboy" Rowe(throw)	5.00	3.75	1.50
C22 Julius Solters	5.00	3.75	1.50
C23 "Hal" Trosky	5.00	3.75	1.50
C24 Joe Vosmik(kneel)	5.00	3.75	1.50
C25 Johnnie Whitehead (throw)	5.00	3.75	1.50
D1 Buddy Bates(M)	12.50	9.00	4.00
D2 Del Bissonette(M)	12.50	9.00	4.00
D3 Lincoln Blakely(T)	12.50	9.00	4.00
D4 Isaac J. Boone(T)	12.50	9.00	4.00
D5 John H. Burnett(T)	12.50	9.00	4.00
D6 Leon Chagnon(M)	12.50	9.00	4.00
D7 Gus Dugas(M)	12.50	9.00	4.00
D8 Henry N. Erickson	12.50	9.00	4.00
D9 Art Funk(T)	12.50	9.00	4.00
D10 George Granger(M)	12.50	9.00	4.00
D11 Thomas G. Heath	12.50	9.00	4.00
D12 Phil Hensick(M)	12.50	9.00	4.00
D13 LeRoy Hermann(T)	12.50	9.00	4.00
D14 Henry Johnson(M)	12.50	9.00	4.00
D15 Hal King(M)	12.50	9.00	4.00
D16 Charles S. Lucas(T)	12.50	9.00	4.00
D17 Edward S. Miller(T)	12.50	9.00	4.00
D18 Jake F. Mooty(T)	12.50	9.00	4.00
D19 Guy Moreau	12.50	9.00	4.00
D20 George Murray(T)	12.50	9.00	4.00
D21 Glen Myatt(M)	12.50	9.00	4.00
D22 Lauri Myllykarqos(M)	12.50	9.00	4.00
D23 Franci J. Nicholas(T)	12.50	9.00	4.00
D24 Bill O'Brien	12.50	9.00	4.00
D25 Thomas Oliver(T)	12.50	9.00	4.00
D26 James Pattison(T)	12.50	9.00	4.00
D27 Crip Polli(M)	12.50	9.00	4.00
D28 Harlin Pool(T)	12.50	9.00	4.00
D29 Walter Purcey(M)	12.50	9.00	4.00
D30 Bill Rhiel(M)	12.50	9.00	4.00
D31 Ben Sankey(M)	12.50	9.00	4.00
D32 Leslie Scarsella(T)	12.50	9.00	4.00
D33 Bob Seeds(M)	12.50	9.00	4.00
D34 Frank Shaughnessy(M)	12.50	9.00	4.00
D35 Harry Smythe(M)	12.50	9.00	4.00
D36 Ben Tate(M)	12.50	9.00	4.00
D37 Fresco Thompson(M)	12.50	9.00	4.00
D38 Charles Wilson(M)	12.50	9.00	4.00
D39 Francis Wistert(horz)(T)	12.50	9.00	4.00

PEPSI COLA

BASEBALL GAME GIVEAWAY

1929 R316 (101)

The 1929 R316 Portraits and Action Baseball set features 101 unnumbered, blank backed, black and white cards. The name of the player is written in script at the bottom of the card. The Hadley, Haines, Siebold, and Todt cards are considered scarce.

	MINT	VG-E	F-G
COMPLETE SET	900.00	675.00	300.00
COMMON PLAYER	6.00	4.50	2.00
1 Ethan N. Allen	6.00	4.50	2.00
2 Dale Alexander	6.00	4.50	2.00
3 Larry Benton	6.00	4.50	2.00
4 Moe Berg	6.00	4.50	2.00
5 Max Bishop	6.00	4.50	2.00
6 Del Bissonette	6.00	4.50	2.00
7 Lucerne A. Blue	6.00	4.50	2.00
8 James Bottomley	10.00	7.00	3.00
9 Guy T. Bush	6.00	4.50	2.00
10 Harold G. Carlson	6.00	4.50	2.00
11 Owen Carroll	6.00	4.50	2.00
12 Chalmers W. Cissell	6.00	4.50	2.00
13 Earl Combs	10.00	7.00	3.00
14 Hugh M. Critz	6.00	4.50	2.00
15 H. J. DeBerry	6.00	4.50	2.00
16 Pete Donohue	6.00	4.50	2.00
17 Taylor Douthit	6.00	4.50	2.00
18 Chas. W. Dressen	7.00	5.25	2.50
19 Jimmy Dykes	7.00	5.25	2.50
20 Howard Ehmke	7.00	5.25	2.50
21 Elwood English	6.00	4.50	2.00
22 Urban Faber	10.00	7.00	3.00
23 Fred Fitzsimmons	6.00	4.50	2.00
24 Lewis A. Fonseca	6.00	4.50	2.00
25 Horace H. Ford	6.00	4.50	2.00
26 Jimmy Foxx	25.00	18.50	8.75
27 Frank Frisch	15.00	11.00	5.00
28 Lou Gehrig	45.00	34.00	15.00
29 Charles Gehringer	13.00	9.50	4.00
30 Leon Goslin	12.00	8.75	4.00
31 George Grantham	6.00	4.50	2.00
32 Burleigh Grimes	12.00	8.75	4.00
33 Robert Grove	20.00	15.00	6.50
34 Bump Hadley	80.00	60.00	25.00
35 Charlie Hafey	10.00	7.00	3.00
36 Jesse J. Haines	125.00	90.00	40.00
37 Harvey Hendrick	6.00	4.50	2.00
38 Floyd C. Herman	6.00	4.50	2.00
39 Andy High	6.00	4.50	2.00
40 Urban J. Hodapp	6.00	4.50	2.00
41 Frank Hogan	6.00	4.50	2.00
42 Rogers Hornsby	25.00	18.50	8.75
43 Waite Hoyt	12.00	8.75	4.00
44 Willis Hudlin	6.00	4.50	2.00
45 Frank O. Hurst	6.00	4.50	2.00
46 Charlie Jamieson	6.00	4.50	2.00
47 Roy C. Johnson	6.00	4.50	2.00
48 Percy Jones	6.00	4.50	2.00
49 Sam Jones	6.00	4.50	2.00
50 Joseph Judge	6.00	4.50	2.00

	MINT	VG-E	F-G
51 Willie Kamm	6.00	4.50	2.00
52 Charles Klein	10.00	7.00	3.00
53 Mark Koenig	6.00	4.50	2.00
54 Ralph Kress	6.00	4.50	2.00
55 Fred M. Leach	6.00	4.50	2.00
56 Fred Lindstrom	10.00	7.00	3.00
57 Ad Liska	6.00	4.50	2.00
58 Fred Lucas	6.00	4.50	2.00
59 Fred Maguire	6.00	4.50	2.00
60 Perce L. Malone	6.00	4.50	2.00
61 Harry Manush	10.00	7.00	3.00
62 Walter Maranville	10.00	7.00	3.00
63 Douglas McWeeney	6.00	4.50	2.00
64 Oscar Melillo	6.00	4.50	2.00
65 Ed "Bing" Miller	6.00	4.50	2.00
66 Frank O'Doul	7.00	5.25	2.50
67 Melvin Ott	20.00	15.00	6.50
68 Herbert Pennock	13.00	9.50	4.00
69 William W. Regan	6.00	4.50	2.00
70 Harry F. Rice	6.00	4.50	2.00
71 Sam Rice	10.00	7.00	3.00
72 Lance Richbourg	6.00	4.50	2.00
73 Eddie Rommel	6.00	4.50	2.00
74 Chas. H. Root	6.00	4.50	2.00
75 Ed Roush	10.00	7.00	3.00
76 Harold Ruel	6.00	4.50	2.00
77 Charlie Ruffing	12.00	8.75	4.00
78 Jack Russell	6.00	4.50	2.00
79 Babe Ruth	60.00	45.00	20.00
80 Fred Schulte	6.00	4.50	2.00
81 Joe Sewell	10.00	7.00	3.00
82 Luke Sewell	6.00	4.50	2.00
83 Art Shires	6.00	4.50	2.00
84 Henry Seibold	80.00	60.00	25.00
85 Al Simmons	13.00	9.50	4.00
86 Bob Smith	6.00	4.50	2.00
87 Riggs Stephenson	7.00	5.25	2.50
87 Wm H. Terry	15.00	11.00	5.00
89 Alphonse Thomas	6.00	4.50	2.00
90 Lafayette Thompson	6.00	4.50	2.00
91 Phil Todt	80.00	60.00	25.00
92 Harold J. Traynor	13.00	9.50	4.00
93 Dazzy Vance	10.00	7.00	3.00
94 Lloyd Waner	10.00	7.00	3.00
95 Paul Waner	12.00	8.75	4.00
96 Jimmy Welsh	6.00	4.50	2.00
97 Earl Whitehill	6.00	4.50	2.00
98 A. C. Whitney	6.00	4.50	2.00
99 Claude Willoughby	6.00	4.50	2.00
100 Hack Wilson	10.00	7.00	3.00
101 Tom Zachary	6.00	4.50	2.00

R337 SERIES OF 24 (24)

2 5/16" X 2 13/16"

The "Series of 24" set is reminiscent of the R302 issues (MP & Co.) in its rough artwork and use of color. Produced about 1932, this issue is numbered 401—424, with the three missing numbers — 403, 413, and 414 — probably corresponding to the three known unnumbered players.

	MINT	VG-E	F-G
COMPLETE SET	900.00	650.00	300.00
COMMON PLAYER	35.00	25.00	10.00

	MINT	VG-E	F-G
401 Johnny Vergez, Giants	35.00	25.00	10.00
402 Babe Ruth, N.Y. Yankees	200.00	150.00	65.00
404 Pipgras, Red Sox, Out at First Base	35.00	25.00	10.00
405 Bill Terry, Giants	60.00	45.00	20.00
406 George Connally, Cleveland	35.00	25.00	10.00
407 Wilson Clark, Brooklyn	35.00	25.00	10.00
408 "Lefty" Grove, Athletics	80.00	60.00	25.00
409 Henry Johnson, Red Sox	35.00	25.00	10.00
410 Jimmy Dykes, White Sox	35.00	25.00	10.00
411 Henry Hine Schuble, Detroit	35.00	25.00	10.00
412 Harris, Washington, Makes Home Run	35.00	25.00	10.00

	MINT	VG-E	F-G
415 Safe At Third Base (Al Simmons)	50.00	38.00	17.00
416 A Safe Leap to Second Base (Henry Manush)	50.00	38.00	17.00
417 Glen Myatt, Cleveland	35.00	25.00	10.00
418 Babe Herman, Chicago Cubs	35.00	25.00	10.00
419 Frank Frisch, St. L. Cardinals	60.00	45.00	20.00
420 A Safe Slide to the Home Plate	35.00	25.00	10.00
421 Paul Waner, Pirates	60.00	45.00	20.00
422 Jimmy Wilson, Cardinals	35.00	25.00	10.00
423 Charles Grimm, Chicago Natl.	35.00	25.00	10.00
424 Dick Bartell, Phila. Natl. at bat	35.00	25.00	10.00
Jimmy Fox, Athletics	100.00	70.00	30.00
Roy Johnson, Red Sox	35.00	25.00	10.00
Traynor, Pitss is out	35.00	25.00	10.00

1947 R346/ W518 BLUE TINT (48)

2" X 2 5/8"

The 1947 R346 Blue Tint set contains 48 blank backed, numbered cards. The W518 set is exactly the same except for slight differences in card size and slight differences in the dimension of the cards. Card no. 2, Durocher, is listed with either Brooklyn or the New York Giants. Number 18, Ott, is listed with the New York Giants or with no team designation. The cards were issued in strips.

	MINT	VG-E	F-G
COMPLETE SET	250.00	175.00	70.00
COMMON PLAYER	3.50	2.50	1.20

	MINT	VG-E	F-G
1 Bill Johnson	3.50	2.50	1.20
2 Leo Durocher(2)	8.00	6.00	2.50
3 Marty Marion	5.00	3.75	1.75
4 Ewell Blackwell	4.00	3.00	1.40
5 John Lindell	3.50	2.50	1.20
6 Larry Jansen	3.50	2.50	1.20
7 Ralph Kiner	7.00	5.25	2.50
8 Chuck Dressen	4.00	3.00	1.40
9 Bobby Brown	3.50	2.50	1.20
10 Luke Appling	6.00	4.50	2.00
11 Bill Nicholson	3.50	2.50	1.20
12 Phil Masi	3.50	2.50	1.20
13 Frank Shea	3.50	2.50	1.20
14 Bob Dillinger	3.50	2.50	1.20
15 Pete Suder	3.50	2.50	1.20
16 Joe DiMaggio	60.00	45.00	20.00
17 John Corriden	3.50	2.50	1.20
18 Mel Ott(2)	20.00	15.00	6.50
19 Warren Rosar	3.50	2.50	1.20
20 Warren Spahn	12.00	8.75	4.00
21 Allie Reynolds	3.50	2.50	1.20
22 Lou Boudreau	7.00	5.25	2.50
23 Hank Majeski	3.50	2.50	1.20
24 Frank Crosetti	5.00	3.75	1.75

	MINT	VG-E	F-G
25 Gus Niarhos	3.50	2.50	1.20
26 Bruce Edwards	3.50	2.50	1.20
27 Rudy York	4.00	3.00	1.40
28 Don Black	3.50	2.50	1.20
29 Lou Gehrig	60.00	45.00	20.00
30 Johnny Mize	6.00	4.50	2.00
31 Ed Stanky	5.00	3.75	1.75
32 Vic Raschi	5.00	3.75	1.75
33 Cliff Mapes	3.50	2.50	1.20
34 Enos Slaughter	6.00	4.50	2.00
35 Hank Greenberg	10.00	7.00	3.00
36 Jackie Robinson	25.00	18.50	8.75
37 Frank Hiller	3.50	2.50	1.20
38 Bob Elliot	3.50	2.50	1.20
39 Harry Walker	4.00	3.00	1.40
40 Ed Lopat	5.00	3.75	1.75
41 Bobby Thomson	6.00	4.50	2.00
42 Tommy Henrich	6.00	4.50	2.00
43 Bobby Feller	16.00	12.00	5.50
44 Ted Williams	45.00	34.00	15.00
45 Dixie Walker	3.50	2.50	1.20
46 Johnny Vandermeer	5.00	3.75	1.75
47 Clint Hartung	3.50	2.50	1.20
48 Charlie Keller	4.00	3.00	1.40

1958 SAN FRANCISCO (25)
CALL—BULLETIN

2" X 4"

The 1958 San Francisco Call—Bulletin set of 25 unnumbered cards features black print on orange paper. These cards were given away as inserts in the San Francisco Call—Bulletin newspaper. The backs of the cards list the Giants home schedule and a radio station ad. The cards are entitled "Giant Payoff" and features San Francisco Giant players only. The bottom part of the card (tab) could be detached as a ticket stub; hence, cards with the tab intact are worth approximately 30% more than the prices listed below. The ACC designation is M126.

	MINT	VG-E	F-G
COMPLETE SET	250.00	175.00	80.00
COMMON PLAYER	7.50	5.75	2.50
1 John Antonelli	8.50	6.50	3.00
2 Curt Barclay	7.50	5.75	2.50
3 Tom Bowers	7.50	5.75	2.50
4 Ed Bressoud	7.50	5.75	2.50
5 Orlando Cepeda	15.00	11.00	5.00
6 Ray Crone	7.50	5.75	2.50
7 Jim Davenport	7.50	5.75	2.50
8 Paul Giel	7.50	5.75	2.50
9 Ruben Gomez	7.50	5.75	2.50
10 Marv Grissom	7.50	5.75	2.50
11 Ray Jablonski	7.50	5.75	2.50
12 Willie Kirkland	7.50	5.75	2.50

	MINT	VG-E	F-G
13 Whitey Lockman	7.50	5.75	2.50
14 Willie Mays	80.00	60.00	25.00
15 Mike McCormick	7.50	5.75	2.50
16 Stu Miller	7.50	5.75	2.50
17 Ray Monzant	7.50	5.75	2.50
18 Danny O'Connell	7.50	5.75	2.50
19 Bill Rigney	10.00	7.00	3.00
20 Hank Sauer	11.00	8.00	3.50
21 Bob Schmidt	7.50	5.75	2.50
22 Daryl Spencer	7.50	5.75	2.50
23 Valmy Thomas	7.50	5.75	2.50
24 Bobby Thomson	13.00	9.50	4.00
26 Al Worthington	7.50	5.75	2.50

1948 SIGNAL OIL (24)

2 3/8" X 3 1/2"

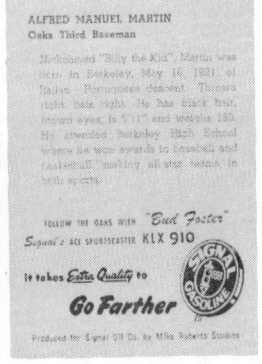

This set of 24 color photos of Oakland Oaks (PCL) was given away at local gas stations. The cards are not numbered and are found with either blue or black printing on the back. The ACC designation is UO10.

	MINT	VG-E	F-G
COMPLETE SET	210.00	150.00	65.00
COMMON PLAYER	8.00	6.00	2.50
1 John Babich	8.00	6.00	2.50
2 Ralph Buxton	8.00	6.00	2.50
3 Loyd Christopher	8.00	6.00	2.50
4 Merrill Coombs	8.00	6.00	2.50
5 Melvin Duezabou	8.00	6.00	2.50
6 Nicholas Etten	12.00	8.75	4.00
7 Bud Foster	8.00	6.00	2.50
8 Charles Gassaway	8.00	6.00	2.50
9 Will Hafey	8.00	6.00	2.50
10 Ray Hamrick	8.00	6.00	2.50
11 Brooks Holder	16.00	12.00	5.50
12 Earl Jones	8.00	6.00	2.50

	MINT	VG-E	F-G
13 Harry Lavagetto	10.00	7.00	3.00
14 Robert Lillard	8.00	6.00	2.50
15 Dario Lodigiani	8.00	6.00	2.50
16 Ernie Lombardi	11.00	8.00	3.50
17 Alfred Martin	25.00	18.50	8.75
18 George Metkovich	8.00	6.00	2.50
19 William Raimondi	8.00	6.00	2.50
20 Les Scarsella	8.00	6.00	2.50
21 Floyd Speer	8.00	6.00	2.50
22 Casey Stengel	25.00	18.50	8.75
23 Maurice Van Robays	8.00	6.00	2.50
24 Aldon Wilkie	8.00	6.00	2.50

The 1947 Signal Oil set of 89 black and white, unnumbered drawings, by Al DeMaree, features Pacific Coast League players from five teams-- Hollywood, Los Angeles, Oakland, Sacramento and Seattle. The Sacramento player cards and to a greater extent the Seattle player cards are more difficult to obtain. The highlights of the careers of the players appear on the backgrounds of the cards as cartoons. Four players appear with two teams--Frank Dasso, Guy Fletcher, Red Mann, and Bill Ramsey. Woody Williams is considered quite scarce and Charles Ripple is somewhat less scarce. The ACC designation is UO-11.

Donald Edwin Osborn

Angel Pitcher
Nickname, "Wizard of Oz"
Throws right, bats right
Height—6'
Weight—180 lbs.

Born Midas, Idaho, June 23, 1910. Scotch-Irish descent. Attended high school Sandpoint, Michigan. Father is rancher. Suffered broken hand from line drive in first pro. game. Owes most in baseball to "Dutch" Reuther, who acted as friend, guide, and philosopher. Wants to be construction contractor. Hobbies: hunting, fishing, bowling and golf.

Professional Experience: 1935, Globe, Arizona Lea.; 1936-37-38 and part of 1939, Seattle, P.C.L.; part of 1939, 1940-41-42, Vancouver, W. Intl. Lea.; 1943-44-45, Los Angeles, P.C.L.

FOLLOW THE ANGELS WITH
Fred Haney
Signal's ACE SPORTSCASTER
KLAC DIAL 570

FOR BETTER CAR PERFORMANCE
REMEMBER . . .
It takes Extra Quality to **Go Farther**
. . . and SIGNAL is the
Famous "GO FARTHER" Gasoline

	MINT	VG-E	F-G			MINT	VG-E	F-G
COMPLETE SET	850.00	650.00	300.00	44 Bud Foster		4.25	3.25	1.50
COMMON PLAYER	4.25	3.25	1.50	45 Sherriff Gassaway		4.25	3.25	1.50
				46 Tom Hafey		4.25	3.25	1.50
1 Ed Albosta	4.25	3.25	1.50	47 Brooks Holder		4.25	3.25	1.50
2 Carl Cox	4.25	3.25	1.50	48 Gene Lillard		4.25	3.25	1.50
3 Frank Dasso	4.25	3.25	1.50	49 Dario Lodigiani		4.25	3.25	1.50
4 Tod Davis	4.25	3.25	1.50	50 Hershel Martin		4.25	3.25	1.50
5 Jimmy Delsing	4.25	3.25	1.50	51 Cotton Pippen		4.25	3.25	1.50
6 Jimmy Dykes	8.00	6.00	2.50	52 Bill Raimondi		4.25	3.25	1.50
7 Paul Gregory	4.25	3.25	1.50	53 Tony Sabol		4.25	3.25	1.50
8 Fred Haney	6.00	4.50	2.00	54 Les Scarsella		4.25	3.25	1.50
9 Francis Kelleher	4.25	3.25	1.50	55 Floyd Speer		4.25	3.25	1.50
10 Joe Krakauskas	4.25	3.25	1.50	56 Casey Stengel		40.00	30.00	13.00
11 Al Libke	4.25	3.25	1.50	57 Maurice Van Robays		4.25	3.25	1.50
12 Tony Lupien	4.25	3.25	1.50	58 Bud Beasley		20.00	15.00	6.50
13 Xavier Rescigno	4.25	3.25	1.50	59 Frank Dasso		20.00	15.00	6.50
14 Jack Sherman	4.25	3.25	1.50	60 Ed Fitzgerald		20.00	15.00	6.50
15 Andy Skurski	4.25	3.25	1.50	61 Guy Fletcher		20.00	15.00	6.50
16 Glen Stewart	4.25	3.25	1.50	62 Tony Freitas		20.00	15.00	6.50
17 Al Unser	5.00	3.75	1.75	63 Red Mann		20.00	15.00	6.50
18 Fred Vaughn	4.25	3.25	1.50	64 Joe Marty		20.00	15.00	6.50
19 Woody Williams	150.00	110.00	50.00	65 Steve Mesner		20.00	15.00	6.50
20 Dutch Zernial	6.00	4.50	2.00	66 Bill Ramsey		20.00	15.00	6.50
21 Red Adams	4.25	3.25	1.50	67 Chas. Ripple		100.00	70.00	30.00
22 Larry Barton	4.25	3.25	1.50	68 John Rizzo		20.00	15.00	6.50
23 Cliff Chambers	4.25	3.25	1.50	69 Al Smith		20.00	15.00	6.50
24 Lloyd Christoper	4.25	3.25	1.50	70 Ronnie Smith		20.00	15.00	6.50
25 Cece Garriott	4.25	3.25	1.50	71 Tommy Thompson		20.00	15.00	6.50
26 Al Glossop	4.25	3.25	1.50	72 Jim Warner		30.00	22.50	10.50
27 Bill Kelly	4.25	3.25	1.50	73 Ed Zipay		20.00	15.00	6.50
28 Red Lynn	4.25	3.25	1.50	74 Kewpie Barrett		20.00	15.00	6.50
29 Eddie Malone	4.25	3.25	1.50	75 Herman Besse		20.00	15.00	6.50
30 Dutch McCall	4.25	3.25	1.50	76 Guy Fletcher		20.00	15.00	6.50
31 Don Osborn	4.25	3.25	1.50	77 Jack Jakucki		20.00	15.00	6.50
32 John Ostrowski	4.25	3.25	1.50	78 Bob Johnson		20.00	15.00	6.50
33 Reggie Otero	4.25	3.25	1.50	79 Pete Jonas		20.00	15.00	6.50
34 Ray Prim	4.25	3.25	1.50	80 Hillis Layne		20.00	15.00	6.50
35 Ed Sauer	4.25	3.25	1.50	81 Red Mann		20.00	15.00	6.50
36 Bill Schuster	4.25	3.25	1.50	82 Lou Novikoff		22.00	16.50	7.50
37 Tuck Stainback	4.25	3.25	1.50	83 John O'Neill		20.00	15.00	6.50
38 Lou Stringer	4.25	3.25	1.50	84 Bill Ramsey		20.00	15.00	6.50
39 Vic Buccola	4.25	3.25	1.50	85 Mickey Rocco		20.00	15.00	6.50
40 Mickey Burnett	4.25	3.25	1.50	86 Geo. Scharein		20.00	15.00	6.50
41 Ralph Buxton	4.25	3.25	1.50	87 Hal Sueme		20.00	15.00	6.50
42 Vince DiMaggio	20.00	15.00	6.50	88 Jo Jo White		20.00	15.00	6.50
43 Dizz Duezabou	4.25	3.25	1.50	89 Tony York		20.00	15.00	6.50

1947 SMITH'S CLOTHING (25)

2″ X 3″

Popular BILLY RAIMONDI, 33, has been Oak property since '31. Billy, the PCL's top receiver, batted an even .300 last year. Managed Acorns part of '45. Believes it's mighty bad luck to cross bats or walk between umpire and catcher. He's a San Franciscan.

Smiths

12th and Washington, Oakland

Largest men's and boys' store west of Chicago

BILLY RAIMONDI
Oaks Catcher   2

The 1947 Smith's Clothing set of 25 black and white, numbered cards features players from the Oakland Oaks only and is similar to the Remar Bread set. The backs give brief player biographies and a Smith's ad. The set is on very thin stock paper. The Max Marshall card is quite scarce. The ACC designation is H801-3A.

	MINT	VG-E	F-G
COMPLETE SET	325.00	250.00	120.00
COMMON PLAYER	7.50	5.75	2.50

		MINT	VG-E	F-G
1	Charles(Casey)Stengel	30.00	22.50	10.50
2	Billy Raimondi	7.50	5.75	2.50
3	Les Scarsella	7.50	5.75	2.50
4	Brooks Holder	7.50	5.75	2.50
5	Ray Hamrick	7.50	5.75	2.50
6	Gene Lillard	7.50	5.75	2.50
7	Maurice Van Robays	7.50	5.75	2.50
8	Charlie Gassaway	7.50	5.75	2.50
9	Henry(Cotton)Pippen	7.50	5.75	2.50
10	James Arnold	7.50	5.75	2.50
11	Ralph(Buck)Buxton	7.50	5.75	2.50
12	Ambrose(Bo)Palica	7.50	5.75	2.50

		MINT	VG-E	F-G
13	Tony Sabot	7.50	5.75	2.50
14	Ed Kearse	7.50	5.75	2.50
15	Bill Hart	7.50	5.75	2.50
16	Donald(Snuffy)Smith	7.50	5.75	2.50
17	Oral(Mickey)Burnett	7.50	5.75	2.50
18	Tom Hafey	7.50	5.75	2.50
19	Will Hafey	7.50	5.75	2.50
20	Paul Gillespie	20.00	15.00	6.50
21	Damon Hayes	25.00	18.50	8.75
22	Max Marshall	125.00	90.00	40.00
23	Mel(Dizz)Duezabou	7.50	5.75	2.50
24	Mel Reeves	7.50	5.75	2.50
25	Joe Faria	15.00	11.00	5.00

1948 SMITH'S CLOTHING (25)

2″ X 3″

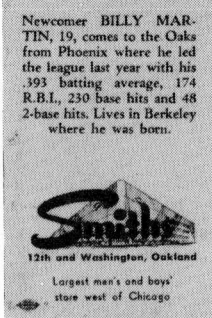

Newcomer BILLY MARTIN, 19, comes to the Oaks from Phoenix where he led the league last year with his .393 batting average, 174 R.B.I., 230 base hits and 48 2-base hits. Lives in Berkeley where he was born.

Smiths

12th and Washington, Oakland

Largest men's and boys' store west of Chicago

BILLY MARTIN
Oaks Third Baseman   17.

The 1948 Smith's Clothing set of 25 black and white, numbered cards features Oakland Oaks players only and is printed on a much heavier stock than the 1947 Smith's set. The cards have a glossy finish. All cards feature full body shots showing players in either fielding, batting, or pitching positions. The ACC designation is H801-3B.

	MINT	VG-E	F-G
COMPLETE SET	190.00	150.00	70.00
COMMON PLAYER	7.50	5.75	2.50

		MINT	VG-E	F-G
1	Billy Raimondi	7.50	5.75	2.50
2	Brooks Holder	7.50	5.75	2.50
3	Will Hafey	7.50	5.75	2.50
4	Nick Etten	15.00	11.00	5.00
5	Lloyd Christopher	7.50	5.75	2.50
6	Les Scarsella	7.50	5.75	2.50
7	Ray Hamrick	7.50	5.75	2.50
8	Gene Lillard	7.50	5.75	2.50
9	Maurice Van Robays	7.50	5.75	2.50
10	Charlie Gassaway	7.50	5.75	2.50
11	Ralph Buxton	7.50	5.75	2.50
12	Tom Hafey	7.50	5.75	2.50

		MINT	VG-E	F-G
13	Damon Hayes	7.50	5.75	2.50
14	Mel"Dizz"Duezabou	7.50	5.75	2.50
15	Dario Lodigiani	7.50	5.75	2.50
16	Vic Buccola	7.50	5.75	2.50
17	Billy Martin	30.00	22.50	10.50
18	Floyd Speer	7.50	5.75	2.50
19	Eddie Samcoff	7.50	5.75	2.50
20	Casey Stengel	30.00	22.50	10.50
21	Floyd Hittle	7.50	5.75	2.50
22	John Babich	7.50	5.75	2.50
23	Merrill Combs	8.00	6.00	2.50
24	Eddie Murphy	7.50	5.75	2.50
25	Bob Klinger	7.50	5.75	2.50

1948 SOMMER & KAUFMAN (30)   2" X 3"

LEFTY O'DOUL
Seals Manager

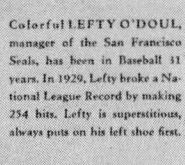

Colorful LEFTY O'DOUL, manager of the San Francisco Seals, has been in Baseball 31 years. In 1929, Lefty broke a National League Record by making 254 hits. Lefty is superstitious, always puts on his left shoe first.

BOYS' SHOP
Sommer & Kaufmann
838 MARKET ST.   2600 OCEAN AVE.
SAN FRANCISCO   SAN FRANCISCO
35 FOURTH AVE. SAN MATEO

The 1948 Sommer and Kaufman set of 30 numbered, black and white cards features players from the San Francisco Seals of the Pacific Coast League. The ACC designation is H801-4A. The backs give brief player biographies and a Sommer and Kaufman ad. The 1948 set can be distinguished from the 1949 set by the script writing of "Sommer and Kaufman". The 1949 set has "Sommer and Kaufman" in fancy print.

	MINT	VG-E	F-G
COMPLETE SET	600.00	450.00	200.00
COMMON PLAYER	20.00	15.00	6.50

		MINT	VG-E	F-G
1	Lefty O'Doul	24.00	18.00	8.50
2	Jack Herndon Brewer	20.00	15.00	6.50
3	Cornelius F. Dempsey	20.00	15.00	6.50
4	"Tommy" Fine	20.00	15.00	6.50
5	Kenneth Harlin Gables	20.00	15.00	6.50
6	Robert Emmett Joyce	20.00	15.00	6.50
7	Alfred Woodrow Lien	20.00	15.00	6.50
8	Cliff Melton	20.00	15.00	6.50
9	Frank S. Shofner	20.00	15.00	6.50
10	Don Trower	20.00	15.00	6.50
11	Joe Brovia	20.00	15.00	6.50
12	Dino Paul Restelli	20.00	15.00	6.50
13	"Gene" Woodling	22.00	16.50	7.50
14	Benjamin J. Guintini	20.00	15.00	6.50
15	Felix Mackiewicz	20.00	15.00	6.50

		MINT	VG-E	F-G
16	John Patrick Tobin	20.00	15.00	6.50
17	Manuel Ruiz Perez, Jr.	20.00	15.00	6.50
18	William George Werle	20.00	15.00	6.50
19	Homer E. Howell, Jr.	20.00	15.00	6.50
20	Wilfred "Bill" Leonard	20.00	15.00	6.50
21	Bruce Ogrodowski	20.00	15.00	6.50
22	R. "Dick" Lajeskie	20.00	15.00	6.50
23	Hugh Luby	20.00	15.00	6.50
24	Roy Melvin Nicely	20.00	15.00	6.50
25	Raymond Joseph Orteig	20.00	15.00	6.50
26	Michael D. Rocco	20.00	15.00	6.50
27	Del Edward Young	20.00	15.00	6.50
28	Joe Sprinz	20.00	15.00	6.50
29	Leo "Doc" Hughes	20.00	15.00	6.50
30	Don Rode-Albert Bero-Charlie Barnes(Bat boys)	20.00	15.00	6.50

1949 SOMMER & KAUFMAN (28)   2" X 3"

FLOYD J. "ARKY" VAUGHAN
Seals Out and Infielder 18

FLOYD JOSEPH "ARKY" VAUGHAN, born March 9, 1912, Clifty, Ark. Lives in Ukiah, Calif. Outfielder and infielder. Played with Wichita, Kans., in 1931. With Pittsburgh, 1932-41. Led National League in hitting with .385 in 1935. With Brooklyn, 1942-48. Inactive, 1944-46. Throws right, bats left.

Sommer & Kaufmann
838 MARKET ST.   2600 OCEAN AVE.
SAN FRANCISCO
35 FOURTH AVE. SAN MATEO
Famous for Boys' "Hot Rod" Shoes

The 1949 Sommer and Kaufman set of 28 numbered, black and white cards features players of the San Francisco Seals of the Pacific Coast League. Card number 24 is not known to exist. The ACC designation is H801-4B.

	MINT	VG-E	F-G
COMPLETE SET	560.00	400.00	150.00
COMMON PLAYER	20.00	15.00	6.50

		MINT	VG-E	F-G
1	"Lefty" O'Doul	24.00	18.00	8.50
2	Jack Brewer	20.00	15.00	6.50
3	Kenneth H. Gables	20.00	15.00	6.50
4	"Con" Dempsey	20.00	15.00	6.50
5	Alfred Lien	20.00	15.00	6.50
6	"Cliff" Melton	20.00	15.00	6.50
7	"Steve" Nagy	20.00	15.00	6.50
8	"Manny" Perez	20.00	15.00	6.50
9	"Roy" Jarvis	20.00	15.00	6.50
10	Roy Partee	20.00	15.00	6.50
11	Reno Cheso	20.00	15.00	6.50
12	"Dick" Lajeskie	20.00	15.00	6.50
13	Roy M. Nicely	20.00	15.00	6.50

		MINT	VG-E	F-G
14	"Mickey" Rocco	20.00	15.00	6.50
15	Frank Shofaer	20.00	15.00	6.50
16	Richard Brooks Holder	20.00	15.00	6.50
17	Dino Restelli	20.00	15.00	6.50
18	Floyd J. "Arky" Vaughn	22.00	16.50	7.50
19	Jackie Baccioccu	20.00	15.00	6.50
20	Robert F. Drilling	20.00	15.00	6.50
21	Del E. Young	20.00	15.00	6.50
22	Joseph D. Sprinz	20.00	15.00	6.50
23	Leo E. "Doc" Hughes	20.00	15.00	6.50
24	unknown	does not exist		xxxx
25	Bert Elmer Singleton	20.00	15.00	6.50
26	John "Gene" Brocker	20.00	15.00	6.50
27	"Jack" Tobin	20.00	15.00	6.50
28	Walter Judnich	20.00	15.00	6.50
29	Harry "Hal" Foldman	20.00	15.00	6.50

— No. 2 —
GEORGE HERMAN "BABE" RUTH
(BASEBALL)

Babe Ruth, the "Home Run King", is the greatest hero of the game of baseball. His amazing feats of the diamond are almost as well known in far off Japan as in the country, Born in Baltimore in 1894, Babe played the game as a kid, and strange as it seems, he was a catcher. He later became a successful "southpaw" pitcher, but because of his tremendous hitting power, he was converted into an outfielder. His first contract was for $600. Years later in 1930, he received $80,000 for a single season, the highest salary ever paid a baseball player. He established many records, but is best known for his thundering home runs. His record of sixty in the 1927 season has never been beaten. He has clouted 687 homers during his professional career, forty-two of them coming in the ten world's series which have given the "Sultan of Swat" another record.

His career is crowded with attractive and sportsman. This complete series is one of a 48 lot limited series. Preserve them. START YOUR COLLECTION NOW.

SPORT KINGS CHEWING GUM
THE GOUDEY GUM CO.   BOSTON
Made by the originators of
INDIAN and BIG LEAGUE GUM

The 1933 Sport Kings set, by Goudey Gum, features a variety of sports figures, baseball players being the most valuable as Ruth, Cobb, and Hubbell are included.

	MINT	VG-E	F-G
COMPLETE SET	425.00	325.00	125.00
COMMON PLAYER (1-24)	5.25	3.75	1.75
COMMON PLAYER (25-48)	6.25	4.75	2.25
1 Ty Cobb: baseball	100.00	70.00	30.00
2 Babe Ruth: baseball	200.00	150.00	65.00
3 Nat Holman: basketball	7.50	5.75	2.50
4 Red Grange: football	20.00	15.00	6.50
5 Ed Wachter: basketball	7.50	5.75	2.50
6 James Thorpe: football	30.00	22.50	10.50
7 B. Walthour Sr.: bicyc	5.25	3.75	1.75
8 Walter Hagen: golf	5.25	3.75	1.75
9 Ed Blood: skiing	5.25	3.75	1.75
10 Anton Lekang: skiing	5.25	3.75	1.75
11 C. Jewtraw: ice skat	5.25	3.75	1.75
12 Bubby McLean: ice skat	5.25	3.75	1.75
13 Laverne Fator: jockey	5.25	3.75	1.75
14 Jim Londos: wrestling	5.25	3.75	1.75
15 R. McNamara: bicycling	5.25	3.75	1.75
16 William Tilden: tennis	5.25	3.75	1.75
17 Jack Dempsey: boxing	20.00	15.00	6.50
18 Gene Tunney: boxing	16.00	12.00	5.50
19 Eddie Shore: hockey	7.50	5.75	2.50
20 D. Kahanamoka: swim	5.25	3.75	1.75
21 J. Weissmuller: swim	25.00	18.50	8.75
22 Gene Sarazen: golf	5.25	3.75	1.75
23 Vincent Richards: ten	5.25	3.75	1.75
24 Howard Morenz: hockey	7.50	5.75	2.50
25 Ralph Snoddy: speedboat	6.25	4.75	2.25
26 James R. Wedell: aviat	6.25	4.75	2.25
27 Col. R. Turner: aviat	6.25	4.75	2.25
28 James Doolittle: aviat	6.25	4.75	2.25
29 "Ace" Bailey: hockey	6.25	4.75	2.25
30 "Ching" Johnson: hockey	7.50	5.75	2.50
31 B. WalthourJr.: cycling	6.25	4.75	2.25
32 Joe Lopchick: basket	10.00	7.00	3.00
33 Eddie Burke: basketball	7.50	5.75	2.50
34 Irving Jaffe: ice skat	6.25	4.75	2.25
35 Knute Rockne: football	30.00	22.50	10.50
36 Willie Hoppe: billiards	6.25	4.75	2.25
37 Helene Madison: swim	6.26	1.76	2.26
38 Bobby Jones: golf	7.50	5.75	2.50
39 Jack Westrope: jockey	6.25	4.75	2.25
40 Don George: wrestling	6.25	4.75	2.25
41 Jim Browning: wrestling	6.25	4.75	2.25
42 Carl Hubbell: baseball	30.00	22.50	10.50
43 Primo Carnera: boxing	6.25	4.75	2.25
44 Max Baer: boxing	7.50	5.75	2.50
45 Babe Didrickson: track	25.00	18.50	8.75
46 Ellsworth Vine: tennis	6.25	4.75	2.25
47 J. H. Stevens: bob-sled	6.25	4.75	2.25
48 L. Seppala: dog-sled	6.25	4.75	2.25

PC748 DORMAND POSTCARD

This 173 card set contains all the players inducted into the Hall of Fame through 1980, with the players pictures taken almost exclusively from older card sets.

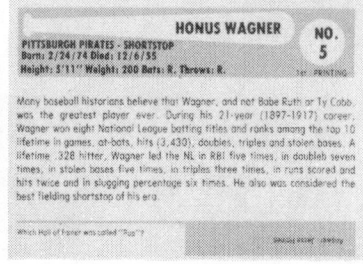

	MINT	VG-E	F-G
COMPLETE SET	13.00	10.00	4.00
COMMON PLAYER	.05	.03	.01
1 Babe Ruth-36	.50	.40	.18
2 Ty Cobb-36	.40	.30	.13
3 Walter Johnson-36	.30	.25	.10
4 Christy Mathewson-36	.30	.25	.10
5 Honus Wagner-36	.30	.25	.10
6 Morgan Bulkley-37	.05	.03	.01
7 Ban Johnson-37	.05	.03	.01
8 Larry Lajoie-37	.20	.15	.06
9 Connie Mack-37	.20	.15	.06
10 John McGraw-37	.10	.07	.03
11 Tris Speaker-37	.10	.07	.03
12 George Wright-37	.05	.03	.01
13 Cy Young-37	.10	.07	.03
14 Grover Alexander-38	.10	.07	.03
15 Alexander Cartwright-38	.05	.03	.01
16 Henry Chadwick-38	.05	.03	.01
17 Cap Anson-39	.05	.03	.01
18 Eddie Collins-39	.05	.03	.01
19 Charles Comiskey-39	.05	.03	.01
20 Candy Cummings-39	.05	.03	.01
21 Buck Ewing-39	.05	.03	.01
22 Lou Gehrig-39	.40	.30	.13
23 Willie Keeler-39	.05	.03	.01
24 Hoss Radbourne-39	.05	.03	.01
25 George Sisler-39	.05	.03	.01
26 Albert Spalding-39	.05	.03	.01
27 Rogers Hornsby-42	.30	.25	.10
28 Judge Landis-44	.05	.03	.01
29 Roger Bresnahan-45	.05	.03	.01
30 Dan Brouthers-45	.05	.03	.01
31 Fred Clarke-45	.05	.03	.01
32 James Collins-45	.05	.03	.01
33 Ed Delahanty-45	.05	.03	.01
34 Hugh Duffy-45	.05	.03	.01
35 Hughie Jennings-45	.05	.03	.01
36 Mike "King" Kelly-45	.05	.03	.01
37 James O'Rourke-45	.05	.03	.01
38 Wilbert Robinson-45	.05	.03	.01
39 Jesse Burkett-46	.05	.03	.01
40 Frank Chance-46	.10	.07	.03
41 Jack Chesbro-46	.05	.03	.01
42 John Evers-46	.10	.07	.03
43 Clark Griffith-46	.05	.03	.01
44 Thomas McCarthy-46	.05	.03	.01
45 Joe McGinnity-46	.05	.03	.01
46 Eddie Plank-46	.10	.07	.03
47 Joe Tinker-46	.10	.07	.03
48 Rube Waddell-46	.05	.03	.01
49 Ed Walsh-46	.05	.03	.01
50 Mickey Cochrane-47	.10	.07	.03
51 Frankie Frisch-47	.15	.11	.05
52 Lefty Grove-47	.20	.15	.06
53 Carl Hubbell-47	.10	.07	.03
54 Herb Pennock-48	.05	.03	.01
55 Pie Traynor-48	.10	.07	.03
56 Three Finger Brown-49	.05	.03	.01
57 Charlie Gehringer-49	.10	.07	.03
58 Kid Nichols-49	.05	.03	.01
59 Jimmie Foxx-51	.30	.25	.10
60 Mel Ott-51	.20	.15	.06
61 Harry Heilmann-52	.10	.07	.03
62 Paul Waner-52	.05	.03	.01
63 Ed Barrow-53	.05	.03	.01
64 Chief Bender-53	.05	.03	.01
65 Tom Connolly-53	.05	.03	.01
66 Dizzy Dean-53	.30	.25	.10
67 Bill Klem-53	.05	.03	.01

	MINT	VG-E	F-G
68 Al Simmons-53	.10	.07	.03
69 Bobby Wallace-53	.05	.03	.01
70 Harry Wright-53	.05	.03	.01
71 Bill Dickey-54	.20	.15	.06
72 Rabbit Maranville-54	.05	.03	.01
73 Bill Terry-54	.10	.07	.03
74 Home Run Baker-55	.05	.03	.01
75 Joe DiMaggio-55	.40	.30	.13
76 Gabby Hartnett-55	.05	.03	.01
77 Ted Lyons-55	.05	.03	.01
78 Ray Schalk-55	.05	.03	.01
79 Dazzy Vance-55	.05	.03	.01
80 Joe Cronin-56	.10	.07	.03
81 Hank Greenberg-56	.10	.07	.03
82 Sam Crawford-57	.05	.03	.01
83 Joe McCarthy-57	.05	.03	.01
84 Zack Wheat-59	.05	.03	.01
85 Max Carey-61	.05	.03	.01
86 Billy Hamilton-61	.05	.03	.01
87 Bob Feller-62	.20	.15	.06
88 Bill McKechnie-62	.05	.03	.01
89 Jackie Robinson-62	.25	.20	.08
90 Edd Roush-62	.05	.03	.01
91 John Clarkson-63	.05	.03	.01
92 Elmer Flick-63	.05	.03	.01
93 Sam Rice-63	.05	.03	.01
94 Eppa Rixey-63	.05	.03	.01
95 Luke Appling-64	.05	.03	.01
96 Red Faber-64	.05	.03	.01
97 Burleigh Grimes-64	.05	.03	.01
98 Miller Huggins-64	.05	.03	.01
99 Tim Keefe-64	.05	.03	.01
100 Heinie Manush-64	.05	.03	.01
101 John Ward-64	.05	.03	.01
102 Pud Galvin-65	.05	.03	.01
103 Casey Stengel-66	.20	.15	.06
104 Ted Williams-66	.30	.25	.10
105 Branch Rickey-67	.05	.03	.01
106 Red Ruffing-67	.05	.03	.01
107 Lloyd Waner-67	.05	.03	.01
108 KiKi Cuyler-68	.05	.03	.01
109 Goose Goslin-68	.05	.03	.01
110 Joe Medwick-68	.05	.03	.01
111 Roy Campanella-69	.25	.20	.08
112 Stan Coveleski-69	.05	.03	.01
113 Waite Hoyt-69	.05	.03	.01
114 Stan Musial-69	.25	.20	.08
115 Lou Boudreau-70	.05	.03	.01
116 Earle Combs-70	.05	.03	.01
117 Ford Frick-70	.05	.03	.01
118 Jesse Haines-70	.05	.03	.01
119 Dave Bancroft-71	.05	.03	.01
120 Jake Beckley-71	.05	.03	.01
121 Chick Hafey-71	.05	.03	.01
122 Harry Hooper-71	.05	.03	.01
123 Joe Kelley-71	.05	.03	.01
124 Rube Marquard-71	.05	.03	.01
125 Satchel Paige-71	.15	.11	.05
126 George Weiss-71	.05	.03	.01
127 Yogi Berra-72	.20	.15	.06
128 Josh Gibson-72	.10	.07	.03
129 Lefty Gomez-72	.10	.07	.03
130 Will Harridge-72	.05	.03	.01
131 Sandy Koufax-72	.15	.11	.05
132 Buck Leonard-72	.05	.03	.01
133 Early Wynn-72	.05	.03	.01
134 Ross Youngs-72	.05	.03	.01
135 Roberto Clemente-73	.20	.15	.06
136 Billy Evans-73	.05	.03	.01
137 Monte Irvin-73	.05	.03	.01

1980 TCMA HOF (CONTINUED)

	MINT	VG-E	F-G		MINT	VG-E	F-G
138 George Kelly-73	.05	.03	.01	156 Fred Lindstrom-76	.05	.03	.01
139 Warren Spahn-73	.10	.07	.03	157 Robin Roberts-76	.10	.07	.03
140 Mickey Welch-73	.05	.03	.01	158 Ernie Banks-77	.20	.15	.06
141 Cool Papa Bell-74	.05	.03	.01	159 Martin Dihigo-77	.05	.03	.01
142 Jim Bottomley-74	.05	.03	.01	160 John Henry Lloyd-77	.05	.03	.01
143 Jocko Conlan-74	.05	.03	.01	161 Al Lopez-77	.05	.03	.01
144 Whitey Ford-74	.10	.07	.03	162 Amos Rusie-77	.05	.03	.01
145 Mickey Mantle-74	.40	.30	.13	163 Joe Sewell-77	.05	.03	.01
146 Sam Thompson-74	.05	.03	.01	164 Addie Joss-78	.05	.03	.01
147 Earl Averill-75	.05	.03	.01	165 Larry McPhail-78	.05	.03	.01
148 Bucky Harris-75	.05	.03	.01	166 Eddie Mathews-78	.10	.07	.03
149 Billy Herman-75	.05	.03	.01	167 Warren Giles-79	.05	.03	.01
150 Judy Johnson-75	.05	.03	.01	168 Willie Mays-79	.30	.25	.10
151 Ralph Kiner-75	.10	.07	.03	169 Hack Wilson-79	.05	.03	.01
152 Oscar Charleston-76	.05	.03	.01	170 Duke Snider-80	.20	.15	.06
153 Roger Connor-76	.05	.03	.01	171 Al Kaline-80	.20	.15	.06
154 Cal Hubbard-76	.05	.03	.01	172 Chuck Klein-80	.05	.03	.01
155 Bob Lemon-76	.10	.07	.03	173 Tom Yawkey-80	.05	.03	.01

1976 SSPC (630)

2 1/2" X 3 1/2"

LOS ANGELES DODGERS

10

Third Baseman
5' 9", 185 lbs.
Bn. 2/15/48

RONALD CHARLES CEY

Ron had the best of his 3 N●L● seasons in '75, hitting .283 with 29 homers, 2 triples, 25 homers, and 101 RBI - fifth in the N●L● Nicknamed "The Penguin," he joined the L●A● organization in '68 and led the Northwest League in RBI in his first year. After topping the P●C●L● in RBI in '71, he got a late season trial with L●A● Spent most of '72 in the P●C●L●, and after hitting .329 returned to the Dodgers, taking over at the hot corner in '73. Helped L●A● to the N●L● title in '74, hitting .313 in the playoffs. In 482 big league games, Ron has 68 doubles, 8 triples, 59 homers, 281 RBI, and a .264 average.

CARD # 75   ° SSPC 1975

The 1976 SSPC set is the first truly "major" collector issue baseball card set. Sometime called "The Pure Card" set because of the lack of extraneous material on the front of the card, this set contains no known scarcities.

	MINT	VG-E	F-G		MINT	VG-E	F-G
COMPLETE SET	35.00	25.00	10.00	25 Clay Carroll	.05	.03	.01
COMMON PLAYER	.05	.03	.01	26 Pat Darcy	.05	.03	.01
				27 Don Gullett	.08	.06	.02
1 Buzz Capra	.05	.03	.01	28 Clay Kirby	.05	.03	.01
2 Tom House	.05	.03	.01	29 Gary Nolan	.05	.03	.01
3 Max Leon	.05	.03	.01	30 Fred Norman	.05	.03	.01
4 Carl Morton	.05	.03	.01	31 Johnny Bench	1.00	.70	.30
5 Phil Niekro	.12	.08	.04	32 Bill Plummer	.05	.03	.01
6 Mike Thompson	.05	.03	.01	33 Darrel Chaney	.05	.03	.01
7 Elias Sosa	.05	.03	.01	34 Dave Concepcion	.12	.08	.04
8 Larvell Blanks	.05	.03	.01	35 Terry Crowley	.05	.03	.01
9 Darrell Evans	.05	.03	.01	36 Dan Driessen	.05	.03	.01
10 Rod Gilbreath	.05	.03	.01	37 Doug Flynn	.05	.03	.01
11 Mike Lum	.05	.03	.01	38 Joe Morgan	.30	.25	.10
12 Craig Robinson	.05	.03	.01	39 Tony Perez	.20	.15	.06
13 Earl Williams	.05	.03	.01	40 Ken Griffey	.15	.11	.05
14 Vic Correll	.05	.03	.01	41 Pete Rose	1.50	1.10	.50
15 Biff Pocoroba	.05	.03	.01	42 Ed Armbrister	.05	.03	.01
16 Dusty Baker	.15	.11	.05	43 John Vukovich	.05	.03	.01
17 Ralph Garr	.08	.06	.02	44 George Foster	.40	.30	.13
18 Cito Gaston	.05	.03	.01	45 Cesar Geronimo	.05	.03	.01
19 Dave May	.05	.03	.01	46 Merv Rettenmund	.05	.03	.01
20 Rowland Office	.05	.03	.01	47 Jim Crawford	.05	.03	.01
21 Bob Beall	.05	.03	.01	48 Ken Forsch	.05	.03	.01
22 Sparky Anderson	.12	.08	.04	49 Doug Konieczny	.05	.03	.01
23 Jack Billingham	.05	.03	.01	50 Joe Niekro	.08	.06	.02
24 Pedro Borbon	.05	.03	.01	51 Cliff Johnson	.05	.03	.01

BASEBALL HISTORY CARDS

225

#	Name	MINT	VG-E	F-G
52	Skip Jutze	.05	.03	.01
53	Milt May	.05	.03	.01
54	Rob Andrews	.05	.03	.01
55	Ken Boswell	.05	.03	.01
56	Tommy Helms	.05	.03	.01
57	Roger Metzger	.05	.03	.01
58	Larry Milbourne	.05	.03	.01
59	Doug Rader	.05	.03	.01
60	Bob Watson	.10	.07	.03
61	Enos Cabell	.05	.03	.01
62	Jose Cruz	.08	.06	.02
63	Cesar Cedeno	.25	.20	.08
64	Greg Gross	.05	.03	.01
65	Wilbur Howard	.05	.03	.01
66	Al Downing	.05	.03	.01
67	Burt Hooton	.15	.11	.05
68	Charlie Hough	.05	.03	.01
69	Tommy John	.25	.20	.08
70	A. Messersmith	.10	.07	.03
71	Doug Rau	.05	.03	.01
72	Rick Rhoden	.05	.03	.01
73	Don Sutton	.25	.20	.08
74	Rick Auerbach	.05	.03	.01
75	Ron Cey	.15	.11	.05
76	Ivan deJesus	.05	.03	.01
77	Steve Garvey	1.00	.70	.30
78	Lee Lacy	.05	.03	.01
79	Dave Lopes	.12	.08	.04
80	Ken McMullen	.05	.03	.01
81	Joe Ferguson	.05	.03	.01
82	Paul Powell	.05	.03	.01
83	Steve Yeager	.05	.03	.01
84	Willie Crawford	.05	.03	.01
85	Henry Cruz	.05	.03	.01
86	Charlie Manuel	.05	.03	.01
87	Manny Mota	.10	.07	.03
88	Tom Paciorek	.05	.03	.01
89	Jim Wynn	.08	.06	.02
90	Walt Alston	.08	.06	.02
91	Bill Buckner	.15	.11	.05
92	Jim Barr	.05	.03	.01
93	Mike Caldwell	.10	.07	.03
94	John D'Acquisto	.05	.03	.01
95	Dave Heaverlo	.05	.03	.01
96	Gary LaVelle	.08	.06	.02
97	John Montefusco	.08	.06	.02
98	Charlie Williams	.05	.03	.01
99	Chris Arnold	.05	.03	.01
100	Mark Hill	.05	.03	.01
101	Dave Rader	.05	.03	.01
102	Bruce Miller	.05	.03	.01
103	Willie Montanez	.08	.06	.02
104	Steve Ontiveros	.05	.03	.01
105	Chris Speier	.05	.03	.01
106	Derrel Thomas	.05	.03	.01
107	Gary Thomasson	.05	.03	.01
108	Glenn Adams	.05	.03	.01
109	Von Joshua	.05	.03	.01
110	Gary Matthews	.10	.07	.03
111	Bobby Murcer	.12	.08	.04
112	Horace Speed	.05	.03	.01
113	Wes Westrum	.05	.03	.01
114	Rich Folkers	.05	.03	.01
115	Alan Foster	.05	.03	.01
116	Dave Freisleben	.05	.03	.01
117	Dan Frisella	.05	.03	.01
118	Randy Jones	.15	.11	.05
119	Dan Spillner	.05	.03	.01
120	Larry Hardy	.05	.03	.01
121	Randy Hundley	.05	.03	.01
122	Fred Kendall	.05	.03	.01
123	John McNamara	.05	.03	.01
124	Tito Fuentes	.05	.03	.01
125	Enzo Hernandez	.05	.03	.01
126	Steve Huntz	.05	.03	.01
127	Mike Ivie	.08	.06	.02
128	Hector Torres	.05	.03	.01
129	Ted Kubiak	.05	.03	.01
130	John Grubb	.05	.03	.01
131	John Scott	.05	.03	.01
132	Bob Tolan	.05	.03	.01
133	Dave Winfield	.75	.55	.25
134	Bill Gogolewski	.05	.03	.01
135	Dan Osborn	.05	.03	.01
136	Jim Kaat	.15	.11	.05
137	Claude Osteen	.05	.03	.01
138	Cecil Upshaw	.05	.03	.01
139	Wilbur Wood	.05	.03	.01
140	Lloyd Allen	.05	.03	.01
141	Brian Downing	.08	.06	.02
142	Jim Essian	.05	.03	.01
143	Bucky Dent	.10	.07	.03
144	Jorge Orta	.05	.03	.01
145	Lee Richard	.05	.03	.01
146	Bill Stein	.05	.03	.01
147	Ken Henderson	.05	.03	.01
148	Carlos May	.05	.03	.01
149	Nyls Nyman	.05	.03	.01
150	Bob Coluccio	.05	.03	.01
151	Chuck Tanner	.08	.06	.02
152	Pat Kelly	.05	.03	.01
153	Jerry Hairston	.05	.03	.01
154	Pete Varney	.05	.03	.01
155	Bill Melton	.05	.03	.01
156	Rich Gossage	.20	.15	.06
157	Terry Forster	.10	.07	.03
158	Rich Hinton	.05	.03	.01
159	Nelson Briles	.05	.03	.01
160	Al Fitzmorris	.05	.03	.01
161	Steve Mingori	.05	.03	.01
162	Marty Pattin	.05	.03	.01
163	Paul Splittorff	.08	.06	.02
164	Dennis Leonard	.12	.08	.04
165	Buck Martinez	.05	.03	.01
166	Bob Stinson	.05	.03	.01
167	George Brett	1.25	.90	.40
168	Harmon Killebrew	.60	.45	.20
169	John Mayberry	.08	.06	.02
170	Fred Patek	.05	.03	.01
171	Cookie Rojas	.05	.03	.01
172	Rodney Scott	.05	.03	.01
173	Tony Solaita	.05	.03	.01
174	Frank White	.08	.06	.02
175	Al Cowens	.08	.06	.02
176	Hal McRae	.05	.03	.01
177	Amos Otis	.12	.08	.04
178	Vada Pinson	.12	.08	.04
179	Jim Wohlford	.05	.03	.01
180	Doug Bird	.05	.03	.01
181	Mark Littell	.05	.03	.01
182	Bob McClure	.05	.03	.01
183	Steve Busby	.05	.03	.01
184	Fran Healy	.05	.03	.01
185	Whitey Herzog	.10	.07	.03
186	Andy Hassler	.05	.03	.01
187	Nolan Ryan	.80	.60	.25
188	Bill Singer	.05	.03	.01
189	Frank Tanana	.12	.08	.04
190	Ed Figueroa	.05	.03	.01
191	Dave Collins	.08	.06	.02
192	Dick Williams	.08	.06	.02
193	Ellie Rodriguez	.05	.03	.01
194	Dave Chalk	.05	.03	.01
195	Winston Llenas	.05	.03	.01
196	Rudy Meoli	.05	.03	.01
197	Orlando Ramirez	.05	.03	.01
198	Jerry Remy	.05	.03	.01
199	Billy Smith	.05	.03	.01
200	Bruce Bochte	.10	.07	.03
201	Joe Lahoud	.05	.03	.01
202	Morris Nettles	.05	.03	.01
203	Mickey Rivers	.10	.07	.03
204	Leroy Stanton	.05	.03	.01
205	Vic Albury	.05	.03	.01
206	Tom Burgmeier	.05	.03	.01
207	Bill Butler	.05	.03	.01
208	Bill Campbell	.05	.03	.01
209	Ray Corbin	.05	.03	.01
210	Joe Decker	.05	.03	.01
211	Jim Hughes	.05	.03	.01
212	Ed Bane	.05	.03	.01
213	Glenn Borgman	.05	.03	.01
214	Rod Carew	1.00	.70	.30
215	Steve Brye	.05	.03	.01
216	Dan Ford	.08	.06	.02
217	Tony Oliva	.30	.25	.10
218	Dave Goltz	.08	.06	.02
219	Bert Blyleven	.12	.08	.04
220	Larry Hisle	.10	.07	.03
221	Steve Braun	.05	.03	.01
222	Jerry Terrell	.05	.03	.01
223	Eric Soderholm	.05	.03	.01
224	Phil Roof	.05	.03	.01
225	Dan Thompson	.05	.03	.01
226	Jim Colborn	.05	.03	.01
227	Tom Murphy	.05	.03	.01
228	Ed Rodriguez	.05	.03	.01
229	Jim Slaton	.05	.03	.01
230	Ed Sprague	.05	.03	.01
231	Chas. Moore	.05	.03	.01
232	Darrell Porter	.12	.08	.04
233	Kurt Bevacqua	.05	.03	.01
234	Pedro Garcia	.05	.03	.01
235	Mike Hegan	.05	.03	.01
236	Don Money	.08	.06	.02
237	George Scott	.08	.06	.02
238	Robin Yount	.12	.08	.04

#	Name	MINT	VG-E	F-G
239	Hank Aaron	1.50	1.10	.50
240	Rob Ellis	.05	.03	.01
241	Sixto Lezcano	.10	.07	.03
242	Bob Mitchell	.05	.03	.01
243	Gorman Thomas	.20	.15	.06
244	Bill Travers	.05	.03	.01
245	Pete Broberg	.05	.03	.01
246	Bill Sharp	.05	.03	.01
247	Bobby Darwin	.05	.03	.01
248	Rick Austin	.05	.03	.01
249	Larry Anderson	.05	.03	.01
250	Tom Bianco	.05	.03	.01
251	L. Currence	.05	.03	.01
252	Steve Foucault	.05	.03	.01
253	Bill Hands	.05	.03	.01
254	Steve Hargan	.05	.03	.01
255	Fergie Jenkins	.12	.08	.04
256	Bob Sheldon	.05	.03	.01
257	Jim Umbarger	.05	.03	.01
258	Clyde Wright	.05	.03	.01
259	Bill Fahey	.05	.03	.01
260	Jim Sundberg	.12	.08	.04
261	Leo Cardenas	.05	.03	.01
262	Jim Fregosi	.12	.08	.04
263	Mike Hargrove	.05	.03	.01
264	Toby Harrah	.05	.03	.01
265	Roy Howell	.05	.03	.01
266	Lenny Randle	.05	.03	.01
267	Roy Smalley	.08	.06	.02
268	Jim Spencer	.05	.03	.01
269	Jeff Burroughs	.10	.07	.03
270	Tom Grieve	.08	.06	.02
271	Joe Lovitto	.05	.03	.01
272	Frank Lucchesi	.05	.03	.01
273	Dave Nelson	.05	.03	.01
274	Ted Simmons	.30	.25	.10
275	Lou Brock	.80	.60	.25
276	Ron Fairly	.05	.03	.01
277	Bake McBride	.08	.06	.02
278	Reggie Smith	.20	.15	.06
279	Willie Davis	.05	.03	.01
280	Ken Reitz	.05	.03	.01
281	Buddy Bradford	.05	.03	.01
282	Luis Melendez	.05	.03	.01
283	Mike Tyson	.05	.03	.01
284	Ted Sizemore	.05	.03	.01
285	Mario Guerrero	.05	.03	.01
286	Larry Lintz	.05	.03	.01
287	Ken Rudolph	.05	.03	.01
288	Dick Billings	.05	.03	.01
389	Jerry Mumphrey	.05	.03	.01
290	Mike Wallace	.05	.03	.01
291	Al Hrabosky	.08	.06	.02
292	Ken Reynolds	.05	.03	.01
293	Mike Garman	.05	.03	.01
294	Bob Forsch	.05	.03	.01
295	John Denny	.05	.03	.01
296	H. Rasmussen	.05	.03	.01
297	Lynn McGlothen	.05	.03	.01
298	Mike Barlow	.05	.03	.01
299	Greg Terlecky	.05	.03	.01
300	Red Schoendienst	.08	.06	.02
301	Rick Reuschel	.15	.11	.05
302	Steve Stone	.15	.11	.05
303	Bill Bonham	.05	.03	.01
304	Oscar Zamora	.05	.03	.01
305	Ken Frailing	.05	.03	.01
306	Milt Wilcox	.05	.03	.01
307	Darold Knowles	.05	.03	.01
308	Jim Marshall	.05	.03	.01
309	Bill Madlock	.08	.06	.02
310	Jose Cardenal	.05	.03	.01
311	Rick Monday	.08	.06	.02
312	Jerry Morales	.05	.03	.01
313	Tim Hosley	.05	.03	.01
314	Gene Hiser	.05	.03	.01
315	Don Kessinger	.08	.06	.02
316	Manny Trillo	.08	.06	.02
317	Pete LaCock	.08	.06	.02
318	Geo. Mitterwald	.05	.03	.01
319	Steve Swisher	.05	.03	.01
320	Rob Sperring	.05	.03	.01
321	Vic Harris	.05	.03	.01
322	Ron Dunn	.05	.03	.01
323	Jose Morales	.05	.03	.01
324	Pete Mackanin	.05	.03	.01
325	Jim Cox	.05	.03	.01
326	Larry Parrish	.10	.07	.03
327	Mike Jorgensen	.05	.03	.01
328	Tim Foli	.05	.03	.01
329	Hal Breeden	.05	.03	.01
330	Nate Colbert	.05	.03	.01
331	Pepe Frias	.05	.03	.01
332	Pat Scanlon	.05	.03	.01
333	Bob Bailey	.05	.03	.01
334	Gary Carter	.25	.20	.08
335	Pepe Mangual	.05	.03	.01
336	Larry Biittner	.05	.03	.01
337	Jim Lyttle	.05	.03	.01
338	Gary Roenicke	.05	.03	.01
339	Tony Scott	.05	.03	.01
340	Jerry White	.05	.03	.01
341	Jim Dwyer	.05	.03	.01
342	Ellis Valentine	.12	.08	.04
343	Fred Scherman	.05	.03	.01
344	Dennis Blair	.05	.03	.01
345	Woodie Fryman	.05	.03	.01
346	Chuck Taylor	.05	.03	.01
347	Dan Warthen	.05	.03	.01
348	Dan Carrithers	.05	.03	.01
349	Steve Rogers	.10	.07	.03
350	Dale Murray	.05	.03	.01
351	Duke Snider	.60	.45	.20
352	Ralph Houk	.10	.07	.03
353	John Hiller	.08	.06	.02
354	Mikey Lolich	.15	.11	.05
355	Dave Lemancyzk	.05	.03	.01
356	Lerrin LaGrow	.05	.03	.01
357	Fred Arroyo	.05	.03	.01
358	Joe Coleman	.05	.03	.01
359	Ben Oglivie	.05	.03	.01
360	Willie Horton	.08	.06	.02
361	John Knox	.05	.03	.01
362	Leon Roberts	.05	.03	.01
363	Ron LeFlore	.12	.08	.04
364	G. Sutherland	.05	.03	.01
365	Dan Meyer	.05	.03	.01
366	A. Rodriguez	.05	.03	.01
367	Tom Veryzer	.05	.03	.01
368	Jack Pierce	.05	.03	.01
369	Gene Michael	.12	.08	.04
370	Billy Baldwin	.05	.03	.01
371	Gates Brown	.05	.03	.01
372	Mickey Stanley	.08	.06	.02
373	Terry Humphrey	.05	.03	.01
374	Doyle Alexander	.05	.03	.01
375	Mike Cuellar	.05	.03	.01
376	Wayne Garland	.05	.03	.01
377	Ross Grimsley	.05	.03	.01
378	Grant Jackson	.05	.03	.01
379	Dyar Miller	.05	.03	.01
380	Jim Palmer	.60	.45	.20
381	Mike Torrez	.08	.06	.02
382	Mike Willis	.05	.03	.01
383	Dave Duncan	.05	.03	.01
384	Ellie Hendricks	.05	.03	.01
385	Jim Hutto	.05	.03	.01
386	Bob Bailor	.05	.03	.01
387	Doug DeCinces	.05	.03	.01
388	Bob Grich	.08	.06	.02
389	Lee May	.08	.06	.02
390	Tony Muser	.05	.03	.01
391	Tim Nordbrook	.05	.03	.01
392	Brooks Robinson	1.00	.70	.30
393	Royle Stillman	.05	.03	.01
394	Don Baylor	.25	.20	.08
395	Paul Blair	.05	.03	.01
396	Al Bumbry	.05	.03	.01
397	Larry Harlow	.05	.03	.01
298	Tommy Davis	.08	.06	.02
399	Jim Northrup	.05	.03	.01
400	Ken Singleton	.20	.15	.06
401	Tom Shopay	.05	.03	.01
402	Fred Lynn	1.00	.70	.30
403	Carlton Fisk	.30	.25	.10
404	Cecil Cooper	.20	.15	.06
405	Jim Rice	1.00	.70	.30
406	Juan Beniquez	.05	.03	.01
407	Denny Doyle	.05	.03	.01
408	Dwight Evans	.05	.03	.01
409	Carl Yastrzemski	1.25	.90	.40
410	Rick Burleson	.15	.11	.04
411	Bernie Carbo	.05	.03	.01
412	Doug Griffin	.05	.03	.01
413	Rico Petrocelli	.08	.06	.02
414	Bob Montgomery	.05	.03	.01
415	Tim Blackwell	.05	.03	.01
416	Rick Miller	.05	.03	.01
417	Darrell Johnson	.05	.03	.01
418	Jim Burton	.05	.03	.01
419	Jim Willoughby	.05	.03	.01
420	Rogelio Moret	.05	.03	.01
421	Bill Lee	.08	.06	.02
422	Dick Drago	.05	.03	.01
423	Diego Segui	.05	.03	.01

	MINT	VG-E	F-G
424 Luis Tiant	.15	.11	.05
425 Jim Hunter	.30	.25	.10
426 Rick Sawyer	.05	.03	.01
427 Rudy May	.08	.06	.02
428 Dick Tidrow	.05	.03	.01
429 Sparky Lyle	.12	.08	.04
430 Doc Medich	.05	.03	.01
431 Pat Dobson	.05	.03	.01
432 Dave Pagan	.05	.03	.01
433 Thurman Munson	1.00	.70	.30
434 Chris Chambliss	.08	.06	.02
435 Roy White	.05	.03	.01
436 Walt Williams	.05	.03	.01
437 Graig Nettles	.12	.08	.04
438 Rick Dempsey	.05	.03	.01
439 Bobby Bonds	.12	.08	.04
440 Ed Hermann	.05	.03	.01
441 Sandy Alomar	.05	.03	.01
442 Fred Stanley	.05	.03	.01
443 Terry Whitfield	.05	.03	.01
444 Rich Bladt	.05	.03	.01
445 Lou Piniella	.08	.06	.02
446 Rich Coggins	.05	.03	.01
447 Ed Brinkman	.05	.03	.01
448 Jim Mason	.05	.03	.01
449 Larry Murray	.05	.03	.01
450 Ron Blomberg	.05	.03	.01
451 Elliott Maddox	.05	.03	.01
452 Kerry Dineen	.05	.03	.01
453 Billy Martin	.30	.25	.10
454 Dave Bergman	.05	.03	.01
455 Otto Velez	.05	.03	.01
456 Joe Hoerner	.05	.03	.01
457 Tug McGraw	.12	.08	.04
458 Gene Garber	.05	.03	.01
459 Steve Carlton	.50	.40	.18
460 L. Christenson	.05	.03	.01
461 Tom Underwood	.05	.03	.01
462 Jim Lonborg	.08	.06	.02
463 Jay Johnstone	.05	.03	.01
464 Larry Bowa	.20	.15	.06
465 Dave Cash	.05	.03	.01
466 Ollie Brown	.05	.03	.01
467 Greg Luzinski	.20	.15	.06
468 Johnny Oates	.05	.03	.01
469 Mike Anderson	.05	.03	.01
470 Mike Schmidt	.60	.45	.20
471 Bob Boone	.05	.03	.01
472 Tom Hutton	.05	.03	.01
473 Rich Allen	.10	.07	.03
474 Tony Taylor	.05	.03	.01
475 Jerry Martin	.05	.03	.01
476 Danny Ozark	.05	.03	.01
477 Dick Ruthven	.05	.03	.01
478 Jim Todd	.05	.03	.01
479 Paul Lindblad	.12	.08	.04
480 Rollie Fingers	.25	.20	.08
481 Vida Blue	.08	.06	.02
482 Ken Holtzman	.08	.06	.02
483 Dick Bosman	.05	.03	.01
484 Sonny Siebert	.05	.03	.01
485 Glenn Abbott	.05	.03	.01
486 Stan Bahnsen	.05	.03	.01
487 Mike Norris	.10	.07	.03
488 Alvin Dark	.08	.06	.02
489 C. Washington	.05	.03	.01
490 Joe Rudi	.08	.06	.02
491 Bill North	.05	.03	.01
492 Bert Campaneris	.08	.06	.02
493 Gene Tenace	.08	.06	.02
494 Reggie Jackson	.80	.60	.25
495 Phil Garner	.05	.03	.01
496 Billy Williams	.20	.15	.06
497 Sal Bando	.08	.06	.02
498 Jim Holt	.05	.03	.01
499 Ted Martinez	.05	.03	.01
500 Ray Fosse	.05	.03	.01
501 Matt Alexander	.05	.03	.01
502 Larry Haney	.05	.03	.01
503 Angel Mangual	.05	.03	.01
504 Fred Beene	.05	.03	.01
505 Tom Buskey	.05	.03	.01
506 D. Eckersley	.12	.08	.04
507 Roric Harrison	.05	.03	.01
508 Don Hood	.05	.03	.01
509 Jim Kern	.08	.06	.02
510 Dave LaRoche	.05	.03	.01
511 Fritz Peterson	.05	.03	.01
512 Jim Strickland	.05	.03	.01
513 Rick Waits	.05	.03	.01
514 Alan Ashby	.05	.03	.01
515 John Ellis	.05	.03	.01

	MINT	VG-E	F-G
516 Rick Cerone			
517 Buddy Bell	.10	.07	.03
518 Jack Brohamer	.15	.11	.05
519 Rico Carty	.05	.03	.01
520 Ed Crosby	.08	.06	.02
521 Frank Duffy	.05	.03	.01
522 Duane Kuiper	.05	.03	.01
523 Joe Lis	.05	.03	.01
524 Boog Powell	.05	.03	.01
525 Frank Robinson	.10	.07	.03
526 Oscar Gamble	.50	.40	.18
527 George Hendrick	.08	.06	.02
528 John Lowenstein	.12	.08	.04
529 Rick Manning	.05	.03	.01
530 Tommy Smith	.05	.03	.01
531 Charlie Spikes	.05	.03	.01
532 Steve Kline	.05	.03	.01
533 Ed Kranepool	.05	.03	.01
534 Mike Vail	.05	.03	.01
535 Del Unser	.05	.03	.01
536 Felix Millan	.05	.03	.01
537 Rusty Staub	.05	.03	.01
538 Jesus Alou	.20	.15	.06
539 Wayne Garrett	.05	.03	.01
540 Mike Phillips	.05	.03	.01
541 Joe Torre	.05	.03	.01
542 Dave Kingman	.15	.11	.05
543 Gene Clines	.30	.25	.10
544 Jack Heidemann	.05	.03	.01
545 Bud Harrelson	.05	.03	.01
546 John Stearns	.05	.03	.01
547 John Milner	.08	.06	.02
548 Bob Apodaca	.05	.03	.01
549 Skip Lockwood	.05	.03	.01
550 Ken Sanders	.05	.03	.01
551 Tom Seaver	.05	.03	.01
552 Rick Baldwin	1.00	.70	.30
553 Hank Webb	.05	.03	.01
554 Jon Matlack	.05	.03	.01
555 Randy Tate	.10	.07	.03
556 Tom Hall	.05	.03	.01
557 George Stone	.05	.03	.01
558 Craig Swan	.05	.03	.01
559 Jerry Cram	.10	.07	.03
560 Roy Staiger	.05	.03	.01
561 Kent Tekulve	.05	.03	.01
562 Jerry Reuss	.10	.07	.03
563 John Candelaria	.10	.07	.03
564 Larry Demery	.08	.06	.02
565 Dave Giusti	.05	.03	.01
566 Jim Rooker	.05	.03	.01
567 R. Hernandez	.05	.03	.01
568 Bruce Kison	.05	.03	.01
569 Ken Brett	.05	.03	.01
570 Bob Moose	.05	.03	.01
571 M. Sanguillen	.05	.03	.01
572 Dave Parker	.80	.60	.25
573 Willie Stargell	.80	.60	.25
574 Richie Zisk	.12	.08	.04
575 Rennie Stennett	.05	.03	.01
576 Al Oliver	.20	.15	.06
577 Bill Robinson	.05	.03	.01
578 Bob Robertson	.05	.03	.01
579 Rich Hebner	.05	.03	.01
580 Ed Kirkpatrick	.05	.03	.01
581 Duffy Dyer	.05	.03	.01
582 Craig Reynolds	.05	.03	.01
583 Frank Taveras	.05	.03	.01
584 Willie Randolph	.12	.08	.04
585 Art Howe	.05	.03	.01
586 Dan Murtaugh	.05	.03	.01
587 Rick McKinney	.05	.03	.01
588 Ed Goodson	.05	.03	.01
589 Checklist #1 Brett & Cowens	.40	.30	.13
590 Checklist #2 Hernandez & Brock	.40	.30	.13
591 Checklist #3 Koosman & Snider	.15	.11	.05
592 Checklist #4 M. Wills & J.Knox	.10	.07	.03
593 Checklist #5 Hunter & Ryan	.25	.20	.08
594 Checklist #6 Erskine, Branca and Reese	.15	.11	.05
595 Checklist #7 Mays & Score	.25	.20	.08
596 Larry Cox	.05	.03	.01
597 Gene Mauch	.06	.04	.02
598 W. Wietelmann	.05	.03	.01
599 Wayne Simpson	.05	.03	.01
600 Mel Thomason	.05	.03	.01

1976 SSPC (CONTINUED)

	MINT	VG-E	F-G			MINT	VG-E	F-G
601 Ike Hampton	.05	.03	.01	616 Willie Mays		1.50	1.10	.50
602 Ken Crosby	.05	.03	.01	617 Phil Cavaretta		.10	.07	.03
603 Ralph Rowe	.05	.03	.01	618 Ted Kluszewski		.20	.15	.06
604 Jim Tyrone	.05	.03	.01	619 Elston Howard		.30	.25	.10
605 Mke Kelleher	.05	.03	.01	620 Alex Grammas		.05	.03	.01
606 Mario Mendoza	.05	.03	.01	621 Mickey Vernon		.08	.06	.02
607 Mike Rogodzinski	.05	.03	.01	622 Dick Sisler		.05	.03	.01
608 Bob Gallagher	.05	.03	.01	623 Harvey Haddix		.05	.03	.01
609 Jerry Koosman	.12	.08	.04	624 Bobby Winkles		.05	.03	.01
610 Joe Frazier	.05	.03	.01	625 John Pesky		.05	.03	.01
611 Karl Kuehl	.05	.03	.01	626 Jim Davenport		.05	.03	.01
612 Frank LaCorte	.05	.03	.01	627 Dave Tomlin		.05	.03	.01
613 Ray Bare	.05	.03	.01	628 Roger Craig		.08	.06	.02
614 Billy Muffett	.05	.03	.01	629 Joe Amalfitano		.05	.03	.01
615 Bill Laxton	.05	.03	.01	630 Jim Reese		.05	.03	.01

1953 STAHL MEYER (9)　　　　　3 1/4" X 4 1/2"

MICKEY MANTLE

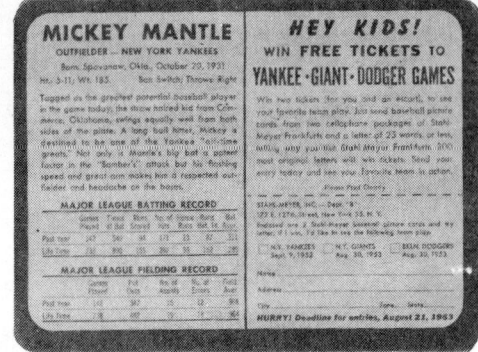

The 1953 Stahl Meyer set contains nine cards. This full color, unnumbered set contains three players from each of the three New York teams. The cards have white borders. The Lockman card is the most plentiful of any in this set.

	MINT	VG-E	F-G
COMPLETE SET	1700.00	1300.00	600.00
COMMON PLAYER	90.00	65.00	30.00
1 Hank Bauer	100.00	70.00	30.00
2 Roy Campanella	275.00	200.00	80.00
3 Gil Hodges	150.00	120.00	50.00
4 Monte Irvin	125.00	90.00	40.00
5 Whitey Lockman	75.00	55.00	24.00
6 Mickey Mantle	800.00	600.00	250.00
7 Phil Rizzuto	150.00	110.00	50.00
8 Duke Snider	200.00	150.00	65.00
9 Bobby Thomson	100.00	70.00	30.00

1954 STAHL MEYER (12)　　　　　3 1/4" X 4 1/2"

DUKE SNIDER

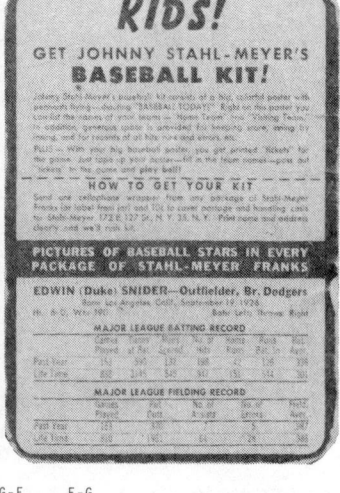

The 1954 Stahl Meyer set of 12 full color, unnumbered cards includes four players from each of the three New York teams. The cards have yellow borders and the backs, oriented horizontally, include an ad for a baseball kit and the player's statistics. No player biography is included on the back.

	MINT	VG-E	F-G
COMPLETE SET	2800.00	2100.00	900.00
COMMON PLAYER	110.00	85.00	35.00
1 Hank Bauer	110.00	85.00	35.00
2 Carl Erskine	110.00	85.00	35.00
3 Gil Hodges	150.00	110.00	50.00
4 Monte Irvin	125.00	90.00	40.00
5 Whitey Lockman	110.00	85.00	35.00
6 Mickey Mantle	1000.00	700.00	300.00
7 Willie Mays	1000.00	700.00	300.00
8 Gil McDougald	110.00	85.00	35.00
9 Don Mueller	110.00	85.00	35.00
10 Don Newcombe	125.00	90.00	40.00
11 Phil Rizzuto	150.00	110.00	50.00
12 Duke Snider	225.00	160.00	70.00

1955 STAHL MEYER (12) 3 1/4" X 4 1/2"

PHIL RIZZUTO

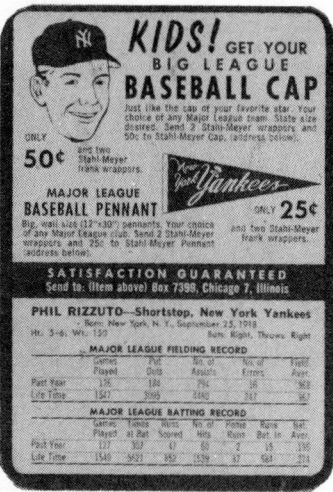

The 1955 Stahl Meyer set of 12 full color, unnumbered cards contains four players each from the three New York teams. As in the 1954 set, the cards have yellow borders; however, the backs of the cards contain a sketch of Mickey Mantle with an ad for a baseball cap or a pennant.

	MINT	VG-E	F-G
COMPLETE SET	2000.00	1400.00	600.00
COMMON PLAYER	100.00	75.00	30.00

		MINT	VG-E	F-G
1 Hank Bauer	100.00	75.00	30.00
2 Carl Erskine	100.00	75.00	30.00
3 Gil Hodges	150.00	110.00	50.00
4 Monte Irvin	125.00	90.00	40.00
5 Whitey Lockman	100.00	75.00	30.00
6 Mickey Mantle	900.00	650.00	300.00

	MINT	VG-E	F-G
7 Gil McDougald	100.00	75.00	30.00
8 Don Mueller	100.00	75.00	30.00
9 Don Newcombe	125.00	90.00	40.00
10 Dusty Rhodes	100.00	75.00	30.00
11 Phil Rizzuto	150.00	110.00	50.00
12 Duke Snider	200.00	150.00	65.00

1962 SUGARDALE (22) 3 3/4" X 5 1/8"

The 1962 Sugardale Meats set of 22 black and white, numbered and lettered cards features the Cleveland Indians and the Pittsburgh Pirates. The Indians are numbered while the Pirates are lettered.

The backs, in red print, give player tips. The Bob Nieman card was just recently discovered and is quite scarce. The SCB designation is F174-1.

CLEVELAND INDIANS PITCHER

	MINT	VG-E	F-G
COMPLETE SET	480.00	370.00	170.00
COMMON PLAYER	21.00	15.50	7.00

	MINT	VG-E	F-G
1 Barry Latman	21.00	15.50	7.00
2 Gary Bell	21.00	15.50	7.00
3 Dick Donovan	21.00	15.50	7.00

	MINT	VG-E	F-G
4 Frank Funk	21.00	15.50	7.00
5 Jim Perry	30.00	22.50	10.50
6 not issued	xx.xx	xx.xx	xx.xx
7 John Romano	21.00	15.50	7.00
8 Ty Cline	21.00	15.50	7.00
9 Tito Francona	25.00	18.50	8.75
10 Bob Nieman	60.00	45.00	20.00

	MINT	VG-E	F-G			MINT	VG-E	F-G
11 Willie Kirkland	21.00	15.50	7.00		17 Ray Katt	21.00	15.50	7.00
12 Woody Held	21.00	15.50	7.00		18 Mel McGaha	21.00	15.50	7.00
13 Jerry Kindall	21.00	15.50	7.00		19 Pedro Ramos	21.00	15.50	7.00
14 Bubba Phillips	21.00	15.50	7.00		A. Dick Groat	30.00	22.50	10.50
15 Mel Harder	21.00	15.50	7.00		B. Robert Clemente	100.00	70.00	30.00
16 Salty Parker	21.00	15.50	7.00		C. Don Hoak	21.00	15.50	7.00
					D. Dick Stuart	21.00	15.50	7.00

1963 SUGARDALE (31)   3 3/4'' X 5 1/8''

The 1963 Sugardale Meats set of 31 black and white, numbered and lettered cards features the Cleveland Indians and Pittsburgh Pirates. The Cleveland Indians player cards are numbered while the Pittsburgh Pirates players cards are lettered. The backs are printed in red and give player tips. The 1963 Sugardale set can be distinguished from the 1962 Sugardale set by examining the biographies on the card for mention of the 1962 season. The Perry and Skinner cards were withdrawn after June trades and are difficult to obtain.

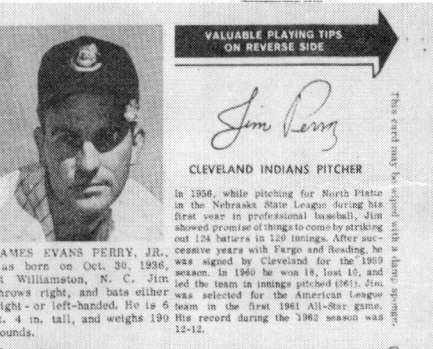

	MINT	VG-E	F-G			MINT	VG-E	F-G
COMPLETE SET	625.00	460.00	220.00		19 Pedro Ramos	21.00	15.50	7.00
COMMON PLAYER	21.00	15.50	7.00		20 Al Luplow	21.00	15.50	7.00
					21 not issued	xx.xx	xx.xx	x.xx
1 Barry Latman	21.00	15.50	7.00		22 not issued	xx.xx	xx.xx	x.xx
2 Gary Bell	21.00	15.50	7.00		23 Jim Grant	25.00	18.50	8.75
3 Dick Donovan	21.00	15.50	7.00		24 Victor Davalillo	21.00	15.50	7.00
4 Joe Adcock	30.00	22.50	10.50		25 Jerry Walker	21.00	15.50	7.00
5 Jim Perry	80.00	60.00	25.00		26 Sam McDowell	30.00	22.50	10.50
6 not issued	xx.xx	xx.xx	xx.xx		27 Fred Whitfield	21.00	15.50	7.00
7 John Romano	21.00	15.50	7.00		28 Jack Kralick	21.00	15.50	7.00
8 Mike de la Hoz	21.00	15.50	7.00		29 not issued	xx.xx	xx.xx	x.xx
9 Tito Francona	25.00	18.50	8.75		30 not issued	xx.xx	xx.xx	x.xx
10 Gene Green	21.00	15.50	7.00		31 not issued	xx.xx	xx.xx	x.xx
11 Willie Kirkland	21.00	15.50	7.00		32 not issued	xx.xx	xx.xx	x.xx
12 Woody Held	21.00	15.50	7.00		33 Bob Allen	21.00	15.50	7.00
13 Jerry Kindall	21.00	15.50	7.00		A. Don Cardwell	21.00	15.50	7.00
14 Max Alvis	21.00	15.50	7.00		B. Bob Skinner	50.00	38.00	17.00
15 Mel Harder	21.00	15.50	7.00		C. Don Schwall	21.00	15.50	7.00
16 George Strickland	21.00	15.50	7.00		D. Jim Pagliaroni	21.00	15.50	7.00
17 Elmer Valo	21.00	15.50	7.00		E. Dick Schofield	21.00	15.50	7.00
18 Birdie Tebbetts	25.00	18.50	8.75					

1966 JOHNSON VS. GOLDWATER SET

1971 SEARS CONGRESSIONAL SET

1946 SUNBEAM BREAD (21)

2" X 3"

GERALD STALEY
1946 Solons Pitcher
Photo by Joe Benelli

GERALD "JERRY" STA-LEY, 26, born Vancouver, Wash.; first season with Solons. Greatest baseball thrill: pitching a perfect game—no hits, no runs, no walks—on Guadalcanal for his Army unit. Most exciting experience: getting shot at. Won first professional game.

The 1946 Sunbeam Bread set of 21 black and white, unnumbered cards features the Sacramento Solons only. There is a reference to the "1946 Solons" on the fronts of the cards and small yellow and red bread loafs on the backs of the cards. The backs are in blue print and give a brief biography and a Sunbeam Bread ad. The ACC designation is D315-1.

	MINT	VG-E	F-G
COMPLETE SET	200.00	150.00	70.00
COMMON PLAYER	10.00	7.00	3.00
1 Beasley, Bud	10.00	7.00	3.00
2 Calvey, Jack	10.00	7.00	3.00
3 Corbett, Gene	10.00	7.00	3.00
4 Conroy, Bill	10.00	7.00	3.00
5 Fletcher, Guy	10.00	7.00	3.00
6 Tony Freitas	10.00	7.00	3.00
7 Ted Greenhalgh	10.00	7.00	3.00
8 Jarlett, Al	10.00	7.00	3.00
9 Landrum	10.00	7.00	3.00
10 Lillard, Gene	12.50	9.00	4.00

	MINT	VG-E	F-G
11 Garth Mann	10.00	7.00	3.00
12 Marcucci	12.50	9.00	4.00
13 Marty, Joe	18.00	13.50	6.00
14 Mesner, Steve	12.50	9.00	4.00
15 Herm Pillette	10.00	7.00	3.00
16 Sheely, Earl	10.00	7.00	3.00
17 Smith, Al	10.00	7.00	3.00
18 Staley, Gerald	11.00	8.00	3.50
19 Thompson, Averett	10.00	7.00	3.00
20 White, Jo Jo	10.00	7.00	3.00
21 Zipay, Bud	10.00	7.00	3.00

1947 SUNBEAM BREAD (26)

2" X 3"

GENE BABBIT
1947 Solons Pitcher
Photo by Joe Benelli

THE BREAD THAT BROADCASTS BASEBALL

The 1947 Sunbeam Bread set of 26 black and white, unnumbered cards features the Sacramento Solons only. This set is distinguishable from the 1946 set by a reference to the "1947 Solons" on the fronts of the cards and a colored Sunbeam Bread loaf filling the entire back of the card. This issue is printed on very thin paper stock. The ACC designation is D315-2.

	MINT	VG-E	F-G
COMPLETE SET	200.00	150.00	70.00
COMMON PLAYER	8.50	6.50	3.00
1 Gene Babbit	8.50	6.50	3.00
2 Bob Barthelson	8.50	6.50	3.00
3 Bud Beasley	8.50	6.50	3.00
4 Chuck Cronin	8.50	6.50	3.00
5 Eddie Fernandes	8.50	6.50	3.00
6 Ed Fitzgerald	8.50	6.50	3.00
7 Van Fletcher	8.50	6.50	3.00
8 Tony Freitas	8.50	6.50	3.00
9 Garth Mann	8.50	6.50	3.00
10 Joe Marty	12.50	9.00	4.00
11 Lou McCollum	8.50	6.50	3.00
12 Steve Mesner	8.50	6.50	3.00
13 Frank Nelson	8.50	6.50	3.00

	MINT	VG-E	F-G
14 Tommy Nelson	8.50	6.50	3.00
15 Joe Orengo	8.50	6.50	3.00
16 Hugh Orhan	8.50	6.50	3.00
17 Nick Pesut	8.50	6.50	3.00
18 Bill Ramsey	8.50	6.50	3.00
19 Johnny Rizzo	8.50	6.50	3.00
20 Mike Schemer	8.50	6.50	3.00
21 Al Smith	8.50	6.50	3.00
22 Tommy Thompson	8.50	6.50	3.00
23 Jim Warner	10.00	7.00	3.00
24 Mel Wasley	10.00	7.00	3.00
25 Leo Wells	8.50	6.50	3.00
26 Eddie Zipay	8.50	6.50	3.00

1948 SWELL GUM SPORT THRILLS (20)

2 1/2" X 3"

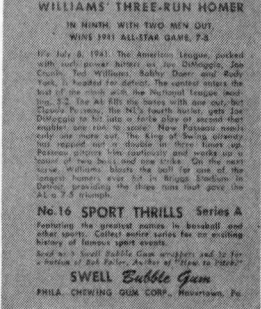

The 1948 Swell Gum Sports Thrills set of 20 black and white, numbered cards highlights events from baseball history. The cards have picture framed borders with the title "Sports Thrills Highlights in the World of Sport" on the front. The backs of the cards give the story of the event pictured on the front. Cards numbers 9, 11, 16 and 20 are more difficult to obtain than the other cards in this set. The ACC designation is R448.

	MINT	VG-E	F-G
COMPLETE SET	175.00	125.00	55.00
COMMON CARDS	6.00	4.50	2.00
1 Greatest Single Inning (Athletics' 10-Run Rally)	6.00	4.50	2.00
2 Amazing Record (Reiser's Debut With Dodgers)	6.00	4.50	2.00
3 Dramatic Debut (Jackie Robinson Rookie of Year)	12.50	9.00	4.00
4 Greatest Pitcher (Greatest Pitcher Of Them All)(W Johnson)	12.50	9.00	4.00
5 Three Strikes Not Out (Lost Third Strike Changes Tide Of 1941 World Series)	6.00	4.50	2.00
6 Home Run Wins Series (Bill Dickey's Last Home Run)	8.00	6.00	2.50
7 Never Say Die Pitcher (Schumacher's Pitching)	6.00	4.50	2.00
8 Five Strikeouts! (Nationals Lose All-Star Game) (Hubbell)	8.00	6.00	2.50
9 Greatest Catch (Al Gionfriddo's Catch)	10.00	7.00	3.00
10 No Hits! No Runs! (Vander Meer Comes Back)	7.00	5.25	2.50
11 Bases Loaded (Alexander The Great)	12.50	9.00	4.00
12 Most Dramatic Home Run (Babe Ruth Points)	30.00	22.50	10.50
13 Winning Run (Bridges' Pitching, Goslin's Single Wins 1935 World Series)	6.00	4.50	2.00
14 Great Slugging! (Lou Gehrig's Four Homers)	25.00	18.50	8.75
15 Four Men To Stop Him (It Took Four Men To Stop Joe DiMaggio's Bat Streak)	15.00	11.00	5.00
16 Three Run Homer In Ninth (William's Three-Run Homer)	30.00	22.50	10.50
17 Football Block! (Lindell's Football Block Paves Way For Yank's Series Victory)	6.00	4.50	2.00
18 Home Run To Fame (Reese's Grand Slam Homer)	9.00	6.75	3.00
19 Strikeout Record (Feller Whiffs Five)	12.50	9.00	4.00
20 Rifle Arm! (Furillo's Rifle Arm)	15.00	11.00	5.00

1957 SWIFTS FRANKS (18)

3 1/2" X 4"

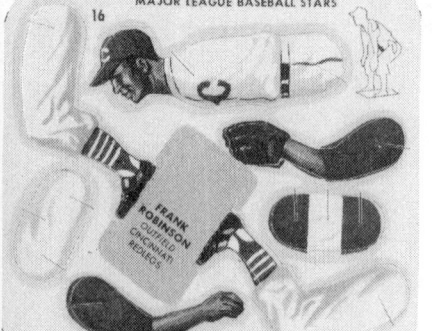

The 18 full color, numbered cards issued in 1957 by the Swift Company are die-cut. Each card consists of several pieces which can be punched out and assembled to form a stand-up model of a player. The ACC designation is F162.

	MINT	VG-E	F-G
COMPLETE SET	700.00	500.00	175.00
COMMON PLAYER	36.00	26.00	8.00
1 John Podres	36.00	26.00	8.00
2 Gus Triandos	36.00	26.00	8.00
3 Dale Long	36.00	26.00	8.00
4 Billy Pierce	40.00	30.00	10.00
5 Ed Bailey	36.00	26.00	8.00
6 Vic Wertz	36.00	26.00	8.00
7 Nelson Fox	45.00	33.00	12.00
8 Ken Boyer	45.00	33.00	12.00
9 Gil McDougald	40.00	30.00	10.00
10 Junior Gilliam	45.00	33.00	12.00
11 Eddie Yost	36.00	26.00	8.00
12 Johnny Logan	36.00	26.00	8.00
13 Hank Aaron	150.00	100.00	40.00
14 Bill Tuttle	36.00	26.00	8.00
15 Jackie Jensen	45.00	33.00	12.00
16 Frank Robinson	70.00	50.00	20.00
17 Richie Ashburn	45.00	33.00	12.00
18 Rocky Colavito	45.00	33.00	12.00

1933 TATOO ORBIT (60)

The 1933 Tatoo—Orbit set contains 60 unnumbered, color cards. Blaeholder and Hadley, and to a lesser degree Andrews and Hornsby are considered more difficult to obtain than the other cards in this set. The ACC designation is R305.

	MINT	VG-E	F-G
COMPLETE SET	850.00	650.00	300.00
COMMON PLAYER	12.00	8.75	4.00

	MINT	VG-E	F-G
1 Dale Alexander	12.00	8.75	4.00
2 Ivy Andrews	20.00	15.00	6.50
3 Earl Averill	16.00	12.00	5.50
4 Dick Bartell	12.00	8.75	4.00
5 Wally Berger	12.00	8.75	4.00
6 George Blaeholder	40.00	30.00	13.00
7 Irving Burns	12.00	8.75	4.00
8 Guy Bush	12.00	8.75	4.00
9 Bruce Campbell	12.00	8.75	4.00
10 Chalmers Cissell	12.00	8.75	4.00
11 Watson Clark	12.00	8.75	4.00
12 Mickey Cochrane	20.00	15.00	6.50
13 Phil Collins	12.00	8.75	4.00
14 Kiki Cuyler	16.00	12.00	5.50
15 Dizzy Dean	50.00	38.00	17.00
16 Jimmy Dykes	12.00	8.75	4.00
17 George Earnshaw	12.00	8.75	4.00
18 Woody English	12.00	8.75	4.00
19 Lou Fonseca	12.00	8.75	4.00
20 Jimmy Foxx	40.00	30.00	13.00
21 Burleigh Grimes	16.00	12.00	5.50
22 Charlie Grimm	12.00	8.75	4.00
23 Lefty Grove	30.00	22.50	10.50
24 Frank Grube	12.00	8.75	4.00
25 George Haas	12.00	8.75	4.00
26 Bump Hadley	40.00	30.00	13.00
27 Chick Hafey	16.00	12.00	5.50
28 Jess Haines	16.00	12.00	5.50
29 Bill Hallahan	12.00	8.75	4.00
30 Mel Harder	12.00	8.75	4.00

	MINT	VG-E	F-G
31 Gabby Hartnett	16.00	12.00	5.50
32 Babe Herman	12.00	8.75	4.00
33 Bill Herman	16.00	12.00	5.50
34 Rogers Hornsby	50.00	38.00	17.00
35 Roy Johnson	12.00	8.75	4.00
36 Smead Jolly	12.00	8.75	4.00
37 Billy Jurges	12.00	8.75	4.00
38 Willie Kamm	12.00	8.75	4.00
39 Mark Koenig	12.00	8.75	4.00
40 Jim Levey	12.00	8.75	4.00
41 Ernie Lombardi	13.00	9.50	4.00
42 Red Lucas	12.00	8.75	4.00
43 Ted Lyons	16.00	12.00	5.50
44 Connie Mack	25.00	18.50	8.75
45 Pat Malone	12.00	8.75	4.00
46 Pepper Martin	13.00	9.50	4.00
47 Marty McManus	12.00	8.75	4.00
48 Frank O'Doul	13.00	9.50	4.00
49 Dick Porter	12.00	8.75	4.00
50 Carl N. Reynolds	12.00	8.75	4.00
51 Charlie Root	12.00	8.75	4.00
52 Bob Seeds	12.00	8.75	4.00
53 Al Simmons	16.00	12.00	5.50
54 Riggs Stephenson	13.00	9.50	4.00
55 Lyle Tinning	12.00	8.75	4.00
56 Joe Vosmik	12.00	8.75	4.00
57 Rube Walberg	12.00	8.75	4.00
58 Paul Waner	16.00	12.00	5.50
59 Lon Warneke	12.00	8.75	4.00
60 Arthur Whitney	12.00	8.75	4.00

19th CENTURY SCORECARD

1947 TIP TOP (164)

2 1/4" X 3"

HARRY LAVAGETTO
Third Base, Brooklyn, N.Y.

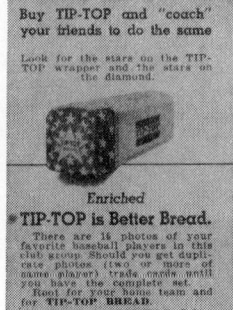

Buy TIP-TOP and "coach" your friends to do the same

Look for the stars on the TIP-TOP wrapper and the stars on the diamond.

Enriched

*TIP-TOP is Better Bread.

There are 16 photos of your favorite baseball players in this club group. Should you get duplicate photos (two or more of same players) trade cards until you have the complete set. Root for your home team and for TIP-TOP BREAD.

Compliments of TIP-TOP Bakers

The 1947 Tip Top Bread issue contains 164 unnumbered cards. The cards were issued in the following cities: Boston (Red Sox and Braves), Chicago (White Sox and Cubs), Detroit, New York (Yankees and Giants), Brooklyn, Pittsburgh, and St. Louis (Browns and Cardinals). Each city issued cards only of players on their home teams. Scarcer cards include those of the Red Sox, White Sox, Tigers, Braves and Cubs. The ACC designation is D323.

	MINT	VG-E	F-G
COMPLETE SET	3600.00	2700.00	1200.00
COMMON PLAYER	10.00	7.00	3.00
1 Leon Culberson	30.00	22.50	10.50
2 Dom DiMaggio	50.00	38.00	17.00
3 Joe Dobson	30.00	22.50	10.50
4 Bob Doerr	35.00	26.00	12.00
5 Dave "Boo" Ferris	30.00	22.50	10.50
6 Mickey Harris	30.00	22.50	10.50
7 Frank Hayes	30.00	22.50	10.50
8 Cecil Hughson	30.00	22.50	10.50
9 Earl Johnson	30.00	22.50	10.50
10 Roy Partee	30.00	22.50	10.50
11 Johnny Pesky	35.00	26.00	12.00
12 Rip Russell	30.00	22.50	10.50
13 Hal Wagner	30.00	22.50	10.50
14 Rudy York	35.00	26.00	12.00
15 Bill Zuber	30.00	22.50	10.50
16 Floyd Baker	30.00	22.50	10.50
17 Earl Caldwell	30.00	22.50	10.50
18 Lloyd Christopher	30.00	22.50	10.50
19 George Dickey	30.00	22.50	10.50
20 Ralph Hodgin	30.00	22.50	10.50
21 Bob Kennedy	35.00	26.00	12.00
22 Joe Kuhel	30.00	22.50	10.50
23 Thornton Lee	30.00	22.50	10.50
24 Ed Lopat	45.00	34.00	15.00
25 Cass Michaels	30.00	22.50	10.50
26 John Rigney	30.00	22.50	10.50
27 "Mike" Tresh	30.00	22.50	10.50
28 Thurman Tucker	30.00	22.50	10.50
29 Jack Wallasca	30.00	22.50	10.50
30 Taft Wright	30.00	22.50	10.50
31 Walter Hoot Evers	30.00	22.50	10.50
32 John Gorsica	30.00	22.50	10.50
33 Fred Hutchinson	45.00	34.00	15.00
34 George Kell	45.00	34.00	15.00
35 Eddie Lake	30.00	22.50	10.50
36 Ed Mayo	30.00	22.50	10.50
37 Arthur Mills	30.00	22.50	10.50
38 "Pat" Mullin	30.00	22.50	10.50
39 James Outlaw	30.00	22.50	10.50
40 Frank "Stub" Overmire	30.00	22.50	10.50
41 Robert "Bob" Swift	30.00	22.50	10.50
42 Geo. "Birdie" Tebbetts	30.00	22.50	10.50
43 Paul "Diz" Trout	30.00	22.50	10.50
44 Virgil Trucks	30.00	22.50	10.50
45 Richard"Dick"Wakefield	30.00	22.50	10.50
46 Larry Berra	40.00	30.00	13.00
47 Floyd "Bill" Bevans	10.00	7.00	3.00
48 Bobby Brown	16.00	12.00	5.50
49 Thomas Bryne	10.00	7.00	3.00
50 Frank Crosetti	15.00	11.00	5.00
51 Tom Henrich	25.00	18.50	8.75
52 Charlie Keller	11.00	8.00	3.50
53 Johnny Lindell	10.00	7.00	3.00
54 Joe Page	11.00	8.00	3.50
55 Mel Queen	10.00	7.00	3.00
56 Al Reynolds	15.00	11.00	5.00
57 Phil Rizzuto	40.00	30.00	13.00
58 Aaron Robinson	10.00	7.00	3.00
59 George Stirnweiss	16.00	12.00	5.50
60 Charles Wensloff	16.00	12.00	5.50

	MINT	VG-E	F-G
61 John Berardino	12.50	9.00	4.00
62 Clifford Fannin	10.00	7.00	3.00
63 Dennis Galehouse	10.00	7.00	3.00
64 "Jeff" Heath	10.00	7.00	3.00
65 Walter Judnick	10.00	7.00	3.00
66 Jack Kramer	10.00	7.00	3.00
67 Paul Lehner	10.00	7.00	3.00
68 Lester Moss	10.00	7.00	3.00
69 "Bob" Muncrief	10.00	7.00	3.00
70 Nelson Potter	10.00	7.00	3.00
71 Fred Sanford	10.00	7.00	3.00
72 Joe Schultz	10.00	7.00	3.00
73 Vern Stephens	10.00	7.00	3.00
74 Jerry Witte	10.00	7.00	3.00
75 Al Zarilla	10.00	7.00	3.00
76 Charles Barrett	25.00	18.50	8.75
77 "Hank" Camelli	25.00	18.50	8.75
78 Dick Culler	25.00	18.50	8.75
79 "Nanny" Fernandez	25.00	18.50	8.75
80 "Si" Johnson	25.00	18.50	8.75
81 Danny Litwhiler	25.00	18.50	8.75
82 Phil Masi	25.00	18.50	8.75
83 Carvel Rowell	25.00	18.50	8.75
84 Connie Ryan	25.00	18.50	8.75
85 John Sain	35.00	26.00	12.00
86 Ray Sanders	25.00	18.50	8.75
87 "Sibby" Sisti	25.00	18.50	8.75
88 Billy Southworth	25.00	18.50	8.75
89 Warren Spahn	50.00	38.00	17.00
90 Ed Wright	25.00	18.50	8.75
91 Bob Bragan	10.00	7.00	3.00
92 Ralph Branca	12.00	8.75	4.00
93 Hugh Casey	10.00	7.00	3.00
94 Bruce Edwards	10.00	7.00	3.00
95 Hal Gregg	10.00	7.00	3.00
96 Joe Hatten	10.00	7.00	3.00
97 Gene Hermanski	10.00	7.00	3.00
98 John Jorgensen	10.00	7.00	3.00
99 Harry Lavagetto	10.00	7.00	3.00
100 Vic Lombardi	10.00	7.00	3.00
101 Frank Melton	10.00	7.00	3.00
102 Ed Miksis	10.00	7.00	3.00
103 Marv Rackley	10.00	7.00	3.00
104 Ed Stevens	10.00	7.00	3.00
105 Phil Cavaretta	35.00	26.00	12.00
106 Bob Chipman	25.00	18.50	8.75
107 Stanley Hack	30.00	22.50	10.50
108 Don Johnson	25.00	18.50	8.75
109 Emil Kush	25.00	18.50	8.75
110 Bill Lee	25.00	18.50	8.75
111 Mickey Livingston	25.00	18.50	8.75
112 Harry Lowrey	30.00	22.50	10.50
113 Clyde McCullough	25.00	18.50	8.75
114 Andy Pafko	30.00	22.50	10.50
115 Marv Rickert	25.00	18.50	8.75
116 John Schmitz	25.00	18.50	8.75
117 "Bobby" Sturgeon	25.00	18.50	8.75
118 Ed Waitkus	25.00	18.50	8.75
119 Henry Wyse	25.00	18.50	8.75
120 Bill Ayers	10.00	7.00	3.00
121 Robert Blattner	10.00	7.00	3.00
122 Mike Budnick	10.00	7.00	3.00
123 Sid Gordon	10.00	7.00	3.00

1947 TIP TOP (CONTINUED)

		MINT	VG-E	F-G
124	Clinton Hartung	10.00	7.00	3.00
125	Monte Kennedy	10.00	7.00	3.00
126	Dave Koslo	10.00	7.00	3.00
127	Carroll Lockman	10.00	7.00	3.00
128	Jack Lohrke	10.00	7.00	3.00
129	Ernie Lombardi	15.00	11.00	5.00
130	Willard Marshall	10.00	7.00	3.00
131	John Mize	16.00	12.00	5.50
132	Eugene Thompson	has not been verified		
133	Ken Trinkle	10.00	7.00	3.00
134	Bill Voiselle	10.00	7.00	3.00
135	Mickey Witek	10.00	7.00	3.00
136	Eddie Basinski	13.00	9.50	4.00
137	Ernie Bonham	13.00	9.50	4.00
138	Bill Cox	13.00	9.50	4.00
139	Elbie Fletcher	13.00	9.50	4.00
140	Frank Gustine	13.00	9.50	4.00
141	Kirby Higbe	13.00	9.50	4.00
142	Leroy Jarvis	13.00	9.50	4.00
143	Ralph Kiner	25.00	18.50	8.75

		MINT	VG-E	F-G
144	Fred Ostermueller	13.00	9.50	4.00
145	"Preacher" Roe	18.00	13.50	6.00
146	Jim Russell	13.00	9.50	4.00
147	"Rip" Sewell	13.00	9.50	4.00
148	Nick Strincevich	13.00	9.50	4.00
149	Honus Wagner	40.00	30.00	13.00
150	Alpha Brazle	10.00	7.00	3.00
151	Ken Burkhart	10.00	7.00	3.00
152	Bernard Creger	10.00	7.00	3.00
153	Joffre Cross	10.00	7.00	3.00
154	Chas. E. Diering	10.00	7.00	3.00
155	Ervin Dusak	10.00	7.00	3.00
156	Joe Garagiola	20.00	15.00	6.50
157	Tony Kaufmann	10.00	7.00	3.00
158	George Kurowski	10.00	7.00	3.00
159	Marty Marion	15.00	11.00	5.00
160	George Munger	10.00	7.00	3.00
161	Del Rice	10.00	7.00	3.00
162	Dick Sisler	10.00	7.00	3.00
163	Enos Slaughter	16.00	12.00	5.50
164	Ted Wilks	10.00	7.00	3.00

1951 TOPPS BLUE BACKS (52)   2" X 2 5/8"

The 1951 Topps Blue Back set of 52 cards can be used to play a baseball game. Blue Backs are more difficult to obtain than the Red Backs.

	MINT	VG-E	F-G
COMPLETE SET	425.00	340.00	150.00
COMMON PLAYER	8.50	6.50	3.00
1 Eddie Yost	10.00	7.00	3.00
2 "Hank" Majeski	8.50	6.50	3.00
3 Richie Ashburn	12.00	8.75	4.00
4 Del Ennis	8.50	6.50	3.00
5 Johnny Pesky	8.50	6.50	3.00
6 Al "Red" Schoendienst	11.00	8.00	3.50
7 Gerry Staley	8.50	6.50	3.00
8 Dick Sisler	8.50	6.50	3.00
9 Johnny Sain	11.00	8.00	3.50
10 Joe Page	10.00	7.00	3.00
11 Johnny Groth	8.50	6.50	3.00
12 Sam Jethroe	8.50	6.50	3.00
13 "Mickey" Vernon	10.00	7.00	3.00
14 "Red" Munger	8.50	6.50	3.00
15 Eddie Joost	8.50	6.50	3.00
16 Murry Dickson	8.50	6.50	3.00
17 Roy Smalley	8.50	6.50	3.00
18 Ned Garver	8.50	6.50	3.00
19 Phil Masi	8.50	6.50	3.00
20 Ralph Branca	10.00	7.00	3.00
21 Billy Johnson	8.50	6.50	3.00
22 Bob Kuzava	8.50	6.50	3.00
23 "Dizzy" Trout	8.50	6.50	3.00
24 Sherman Lollar	8.50	6.50	3.00
25 Sam Mele	8.50	6.50	3.00

	MINT	VG-E	F-G
26 Chico Carrasquel	8.50	6.50	3.00
27 Andy Pafko	8.50	6.50	3.00
28 Harry Brecheen	8.50	6.50	3.00
29 Granville Hamner	8.50	6.50	3.00
30 Enos Slaughter	14.00	10.50	4.75
31 Lou Brissie	8.50	6.50	3.00
32 Bob Elliott	8.50	6.50	3.00
33 Don Lenhardt	8.50	6.50	3.00
34 Earl Torgeson	8.50	6.50	3.00
35 Tommy Byrne	8.50	6.50	3.00
36 Cliff Fannin	8.50	6.50	3.00
37 Bobby Doerr	9.00	6.75	3.00
38 Irv Noren	8.50	6.50	3.00
39 Ed Lopat	11.00	8.00	3.50
40 Vic Wertz	8.50	6.50	3.00
41 Johnny Schmitz	8.00	6.50	3.00
42 Bruce Edwards	8.00	6.50	3.00
43 Willie Jones	8.00	6.50	3.00
44 Johnny Wyrostek	8.00	6.50	3.00
45 Billy Pierce	11.00	8.00	3.50
46 Gerry Priddy	8.00	6.50	3.00
47 Herman Wehmeier	8.00	6.50	3.00
48 Billy Cox	8.00	6.50	3.00
49 Henry Sauer	9.00	6.75	3.00
50 Johnny Mize	18.00	13.50	6.00
51 Eddie Waitkus	8.00	6.50	3.00
52 Sam Chapman	8.00	6.50	3.00

1951 TOPPS RED BACKS (52)   2" X 2 5/8"

The 1951 Topps Red Back set of 52 cards can be used to play a baseball game. Card number 36 Zernial is found with the Chicago or Philadelphia team and number 52 Holmes with the Boston or Hartford team.

	MINT	VG-E	F-G
COMPLETE SET	225.00	170.00	75.00
COMMON PLAYER	3.00	2.25	1.00
1 Larry "Yogi" Berra	17.00	12.50	6.00
2 Sid Gordon	3.00	2.25	1.00
3 Ferris Fain	3.50	2.50	1.20
4 Vern Stephens	3.00	2.25	1.00
5 Phil Rizzuto	10.00	7.00	3.00
6 Allie Reynolds	4.50	3.50	1.60
7 Howie Pollet	3.00	2.25	1.00
8 Early Wynn	8.00	6.00	2.50
9 Roy Sievers	3.00	2.25	1.00
10 Mel Parnell	3.00	2.25	1.00
11 Gene Hermanski	3.00	2.25	1.00
12 Jim Hegan	3.00	2.25	1.00
13 Dale Mitchell	3.00	2.25	1.00
14 Wayne Terwilliger	3.00	2.25	1.00
15 Ralph Kiner	8.50	6.50	3.00
16 Preacher Roe	4.00	3.00	1.40
17 Dave Bell	3.00	2.25	1.00
18 Gerry Coleman	3.50	2.50	1.20
19 Dick Kokos	3.00	2.25	1.00
20 Dom DiMaggio	5.50	4.25	2.00
21 Larry Jansen	3.00	2.25	1.00
22 Bob Feller	13.00	9.50	4.00
23 Ray Boone	3.00	2.25	1.00
24 Hank Bauer	4.00	3.00	1.40
25 Cliff Chambers	3.00	2.25	1.00
26 Luke Easter	3.50	2.50	1.20

	MINT	VG-E	F-G
27 Wally Westlake	3.00	2.25	1.00
28 Elmer Valo	3.00	2.25	1.00
29 Bob Kennedy	3.50	2.50	1.20
30 Warren Spahn	11.00	8.00	3.50
31 Gil Hodges	10.00	7.00	3.00
32 Henry Thompson	3.00	2.25	1.00
33 William Werle	3.00	2.25	1.00
34 Grady Hatton	3.00	2.25	1.00
35 Al Rosen	6.00	4.50	2.00
36a Gus Zernial (Chi.)	10.00	7.00	3.00
36b Gus Zernial (Phil.)	10.00	7.00	3.00
37 Wes Westrum	3.00	2.25	1.00
38 Duke Snider	13.00	9.50	4.00
39 Ted Kluszewski	4.50	3.50	1.60
40 Mike Garcia	3.50	2.50	1.20
41 Whitey Lockman	3.00	2.25	1.00
42 Ray Scarborough	3.00	2.25	1.00
43 Maurice McDermott	3.00	2.25	1.00
44 Sid Hudson	3.00	2.25	1.00
45 Andy Seminick	3.00	2.25	1.00
46 Billy Goodman	3.00	2.25	1.00
47 Tommy Glaviano	3.00	2.25	1.00
48 Eddie Stanky	3.50	2.50	1.20
49 Al Zarilla	3.00	2.25	1.00
50 Monte Irvin	6.50	5.00	2.25
51 Eddie Robinson	3.00	2.25	1.00
52a Tommy Holmes (Bost.)	10.00	7.00	3.00
52b Tommy Holmes (Hart.)	10.00	7.00	3.00

1951 TOPPS TEAM CARDS (9)   2 1/16" X 5 1/4"

The 1951 Topps Team Cards are nine unnumbered black & white with yellow border team cards with or without the "1950" date on their front. There are essentially no differences in values for the dated or undated team cards.

BOSTON RED SOX

FRONT ROW (left to right): Piersall, Pesky, Littlefield, Bat Boy Fitzpatrick, Maxwell, Goodman, Stringer.

SECOND ROW (left to right): Kinder, Rosar, McDonald, Zarilla, Coach Combs, Manager O'Neill, Coach Schreiber, Coach Susce, Doerr, Traveling Secretary Dowd.

THIRD ROW (left to right): Trainer Fadden, DiMaggio, Wright, Parnell, Batts, Stobbs, Vollmer, McDermott, Stevens, Equipment Manager Orlando.

BACK ROW (left to right): Masterson, Nixon, Dobson, Taylor, Dropo, Atkins, Williams, Tebbetts, Hatfield.

	MINT	VG-E	F-G
COMPLETE SET	500.00	380.00	160.00
COMMON TEAM	45.00	35.00	15.00
Boston Red Sox	110.00	80.00	35.00
Brooklyn Dodgers	80.00	60.00	25.00
Chicago White Sox	70.00	50.00	23.00

	MINT	VG-E	F-G
Cincinnati Reds	45.00	35.00	15.00
New York Giants	90.00	70.00	30.00
Philadelphia Athletics	50.00	38.00	17.00
Philadelphia Phillies	50.00	38.00	17.00
St. Louis Cardinals	100.00	70.00	30.00
Washington Senators	50.00	38.00	17.00

1951 TOPPS CONNIE MACK (11) ALL-STAR
2 1/16" X 5 1/4"

Defensive Giant of the Midway, scrappy Eddie Collins of Connie Mack's 1910-11-13-14 World Championship Athletics, paced the American League's second basemen in fielding nine times. No major leaguer has matched his 25 years as an active player, during which time he attained a lifetime batting average of .333.

Fold on dotted lines to make figure stand. Collect the whole series of Connie Mack's All-Time All-Star Team
(11 in the Series)

The 1951 Topps Connie Mack All Stars are 11 die-cut cards which after removal of the back can be folded to form a standing figure. Without tops their value drops to less than half their normal value.

	MINT	VG-E	F-G
COMPLETE SET	2650.00	2000.00	800.00
COMMON PLAYER	75.00	55.00	25.00
Grover C. Alexander	300.00	225.00	100.00
Mickey Cochrane	150.00	110.00	50.00
Ed Collins	100.00	70.00	30.00
Jimmy Collins	75.00	55.00	25.00

	MINT	VG-E	F-G
Lou Gehrig	500.00	400.00	150.00
Walter Johnson	450.00	350.00	150.00
Connie Mack	225.00	160.00	70.00
Christy Mathewson	150.00	110.00	50.00
Babe Ruth	550.00	450.00	200.00
Tris Speaker	125.00	90.00	40.00
Honus Wagner	175.00	125.00	60.00

1951 TOPPS CURRENT ALL-STAR (11)
2 1/16" X 5 1/

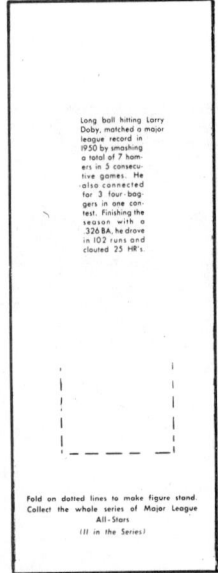

Long ball hitting Larry Doby, matched a major league record in 1950 by smashing a total of 7 homers in 3 consecutive games. He also connected for 3 four-baggers in one contest. Finishing the season with a .326 BA, he drove in 102 runs and clouted 25 HR's.

Fold on dotted lines to make figure stand. Collect the whole series of Major League All-Stars
(11 in the Series)

The 1951 Topps Current All Stars are 11 rare, die-cut cards which after removal of the back can be folded to form a standing figure. Without tops their valure drops to about half their normal value.

	MINT	VG-E	F-G
COMPLETE SET	2400.00	1750.00	800.00
COMMON PLAYER	200.00	150.00	65.00
Yogi Berra	500.00	400.00	150.00
Larry Doby	250.00	180.00	80.00
Walt Dropo	350.00	250.00	100.00
Hoot Evers	200.00	150.00	65.00

	MINT	VG-E	F-G
George Kell	250.00	180.00	80.00
Ralph Kiner	350.00	250.00	100.00
Jim Konstanty	4000.00	3000.00	1500.00
Bob Lemon	400.00	300.00	125.00
Phil Rizzuto	500.00	400.00	125.00
Robin Roberts	4000.00	3000.00	1500.00
Eddie Stanky	4000.00	3000.00	1500.00

Nearly 30 years ago, the Topps Chewing Gum Company issued its first major set of current players. To this date, this 1952 set of 407 cards remains one of the most popular and most talked about post-World War II card issues. The set was issued in six series released consecutively during the spring (and possibly the fall) of 1952.

The first series contains 80 cards. It was originally issued with black printed backs. At least two major printings of these black backs were produced, as errors on the backs of card numbers 48 and 49 were released initially and corrected during a later print run. Consequent to the black-back printing, at least one further large printing of cards 1-80 was released with red printed backs. No red-back errors in cards 48 and 49 are known and the red-back cards are more plentiful than the black-back cards.

The second series contains card numbers 81 through 130. This series has no known errors or anomalies of significance and had quite a large distribution, as there appear to be more cards from this series available than any of the other five series. The third series includes card numbers 131 through 190. This series also produced no known errors or anomalies. The fourth series contains card numbers 191 through 250. For years veteran collectors questioned whether this series ended at number 250 or 252. The past year has produced unquestionnable verification that the fourth series ends at number 250. The fifth series of 1952 Topps cards was produced to a lesser degree than any of the previous four series. It begins at 251 and ends at 310, and is called the "semi-high" series by collectors. The Topps rookie card of Willie Mays is in this series.

The last, or sixth, series contains numbers 311 through 407. Because of very limited distribution, the 97 cards in this series are called the 1952 Topps "high numbers," and are considered the scarcest regular issue Topps cards. There appears to be a preponderance of these cards currently emanating from Canada, which indicates that these cards were preferentially issued north of the American border. Reliable sources suggest that the 1952 high-numbered series was also distributed mixed with the 1953 Topps regular issue cards in some areas of the country. The first Topps cards of many superstars, for instance Mickey Mantle, are included in the high numbers, a fact which further adds to their mystique.

For the past 29 years, there has been much conjecture concerning the complexities of this set. In June at a baseball card show in Baltimore, Maryland, a person brought in uncut sheets of 1952 Topps cards, with varying quantities of cards per sheet. He was immediately overwhelmed by interested collectors and zealous dealers, and many of these uncut sheets were placed in auction and sold. While the mayhem created by the appearance of these uncut sheets precluded any systematic study of them, the bits and pieces gathered from several of the collectors and dealers present at the show has made possible the following discussion of the method of issue of cards in the 1952 Topps set. Accompanying photographs should help to verify the theories.

From the size of the uncut sheets seen at this show (they were partial sheets with a maximum of 25 cards on any one sheet) and in particular those that we were fortunate enough to photograph, the distribution of the high-numbered series and the semi-high numbered series have been determined with reasonable certainty. Extrapolation based on what was learned from these two series has generated some very plausible theories for the other four series.

An uncut sheet of 1954 Topps is presented (for both its own intrinsic value and) to substantiate the theory projected for the number of cards presented on a 1952 uncut sheet. Cards from the 1954 Topps series and cards from the 1952 Topps series are the same size; therefore, we might logically deduce that 1952 Topps cards were printed on sheets of the same size — 100 cards per sheet. This size is corroborated by the oversized borders (signifying the edge of a sheet) on two sides of all the 25-card sheets photographed (see picture of high-number sheet). Three of the four quadrants of the high numbers have been photographed (because of space limitations only one is pictured here). The schematics pictured on the following page depict the two possible configurations of the 1952 high numbered sheet. All but the southwest quadrant have been seen and are the same on both configurations. Whichever configuration of the southwest quadrant is correct, it can be proposed with certainty that three cards of the high numbers were double printed — 311, Mantle; 312, Robinson; and 213, Thompson. Variations of the stitching on the ball on the back of these three cards has been found (see figure).

From the two 15-card sheets of "semi-high" cards and their respective wide borders, we can deduce that in this series of 60 cards, 40 were doubly printed and 20 were singly printed (see picture). The 20 doubly printed cards indicated by these sheets are card numbers 281 to 300. Two other independent sources — one, a find of three unopened vending boxes of semi-high numbers containing 1620 cards; the other, a dealer with a considerable stock in semi-high numbers — verified the scarcity of these twenty cards.

We can now suggest the following about the other four 1952 Topps series:

Series 1-80 contains 20 doubly printed cards and 60 singly printed cards
Series 81-130 contains 50 doubly printed cards (i.e. no scarcities)
Series 131-190 contains 40 doubly printed cards and 20 singly printed cards
Series 191-250 contains 40 doubly printed cards and 20 singly printed cards

One further hypothesis, based solely on the known partial sheets of semi-high cards and not the maverick (97 cards) high number partial sheets, is that the cards in the first four series were, like the semi-highs, printed in sequentially numbered columns beginning with the 1 digit and ending with the 0 digit number (i.e., 261-270, 271-280, etc.). If that is the case, the scarce or singly printed numbers in each of the first four series would be groups of ten consecutive numbers beginning with the N1 number and ending with the (N+1) 0 number. While this hypothesis is plausible, it has by no means been verified. Hopefully, at some future date, uncut sheets of these series will surface and we can unlock the mystery of the 1952 Topps Baseball card set (once and for all).

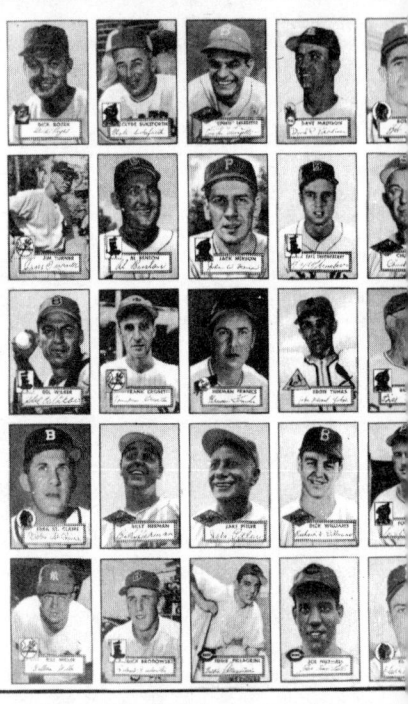

PICTURED ABOVE AND BELOW ARE THE UPPER LEFT AND LOWER RIGHT (AS VIEW FROM THE BACK OF THE CARDS) PORTIONS OF A SEMI-HIGH FULL SHEET (NOTE THE BORDERS). AT THE LOWER RIGHT IS A PICTURE OF THE OBVERSE OF THE SHEET BELOW. NOTICE THE 280's AND 290's COLUMNS ARE CURIOUSLY MISSING FROM THE SEQUENCE IN THE SHEET BELOW, SUGGESTING THEY WERE PRINTED BUT ONCE ON THE FULL SHEET OF SEMI-HIGH NUMBERS.

PICTURED IS THE UPPER LEFT QUADRANT OF A 1952 TOPPS NUMBER SHEET. THREE OF THE FOUR QUADRANTS ARE KNOWN (SCHEMATIC ON THE NEXT PAGE).

1954 TOPPS UNCUT SHEET—SHEET CONTAINS EXACTLY 100 CARDS.

3	383	393	403	316	326	336	346	356
4	384	394	404	317	327	337	347	357
5	385	395	405	318	328	338	348	358
6	386	396	406	319	329	339	349	359
7	387	397	407	320	330	340	350	360
1	331	341	351	311	368	378	388	398
2	332	342	352	312	369	379	389	399
3	333	343	353	313	370	380	390	400
4	334	344	354	361	371	381	391	401
5	335	345	355	362	372	382	392	402

363	373	383	393	403	316	326	336	346	356
364	374	384	394	404	317	327	337	347	357
365	375	385	395	405	318	328	338	348	358
366	376	386	396	406	319	329	339	349	359
367	377	387	397	407	320	330	340	350	360
321	331	341	351	311	368	378	388	398	
322	332	342	352	312	369	379	389	399	
323	333	343	353	313	370	380	390	400	
324	334	344	354	314	361	371	381	391	401
325	335	345	355	315	362	372	382	392	402

POSSIBLE CONFIGURATION (AS VIEWED FROM BACK OF SHEET) OF TOPPS HIGH NUMBER SHEET. THE LOWER LEFT QUADRANT IS THE ONLY PORTION DIFFERENT IN THE TWO CONFIGURATIONS.

THE SCHEMATIC ABOVE SHOWS THE "ARROWS," WHICH FORM THE STITCHING ON THE BALL, ARE POINTED EITHER TO THE LEFT OR TO THE RIGHT. HIGH NUMBERS 311, 312 AND 313 EXIST IN BOTH VARIATIONS, INDICATING THESE THREE HIGH NUMBERS WERE DOUBLY PRINTED ON THE SHEET. NO VARIATIONS OF THIS TYPE HAVE YET BEEN FOUND IN ANY OF THE OTHER FIVE 1952 TOPPS SERIES.

1952 TOPPS (407)   2 5/8" X 3 5/8"

The 1952 Topps set is Topps' first truly major set. Card nos. 1-80 were issued with red or black backs, both of which are less plentiful than card nos. 81-250. Card no. 48 (Page)

and no. 49 (Sain) can found with each other's wri up on their back. Card n 251-310 are somewhat scar and nos. 311-407 are qu scarce.

ROBERT WILLIAM ANDREW FELLER
Pitcher: Cleveland Indians   Home: Grand Prairie, Texas
Born: Nov. 3, 1918, Van Meter, Ia.   Eyes: Brown
Ht. 6' Wt. 185 Hair Brown Throws: Right Bats: Right

"Rapid Robert" came right off a farm and started hurling for the Indians in 1938. Outside of 3 years in the Navy, he's been taking his regular turn on the mound for 13 years. In '51 Bob was the top hurler in the American League and became the 3rd man in Baseball History to pitch 3 no-hit games in a career. The Player of the Year in 1940, he's pitched ten 1-hit games, led the League in Strikeouts 7 times and set a Strikeout mark of 348 in '46.

MAJOR LEAGUE PITCHING RECORD

	Games	Innings Pitched	W	L	Pct.	Hits	Runs	Strike Outs	Walks	Ern. Runs	ERA
PAST YEAR	33	250	22	8	.733	239	﹖105	111	95	97	3.49
LIFE-TIME	452	3179	230	131	.637	2628	1225	2338	1528	1101	3.12

© T. C. G.   ☆ TOPPS BASEBALL ☆   PRTD. IN U.S.A.

	MINT	VG-E	F-G		MINT	VG-E	F-G
COMPLETE SET	9000.00	7000.00	3000.00	59 Robin Roberts	10.00	7.00	3.00
COMMON PLAYER (1-80)	3.25	2.50	1.00	60 Sid Hudson	3.25	2.50	1.00
COMMON PLAYER (81-250)	2.75	2.00	.80	61 "Tookie" Gilbert	3.25	2.50	1.00
COMMON PLAYER (251-310)	10.50	8.25	3.50	62 Chuck Stobbs	3.25	2.50	1.00
COMMON PLAYER (311-407)	40.00	30.00	13.00	63 Howie Pollet	3.25	2.50	1.00
				64 Roy Sievers	3.25	2.50	1.00
1 Andy Pafko	20.00	15.00	6.50	65 Enos Slaughter	6.50	5.00	2.25
2 James Runnels	3.25	2.50	1.00	66 Preacher Roe	5.00	3.75	1.75
3 Henry Thompson	3.25	2.50	1.00	67 Allie Reynolds	6.00	4.50	2.00
4 Don Lenhardt	3.25	2.50	1.00	68 Cliff Chambers	3.25	2.50	1.00
5 Larry Jansen	3.25	2.50	1.00	69 Virgil Stallcup	3.25	2.50	1.00
6 Grady Hatton	3.25	2.50	1.00	70 Al Zarilla	3.25	2.50	1.00
7 Wayne Terwilliger	3.25	2.50	1.00	71 Tom Upton	3.25	2.50	1.00
8 Fred Marsh	3.25	2.50	1.00	72 Karl Olson	3.25	2.50	1.00
9 Robert Hogue	3.25	2.50	1.00	73 William Werle	3.25	2.50	1.00
10 Al Rosen	7.50	5.75	2.50	74 Andy Hansen	3.25	2.50	1.00
11 Phil Rizzuto	14.00	10.50	4.75	75 Wes Westrum	3.25	2.50	1.00
12 Romanus Basgall	3.25	2.50	1.00	76 Eddie Stanky	4.00	3.00	1.40
13 Johnny Wyrostek	3.25	2.50	1.00	77 Bob Kennedy	4.00	3.00	1.40
14 Bob Elliott	3.25	2.50	1.00	78 Ellis Kinder	3.25	2.50	1.00
15 Johnny Pesky	3.50	2.50	1.20	79 Gerald Staley	3.25	2.50	1.00
16 Gene Hermanski	3.25	2.50	1.00	80 Herman Wehmeier	3.25	2.50	1.00
17 Jim Hegan	3.25	2.50	1.00	81 Vernon Law	3.00	2.25	1.00
18 Merrill Combs	3.25	2.50	1.00	82 Duane Pillette	2.75	2.00	.80
19 Johnny Bucha	3.25	2.50	1.00	83 Billy Johnson	2.75	2.00	.80
20 Billy Loes	3.25	2.50	1.00	84 Vern Stephens	2.75	2.00	.80
21 Ferris Fain	4.00	3.00	1.40	85 Bob Kuzava	2.75	2.00	.80
22 Dom DiMaggio	6.50	5.00	2.25	86 Ted Gray	2.75	2.00	.80
23 Billy Goodman	3.25	2.50	1.00	87 Dale Coogan	2.75	2.00	.80
24 Luke Easter	3.50	2.50	1.20	88 Bob Feller	20.00	15.00	6.50
25 John Groth	3.25	2.50	1.00	89 Johnny Lipton	2.75	2.00	.80
26 Monte Irvin	7.00	5.25	2.50	90 Mickey Grasso	2.75	2.00	.80
27 Sam Jethroe	3.25	2.50	1.00	91 "Red" Schoendienst	4.00	3.00	1.40
28 Jerry Priddy	3.25	2.50	1.00	92 Dale Mitchell	2.75	2.00	.80
29 Ted Kluszewski	5.00	3.75	1.75	93 Al Sima	2.75	2.00	.80
30 Mel Parnell	3.25	2.50	1.00	94 Sam Mele	2.75	2.00	.80
31 Gus Zernial	3.25	2.50	1.00	95 Ken Holcombe	2.75	2.00	.80
32 Eddie Robinson	3.25	2.50	1.00	96 Willard Marshall	2.75	2.00	.80
33 Warren Spahn	13.00	9.50	4.00	97 Earl Torgeson	2.75	2.00	.80
34 Elmer Valo	3.25	2.50	1.00	98 Billy Pierce	4.00	3.00	1.40
35 Hank Sauer	6.00	4.50	2.00	99 Gene Woodling	3.50	2.50	1.20
36 Gil Hodges	12.00	8.75	4.00	100 Del Rice	2.75	2.00	.80
37 Duke Snider	18.00	13.50	6.00	101 Max Lanier	2.75	2.00	.80
38 Wally Westlake	3.25	2.50	1.00	102 Bill Kennedy	2.75	2.00	.80
39 "Dizzy" Trout	3.25	2.50	1.00	103 Cliff Mapes	2.75	2.00	.80
40 Irv Noren	3.25	2.50	1.00	104 Don Kolloway	2.75	2.00	.80
41 Bob Wellman	3.25	2.50	1.00	105 John Pramesa	2.75	2.00	.80
42 Lou Kretlow	3.25	2.50	1.00	106 Mickey Vernon	3.50	2.50	1.20
43 Ray Scarborough	3.25	2.50	1.00	107 Connie Ryan	2.75	2.00	.80
44 Con Dempsey	3.25	2.50	1.00	108 Jim Konstanty	3.50	2.50	1.20
45 Eddie Joost	3.25	2.50	1.00	109 Ted Wilks	2.75	2.00	.80
46 Gordon Goldsberry	3.25	2.50	1.00	110 "Dutch" Leonard	2.75	2.00	.80
47 Willie Jones	3.25	2.50	1.00	111 "Peanuts" Lowery	2.75	2.00	.80
48a Joe Page(correct)	5.00	3.75	1.75	112 Henry Majeski	2.75	2.00	.80
48b Joe Page(error)	75.00	55.00	24.00	113 Dick Sisler	2.75	2.00	.80
49a Johnny Sain(correct)	6.00	4.50	2.00	114 Willard Ramsdell	2.75	2.00	.80
49b Johnny Sain(error)	55.00	42.00	19.00	115 "Red" Munger	2.75	2.00	.80
50 Marv Rickert	3.25	2.50	1.00	116 Carl Scheib	2.75	2.00	.80
51 Jim Russell	3.25	2.50	1.00	117 Sherman Lollar	2.75	2.00	.80
52 Don Mueller	3.25	2.50	1.00	118 Ken Raffensberger	2.75	2.00	.80
53 Chris Van Cuyk	3.25	2.50	1.00	119 Mickey McDermott	2.75	2.00	.80
54 Leo Kiely	3.25	2.50	1.00	120 Bob Chakales	2.75	2.00	.80
55 Ray Boone	3.25	2.50	1.00	121 Gus Niarhos	2.75	2.00	.80
56 Thomas Glaviano	3.25	2.50	1.00	122 Jackie Jensen	4.50	3.50	1.60
57 Ed Lopat	6.00	4.50	2.00	123 Eddie Yost	2.75	2.00	.80
58 Bob Mahoney	3.25	2.50	1.00				

1952 TOPPS (CONTINUED)

	MINT	VG-E	F-G		MINT	VG-E	F-G
124 Monte Kennedy	2.75	2.00	.80	217 "Snuffy" Stirnweiss	2.75	2.00	.80
125 Bill Rigney	3.00	2.25	1.00	218 Clyde McCullough	2.75	2.00	.80
126 Fred Hutchison	4.00	3.00	1.40	219 Bobby Shantz	7.00	5.25	2.50
127 Paul Minner	2.75	2.00	.80	220 Joe Preska	2.75	2.00	.80
128 Don Bollweg	2.75	2.00	.80	221 Granny Hamner	2.75	2.00	.80
129 Johnny Mize	7.00	5.25	2.50	222 Hoot Evers	2.75	2.00	.80
130 Sheldon Jones	2.75	2.00	.80	223 Del Ennis	3.00	2.25	1.00
131 Morris Martin	2.75	2.00	.80	224 Bruce Edwards	2.75	2.00	.80
132 Clyde Klutz	2.75	2.00	.80	225 Frank Baumholtz	2.75	2.00	.80
133 Al Widmar	2.75	2.00	.80	226 Dave Philley	2.75	2.00	.80
134 Joe Tipton	2.75	2.00	.80	227 Joe Garagiola	10.00	7.00	3.00
135 Dixie Howell	2.75	2.00	.80	228 Al Brazle	2.75	2.00	.80
136 Johnny Schmitz	2.75	2.00	.80	229 Gene Beardon	2.75	2.00	.80
137 Roy McMillan	2.75	2.00	.80	230 Matt Batts	2.75	2.00	.80
138 Bill MacDonald	2.75	2.00	.80	231 Sam Zoldak	2.75	2.00	.80
139 Ken Wood	2.75	2.00	.80	232 Billy Cox	2.75	2.00	.80
140 Johnny Antonelli	3.00	2.25	1.00	233 Bob Friend	3.00	2.25	1.00
141 Clint Hartung	3.00	2.25	1.00	234 Steve Souchock	2.75	2.00	.80
142 Harry Perkowski	2.75	2.00	.80	235 Walt Dropo	2.75	2.00	.80
143 Les Moss	2.75	2.00	.80	236 Ed Fitzgerald	2.75	2.00	.80
144 Ed Blake	2.75	2.00	.80	237 Jerry Coleman	3.00	2.25	1.00
145 Joe Haynes	2.75	2.00	.80	238 Art Houtteman	2.75	2.00	.80
146 Frank House	2.75	2.00	.80	239 Rocky Bridges	2.75	2.00	.80
147 Bob Young	2.75	2.00	.80	240 Jack Phillips	2.75	2.00	.80
148 Johnny Klippstein	2.75	2.00	.80	241 Tommy Byrne	2.75	2.00	.80
149 Dick Kryhoski	2.75	2.00	.80	242 Tom Poholsky	2.75	2.00	.80
150 Ted Beard	2.75	2.00	.80	243 Larry Doby	5.00	5.25	2.50
151 Wally Post	2.75	2.00	.80	244 Vic Wertz	3.00	2.25	1.00
152 Al Evans	2.75	2.00	.80	245 Sherry Robertson	2.75	2.00	.80
153 Bob Rush	2.75	2.00	.80	246 George Kell	4.00	3.00	1.40
154 Joe Muir	2.75	2.00	.80	247 Randy Gumpert	2.75	2.00	.80
155 Frank Overmire	2.75	2.00	.80	248 Frank Shea	2.75	2.00	.80
156 Frank Hiller	2.75	2.00	.80	249 Bobby Adams	2.75	2.00	.80
157 Bob Usher	2.75	2.00	.80	250 Carl Erskine	7.50	5.75	2.50
158 Eddie Waitkus	2.75	2.00	.80	251 Chico Carrasquel	10.50	8.25	3.50
159 Saul Rogovin	2.75	2.00	.80	252 Vern Bickford	10.50	8.25	3.50
160 Owen Friend	2.75	2.00	.80	253 Johnny Berardino	12.00	8.75	4.00
161 Bud Byerly	2.75	2.00	.80	254 Joe Dobson	10.50	8.25	3.50
162 Del Crandall	3.00	2.25	1.00	255 Clyde Vollmer	10.50	8.25	3.50
163 Stan Rojek	2.75	2.00	.80	256 Pete Suder	10.50	8.25	3.50
164 Walt Dubiel	2.75	2.00	.80	257 Bobby Avila	12.00	8.75	4.00
165 Eddie Kazak	2.75	2.00	.80	258 Steve Gromek	10.50	8.25	3.50
166 Paul LaPalme	2.75	2.00	.80	259 Bob Addis	10.50	8.25	3.50
167 Bill Howerton	2.75	2.00	.80	260 Pete Castiglione	10.50	8.25	3.50
168 Charlie Silvera	2.75	2.00	.80	261 Willie Mays	375.00	280.00	125.00
169 Howie Judson	2.75	2.00	.80	262 Virgil Trucks	10.50	8.25	3.50
170 Gus Bell	2.75	2.00	.80	263 Harry Brecheen	11.00	8.00	3.50
171 Ed Erautt	2.75	2.00	.80	264 Roy Hartsfield	10.50	8.25	3.50
172 Eddie Miksis	2.75	2.00	.80	265 Chuck Diering	10.50	8.25	3.50
173 Roy Smalley	2.75	2.00	.80	266 Murry Dickson	10.50	8.25	3.50
174 Clarence Marshall	2.75	2.00	.80	267 Sid Gordon	10.50	8.25	3.50
175 Billy Martin	14.00	10.50	4.75	268 Bob Lemon	50.00	38.00	17.00
176 Hank Edwards	2.75	2.00	.80	269 Willard Nixon	10.50	8.25	3.50
177 Bill Wight	2.75	2.00	.80	270 Lou Brissie	10.50	8.25	3.50
178 Cass Michaels	2.75	2.00	.80	271 Jim Delsing	10.50	8.25	3.50
179 Frank Smith	2.75	2.00	.80	272 Mike Garcia	12.00	8.75	4.00
180 Charley Maxwell	2.75	2.00	.80	273 Erv Palica	10.50	8.25	3.50
181 Bob Swift	2.75	2.00	.80	274 Ralph Branca	12.00	8.75	4.00
182 Billy Hitchcock	2.75	2.00	.80	275 Pat Mullin	10.50	8.25	3.50
183 Erv Dusak	2.75	2.00	.80	276 Jim Wilson	10.50	8.25	3.50
184 Bob Ramazotti	2.75	2.00	.80	277 Early Wynn	50.00	38.00	17.00
185 Bill Nicholson	2.75	2.00	.80	278 Al Clark	10.50	8.25	3.50
186 Walt Masterson	2.75	2.00	.80	279 Ed Stewart	10.50	8.25	3.50
187 Bob Miller	2.75	2.00	.80	280 Cloyd Boyer	10.50	8.25	3.50
188 Clarence Podbielan	2.75	2.00	.80	281 Tommy Brown	10.50	8.25	3.50
189 Pete Reiser	3.50	2.50	1.20	282 Birdie Tebbetts	10.50	8.25	3.50
190 Don Johnson	2.75	2.00	.80	283 Phil Masi	10.50	8.25	3.50
191 "Yogi" Berra	30.00	22.50	10.50	284 Hank Arft	10.50	8.25	3.50
192 Myron Ginsberg	2.75	2.00	.80	285 Cliff Fannin	10.50	8.25	3.50
193 Harry Simpson	2.75	2.00	.80	286 Joe DeMaestri	10.50	8.25	3.50
194 Joe Hatton	2.75	2.00	.80	287 Steve Bilko	10.50	8.25	3.50
195 "Minnie" Minoso	5.50	4.25	2.00	288 Chet Nichols	10.50	8.25	3.50
196 Solly Hemus	2.75	2.00	.80	289 Tommy Holmes	12.00	8.75	4.00
197 George Strickland	2.75	2.00	.80	290 Joe Astroth	10.50	8.25	3.50
198 Phil Haugstad	2.75	2.00	.80	291 Gil Coan	10.50	8.25	3.50
199 George Zuverink	2.75	2.00	.80	292 Floyd Baker	10.50	8.25	3.50
200 Ralph Houk	5.00	3.75	1.75	293 Sibby Sisti	10.50	8.25	3.50
201 Alex Kellner	2.75	2.00	.80	294 Walker Cooper	10.50	8.25	3.50
202 Joe Collins	2.75	2.00	.80	295 Phil Cavaretta	12.00	8.75	4.00
203 Curt Simmons	3.00	2.25	1.00	296 "Red" Rolfe	12.00	8.75	4.00
204 Ron Northey	2.75	2.00	.80	297 Andy Seminick	10.50	8.25	3.50
205 Clyde King	2.75	2.00	.80	298 Bob Ross	10.50	8.25	3.50
206 Joe Ostrowski	2.75	2.00	.80	299 Ray Murray	10.50	8.25	3.50
207 Mickey Harris	2.75	2.00	.80	300 Barney McCosky	10.50	8.25	3.50
208 Marlin Stuart	2.75	2.00	.80	301 Bob Porterfield	10.50	8.25	3.50
209 Howie Fox	2.75	2.00	.80	302 Max Surkont	10.50	8.25	3.50
210 Dick Fowler	2.75	2.00	.80	303 Harry Dorish	10.50	8.25	3.50
211 Ray Coleman	2.75	2.00	.80	304 Sam Dente	10.50	8.25	3.50
212 Ned Garver	2.75	2.00	.80	305 Paul Richards	12.00	8.75	4.00
213 "Nippy" Jones	2.75	2.00	.80	306 Lou Sleater, Jr.	10.50	8.25	3.50
214 Johnny Hopp	3.00	2.25	1.00	307 Frank Campos	10.50	8.25	3.50
215 Hank Bauer	4.50	3.50	1.60	308 Luis Aloma	10.50	8.25	3.50
216 Richie Ashburn	5.50	4.25	2.00	309 Jim Busby	10.50	8.25	3.50
				310 George Metkovich	10.50	8.25	3.50

1952 TOPPS (CONTINUED)

	MINT	VG-E	F-G
311 Mickey Mantle (dp)	1500.00	900.00	300.00
312 Jackie Robinson ('dp)	325.00	250.00	100.00
313 Bobby Thomson (dp)	75.00	55.00	25.00
314 Roy Campanella	350.00	250.00	100.00
315 Leo Durocher	100.00	70.00	30.00
316 Dave Williams	40.00	30.00	13.00
317 Conrado Marrerro	40.00	30.00	13.00
318 Harold Gregg	40.00	30.00	13.00
319 Al Walker	40.00	30.00	13.00
320 John Rutherford	40.00	30.00	13.00
321 Joe Black	50.00	38.00	17.00
322 Randy Jackson	40.00	30.00	13.00
323 Bubba Church	40.00	30.00	13.00
324 Warren Hacker	40.00	30.00	13.00
325 Bill Serena	40.00	30.00	13.00
326 George Shuba	40.00	30.00	13.00
327 Al Wilson	40.00	30.00	13.00
328 Bob Borkowski	40.00	30.00	13.00
329 Ike Delock	40.00	30.00	13.00
330 "Turk" Lown	40.00	30.00	13.00
331 Tom Morgan	40.00	30.00	13.00
332 Anthony Bartirome	40.00	30.00	13.00
333 "Peewee" Reese	175.00	130.00	60.00
334 Wilmer Mizell	40.00	30.00	13.00
335 Ted Lepcio	40.00	30.00	13.00
336 "Dave" Koslo	40.00	30.00	13.00
337 Jim Hearn	40.00	30.00	13.00
338 Sal Yvars	40.00	30.00	13.00
339 Russ Meyer	40.00	30.00	13.00
340 Bob Hooper	40.00	30.00	13.00
341 Hal Jeffcoat	40.00	30.00	13.00
342 Clem Labine	40.00	30.00	13.00
343 Dick Gernert	40.00	30.00	13.00
344 Ewell Blackwell	50.00	38.00	17.00
345 Charles White	40.00	30.00	13.00
346 George Spencer	40.00	30.00	13.00
347 Joe Adcock	50.00	38.00	17.00
348 Robert Kelly	40.00	30.00	13.00
349 Bob Cain	40.00	30.00	13.00
350 Cal Abrams	40.00	30.00	13.00
351 Alvin Dark	60.00	45.00	20.00
352 Karl Drews	40.00	30.00	13.00
353 Bobby Del Greco	40.00	30.00	13.00
354 Fred Hatfield	40.00	30.00	13.00
355 Bobby Morgan	40.00	30.00	13.00
356 Toby Atwell	40.00	30.00	13.00
357 Smokey Burgess	40.00	30.00	13.00

	MINT	VG-E	F-G
358 John Kucab	40.00	30.00	13.00
359 Dee Fondy	40.00	30.00	13.00
360 George Crowe	40.00	30.00	13.00
361 William Posedel	40.00	30.00	13.00
362 Ken Heintzelman	40.00	30.00	13.00
363 Dick Rozek	40.00	30.00	13.00
364 Clyde Sukeforth	40.00	30.00	13.00
365 Cookie Lavagetto	50.00	38.00	17.00
366 Dave Madison	40.00	30.00	13.00
367 Ben Thorpe	40.00	30.00	13.00
368 Ed Wright	40.00	30.00	13.00
369 Dick Groat	80.00	60.00	25.00
370 Billy Hoeft	40.00	30.00	13.00
371 Bobby Hofman	40.00	30.00	13.00
372 Gil McDougald	80.00	60.00	25.00
373 Jim Turner	40.00	30.00	13.00
374 John Benton	40.00	30.00	13.00
375 John Merson	40.00	30.00	13.00
376 Faye Throneberry	40.00	30.00	13.00
377 Chuck Dressen	50.00	38.00	17.00
378 Leroy Fusselman	40.00	30.00	13.00
379 Joseph Rossi	40.00	30.00	13.00
380 Clem Koshorek	40.00	30.00	13.00
381 Milton Stock	40.00	30.00	13.00
382 Sam Jones	40.00	30.00	13.00
383 Del Wilber	40.00	30.00	13.00
384 Frank Crosetti	100.00	70.00	30.00
385 Herman Franks	50.00	38.00	17.00
386 John Yuhas	40.00	30.00	13.00
387 William Meyer	40.00	30.00	13.00
388 Bob Chipman	40.00	30.00	13.00
389 Ben Wade	40.00	30.00	13.00
390 Glenn Nelson	40.00	30.00	13.00
391 Ben Chapman	40.00	30.00	13.00
392 Hoyt Wilhelm	110.00	80.00	30.00
393 Ebba St. Claire	40.00	30.00	13.00
394 Billy Herman	80.00	60.00	25.00
395 Jake Pitler	40.00	30.00	13.00
396 R. Williams	60.00	45.00	20.00
397 Forrest Main	40.00	30.00	13.00
398 Hal Rice	40.00	30.00	13.00
399 Jim Fridley	40.00	30.00	13.00
400 Bill Dickey	275.00	200.00	90.00
401 Bob Schultz	40.00	30.00	13.00
402 Earl Harrist	40.00	30.00	13.00
403 W. Miller	40.00	30.00	13.00
404 Dick Brodowski	40.00	30.00	13.00
405 Ed Pellagrini	40.00	30.00	13.00
406 Joe Nuxhall	50.00	38.00	17.00
407 Ed Mathews	425.00	325.00	125.00

1953 TOPPS (280)   2 5/8" X 3 5/8"

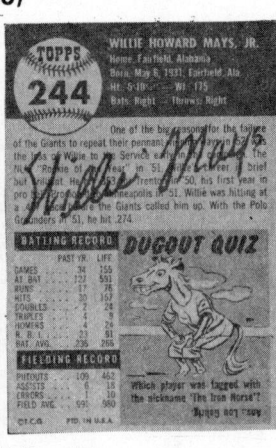

The 1953 Topps set feature line drawing color cards whos red or black bottom portio "bleeds" to the edge of th card. Card nos. 253, 261, 26 268, 271, and 275 were no issued. Card nos. 221-28 are more difficult to obtai As the red and black colo on the bottom edge chi and notch quite easily, mir cards are at a premium i this set.

	MINT	VG-E	F-G
COMPLETE SET	1650.00	1100.00	450.00
COMMON PLAYER (1-165)	2.00	1.25	.50
COMMON PLAYER (166-220)	1.50	.90	.40
COMMON PLAYER (221-280)	10.00	7.00	3.00
1 Jackie Robinson	45.00	25.00	10.00
2 Luke Easter	2.50	1.80	.80
3 George Crowe	2.00	1.25	.50
4 Ben Wade	2.00	1.25	.50
5 Joe Dobson	2.00	1.25	.50
6 Sam Jones	2.00	1.25	.50
7 Bob Borkowski	2.00	1.25	.50
8 Clem Koshorek	2.00	1.25	.50
9 Joe Collins	2.00	1.25	.60

	MINT	VG-E	F-G
10 "Smokey" Burgess	2.50	1.80	.80
11 Sal Yvars	2.00	1.25	.50
12 Howie Judson	2.00	1.25	.50
13 Connie Marrero	2.00	1.25	.50
14 Clem Labine	2.00	1.25	.50
15 "Bobo" Newsom	2.50	1.80	.80
16 "Peanuts" Lowrey	2.00	1.25	.50
17 Billy Hitchcock	2.00	1.25	.50
18 Ted Lepcio	2.00	1.25	.50
19 Mel Parnell	2.00	1.25	.50
20 Hank Thompson	2.00	1.25	.50
21 Billy Johnson	2.00	1.25	.50
22 Howie Fox	2.00	1.25	.50

247

#	Name	MINT	VG-E	F-G
23	Toby Atwell	2.00	1.25	.50
24	Ferris Fain	2.50	1.80	.80
25	Ray Boone	2.00	1.25	.50
26	Dale Mitchell	2.00	1.25	.50
27	Roy Campanella	28.00	21.00	10.00
28	Eddie Pellagrini	2.00	1.25	.50
29	Hal Jeffcoat	2.00	1.25	.50
30	Willard Nixon	2.00	1.25	.50
31	Ewell Blackwell	2.50	1.80	.80
32	Clyde Vollmer	2.00	1.25	.50
33	Bob Kennedy	2.50	1.80	.80
34	George Shuba	2.00	1.25	.50
35	Irv Noren	2.00	1.25	.50
36	Johnny Groth	2.00	1.25	.50
37	Ed Mathews	11.00	8.00	3.50
38	Jim Hearn	2.00	1.25	.50
39	Eddie Miksis	2.00	1.25	.50
40	John Lipon	2.00	1.25	.50
41	Enos Slaughter	5.00	3.75	1.75
42	Gus Zernial	2.00	1.25	.50
43	Gil McDougald	3.00	2.25	1.00
44	Ellis Kinder	2.00	1.25	.50
45	Grady Hatton	2.00	1.25	.50
46	Johnny Klippstein	2.00	1.25	.50
47	"Bubba" Church	2.00	1.25	.50
48	Bob Del Greco	2.00	1.25	.50
49	Faye Throneberry	2.00	1.25	.50
50	Chuck Dressen	2.50	1.80	.80
51	Frank Campos	2.00	1.25	.50
52	Ted Gray	2.00	1.25	.50
53	Sherman Lollar	2.00	1.25	.50
54	Bob Feller	18.00	13.50	6.00
55	Maurice McDermott	2.00	1.25	.50
56	Gerry Staley	2.00	1.25	.50
57	Carl Scheib	2.00	1.25	.50
58	George Metkovich	2.00	1.25	.50
59	Karl Drews	2.00	1.25	.50
60	Cloyd Boyer	2.00	1.25	.50
61	Early Wynn	9.00	6.75	3.00
62	Monte Irvin	6.00	4.50	2.00
63	Gus Niarhos	2.00	1.25	.50
64	Dave Philley	2.00	1.25	.50
65	Earl Harrist	2.00	1.25	.50
66	"Minnie" Minoso	4.00	3.00	1.40
67	Roy Sievers	2.00	1.25	.50
68	Del Rice	2.00	1.25	.50
69	Dick Brodowski	2.00	1.25	.50
70	Ed Yuhas	2.00	1.25	.50
71	Tony Bartirome	2.00	1.25	.50
72	Fred Hutchison	3.00	2.25	1.00
73	Eddie Robinson	2.00	1.25	.50
74	Joe Rossi	2.00	1.25	.50
75	Mike Garcia	2.50	1.80	.80
76	"Peewee" Reese	10.00	7.00	3.00
77	John Mize	6.00	4.50	2.00
78	Al Schoendienst	3.50	2.50	1.20
79	Johnny Wyrostek	2.00	1.25	.50
80	Jim Hegan	2.00	1.25	.50
81	Joe Black	2.50	1.80	.80
82	*Mickey Mantle*	200.00	150.00	65.00
83	Howie Pollet	2.00	1.25	.50
84	Bob Hooper	2.00	1.25	.50
85	Bobby Morgan	2.00	1.25	.50
86	Billy Martin	11.00	8.00	3.50
87	Ed Lopat	4.50	3.50	1.60
88	Willie Jones	2.00	1.25	.50
89	Chuck Stobbs	2.00	1.25	.50
90	Hank Edwards	2.00	1.25	.50
91	Ebba St. Claire	2.00	1.25	.50
92	Paul Minner	2.00	1.25	.50
93	Hal Rice	2.00	1.25	.50
94	Bill Kennedy	2.00	1.25	.50
95	Willard Marshall	2.00	1.25	.50
96	Virgil Trucks	2.00	1.25	.50
97	Don Kolloway	2.00	1.25	.50
98	Cal Abrams	2.00	1.25	.50
99	Dave Madison	2.00	1.25	.50
100	Bill Miller	2.00	1.25	.50
101	Ted Wilks	2.00	1.25	.50
102	Connie Ryan	2.00	1.25	.50
103	Joe Astroth	2.00	1.25	.50
104	Yogi Berra	22.00	16.50	7.50
105	Joe Nuxhall	2.50	1.80	.80
106	Johnny Antonelli	2.50	1.80	.80
107	Danny O'Connell	2.00	1.25	.50
108	Bob Porterfield	2.00	1.25	.50
109	Alvin Dark	2.50	1.80	.80
110	Herman Wehmeier	2.00	1.25	.50
111	Hank Sauer	2.50	1.80	.80
112	Ned Garver	2.00	1.25	.50
113	Jerry Priddy	2.00	1.25	.50
114	Phil Rizzuto	11.00	8.00	3.50
115	George Spencer	2.00	1.25	.50
116	Frank Smith	2.00	1.25	.50
117	Sid Gordon	2.00	1.25	.50
118	Gus Bell	2.00	1.25	.50
119	John Sain	3.50	2.50	1.20
120	Davey Williams	2.00	1.25	.50
121	Walter Dropo	2.00	1.25	.50
122	Elmer Valo	2.00	1.25	.50
123	Tommy Byrne	2.00	1.25	.50
124	Sibby Sisti	2.00	1.25	.50
125	Dick Williams	3.00	2.25	1.00
126	Bill Connelly	2.00	1.25	.50
127	Clint Courtney	2.00	1.25	.50
128	Wilmer Mizell	2.00	1.25	.50
129	Keith Thomas	2.00	1.25	.50
130	"Turk" Lown	2.00	1.25	.50
131	Harry Byrd	2.00	1.25	.50
132	Tom Morgan	2.00	1.25	.50
133	Gil Coan	2.00	1.25	.50
134	"Rube" Walker	2.00	1.25	.50
135	Al Rosen	6.50	5.00	2.25
136	Ken Heintzelman	2.00	1.25	.50
137	John Rutherford	2.00	1.25	.50
138	George Kell	3.00	2.25	1.00
139	Sammy White	2.00	1.25	.50
140	Tommy Glaviano	2.00	1.25	.50
141	Allie Reynolds	4.00	3.00	1.40
142	Vic Wertz	2.00	1.25	.50
143	Billy Pierce	3.50	2.50	1.20
144	Bob Schultz	2.00	1.25	.50
145	Harry Dorish	2.00	1.25	.50
146	Granny Hamner	2.00	1.25	.50
147	Warren Spahn	12.00	8.75	4.00
148	Mickey Grasso	2.00	1.25	.50
149	Dom DiMaggio	6.50	5.00	2.25
150	Harry Simpson	2.00	1.25	.50
151	Hoyt Wilhelm	5.00	3.75	1.75
152	Bob Adams	2.00	1.25	.50
153	Andy Seminick	2.00	1.25	.50
154	Dick Groat	3.00	2.25	1.00
155	"Dutch" Leonard	2.00	1.25	.50
156	Jim Rivera	2.00	1.25	.50
157	Bob Addis	2.00	1.25	.50
158	John Logan	2.00	1.25	.50
159	Wayne Terwilliger	2.00	1.25	.50
160	Bob Young	2.00	1.25	.50
161	Vern Bickford	2.00	1.25	.50
162	Ted Kluszewski	4.00	3.00	1.40
163	Fred Hatfield	2.00	1.25	.50
164	Frank Shea	2.00	1.25	.50
165	Billy Hoeft	2.00	1.25	.50
166	Bill Hunter	1.50	.90	.40
167	Art Schult	1.50	.90	.40
168	Willard Schmidt	1.50	.90	.40
169	"Dizzy" Trout	1.50	.90	.40
170	Bill Werle	1.50	.90	.40
171	Bill Glynn	1.50	.90	.40
172	Rip Repulski	1.50	.90	.40
173	Preston Ward	1.50	.90	.40
174	Billy Loes	1.50	.90	.40
175	Ronnie Kline	1.50	.90	.40
176	Don Hoak	1.50	.90	.40
177	Jim Dyck	1.50	.90	.40
178	Jim Waugh	1.50	.90	.40
179	Gene Hermanski	1.50	.90	.40
180	Virgil Stallcup	1.50	.90	.40
181	Al Zarilla	1.50	.90	.40
182	Bobby Hofman	1.50	.90	.40
183	Stu Miller	1.50	.90	.40
184	Hal Brown	1.50	.90	.40
185	Jim Pendleton	1.50	.90	.40
186	Charlie Bishop	1.50	.90	.40
187	Jim Fridley	1.50	.90	.40
188	Andy Carey	1.50	.90	.40
189	Ray Jablonski	1.50	.90	.40
190	Dixie Walker	1.50	.90	.40
191	Ralph Kiner	8.00	6.00	2.50
192	Wally Westlake	1.50	.90	.40
193	Mike Clark	1.50	.90	.40
194	Eddie Kazak	1.50	.90	.40
195	Ed McGhee	1.50	.90	.40
196	Bob Keegan	1.50	.90	.40
197	Del Crandell	2.00	1.50	.60
198	Forrest Main	1.50	.90	.40
199	Marion Fricano	1.50	.90	.40
200	Gordon Goldsberry	1.50	.90	.40
201	Paul LaPalme	1.50	.90	.40
202	Carl Sawatski	1.50	.90	.40
203	Cliff Fannin	1.50	.90	.40
204	Dick Bokelman	1.50	.90	.40
205	Vern Benson	1.50	.90	.40
206	Ed Bailey	1.50	.90	.40
207	Whitey Ford	10.00	7.00	3.00
208	Jim Wilson	1.50	.90	.40
209	Jim Greengrass	1.50	.90	.40

248

1953 TOPPS (CONTINUED)

	MINT	VG-E	F-G
210 Bob Cerv	1.50	.90	.40
211 J. W. Porter	1.50	.90	.40
212 Jack Dittmer	1.50	.90	.40
213 Ray Scarborough	1.50	.90	.40
214 Bill Bruton	1.50	.90	.40
215 Gene Conley	1.50	.90	.40
216 Jim Hughes	1.50	.90	.40
217 Murray Wall	1.50	.90	.40
218 Les Fusselman	1.50	.90	.40
219 Pete Runnels	1.50	.90	.40
220 Satchel Paige	27.00	20.00	8.00
221 Bob Milliken	10.00	7.00	3.00
222 Vic Janowicz	10.00	7.00	3.00
223 Johnny O'Brien	10.00	7.00	3.00
224 Lou Sleater	10.00	7.00	3.00
225 Bobby Shantz	13.00	9.50	4.00
226 Ed Erautt	10.00	7.00	3.00
227 Morris Martin	10.00	7.00	3.00
228 Hal Newhouser	13.00	9.50	4.00
229 Rockey Krsnich	10.00	7.00	3.00
230 Johnny Lindell	10.00	7.00	3.00
231 Solly Hemus	10.00	7.00	3.00
232 Dick Kokos	10.00	7.00	3.00
233 Al Aber	10.00	7.00	3.00
234 Ray Murray	10.00	7.00	3.00
235 John Hetki	10.00	7.00	3.00
236 Harry Perkowski	10.00	7.00	3.00
237 Bud Podbielan	10.00	7.00	3.00
238 Cal Hogue	10.00	7.00	3.00
239 Jim Delsing	10.00	7.00	3.00
240 Freddie Marsh	10.00	7.00	3.00
241 Al Sima	10.00	7.00	3.00

	MINT	VG-E	F-G
242 Charlie Silvera	10.00	7.00	3.00
243 Carlos Bernier	10.00	7.00	3.00
244 Willie Mays	600.00	350.00	150.00
245 Bill Norman	10.00	7.00	3.00
246 Roy Face	13.00	9.50	4.00
247 Mike Sandlock	10.00	7.00	3.00
248 Gene Stephens	10.00	7.00	3.00
249 Ed O'Brien	10.00	7.00	3.00
250 Bob Wilson	10.00	7.00	3.00
251 Sid Hudson	10.00	7.00	3.00
252 Henry Foiles	10.00	7.00	3.00
254 Preacher Roe	20.00	15.00	6.50
255 Dixie Howell	10.00	7.00	3.00
256 Les Peden	10.00	7.00	3.00
257 Bob Boyd	10.00	7.00	3.00
258 Jim Gilliam	30.00	22.50	10.50
259 Roy McMillan	10.00	7.00	3.00
260 Sam Calderone	10.00	7.00	3.00
262 Bob Oldis	10.00	7.00	3.00
263 Johnny Podres	18.00	13.50	6.00
264 Gene Woodling	16.00	12.00	5.50
265 Jackie Jensen	18.00	13.50	6.00
266 Bob Cain	10.00	7.00	3.00
269 Duane Pillette	10.00	7.00	3.00
270 Vern Stephens	10.00	7.00	3.00
272 Bill Antonello	10.00	7.00	3.00
273 Harvey Haddix	12.00	8.75	4.00
274 John Riddle	10.00	7.00	3.00
276 Ken Raffensberger	10.00	7.00	3.00
277 Don Lund	10.00	7.00	3.00
278 Willie Miranda	10.00	7.00	3.00
279 Joe Coleman	10.00	7.00	3.00
280 Milt Bolling	15.00	8.00	3.00

1954 TOPPS (250)

2 5/8" X 3 5/8"

The 1954 Topps set features a large bust picture of the player plus a smaller insert picture of the player in action.

Ted Williams is portrayed on card nos. 1 and 250, while card no. 128 is the Hank Aaron rookie card.

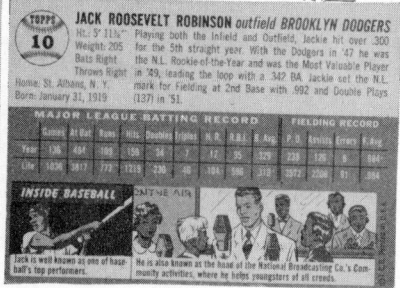

	MINT	VG-E	F-G
COMPLETE SET	725.00	575.00	250.00
COMMON PLAYER	1.10	.80	.35
1 Ted Williams	45.00	35.00	15.00
2 Gus Zernial	1.25	.90	.40
3 Monte Irvin	5.50	4.25	2.00
4 Hank Sauer	1.50	1.10	.50
5 Ed Lopat	3.00	2.25	1.00
6 "Pete" Runnels	1.10	.80	.35
7 Ted Kluszewski	3.00	2.25	1.00
8 Bob Young	1.10	.80	.35
9 Harvey Haddix	1.25	.90	.40
10 Jackie Robinson	24.00	18.00	8.50
11 Paul Leslie Smith	1.10	.90	.35
12 Del Crandall	1.25	.90	.40
13 Billy Martin	8.00	6.00	2.50
14 "Preacher" Roe	2.50	1.80	.80
15 Al Rosen	6.00	4.50	2.00
16 Vic Janowicz	1.10	.80	.35
17 Phil Rizzuto	9.50	7.00	3.00
18 Walt Dropo	1.10	.80	.35
19 Johnny Lipon	1.10	.80	.35
20 Warren Spahn	10.00	7.00	3.00
21 Bobby Shantz	1.50	1.10	.50
22 Jim Greengrass	1.10	.80	.35
23 Luke Easter	1.25	.90	.40
24 Granny Hamner	1.10	.80	.35
25 Harvey Kuenn	1.50	1.10	.50
26 Ray Jablonski	1.10	.80	.35
27 Ferris Fain	1.25	.90	.40

	MINT	VG-E	F-G
28 Paul Minner	1.10	.80	.35
29 Jim Hegan	1.10	.80	.35
30 Ed Mathews	11.00	8.00	3.50
31 Johnny Klippstein	1.10	.80	.35
32 Duke Snider	16.00	12.00	5.50
33 Johnny Schmitz	1.10	.80	.35
34 Jim Rivera	1.10	.80	.35
35 Jim Gilliam	3.00	2.25	1.00
36 Hoyt Wilhelm	3.50	2.50	1.20
37 Whitey Ford	12.00	8.75	4.00
38 Eddie Stanky	1.25	.90	.40
39 Sherm Lollar	1.10	.80	.35
40 Mel Parnell	1.10	.80	.35
41 Willie Jones	1.10	.80	.35
42 Don Mueller	1.10	.80	.35
43 Dick Groat	1.25	.90	.40
44 Ned Garver	1.10	.80	.35
45 Richie Ashburn	3.00	2.25	1.00
46 Ken Raffensberger	1.10	.80	.35
47 Ellis Kinder	1.10	.80	.35
48 William Hunter	1.10	.80	.35
49 Ray Murray	1.10	.80	.35
50 Yogi Berra	20.00	15.00	6.50
51 Johnny Lindell	1.10	.80	.35
52 Vic Power	1.50	1.10	.50
53 Johnny Dittmar	1.10	.80	.35
54 Vern Stephens	1.10	.80	.35
55 Phil Cavaretta	1.50	1.10	.50
56 Willie Miranda	1.10	.80	.35
57 Luis Aloma	1.10	.80	.35

	MINT	VG-E	F-G
58 Bob Wilson	1.10	.80	.35
59 Gene Conley	1.10	.80	.35
60 Frank Baumholtz	1.10	.80	.35
61 Bob Cain	1.10	.80	.35
62 Eddie Robinson	1.25	.90	.40
63 Johnny Pesky	1.50	1.10	.50
64 Hank Thompson	1.50	1.10	.50
65 Bob Swift	1.10	.80	.35
66 Thad Lepcio	1.10	.80	.35
67 Jim Willis	1.10	.80	.35
68 Sam Calderone	1.10	.80	.35
69 Bud Podbelian	1.10	.80	.35
70 Larry Doby	3.50	2.50	1.20
71 Frank Smith	1.10	.80	.35
72 Preston Ward	1.10	.80	.35
73 Wayne Terwilliger	1.10	.80	.35
74 Bill Taylor	1.10	.80	.35
75 Fred Haney	1.50	1.10	.50
76 Bob Scheffing	1.10	.80	.35
77 Ray Boone	1.10	.80	.35
78 Ted Kazanski	1.10	.80	.35
79 Andy Pafko	1.10	.80	.35
80 Jackie Jensen	2.00	1.50	.60
81 Dave Hoskins	1.10	.80	.35
82 Milt Bolling	1.10	.80	.35
83 Joe Collins	1.10	.80	.35
84 Dick Cole	1.10	.80	.35
85 Bob Turley	2.00	1.50	.60
86 Billy Herman	2.50	1.80	.80
87 Roy Face	1.50	1.10	.50
88 Matt Batts	1.10	.80	.35
89 Howie Pollet	1.10	.80	.35
90 Willie Mays	100.00	70.00	30.00
91 Bob Oldis	1.10	.80	.35
92 Wally Westlake	1.10	.80	.35
93 Sid Hudson	1.10	.80	.35
94 Ernie Banks	45.00	34.00	15.00
95 Hal Rice	1.10	.80	.35
96 Charlie Silvera	1.10	.80	.35
97 Jerald Hal Lane	1.10	.80	.35
98 Joe Black	1.25	.90	.40
99 Bobby Hofman	1.10	.80	.35
100 Bob Keegan	1.10	.80	.35
101 Gene Woodling	1.25	.90	.40
102 Gil Hodges	10.00	7.00	3.00
103 Jim Lemon	1.10	.80	.35
104 Mike Sandlock	1.10	.80	.35
105 Andy Carey	1.10	.80	.35
106 Dick Kokos	1.10	.80	.35
107 Duane Pillette	1.10	.80	.35
108 Thornton Kipper	1.10	.80	.35
109 Bill Bruton	1.10	.80	.35
110 Harry Dorish	1.10	.80	.35
111 Jim Delsing	1.10	.80	.35
112 Bill Renna	1.10	.80	.35
113 Bob Boyd	1.10	.80	.35
114 Dean Stone	1.10	.80	.35
115 Rip Repulski	1.10	.80	.35
116 Steve Bilko	1.10	.80	.35
117 Solly Hemus	1.10	.80	.35
118 Carl Scheib	1.10	.80	.35
119 Johnny Antonelli	1.25	.90	.40
120 Roy McMillan	1.10	.80	.35
121 Clem Labine	1.10	.80	.35
122 Johnny Logan	1.10	.80	.35
123 Bobby Adams	1.10	.80	.35
124 Marion Fricano	1.10	.80	.35
125 Harry Perkowski	1.10	.80	.35
126 Ben Wade	1.10	.80	.35
127 Steve O'Neill	1.10	.80	.35
128 Hank Aaron	180.00	125.00	50.00
129 Forrest Jacobs	1.10	.80	.35
130 Hank Bauer	2.50	1.80	.80
131 Reno Bertoia	1.10	.80	.35
132 Tom Lasorda	4.50	3.50	1.60
133 Dave Baker	1.10	.80	.35
134 Cal Hogue	1.10	.80	.35
135 Joe Presko	1.10	.80	.35
136 Connie Ryan	1.10	.80	.35
137 Wally Moon	2.50	1.80	.80
138 Bob Borkowski	1.10	.80	.35
139 The O'Brien's	2.00	1.50	.60
140 Tom Wright	1.10	.80	.35
141 Joe Jay	1.10	.80	.35
142 Tom Poholsky	1.10	.80	.35
143 Ralston Hemsley	1.10	.80	.35
144 Bill Werle	1.10	.80	.35
145 Elmer Valo	1.10	.80	.35
146 Johnny Riddle	1.10	.80	.35
147 Don Johnson	1.10	.80	.35
148 Bob Trice	1.10	.80	.35
149 Al Robertson	1.10	.80	.35
150 Dick Kryhoski	1.10	.80	.35

	MINT	VG-E	F-G
151 Alex Grammas	1.10	.80	.35
152 Michael Blyzka	1.10	.80	.35
153 Al Walker	1.10	.80	.35
154 Mike Fornieles	1.10	.80	.35
155 Bob Kennedy	1.25	.90	.40
156 Joe Coleman	1.10	.80	.35
157 Don Lenhardt	1.10	.80	.35
158 Peanuts Lowrey	1.10	.80	.35
159 Dave Philley	1.10	.80	.35
160 Ralph Kress	1.10	.80	.35
161 John Hetki	1.10	.80	.35
162 Herman Wehmeier	1.10	.80	.35
163 Frank House	1.10	.80	.35
164 Stu Miller	1.10	.80	.35
165 Jim Pendleton	1.10	.80	.35
166 Johnny Podres	2.00	1.50	.60
167 Don Lund	1.10	.80	.35
168 Morrie Martin	1.10	.80	.35
169 Jim Hughes	1.10	.80	.35
170 James Rhodes	1.25	.90	.40
171 Leo Kiely	1.10	.80	.35
172 Harold Brown	1.10	.80	.35
173 Jack Harshman	1.10	.80	.35
174 Tom Qualters	1.10	.80	.35
175 Frank Leja	1.10	.80	.35
176 Robert Keeley	1.10	.80	.35
177 Bob Milliken	1.10	.80	.35
178 Bill Glynn	1.10	.80	.35
179 Gair Allie	1.10	.80	.35
180 Wes Westrum	1.10	.80	.35
181 Mel Roach	1.10	.80	.35
182 Chuck Harmon	1.10	.80	.35
183 Earle Combs	2.50	1.80	.80
184 Ed Bailey	1.10	.80	.35
185 Chuck Stobbs	1.10	.80	.35
186 Karl Olson	1.10	.80	.35
187 Henry Manush	2.50	1.80	.80
188 Dave Jolly	1.10	.80	.35
189 Floyd Ross	1.10	.80	.35
190 Ray Herbert	1.10	.80	.35
191 John Schofield	1.10	.80	.35
192 Ellis Deal	1.10	.80	.35
193 Johnny Hopp	1.50	1.10	.50
194 Bill Sarni	1.10	.80	.35
195 Bill Consolo	1.10	.80	.35
196 Stanley Jok	1.10	.80	.35
197 Lynwood Rowe	1.50	1.10	.50
198 Carl Sawatski	1.10	.80	.35
199 Glenn Nelson	1.10	.80	.35
200 Larry Jansen	1.10	.80	.35
201 Al Kaline	50.00	38.00	17.00
202 Bob Purkey	1.10	.80	.35
203 Harry Brecheen	1.25	.90	.40
204 Angel Scull	1.10	.80	.35
205 Johnny Sain	2.50	1.80	.80
206 Ray Crone	1.10	.80	.35
207 Tom Oliver	1.10	.80	.35
208 Grady Hatton	1.10	.80	.35
209 Chuck Thompson	1.10	.80	.35
210 Bob Buhl	1.25	.90	.40
211 Don Hoak	1.10	.80	.35
212 Bob Micelotta	1.10	.80	.35
213 Johnny Fitzpatrick	1.10	.80	.35
214 Arnold Portocarrero	1.10	.80	.35
215 Warren McGhee	1.10	.80	.35
216 Al Sima	1.10	.80	.35
217 Paul Schreiber	1.10	.80	.35
218 Fred Marsh	1.10	.80	.35
219 Chuck Kress	1.10	.80	.35
220 Ruben Gomez	1.10	.80	.35
221 Dick Brodowski	1.10	.80	.35
222 Bill Wilson	1.10	.80	.35
223 Joe Haynes	1.10	.80	.35
224 Dick Weik	1.10	.80	.35
225 Don Liddle	1.10	.80	.35
226 Jehosie Heard	1.10	.80	.35
227 Colonel Mills	1.10	.80	.35
228 Gene Hermanski	1.10	.80	.35
229 Robert Talbot	1.10	.80	.35
230 Bob Kuzava	1.10	.80	.35
231 Roy Smalley	1.10	.80	.35
232 Lou Limmer	1.10	.80	.35
233 Augie Galan	1.10	.80	.35
234 Jerry Lynch	1.10	.80	.35
235 Vernon Law	1.25	.90	.40
236 Paul Penson	1.10	.80	.35
237 Dominic Ryba	1.10	.80	.35
238 Al Aber	1.10	.80	.35
239 Bill Skowron	2.00	1.50	.60
240 Sam Mele	1.10	.80	.35
241 Robert Miller	1.10	.80	.35
242 Curt Roberts	1.10	.80	.35
243 Ray Blades	1.10	.80	.35
244 Leroy Wheat	1.10	.80	.35

	MINT	VG-E	F-G
245 Roy Sievers	1.25	.90	.40
246 Howie Fox	1.10	.80	.35
247 Ed Mayo	1.10	.80	.35

	MINT	VG-E	F-G
248 Alphonse Smith	1.10	.80	.35
249 Wilmer Mizell	1.10	.80	.35
250 Ted Williams	45.00	35.00	15.00

1955 TOPPS (210)

2 5/8" X 3 5/8"

The 1955 Topps set features a large bust picture of the player plus a smaller full length insert photo of the same player. The card fronts are oriented horizontally rather than vertically as in Topps three previous issues. Card nos. 175, 186, 203, and 209 were not issued. Card nos. 161—210 are more difficult to obtain.

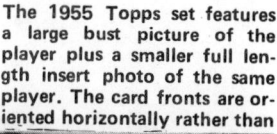

ROBERTO CLEMENTE

	MINT	VG-E	F-G
COMPLETE SET	650.00	500.00	200.00
COMMON PLAYER (1-160)	.65	.45	.20
COMMON PLAYER (161-210)	2.50	1.75	.80
1 Dusty Rhodes	3.50	1.50	.50
2 Ted Williams	30.00	22.50	10.50
3 Art Fowler	1.00	.70	.30
4 Al Kaline	11.00	8.00	3.50
5 Jim Gilliam	2.50	1.80	.80
6 Stan Hack	1.00	.70	.30
7 Jim Hegan	.65	.45	.20
8 Harold Smith	.65	.45	.20
9 Robert Miller	.65	.45	.20
10 Bob Keegan	.65	.45	.20
11 Ferris Fain	1.00	.70	.30
12 Vernon Thies	.65	.45	.20
13 Fred Marsh	.65	.45	.20
14 Jim Finigan	.65	.45	.20
15 Jim Pendleton	.65	.45	.20
16 Roy Sievers	.65	.45	.20
17 Bobby Hofman	.65	.45	.20
18 Russ Kemmerer	.65	.45	.20
19 Billy Herman	2.00	1.50	.60
20 Andy Carey	.65	.45	.20
21 Alex Grammas	.65	.45	.20
22 Bill Skowron	1.50	1.10	.50
23 Jack Parks	.65	.45	.20
24 Hal Newhouser	1.50	1.10	.50
25 John Podres	1.50	1.10	.50
26 Dick Groat	1.50	1.10	.50
27 Bill Gardner	.65	.45	.20
28 Ernie Banks	11.00	8.00	3.50
29 Herman Wehmeier	.65	.45	.20
30 Vic Power	.65	.45	.20
31 Warren Spahn	8.50	6.50	3.00
32 Warren McGhee	.65	.45	.20
33 Tom Qualters	.65	.45	.20
34 Wayne Terwilliger	.65	.45	.20
35 Dave Jolly	.65	.45	.20
36 Leo Kiely	.65	.45	.20
37 Joe Cunningham	.65	.45	.20
38 Bob Turley	1.25	.90	.40
39 Bill Glynn	.65	.45	.20
40 Don Hoak	.65	.45	.20
41 Chuck Stobbs	.65	.45	.20
42 John McCall	.65	.45	.20
43 Harvey Haddix	.65	.45	.20
44 Harold Valentine	.65	.45	.20
45 Hank Sauer	1.00	.70	.30
46 Ted Kazanski	.65	.45	.20
47 Hank Aaron	40.00	30.00	13.00
48 Bob Kennedy	.75	.55	.25
49 J. W. Porter	.65	.45	.20
50 Jackie Robinson	22.00	16.50	7.50
51 Jim Hughes	.65	.45	.20
52 Bill Tremel	.65	.45	.20
53 Bill Taylor	.65	.45	.20
54 Lou Limmer	.65	.45	.20
55 Rip Repulski	.65	.45	.20

	MINT	VG-E	F-G
56 Ray Jablonski	.65	.45	.20
57 Bill O'Dell	.65	.45	.20
58 Jim Rivera	.65	.45	.20
59 Gair Allie	.65	.45	.20
60 Dean Stone	.65	.45	.20
61 Forrest Jacobs	.65	.45	.20
62 Thornton Kipper	.65	.45	.20
63 Joe Collins	.65	.45	.20
64 Gus Triandos	1.00	.70	.30
65 Ray Boone	.65	.45	.20
66 Ron Jackson	.65	.45	.20
67 Wally Moon	1.00	.70	.30
68 Jim Davis	.65	.45	.20
69 Ed Bailey	.65	.45	.20
70 Al Rosen	5.00	3.75	1.75
71 Ruben Gomez	.65	.45	.20
72 Karl Olson	.65	.45	.20
73 Jack Shepard	.65	.45	.20
74 Robert Borkowski	.65	.45	.20
75 Sandy Amoros	.65	.45	.20
76 Howie Pollet	.65	.45	.20
77 Arnold Portocarrero	.65	.45	.20
78 Gordon Jones	.65	.45	.20
79 Clyde Schell	.65	.45	.20
80 Bob Grim	.65	.45	.20
81 Gene Conley	.65	.45	.20
82 Chuck Harmon	.65	.45	.20
83 Tom Brewer	.65	.45	.20
84 Camilo Pascual	1.00	.70	.30
85 Don Mossi	.65	.45	.20
86 Bill Wilson	.65	.45	.20
87 Frank House	.65	.45	.20
88 Bob Skinner	.65	.45	.20
89 Joe Frazier	.65	.45	.20
90 Karl Spooner	.65	.45	.20
91 Milt Bolling	.65	.45	.20
92 Don Zimmer	1.00	.70	.30
93 Steve Bilko	.65	.45	.20
94 Reno Bertoia	.65	.45	.20
95 Preston Ward	.65	.45	.20
96 Chuck Bishop	.65	.45	.20
97 Carlos Paula	.65	.45	.20
98 John Riddle	.65	.45	.20
99 Frank Leja	.65	.45	.20
100 Monte Irvin	4.50	3.50	1.60
101 Johnny Gray	.65	.45	.20
102 Wally Westlake	.65	.45	.20
103 Chuck White	.65	.45	.20
104 Jack Harshman	.65	.45	.20
105 Chuck Diering	.65	.45	.20
106 Frank Sullivan	.65	.45	.20
107 Curt Roberts	.65	.45	.20
108 Al Walker	.65	.45	.20
109 Ed Lopat	2.00	1.50	.60
110 Gus Zernial	.65	.45	.20
111 Bob Milliken	.65	.45	.20
112 Nelson King	.65	.45	.20
113 Harry Brecheen	.65	.45	.20
114 Louis Ortiz	.65	.45	.20

	MINT	VG-E	F-G
115 Ellis Kinder	.65	.45	.20
116 Tom Hurd	.65	.45	.20
117 Mel Roach	.65	.45	.20
118 Bob Purkey	.65	.45	.20
119 Bob Lennon	.65	.45	.20
120 Ted Kluszewski	2.50	1.80	.80
121 Bill Renna	.65	.45	.20
122 Carl Sawatski	.65	.45	.20
123 Sandy Koufax	30.00	22.50	10.50
124 Harmon Killebrew	13.50	10.00	4.50
125 Ken Boyer	3.50	2.50	1.20
126 Dick Hall	.65	.45	.20
127 Dale Long	.65	.45	.20
128 Ted Lepcio	.65	.45	.20
129 Elvin Tappe	.65	.45	.20
130 Ed Smith	.65	.45	.20
131 Grady Hatton	.65	.45	.20
132 Bob Trice	.65	.45	.20
133 Dave Hoskins	.65	.45	.20
134 Joe Jay	.65	.45	.20
135 Johnny O'Brien	.65	.45	.20
136 Vernon Stewart	.65	.45	.20
137 Harry Elliott	.65	.45	.20
138 Ray Herbert	.65	.45	.20
139 Steve Kraly	.65	.45	.20
140 Mel Parnell	.65	.45	.20
141 Tom Wright	.65	.45	.20
142 Gerry Lynch	.65	.45	.20
143 John Schofield	.65	.45	.20
144 John Amalfitano	.65	.45	.20
145 Elmer Valo	.65	.45	.20
146 Dick Donovan	.65	.45	.20
147 Hugh Pepper	.65	.45	.20
148 Hector Brown	.65	.45	.20
149 Ray Crone	.65	.45	.20
150 Michael Higgins	.65	.45	.20
151 Ralph Kress	.65	.45	.20
152 Harry Agganis	1.00	.70	.30
153 "Bud" Podbelian	.65	.45	.20
154 Willie Miranda	.65	.45	.20
155 Eddie Mathews	10.00	7.00	3.00
156 Joe Black	2.00	1.50	.60
157 Robert Miller	.65	.45	.20
158 Tommy Carroll	.65	.45	.20
159 Johnny Schmitz	.65	.45	.20
160 Ray Narleski	.65	.45	.20

	MINT	VG-E	F-G
161 Chuck Tanner	4.00	3.00	1.40
162 Joe Coleman	2.50	1.75	.80
163 Faye Throneberry	2.50	1.75	.80
164 Roberto Clemente	100.00	70.00	30.00
165 Don Johnson	2.50	1.75	.80
166 Hank Bauer	5.00	3.75	1.75
167 Thomas Casagrande	2.50	1.75	.80
168 Duane Pillette	2.50	1.75	.80
169 Bob Oldis	2.50	1.75	.80
170 Jim Pearce (dp)	1.00	.70	.30
171 Dick Brodowski	2.50	1.75	.80
172 Frank Baumholtz(dp)	1.00	.70	.30
173 Johnny Kline	2.50	1.75	.80
174 Rudy Minarcin	2.50	1.75	.80
176 Norbert Zauchin	2.50	1.75	.80
177 Al Robertson	2.50	1.75	.80
178 Bobby Adams	3.00	2.25	1.00
179 Jim Bolger	2.50	1.75	.80
180 Clem Labine	2.50	1.75	.80
181 Roy McMillan	2.50	1.75	.80
182 Humberto Robinson	2.50	1.75	.80
183 Anthony Jacobs	2.50	1.75	.80
184 Harry Perkowski(dp)	1.00	.70	.30
185 Don Ferrarese	2.50	1.75	.80
187 Gil Hodges	25.00	18.50	8.75
188 Charlie Silvera (dp)	1.25	.90	.40
189 Phil Rizzuto	20.00	15.00	6.50
190 Gene Woodling	3.00	2.25	1.00
191 Eddie Stanky	3.00	2.25	1.00
192 Jim Delsing	2.50	1.75	.80
193 Johnny Sain	5.00	3.75	1.75
194 Willie Mays	200.00	130.00	50.00
195 Ed Roebuck	2.50	1.75	.80
196 Gale Wade	2.50	1.75	.80
197 Al Smith	2.50	1.75	.80
198 Yogi Berra	35.00	25.00	10.00
199 Odbert Hamric	2.50	1.75	.80
200 Jackie Jensen	4.00	3.00	1.40
201 Sherman Lollar	2.50	1.75	.80
202 Jim Owens	2.50	1.75	.80
204 Frank Smith	2.50	1.75	.80
205 Gene Freese	2.50	1.75	.80
206 Pete Daley	2.50	1.75	.80
207 Bill Consolo	2.50	1.75	.80
208 Ray Moore	2.50	1.75	.80
210 Duke Snider	90.00	50.00	30.00

1955 TOPPS DOUBLE HEADER (66) 2 1/16" X 4 7/8"

The 1955 Topps doubleheader set contains 66 cards, each featuring two players. Each player is numbered separately. The cards are perforated for folding, and by using the same lower part of the card, a different player appears in the folded position than in the unfolded position. When the cards are placed side by side, a continuous ballpark background is formed. The set is not an insert but a separate Topps issue.

	MINT	VG-E	F-G
COMPLETE SET	1000.00	700.00	300.00
COMMON PLAYER	11.50	8.50	4.00
1-2 Rosen,Diering	15.00	11.00	5.00
3-4 Irvin,Kemmerer	17.00	12.50	6.00
5-6 Kazanski,Jones	11.50	8.50	4.00

		MINT	VG-E	F-G
7-8 Taylor,O'Dell		11.50	8.50	4.00
9-10 Porter,Kipper		11.50	8.50	4.00
11-12 Roberts,Portoc.		11.50	8.50	4.00
13-14 Westlake,House		11.50	8.50	4.00
15-16 Walker,Limmer		11.50	8.50	4.00
17-18 Stone,White		11.50	8.50	4.00

The 1956 Topps series contains a bust picture of the player plus a smaller insert of the player in an action pose. Two unnumbered checklist cards exist and are quite scarce. Team card nos. 11, 72, 85, 90, and 100 exist in three varieties: 1)dated 1955, 2)undated with the team name to the left, and 3)undated with the team name centered.

	MINT	VG-E	F-G
COMPLETE SET	480.00	390.00	160.00
COMMON PLAYERS (1-180)	.55	.40	.15
COMMON PLAYERS (181-260)	.75	.60	.25
COMMON PLAYERS (261-340)	.55	.40	.15
1 William Harridge	4.00	3.00	1.40
2 Warren Giles	2.50	1.80	.80
3 Elmer Valo	.55	.40	.15
4 Carlos Paula	.55	.40	.15
5 Ted Williams	24.00	18.00	8.50
6 Ray Boone	.55	.40	.15
7 Ron Negray	.55	.40	.15
8 Walter Alston	1.25	.90	.40
9 Ruben Gomez	.55	.40	.15
10 Warren Spahn	8.00	6.00	2.50
11A Chicago Cubs	1.50	1.10	.50
11B Chicago Cubs(Dated)	5.00	3.75	1.75
12 Andy Carey	.55	.40	.15
13 Roy Face	.75	.55	.25
14 Ken Boyer	1.50	1.10	.50
15 Ernie Banks	9.00	6.75	3.00
16 Hector Lopez	.55	.40	.15
17 Gene Conley	.55	.40	.15
18 Dick Donovan	.55	.40	.15
19 Chuck Diering	.55	.40	.15
20 Al Kaline	9.00	6.75	3.00
21 Joe Collins	.55	.40	.15
22 Jim Finigan	.55	.40	.15
23 Freddie Marsh	.55	.40	.15
24 Dick Groat	1.00	.70	.30
25 Ted Kluszewski	2.25	1.65	.75
26 Grady Hatton	.55	.40	.15
27 Nelson Burbrink	.55	.40	.15
28 Bobby Hofman	.55	.40	.15
29 Jack Harshman	.55	.40	.15
30 Jackie Robinson	19.00	14.50	6.50
31 Hank Aaron	30.00	22.50	10.50
32 Frank House	.55	.40	.15
33 Roberto Clemente	21.00	15.50	7.00
34 Tom Brewer	.55	.40	.15
35 Al Rosen	4.00	3.00	1.40
36 Rudy Minarcin	.55	.40	.15
37 Alex Grammas	.55	.40	.15
38 Bob Kennedy	.75	.55	.25
39 Don Mossi	.55	.40	.15
40 Bob Turley	1.25	.90	.40
41 Hank Sauer	.75	.55	.25
42 Sandy Amoros	.55	.40	.15
43 Ray Moore	.55	.40	.15
44 "Windy" McCall	.55	.40	.15
45 Gus Zernial	.55	.40	.15
46 Gene Freese	.55	.40	.15
47 Art Fowler	.55	.40	.15
48 Jim Hegan	.55	.40	.15
49 Pedro Ramos	.55	.40	.15
50 "Dusty" Rhodes	.75	.55	.25
51 Ernie Oravetz	.55	.40	.15
52 Bob Grim	.55	.40	.15
53 Arnie Portocarrero	.55	.40	.15
54 Bob Keegan	.55	.40	.15
55 Wally Moon	.75	.55	.25
56 Dale Long	.55	.40	.15
57 Duke Maas	.55	.40	.15
58 Ed Roebuck	.55	.40	.15
59 Jose Santiago	.55	.40	.15
60 Mayo Smith	.55	.40	.15
61 Bill Skowron	1.25	.90	.40
62 Hal Smith	.55	.40	.15
63 Roger Craig	.75	.55	.25
64 Luis Arroyo	.55	.40	.15
65 Johnny O'Brien	.55	.40	.15
66 Bob Speake	.55	.40	.15
67 Vic Power	.55	.40	.15
68 Chuck Stobbs	.55	.40	.15
69 Chuck Tanner	1.00	.70	.30
70 "Jim" Rivera	.55	.40	.15
71 Frank Sullivan	.55	.40	.15
72A Phillies	1.50	1.10	.50
72B Phillies (Dated)	5.00	3.75	1.75
73 Wayne Terwilliger	.55	.40	.15
74 Jim King	.55	.40	.15
75 Roy Sievers	.75	.55	.25
76 Ray Crone	.55	.40	.15
77 Harvey Haddix	.75	.55	.25
78 Herman Wehmeier	.55	.40	.15
79 Sandy Koufax	15.00	11.00	5.00
80 Gus Triandos	.75	.55	.25
81 Wally Westlake	.55	.40	.15
82 Bill Renna	.55	.40	.15
83 Karl Spooner	.55	.40	.15
84 "Babe" Birrer	.55	.40	.15
85A Cleveland Indians	1.50	1.10	.50
85B Indians Team (Dated)	5.00	3.75	1.75
86 Ray Jablonski	.55	.40	.15
87 Dean Stone	.55	.40	.15
88 Johnny Kucks	.55	.40	.15
89 Norm Zauchin	.55	.40	.15
90A Cincinnati Redlegs	1.50	1.10	.50
90B Reds Team (Dated)	5.00	3.75	1.75
91 Gail Harris	.55	.40	.15
92 Bob "Red" Wilson	.55	.40	.15
93 George Susce	.55	.40	.15
94 Ronnie Kline	.55	.40	.15
95A Milwaukee Braves	1.50	1.10	.50
95B Braves Team (Dated)	5.00	3.75	1.75
96 Bill Tremel	.55	.40	.15
97 Jerry Lynch	.55	.40	.15
98 Camilo Pascual	.75	.55	.25
99 Don Zimmer	1.00	.70	.30
100A Baltimore Orioles	1.50	1.10	.50
100B Orioles Team (Dated)	5.00	3.75	1.75
101 Roy Campanella	16.00	12.00	5.50
102 Jim Davis	.55	.40	.15
103 "Willie" Miranda	.55	.40	.15
104 Bob Lennon	.55	.40	.15
105 Al Smith	.55	.40	.15
106 Joe Astroth	.55	.40	.15
107 Ed Mathews	8.50	6.50	3.00
108 Laurin Pepper	.55	.40	.15
109 Enos Slaughter	3.50	2.50	1.20
110 Yogi Berra	13.00	9.50	4.00
111 Boston Red Sox	2.00	1.50	.60
112 Dee Fondy	.55	.40	.15
113 Phil Rizzuto	7.50	5.75	2.50
114 Jim Owens	.55	.40	.15
115 Jackie Jensen	1.25	.90	.40
116 Eddie O'Brien	.55	.40	.15
117 Virgil Trucks	.55	.40	.15

1956 TOPPS (CONTINUED)

	MINT	VG-E	F-G
118 Nelson Fox	2.00	1.50	.60
119 Larry Jackson	.55	.40	.15
120 Richie Ashburn	2.00	1.50	.60
121 Pittsburgh Pirates	1.50	1.10	.50
122 Willard Nixon	.55	.40	.15
123 Roy McMillan	.55	.40	.15
124 Don Kaiser	.55	.40	.15
125 "Minnie" Minoso	2.00	1.50	.60
126 Jim Brady	.55	.40	.15
127 Willie Jones	.55	.40	.15
128 Eddie Yost	.55	.40	.15
129 "Jake" Martin	.55	.40	.15
130 Willie Mays	32.00	24.00	11.00
131 Bob Roselli	.55	.40	.15
132 Bobby Avila	.55	.40	.15
133 Ray Narleski	.55	.40	.15
134 Cardinals	1.50	1.10	.50
135 Mickey Mantle	65.00	48.00	22.00
136 Johnny Logan	.55	.40	.15
137 Al Silvera	.55	.40	.15
138 Johnny Antonelli	.75	.55	.25
139 Tommy Carroll	.55	.40	.15
140 Herb Score	1.50	1.10	.50
141 Joe Frazier	.55	.40	.15
142 Gene Baker	.55	.40	.15
143 Jim Piersall	1.25	.90	.40
144 Leroy Powell	.55	.40	.15
145 Gil Hodges	8.00	6.00	2.50
146 Washington Nationals	1.50	1.10	.50
147 Earl Torgeson	.55	.40	.15
148 Al Dark	.75	.55	.25
149 "Dixie"Howell	.55	.40	.15
150 "Duke" Snider	12.50	9.00	4.00
151 "Spook" Jacobs	.55	.40	.15
152 Billy Hoeft	.55	.40	.15
153 Frank Thomas	.55	.40	.15
154 David Pope	.55	.40	.15
155 Harvey Kuenn	1.25	.90	.40
156 Wes Westrum	.55	.40	.15
157 Dick Brodowski	.55	.40	.15
158 Wally Post	.55	.40	.15
159 Clint Courtney	.55	.40	.15
160 Billy Pierce	1.25	.90	.40
161 Joe DeMaestri	.55	.40	.15
162 Dave "Gus" Bell	.55	.40	.15
163 Gene Woodling	.75	.55	.25
164 Harmon Killebrew	6.00	4.50	2.00
165 "Red" Schoendienst	1.50	1.10	.50
166 Brooklyn Dodgers	4.00	3.00	1.40
167 Harry Dorish	.55	.40	.15

	MINT	VG-E	F-G
168 Sammy White	.55	.40	.15
169 Bob Nelson	.55	.40	.15
170 Bill Virdon	2.00	1.50	.60
171 Jim Wilson	.55	.40	.15
172 Frank Torre	.55	.40	.15
173 Johnny Podres	1.50	1.10	.50
174 Glen Gorbous	.55	.40	.15
175 Del Crandall	.75	.55	.25
176 Alex Kellner	.55	.40	.15
177 Hank Bauer	1.50	1.10	.50
178 Joe Black	.75	.55	.25
179 Harry Chiti	.55	.40	.15
180 Robin Roberts	6.50	5.00	2.25
181 "Billy" Martin	6.50	5.00	2.25
182 Paul Minner	.75	.60	.25
183 Stan Lopata	.75	.60	.25
184 Don Bessent	.75	.60	.25
185 Bill Bruton	.75	.60	.25
186 Ron Jackson	.75	.60	.25
187 Early Wynn	6.00	4.50	2.00
188 Chicago White Sox	2.00	1.50	.60
189 Ned Garver	.75	.55	.25
190 Carl Furillo	2.50	1.80	.80
191 Frank Lary	.75	.60	.25
192 "Smokey" Burgess	.75	.60	.25
193 Wilmer Mizell	.75	.60	.25
194 Monte Irvin	4.00	3.00	1.40
195 George Kell	1.50	1.10	.50
196 Tom Poholsky	.75	.60	.25
197 Granny Hamner	.75	.60	.25
198 Ed Fitzgerald	.75	.60	.25
199 Hank Thompson	.75	.60	.25
200 Bob Feller	13.00	9.50	4.00
201 Rip Repulski	.75	.60	.25
202 Jim Hearn	.75	.60	.25
203 Bill Tuttle	.75	.60	.25
204 Art Swanson	.75	.60	.25
205 "Whitey" Lockman	.75	.60	.25
206 Erv Palica	.75	.60	.25
207 Jim Small	.75	.60	.25
208 Elston Howard	4.00	3.00	1.40
209 Max Surkont	.75	.60	.25
210 Mike Garcia	.75	.60	.25
211 Murry Dickson	.75	.60	.25
211 Johnny Temple	.75	.60	.25
213 Detroit Tigers	2.00	1.50	.60
214 Bob Rush	.75	.60	.25
215 Tommy Byrne	.75	.60	.25
216 Jerry Schoonmaker	.75	.60	.25
217 Billy Klaus	.75	.60	.25
218 Joe Nuxhall	.75	.60	.25

JAPANESE BASEBALL CARD

Powell

1970 CARL ALDANA ORIOLES SET

1956 TOPPS (CONTINUED)

	MINT	VG-E	F-G.
219 Lew Burdette	1.00	.70	.30
220 Del Ennis	.75	.60	.25
221 Bob Friend	.75	.60	.25
222 Dave Philley	.75	.60	.25
223 Randy Jackson	.75	.60	.25
224 "Bud" Podbelian	.75	.60	.25
225 Gil McDougald	1.25	.90	.40
226 New York Giants	3.00	2.25	1.00
227 Russ Meyer	.75	.60	.25
228 "Mickey" Vernon	.75	.60	.25
229 Harry Brecheen	.75	.60	.25
230 "Chico" Carrasquel	.75	.60	.25
231 Bob Hale	.75	.60	.25
232 "Toby" Atwell	.75	.60	.25
233 Carl Erskine	2.00	1.50	.60
234 "Pete" Runnels	.75	.60	.25
235 Don Newcombe	3.50	2.50	1.20
236 Athletics	1.50	1.10	.50
237 Jose Valdivielso	.75	.60	.25
238 Walt Dropo	.75	.60	.25
239 Harry Simpson	.75	.60	.25
240 "Whitey" Ford	11.00	8.00	3.50
241 Don Mueller	.75	.60	.25
242 Hershell Freeman	.75	.60	.25
243 Sherm Lollar	.75	.60	.25
244 Bob Buhl	.75	.60	.25
245 Billy Goodman	.75	.60	.25
246 Tom Gorman	.75	.60	.25
247 Bill Sarni	.75	.60	.25
248 "Bob" Porterfield	.75	.60	.25
249 Johnny Klippstein	.75	.60	.25
250 Larry Doby	2.00	1.50	.60
251 New York Yankees	6.00	4.50	2.00
252 Vernon Law	.75	.60	.25
253 Irv Noren	.75	.60	.25
254 George Crowe	.75	.60	.25
255 Bob Lemon	6.50	5.00	2.25
256 Tom Hurd	.75	.60	.25
257 Bobby Thomson	2.00	1.50	.60
258 Art Ditmar	.75	.60	.25
259 Sam Jones	.75	.60	.25
260 "Peewee" Reese	8.00	6.00	2.50
261 Bobby Shantz	1.00	.70	.30
262 Howie Pollet	.55	.40	.15
263 Bob Miller	.55	.40	.15
264 Ray Monzant	.55	.40	.15
265 Sandy Consuegra	.55	.40	.15
266 Don Ferrarese	.55	.40	.15
267 Bob Nieman	.55	.40	.15
268 Dale Mitchell	.55	.40	.15
269 Jack Meyer	.55	.40	.15
270 Billy Loes	.55	.40	.15
271 Foster Castleman	.55	.40	.15
272 Danny O'Connell	.55	.40	.15
273 Walker Cooper	.55	.40	.15
274 Frank Baumholtz	.55	.40	.15
275 Jim Greengrass	.55	.40	.15
276 George Zuverink	.55	.40	.15
277 Daryl Spencer	.55	.40	.15
278 Chet Nichols	.55	.40	.15
279 Johnny Groth	.55	.40	.15
280 Jim Gilliam	2.00	1.50	.60
281 Art Houtteman	.55	.40	.15
282 Warren Hacker	.55	.40	.15
283 Hal Smith	.55	.40	.15
284 "Ike" Delock	.55	.40	.15
285 Eddie Miksis	.55	.40	.15
286 Bill Wight	.55	.40	.15
287 Bobby Adams	.55	.40	.15
288 Bob Cerv	.55	.40	.15
289 Hal Jeffcoat	.55	.40	.15
290 Curt Simmons	.75	.55	.25
291 Frank Kellert	.55	.40	.15
292 Luis Aparicio	3.00	2.25	1.00
293 Stu Miller	.55	.40	.15
294 Ernie Johnson	.55	.40	.15
295 Clem Labine	.55	.40	.15
296 Andy Seminick	.55	.40	.15
297 Bob Skinner	.55	.40	.15
298 Johnny Schmitz	.55	.40	.15
299 Charley Neal	.55	.40	.15
300 Vic Wertz	.75	.55	.25
301 Marv Grissom	.55	.40	.15
302 Eddie Robinson	.55	.40	.15
303 Jim Dyck	.55	.40	.15
304 Frank Malzone	.55	.40	.15
305 Brooks Lawrence	.55	.40	.15
306 Curt Roberts	.55	.40	.15
307 Hoyt Wilhelm	2.50	1.80	.80
308 Chuck Harmon	.55	.40	.15
309 Don Blasingame	.55	.40	.15
310 Steve Gromek	.55	.40	.15
311 Hal Naragon	.55	.40	.15
312 Andy Pafko	.55	.40	.15
313 Gene Stephens	.55	.40	.15
314 Hobie Landrith	.55	.40	.15
315 Milt Bolling	.55	.40	.15
316 Jerry Coleman	.75	.55	.25
317 Al Aber	.55	.40	.15
318 Fred Hatfield	.55	.40	.15
319 John Crimian	.55	.40	.15
320 Joe Adcock	.75	.55	.25
321 Jim Konstanty	.75	.55	.25
322 Karl Olson	.55	.40	.15
323 Willard Schmidt	.55	.40	.15
324 "Rocky" Bridges	.55	.40	.15
325 Don Liddle	.55	.40	.15
326 Connie Johnson	.55	.40	.15
327 Bob Wiesler	.55	.40	.15
328 Preston Ward	.55	.40	.15
329 Lou Berberet	.55	.40	.15
330 Jim Busby	.55	.40	.15
331 Dick Hall	.55	.40	.15
332 Don Larsen	2.50	1.80	.80
333 "Rube" Walker	.55	.40	.15
334 Bob Miller	.55	.40	.15
335 Don Hoak	.55	.40	.15
336 Ellis Kinder	.55	.40	.15
337 Bobby Morgan	.55	.40	.15
338 Jim Delsing	.55	.40	.15
339 Rance Pless	.55	.40	.15
340 "Mickey" McDermott	.75	.50	.20
Checklist 1/3	10.00	7.00	3.00
Checklist 2/4	10.00	7.00	3.00

UNCLASSIFIED RAWLINGS CARD

1957 TOPPS (407)

2 1/2" X 3 1/2"

Koufax

BROOKLYN DODGERS

The 1957 Topps set marks the first year of the now standard 3½" x 2½" card Card nos. 265-352 are much scarcer than the other cards in the set. Four unnumbered checklist cards were also issued and are quite scarce.

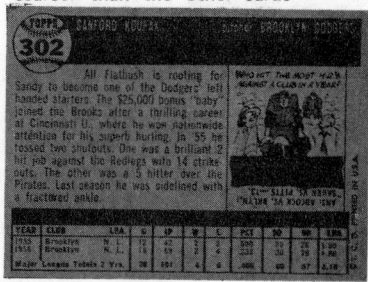

	MINT	VG-E	F-G
COMPLETE SET	700.00	525.00	200.00
COMMON PLAYER (1-264)	.50	.37	.16
COMMON PLAYER (265-352)	2.50	1.75	.80
COMMON PLAYER (353-407)	.60	.45	.20
1 *Ted Williams*	27.00	20.00	8.00
2 *Yogi Berra*	12.00	8.75	4.00
3 Dale Long	.50	.37	.16
4 Johnny Logan	.50	.37	.16
5 Sal Maglie	.80	.60	.25
6 Hector Lopez	.50	.37	.16
7 Luis Aparicio	1.50	1.10	.50
8 Don Mossi	.50	.37	.16
9 Johnny Temple	.50	.37	.16
10 *Willie Mays*	28.00	21.00	10.00
11 George Zuverink	.50	.37	.16
12 Dick Groat	.75	.55	.25
13 Wally Burnette	.50	.37	.16
14 Bob Nieman	.50	.37	.16
15 Robin Roberts	5.00	3.75	1.75
16 Walt Moryn	.50	.37	.16
17 W. Gardner	.50	.37	.16
18 Don Drysdale	9.00	6.75	3.00
19 Bob Wilson	.50	.37	.16
20 *Hank Aaron*	30.00	22.50	10.50
21 Frank Sullivan	.50	.37	.16
22 Jerry Snyder	.50	.37	.16
23 Sherm Lollar	.50	.37	.16
24 Bill Mazeroski	1.00	.70	.30
25 Whitey Ford	6.00	4.50	2.00
26 Bob Boyd	.50	.37	.16
27 Ted Kazanski	.50	.37	.16
28 Gene Conley	.50	.37	.16
29 Whitey Herzog	.75	.55	.25
30 "Peewee" Reese	6.00	4.50	2.00
31 Ron Northey	.50	.37	.16
32 Hershell Freeman	.50	.37	.16
33 Jim Small	.50	.37	.16
34 Tom Sturdivant	.50	.37	.16
35 Frank Robinson	16.00	12.00	5.50
36 Bob Grim	.50	.37	.16
37 Frank Torre	.50	.37	.16
38 Nelson Fox	2.00	1.50	.60
39 Al Worthington	.50	.37	.16
40 Early Wynn	4.00	3.00	1.50
41 H. W. Smith	.50	.37	.16
42 Dee Fondy	.50	.37	.16
43 Connie Johnson	.50	.37	.16
44 Joe DeMaestri	.50	.37	.16
45 Carl Furillo	2.00	1.50	.60
46 Robert J. Miller	.50	.37	.16
47 Don Blasingame	.50	.37	.16
48 Bill Bruton	.50	.37	.16
49 Daryl Spencer	.50	.37	.16
50 Herb Score	.75	.55	.25
51 Clint Courtney	.50	.37	.16
52 Lee Walls	.50	.37	.16
53 Clem Labine	.50	.37	.16
54 Elmer Valo	.50	.37	.16
55 Ernie Banks	8.00	6.00	2.50
56 Dave Sisler	.50	.37	.16
57 Jim Lemon	.50	.37	.16
58 Ruben Gomez	.50	.37	.16
59 Dick Williams	.75	.55	.25

	MINT	VG-E	F-G
60 Billy Hoeft	.50	.37	.16
61 James Rhodes	.75	.55	.25
62 Billy Martin	5.50	4.25	2.00
63 Ike Delock	.50	.37	.16
64 Pete Runnels	.50	.37	.16
65 Wally Moon	.75	.55	.25
66 Brooks Lawrence	.50	.37	.16
67 Chico Carrasquel	.50	.37	.16
68 Ray Crone	.50	.37	.16
69 Roy McMillan	.50	.37	.16
70 Richie Ashburn	1.50	1.10	.50
71 Murry Dickson	.50	.37	.16
72 Bill Tuttle	.50	.37	.16
73 George Crowe	.50	.37	.16
74 Vito Valentinetti	.50	.37	.16
75 Jim Piersall	1.00	.70	.30
76 *Roberto Clemente*	16.00	12.00	5.50
77 Paul Foytack	.50	.37	.16
78 Vic Wertz	.50	.37	.16
79 Lindy McDaniel	.50	.37	.16
80 Gil Hodges	6.50	5.00	2.25
81 Herman Wehmeier	.50	.37	.16
82 Elston Howard	2.00	1.50	.60
83 L. Skizas	.50	.37	.16
84 Moe Drabowsky	.50	.37	.16
85 Larry Doby	1.50	1.10	.50
86 Bill Sarni	.50	.37	.16
87 Tom Gorman	.50	.37	.16
88 Harvey Kuenn	1.00	.70	.30
89 Roy Sievers	.75	.55	.25
90 Warren Spahn	7.00	5.25	2.50
91 Mack Burk	.50	.37	.16
92 Mickey Vernon	.75	.55	.25
93 Hal Jeffcoat	.50	.37	.16
94 Bobby Del Greco	.50	.37	.16
95 *Mickey Mantle*	55.00	40.00	15.00
96 Hank Aguirre	.50	.37	.16
97 New York Yankees	3.00	2.25	1.00
98 Alvin Dark	.75	.55	.25
99 Bob Keegan	.50	.37	.16
100 Giles & Harridge	1.50	1.10	.50
101 Chuck Stobbs	.50	.37	.16
102 Ray Boone	.50	.37	.16
103 Joe Nuxhall	.75	.55	.25
104 Hank Foiles	.50	.37	.16
105 Johnny Antonelli	.75	.55	.25
106 Ray Moore	.50	.37	.16
107 Jim Rivera	.50	.37	.16
108 Tommy Byrne	.50	.37	.16
109 Hank Thompson	.50	.37	.16
110 Bill Virdon	1.25	.90	.40
111 H. R. Smith	.50	.37	.16
112 Tom Brewer	.50	.37	.16
113 Wilmer Mizell	.50	.37	.16
114 Milwaukee Braves	1.25	.90	.40
115 Jim Gilliam	1.50	1.10	.50
116 Mike Fornieles	.50	.37	.16
117 Joe Adcock	.75	.55	.25
118 Bob Porterfield	.50	.37	.16
119 Stan Lopata	.50	.37	.16
120 Bob Lemon	5.00	3.75	1.75
121 Cletis Boyer	.50	.37	.16
122 Ken Boyer	1.25	.90	.40
123 S. Ridzik	.50	.37	.16

	MINT	VG-E	F-G		MINT	VG-E	F-G
124 Dave Philley	.50	.37	.16	217 Gene Stephens	.50	.37	.16
125 Al Kaline	8.00	6.00	2.50	218 Ray Jablonski	.50	.37	.16
126 Bob Wiesler	.50	.37	.16	219 Tom Acker	.50	.37	.16
127 Bob Buhl	.50	.37	.16	220 Jackie Jensen	1.00	.70	.30
128 Ed Bailey	.50	.37	.16	221 Dixie Howell	.50	.37	.16
129 Saul Rogovin	.50	.37	.16	222 Alex Grammas	.50	.37	.16
130 Don Newcombe	2.00	1.50	.60	223 Frank House	.50	.37	.16
131 Milt Bolling	.50	.37	.16	224 Marv Blaylock	.50	.37	.16
132 Art Ditmar	.50	.37	.16	225 Hank Simpson	.50	.37	.16
133 Del Crandall	.75	.55	.25	226 Preston Ward	.50	.37	.16
134 Don Kaiser	.50	.37	.16	227 Gerry Staley	.50	.37	.16
135 Bill Skowron	1.25	.90	.40	228 "Smokey" Burgess	.75	.55	.25
136 Jim Hegan	.50	.37	.16	229 George Susce	.50	.37	.16
137 Bob Rush	.50	.37	.16	230 George Kell	1.00	.70	.30
138 Minnie Minoso	1.50	1.10	.50	231 Solly Hemus	.50	.37	.16
139 Lou Kretlow	.50	.37	.16	232 Whitey Lockman	.50	.37	.16
140 Frank Thomas	.50	.37	.16	233 Art Fowler	.50	.37	.16
141 Al Aber	.50	.37	.16	234 Dick Cole	.50	.37	.16
142 Charley Thompson	.50	.37	.16	235 Tom Poholsky	.50	.37	.16
143 Andy Pafko	.50	.37	.16	236 Moe Ginsberg	.50	.37	.16
144 Ray Narleski	.50	.37	.16	237 Foster Castleman	.50	.37	.16
145 Al Smith	.50	.37	.16	238 Eddie Robinson	.50	.37	.16
146 Don Ferrarese	.50	.37	.16	239 Tom Morgan	.50	.37	.16
147 Al Walker	.50	.37	.16	240 Hank Bauer	1.25	.90	.40
148 Don Mueller	.50	.37	.16	241 Joe Lonnett	.50	.37	.16
149 Bob Kennedy	.75	.55	.25	242 Charlie Neal	.50	.37	.16
150 Bob Friend	.75	.55	.25	243 St. Louis Cardinals	1.00	.70	.30
151 Willie Miranda	.50	.37	.16	244 Billy Loes	.50	.37	.16
152 Jack Harshman	.50	.37	.16	245 Rip Repulski	.50	.37	.16
153 Karl Olson	.50	.37	.16	246 Jose Valdivielso	.50	.37	.16
154 "Red" Schoendienst	1.00	.70	.30	247 Turk Lown	.50	.37	.16
155 Jim Brosnan	.50	.37	.16	248 Jim Finigan	.50	.37	.16
156 Gus Triandos	.50	.37	.16	249 Dave Pope	.50	.37	.16
157 Wally Post	.50	.37	.16	250 Ed Mathews	7.00	5.25	2.50
158 Curt Simmons	.75	.55	.25	251 Baltimore Orioles	1.00	.70	.30
159 Solly Drake	.50	.37	.16	252 Carl Erskine	1.25	.90	.40
160 Billy Pierce	1.25	.90	.40	253 Gus Zernial	.50	.37	.16
161 Pittsburgh Pirates	.80	.60	.25	254 Ron Negray	.50	.37	.16
162 Jack Meyer	.50	.37	.16	255 Charlie Silvera	.50	.37	.16
163 Sammy White	.50	.37	.16	256 Ron Kline	.50	.37	.16
164 Tommy Carroll	.50	.37	.16	257 Walt Dropo	.50	.37	.16
165 Ted Kluszewski	1.50	1.10	.50	258 Steve Gromek	.50	.37	.16
166 Elroy Face	.75	.55	.25	259 Eddie O'Brien	.50	.37	.16
167 Vic Power	.50	.37	.16	260 Del Ennis	.50	.37	.16
168 Frank Lary	.50	.37	.16	261 Bob Chakales	.50	.37	.16
169 Herb Plews	.50	.37	.16	262 Bobby Thomson	1.25	.90	.40
170 Duke Snider	10.00	7.00	3.00	263 George Strickland	.50	.37	.16
171 Boston Red Sox	1.00	.70	.30	264 Bob Turley	1.25	.90	.40
172 Gene Woodling	.75	.55	.25	265 Harvey Haddix	3.00	2.25	1.00
173 Roger Craig	.75	.55	.25	266 K. Kuhn	2.50	1.75	.80
174 Willie Jones	.50	.37	.16	267 D. Kravitz	2.50	1.75	.80
175 Don Larsen	1.50	1.10	.50	268 Joe Collum	2.50	1.75	.80
176 Gene Baker	.75	.55	.25	269 Bob Cerv	2.50	1.75	.80
177 Eddie Yost	.50	.37	.16	270 Washington Senators	4.00	3.00	1.40
178 Don Bessent	.50	.37	.16	271 Danny O'Connell	2.50	1.75	.80
179 Ernie Oravetz	.50	.37	.16	272 Bobby Shantz	5.00	3.75	1.75
180 Dave Bell	.50	.37	.16	273 Jim Davis	2.50	1.75	.80
181 Dick Donovan	.50	.37	.16	274 Don Hoak	2.50	1.75	.80
182 Hobie Landrith	.50	.37	.16	275 Cleveland Indians	4.00	3.00	1.40
183 Chicago Cubs	.80	.60	.25	276 Jim Pyburn	2.50	1.75	.80
184 Tito Francona	.50	.37	.16	277 Johnny Podres	7.00	5.25	2.50
185 Johnny Kucks	.50	.37	.16	278 Fred Hatfield	2.50	1.75	.80
186 Jim King	.50	.37	.16	279 R. Thurman	2.50	1.75	.80
187 Virgil Trucks	.50	.37	.16	280 Alex Kellner	2.50	1.75	.80
188 Felix Mantilla	.50	.37	.16	281 Gail Harris	2.50	1.75	.80
189 Willard Nixon	.50	.37	.16	282 Jack Dittmar	2.50	1.75	.80
190 Randy Jackson	.50	.37	.16	283 Wes Covington	2.50	1.75	.80
191 Joe Margoneri	.50	.37	.16	284 Don Zimmer	5.00	3.75	1.75
192 Gerry Coleman	.75	.55	.25	285 Ned Garver	2.50	1.75	.80
193 Del Rice	.50	.37	.16	286 Bobby Richardson	8.00	6.00	2.50
194 Hal Brown	.50	.37	.16	287 Sam Jones	2.50	1.75	.80
195 Bobby Avila	.50	.37	.16	288 Ted Lepcio	2.50	1.75	.80
196 Larry Jackson	.50	.37	.16	289 Jim Bolger	2.50	1.75	.80
197 Hank Sauer	.75	.55	.25	290 Andy Carey	2.50	1.75	.80
198 Detroit Tigers	1.00	.70	.30	291 Jim McCall	2.50	1.75	.80
199 Vern Law	.75	.55	.25	292 W. Klaus	2.50	1.75	.80
200 Gil McDougald	1.00	.70	.30	293 Tom Abernathy	2.50	1.75	.80
201 Sandy Amoros	.50	.37	.16	294 Rocky Bridges	2.50	1.75	.80
202 Dick Gernert	.50	.37	.16	295 Joe Collins	2.50	1.75	.80
203 Hoyt Wilhelm	2.00	1.50	.60	296 Johnny Klippstein	2.50	1.75	.80
204 Athletics	.80	.60	.25	297 Jim Crimian	2.50	1.75	.80
205 Charlie Maxwell	.50	.37	.16	298 Irv Noren	2.50	1.75	.80
206 Willard Schmidt	.50	.37	.16	299 Chuck Harmon	2.50	1.75	.80
207 Gordon Hunter	.50	.37	.16	300 Mike Garcia	3.00	2.25	1.00
208 Lou Burdette	1.00	.70	.30	301 S. Esposito	2.50	1.75	.80
209 Bob Skinner	.50	.37	.16	302 Sandy Koufax	85.00	60.00	25.00
210 Roy Campanella	13.00	9.50	4.00	303 Billy Goodman	2.50	1.75	.80
211 Camilo Pascual	.50	.37	.16	304 J. Cunningham	2.50	1.75	.80
212 Rocco Colavito	3.00	2.25	1.00	305 H. Fernandez	2.50	1.75	.80
213 Les Moss	.50	.37	.16	306 Don Johnson	2.50	1.75	.80
214 Phillies	1.00	.70	.30	307 J. D. Phillips	2.50	1.75	.80
215 Enos Slaughter	2.00	1.50	.60	308 Richard Hall	2.50	1.75	.80
216 Marv Grissom	.50	.37	.16	309 Jim Busby	2.50	1.75	.80
				310 Max Surkont	2.50	1.75	.80

1957 TOPPS (CONTINUED)

	MINT	VG-E	F-G
311 A. Pilarcik	2.50	1.75	.80
312 Tony Kubek	11.00	8.00	3.50
313 Mel Parnell	2.50	1.75	.80
314 Ed Bouchee	2.50	1.75	.80
315 Lou Berberet	2.50	1.75	.80
316 W. O'Dell	2.50	1.75	.80
317 New York Giants	8.00	6.00	2.50
318 Mickey McDermott	2.50	1.75	.80
319 Gino Cimoli	2.50	1.75	.80
320 N. Chrisley	2.50	1.75	.80
321 J. Murff	2.50	1.75	.80
322 Cincinnati Redlegs	10.00	7.00	3.00
323 Wes Westrum	2.50	1.75	.80
324 Brooklyn Dodgers	13.50	10.00	4.50
325 Frank Bolling	2.50	1.75	.80
326 P. Ramos	2.50	1.75	.80
327 Jim Pendleton	2.50	1.75	.80
328 Brooks Robinson	85.00	60.00	25.00
329 Chicago white Sox	5.00	3.75	1.75
330 Jim Wilson	2.50	1.75	.80
331 Ray Katt	2.50	1.75	.80
332 R. Bowman	2.50	1.75	.80
333 Ernie Johnson	2.50	1.75	.80
334 G. Schoonmaker	2.50	1.75	.80
335 Granny Hamner	2.50	1.75	.80
336 H. Sullivan	3.00	2.25	1.00
337 R. Valdes	2.50	1.75	.80
338 Jim Bunning	9.00	6.75	3.00
339 Bob Speake	2.50	1.75	.80
340 W. Wight	2.50	1.75	.80
341 D. Gross	2.50	1.75	.80
342 Gene Mauch	6.00	4.50	2.00
343 Taylor Phillips	2.50	1.75	.80
344 Paul LaPalme	2.50	1.75	.80
345 P. Smith	2.50	1.75	.80
346 Dick Littlefield	2.50	1.75	.80
347 Hal Naragon	2.50	1.75	.80
348 Jim Hearn	2.50	1.75	.80
349 N. King	2.50	1.75	.80
350 Eddie Miksis	2.50	1.75	.80
351 D. Hillman	2.50	1.75	.80
352 Ellis Kinder	2.50	1.75	.80
353 Cal Neeman	.60	.45	.20
354 W. Coleman	.60	.45	.20
355 Frank Malzone	.60	.45	.20
356 Faye Throneberry	.60	.45	.20
357 Earl Torgeson	.60	.45	.20
358 Gerry Lynch	.60	.45	.20
359 Tom Cheney	.60	.45	.20
360 Johnny Groth	.60	.45	.20

	MINT	VG-E	F-G
361 C. Barclay	.60	.45	.20
362 R. Mejias	.60	.45	.20
363 Eddie Kasko	.60	.45	.20
364 C. McLish	.60	.45	.20
365 O. Virgil	.60	.45	.20
366 Ken Lehman	.60	.45	.20
367 Ed Fitzgerald	.60	.45	.20
368 Bob Purkey	.60	.45	.20
369 M. Graff	.60	.45	.20
370 Warren Hacker	.60	.45	.20
371 Bob Lennon	.60	.45	.20
372 N. Zauchin	.60	.45	.20
373 T. P. Whisenant	.60	.45	.20
374 D. Cardwell	.60	.45	.20
375 J. Landis	.60	.45	.20
376 D. Elston	.60	.45	.20
377 A. Rodgers	.60	.45	.20
378 B. E. Singleton	.60	.45	.20
379 D. Lee	.60	.45	.20
380 Walker Cooper	.60	.45	.20
381 Dean Stone	.60	.45	.20
382 Jim Brideweser	.60	.45	.20
383 J. Pizarro	.60	.45	.20
384 B. G. Smith	.60	.45	.20
385 Art Houtteman	.60	.45	.20
386 L. Luttrell	.60	.45	.20
387 Jack Sanford	.60	.45	.20
388 P. Daley	.60	.45	.20
389 Dave Jolly	.60	.45	.20
390 R. Bertoia	.60	.45	.20
391 R. Terry	.75	.55	.25
392 Chuck Tanner	1.00	.70	.30
393 R. Sanchez	.60	.45	.20
394 Luis Arroyo	.60	.45	.20
395 J. M. Phillips	.60	.45	.20
396 K. Wise	.60	.45	.20
397 R. Smalley	.60	.45	.20
398 A. Cicotte	.60	.45	.20
399 Bill Consolo	.60	.45	.20
400 Dodgers' Sluggers	10.00	7.00	3.00
401 E. Battey	.60	.45	.20
402 J. Pisani	.60	.45	.20
403 R. Hyde	.60	.45	.20
404 H. Anderson	.60	.45	.20
405 D. Maas	.60	.45	.20
406 R. Hale	.60	.45	.20
407 Berra-Mantle	13.00	9.50	4.00
Checklist 1-2	5.00	3.75	1.75
Checklist 2-3	10.00	7.00	3.00
Checklist 3-4	10.00	7.00	3.00
Checklist 4-5	10.00	7.00	3.00

1958 TOPPS (495)

2 1/2'' X 3 1/2''

The 1958 Topps set cont Topps first use of All-player cards chosen fro national publication. (numbers 475-495 are S Magazine All-Star selecti Card number 145 was issued. Cards with ye lettering are designated (YL) or (YT) in the check depending on whether player's name or his t name is printed yellow rather than the n common white letter Team cards 377, 397, 428 were issued both v alphabetical checklist b and numerical checklist ba

	MINT	VG-E	F-G
COMPLETE SET	400.00	300.00	140.00
COMMON PLAYER	.35	.25	.10

	MINT	VG-E	F-G		MINT	VG-E	F-G
1 Ted Williams	25.00	15.00	6.00	24A Hobie Landrith	.35	.25	.10
2A Bob Lemon	4.25	3.25	1.50	24B Hobie Landrith(YL)	5.00	3.75	1.75
2B Bob Lemon(YT)	10.00	7.00	3.00	25 Don Drysdale	4.50	3.50	1.60
3 Alex Kellner	.35	.25	.10	26 Ron Jackson	.35	.25	.10
4 Hank Foiles	.35	.25	.10	27 Bud Freeman	.35	.25	.10
5 Willie Mays	23.00	17.00	8.00	28 Jim Busby	.35	.25	.10
6 George Zuverink	.35	.25	.10	29 Ted Lepcio	.35	.25	.10
7 Dale Long	.35	.25	.10	30A Hank Aaron	23.00	17.00	8.00
8A Eddie Kasko	.35	.25	.10	30B Hank Aaron(YL)	50.00	38.00	17.00
8B Eddie Kasko(YL)	5.00	3.75	1.75	31 Tex Clevenger	.35	.25	.10
9 Hank Bauer	1.00	.70	.30	32A J.W. Porter	.35	.25	.10
10 Lou Burdette	1.00	.70	.30	32B J.W. Porter(YL)	5.00	3.75	1.75
11A Jim Rivera	.35	.25	.10	33A Cal Neeman	.35	.25	.10
11B Jim Rivera (YT)	3.00	2.25	1.00	33B Cal Neeman(YT)	3.00	2.25	1.00
12 George Crowe	.35	.25	.10	34 Bob Thurman	.35	.25	.10
13A Billy Hoeft	.35	.25	.10	35A Don Mossi	.35	.25	.10
13B Billy Hoeft(YL)	5.00	3.75	1.75	35B Don Mossi(YT)	3.00	2.25	1.00
14 Rip Repulski	.35	.25	.10	36 Ted Kazanski	.35	.25	.10
15 Jim Lemon	.35	.25	.10	37 Mike McCormick	.35	.25	.10
16 Charley Neal	.35	.25	.10	38 Dick Gernert	.35	.25	.10
17 Felix Mantilla	.35	.25	.10	39 Bob Martyn	.35	.25	.10
18 Frank Sullivan	.35	.25	.10	40 George Kell	.75	.55	.25
19 New York Giants	1.00	.70	.30	41 Dave Hillman	.35	.25	.10
20A Gil McDougald	1.00	.70	.30	42 John Roseboro	.60	.45	.20
20B Gil McDougald(YL)	8.00	6.00	2.50	43 Sal Maglie	.75	.55	.25
21 Curt Barclay	.35	.25	.10	44 Washington Senators	.60	.45	.20
22 Hal Naragon	.35	.25	.10	45 Dick Groat	.60	.45	.20
23A Bill Tuttle	.35	.25	.10	46A Lou Sleater	.35	.25	.10
23B Bill Tuttle(YL)	5.00	3.75	1.75	46B Lou Sleater(YL)	5.00	3.75	1.75

1957 TOPPS BASEBALL CHECKLISTS

	MINT	VG-E	F-G
47 Roger Maris	7.00	5.25	2.50
48 Chuck Harmon	.35	.25	.10
49 Smokey Burgess	.50	.40	.18
50A Billy Pierce	1.00	.70	.30
50B Billy Pierce(YT)	5.00	3.75	1.75
51 Del Rice	.35	.25	.10
52A Bob Clemente	13.00	9.50	4.00
52B Bob Clemente(YT)	30.00	22.50	10.50
53A Morrie Martin	.35	.25	.10
53B Morrie Martin(YL)	5.00	3.75	1.75
54 Norm Siebern	.35	.25	.10
55 Chico Carrasquel	.35	.25	.10
56 Bill Fischer	.35	.25	.10
57A Tim Thompson	.35	.25	.10
57B Tim Thompson (YL)	5.00	3.75	1.75
58A Art Schult	.35	.25	.10
58B Art Schult(YT)	3.00	2.25	1.00
59 Dave Sisler	.35	.25	.10
60A Del Ennis	.50	.40	.18
60B Del Ennis(YL)	5.00	3.75	1.75
61A Darrell Johnson	.35	.25	.10
61B Darrell Johnson(YL)	5.00	3.75	1.75
62 Joe DeMaestri	.35	.25	.10
63 Joe Nuxhall	.50	.40	.18
64 Joe Lonnett	.35	.25	.10
65A Von McDaniel	.35	.25	.10
65B Von McDaniel(YL)	5.00	3.75	1.75
66 Lee Walls	.35	.25	.10
67 Joe Ginsberg	.35	.25	.10
68 Daryl Spencer	.35	.25	.10
69 Wally Burnette	.35	.25	.10
70A Al Kaline	7.50	5.75	2.50
70B Al Kaline(YL)	30.00	22.50	10.50
71 Dodgers Team	1.25	.90	.40
72 Bud Byerly	.35	.25	.10
73 Pete Daley	.35	.25	.10
74 Roy Face	.50	.40	.18
75 Gus Bell	.35	.25	.10
76A Dick Farrell	.35	.25	.10
76B Dick Farrell (YT)	3.00	2.25	1.00
77A Don Zimmer	1.00	.70	.30
77B Don Zimmer(YT)	5.00	3.75	1.75
78A Ernie Johnson	.35	.25	.10
78B Ernie Johnson(YL)	5.00	3.75	1.75
79A Dick Williams	.75	.55	.25
79B Dick Williams(YT)	not verified		xxx
80 Dick Drott	.35	.25	.10
81A Steve Boros	.35	.25	.10
81B Steve Boros(YT)	3.00	2.25	1.00
82 Ronnie Kline	.35	.25	.10
83 Bob Hazle	.35	.25	.10
84 Billy O'Dell	.35	.25	.10
85A Luis Aparicio	1.50	1.10	.50
85B Luis Aparicio(YT)	6.00	4.50	1.60
86 Valmy Thomas	.35	.25	.10
87 Johnny Kucks	.35	.25	.10
88 Duke Snider	8.00	6.00	2.50
89 Billy Klaus	.35	.25	.10
90 Robin Roberts	4.00	3.00	1.40
91 Chuck Tanner	.75	.55	.25
92A Clint Courtney	.35	.25	.10
92B Clint Courtney(YL)	5.00	3.75	1.75
93 Sandy Amoros	.35	.25	.10
94 Bob Skinner	.35	.25	.10
95 Frank Bolling	.35	.25	.10
96 Joe Durham	.35	.25	.10
97A Larry Jackson	.35	.25	.10
97B Larry Jackson(YL)	5.00	3.75	1.75
98A Billy Hunter	.35	.25	.10
98B Billy Hunter(YL)	5.00	3.75	1.75
99 Bobby Adams	.35	.25	.10
100A Early Wynn	3.50	2.50	1.20
100B Early Wynn(YT)	10.00	7.00	3.00
101A Bobby Richardson	1.00	.70	.30
101B Bobby Richardson(YL)	6.00	4.50	1.60
102 George Strickland	.35	.25	.10
103 Jerry Lynch	.35	.25	.10
104 Jim Pendleton	.35	.25	.10
105 Billy Gardner	.35	.25	.10
106 Dick Schofield	.35	.25	.10
107 Ossie Virgil	.35	.25	.10
108A Jim Landis	.35	.25	.10
108B Jim Landis(YT)	3.00	2.25	1.00
109 Herb Plews	.35	.25	.10
110 Johnny Logan	.35	.25	.10
111 Stu Miller	.35	.25	.10
112 Gus Zernial	.35	.25	.10
113 Jerry Walker	.35	.25	.10
114 Irv Noren	.35	.25	.10
115 Jim Bunning	1.25	.90	.40
116 Dave Philley	.35	.25	.10
117 Frank Torre	.35	.25	.10
118 Harvey Haddix	.50	.40	.18

	MINT	VG-E	F-G
119 Harry Chiti	.35	.25	.10
120 Johnny Podres	1.00	.70	.30
121 Eddie Miksis	.35	.25	.10
122 Walt Moryn	.35	.25	.10
123 Dick Tomanek	.35	.25	.10
124 Bobby Usher	.35	.25	.10
125 Al Dark	.60	.45	.20
126 Stan Palys	.35	.25	.10
127 Tom Sturdivant	.35	.25	.10
128 Willie Kirkland	.35	.25	.10
129 Jim Derrington	.35	.25	.10
130 Jackie Jensen	2.00	1.50	.60
131 Bob Henrich	.35	.25	.10
132 Vernon Law	.50	.40	.18
133 Russ Nixon	.35	.25	.10
134 Phillies	.70	.50	.20
135 Mike Drabowsky	.35	.25	.10
136 Jim Finigan	.35	.25	.10
137 Russ Kemmerer	.35	.25	.10
138 Earl Torgeson	.35	.25	.10
139 George Brunet	.35	.25	.10
140 Wes Covington	.35	.25	.10
141 Ken Lehman	.35	.25	.10
142 Enos Slaughter	1.75	1.25	.55
143 Billy Muffett	.35	.25	.10
144 Bobby Morgan	.35	.25	.10
146 Dick Gray	.35	.25	.10
147 Don McMahon	.35	.25	.10
148 Billy Consolo	.35	.25	.10
149 Tom Acker	.35	.25	.10
150 Mickey Mantle	32.00	24.00	11.00
151 Buddy Pritchard	.35	.25	.10
152 Johnny Antonelli	.50	.40	.18
153 Les Moss	.35	.25	.10
154 Harry Byrd	.35	.25	.10
155 Hector Lopez	.35	.25	.10
156 Dick Hyde	.35	.25	.10
157 Dee Fondy	.35	.25	.10
158 Cleveland Indians	.70	.50	.20
159 Taylor Phillips	.35	.25	.10
160 Don Hoak	.35	.25	.10
161 Don Larsen	1.50	1.10	.50
162 Gil Hodges	5.50	4.25	2.00
163 Jim Wilson	.35	.25	.10
164 Bob Taylor	.35	.25	.10
165 Bob Nieman	.35	.25	.10
166 Danny O'Connell	.35	.25	.10
167 Frank Baumann	.35	.25	.10
168 Joe Cunningham	.35	.25	.10
169 Ralph Terry	.35	.25	.10
170 Vic Wertz	.35	.25	.10
171 Harry Anderson	.35	.25	.10
172 Don Gross	.35	.25	.10
173 Eddie Yost	.35	.25	.10
174 Athletics	.60	.45	.20
175 Marv Throneberry	.60	.45	.20
176 Bob Buhl	.35	.25	.10
177 Al Smith	.35	.25	.10
178 Ted Kluszewski	1.25	.90	.40
179 Willy Miranda	.35	.25	.10
180 Lindy McDaniel	.35	.25	.10
181 Willie Jones	.35	.25	.10
182 Joe Caffie	.35	.25	.10
183 Dave Jolly	.35	.25	.10
184 Elvin Tappe	.35	.25	.10
185 Ray Boone	.35	.25	.10
186 Jack Meyer	.35	.25	.10
187 Sandy Koufax	10.00	7.00	3.00
188 Milt Bolling	.35	.25	.10
189 George Susce	.35	.25	.10
190 Red Schoendienst	1.00	.70	.30
191 Art Ceccarelli	.35	.25	.10
192 Milt Graff	.35	.25	.10
193 Jerry Lumpe	.35	.25	.10
194 Roger Craig	.50	.40	.18
195 Whitey Lockman	.50	.40	.18
196 Mike Garcia	.50	.40	.18
197 Haywood Sullivan	.50	.40	.18
198 Bill Virdon	1.00	.70	.30
199 Don Blasingame	.35	.25	.10
200 Bob Keegan	.35	.25	.10
201 Jim Bolger	.35	.25	.10
202 Woody Held	.35	.25	.10
203 Al Walker	.35	.25	.10
204 Leo Kiely	.35	.25	.10
205 Johnny Temple	.35	.25	.10
206 Bob Shaw	.35	.25	.10
207 Solly Hemus	.35	.25	.10
208 Cal McLish	.35	.25	.10
209 Bob Anderson	.35	.25	.10
210 Wally Moon	.50	.40	.18
211 Pete Burnside	.35	.25	.10
212 Bubba Phillips	.35	.25	.10
213 Red Wilson	.35	.25	.10

	MINT	VG-E	F-G
214 Willard Schmidt	.35	.25	.10
215 Jim Gilliam	1.50	1.10	.50
216 Cardinals	.80	.60	.25
217 Jack Harshman	.35	.25	.10
218 Dick Rand	.35	.25	.10
219 Camilo Pascual	.50	.40	.18
220 Tom Brewer	.35	.25	.10
221 Jerry Kindall	.35	.25	.10
222 Bud Daley	.35	.25	.10
223 Andy Pafko	.35	.25	.10
224 Bob Grim	.35	.25	.10
225 Billy Goodman	.35	.25	.10
226 Bob Smith	.35	.25	.10
227 Gene Stephens	.35	.25	.10
228 Duke Maas	.35	.25	.10
229 Frank Zupo	.35	.25	.10
230 Richie Ashburn	1.25	.90	.40
231 Lloyd Merritt	.35	.25	.10
232 Reno Bertoia	.35	.25	.10
233 Mickey Vernon	.50	.40	.18
234 Carl Sawatski	.35	.25	.10
235 Tom Gorman	.35	.25	.10
236 Ed Fitzgerald	.35	.25	.10
237 Bill Wight	.35	.25	.10
238 Bill Mazeroski	.75	.55	.25
239 Chuck Stobbs	.35	.25	.10
240 Moose Skowron	1.00	.70	.30
241 Dick Littlefield	.35	.25	.10
242 Johnny Klippstein	.35	.25	.10
243 Larry Raines	.35	.25	.10
244 Don Demeter	.35	.25	.10
245 Frank Lary	.35	.25	.10
246 New York Yankees	1.50	1.10	.50
247 Casey Wise	.35	.25	.10
248 Herm Wehmeier	.35	.25	.10
249 Ray Moore	.35	.25	.10
250 Roy Sievers	.35	.25	.10
251 Warren Hacker	.35	.25	.10
252 Bob Trowbridge	.35	.25	.10
253 Don Mueller	.35	.25	.10
254 Alex Grammas	.35	.25	.10
255 Bob Turley	.75	.55	.25
256 Chicago White Sox	.70	.50	.20
257 Hal Smith	.35	.25	.10
258 Carl Erskine	1.00	.70	.30
259 Al Pilarcik	.35	.25	.10
260 Frank Malzone	.35	.25	.10
261 Turk Lown	.35	.25	.10
262 Johnny Groth	.35	.25	.10
263 Eddie Bressoud	.35	.25	.10
264 Jack Sanford	.35	.25	.10
265 Pete Runnels	.35	.25	.10
266 Connie Johnson	.35	.25	.10
267 Sherm Lollar	.35	.25	.10
268 Granny Hamner	.35	.25	.10
269 Paul Smith	.35	.25	.10
270 Warren Spahn	5.00	3.75	1.75
271 Billy Martin	2.00	1.50	.50
272 Ray Crone	.35	.25	.10
273 Hal Smith	.35	.25	.10
274 Rocky Bridges	.35	.25	.10
275 Elston Howard	2.00	1.50	.50
276 Bobby Avila	.35	.25	.10
277 Virgil Trucks	.35	.25	.10
278 Mack Burk	.35	.25	.10
279 Bob Boyd	.35	.25	.10
280 Jim Piersall	1.00	.70	.30
281 Sam Taylor	.35	.25	.10
282 Paul Foytack	.35	.25	.10
283 Ray Shearer	.35	.25	.10
284 Ray Katt	.35	.25	.10
285 Frank Robinson	6.50	5.00	2.25
286 Gino Cimoli	.35	.25	.10
287 Sam Jones	.35	.25	.10
288 Harmon Killebrew	4.50	3.50	1.60
289 Burdette - Shantz	.60	.45	.20
290 Dick Donovan	.35	.25	.10
291 Don Landrum	.35	.25	.10
292 Ned Garver	.35	.25	.10
293 Gene Freese	.35	.25	.10
294 Hal Jeffcoat	.35	.25	.10
295 Minnie Minoso	1.25	.90	.40
296 Ryne Duren	.50	.40	.18
297 Don Buddin	.35	.25	.10
298 Jim Hearn	.35	.25	.10
299 Harry Simpson	.35	.25	.10
300 Harridge - Giles	1.50	1.10	.50
301 Randy Jackson	.35	.25	.10
302 Mike Baxes	.35	.25	.10
303 Neil Chrisley	.35	.25	.10
304 Kuenn - Kaline	1.50	1.10	.50
305 Clem Labine	.35	.25	.10
306 Whammy Douglas	.35	.25	.10

	MINT	VG-E	F-G
307 Brooks Robinson	7.00	5.25	2.50
308 Paul Giel	.35	.25	.10
309 Gail Harris	.35	.25	.10
310 Ernie Banks	8.00	6.00	2.50
311 Bob Purkey	.35	.25	.10
312 Boston Red Sox	.80	.60	.25
313 Bob Rush	.35	.25	.10
314 Snider - Alston	1.75	1.25	.55
315 Bob Friend	.50	.40	.18
316 Tito Francona	.35	.25	.10
317 Albie Pearson	.35	.25	.10
318 Frank House	.35	.25	.10
319 Lou Skizas	.35	.25	.10
320 Whitey Ford	6.00	4.50	2.00
321 Kluszewski - Williams	2.00	1.50	.60
322 Harding Peterson	.50	.40	.18
323 Elmer Valo	.35	.25	.10
324 Hoyt Wilhelm	1.50	1.10	.50
325 Joe Adcock	.50	.40	.18
326 Bob Miller	.35	.25	.10
327 Chicago Cubs	.70	.50	.20
328 Ike Delock	.35	.25	.10
329 Bob Cerv	.35	.25	.10
330 Ed Bailey	.35	.25	.10
331 Pedro Ramos	.35	.25	.10
332 Jim King	.35	.25	.10
333 Andy Carey	.35	.25	.10
334 Friend - Pierce	.60	.45	.20
335 Ruben Gomez	.35	.25	.10
336 Bert Hamric	.35	.25	.10
337 Hank Aguirre	.35	.25	.10
338 Walt Dropo	.35	.25	.10
339 Fred Hatfield	.35	.25	.10
340 Don Newcombe	1.50	1.10	.50
341 Pittsburgh Pirates	.70	.50	.20
342 Jim Brosnan	.35	.25	.10
343 Orlando Cepeda	3.50	2.50	1.20
344 Bob Porterfield	.35	.25	.10
345 Jim Hegan	.35	.25	.10
346 Steve Bilko	.35	.25	.10
347 Don Rudolph	.35	.25	.10
348 Chico Fernandez	.35	.25	.10
349 Murry Dickson	.35	.25	.10
350 Ken Boyer	1.25	.90	.40
351 Braves Fence Busters	3.00	2.25	1.00
352 Herb Score	.75	.55	.25
353 Stan Lopata	.35	.25	.10
354 Art Ditmar	.36	.26	.10
355 Bill Bruton	.35	.25	.10
356 Bob Malkmus	.35	.25	.10
357 Danny McDevitt	.35	.25	.10
358 Gene Baker	.35	.25	.10
359 Billy Loes	.35	.25	.10
360 Roy McMillan	.35	.25	.10
361 Mike Fornieles	.35	.25	.10
362 Ray Jablonski	.35	.25	.10
363 Don Elston	.35	.25	.10
364 Earl Battey	.35	.25	.10
365 Tom Morgan	.35	.25	.10
366 Gene Green	.35	.25	.10
367 Jack Urban	.35	.25	.10
368 Rocky Colavito	1.25	.90	.40
369 Ralph Lumenti	.35	.25	.10
370 Yogi Berra	8.00	6.00	2.50
371 Marty Keough	.35	.25	.10
372 Don Cardwell	.35	.25	.10
373 Joe Pignatano	.35	.25	.10
374 Brooks Lawrence	.35	.25	.10
375 Pee Wee Reese	5.00	3.75	1.75
376 Charley Rabe	.35	.25	.10
377A Milwaukee (alph)	1.00	.70	.30
377B Milwaukee (num)	5.00	3.75	1.75
378 Hank Sauer	.50	.40	.18
379 Ray Herbert	.35	.25	.10
380 Charley Maxwell	.35	.25	.10
381 Hal Brown	.35	.25	.10
382 Al Cicotte	.35	.25	.10
383 Lou Berberet	.35	.25	.10
384 John Goryl	.35	.25	.10
385 Wilmer Mizell	.35	.25	.10
386 Birdie's Sluggers	1.25	.90	.40
387 Wally Post	.35	.25	.10
388 Billy Moran	.35	.25	.10
389 Bill Taylor	.35	.25	.10
390 Del Crandall	.50	.40	.18
391 Dave Melton	.35	.25	.10
392 Bennie Daniels	.35	.25	.10
393 Tony Kubek	1.00	.70	.30
394 Jim Grant	.35	.25	.10
395 Willard Nixon	.35	.25	.10
396 Dutch Cotterer	.35	.25	.10
397A Detroit (alph)	1.00	.70	.30
397A Detroit (num)	5.00	3.75	1.75

		MINT	VG-E	F-G
398	Gene Woodling	.35	.25	.10
399	Marv Grissom	.35	.25	.10
400	Nellie Fox	1.50	1.10	.50
401	Don Bessent	.35	.25	.10
402	Bobby Gene Smith	.35	.25	.10
403	Steve Korchek	.35	.25	.10
404	Curt Simmons	.50	.40	.18
405	Ken Aspromonte	.35	.25	.10
406	Vic Power	.35	.25	.10
407	Carlton Willey	.35	.25	.10
408A	Baltimore (alph)	1.00	.70	.30
408B	Baltimore (num)	5.00	3.75	1.75
409	Frank Thomas	.35	.25	.10
410	Murray Wall	.35	.25	.10
411	Tony Taylor	.35	.25	.10
412	Jerry Staley	.35	.25	.10
413	Jim Davenport	.35	.25	.10
414	Sammy White	.35	.25	.10
415	Bob Bowman	.35	.25	.10
416	Foster Castelman	.35	.25	.10
417	Carl Furillo	1.25	.90	.40
418	Mantle-Aaron	6.00	4.50	2.00
419	Bobby Shantz	.60	.45	.20
420	Vada Pinson	2.00	1.50	.60
421	Dixie Howell	.35	.25	.10
422	Norm Zauchin	.35	.25	.10
423	Phil Clark	.35	.25	.10
424	Larry Doby	1.25	.90	.40
425	Sam Esposito	.35	.25	.10
426	Johnny O'Brien	.35	.25	.10
427	Al Worthington	.35	.25	.10
428A	Cincinnatti (alph)	1.00	.70	.30
428B	Cincinnatti (num)	5.00	3.75	1.75
429	Gus Triandos	.35	.25	.10
430	Bobby Thomson	1.00	.70	.30
431	Gene Conley	.35	.25	.10
432	John Powers	.35	.25	.10
433	Pancho Herrera	.60	.45	.20
434	Harvey Kuenn	.75	.55	.25
435	Ed Roebuck	.35	.25	.10
436	Mays-Snider	4.50	3.50	1.60
437	Bob Speake	.35	.25	.10
438	Whitey Herzog	.50	.40	.18
439	Ray Narleski	.35	.25	.10
440	Ed Mathews	6.00	4.50	2.00
441	Jim Marshall	.35	.25	.10
442	Phil Paine	.35	.25	.10
443	Billy Harrell*	2.50	1.80	.80
444	Danny Kravitz	.35	.25	.10

		MINT	VG-E	F-G
445	Bob Smith	.35	.25	.10
446	Carroll Hardy*	2.50	1.80	.80
447	Ray Monzant	.35	.25	.10
448	Charlie Lau	.50	.40	.18
449	Gene Fodge	.35	.25	.10
450	P. Ward*	2.50	1.80	.80
451	Joe Taylor	.35	.25	.10
452	Roman Mejias	.35	.25	.10
453	Tom Qualters	.35	.25	.10
454	Harry Hanebrink	.35	.25	.10
455	Hal Griggs	.35	.25	.10
456	Dick Brown	.35	.25	.10
457	Milt Pappas	.75	.55	.25
458	Julio Becquer	.35	.25	.10
459	Ron Blackburn	.35	.25	.10
460	Chuck Essegian	.35	.25	.10
461	Ed Mayer	.35	.25	.10
462	G. Geiger*	2.50	1.80	.80
463	Vito Valentinetti	.35	.25	.10
464	Curt Flood	1.25	.90	.40
465	Arnie Portocarrero	.35	.25	.10
466	Pete Whisenant	.35	.25	.10
467	Glen Hobbie	.35	.25	.10
468	Bob Schmidt	.35	.25	.10
469	Don Ferrarese	.35	.25	.10
470	R. C. Stevens	.35	.25	.10
471	Lenny Green	.35	.25	.10
472	Joe Jay	.35	.25	.10
473	Bill Renna	.35	.25	.10
474	Roman Semproch	.35	.25	.10
475	Haney-Stengel	2.50	1.80	.80
476	Stan Musial, AS	3.50	2.50	1.20
477	Bill Skowron, AS	.50	.40	.18
478	Johnny Temple, AS	.40	.30	.13
479	Nellie Fox, AS	1.00	.70	.30
480	Eddie Mathews, AS	2.75	2.00	.90
481	Frank Malzone, AS	.40	.30	.13
482	Ernie Banks, AS	3.00	2.25	1.00
483	Luis Aparicio, AS	.75	.55	.25
484	Frank Robinson, AS	2.75	2.00	.90
485	Ted Williams, AS	5.00	3.75	1.75
486	Willie Mays, AS	5.50	4.25	2.00
487	Mickey Mantle, AS	5.00	3.75	1.75
488	Hank Aaron, AS	5.50	4.25	2.00
489	Jackie Jensen, AS	.50	.40	.18
490	Ed Bailey, AS	.40	.30	.13
491	Sherm Lollar, AS	.40	.30	.13
492	Bob Friend, AS	.40	.30	.13
493	Bob Turley, AS	.50	.40	.18
494	Warren Spahn, AS	2.50	1.80	.80
495	Herb Score, AS	.50	.40	.18

STAR CAL DECAL — TYPE 1

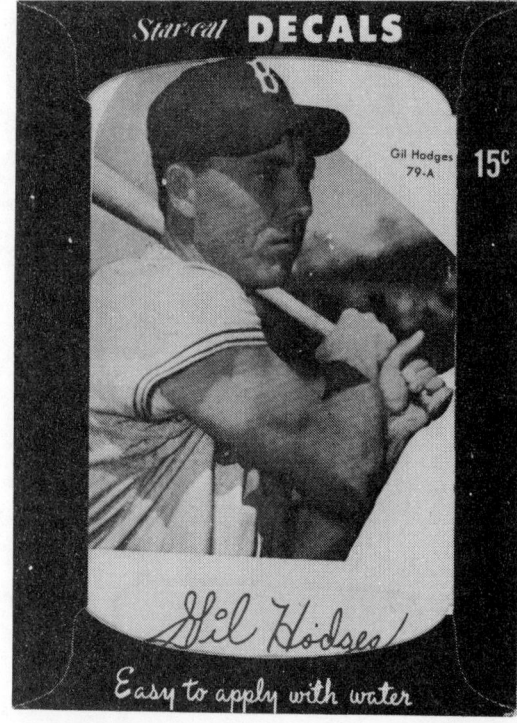

1959 TOPPS (572)   2 1/2" X 3 1/2"

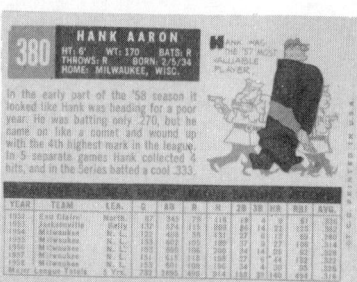

The 1959 Topps set contains bust pictures of the players in a colored circle. Card nos. 551-572 are The Sporting News All-Star selections. High numbers 507-572 have the card number in a black background on the reverse rather than a green background as in the lower numbers. The high numbers are more difficult to obtain. Several cards in the 300's exist with or without an extra traded or option line on the back of the card.

	MINT	VG-E	F-G
COMPLETE SET	400.00	300.00	140.00
COMMON PLAYER (1-110)	.30	.24	.10
COMMON PLAYER (111-506)	.25	.20	.08
COMMON PLAYER (507-572)	1.15	.85	.35
1 Ford Frick	1.50	1.10	.50
2 Eddie Yost	.30	.24	.10
3 Don McMahon	.30	.24	.10
4 Albie Pearson	.30	.24	.10
5 Dick Donovan	.30	.24	.10
6 Alex Grammas	.30	.24	.10
7 Al Pilarcik	.30	.24	.10
8 Team - Phillies	.50	.40	.18
9 Paul Giel	.30	.24	.10
10 Mickey Mantle	24.00	18.00	8.50
11 Billy Hunter	.30	.24	.10
11 Vern Law	.50	.40	.18
13 Dick Gernert	.30	.24	.10
14 Pete Whisenant	.30	.24	.10
15 Dick Drott	.30	.24	.10
16 Joe Pignatano	.30	.24	.10
17 Danny's Stars	.60	.45	.20
18 Jack Urban	.30	.24	.10
19 Eddie Bressoud	.30	.24	.10
20 Duke Snider	7.00	5.25	2.50
21 C. Johnson	.30	.24	.10
22 Al Smith	.30	.24	.10
23 Murry Dickson	.30	.24	.10
24 Red Wilson	.30	.24	.10
25 Don Hoak	.30	.24	.10
26 Chuck Stobbs	.30	.24	.10
27 Andy Pafko	.30	.24	.10
28 R. Worthington	.30	.24	.10
29 Jim Bolger	.30	.24	.10
30 Nellie Fox	2.00	1.50	.60
31 Ken Lehman	.30	.24	.10
32 Don Buddin	.30	.24	.10
33 Ed Fitzgerald	.30	.24	.10
34 Pitchers Beware	1.25	.90	.40
35 Ted Kluszewski	1.25	.90	.40
36 Hank Aguirre	.30	.24	.10
37 Gene Green	.30	.24	.10
38 Morrie Martin	.30	.24	.10
39 Ed Bouchee	.30	.24	.10
40 Warren Spahn	5.50	4.25	2.00
41 Bob Martyn	.30	.24	.10
42 Murray Wall	.30	.24	.10
43 Steve Bilko	.30	.24	.10
44 Vito Valentinetti	.30	.24	.10
45 Andy Carey	.30	.24	.10
46 R. Henry	.30	.24	.10
47 Jim Finigan	.30	.24	.10
48 Team - Orioles	.50	.40	.18
49 B. Hall	.30	.24	.10
50 Willie Mays	18.00	13.50	6.00
51 R. Coleman	.30	.24	.10
52 Coot Veal	.30	.24	.10
53 Stan Williams	.30	.24	.10
54 Mel Roach	.30	.24	.10
55 Tom Brewer	.30	.24	.10
56 Carl Sawatski	.30	.24	.10
57 Al Cicotte	.30	.24	.10
58 Eddie Miksis	.30	.24	.10
59 Irv Noren	.30	.24	.10

	MINT	VG-E	F-G
60 Bob Turley	.60	.45	.20
61 Dick Brown	.30	.24	.10
62 Tony Taylor	.30	.24	.10
63 Jim Hearn	.30	.24	.10
64 Joe DeMaestri	.30	.24	.10
65 Frank Torre	.30	.24	.10
66 Joe Ginsberg	.30	.24	.10
67 Brooks Lawrence	.30	.24	.10
68 Dick Schofield	.30	.24	.10
69 Team - Giants	.60	.45	.20
70 Harvey Kuenn	.60	.45	.20
71 Don Bessent	.30	.24	.10
72 Bill Renna	.30	.24	.10
73 Ron Jackson	.30	.24	.10
74 Directing Power	.50	.40	.18
75 Sam Jones	.30	.24	.10
76 Bobby Richardson	.50	.40	.18
77 John Goryl	.30	.24	.10
78 Pedro Ramos	.30	.24	.10
79 Harry Chiti	.30	.24	.10
80 Minnie Minoso	1.00	.70	.30
81 Hal Jeffcoat	.30	.24	.10
82 B. Boyd	.30	.24	.10
83 B. Smith	.30	.24	.10
84 Reno Bertoia	.30	.24	.10
85 Harry Anderson	.30	.24	.10
86 Bob Keegan	.30	.24	.10
86 Danny O'Connell	.30	.24	.10
88 Herb Score	.60	.45	.20
89 Billy Gardner	.30	.24	.10
90 Bill Skowron	1.00	.70	.30
91 Herb Moford	.30	.24	.10
92 Dave Philley	.30	.24	.10
93 Julie Becquer	.30	.24	.10
94 Team - White Sox	.50	.40	.18
95 Carl Willey	.30	.24	.10
96 Lou Berberet	.30	.24	.10
97 Jerry Lynch	.30	.24	.10
98 Arnie Portocarrero	.30	.24	.10
99 Ted Kazanski	.30	.24	.10
100 Bob Cerv	.30	.24	.10
101 Alex Kellner	.30	.24	.10
102 Felipe Alou	.75	.55	.25
103 Billy Goodman	.30	.24	.10
104 Del Rice	.30	.24	.10
105 Lee Walls	.30	.24	.10
106 Hal Woodeshick	.30	.24	.10
107 Norm Larker	.30	.24	.10
108 Zack Monroe	.30	.24	.10
109 Bob Schmidt	.30	.24	.10
110 George Witt	.30	.24	.10
111 Team - Redlegs	.60	.45	.20
112 Billy Consolo	.25	.20	.08
113 Taylor Phillips	.25	.20	.08
114 Earl Battey	.25	.20	.08
115 Mickey Vernon	.50	.40	.18
116 Bob Allison	.75	.55	.25
117 John Blanchard	.25	.20	.08
118 John Buzhardt	.25	.20	.08
119 John Callison	.50	.40	.18
120 Chuck Coles	.25	.20	.08
121 Bob Conley	.25	.20	.08
122 Bennie Daniels	.25	.20	.08
123 D. Dillard	.25	.20	.08

	MINT	VG-E	F-G
124 Dan Dobbek	.25	.20	.08
125 Ron Fairly	.50	.40	.18
126 Ed Haas	.25	.20	.08
127 Kent Hadley	.25	.20	.08
128 Bob Hartman	.25	.20	.08
129 Frank Herrera	.25	.20	.08
130 Lou Jackson	.25	.20	.08
131 Deron Johnson	.40	.30	.13
132 Don Lee	.25	.20	.08
133 Bob Lillis	.25	.20	.08
134 Jim McDaniel	.25	.20	.08
135 Gene Oliver	.25	.20	.08
136 Jim O'Toole	.50	.40	.18
137 D. Ricketts	.25	.20	.08
138 John Romano	.25	.20	.08
139 Ed Sadowski	.25	.20	.08
140 C. Secrest	.25	.20	.08
141 Joe Shipley	.25	.20	.08
142 Dick Stigman	.25	.20	.08
143 Willie Tasby	.25	.20	.08
144 Jerry Walker	.25	.20	.08
145 Dom Zanni	.25	.20	.08
146 Jerry Zimmerman	.25	.20	.08
147 Cubs Clubbers	1.25	.90	.40
148 Mike McCormick	.25	.20	.08
149 Jim Bunning	.80	.60	.25
150 Stan Musial	9.00	6.75	3.00
151 Bob Malkmus	.25	.20	.08
152 John Klippstein	.25	.20	.08
153 J. Marshall	.25	.20	.08
154 Ray Herbert	.25	.20	.08
155 Enos Slaughter	1.75	1.25	.55
156 Ace Hurlers	.60	.45	.20
157 Felix Mantilla	.25	.20	.08
158 Walt Dropo	.25	.20	.08
159 Bob Shaw	.25	.20	.08
160 Dick Groat	.40	.30	.13
161 Frank Baumann	.25	.20	.08
162 B. G. Smith	.25	.20	.08
163 Sandy Koufax	10.00	7.00	3.00
164 Johnny Groth	.25	.20	.08
165 Bill Bruton	.25	.20	.08
166 Destruction Crew	.60	.45	.20
167 Duke Maas	.25	.20	.08
168 Carroll Hardy	.25	.20	.08
169 Ted Abernathy	.25	.20	.08
170 Gene Woodling	.40	.30	.13
171 W. Schmidt	.25	.20	.08
172 Team - Athletics	.50	.40	.18
173 Bill Monbouquette	.25	.20	.08
174 Jim Pendleton	.25	.20	.08
175 D. Farrell	.25	.20	.08
176 P. Ward	.25	.20	.08
177 J. Briggs	.25	.20	.08
178 Ruben Amaro	.25	.20	.08
179 Don Rudolph	.25	.20	.08
180 Yogi Berra	7.50	5.75	2.50
181 Bob Porterfield	.25	.20	.08
182 Milt Graff	.25	.20	.08
183 Stu Miller	.25	.20	.08
184 Harvey Haddix	.40	.30	.13
185 Jim Busby	.25	.20	.08
186 Mudcat Grant	.25	.20	.08
187 Bubba Phillips	.25	.20	.08
188 Juan Pizzaro	.25	.20	.08
189 Neil Chrisley	.25	.20	.08

	MINT	VG-E	F-G
190 Bill Virdon	.75	.55	.25
191 Russ Kemmerer	.25	.20	.08
192 Charlie Beamon	.25	.20	.08
193 Sammy Taylor	.25	.20	.08
194 Jim Brosnan	.25	.20	.08
195 Rip Repulski	.25	.20	.08
196 Billy Morgan	.25	.20	.08
197 Ray Semproch	.25	.20	.08
198 Jim Davenport	.25	.20	.08
199 Leo Kiely	.25	.20	.08
200 Warren Giles	1.00	.70	.30
201 Tom Acker	.25	.20	.08
202 Roger Maris	4.50	3.50	1.60
203 Ossie Virgil	.25	.20	.08
204 Casey Wise	.25	.20	.08
205 Don Larsen	.75	.55	.25
206 Carl Furillo	1.00	.70	.30
207 George Strickland	.25	.20	.08
208 Willie Jones	.25	.20	.08
209 Lenny Green	.25	.20	.08
210 Ed Bailey	.25	.20	.08
211 B. Blaylock	.25	.20	.08
212 Fence Busters	3.00	2.25	1.00
213 Jim Rivera	.25	.20	.08
214 Marcelino Solis	.25	.20	.08
215 Jim Lemon	.25	.20	.08
216 Andre Rodgers	.25	.20	.08
217 Carl Erskine	1.00	.70	.30
218 Roman Mejias	.25	.20	.08
219 George Zuverink	.25	.20	.08
220 Frank Malzone	.25	.20	.08
221 B. Bowman	.25	.20	.08
222 Bobby Shantz	.40	.30	.13
223 Team - Cardinals	.60	.45	.20
224 Claude Osteen	.40	.30	.13
225 Johnny Logan	.25	.20	.08
226 Art Ceccarelli	.25	.20	.08
227 H. W. Smith	.25	.20	.08
228 Don Gross	.25	.20	.08
229 Vic Power	.25	.20	.08
230 B. Fischer	.25	.20	.08
231 Ellis Burton	.25	.20	.08
232 Eddie Kasko	.25	.20	.08
233 Paul Foytack	.25	.20	.08
234 Chuck Tanner	.50	.40	.18
235 Valmy Thomas	.25	.20	.08
236 Ted Bowsfield	.25	.20	.08
237 Run Preventers	.50	.40	.18
238 Gene Baker	.25	.20	.08
239 Bob Trowbridge	.25	.20	.08
240 Hank Bauer	.60	.45	.20
241 Billy Muffett	.25	.20	.08
242 Ron Samford	.25	.20	.08
243 Marv Grissom	.25	.20	.08
244 T. Gray	.25	.20	.08
245 Ned Garver	.25	.20	.08
246 J. W. Porter	.25	.20	.08
247 Don Ferrarese	.25	.20	.08
248 Team - Red Sox	.60	.45	.20
249 Bobby Adams	.25	.20	.08
250 Billy O'Dell	.25	.20	.08
251 Cletis Boyer	.25	.20	.08
252 Ray Boone	.25	.20	.08
253 Seth Morehead	.25	.20	.08
254 Zeke Bella	.25	.20	.08

	MINT	VG-E	F-G
255 D. Ennis	.40	.30	.13
256 J. Davis	.25	.20	.08
257 Leon Wagner	.25	.20	.08
258 Fred Kipp	.25	.20	.08
259 Jim Pisoni	.25	.20	.08
260 Early Wynn	3.00	2.25	1.00
261 Gene Stephens	.25	.20	.08
262 Hitters' Foes	.80	.60	.25
263 B. Daley	.25	.20	.08
264 C. Carrasquel	.25	.20	.08
265 R. Kline	.25	.20	.08
266 W. Held	.25	.20	.08
267 J. Romonosky	.25	.20	.08
268 T. Francona	.25	.20	.08
269 J. Mayer	.25	.20	.08
270 Gil Hodges	3.75	2.75	1.25
271 O. Pena	.25	.20	.08
272 J. Lumpe	.25	.20	.08
273 J. Jay	.25	.20	.08
274 J. Kindall	.25	.20	.08
275 J. Sanford	.25	.20	.08
276 P. Daley	.25	.20	.08
277 T. Lown	.25	.20	.08
278 C. Essegian	.25	.20	.08
279 E. Johnson	.25	.20	.08
280 F. Bolling	.25	.20	.08
281 W. Craddock	.25	.20	.08
282 R. C. Stevens	.25	.20	.08
283 R. Heman	.25	.20	.08
284 S. Korcheck	.25	.20	.08
285 J. Cunningham	.25	.20	.08
286 D. Stone	.25	.20	.08
287 D. Zimmer	.50	.40	.18
288 D. Dotterer	.25	.20	.08
289 J. Kucks	.25	.20	.08
290 W. Covington	.25	.20	.08
291 Pitch Partners	.40	.30	.13
292 D. Williams	.40	.30	.13
293 R. Moore	.25	.20	.08
294 H. Foiles	.25	.20	.08
295 B. Martin	1.75	1.25	.55
296 E. Broglio	.25	.20	.08
297 J. Brandt	.25	.20	.08
298 T. Clevenger	.25	.20	.08
299 B. Klaus	.25	.20	.08
300 R. Ashburn	1.00	.70	.30
301 E. Averill	.25	.20	.08
302 D. Mossi	.25	.20	.08
303 M. Keough	.25	.20	.08
304 Team - Cubs	.50	.40	.18
305 C. Raydon	.25	.20	.00
306 J. Gilliam	1.25	.90	.40
307 C. Barclay	.25	.20	.08
308 N. Siebern	.25	.20	.08
309 S. Maglie	.40	.30	.13
310 L. Aparicio	1.25	.90	.40
311 Norm Zauchin	.25	.20	.08
312 Don Newcombe	.75	.55	.25
313 Frank House	.25	.20	.08
314 Don Cardwell	.25	.20	.08
315 Joe Adcock	.40	.30	.13
316A Ralph Lumenti(Opt.)	.25	.20	.08
316B Ralph Lumenti(No Opt)	10.00	7.00	3.00
317 Hitting Kings	2.50	1.80	.80
Ashburn, Mays	.25	.20	.08
318 Rocky Bridges	.25	.20	.08
319 Dave Hillmann	.25	.20	.08
320 Bob Skinner	.25	.20	.08
321A Giallombardo(Opt.)	.25	.20	.08
321B Giallombardo(No Opt)	10.00	7.00	3.00
322A Hanebrink(Traded)	.25	.20	.08
322A Hanebrink(No Trade)	10.00	7.00	3.00
323 Frank Sullivan	.25	.20	.08
324 Don Demeter	.25	.20	.08
325 Ken Boyer	1.00	.70	.30
326 Marv Throneberry	.40	.30	.13
327 Gary Bell	.25	.20	.08
328 Lou Skizas	.25	.20	.08
329 Team - Tigers	.60	.45	.20
330 Gus Triandos	.25	.20	.08
331 Steve Boros	.25	.20	.08
332 Ray Monzant	.25	.20	.08
333 Harry Simpson	.25	.20	.08
334 Glen Hobbie	.25	.20	.08
335 Johnny Temple	.25	.20	.08
336A Billy Loes(Traded)	.25	.20	.08
336B Billy Loes(No Trade)	10.00	7.00	3.00
337 George Crowe	.25	.20	.08
338 Sparky Anderson	1.00	.70	.30
339 Roy Face	.40	.30	.13
340 Roy Sievers	.25	.20	.08
341 Tom Qualters	.25	.20	.08
342A Ray Jablonski(Traded)	.25	.20	.08
342B Ray Jablonski(No Trade)	xx	not	verified
343 Bill Hoeft	.25	.20	.08
344 Russ Nixon	.25	.20	.08
345 Gil McDougald	.50	.40	.18
346 Batter Bafflers	.40	.30	.13
Brewer, Sisler	.25	.20	.08

	MINT	VG-E	F-G
347 Bob Buhl	.25	.20	.08
348 Ted Lepcio	.25	.20	.08
349 Hoyt Wilhelm	1.00	.70	.30
350 Ernie Banks	6.00	4.50	2.00
351 Earl Torgeson	.25	.20	.08
352 Robin Roberts	3.25	2.40	1.10
353 Curt Flood	.60	.45	.20
354 Pete Burnside	.25	.20	.08
355 Jim Piersall	.60	.45	.20
356 Bob Mabe	.25	.20	.08
357 Dick Stuart	.50	.40	.18
358 Ralph Terry	.25	.20	.08
359A Bill White(Traded)	.50	.40	.18
359B Bill White(No Trade)	xx	not	verified
360 Al Kaline	5.50	4.25	2.00
361 Willard Nixon	.25	.20	.08
362A Dolan Nichols(Opt.)	.25	.20	.08
362B Dolan Nichols(No Opt)	10.00	7.00	3.00
363 Bobby Avila	.25	.20	.08
364 Danny McDevitt	.25	.20	.08
365 Gus Bell	.25	.20	.08
366 Humberto Robinson	.25	.20	.08
367 Cal Neeman	.25	.20	.08
368 D. Mueller	.25	.20	.08
369 D. Tomanek	.25	.20	.08
370 P. Runnels	.25	.20	.08
371 D. Brodowski	.25	.20	.08
372 J. Hegan	.25	.20	.08
373 H. Plews	.25	.20	.08
374 A. Ditmar	.25	.20	.08
375 B. Nieman	.25	.20	.08
376 H. Naragon	.25	.20	.08
377 J. Antonelli	.40	.30	.13
378 G. Harris	.25	.20	.08
379 B. Miller	.25	.20	.08
380 Hank Aaron	16.00	12.00	5.50
381 M. Baxes	.25	.20	.08
382 C. Simmons	.40	.30	.13
383 Words of Wisdom	1.00	.70	.30
384 D. Sisler	.25	.20	.08
385 S. Lollar	.25	.20	.08
386 J. Delsing	.25	.20	.08
387 D. Drysdale	3.50	2.50	1.20
388 B. Will	.25	.20	.08
389 J. Nuxhall	.40	.30	.13
390 O. Cepeda	1.25	.90	.40
391 M. Pappas	.40	.30	.13
392 W. Herzog	.40	.30	.13
393 F. Lary	.25	.20	.08
394 R. Jackson	.25	.20	.08
395 E. Howard	1.50	1.10	.50
396 B. Rush	.25	.20	.08
397 Team - Senators	.50	.40	.18
398 W. Post	.25	.20	.08
399 L. Jackson	.25	.20	.08
400 J. Jensen	.60	.45	.20
401 R. Blackburn	.25	.20	.08
402 H. Lopez	.25	.20	.08
403 C. Labine	.25	.20	.08
404 H. Sauer	.40	.30	.13
405 R. McMillan	.25	.20	.08
406 S. Drake	.25	.20	.08
407 M. Drabowsky	.25	.20	.08
408 Keystone Combo	1.00	.70	.30
409 G. Zernial	.25	.20	.08
410 B. Pierce	.80	.60	.25
411 W. Lockman	.25	.20	.08
412 S. Lopata	.25	.20	.08
413 C. Pascual	.40	.30	.13
414 D. Long	.25	.20	.08
415 B. Mazeroski	.50	.40	.18
416 H. Sullivan	.40	.30	.13
417 V. Trucks	.25	.20	.08
418 G. Cimoli	.25	.20	.08
419 Team - Braves	.60	.45	.20
420 R. Colavito	1.00	.70	.30
421 H. Wehmeier	.25	.20	.08
422 H. Landrith	.25	.20	.08
423 B. Grim	.25	.20	.08
424 K. Aspromonte	.25	.20	.08
425 D. Crandall	.40	.30	.13
426 J. Staley	.25	.20	.08
427 C. Neal	.25	.20	.08
428 Buc Hill Aces	.60	.40	.18
429 B. Thomson	.60	.45	.20
430 Whitey Ford	5.00	3.75	1.75
431 W. Douglas	.25	.20	.08
432 S. Burgess	.25	.20	.08
433 B. Harrell	.25	.20	.08
434 H. Griggs	.25	.20	.08
435 F. Robinson	5.00	3.75	1.75
436 G. Hamner	.25	.20	.08
437 Ike Delock	.25	.20	.08
438 S. Esposito	.25	.20	.08
439 B. Robinson	6.00	4.50	2.00
440 L. Burdette	2.50	1.80	.80
441 J. Roseboro	.25	.20	.08
442 R. Narleski	.25	.20	.08
443 D. Spencer	.25	.20	.08

	MINT	VG-E	F-G			MINT	VG-E	F-G
444 Ron Hansen	.25	.20	.08	508 Art Fowler	1.15	.85	.35
445 Cal McLish	.25	.20	.08	509 Norm Cash	2.00	1.50	.60
446 Rocky Nelson	.25	.20	.08	510 Team - Yankees	3.00	2.25	1.00
447 Bob Anderson	.25	.20	.08	511 George Susce	1.15	.85	.35
448 Vada Pinson	1.25	.90	.40	512 George Altman	1.15	.85	.35
449 Tom Gorman	.25	.20	.08	513 Tommy Carroll	1.15	.85	.35
450 Ed Mathews	5.00	3.75	1.75	514 Bob Gibson	16.00	12.00	5.50
451 Jimmy Constable	.25	.20	.08	515 Harmon Killebrew	7.50	5.75	2.50
452 Chico Fernandez	.25	.20	.08	516 M. Garcia	1.50	1.10	.50
453 Les Moss	.25	.20	.08	517 J. Koppe	1.15	.85	.35
454 P. Clark	.25	.20	.08	518 M. Cuellar	1.50	1.10	.50
455 L. Doby	.75	.55	.25	519 Infield Power	1.50	1.10	.50
456 J. Casale	.25	.20	.08	520 D. Elston	1.15	.85	.35
457 Team - Dodgers	1.00	.70	.30	521 G. Geiger	1.15	.85	.35
458 G. Jones	.25	.20	.08	522 G. Snyder	1.15	.85	.35
459 B. Tuttle	.25	.20	.08	523 H. Bright	1.15	.85	.35
460 B. Friend	.40	.30	.13	524 L. Osborne	1.15	.85	.35
461 Mantle Hits H. R.	4.00	3.00	1.40	525 J. Coates	1.15	.85	.35
462 Colavito's Catch	.60	.45	.20	526 B. Speake	1.15	.85	.35
463 Kaline Bat Champ	1.50	1.10	.50	527 S. Hemus	1.15	.85	.35
464 Mays' Series Catch	2.50	1.80	.80	528 Team - Pirates	2.00	1.50	.60
465 Sievers Sets Mark	.40	.30	.13	529 G. Bamberger	2.00	1.50	.60
466 Pierce All-Star	.50	.40	.18	530 W. Moon	1.50	1.10	.50
467 Aaron Clubs H. R.	2.50	1.80	.80	531 R. Webster	1.15	.85	.35
468 Snider's Play	1.75	1.25	.55	532 M. Freeman	1.15	.85	.35
469 Hustler Banks	1.75	1.25	.55	533 D. Johnson	1.15	.85	.35
470 Musial's 3000th Hit	2.00	1.50	.60	534 F. Throneberry	1.15	.85	.35
471 T. Sturdivant	.25	.20	.08	535 R. Gomez	1.15	.85	.35
472 G. Freese	.25	.20	.08	536 D. Kravitz	1.15	.85	.35
473 M. Fornieles	.25	.20	.08	537 R. Arias	1.15	.85	.35
474 M. Thacker	.25	.20	.08	538 C. King	1.15	.85	.35
475 J. Harshman	.25	.20	.08	539 G. Blaylock	1.15	.85	.35
476 Team - Indians	.50	.40	.18	540 W. Miranda	1.15	.85	.35
477 B. Latman	.25	.20	.08	541 B. Thurman	1.15	.85	.35
478 Bob Clemente	11.50	8.25	3.75	542 J. Perry	1.50	1.10	.50
479 L. McDaniel	.25	.20	.08	543 Corsair Trio	5.00	3.75	1.75
480 R. Schoendienst	.75	.55	.25	544 L. Tate	1.15	.85	.35
481 C. Maxwell	.25	.20	.08	545 Tom Morgan	1.15	.85	.35
482 Russ Meyer	.25	.20	.08	546 Al Schroll	1.15	.85	.35
483 C. Courtney	.25	.20	.08	547 Jim Baxes	1.15	.85	.35
484 W. Kirkland	.25	.20	.08	548 Elmer Singleton	1.15	.85	.35
485 R. Duren	.40	.30	.13	549 Howie Nunn	1.15	.85	.35
486 S. White	.25	.20	.08	550 Roy Campanella	16.00	12.00	5.50
487 H. Brown	.25	.20	.08	551 F. Haney, AS	1.25	.90	.40
488 W. Moryn	.25	.20	.08	552 C. Stengel, AS	4.00	3.00	1.40
489 John Powers	.25	.20	.08	553 O. Cepeda, AS	1.50	1.10	.50
490 F. Thomas	.25	.20	.08	554 B. Skowron, AS	1.50	1.10	.50
491 D. Blasingame	.25	.20	.08	555 B. Mazeroski, AS	1.25	.90	.40
492 G. Conley	.25	.20	.08	556 N. Fox, AS	1.50	1.10	.50
493 J. Landis	.25	.20	.08	557 K. Boyer, AS	1.50	1.10	.50
494 D. Pavletich	.25	.20	.08	558 F. Malzone, AS	1.25	.90	.40
495 J. Podres	.50	.40	.18	559 E. Banks, AS	6.00	4.50	2.00
496 W. Terwilliger	.25	.20	.08	560 L. Aparicio, AS	1.50	1.10	.50
497 H. R. Smith	.25	.20	.08	561 H. Aaron, AS	11.00	8.00	3.50
498 D. Hyde	.25	.20	.08	562 A. Kaline, AS	6.00	4.50	2.00
499 J. O'Brien	.25	.20	.08	563 W. Mays, AS	11.00	8.00	3.50
500 V. Wertz	.25	.20	.08	564 M. Mantle, AS	14.00	10.50	4.75
501 B. Tiefenauer	.25	.20	.08	565 W. Covington, AS	1.25	.90	.40
502 A. Dark	.50	.40	.18	566 R. Sievers, AS	1.25	.90	.40
503 Jim Owens	.25	.20	.08	567 D. Crandall, AS	1.25	.90	.40
504 Ossie Alvarez	.25	.20	.08	568 G. Triandos, AS	1.25	.90	.40
505 Tony Kubek	.60	.45	.20	569 B. Friend, AS	1.25	.90	.40
506 Bob Purkey	.25	.20	.08	570 B. Turley, AS	1.25	.90	.40
507 Bob Hall	1.15	.85	.35	571 W. Spahn, AS	4.00	3.00	1.40
				572 B. Pierce, AS	1.50	1.10	.50

bob cerv — KANSAS CITY ATHLETICS OUTFIELD

jim bolger — CHICAGO CUBS OUTFIELD

mickey mantle — NEW YORK YANKEES OUTFIELD

1959 TOPPS ADVERTISING PANEL

1960 TOPPS (572)

The 1960 Topps set is Topps only issue in the 2 1/2″ X 3 1/2″ card size which utilizes a horizontal format front.

High numbers 507–572 are somewhat more difficult to obtain. Card nos. 553–572 are Sport Magazine All-Star selections.

	MINT	VG-E	F-G
COMPLETE SET	350.00	260.00	110.00
COMMON PLAYER (1-440)	.22	.17	.07
COMMON PLAYER (441-506)	.45	.35	.15
COMMON PLAYER (507-572)	1.00	.75	.30
1 Early Wynn	3.00	2.00	.80
2 Roman Mejias	.22	.17	.07
3 Joe Adcock	.30	.25	.10
4 Bob Purkey	.22	.17	.07
5 Wally Moon	.30	.25	.10
6 Lou Berberet	.22	.17	.07
7 Master & Mentor	2.00	1.50	.60
Mays & Rigney			
8 Bud Daley	.22	.17	.07
9 Faye Throneberry	.22	.17	.07
10 Ernie Banks	4.50	3.50	1.60
11 Norm Siebern	.22	.17	.07
12 Milt Pappas	.30	.25	.10
13 Wally Post	.22	.17	.07
14 Jim Grant	.22	.17	.07
15 Pete Runnels	.22	.17	.07
16 Ernie Broglio	.22	.17	.07
17 Johnny Callison	.22	.17	.07
18 Team - Dodgers	.60	.45	.20
19 Felix Mantilla	.22	.17	.07
20 Roy Face	.30	.25	.10
21 Dutch Dotterer	.22	.17	.07
22 Rocky Bridges	.22	.17	.07
23 Eddie Fisher	.22	.17	.07
24 Dick Gray	.22	.17	.07
25 Roy Sievers	.30	.25	.10
26 Wayne Terwilliger	.22	.17	.07
27 Dick Drott	.22	.17	.07
28 Brooks Robinson	4.50	3.50	1.60
29 Clem Labine	.22	.17	.07
30 Tito Francona	.22	.17	.07
31 Sammy Esposito	.22	.17	.07
32 Soph Stalwarts	.40	.30	.13
Toole & Pinson			
33 Tom Morgan	.22	.17	.07
34 George Anderson	.75	.55	.25
35 Whitey Ford	4.25	3.25	1.50
36 Russ Nixon	.22	.17	.07
37 Bill Bruton	.22	.17	.07
38 Jerry Casale	.22	.17	.07
39 Earl Averill	.22	.17	.07
40 Joe Cunningham	.22	.17	.07
41 Barry Latman	.22	.17	.07
42 Hobie Landrith	.22	.17	.07
43 Team - Senators	.40	.30	.13
44 Bob Locke	.22	.17	.07
45 Roy McMillan	.22	.17	.07
46 Jerry Fisher	.22	.17	.07
47 Don Zimmer	.40	.30	.13
48 Hal W. Smith	.22	.17	.07
49 Curt Raydon	.22	.17	.07
50 Al Kaline	4.50	3.50	1.60
51 Jim Coates	.22	.17	.07
52 Dave Philley	.22	.17	.07
53 Jackie Brandt	.22	.17	.07
54 Mike Fornieles	.22	.17	.07
55 Bill Mazeroski	.40	.30	.13
56 Steve Korcheck	.22	.17	.07
57 Win - Savers	.30	.25	.10
Lown & Staley			
58 Gino Cimoli	.22	.17	.07
59 Juan Pizarro	.22	.17	.07

	MINT	VG-E	F-G
60 Gus Triandos	.22	.17	.07
61 Eddie Kasko	.22	.17	.07
62 Roger Craig	.30	.25	.10
63 George Strickland	.22	.17	.07
64 Jack Meyer	.22	.17	.07
65 Elston Howard	1.50	1.10	.50
66 Bob Trowbridge	.22	.17	.07
67 Jose Pagan	.22	.17	.07
68 Dave Hillman	.22	.17	.07
69 Billy Goodman	.22	.17	.07
70 Lew Burdette	.50	.40	.18
71 Marty Keough	.22	.17	.07
72 Team - Tigers	.60	.45	.20
73 Bob Gibson	3.50	2.50	1.20
74 Walt Moryn	.22	.17	.07
75 Vic Power	.22	.17	.07
76 Bill Fischer	.22	.17	.07
77 Hank Foiles	.22	.17	.07
78 Bob Grim	.22	.17	.07
79 Walt Dropo	.22	.17	.07
80 Johnny Antonelli	.30	.25	.10
81 Russ Snyder	.22	.17	.07
82 Ruben Gomez	.22	.17	.07
83 Tony Kubek	.60	.45	.20
84 Hal R. Smith	.22	.17	.07
85 Frank Lary	.22	.17	.07
86 Dick Gernert	.22	.17	.07
87 John Romonosky	.22	.17	.07
88 John Roseboro	.22	.17	.07
89 Hal Brown	.22	.17	.07
90 Bobby Avila	.22	.17	.07
91 Bennie Daniels	.22	.17	.07
92 Whitey Herzog	.30	.25	.10
93 Art Schult	.22	.17	.07
94 Leo Kiely	.22	.17	.07
95 Frank Thomas	.22	.17	.07
96 Ralph Terry	.22	.17	.07
97 Ted Lepcio	.22	.17	.07
98 Gordon Jones	.22	.17	.07
99 Lenny Green	.22	.17	.07
100 Nellie Fox	1.50	1.10	.50
101 Bob Miller	.22	.17	.07
102 Kent Hadley	.22	.17	.07
103 Dick Farrell	.22	.17	.07
104 Dick Schofield	.22	.17	.07
105 Larry Sherry	.30	.25	.10
106 Billy Gardner	.22	.17	.07
107 Carlton Willey	.22	.17	.07
108 Pete Daley	.22	.17	.07
109 Clete Boyer	.22	.17	.07
110 Cal McLish	.22	.17	.07
111 Vic Wertz	.30	.25	.10
112 Jack Harshman	.22	.17	.07
113 Bob Skinner	.22	.17	.07
114 Ken Aspromonte	.22	.17	.07
115 Fork & Knuckler	.75	.55	.25
(Face & Wilhelm)			
116 Jim Rivera	.22	.17	.07
117 Tom Borland	.22	.17	.07
118 Bob Bruce	.22	.17	.07
119 Chico Cardenas	.22	.17	.07
120 Duke Carmel	.22	.17	.07
121 Camilo Carreon	.22	.17	.07
122 Don Dillard	.22	.17	.07
123 Dan Dobbek	.22	.17	.07
124 Jim Donohue	.22	.17	.07
125 Dick Ellsworth	.22	.17	.07

	MINT	VG-E	F-G
126 Chuck Estrada	.22	.17	.07
127 Ron Hansen	.22	.17	.07
128 Bill Harris	.22	.17	.07
129 Bob Hartman	.22	.17	.07
130 Frank Herrera	.22	.17	.07
131 Ed Hobaugh	.22	.17	.07
132 F. Howard	1.75	.60	.25
133 M. Javier	.22	.17	.07
134 D. Johnson	.22	.17	.07
135 K. Johnson	.22	.17	.07
136 J. Kaat	1.25	.90	.40
137 L. Klimchock	.22	.17	.07
138 A. Mahaffey	.22	.17	.07
139 C. Mathias	.22	.17	.07
140 J. Navarro	.22	.17	.07
141 J. Proctor	.22	.17	.07
142 B. Short	.22	.17	.07
143 A. Spangler	.22	.17	.07
144 A. Stieglitz	.22	.17	.07
145 J. Umbricht	.22	.17	.07
146 T. Wieand	.22	.17	.07
147 B. Will	.22	.17	.07
148 Carl Yastrzemski	28.00	21.00	10.00
149 B. Nieman	.22	.17	.07
150 B. Pierce	.75	.55	.25
151 Team - Giants	.50	.40	.18
152 G. Harris	.22	.17	.07
153 B. Thomson	.50	.40	.18
154 J. Davenport	.22	.17	.07
155 C. Neal	.22	.17	.07
156 A. Ceccarelli	.22	.17	.07
157 R. Nelson	.22	.17	.07
158 W. Covington	.22	.17	.07
159 J. Piersall	.40	.30	.13
160 Rival All-Stars	3.00	2.25	1.00
161 R. Narleski	.22	.17	.07
162 S. Taylor	.22	.17	.07
163 H. Lopez	.22	.17	.07
164 Team - Reds	.50	.40	.18
165 J. Sanford	.22	.17	.07
166 C. Essegian	.22	.17	.07
167 V. Thomas	.22	.17	.07
168 A. Grammas	.22	.17	.07
169 J. Striker	.22	.17	.07
170 D. Crandall	.30	.25	.10
171 J. Groth	.22	.17	.07
172 W. Kirkland	.22	.17	.07
173 B. Martin	1.50	1.10	.50
174 Team - Indians	.50	.40	.18
175 P. Ramos	.22	.17	.07
176 V. Pinson	.80	.60	.25
177 J. Kucks	.22	.17	.07
178 W. Held	.22	.17	.07
179 R. Coleman	.22	.17	.07
180 H. Simpson	.22	.17	.07
181 B. Loes	.22	.17	.07
182 G. Hobbie	.22	.17	.07
183 E. Grba	.22	.17	.07
184 G. Geiger	.22	.17	.07
185 J. Owens	.22	.17	.07
186 D. Sisler	.22	.17	.07
187 J. Hook	.22	.17	.07
188 D. Williams	.30	.25	.10
189 D. McMahon	.22	.17	.07
190 G. Woodling	.30	.25	.10
191 J. Klippstein	.22	.17	.07
192 D. O'Connell	.22	.17	.07
193 D. Hyde	.22	.17	.07
194 B. G. Smith	.22	.17	.07
195 L. McDaniel	.22	.17	.07
196 A. Carey	.22	.17	.07
197 R. Kline	.22	.17	.07
198 J. Lynch	.22	.17	.07
199 D. Donovan	.22	.17	.07
200 Willie Mays	16.00	12.00	5.50
201 L. Osborne	.22	.17	.07
202 F. Kipp	.22	.17	.07
203 S. White	.22	.17	.07
204 R. Duren	.22	.17	.07
205 J. Logan	.22	.17	.07
206 C. Osteen	.22	.17	.07
207 B. Boyd	.22	.17	.07
208 Team - White Sox	.50	.40	.18
209 R. Blackburn	.22	.17	.07
210 H. Killebrew	3.25	2.40	1.10
211 T. Phillips	.22	.17	.07
212 W. Alston	.50	.40	.18
213 C. Dressen	.30	.25	.10
214 Jimmy Dykes	.30	.25	.10
215 Bob Elliott	.22	.17	.07
216 Joe Gordon	.22	.17	.07
217 Charlie Grimm	.30	.25	.10
218 Solly Hemus	.22	.17	.07

	MINT	VG-E	F-G
219 Fred Hutchinson	.50	.40	.18
220 Billy Jurges	.22	.17	.07
221 Cookie Lavagetto	.22	.17	.07
222 Al Lopez	1.00	.70	.30
223 Danny Murtaugh	.30	.25	.10
224 P. Richards	.30	.25	.10
225 B. Rigney	.22	.17	.07
226 E. Sawyer	.22	.17	.07
227 C. Stengel	3.00	2.25	1.00
228 E. Johnson	.22	.17	.07
229 J. Morgan	.22	.17	.07
230 Mound Magicians	1.00	.70	.30
231 Hal Naragon	.22	.17	.07
232 Jim Busby	.22	.17	.07
233 Don Elston	.22	.17	.07
234 Don Demeter	.22	.17	.07
235 Gus Bell	.22	.17	.07
236 D. Ricketts	.22	.17	.07
237 E. Valo	.22	.17	.07
238 D. Kravitz	.22	.17	.07
239 J. Shipley	.22	.17	.07
240 L. Aparicio	1.00	.70	.30
241 A. Pearson	.22	.17	.07
242 Team - Cardinals	.50	.40	.18
243 B. Phillips	.22	.17	.07
244 H. Griggs	.22	.17	.07
245 E. Yost	.22	.17	.07
246 L. Maye	.22	.17	.07
247 G. McDougald	.50	.40	.18
248 D. Rice	.22	.17	.07
249 E. Wilson	.22	.17	.07
250 Stan Musial	8.00	6.00	2.50
251 B. Malkmus	.22	.17	.07
252 R. Herbert	.22	.17	.07
253 E. Bressoud	.22	.17	.07
254 A. Portocarrero	.22	.17	.07
255 J. Gilliam	1.00	.70	.30
256 D. Brown	.22	.17	.07
257 G. Coleman	.22	.17	.07
258 D. Groat	1.00	.70	.30
259 G. Altman	.22	.17	.07
260 Power Plus	.50	.40	.18
261 P. Burnside	.22	.17	.07
262 H. Bauer	.50	.40	.18
263 D. Johnson	.22	.17	.07
264 R. Roberts	3.00	2.25	1.00
265 R. Repulski	.22	.17	.07
266 J. Jay	.22	.17	.07
267 J. Marshall	.22	.17	.07
268 A. Worthington	.22	.17	.07
269 G. Green	.22	.17	.07
270 B. Turley	.40	.30	.13
271 J. Becquer	.22	.17	.07
272 F. Green	.22	.17	.07
273 N. Chrisley	.22	.17	.07
274 T. Acker	.22	.17	.07
275 C. Flood	.40	.30	.13
276 K. McBride	.22	.17	.07
277 H. Bright	.22	.17	.07
278 S. Williams	.22	.17	.07
279 C. Tanner	.40	.30	.13
280 F. Sullivan	.22	.17	.07
281 R. Boone	.22	.17	.07
282 J. Nuxhall	.30	.25	.10
283 J. Blanchard	.22	.17	.07
284 D. Gross	.22	.17	.07
285 H. Anderson	.22	.17	.07
286 R. Semproch	.22	.17	.07
287 F. Alou	.30	.25	.10
288 B. Mabe	.22	.17	.07
289 W. Jones	.22	.17	.07
290 J. Lumpe	.22	.17	.07
291 B. Keegan	.22	.17	.07
292 Dodger Backstops	.30	.25	.10
293 G. Conley	.22	.17	.07
294 T. Taylor	.22	.17	.07
295 G. Hodges	3.50	2.50	1.20
296 N. Chittum	.22	.17	.07
297 R. Bertoia	.22	.17	.07
298 G. Witt	.22	.17	.07
299 E. Torgeson	.22	.17	.07
300 Hank Aaron	16.00	12.00	5.50
301 J. Davie	.22	.17	.07
302 Team - Phillies	.50	.40	.18
303 B. O'Dell	.22	.17	.07
304 J. Ginsberg	.22	.17	.07
305 R. Ashburn	1.00	.70	.30
306 F. Baumann	.22	.17	.07
307 G. Oliver	.22	.17	.07
308 Dick Hall	.22	.17	.07
309 Bob Hale	.22	.17	.07
310 Frank Malzone	.22	.17	.07
311 Raul Sanchez	.22	.17	.07
312 Charley Lau	.30	.25	.10

	MINT	VG-E	F-G			MINT	VG-E	F-G
313 Turk Lown	.22	.17	.07	406 B. Klaus	.22	.17	.07
314 Chico Fernandez	.22	.17	.07	407 G. Peters	.22	.17	.07
315 Bobby Shantz	.30	.25	.10	408 C. Furillo	1.00	.70	.30
316 Willie McCovey	18.00	13.50	6.00	409 R. Samford	.22	.17	.07
317 Pumpsie Green	.22	.17	.07	410 S. Jones	.22	.17	.07
318 J. Baxes	.22	.17	.07	411 E. Bailey	.22	.17	.07
319 J. Koppe	.22	.17	.07	412 B. Anderson	.22	.17	.07
320 B. Allison	.40	.30	.13	413 Team - Athletics	.40	.30	.13
321 R. Fairly	.40	.30	.13	414 Don Williams	.22	.17	.07
322 W. Tasby	.22	.17	.07	415 B. Cerv	.22	.17	.07
323 J. Romano	.22	.17	.07	416 H. Robinson	.22	.17	.07
324 J. Perry	.50	.40	.18	417 C. Cottier	.22	.17	.07
325 J. O'Toole	.30	.25	.10	418 D. Mossi	.22	.17	.07
326 B. Clemente	10.00	7.00	3.00	419 G. Crowe	.22	.17	.07
327 R. Sadecki	.22	.17	.07	420 E. Mathews	3.50	2.50	1.20
328 E. Battey	.22	.17	.07	421 D. Maas	.22	.17	.07
329 Z. Monroe	.22	.17	.07	422 J. Powers	.22	.17	.07
330 H. Kuenn	.50	.40	.18	423 E. Fitzgerald	.22	.17	.07
331 H. Mason	.22	.17	.07	424 P. Whisenant	.22	.17	.07
332 Team -Yankees	1.00	.70	.30	425 J. Podres	.50	.40	.18
333 D. McDevitt	.22	.17	.07	426 R. Jackson	.22	.17	.07
334 T. Abernathy	.22	.17	.07	427 A. Grunwald	.22	.17	.07
335 R. Schoendienst	.50	.40	.18	428 A. Smith	.22	.17	.07
336 I. Delock	.22	.17	.07	429 A. L. Kings	.50	.40	.18
337 C. Neeman	.22	.17	.07	430 A. Ditmar	.22	.17	.07
338 R. Monzant	.22	.17	.07	431 A. Rodgers	.22	.17	.07
339 H. Chiti	.22	.17	.07	432 C. Stobbs	.22	.17	.07
340 H. Haddix	.30	.25	.10	433 I. Noren	.22	.17	.07
341 C. Hardy	.22	.17	.07	434 B. Lawrence	.22	.17	.07
342 C. Wise	.22	.17	.07	435 G. Freese	.22	.17	.07
343 S. Koufax	9.00	6.75	3.00	436 M. Throneberry	.30	.25	.10
344 C. Courtney	.22	.17	.07	437 B. Friend	.30	.25	.10
345 D. Newcombe	.75	.55	.25	438 J. Coker	.22	.17	.07
346 J. C. Martin	.22	.17	.07	439 T. Brewer	.22	.17	.07
347 E. Bouchee	.22	.17	.07	440 J. Lemon	.22	.17	.07
348 B. Shetrone	.22	.17	.07	441 Gary Bell	.45	.35	.15
349 M. Drabowsky	.22	.17	.07	442 Joe Pignatano	.45	.35	.15
350 Mickey Mantle	22.00	15.60	7.50	443 Charley Maxwell	.45	.35	.15
351 D. Nottebart	.22	.17	.07	444 Jerry Kindall	.45	.35	.15
352 Cincy Clouters	1.00	.70	.30	445 Warren Spahn	4.00	3.00	1.40
353 D. Larsen	.40	.30	.13	446 E. Burton	.45	.35	.15
354 B. Lillis	.22	.17	.07	447 R. Moore	.45	.35	.15
355 B. White	.30	.25	.10	448 J. Gentile	.45	.35	.15
356 J. Amalfitano	.22	.17	.07	449 J. Brosnan	.45	.35	.15
357 A. Schroll	.22	.17	.07	450 O. Cepeda	2.50	1.80	.80
358 J. De Maestri	.22	.17	.07	451 C. Simmons	.45	.35	.15
359 B. Gilbert	.22	.17	.07	452 R. Webster	.45	.35	.15
360 H. Score	.50	.40	.18	453 V. Law	.60	.45	.20
361 B. Oldis	.22	.17	.07	454 H. Woodshick	.45	.35	.15
362 R. Kemmerer	.22	.17	.07	455 Coaches - Orioles	.60	.45	.20
363 G. Stephens	.22	.17	.07	456 Coaches - Red Sox	.60	.45	.20
364 P. Foytack	.22	.17	.07	457 Coaches - Cubs	.60	.45	.20
365 M. Minoso	.80	.60	.25	458 Coaches - White Sox	.60	.45	.20
366 D. Green	.60	.45	.20	459 Coaches - Reds	.60	.45	.20
367 B. Tuttle	.22	.17	.07	460 Coaches - Indians	.60	.45	.20
368 D. Spencer	.22	.17	.07	461 Coaches - Tigers	.60	.45	.20
369 B. Hoeft	.22	.17	.07	462 Coaches - Athletics	.60	.45	.20
370 B. Skowron	.80	.60	.25	463 Coaches - Dodgers	.60	.45	.20
371 B. Byerly	.22	.17	.07	464 Coaches - Braves	.60	.45	.20
372 F. House	.22	.17	.07	465 Coaches - Yankees	.90	.70	.30
373 D. Hoak	.22	.17	.07	466 Coaches - Phillies	.60	.45	.20
374 B. Buhl	.22	.17	.07	467 Coaches - Pirates	.60	.45	.20
375 D. Long	.22	.17	.07	468 Coaches - Cardinals	.60	.45	.20
376 J. Briggs	.22	.17	.07	469 Coaches - Giants	.60	.45	.20
377 R. Maris	4.50	3.50	1.60	470 Coaches - Senators	.60	.45	.20
378 S. Miller	.22	.17	.07	471 N. Garver	.45	.35	.15
379 R. Wilson	.22	.17	.07	472 A. Dark	.60	.45	.20
380 B. Shaw	.22	.17	.07	473 A. Cicotte	.45	.35	.20
381 Team - Braves	.50	.40	.18	474 H. Sullivan	.60	.45	.20
382 T. Bowsfield	.22	.17	.07	475 D. Drysdale	4.00	3.00	1.40
383 L. Wagner	.22	.17	.07	476 L. Johnson	.45	.35	.15
384 D. Cardwell	.22	.17	.07	477 D. Ferrarese	.45	.35	.15
385 World Series 1	.75	.55	.25	478 F. Torre	.45	.35	.15
386 World Series 2	.75	.55	.25	479 G. Maranda	.45	.35	.15
387 World Series 3	.75	.55	.25	480 Y. Berra	6.00	4.50	2.00
388 World Series 4	.75	.55	.25	481 W. Stock	.45	.35	.20
389 World Series 5	.75	.55	.25	482 F. Bolling	.45	.35	.20
390 World Series 6	.75	.55	.25	483 C. Pascual	.60	.45	.20
391 W. S. Composite	.75	.55	.25	484 Team - Pirates	1.00	.70	.30
392 T. Clevenger	.22	.17	.07	485 K. Boyer	1.25	.90	.40
393 S. Burgess	.30	.25	.10	486 B. Del Greco	.45	.35	.15
394 N. Larker	.22	.17	.07	487 T. Sturdivant	.45	.35	.15
395 H. Wilhelm	1.00	.70	.30	488 N. Cash	1.25	.90	.40
396 S. Bilko	.22	.17	.07	489 S. Ridzik	.45	.35	.15
397 B. Blasingame	.22	.17	.07	490 F. Robinson	5.50	4.25	2.00
398 M. Cuellar	.30	.25	.10	491 M. Roach	.45	.35	.15
399 Young Stars	.30	.25	.10	492 L. Jackson	.45	.35	.15
400 R. Colavito	1.00	.70	.30	493 D. Snider	5.50	4.25	2.00
401 Bob Duliba	.22	.17	.07	494 Team - Orioles	.75	.55	.25
402 Dick Stuart	.30	.25	.10	495 S. Lollar	.45	.35	.15
403 Ed Sadowski	.22	.17	.07	496 B. Virdon	1.00	.70	.30
404 Bob Rush	.22	.17	.07	497 J. Tsitouris	.45	.35	.15
405 Bobby Richardson	.50	.40	.18	498 A. Pilarcik	.45	.35	.15
				499 J. James	.45	.35	.15

1960 TOPPS (CONTINUED)

	MINT	VG-E	F-G			MINT	VG-E	F-G
500 Johnny Temple	.45	.35	.15	536 W. Hawkins		1.00	.75	.30
501 Bob Schmidt	.45	.35	.15	537 Team - Red Sox		2.00	1.50	.60
502 Jim Bunning	1.00	.70	.30	538 F. Barnes		1.00	.75	.30
503 Don Lee	.45	.35	.15	539 G. Baker		1.00	.75	.30
504 Seth Morehead	.45	.35	.15	540 J. Walker		1.00	.75	.30
505 T. Kluszewski	1.25	.90	.40	541 T. Curry		1.00	.75	.30
506 L. Walls	.45	.35	.15	542 K. Hamlin		1.00	.75	.30
507 D. Stigman	1.00	.75	.30	543 E. Chacon		1.00	.75	.30
508 B. Consolo	1.00	.75	.30	544 B. Monbouquette		1.00	.75	.30
509 T. Davis	2.00	1.50	.60	545 Carl Sawatski		1.00	.75	.30
510 J. Staley	1.00	.75	.30	546 Hank Aguirre		1.00	.75	.30
511 K. Walters	1.00	.75	.30	547 Bob Aspromonte		1.00	.75	.30
512 J. Gibbon	1.00	.75	.30	548 Don Mincher		1.00	.75	.30
513 Team - Cubs	2.00	1.50	.60	549 John Buzhardt		1.00	.75	.30
514 S. Barber	1.00	.75	.30	550 J. Landis		1.00	.75	.30
515 S. Lopata	1.00	.75	.30	551 E. Rakow		1.00	.75	.30
516 M. Kutyna	1.00	.75	.30	552 W. Bond		1.00	.75	.30
517 C. James	1.00	.75	.30	553 B. Skowron, AS		1.50	1.10	.50
518 T. Gonzales	1.00	.75	.30	554 W. McCovey, AS		7.50	5.75	2.50
519 E. Roebuck	1.00	.75	.30	555 N. Fox, AS		2.00	1.50	.60
520 D. Buddin	1.00	.75	.30	556 C. Neal, AS		1.25	.90	.40
521 M. Lee	1.00	.75	.30	557 F. Malzone, AS		1.25	.90	.40
522 K. Hunt	1.00	.75	.30	558 E. Mathews, AS		4.50	3.50	1.60
523 C. Dalrymple	1.00	.75	.30	599 L. Aparicio, AS		2.00	1.50	.60
524 B. Henry	1.00	.75	.30	560 E. Banks, AS		5.50	4.25	2.00
525 M. Breeding	1.00	.75	.30	561 A. Kaline, AS		5.50	4.25	2.00
526 Paul Giel	1.00	.75	.30	562 J. Cunningham, AS		1.25	.90	.40
527 Jose Valdivielso	1.00	.75	.30	563 M. Mantle, AS		15.00	11.00	5.00
528 Ben Johnson	1.00	.75	.30	564 W. Mays, AS		12.00	8.75	4.00
529 Norm Sherry	1.25	.90	.40	565 R. Maris, AS		5.00	3.75	1.75
530 Mike McCormick	1.25	.90	.40	566 H. Aaron, AS		12.00	8.75	4.00
531 Sandy Amoros	1.00	.75	.30	567 S. Lollar, AS		1.25	.90	.40
532 Mike Garcia	1.25	.90	.40	568 D. Crandall, AS		1.25	.90	.40
533 Lou Clinton	1.00	.75	.30	569 C. Pascual, AS		1.25	.90	.40
534 Ken Mackenzie	1.00	.75	.30	570 D. Drysdale, AS		3.50	2.50	1.20
535 Whitey Lockman	1.00	.75	.30	571 B. Pierce, AS		1.50	1.10	.50
				572 J. Antonelli, AS		1.25	.90	.40

1961 TOPPS (589) 2 1/2" X 3 1/2"

The 1961 Topps set witnesses a return to the vertical format card with which Topps has continued until the present. Card nos. 426, 587, and 588 were not issued. Card no. 426 was intended to be the Braves Team card. Card nos. 401-410 are Baseball Thrills; card nos. 471-486 are Most Valuable Player cards from 1950-1960; and card nos. 566-589 are The Sporting News All-Star selections. There were two card nos. 463 issued-Jack Fisher and the Milwaukee Braves team card. High numbers 523-589 are more difficult to obtain.

	MINT	VG-E	F-G			MINT	VG-E	F-G
COMPLETE SET	750.00	575.00	260.00	23 Don Demeter		.21	.16	.06
COMMON PLAYER (1-522)	.21	.16	.06	24 Ken Johnson		.21	.16	.06
COMMON PLAYER (523-589)	5.50	4.25	1.75	25 Heavy Artillery		1.00	.70	.30
				26 Wes Stock		.21	.16	.06
1 Dick Groat	1.50	.75	.30	27 Jerry Kindall		.21	.16	.06
2 Roger Maris	5.00	3.75	1.75	28 Hector Lopez		.21	.16	.06
3 John Buzhardt	.21	.16	.06	29 Don Nottebart		.21	.16	.06
4 Lenny Green	.21	.16	.06	30 Nellie Fox		1.25	.90	.40
5 John Romano	.21	.16	.06	31 Bob Schmidt		.21	.16	.06
6 Ed Roebuck	.21	.16	.06	32 Ray Sadecki		.21	.16	.06
7 White Sox Team	.40	.30	.13	33 Gary Geiger		.21	.16	.06
8 Dick Williams	.30	.25	.10	34 Wynn Hawkins		.21	.16	.06
9 Bob Purkey	.21	.16	.06	35 Ron Santo		1.25	.90	.40
10 Brooks Robinson	4.50	3.50	1.60	36 Jack Kralick		.21	.16	.06
11 Curt Simmons	.30	.25	.10	37 Charley Maxwell		.21	.16	.06
12 Moe Thacker	.21	.16	.06	38 Bob Lillis		.21	.16	.06
13 Chuck Cottier	.21	.16	.06	39 Leo Posada		.21	.16	.06
14 Don Mossi	.21	.16	.06	40 Bob Turley		.40	.30	.13
15 Willie Kirkland	.21	.16	.06	41 N. L. Bat Leaders		.55	.40	.18
16 Billy Muffet	.21	.16	.06	42 A. L. Bat Leaders		.55	.40	.18
17 Check List 1	.21	.16	.06	43 N. L. HR Leaders		.55	.40	.18
18 Jim Grant	.21	.16	.06	44 A. L. HR Leaders		.55	.40	.18
19 Cletis Boyer	.21	.16	.06	45 N. L. Era Leaders		.55	.40	.18
20 Robin Roberts	3.00	2.25	1.00	46 A. L. Era Leaders		.55	.40	.18
21 Zorro Versalles	.40	.30	.13	47 N. L. Pit. Leaders		.55	.40	.18
22 Clem Labine	.21	.16	.06	48 A. L. Pit. Leaders		.55	.40	.18

#	Name	MINT	VG-E	F-G
49	N. L. S.O. Leaders	.55	.40	.18
50	A. L. S.O. Leaders	.55	.40	.18
51	Tigers Team	.45	.35	.15
52	George Crowe	.21	.16	.06
53	Russ Nixon	.21	.16	.06
54	Earl Francis	.21	.16	.06
55	Jim Davenport	.21	.16	.06
56	Russ Kemmerer	.21	.16	.06
57	Marv Thronebernry	.30	.25	.10
58	Joe Schaffernoth	.21	.16	.06
59	Jim Woods	.21	.16	.06
60	Woodie Held	.21	.16	.06
61	Ron Piche	.21	.16	.06
62	Al Pilarcik	.21	.16	.06
63	Jim Kaat	.75	.55	.25
64	Alex Grammas	.21	.16	.06
65	Ted Kluszewski	1.00	.70	.30
66	Billy Henry	.21	.16	.06
67	Ossie Virgil	.21	.16	.06
68	Deron Johnson	.21	.16	.06
69	Earl Wilson	.21	.16	.06
70	Bill Virdon	.80	.60	.25
71	Jerry Adair	.21	.16	.06
72	Stu Miller	.21	.16	.06
73	Al Spangler	.21	.16	.06
74	Joe Pignatano	.21	.16	.06
75	Lindy Shows Larry	.30	.25	.10
76	Harry Anderson	.21	.16	.06
77	Dick Stigman	.21	.16	.06
78	Lee Walls	.21	.16	.06
79	Joe Ginsberg	.21	.16	.06
80	Harmon Killebrew	3.00	2.25	1.00
81	Tracy Stallard	.21	.16	.06
82	Joe Christopher	.21	.16	.06
83	Bob Bruce	.21	.16	.06
84	Lee Maye	.21	.16	.06
85	Jerry Walker	.21	.16	.06
86	Dodgers Team	.60	.45	.20
87	Joe Amalfitano	.21	.16	.06
88	Richie Ashburn	1.00	.70	.30
89	Billy Martin	1.25	.90	.40
90	Jerry Staley	.21	.16	.06
91	Walt Moryn	.21	.16	.06
92	Hal Naragon	.21	.16	.06
93	Tony Gonzalez	.21	.16	.06
94	John Kucks	.21	.16	.06
95	Norm Cash	.75	.55	.25
96	Bill O'Dell	.21	.16	.06
97	Jerry Lynch	.21	.16	.06
98	Checklist 2	.21	.16	.06
99	Don Buddin	.21	.16	.06
100	Harvey Haddix	.30	.25	.10
101	Bubba Phillips	.21	.16	.06
102	Gene Stephens	.21	.16	.06
103	Ruben Amaro	.21	.16	.06
104	John Blanchard	.21	.16	.06
105	Carl Willey	.21	.16	.06
106	Whitey Herzog	.30	.25	.10
107	Seth Morehead	.21	.16	.06
108	Dan Dobbek	.21	.16	.06
109	John Podres	.40	.30	.13
110	Vada Pinson	1.00	.70	.30
111	Jack Meyer	.21	.16	.06
112	C. Fernandez	.21	.16	.06
113	M. Fornieles	.21	.16	.06
114	Hobie Landrith	.21	.16	.06
115	J. Antonelli	.30	.25	.10
116	Joe DeMaestri	.21	.16	.06
117	Dale Long	.21	.16	.06
118	Chris Cannizzaro	.21	.16	.06
119	A's Big Armor	.30	.25	.10
120	Ed Mathews	3.50	2.50	1.20
121	Eli Grba	.21	.16	.06
122	Cubs Team	.40	.30	.13
123	Billy Gardner	.21	.16	.06
124	J. C. Martin	.21	.16	.06
125	Steve Barber	.21	.16	.06
126	Dick Stuart	.30	.25	.10
127	Ron Kline	.21	.16	.06
128	Rip Repulski	.21	.16	.06
129	Ed Hobaugh	.21	.16	.06
130	Norm Larker	.21	.16	.06
131	Paul Richards	.40	.30	.13
132	Al Lopez	1.00	.70	.30
133	Ralp Houk	.60	.45	.20
134	Mickey Vernon	.30	.25	.10
135	Fred Hutchinson	.50	.40	.18
136	Walt Alston	.60	.45	.20
137	Chuck Dressen	.30	.25	.10
138	Danny Murtaugh	.30	.25	.10
139	Solly Hemus	.21	.16	.06
140	Gus Triandos	.21	.16	.06
141	Billy Williams	2.00	1.50	.60
142	Luis Arroyo	.21	.16	.06
143	Russ Snyder	.21	.16	.06
144	Jim Coker	.21	.16	.06
145	Bob Buhl	.21	.16	.06
146	Marty Keough	.21	.16	.06
147	Ed Rakow	.21	.16	.06
148	Julian Javier	.21	.16	.06
149	Bob Oldis	.21	.16	.06
150	Willie Mays	15.00	11.00	5.00
151	Jim Donohue	.21	.16	.06
152	Earl Torgeson	.21	.16	.06
153	Don Lee	.21	.16	.06
154	Bobby Del Greco	.21	.16	.06
155	John Temple	.21	.16	.06
156	Ken Hunt	.21	.16	.06
157	Cal McLish	.21	.16	.06
158	Pete Daley	.21	.16	.06
159	Orioles Team	.40	.30	.13
160	Whitey Ford	4.25	3.25	1.50
161	Sherman Jones	.21	.16	.06
162	Jay Hook	.21	.16	.06
163	Ed Sadowski	.21	.16	.06
164	Felix Mantilla	.21	.16	.06
165	Gino Cimoli	.21	.16	.06
166	Danny Kravitz	.21	.16	.06
167	Giants Team	.50	.40	.18
168	Tommy Davis	.75	.55	.25
169	Don Elston	.21	.16	.06
170	Al Smith	.21	.16	.06
171	Paul Foytack	.21	.16	.06
172	Don Dillard	.21	.16	.06
173	Beantown Bombers	.30	.25	.10
174	Ray Semproch	.21	.16	.06
175	Gene Freese	.21	.16	.06
176	Ken Aspromonte	.21	.16	.06
177	Don Larsen	.40	.30	.13
178	Bob Nieman	.21	.16	.06
179	Joe Koppe	.21	.16	.06
180	Bobby Richardson	.50	.40	.18
181	Fred Green	.21	.16	.06
182	Dave Nicholson	.21	.16	.06
183	Andre Rodgers	.21	.16	.06
184	Steve Bilko	.21	.16	.06
185	Herb Score	.40	.30	.13
186	Elmer Valo	.21	.16	.06
187	Billy Klaus	.21	.16	.06
188	Jim Marshall	.21	.16	.06
189	Check List 3	.21	.16	.06
190	Stan Williams	.21	.16	.06
191	Mike De La Hoz	.21	.16	.06
192	Dick Brown	.21	.16	.06
193	Gene Conley	.21	.16	.06
194	Gordy Coleman	.21	.16	.06
195	Jerry Casale	.21	.16	.06
196	Ed Bouchee	.21	.16	.06
197	Dick Hall	.21	.16	.06
198	Carl Sawatski	.21	.16	.06
199	Bob Boyd	.21	.16	.06
200	Warren Spahn	3.50	2.50	1.20
201	Pete Whisenant	.21	.16	.06
202	Al Neiger	.21	.16	.06
203	Eddie Bressoud	.21	.16	.06
204	Bob Skinner	.21	.16	.06
205	Bill Pierce	.80	.60	.25
206	Gene Green	.21	.16	.06
207	Dodger Southpaws	1.25	.90	.40
208	Larry Osborne	.21	.16	.06
209	Ken McBride	.21	.16	.06
210	Pete Runnels	.21	.16	.06
211	Bob Gibson	3.50	2.50	1.20
212	Haywood Sullivan	.30	.25	.10
213	Billy Stafford	.21	.16	.06
214	Danny Murphy	.21	.16	.06
215	Gus Bell	.21	.16	.06
216	Ted Bowsfield	.21	.16	.06
217	Mel Roach	.21	.16	.06
218	Hal Brown	.21	.16	.06
219	Gene Mauch	.50	.40	.18
220	Al Dark	.40	.30	.13
221	Mike Higgins	.21	.16	.06
222	Jimmie Dykes	.30	.25	.10
223	Bob Scheffing	.21	.16	.06
224	Joe Gordon	.21	.16	.06
225	Bill Rigney	.21	.16	.06
226	Harry Lavagetto	.21	.16	.06
227	Juan Pizarro	.21	.16	.06
228	N. Y. Yankees	.75	.55	.25
229	Rudy Hernandez	.21	.16	.06
230	Don Hoak	.21	.16	.06
231	Dick Drott	.21	.16	.06
232	Bill White	.30	.25	.10
233	Joe Jay	.21	.16	.06
234	Ted Lepcio	.21	.16	.06
235	Camilo Pascual	.30	.25	.10
236	Don Gile	.21	.16	.06
237	Billy Loes	.21	.16	.06

	MINT	VG-E	F-G
238 Jim Gilliam	1.00	.70	.30
239 Dave Sisler	.21	.16	.06
240 Ron Hansen	.21	.16	.06
241 Al Cicotte	.21	.16	.06
242 Hal (W) Smith	.21	.16	.06
243 Frank Lary	.21	.16	.06
244 Chico Cardenas	.21	.16	.06
245 Joe Adcock	.30	.25	.10
246 Bob Davis	.21	.16	.06
247 Billy Goodman	.21	.16	.06
248 Ed Keegan	.21	.16	.06
249 Cinn. Reds Team	.65	.50	.20
250 Buc Hill Aces	.30	.25	.10
251 Bill Bruton	.21	.16	.06
252 Bill Short	.21	.16	.06
253 Sammy Taylor	.21	.16	.06
254 Ted Sadowski	.21	.16	.06
255 Vic Power	.21	.16	.06
256 Billy Hoeft	.21	.16	.06
257 Carroll Hardy	.21	.16	.06
258 Jack Sanford	.21	.16	.06
259 John Schaive	.21	.16	.06
260 Don Drysdale	3.50	2.50	1.20
261 Charlie Lau	.30	.25	.10
262 Tony Curry	.21	.16	.06
263 Ken Hamlin	.21	.16	.06
264 Glen Hobbie	.21	.16	.06
265 Tony Kubek	.60	.45	.20
266 Lindy McDaniel	.21	.16	.06
267 Norm Siebern	.21	.16	.06
268 Ike Delock	.21	.16	.06
269 Harry Chiti	.21	.16	.06
270 Bob Friend	.30	.25	.10
271 Jim Landis	.21	.16	.06
272 Tom Morgan	.21	.16	.06
273 Check List 4	.21	.16	.06
274 Gary Bell	.21	.16	.06
275 Gene Woodling	.30	.25	.10
276 Ray Rippelmeyer	.21	.16	.06
277 Hank Foiles	.21	.16	.06
278 Don McMahon	.21	.16	.06
279 Jose Pagan	.21	.16	.06
280 Frank Howard	.75	.55	.25
281 Frank Sullivan	.21	.16	.06
282 Faye Throneberry	.21	.16	.06
283 Bob Anderson	.21	.16	.06
284 Dick Gernert	.21	.16	.06
285 Sherm Lollar	.21	.16	.06
286 George Witt	.21	.16	.06
287 Carl Yastrzemski	16.00	12.00	5.50
288 Albie Pearson	.21	.16	.06
289 Ray Moore	.21	.16	.06
290 Stan Musial	8.00	6.00	2.50
291 Tex Clevenger	.21	.16	.06
292 Jim Baumer	.21	.16	.06
293 Tom Sturdivant	.21	.16	.06
294 Don Blasingame	.21	.16	.06
295 Milt Pappas	.30	.25	.10
296 Wes Covington	.21	.16	.06
297 Athletics Team	.40	.30	.13
298 Jim Golden	.21	.16	.06
299 Clay Dalrymple	.21	.16	.06
300 Mickey Mantle	20.00	15.00	6.50
301 Chet Nichols	.21	.16	.06
302 Al Heist	.21	.16	.06
303 Gary Peters	.21	.16	.06
304 Rocky Nelson	.21	.16	.06
305 Mike McCormick	.21	.16	.06
306 World Series Game 1	.65	.50	.20
307 World Series Game 2	.65	.50	.20
308 World Series Game 3	.65	.50	.20
309 World Series Game 4	.65	.50	.20
310 World Series Game 5	.65	.50	.20
311 World Series Game 6	.65	.50	.20
312 World Series Game 7	.65	.50	.20
313 World Series Celeb.	.65	.50	.20
314 Bob Miller	.21	.16	.06
315 Earl Battey	.21	.16	.06
316 Bobby Gene Smith	.21	.16	.06
317 Jim Brewer	.21	.16	.06
318 Danny O'Connell	.21	.16	.06
319 Valmy Thomas	.21	.16	.06
320 Lou Burdette	.60	.45	.20
321 Marv Breeding	.21	.16	.06
322 Billy Kunkel	.21	.16	.06
323 Sammy Esposito	.21	.16	.06
324 Hank Aguirre	.21	.16	.06
325 Wally Moon	.30	.25	.10
326 Dave Hillman	.21	.15	.06
327 Matty Alou	.50	.40	.18
328 Jim O'Toole	.21	.16	.06
329 Julio Becquer	.21	.16	.06
330 Rocky Colavito	1.00	.70	.30
331 Ned Garver	.21	.16	.06

	MINT	VG-E	F-G
332 Dutch Dotterer	.21	.16	.06
333 Fritz Brickell	.21	.16	.06
334 Walt Bond	.21	.16	.06
335 Frank Bolling	.21	.16	.06
336 Don Mincher	.21	.16	.06
337 Al's Aces	1.25	.90	.40
338 Don Landrum	.21	.16	.06
339 Gene Baker	.21	.16	.06
340 Vic Wertz	.21	.16	.06
341 Jim Owens	.21	.16	.06
342 Clint Courtney	.21	.16	.06
343 Earl Robinson	.21	.16	.06
344 Sandy Koufax	8.00	6.00	2.50
345 Jim Piersall	.50	.40	.18
346 Howie Nunn	.21	.16	.06
347 Cardinals Team	.50	.40	.18
348 Steve Boros	.21	.16	.06
349 Danny McDevitt	.21	.16	.06
350 Ernie Banks	4.50	3.50	1.60
351 Jim King	.21	.16	.06
352 Bob Shaw	.21	.16	.06
353 Howie Bedell	.21	.16	.06
354 Billy Harrell	.21	.16	.06
355 Bob Allison	.30	.25	.10
356 Ryne Duren	.30	.25	.10
357 Daryl Spencer	.21	.16	.06
358 Earl Averill	.21	.16	.06
359 Dallas Green	.60	.45	.20
360 Frank Robinson	6.00	4.50	2.00
361 Check List 5	.30	.25	.10
362 Frank Funk	.21	.16	.06
363 John Roseboro	.21	.16	.06
364 Moe Drabowski	.21	.16	.06
365 Jerry Lumpe	.21	.16	.06
366 Eddie Fisher	.21	.16	.06
367 Jim Rivera	.21	.16	.06
368 Bennie Daniels	.21	.16	.06
369 Dave Philley	.21	.16	.06
370 Roy Face	.30	.25	.10
371 Bill Skowron	.75	.55	.25
372 Bob Hendley	.21	.16	.06
373 Red Sox Team	.60	.45	.20
374 Paul Giel	.21	.16	.06
375 Ken Boyer	1.00	.70	.30
376 Mike Roarke	.21	.16	.06
377 Ruben Gomez	.21	.16	.06
378 Wally Post	.21	.16	.06
379 Bobby Shantz	.40	.30	.13
380 Minnie Minoso	.80	.60	.25
381 Dave Wickersham	.21	.16	.06
382 Frank Thomas	.21	.16	.06
383 Frisco 1st Liners	.30	.25	.10
384 Chuck Essegian	.21	.16	.06
385 Jim Perry	.30	.25	.10
386 Joe Hicks	.21	.16	.06
387 Duke Maas	.21	.16	.06
388 Bob Clemente	9.50	7.00	3.00
389 Ralph Terry	.21	.16	.06
390 Del Crandall	.30	.25	.10
391 Winston Brown	.21	.16	.06
392 Reno Bertoia	.21	.16	.06
393 Batter Bafflers	.30	.25	.10
394 Ken Walters	.21	.16	.06
395 Chuck Estrada	.21	.16	.06
396 Bob Aspromonte	.21	.16	.06
397 Hal Woodeshick	.21	.16	.06
398 Hank Bauer	.40	.30	.13
399 Cliff Cook	.21	.16	.06
400 Vern Law	.30	.25	.10
401 Ruth - 60th Homer	3.00	2.25	1.00
402 Perfect Game	.60	.45	.20
403 26-Inning Tie	.30	.25	.10
404 Hornsby 424 Average	.80	.60	.25
405 Gehrig's Streak	2.50	1.80	.80
406 Mantle 565 Ft. H. R.	2.50	1.80	.80
407 Chesbro Wins 41	.30	.25	.10
408 Mathewson Fans 267	1.00	.70	.30
409 Johnson Shutouts	1.00	.70	.30
410 Haddix 12 Innings	.40	.30	.13
411 Tony Taylor	.21	.16	.06
412 Larry Sherry	.30	.25	.10
413 Eddie Yost	.21	.16	.06
414 Dick Donovan	.21	.16	.06
415 Hank Aaron	15.00	11.00	5.00
416 Dick Howser	.40	.30	.13
417 Juan Marichal	3.00	2.25	1.00
418 Ed Bailey	.21	.16	.06
419 Tom Borland	.21	.16	.06
420 Ernie Broglio	.21	.16	.06
421 Ty Cline	.21	.16	.06
422 Bud Daley	.21	.16	.06
423 Charlie Neal	.21	.16	.06
424 Turk Lown	.21	.16	.06
425 Yogi Berra	6.00	4.50	2.00
426 Braves Team (#463)	1.25	.90	.40

	MINT	VG-E	F-G
427 Dick Ellsworth	.21	.16	.06
428 Ray Barker	.21	.16	.06
429 Al Kaline	5.00	3.75	1.75
430 Bill Mazeroski	.50	.40	.18
431 Chuck Stobbs	.21	.16	.06
432 Coot Veal	.21	.16	.06
433 Art Mahaffey	.21	.16	.06
434 Tom Brewer	.21	.16	.06
435 Orlando Cepeda	1.50	1.10	.50
436 Jim Maloney	.30	.25	.10
437 Check List 6	.21	.16	.06
438 Curt Flood	.40	.30	.13
439 Phil Regan	.21	.16	.06
440 Luis Aparicio	1.00	.70	.30
441 Dick Bertell	.21	.16	.06
442 Gordon Jones	.21	.16	.06
443 Duke Snider	5.50	4.25	2.00
444 Joe Nuxhall	.30	.25	.10
445 Frank Malzone	.21	.16	.06
446 Bob Taylor	.21	.16	.06
447 Harry Bright	.21	.16	.06
448 Del Rice	.21	.16	.06
449 Bob Bolin	.21	.16	.06
450 Jim Lemon	.21	.16	.06
451 Power for Ernie	.30	.25	.10
452 Bob Allen	.21	.16	.06
453 Dick Schofield	.21	.16	.06
454 Pumpsie Green	.21	.16	.06
455 Early Wynn	2.50	1.80	.80
456 Hal Bevan	.21	.16	.06
457 John James	.21	.16	.06
458 Willie Tasby	.21	.16	.06
459 Terry Fox	.21	.16	.06
460 Gil Hodges	3.00	2.25	1.00
461 Smoky Burgess	.21	.16	.06
462 Lou Klimchock	.21	.16	.06
463 Jack Fisher	.30	.25	.10
464 Leroy Thomas	.21	.16	.06
465 Roy McMillan	.21	.16	.06
466 Ron Moeller	.21	.16	.06
467 Indians Team	.40	.30	.13
468 John Callison	.21	.16	.03
469 Ralph Lumenti	.21	.16	.03
470 Roy Sievers	.25	.20	.08
471 Phil Rizzuto, MVP	3.00	2.25	1.00
472 Yogi Berra, MVP	4.00	3.00	1.40
473 Bob Shantz, MVP	.75	.55	.25
474 Al Rosen, MVP	1.25	.90	.40
475 Mickey Mantle, MVP	8.00	6.00	2.50
476 Jackie Jensen, MVP	.75	.55	.25
477 Nellie Fox, MVP	1.25	.90	.40
478 Roger Maris, MVP	2.50	1.80	.80
479 Jim Konstanty, MVP	.75	.55	.25
480 Roy Campanella, MVP	4.50	3.50	1.60
481 Hank Sauer, MVP	.75	.55	.25
482 Willie Mays, MVP	6.00	4.50	2.00
483 Don Newcombe, MVP	1.00	.70	.30
484 Hank Aaron, MVP	6.00	4.50	2.00
485 Ernie Banks, MVP	3.50	2.50	1.20
486 Dick Groat, MVP	.75	.55	.25
487 Gene Oliver	.21	.16	.06
488 Joe McClain	.21	.16	.06
489 Walt Dropo	.21	.16	.06
490 Jim Bunning	.80	.60	.25
491 Phillies Team	.50	.40	.18
492 Ron Fairly	.30	.25	.10
493 Don Zimmer	.40	.30	.13
494 Tom Cheney	.21	.16	.06
495 Elston Howard	1.25	.90	.40
496 Ken Mackenzie	.21	.16	.06
397 Willie Jones	.21	.16	.06
498 Ray Herbert	.21	.16	.06
499 Chuck Schilling	.21	.16	.06
500 Harvey Kuenn	.50	.40	.18
501 John Demerit	.21	.16	.06
502 Clarence Coleman	.21	.16	.06
503 Tito Francona	.21	.16	.06
504 Billy Consolo	.21	.16	.06
505 Red Schoendienst	.50	.40	.18
506 Willie Davis	.75	.55	.25
507 Pete Burnside	.21	.16	.06
508 Rocky Bridges	.21	.16	.06
509 Cam Carreon	.21	.16	.06
510 Art Ditmar	.21	.16	.06
511 Joe Morgan	.21	.16	.06
512 Bob Will	.21	.16	.06
513 Jim Brosnan	.21	.16	.06
514 Jake Wood	.21	.16	.06
515 Jackie Brandt	.21	.16	.06
516 Check List 7	.21	.16	.06
517 Willie McCovey	6.50	5.00	2.25
518 Andy Carey	.21	.16	.06
519 Jim Pagliaroni	.21	.16	.06

	MINT	VG-E	F-G
520 Joe Cunningham	.21	.16	.06
521 Brother Battery	.40	.30	.13
522 Dick Farrell	.21	.16	.06
523 Joe Gibbon	5.50	4.25	1.75
524 John Logan	5.50	4.25	1.75
525 Ron Perranoski	5.50	4.25	1.75
526 R. C. Stevens	5.50	4.25	1.75
527 Gene Leek	5.50	4.25	1.75
528 Pedro Ramos	5.50	4.25	1.75
529 Bob Roselli	5.50	4.25	1.75
530 Bob Malkmus	5.50	4.25	1.75
531 Jim Coates	5.50	4.25	1.75
532 Bob Hale	5.50	4.25	1.75
533 Jack Curtis	5.50	4.25	1.75
534 Eddie Kasko	5.50	4.25	1.75
535 Larry Jackson	5.50	4.25	1.75
536 Bill Tuttle	5.50	4.25	1.75
537 Bobby Locke	5.50	4.25	1.75
538 Chuck Hiller	5.50	4.25	1.75
539 John Klippstein	5.50	4.25	1.75
540 Jackie Jensen	8.00	6.00	2.50
541 Roland Sheldon	5.50	4.25	1.75
542 Minnesota Twins Team	8.00	6.00	2.50
543 Roger Craig	8.00	6.00	2.50
544 George Thomas	5.50	4.25	1.75
545 Hoyt Wilhelm	12.00	8.75	4.00
546 Marty Kutyna	5.50	4.25	1.75
547 Leon Wagner	5.50	4.25	1.75
548 Ted Wills	5.50	4.25	1.75
549 Hal R. Smith	5.50	4.25	1.75
550 Frank Baumann	5.50	4.25	1.75
551 George Altman	5.50	4.25	1.75
552 Jim Archer	5.50	4.25	1.75
553 Bill Fischer	5.50	4.25	1.75
554 Pitt. Pirates Team	8.00	6.00	2.50
555 Sam Jones	5.50	4.25	1.75
556 Ken R. Hunt	5.50	4.25	1.75
557 Jose Valdivielso	5.50	4.25	1.75
558 Don Ferrarese	5.50	4.25	1.75
559 Jim Gentile	5.50	4.25	1.75
560 Barry Latman	5.50	4.25	1.75
561 Charley James	5.50	4.25	1.75
562 Bill Monbouquette	5.50	4.25	1.75
563 Bob Cerv	5.50	4.25	1.75
564 Don Cardwell	5.50	4.25	1.75
565 Felipe Alou	7.00	5.25	2.50
566 Paul Richards, AS	7.00	5.25	2.50
567 Danny Murtaugh, AS	7.00	5.25	2.50
568 Bill Skowron, AS	8.00	6.00	2.50
569 Frank Herrera, AS	7.00	5.25	2.50
570 Nellie Fox, AS	8.00	6.00	2.50
571 Bill Mazeroski, AS	7.00	5.25	2.50
572 Brooks Robinson, AS	18.00	13.50	6.00
573 Ken Boyer, AS	8.00	6.00	2.50
574 Luis Aparicio, AS	8.00	6.00	2.50
575 Ernie Banks, AS	18.00	13.50	6.00
576 Roger Maris, AS	16.00	12.00	5.50
577 Hank Aaron, AS	60.00	45.00	20.00
578 Mickey Mantle, AS	80.00	60.00	25.00
579 Willie Mays, AS	60.00	45.00	20.00
580 Al Kaline, AS	18.00	13.50	6.00
581 Frank Robinson, AS	18.00	13.50	6.00
582 Earl Battey, AS	7.00	5.25	2.50
583 Del Crandall, AS	7.00	5.25	2.50
584 Jim Perry, AS	7.00	5.25	2.50
585 Bob Friend, AS	7.00	5.25	2.50
586 Whitey Ford, AS	18.00	13.50	6.00
589 Warren Spahn, AS	18.00	13.50	6.00

1962 TOPPS (598)

2 1/2″ X 3 1/2″

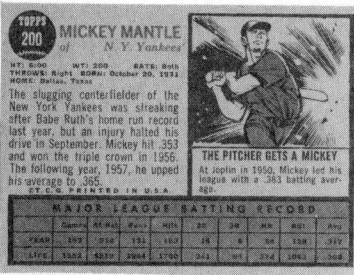

The 1962 Topps set features a series of Babe Ruth Special cards nos. 135-144. Card no. 139 exists as 1) a Babe Ruth Special card, 2) Hal Reniff in an arms over head pose, and 3) Hal Reniff in the same pose as card no. 159. Card nos. 390-399 are the Sporting News National League All-Star selections and card nos. 466-475 are The Sporting News American League All-Star selections. Two different player poses exist of the card nos. 129, 132, 134, 147,174, I76, and 190. High numbers 523-598 are somewhat more difficult to obtain. Set price includes second series pose variations.

	MINT	VG-E	F-G
COMPLETE SET	400.00	300.00	140.00
COMMON PLAYERS (1-412)	.20	.15	.06
COMMON PLAYERS (413-522)	.30	.25	.10
COMMON PLAYERS (523-598)	1.10	.80	.30

	MINT	VG-E	F-G
1 Roger Maris	7.00	4.00	1.50
2 Jim Brosnan	.20	.15	.06
3 Pete Runnels	.20	.15	.06
4 John De Merit	.20	.15	.06
5 Sandy Koufax	8.00	6.00	2.50
6 Marv Breeding	.20	.15	.06
7 Frank Thomas	.20	.15	.06
8 Ray Herbert	.20	.15	.06
9 Jim Davenport	.20	.15	.06
10 Bob Clemente	8.00	6.00	2.50
11 Tom Morgan	.20	.15	.06
12 Harry Craft	.20	.15	.06
13 Dick Howser	.40	.30	.13
14 Bill White	.30	.25	.10
15 Dick Donovan	.20	.15	.06
16 Darrell Johnson	.20	.15	.06
17 John Callison	.20	.15	.06
18 Managers' Dream	4.50	3.50	1.60
19 Ray Washburn	.20	.15	.06
20 Rocky Colavito	1.00	.70	.30
21 Jim Kaat	.75	.55	.25
22A Checklist 1 (Corr.)	.30	.25	.10
22B Checklist 1 (Wrong)	2.00	1.50	.60
23 Norm Larker	.20	.15	.06
24 Tigers Team	.40	.30	.13
25 Ernie Banks	4.00	3.00	1.40
26 C. Cannizzaro	.20	.15	.06
27 Chuck Cottier	.20	.15	.06
28 Minnie Minoso	.80	.60	.25
29 Casey Stengel	3.00	2.25	1.10
30 Ed Mathews	3.50	2.50	1.20
31 Tom Tresh	.40	.30	.13
32 John Roseboro	.20	.15	.06
33 Don Larsen	.40	.30	.13
34 Johnny Temple	.20	.15	.06
35 Don Schwall	.20	.15	.06
36 Don Leppert	.20	.15	.06
37 Tribe Hill Trio	.30	.25	.10
38 Gene Stephens	.20	.15	.06
39 Joe Koppe	.20	.15	.06
40 Orlando Cepeda	1.25	.90	.40
41 Cliff Cook	.20	.15	.06
42 Jim King	.20	.15	.06
43 Dodgers Team	.60	.45	.20
44 Don Taussig	.20	.15	.06
45 B. Robinson	4.00	3.00	1.40
46 Jack Baldschun	.20	.15	.06
47 Bob Will	.20	.15	.06
48 Ralph Terry	.20	.15	.06
49 Hal Jones	.20	.15	.06
50 Stan Musial	7.50	5.75	2.50
51 A. L. Bat Leaders	.50	.40	.18
52 N. L. Bat Leaders	.50	.40	.18
53 A. L. H.R. Leaders	.50	.40	.18
54 N. L. H.R. Leaders	.50	.40	.18
55 A. L. E.R.A. Leaders	.50	.40	.18
56 N. L. E.R.A. Leaders	.50	.40	.18
57 A. L. Wins Leaders	.50	.40	.18
58 N. L. Wins Leaders	.50	.40	.18
59 A. L. S.O. Leaders	.50	.40	.18
60 N. L. S.O. Leaders	.50	.40	.18

	MINT	VG-E	F-G
61 Cardinals Team	.40	.30	.13
62 Steve Boros	.20	.15	.06
63 Tony Cloninger	.20	.15	.06
64 Russ Snyder	.20	.15	.06
65 B. Richardson	.40	.30	.13
66 Cuno Barragon	.20	.15	.06
67 Harvey Haddix	.30	.25	.10
68 Ken Hunt	.20	.15	.06
69 Phil Ortega	.20	.15	.06
70 H. Killebrew	3.00	2.25	1.00
71 Dick Le May	.20	.15	.06
72 Bob's Pupils	.25	.20	.08
73 Nellie Fox	1.00	.70	.30
74 Bob Lillis	.20	.15	.06
75 Milt Pappas	.25	.20	.08
76 Howie Bedell	.20	.15	.06
77 Tony Taylor	.20	.15	.06
78 Gene Green	.20	.15	.06
79 Ed Hobaugh	.20	.15	.06
80 Vada Pinson	.80	.60	.25
81 Jim Pagliaroni	.20	.15	.06
82 Deron Johnson	.20	.15	.06
83 Larry Jackson	.20	.15	.06
84 Lenny Green	.20	.15	.06
85 Gil Hodges	3.00	2.25	1.00
86 D. Clendennon	.20	.15	.06
87 Mike Roarke	.20	.15	.06
88 Ralph Houk	.40	.30	.13
89 Barney Schultz	.20	.15	.06
90 Jim Piersall	.40	.30	.13
91 J. C. Martin	.20	.15	.06
92 Sam Jones	.20	.15	.06
93 J. Blanchard	.20	.15	.06
94 Jay Hook	.20	.15	.06
95 Don Hoak	.20	.15	.06
96 Eli Grba	.20	.15	.06
97 Tito Francona	.20	.15	.06
98 Check List 2	.20	.15	.06
99 John Powell	1.50	1.10	.50
100 Warren Spahn	3.50	2.50	1.20
101 Carroll Hardy	.20	.15	.06
102 Al Schroll	.20	.15	.06
103 D. Blasingame	.20	.15	.06
104 Ted Savage	.20	.15	.06
105 Don Mossi	.20	.15	.06
106 Carl Sawatski	.20	.15	.06
107 M. McCormick	.20	.15	.06
108 Willie Davis	.30	.25	.10
109 Bob Shaw	.20	.15	.06
110 Bill Skowron	.50	.40	.18
111 Dallas Green	.50	.40	.18
112 Hank Foiles	.20	.15	.06
113 W. Sox Team	.40	.30	.13
114 Howie Koplitz	.20	.15	.06
115 Bob Skinner	.20	.15	.06
116 Herb Score	.40	.30	.13
117 Gary Geiger	.20	.15	.06
118 Julian Javier	.20	.15	.06
119 Danny Murphy	.20	.15	.06
120 Bob Purkey	.20	.15	.06
121 B. Hitchcock	.20	.15	.06
122 Norm Bass	.20	.15	.06
123 Mike De La Hoz	.20	.15	.06
124 Bill Pleis	.20	.15	.06

	MINT	VG-E	F-G
125 Gene Woodling	.25	.20	.08
126 Al Cicotte	.20	.15	.06
127 Pride of A's:	.25	.20	.08
Sieburn, Bauer,			
Lumpe			
128 Art Fowler	.20	.15	.06
129A Lee Walls(face rt)	.40	.30	.13
129B Lee Walls(face lft)	3.00	2.25	1.00
130 Frank Bolling	.20	.15	.06
131 Pete Richert	.20	.15	.06
132A Angels Team(w/o photo)	.60	.45	.20
132B Angels Team(w/photo)	3.00	2.25	1.00
133 Felipe Alou	.30	.25	.10
134A Billy Hoeft(face rt)	.40	.30	.13
134B Billy Hoeft(face st)	3.00	2.25	1.00
135 Babe Ruth - 1	2.50	1.80	.80
136 Babe Ruth - 2	2.50	1.80	.80
137 Babe Ruth - 3	2.50	1.80	.80
138 Babe Ruth - 4	2.50	1.80	.80
139A Babe Ruth - 5	2.50	1.80	.80
139B Hal Reniff (port)	5.00	3.75	1.75
139C Hal Reniff (pitch)	20.00	15.00	6.50
140 Babe Ruth - 6	2.50	1.80	.80
141 Babe Ruth 7	2.50	1.80	.80
142 Babe Ruth 8	2.50	1.80	.80
143 Babe Ruth 9	2.50	1.80	.80
144 Babe Ruth - 10	2.50	1.80	.80
145 Barry Latman	.20	.15	.06
146 Don Demeter	.20	.15	.06
147A Bill Kunkel(port)	.40	.30	.13
147B Bill Kunkel(pitch)	3.00	2.25	1.00
148 Wally Post	.20	.15	.06
149 Bob Duliba	.20	.15	.06
150 Al Kaline	4.25	3.25	1.50
151 J. Klippstein	.20	.15	.06
152 Mickey Vernon	.25	.20	.08
153 Pumpsie Green	.20	.15	.06
154 Lee Thomas	.20	.15	.06
155 Stu Miller	.20	.15	.06
156 Merritt Ranew	.20	.15	.06
157 Wes Covington	.20	.15	.06
158 Braves Team	.40	.30	.13
159 Hal Reniff	.40	.30	.13
160 Dick Stuart	.30	.25	.10
161 F. Baumann	.20	.15	.06
162 Sammy Drake	.20	.15	.06
163 Hot Cor. Guard:	.25	.20	.08
Gardner, Boyer			
164 Hal Naragon	.20	.15	.06
165 Jackie Brandt	.20	.15	.06
166 Don Lee	.20	.15	.06
167 Tim McCarver	.40	.30	.13
168 Leo Posada	.20	.15	.06
169 Bob Cerv	.20	.15	.06
170 Ron Santo	.75	.55	.25
171 Dave Sisler	.20	.15	.06
172 F. Hutchinson	.30	.25	.10
173 C. Fernandez	.20	.15	.06
174A Carl Willey(capless)	.40	.30	.13
174B Carl Willey(w/cap)	3.00	2.25	1.00
175 Frank Howard	1.00	.70	.30
176A Eddie Yost(port)	.40	.30	.13
176B Eddie Yost(batting)	3.00	2.25	1.00
177 Bobby Shantz	.30	.25	.10
178 Cam Carreon	.20	.15	.06
179 Tom Sturdivant	.20	.15	.06
180 Bob Allison	.30	.25	.10
181 Paul Brown	.20	.15	.06
182 Bob Nieman	.20	.15	.06
183 Roger Craig	.30	.25	.10
184 H. Sullivan	.30	.25	.10
185 R. Sheldon	.20	.15	.06
186 Mack Jones	.20	.15	.06
187 Gene Conley	.20	.15	.06
188 Chuck Hiller	.20	.15	.06
189 Dick Hall	.20	.15	.06
190A Wally Moon(port)	.60	.45	.20
190B Wally Moon(batting)	4.00	3.00	1.40
191 Jim Brewer	.20	.15	.06
192A Checklist 3(w/o comma)	.40	.30	.13
192B Checklist 3(w/comma)	2.00	1.50	.60
193 Eddie Kasko	.20	.15	.06
194 Dean Chance	.30	.25	.10
195 Joe Cunningham	.20	.15	.06
196 Terry Fox	.20	.15	.06
197 Daryl Spencer	.20	.15	.06
198 Johnny Keane	.20	.15	.06
199 Gaylord Perry	5.50	4.25	2.00
200 Mickey Mantle	18.00	13.50	6.00

	MINT	VG-E	F-G
201 Ike Delock	.20	.15	.06
202 Carl Warwick	.20	.15	.06
203 Jack Fisher	.20	.15	.06
204 J. Weekly	.20	.15	.06
205 Gene Freese	.20	.15	.06
206 Senators Team	.40	.30	.13
207 Pete Burnside	.20	.15	.06
208 Billy Martin	1.00	.70	.30
209 Jim Fregosi	1.25	.90	.40
210 Roy Face	.25	.20	.08
211 Mid. Masters:	.25	.20	.08
Bolling, McMillan			
212 Jim Owens	.20	.15	.06
213 R. Ashburn	.80	.60	.25
214 Dom Zanni	.20	.15	.06
215 Woody Held	.20	.15	.06
216 Ron Kline	.20	.15	.06
217 Walt Alston	.40	.30	.13
218 Joe Torre	1.50	1.10	.50
219 Al Downing	.20	.15	.06
220 Roy Sievers	.25	.20	.08
221 Bill Short	.20	.15	.06
222 J. Zimmerman	.20	.15	.06
223 Alex Grammas	.20	.15	.06
224 Don Rudolph	.20	.15	.06
225 Frank Malzone	.25	.20	.08
226 Giants Team	.45	.35	.15
227 B. Tiefenauer	.20	.15	.06
228 Dale Long	.20	.15	.06
229 J. McFarlane	.20	.15	.06
230 C. Pascual	.25	.20	.08
231 E. Bowman	.20	.15	.06
232 World Series 1	.55	.40	.18
233 World Series 2	.55	.40	.18
234 World Series 3	.55	.40	.18
235 World Series 4	.55	.40	.18
236 World Series 5	.55	.40	.18
237 World Series 6	.55	.40	.18
238 Norm Sherry	.20	.15	.06
239 Cecil Butler	.20	.15	.06
240 George Altman	.20	.15	.06
241 Johnny Kucks	.20	.15	.06
242 Mel McGaha	.20	.15	.06
243 Robin Roberts	3.00	2.25	1.10
244 Don Gile	.20	.15	.06
245 Ron Hansen	.20	.15	.06
246 Art Ditmar	.20	.15	.06
247 J. Pignatano	.20	.15	.06
248 B. Aspromonte	.20	.15	.06
249 Ed Keegan	.20	.15	.06
250 Norm Cash	.75	.55	.25
251 New York Yankees	.75	.55	.25
252 Earl Francis	.20	.15	.06
253 Harry Chiti	.20	.15	.06
254 G. Windhorn	.20	.15	.06
255 Juan Pizarro	.20	.15	.06
256 Elio Chacon	.20	.15	.06
257 Jack Spring	.20	.15	.06
258 Marty Keough	.20	.15	.06
259 Lou Klimchock	.20	.15	.06
260 Bill Pierce	.75	.55	.25
261 George Alusik	.20	.15	.06
262 Bob Schmidt	.20	.15	.06
263 The Right Pitch:	.25	.20	.08
Purkey, Turner,			
Jay			
264 Dick Ellsworth	.25	.20	.08
265 Joe Adcock	.30	.25	.10
266 John Anderson	.20	.15	.06
267 Dan Dobbek	.20	.15	.06
268 Ken McBride	.20	.15	.06
269 Bob Oldis	.20	.15	.06
270 Dick Groat	.30	.25	.10
271 R. Rippelmeyer	.20	.15	.06
272 Earl Robinson	.20	.15	.06
273 Gary Bell	.20	.15	.06
274 Sammy Taylor	.20	.15	.06
275 Norm Siebern	.20	.15	.06
276 Hal Kolstad	.20	.15	.06
277 Checklist 4	.20	.15	.06
278 Ken Johnson	.20	.15	.06
279 Hobie Landrith	.20	.15	.06
280 Johnny Podres	.40	.30	.13
281 Jake Gibbs	.20	.15	.06
282 Dave Hillman	.20	.15	.06
283 Charlie Smith	.20	.15	.06
284 Ruben Amaro	.20	.15	.06
285 Curt Simmons	.25	.20	.08
286 Al Lopez	1.00	.70	.30

REMEMBER THE NATIONAL CONVENTION IS BEING HELD JULY 9 - 12, 1981, IN PLYMOUTH, MICHIGAN

1962 TOPPS (CONTINUED)

	MINT	VG-E	F-G			MINT	VG-E	F-G
287 George Witt	.20	.15	.06	300 Willie Mays		15.00	11.00	5.00
288 Billy Williams	1.50	1.10	.50	301 Galen Cisco		.20	.15	.06
289 Mike Krsnich	.20	.15	.06	302 John Edwards		.20	.15	.06
290 Jim Gentile	.25	.20	.08	303 Frank Torre		.20	.15	.06
291 Hal Stowe	.20	.15	.06	304 Dick Farrell		.20	.15	.06
292 Jerry Kindall	.20	.15	.06	305 Jerry Lumpe		.20	.15	.06
293 Bob Miller	.20	.15	.06	306 Redbird Rippers:		.25	.20	.08
294 Phillies Team	.40	.30	.13	McDaniel, Jackson				
295 Vern Law	.25	.20	.08	307 Jim Grant		.20	.15	.06
296 Ken Hamlin	.20	.15	.06	308 Neil Chrisley		.20	.15	.06
297 Ron Perranoski	.20	.15	.06	309 Moe Morhardt		.20	.15	.06
298 Bill Tuttle	.20	.15	.06	310 Whitey Ford		4.00	3.00	1.40
299 Don Wert	.20	.15	.06	311 Kubek in Action		.50	.40	.18

1962 TOPPS VARIATIONS

With over 2 Million Cards in Stock,
We can fill any Want-List.

Topps & Bowman   *Goudey* ★
Tobacco Cards   *Non Sport Cards* ★
Programs ★ *Yearbooks* ★ *Magazines* ★

Au Sports Memorabilia
Dept. PG3
3328½ Dempster
Skokie, IL 60076
(312) 679-8310

	MINT	VG-E	F-G			MINT	VG-E	F-G
312 Spahn in Action	1.50	1.10	.50	405 Jim Perry		.25	.20	.08
313 Maris in Action	1.25	.90	.40	406 Bob Taylor		.20	.15	.06
314 Colavito in Action	.40	.30	.13	407 Hank Aguirre		.20	.15	.06
315 Ford in Action	1.50	1.10	.50	408 Gus Bell		.20	.15	.06
316 Killebrew in Action	1.00	.70	.30	409 Pirates Team		.45	.35	.15
317 Musial in Action	2.00	1.50	.60	410 Al Smith		.20	.15	.06
318 Mantle in Action	2.75	2.00	.90	411 D. O'Connell		.20	.15	.06
319 McCormick in Action	.25	.20	.08	412 Charlie James		.20	.15	.06
320 Hank Aaron	15.00	11.00	5 00	413 Matty Alou		.40	.30	.13
321 Lee Stange	.20	.15	.06	414 Joe Gaines		.30	.25	.10
322 Al Dark	.30	.25	.10	415 Bill Virdon		.75	.55	.25
323 Don Landrum	.20	.15	.06	416 Bob Scheffing		.30	.25	.10
324 Joe McClain	.20	.15	.06	417 Joe Azcue		.30	.25	.10
325 Luis Aparicio	1.00	.70	.30	418 Andy Carey		.30	.25	.10
326 Tom Parsons	.20	.15	.06	419 Bob Bruce		.30	.25	.10
327 Ozzie Virgil	.20	.15	.06	420 Gus Triandos		.30	.25	.10
328 Ken Walters	.20	.15	.06	421 Ken Mackenzie		.30	.25	.10
329 Bob Bolin	.20	.15	.06	422 Steve Bilko		.30	.25	.10
330 John Romano	.20	.15	.06	423 Rival Aces		.50	.40	.18
331 Moe Drabowsky	.20	.15	.06	424 Al McBean		.30	.25	.10
332 Don Buddin	.20	.15	.06	425 C. Yastrzemski	20.00	15.00	6.50
333 Frank Cipriani	.20	.15	.06	426 Bob Farley		.30	.25	.10
334 Red Sox Team	.50	.40	.18	427 Jake Wood		.30	.25	.10
335 Bill Bruton	.20	.15	.06	428 Joe Hicks		.30	.25	.10
336 Billy Muffett	.20	.15	.06	429 Billy O'Dell		.30	.25	.10
337 Jim Marshall	.20	.15	.06	430 Tony Kubek		.75	.55	.25
338 Billy Gardner	.20	.15	.06	431 Bob Rodgers		.30	.25	.10
339 J. Valdivielso	.20	.15	.06	432 Jim Pendleton		.30	.25	.10
340 Don Drysdale	3.50	2.50	1.20	433 Jim Archer		.30	.25	.10
341 M. Hershberger	.20	.15	.06	434 C. Dalrymple		.30	.25	.10
342 Ed Rakow	.20	.15	.06	435 Larry Sherry		.30	.25	.10
343 Albie Pearson	.20	.15	.06	436 Felix Mantilla		.30	.25	.10
344 Ed Bauta	.20	.15	.06	437 Ray Moore		.30	.25	.10
345 Chuck Schilling	.20	.15	.06	438 Dick Brown		.30	.25	.10
346 Jack Kralick	.20	.15	.06	439 Jerry Buchek		.30	.25	.10
347 Chuck Hinton	.20	.15	.06	440 Joe Jay		.30	.25	.10
348 Larry Burright	.20	.15	.06	441 Check List 6		.30	.25	.10
349 Paul Foytack	.20	.15	.06	442 Wes Stock		.30	.25	.10
350 Frank Robinson	4.25	3.25	1.50	443 Del Crandall		.40	.30	.13
351 Braves' Backstops	.30	.25	.10	444 Ted Wills		.30	.25	.10
352 Frank Sullivan	.20	.15	.06	445 Vic Power		.30	.25	.10
353 B. Mazeroski	.40	.30	.18	446 Don Elston		.30	.25	.10
354 R. Mejias	.20	.15	.06	447 Willie Kirkland		.30	.25	.10
355 Steve Barber	.20	.15	.06	448 Joe Gibbon		.30	.25	.10
356 Tom Haller	.20	.15	.06	449 Jerry Adair		.30	.25	.10
357 Jerry Walker	.20	.15	.06	450 Jim O'Toole		.30	.25	.10
358 Tommy Davis	.40	.30	.18	451 Jose Tartabull		.30	.25	.10
359 Bobby Locke	.20	.15	.06	452 Earl Averill		.30	.25	.10
360 Yogi Berra	4.50	3.50	1.60	453 Cal McLish		.30	.25	.10
361 Bob Hendley	.20	.15	.06	454 Floyd Robinson		.30	.25	.10
362 Ty Cline	.20	.15	.06	455 Luis Arroyo		.30	.25	.10
363 Bob Roselli	.20	.15	.06	456 J. Amalfitano		.30	.25	.10
364 Ken Hunt	.20	.15	.06	457 Lou Clinton		.50	.40	.18
365 Charley Neal	.20	.15	.06	458 Bob Buhl		.30	.25	.10
366 Phil Regan	.20	.15	.06	459 Ed Bailey		.30	.25	.10
367 Check List 5	.20	.15	.06	460 Jim Bunning		.75	.55	.25
368 Bob Tillman	.20	.15	.06	461 Ken Hubbs	1.00	.70	.30
369 Ted Bowsfield	.20	.15	.06	462 Willie Tasby		.50	.40	.18
370 Ken Boyer	1.00	.70	.30	463 Hank Bauer		.40	.30	.13
371 Earl Battey	.20	.15	.06	464 Al Jackson		.30	.25	.10
372 Jack Curtis	.20	.15	.06	465 Reds Team		.75	.55	.25
373 Al Heist	.20	.15	.06	466 Norm Cash, AS		.50	.40	.18
374 Gene Mauch	.30	.25	.10	467 C. Schilling, AS		.40	.30	.13
375 Ron Fairly	.30	.25	.10	468 B. Robinson, AS	3.00	2.25	1.00
376 Bud Daley	.20	.15	.06	469 Luis Aparicio, AS		.75	.55	.25
377 John Orsino	.20	.15	.06	470 Al Kaline, AS	3.00	2.25	1.00
378 Bennie Daniels	.20	.15	.06	471 M. Mantle, AS	7.00	5.25	2.50
379 C. Essegian	.20	.15	.06	472 R. Colavito, AS		.60	.45	.20
380 Lou Burdette	.40	.30	.13	473 Elston Howard, AS		.75	.55	.25
381 C. Cardenas	.20	.15	.06	474 Frank Lary, AS		.40	.30	.13
382 Dick Williams	.30	.25	.10	475 Whitey Ford, AS	2.50	1.80	.80
383 Ray Sadecki	.20	.15	.06	476 Orioles Team		.60	.45	.20
384 K. C. A. Team	.40	.30	.13	477 Andre Rodgers		.30	.25	.10
385 Early Wynn	3.00	2.25	1.10	478 Don Zimmer		.50	.40	.18
386 Don Mincher	.20	.15	.06	479 Joel Horlen		.30	.25	.10
387 Lou Brock	16.00	12.00	5.50	480 Harvey Kuenn		.60	.45	.20
388 Ryne Duren	.25	.20	.08	481 Vic Wertz		.30	.25	.10
389 Smokey Burgess	.25	.20	.08	482 Sam Mele		.30	.25	.10
390 O. Cepeda, AS	1.00	.70	.30	483 Don McMahon		.30	.25	.10
391 B. Mazeroski, AS	.30	.25	.10	484 Dick Schofield		.30	.25	.10
392 Ken Boyer, AS	.50	.40	.18	485 Pedro Ramos	1.25	.90	.40
393 Roy McMillan, AS	.25	.20	.08	486 Jim Gilliam		.30	.25	.10
394 Hank Aaron, AS	5.00	3.75	1.75	487 Jerry Lynch		.30	.25	.10
395 Willie Mays, AS	5.00	3.75	1.75	488 Hal Brown		.30	.25	.10
396 F. Robinson, AS	3.00	2.25	1.00	489 Julio Gotay		.30	.25	.10
397 John Roseboro, AS	.25	.20	.08	490 Clete Boyer		.30	.25	.10
398 Don Drysdale, AS	2.00	1.50	.60	491 Leon Wagner		.30	.25	.10
399 Warren Spahn, AS	2.50	1.80	.80	492 Hal W Smith		.30	.25	.10
400 Elston Howard	1.25	.90	.40	493 D. McDevitt		.30	.25	.10
401 Homer Kings	1.50	1.10	.50	494 Sammy White		.30	.25	.10
402 Gino Cimoli	.20	.15	.06	495 Don Cardwell		.30	.25	.10
403 Chet Nichols	.20	.15	.06	496 Wayne Causey		.30	.25	.10
404 Tim Harkness	.20	.15	.06	497 Ed Bouchee		.30	.25	.10
				498 Jim Donohue				

	MINT	VG-E	F-G			MINT	VG-E	F-G
499 Zoilo Versalles	.40	.30	.13	548 B. Del Greco		1.10	.80	.30
500 Duke Snider	6.00	4.50	2.00	549 Bill Rigney		1.10	.80	.30
501 Claude Osteen	.30	.25	.10	550 Art Mahaffey		1.10	.80	.30
502 Hector Lopez	.30	.25	.10	551 Harry Bright		1.10	.80	.30
503 D. Murtaugh	.30	.25	.10	552 Chicago Cubs		2.00	1.50	.60
504 E. Bressoud	.30	.25	.10	553 Jim Coates		1.10	.80	.30
505 Juan Marichal	2.50	1.80	.80	554 Bubba Morton		1.10	.80	.30
506 J. Maxwell	.30	.25	.10	555 J. Buzhardt		1.10	.80	.30
507 Ernie Broglio	.30	.25	.10	556 Al Spangler		1.10	.80	.30
508 G. Coleman	.30	.25	.10	557 Bob Anderson		1.10	.80	.30
509 Dave Giusti	.30	.25	.10	558 John Goryl		1.10	.80	.30
510 Jim Lemon	.30	.25	.10	559 Mike Higgins		1.10	.80	.30
511 Bubba Phillips	.30	.25	.10	560 Chuck Estrada		1.10	.80	.30
512 Mike Fornieles	.30	.25	.10	561 Gene Oliver		1.10	.80	.30
513 Whitey Herzog	.40	.30	.13	562 Bill Henry		1.10	.80	.30
514 Sherm Lollar	.30	.25	.10	563 K. Aspromonte		1.10	.80	.30
515 Stan Williams	.30	.25	.10	564 Bob Grim		1.10	.80	.30
516 Check List 7	.30	.25	.10	565 Jose Pagan		1.10	.80	.30
517 D. Wickersham	.30	.25	.10	566 Marty Kutyna		1.10	.80	.30
518 Lee Maye	.30	.25	.10	567 Tracy Stallard		1.10	.80	.30
519 Bob Johnson	.30	.25	.10	568 Jim Golden		1.10	.80	.30
520 Bob Friend	.40	.30	.13	569 Ed Sadowski		1.10	.80	.30
521 Jacke Davis	.30	.25	.10	570 Bill Stafford		1.10	.80	.30
522 L. McDaniel	.30	.25	.10	571 Billy Klaus		1.10	.80	.30
523 Russ Nixon	1.10	.80	.30	572 B. G. Miller		1.10	.80	.30
524 Howie Nunn	1.10	.80	.30	573 Johnny Logan		1.10	.80	.30
525 G. Thomas	1.10	.80	.30	574 Dean Stone		1.10	.80	.30
526 H. Woodeshick	1.10	.80	.30	575 Red Schoendienst		2.00	1.50	.60
527 D. McAuliffe	1.10	.80	.30	576 R. Kemmerer		1.10	.80	.30
528 Turk Lown	1.10	.80	.30	577 Dave Nicholson		1.10	.80	.30
529 John Schaive	1.10	.80	.30	578 Jim Duffalo		1.10	.80	.30
530 Bob Gibson	16.00	12.00	5.50	579 Jim Schaffer		1.10	.80	.30
531 Bobby Smith	1.10	.80	.30	580 Bill Monbouquette		1.10	.80	.30
532 Dick Stigman	1.10	.80	.30	581 Mel Roach		1.10	.80	.30
533 Charley Lau	1.25	.90	.40	582 Ron Piche		1.10	.80	.30
534 T. Gonzalez	1.10	.80	.30	583 Larry Osborne		1.10	.80	.30
535 Ed Roebuck	1.10	.80	.30	584 Minn. Twins		2.00	1.50	.60
536 Dick Gernert	1.10	.80	.30	585 Glen Hobbie		1.10	.80	.30
537 Indians Team	2.00	1.50	.60	586 Sam Esposito		1.10	.80	.30
538 Jack Sanford	1.10	.80	.30	587 Frank Funk		1.10	.80	.30
539 Billy Moran	1.10	.80	.30	588 B. Tebbetts		1.10	.80	.30
540 Jim Landis	1.10	.80	.30	589 Bob Turley		1.50	1.10	.50
541 D. Nottebart	1.10	.80	.30	590 Curt Flood		1.50	1.10	.50
542 Dave Philley	1.10	.80	.30	591 Rookie Parade 1		2.00	1.50	.60
543 Bob Allen	1.10	.80	.30	592 Rookie Parade 2		2.00	1.50	.60
544 W. McCovey	20.00	15.00	6.50	593 Rookie Parade 3		2.00	1.50	.60
545 Hoyt Wilhelm	4.00	3.00	1.40	594 Rookie Parade 4		2.00	1.50	.60
546 Moe Thacker	1.10	.80	.30	595 Rookie Parade 5		2.00	1.50	.60
547 D. Ferrarese	1.10	.80	.30	596 Rookie Parade 6		2.00	1.50	.60
				597 Rookie Parade 7		2.00	1.50	.60
				598 Rookie Parade 8		2.00	1.50	.60

1963 TOPPS (576)

2 1/2" X 3 1/2"

The 1963 Topps set contains both semi-high numbers 289–446 and high numbers 447–576. The high numbers are scarcer than the semi-high numbers which in turn are scarcer than the low numbers.

	MINT	VG-E	F-G
COMPLETE SET	550.00	400.00	150.00
COMMON PLAYER (1-288)	.17	.13	.05
COMMON PLAYER (289-446)	.25	.18	.08
COMMON PLAYER (447-506)	.70	.50	.20
COMMON PLAYER (507-576)	1.00	.75	.30

	MINT	VG-E	F-G		MINT	VG-E	F-G
1 N. L. Batting Leaders	.60	.35	.15	8 A. L. Pitch. Leaders	.50	.40	.18
2 A. L. Batting Leaders	.50	.40	.18	9 N. L. S. O. Leaders	.50	.40	.18
3 N. L. HR Leaders	.50	.40	.18	10 A. L. S. O. Leaders	.50	.40	.18
4 A. L. HR Leaders	.50	.40	.18	11 L. Walls	.17	.13	.05
5 N. L. Era Leaders	.50	.40	.18	12 S. Barber	.17	.13	.05
6 A. L. Era Leaders	.50	.40	.18	13 Phillies Team	.35	.27	.12
7 N. L. Pitch. Leaders	.50	.40	.18	14 P. Ramos	.17	.13	.05
				15 K. Hubbs	.75	.55	.25
				16 A. Smith	.17	.13	.05
				17 R. Duren	.20	.15	.06
				18 Buc Blasters	1.00	.70	.30
				19 Pete Burnside	.17	.13	.05
				20 Tony Kubek	.50	.40	.18

	MINT	VG-E	F-G			MINT	VG-E	F-G
21 Marty Keough	.17	.13	.05	113 D. Landrum		.17	.13	.05
22 Curt Simmons	.20	.15	.05	114 D. Osinski		.17	.13	.05
23 Ed Lopat	.50	.40	.18	115 Carl Yastrzemski		12.00	8.75	4.00
24 Bob Bruce	.17	.13	.05	116 Jim Brosnan		.17	.13	.05
25 Al Kaline	4.50	3.50	1.60	117 J. Davis		.17	.13	.05
26 R. Moore	.17	.13	.05	118 Sherm Lollar		.17	.13	.05
27 C. C. Coleman	.17	.15	.05	119 Bob Lillis		.17	.13	.05
28 M. Fornieles	.17	.13	.05	120 Roger Maris		3.25	2.40	1.10
29 Rookie Stars	.30	.25	.10	121 J. Hannan		.17	.13	.05
30 H. Kuenn	.40	.30	.13	122 Julio Gotay		.17	.13	.05
31 Cal Koonce	.17	.13	.05	123 Frank Howard		.75	.55	.25
32 T. Gonzalez	.17	.13	.05	124 Dick Howser		.30	.25	.10
33 Bo Belinski	.20	.15	.05	125 Robin Roberts		2.50	1.80	.80
34 D. Schofield	.17	.13	.05	126 Bob Uecker		1.00	.70	.30
35 John Buzhardt	.17	.13	.05	127 Bill Tuttle		.17	.13	.05
36 J. Kindall	.17	.13	.05	128 Matty Alou		.20	.15	.06
37 Jerry Lynch	.17	.13	.05	129 Gary Bell		.17	.13	.05
38 B. Daley	.17	.13	.05	130 Dick Groat		.25	.20	.08
39 Angels Team	.35	.27	.12	131 Senators Team		.35	.27	.12
40 Vic Power	.17	.13	.05	132 J. Hamilton		.17	.13	.05
41 C. Lau	.20	.15	.05	133 Gene Freese		.17	.13	.05
42 Stan Williams	.17	.13	.05	134 Bob Scheffing		.17	.13	.05
43 Veteran Masters	1.25	.90	.40	135 Richie Ashburn		1.00	.70	.30
44 T. Fox	.17	.13	.05	136 Ike Delock		.17	.13	.05
45 Bob Aspromonte	.17	.13	.05	137 M. Jones		.17	.13	.05
46 Tommy Aaron	.25	.20	.08	138 Pride of N.L.		3.50	2.50	1.20
47 D. Lock	.17	.13	.05	139 E. Averill		.17	.13	.05
48 Birdie Tebbetts	.17	.13	.05	140 F. Lary		.17	.13	.05
49 Dal Maxvill	.17	.13	.05	141 M. Mota		.30	.25	.10
50 Billy Pierce	.60	.45	.20	142 '62 W.S. #1		.50	.40	.18
51 George Alusik	.17	.13	.05	143 '62 W.S. #2		.50	.40	.18
52 Chuck Schilling	.17	.13	.05	144 '62 W.S. #3		.50	.40	.18
53 Joe Moeller	.17	.13	.05	145 '62 W.S. #4		.50	.40	.18
54 Rookie Stars	.75	.55	.25	146 '62 W.S. #5		.50	.40	.18
55 Bill Virdon	.75	.55	.25	147 '62 W.S. #6		.50	.40	.18
56 Dennis Bennett	.17	.13	.05	148 '62 W.S. #7		.50	.40	.18
57 Billy Moran	.17	.13	.05	149 Marv Breeding		.17	.13	.05
58 Bob Will	.17	.13	.05	150 John Podres		.30	.25	.10
59 C. Anderson	.17	.13	.05	151 Pirates Team		.40	.30	.13
60 E. Howard	2.00	1.50	.60	152 Ron Nischwitz		.17	.13	.05
61 E. Bowman	.17	.13	.05	153 Hal Smith		.17	.13	.05
62 B. Hendley	.17	.13	.05	154 Walt Alston		.30	.25	.10
63 Reds Team	.50	.40	.18	155 B. Stafford		.17	.13	.05
64 Dick McAuliffe	.17	.13	.05	156 Ron McMillan		.17	.13	.05
65 J. Brandt	.17	.13	.05	157 Diego Segui		.17	.13	.05
66 M. Joyce	.17	.13	.05	158 Rookie Stars		.17	.13	.05
67 Ed Charles	.17	.13	.05	159 Jim Pagliaroni		.17	.13	.05
68 Friendly Foes	1.50	1.10	.50	160 Juan Pizarro		.17	.13	.05
69 Bud Zipfel	.17	.13	.05	161 Frank Torre		.17	.13	.05
70 Jim O'Toole	.20	.15	.06	162 Twins Team		.35	.27	.12
71 Bobby Wine	.17	.13	.05	163 Don Larsen		.25	.20	.08
72 J. Romano	.17	.13	.05	164 B. Morton		.17	.13	.05
73 Bob Bragan	.17	.13	.05	165 Jim Kaat		.60	.45	.20
74 Denny Lemaster	.17	.13	.05	166 Johnny Keane		.17	.13	.05
75 Bob Allison	.25	.20	.08	167 Jim Fregosi		.50	.40	.18
76 E. Wilson	.17	.13	.05	168 R. Nixon		.17	.13	.05
77 Al Spangler	.17	.13	.05	169 Rookies (G. Perry)		3.00	2.25	1.00
78 Marv Throneberry	.30	.25	.10	170 Joe Adcock		.25	.20	.08
79 1st Ser. Checklist	.17	.13	.05	171 S. Hamilton		.17	.13	.05
80 Jim Gilliam	.80	.60	.25	172 Gene Oliver		.17	.13	.05
81 J. Schaffer	.17	.13	.05	173 Bombers' Best		2.00	1.50	.60
82 Ed Rakow	.17	.13	.05	174 Larry Burright		.17	.13	.05
83 C. James	.17	.13	.05	175 Bob Buhl		.17	.13	.05
84 Ron Kline	.17	.13	.05	176 J. King		.17	.13	.05
85 Tom Haller	.17	.13	.05	177 B. Phillips		.17	.13	.05
86 Charley Maxwell	.17	.13	.05	178 J. Edwards		.17	.13	.05
87 Bob Veale	.17	.13	.05	179 Ron Piche		.17	.13	.05
88 Ron Hansen	.17	.13	.05	180 Bill Skowron		.40	.30	.13
89 D. Stigman	.17	.13	.05	181 Sammy Esposito		.17	.13	.05
90 G. Coleman	.17	.13	.05	182 Albie Pearson		.17	.13	.05
81 D. Green	.17	.13	.05	183 Joe Pepitone		.40	.30	.13
92 Hector Lopez	.17	.13	.05	184 Vern Law		.30	.25	.10
93 Galen Cisco	.17	.13	.05	185 Chuck Hiller		.17	.13	.05
94 Bob Schmidt	.17	.13	.05	186 J. Zimmerman		.17	.13	.05
95 L. Jackson	.17	.13	.05	187 Willie Kirkland		.17	.13	.05
96 Lou Clinton	.17	.13	.05	188 Eddie Bressoud		.17	.13	.05
97 Bob Duliba	.17	.13	.05	189 Dave Giusti		.17	.13	.05
98 G. Thomas	.17	.13	.05	190 Minnie Minoso		.60	.45	.02
99 Jim Umbricht	.17	.13	.05	191 3rd Ser. Checklist		.17	.13	.05
100 J. Cunningham	.17	.13	.05	192 Clay Dalrymple		.17	.13	.05
101 Joe Gibbon	.17	.13	.05	193 A. Rodgers		.17	.13	.05
102 2nd Ser. Checklist	.17	.13	.05	194 Joe Nuxhall		.20	.15	.06
103 Chuck Essegian	.17	.13	.05	195 Manny Jimenez		.17	.13	.05
104 L. Krausse	.17	.13	.05	196 D. Camilli		.17	.13	.05
105 Ron Fairly	.20	.15	.06	197 Roger Craig		.25	.20	.08
106 B. Bolin	.17	.13	.05	198 L. Green		.17	.13	.05
107 Jim Hickman	.17	.13	.05	199 Joe Amalfitano		.17	.13	.05
108 Hoyt Wilhelm	.75	.55	.25	200 Mickey Mantle		28.00	21.00	10.00
109 Lee Maye	.17	.13	.05	201 C. Butler		.17	.13	.05
110 Rich Rollins	.17	.13	.05	202 Red Sox Team		.40	.30	.13
111 A. Jackson	.17	.13	.05	203 Chico Cardenas		.17	.13	.05
112 D. Brown	.17	.13	.05	204 Don Nottebart		.17	.13	.05

1963 TOPPS (CONTINUED)

	MINT	VG-E	F-G			MINT	VG-E	F-G
205 Luis Aparicio	1.00	.70	.30	211 F. Whitfield	.17	.13	.05
206 Ray Washburn	.17	.13	.05	212 Glen Hobbie	.17	.13	.05
207 K. Hunt	.17	.13	.05	213 Bill Hitchcock	.17	.13	.05
208 Rookie Stars	.17	.13	.05	214 Orlando Pena	.17	.13	.05
209 Hobie Landrith	.17	.13	.05	215 Bob Skinner	.17	.13	.05
210 Sandy Koufax	11.00	8.00	3.50				

HARMONY DIARY

1967 BASEBALL STICKERS

	MINT	VG-E	F-G
216 Gene Conley	.17	.13	.05
217 Joe Christopher	.17	.13	.05
218 Tiger Twirlers	.40	.30	.13
219 C. Cottier	.17	.13	.05
220 C. Pascual	.20	.15	.06
221 C. Rojas	.20	.15	.06
222 Cubs Team	.40	.30	.13
223 E. Fisher	.17	.13	.05
224 M. Roarke	.17	.13	.05
225 J. Jay	.17	.13	.05
226 J. Javier	.17	.13	.05
227 J. Grant	.17	.13	.05
228 Rookies	2.25	1.65	.75
229 W. Davis	.30	.25	.10
230 P. Runnels	.17	.13	.05
231 E. Grba	.17	.13	.05
232 F. Malzone	.20	.15	.06
233 C. Stengel	3.00	2.25	1.00
234 D. Nicholson	.17	.13	.05
235 B. O'Dell	.17	.13	.05
236 B. Bryan	.17	.13	.05
237 J. Coates	.17	.13	.05
238 L. Johnson	.17	.13	.05
239 H. Haddix	.20	.15	.06
240 R. Colavito	1.00	.70	.30
241 B. Smith	.17	.13	.05
242 Power Plus	3.50	2.50	1.20
243 D. Leppert	.17	.13	.05
244 J. Tsitouris	.17	.13	.05
245 G. Hodges	2.50	1.80	.80
246 L. Stange	.17	.13	.05
247 Yankees Team	.60	.45	.20
248 T. Francona	.17	.13	.05
249 L. Burke	.17	.13	.05
250 S. Musial	8.00	6.00	2.50
251 J. Lamabe	.17	.13	.05
252 R. Santo	.75	.55	.25
253 Rookies	.17	.13	.05
254 Mike Hershberger	.17	.13	.05
255 B. Shaw	.17	.13	.05
256 J. Lumpe	.17	.13	.05
257 H. Aguirre	.17	.13	.05
258 A. Dark	.25	.20	.08
259 J. Logan	.20	.15	.06
260 J. Gentile	.17	.13	.05
261 B. Miller	.17	.13	.05
262 E. Burton	.17	.13	.05
263 D. Stenhouse	.17	.13	.05
264 P. Linz	.17	.13	.05
265 V. Pinson	.65	.50	.20
266 B. Allen	.17	.13	.05
267 C. Sawatski	.17	.13	.05
268 D. Demeter	.17	.13	.05
269 D. Mincher	.17	.13	.05
270 F. Alou	.20	.15	.06
271 D. Stone	.17	.13	.05
272 D. Murphy	.17	.13	.05
273 S. Taylor	.17	.13	.05
274 4th Ser. Checklist	.17	.13	.05
275 E. Mathews	4.00	3.00	1.40
276 B. Shetrone	.17	.13	.05
277 D. Farrell	.17	.13	.05
278 C. Fernandez	.17	.13	.05
279 W. Moon	.20	.15	.06
280 B. Rodgers	.17	.13	.05
281 T. Sturdivant	.17	.13	.05
282 B. Del Greco	.17	.13	.05
283 R. Sievers	.20	.15	.06
284 D. Sisler	.17	.13	.05
285 D. Stuart	.20	.15	.06
286 S. Miller	.17	.13	.05
287 D. Bertell	.17	.13	.05
288 White Sox Team	.35	.27	.12
289 H. Brown	.25	.18	.08
290 B. White	.30	.25	.10
291 D. Rudolph	.25	.18	.08
292 P. Green	.25	.18	.08
293 B. Pleis	.25	.18	.08
294 B. Rigney	.25	.18	.08
295 E. Roebuck	.25	.18	.08
296 D. Edwards	.25	.18	.08
297 J. Golden	.25	.18	.08
298 D. Dillard	.25	.18	.08
299 Rookies	.25	.18	.08
300 W. Mays	22.00	16.50	7.50
301 B. Fischer	.25	.18	.08
302 W. Herzog	.40	.30	.13
303 E. Francis	.25	.18	.08
304 H. Bright	.25	.18	.08
305 D. Hoak	.25	.18	.08
306 Star Receivers	.40	.30	.13
307 C. Nichols	.25	.18	.08
308 Camilo Carreon	.25	.18	.08
309 Jim Brewer	.25	.18	.08
310 Tommy Davis	.50	.40	.18
311 Joe McClain	.25	.18	.08
312 Colts Team	.50	.40	.18
313 E. Broglio	.25	.18	.08
314 J. Goryl	.25	.18	.08
315 R. Terry	.25	.18	.08
316 N. Sherry	.25	.18	.08
317 S. McDowell	.30	.25	.10
318 G. Mauch	.30	.25	.10
319 J. Gaines	.25	.18	.08
320 W. Spahn	4.00	3.00	1.40
321 G. Cimoli	.25	.18	.08
322 B. Turley	.40	.30	.13
323 B. Mazeroski	.40	.30	.13
324 Rookies	.25	.18	.08
325 J. Sanford	.25	.18	.08
326 H. Foiles	.25	.18	.08
327 P. Foytack	.25	.18	.08
328 D. Williams	.30	.25	.10
329 L. McDaniel	.25	.18	.08
330 C. Hinton	.25	.18	.08
331 Series Foes	.30	.25	.10
332 J. Horlen	.25	.18	.08
333 C. Warwick	.25	.18	.08
334 W. Hawkins	.25	.18	.08
335 L. Wagner	.25	.18	.08
336 E. Bauta	.25	.18	.08
337 Dodgers Team	.50	.40	.18
338 R. Kemmerer	.25	.18	.08
339 T. Bowsfield	.25	.18	.08
340 Y. Berra	6.00	4.50	2.00
341 J. Baldschun	.25	.18	.08
342 G. Woodling	.30	.25	.10
343 J. Pesky	.25	.18	.08
344 D. Schwall	.25	.18	.08
345 B. Robinson	6.00	4.50	2.00
346 B. Hoeft	.25	.18	.08
347 J. Torre	1.25	.90	.40
348 V. Wertz	.25	.18	.08
349 Z. Versalles	.30	.25	.10
350 B. Purkey	.25	.18	.08
351 A. Luplow	.25	.18	.08
352 K. Johnson	.25	.18	.08
353 B. Williams	1.25	.90	.40
354 D. Zanni	.25	.18	.08
355 D. Chance	.25	.18	.08
356 J. Schaive	.25	.18	.08
357 G. Altman	.25	.18	.08
358 M. Pappas	.30	.25	.10
359 H. Sullivan	.30	.25	.10
360 D. Drysdale	4.50	3.50	1.60
361 C. Boyer	.25	.18	.08
362 5th Ser. Checklist	.25	.18	.08
363 D. Radatz	.30	.25	.10
364 H. Goss	.25	.18	.08
365 J. Bunning	.75	.55	.25
366 T. Taylor	.25	.18	.08
367 T. Cloninger	.25	.18	.08
368 E. Bailey	.25	.18	.08
369 J. Lemon	.25	.18	.08
370 D. Donovan	.25	.18	.08
371 R. Kanehl	.25	.18	.08
372 D. Lee	.25	.18	.08
373 J. Campbell	.25	.18	.08
374 C. Osteen	.25	.18	.08
375 K. Boyer	1.00	.70	.30
376 J. Wyatt	.25	.18	.08
377 Orioles Team	.50	.40	.18
378 B. Henry	.25	.18	.08
379 B. Anderson	.25	.18	.08
380 E. Banks	9.00	6.75	3.00
381 F. Baumann	.25	.18	.08
382 R. Houk	.40	.30	.13
383 P. Richert	.25	.18	.08
384 B. Tillman	.25	.18	.08
385 A. Mahaffey	.25	.18	.08
386 Rookies	.25	.18	.08
387 A. McBean	.25	.18	.08
388 J. Davenport	.25	.18	.08
389 F. Sullivan	.25	.18	.08
390 H. Aaron	27.00	20.00	9.00
391 B. Dailey	.25	.18	.08
392 Tribe Thumpers	.30	.25	.10
393 K. MacKenzie	.25	.18	.08
394 T. McCarver	.30	.25	.10
395 D. McMahon	.25	.18	.08
396 J. Koppe	.25	.18	.08
397 K. C. Team	.25	.18	.08
398 B. Powell	1.00	.70	.30
399 D. Ellsworth	.30	.25	.10
400 Frank Robinson	6.50	5.00	2.25

1963 TOPPS (CONTINUED)

	MINT	VG-E	F-G
401 J. Bouton	.75	.55	.25
402 Mickey Vernon	.30	.25	.10
403 R. Perranoski	.30	.25	.10
404 B. Oldis	.25	.18	.08
405 Floyd Robinson	.25	.18	.08
406 H. Koplitz	.25	.18	.08
407 Rookies	.25	.18	.08
408 B. Gardner	.25	.18	.08
409 R. Face	.30	.25	.10
410 E. Battey	.25	.18	.08
411 J. Constable	.25	.18	.08
412 Dod. Big Three	1.50	1.10	.50
413 J. Walker	.25	.18	.08
414 T. Cline	.25	.18	.08
415 B. Gibson	7.00	5.25	2.50
416 A. Grammas	.25	.18	.08
417 Giants Team	.50	.40	.18
418 J. Orsino	.25	.18	.08
419 T. Stallard	.25	.18	.08
420 B. Richardson	.50	.40	.18
421 T. Morgan	.25	.18	.08
422 F. Hutchinson	.50	.40	.18
423 E. Hobaugh	.25	.18	.08
424 C. Smith	.25	.18	.08
425 S. Burgess	.30	.25	.10
426 B. Latman	.25	.18	.08
427 B. Allen	.25	.18	.08
428 C. Boles	.25	.18	.08
429 L. Burdette	.50	.40	.18
430 N. Siebern	.25	.18	.08
431 6th Ser. Checklist	.25	.18	.08
432 R. Mejias	.25	.18	.08
433 D. Menke	.25	.18	.08
434 J. Callison	.25	.18	.08
435 W. Held	.25	.18	.08
436 T. Harkness	.25	.18	.08
437 B. Bruton	.25	.18	.08
438 W. Stock	.25	.18	.08
439 D. Zimmer	.50	.40	.18
440 J. Marichal	2.50	1.80	.80
441 L. Thomas	.25	.18	.08
442 J. C. Hartman	.25	.18	.08
443 J. Piersall	.50	.40	.18
444 J. Maloney	.40	.30	.13
445 N. Cash	.60	.45	.20
446 W. Ford	6.00	4.50	2.00
447 F. Mantilla	.70	.50	.20
448 J. Kralick	.70	.50	.20
449 J. Tartabull	.70	.50	.20
450 B. Friend	1.00	.70	.30
451 Indians Team	1.00	.70	.30
452 B. Schultz	.70	.50	.20
453 J. Wood	.70	.50	.20
454 A. Fowler	.70	.50	.20
455 R. Amaro	.70	.50	.20
456 J. Coker	.70	.50	.20
457 T. Clevenger	.70	.50	.20
458 A. Lopez	1.50	1.10	.50
459 D. Lemay	.70	.50	.20
460 D. Crandall	1.00	.70	.30
461 N. Bass	.70	.50	.20
462 W. Post	.70	.50	.20
463 J. Schaffernoth	.70	.50	.20
464 K. Aspromonte	.70	.50	.20
465 C. Estrada	.70	.50	.20
466 Rookies	.70	.50	.20
467 P. Ortega	.70	.50	.20
468 C. Hardy	.70	.50	.20
469 J. Hook	.70	.50	.20
470 T. Tresh	1.00	.70	.30
471 K. Retzer	.70	.50	.20
472 L. Brock	35.00	26.00	12.00
473 Mets Team	2.00	1.50	.60
474 J. Fisher	.70	.50	.20
475 G. Triandos	.70	.50	.20
476 L. Funk	.70	.50	.20
477 D. Clendenon	.70	.50	.20
478 P. Brown	.70	.50	.20
479 E. Brinkman	.70	.50	.20
480 B. Monbouquette	.70	.50	.20
481 B. Taylor	.70	.50	.20
482 F. Torre	.70	.50	.20
483 J. Owens	.70	.50	.20
484 Dale Long	.70	.50	.20
485 Jim Landis	.70	.50	.20
486 Ray Sadecki	.70	.50	.20
487 John Roseboro	.70	.50	.20
488 Jerry Adair	.70	.50	.20

	MINT	VG-E	F-G
489 Paul Toth	.70	.50	.20
490 Willie McCovey	20.00	15.00	6.50
491 Harry Craft	.70	.50	.20
492 Dave Wickersham	.70	.50	.20
493 Walt Bond	.70	.50	.20
494 P. Regan	.70	.50	.20
495 F. Thomas	.70	.50	.20
496 Rookies	.70	.50	.20
497 B. Daniels	.70	.50	.20
498 E. Kasko	.70	.50	.20
499 J. C. Martin	.70	.50	.20
500 H. Killebrew	9.50	7.00	3.00
501 J. Azcue	.70	.50	.20
502 D. Spencer	.70	.50	.20
503 Braves Team	1.00	.70	.30
504 B. Johnson	.70	.50	.20
505 C. Flood	1.00	.70	.30
506 G. Green	.70	.50	.20
507 R. Sheldon	1.00	.75	.30
508 T. Savage	1.00	.75	.30
509 7th Ser. Checklist	1.00	.75	.30
510 K. McBride	1.00	.75	.30
511 C. Neal	1.00	.75	.30
512 C. McLish	1.00	.75	.30
513 G. Geiger	1.00	.75	.30
514 L. Osborne	1.00	.75	.30
515 D. Elston	1.00	.75	.30
516 P. Goldy	1.00	.75	.30
517 H. Woodeshick	1.00	.75	.30
518 K. Blasingame	1.00	.75	.30
519 C. Raymond	1.00	.75	.30
520 O. Cepeda	4.00	3.00	1.40
521 D. Pfister	1.00	.75	.30
522 Rookies	1.00	.75	.30
523 B. Kunkel	1.00	.75	.30
524 Cards Team	1.50	1.10	.50
525 N. Fox	2.00	1.50	.60
526 D. Hall	1.00	.75	.30
527 E. Sadowski	1.00	.75	.30
528 C. Willey	1.00	.75	.30
529 W. Covington	1.00	.75	.30
530 D. Mossi	1.00	.75	.30
531 S. Mele	1.00	.75	.30
532 S. Boros	1.00	.75	.30
533 B. Shantz	1.50	1.10	.50
534 K. Walters	1.00	.75	.30
535 J. Perry	1.50	1.10	.50
536 N. Larker	1.00	.75	.30
537 Rookies (Rose)	55.00	42.00	19.00
538 G. Brunet	1.00	.75	.30
539 W. Causey	1.00	.75	.30
540 B. Clemente	40.00	30.00	13.00
541 R. Moeller	1.00	.75	.30
542 L. Klimchock	1.00	.75	.30
543 R. Snyder	1.00	.75	.30
544 Rookies (Staub)	3.00	2.25	1.10
545 J. Pagan	1.00	.75	.30
546 Hal Reniff	1.00	.75	.30
547 Gus Bell	1.00	.75	.30
548 T. Satriano	1.00	.75	.30
549 Rookies	1.00	.75	.30
550 D. Snider	15.00	11.00	5.00
551 B. Klaus	1.00	.75	.30
552 Tigers Team	2.00	1.50	.60
553 Rookies (Stargell)	16.00	12.00	5.50
554 H. Fischer	1.00	.75	.30
555 J. Blanchard	1.00	.75	.30
556 A. Worthington	1.00	.75	.30
557 C. Barragan	1.00	.75	.30
558 Rookies	1.00	.75	.30
559 D. Murtaugh	1.00	.75	.30
560 R. Herbert	1.00	.75	.30
561 M. De La Hoz	1.00	.75	.30
562 Rookies	1.00	.75	.30
563 M. McCormick	1.00	.75	.30
564 G. Banks	1.00	.75	.30
565 L. Sherry	1.00	.75	.30
566 C. Cook	1.00	.75	.30
567 J. Duffalo	1.00	.75	.30
568 B. Sadowski	1.00	.75	.30
569 L. Arroyo	1.00	.75	.30
570 F. Bolling	1.00	.75	.30
571 J. Klippstein	1.00	.75	.30
572 Jack Spring	1.00	.75	.30
573 Coot Veal	1.00	.75	.30
574 Hal Kolstad	1.00	.75	.30
575 Don Cardwell	1.00	.75	.30
576 Johnny Temple	1.00	.75	.30

Attend a Sports Memorabilia Show or Convention in your area sometime this year. They are both interesting and enjoyable to all members of the family.

YANKEES

YOGI BERRA　　manager

The 1964 Topps set contains high nos. 523—587 which are somewhat more difficult to obtain than the low numbers.

YOGI BERRA
(New York Yankees — Manager)

Probably the biggest sports story during the Winter season of '63 was the announcement that Yogi Berra was going to manage the New York Yankees in 1964. The Yankee organization couldn't have found a man with greater knowledge and love for the game than Mr. Berra. A three time winner of the American League's Most Valuable Player Award, Yogi has set many records in World Series competition as well as in regular season play. Joining New York in 1946, Yogi first hit over .300 in '48. In 1950, the backstop had one of his finest seasons at the plate as he hit .322 and socked 28 home runs. Two years later, Yogi tied an American League record for catchers by hitting 30 home runs in a single campaign. During his career, the catcher hit 358 circuit clouts which placed him 14th among the all-time home run sluggers.　　(T.C.G. PRINTED IN U.S.A.)

	MINT	VG-E	F-G
COMPLETE SET	250.00	190.00	90.00
COMMON PLAYER (1-429	.17	.13	.06
COMMON PLAYER (430-522)	.22	.17	.07
COMMON PLAYER (523-587)	.35	.25	.10
1 NL ERA Leaders	.60	.35	.15
2 AL ERA Leaders	.50	.40	.18
3 NL Pitch Leaders	.50	.40	.18
4 AL Pitch Leaders	.50	.40	.18
5 NL SO Leaders	.50	.40	.18
6 AL SO Leaders	.50	.40	.18
7 NL Batting Leaders	.50	.40	.18
8 AL Batting Leaders	.50	.40	.18
9 NL HR Leaders	.50	.40	.18
10 AL HR Leaders	.50	.40	.18
11 NL RBI Leaders	.50	.40	.18
12 AL RBI Leaders	.50	.40	.18
13 Hoyt Wilhelm	.75	.55	.25
14 Rookie (Dodgers)	.17	.13	.06
15 Zoilo Versalles	.20	.15	.06
16 John Boozer	.17	.13	.06
17 Willie Kirkland	.17	.13	.06
18 Billy O'Dell	.17	.13	.06
19 Don Wert	.17	.13	.06
20 Bob Friend	.20	.15	.06
21 Yogi Berra	3.75	2.75	1.25
22 Jerry Adair	.17	.13	.06
23 Chris Zachary	.17	.13	.06
24 Carl Sawatski	.17	.13	.06
25 Bill Monbouquette	.17	.13	.06
26 Gino Cimoli	.17	.13	.06
27 Mets Team	.40	.30	.13
28 Claude Osteen	.20	.15	.06
29 Lou Brock	7.00	5.25	2.50
30 Ron Perranoski	.17	.13	.06
31 Dave Nicholson	.17	.13	.06
32 Dean Chance	.50	.40	.18
33 Rookie (Reds)	.17	.13	.06
34 Jim Perry	.20	.15	.06
35 Ed Mathews	3.00	2.25	1.00
36 Hal Reniff	.17	.13	.06
37 Smokey Burgess	.20	.15	.06
38 Jim Wynn	.30	.25	.10
39 Hank Aquirre	.17	.13	.06
40 Dick Groat	.25	.20	.08
41 Friendly Foes	.50	.40	.18
42 Moe Drabowski	.17	.13	.06
43 Roy Sievers	.20	.15	.06
44 Duke Carmel	.17	.13	.06
45 Milt Pappas	.20	.15	.06
46 Ed Brinkman	.17	.13	.06
47 Rookie (Giants)	.17	.13	.06
48 Bob Perry	.17	.13	.06
49 Bill Henry	.17	.13	.06
50 Mickey Mantle	15.00	11.00	5.00
51 Pete Richert	.17	.13	.06
52 Chuck Hinton	.17	.13	.16
53 Denis Menke	.17	.13	.06
54 Sam Mele	.17	.13	.06
55 Ernie Banks	4.50	3.50	1.60
56 Hal Brown	.17	.13	.06
57 Tim Harkness	.17	.13	.06
58 Don Demeter	.17	.13	.06
59 Ernie Broglio	.17	.13	.06
60 Frank Malzone	.20	.15	.06

	MINT	VG-E	F-G
61 Angel Backstops	.17	.13	.06
Rodgers, Sadowski			
62 Ted Savage	.17	.13	.06
63 Johnny Orsino	.17	.13	.06
64 Ted Abernathy	.17	.13	.06
65 Felipe Alou	.20	.15	.06
66 Eddie Fisher	.17	.13	.06
67 Tigers Team	.35	.27	.12
68 Willie Davis	.25	.20	.08
69 Clete Boyer	.17	.13	.06
70 Joe Torre	.60	.45	.20
71 Jack Spring	.17	.13	.06
72 Chico Cardenas	.17	.13	.06
73 Jimmie Hall	.17	.13	.06
74 Rookies(Pirates)	.17	.13	.06
75 Wayne Causey	.17	.13	.06
76 1st Ser. Checklist	.17	.13	.06
77 Jerry Walker	.17	.13	.06
78 Merritt Ranew	.17	.13	.06
79 Bob Heffner	.17	.13	.06
80 Vada Pinson	.60	.45	.20
81 All-Star Vets	1.25	.90	.40
82 Jim Davenport	.17	.13	.06
83 Gus Triandos	.20	.15	.06
84 Carl Willey	.17	.13	.06
85 Pete Ward	.17	.13	.06
86 Al Downing	.17	.13	.06
87 Cardinals Team	.35	.27	.12
88 John Roseboro	.17	.13	.06
89 Boog Powell	.50	.40	.18
90 Earl Battey	.17	.13	.06
91 Bob Bailey	.17	.13	.06
92 Steve Ridzik	.17	.13	.06
93 Gary Geiger	.17	.13	.06
94 Rookie Stars	.17	.13	.06
95 George Altman	.17	.13	.06
96 Bob Buhl	.17	.13	.06
97 Jim Fregosi	.40	.30	.13
98 Bill Bruton	.17	.13	.06
99 Al Stanek	.17	.13	.06
100 Elston Howard	1.00	.70	.30
101 Walt Alston	.25	.20	.08
102 2nd Ser. Checklist	.17	.13	.06
103 Curt Flood	.25	.20	.08
104 Art Mahaffey	.17	.13	.06
105 Woody Held	.17	.13	.06
106 Joe Nuxhall	.20	.15	.06
107 Rookies (W. Sox)	.17	.13	.06
108 John Wyatt	.17	.13	.06
109 Rusty Staub	.60	.45	.20
110 Albie Pearson	.17	.13	.06
111 Don Elston	.17	.13	.06
112 Bob Tillman	.17	.13	.06
113 Grover Powell	.17	.13	.06
114 Don Lock	.17	.13	.06
115 Frank Bolling	.17	.13	.06
116 Rookies (Twins)	.75	.55	.25
117 Earl Francis	.17	.13	.06
118 John Blanchard	.17	.13	.06
119 Gary Kolb	.17	.13	.06
120 Don Drysdale	3.00	2.25	1.00
121 Pete Runnels	.17	.13	.06
122 Don McMahon	.17	.13	.06
123 Jose Pagan	.17	.13	.06

BASEBALL COLLECTIBLES FOR SALE!

285

	MINT	VG-E	F-G
124 Orlando Pena	.17	.13	.06
125 Pete Rose	14.00	10.50	4.75
126 Russ Snyder	.17	.13	.06
127 Rookies (Angels)	.17	.13	.06
128 Mickey Lolich	.50	.40	.18
129 Amado Samuel	.17	.13	.06
130 Gary Peters	.17	.13	.06
131 Steve Boros	.17	.13	.06
132 Braves Team	.35	.27	.12
133 Jim Grant	.17	.13	.06
134 Don Zimmer	.30	.25	.10
135 Johnny Callison	.17	.13	.06
136 World Series 1	.50	.40	.18
137 World Series 2	.50	.40	.18
138 World Series 3	.50	.40	.18
139 World Series 4	.50	.40	.18
140 World Series 5	.50	.40	.18
141 Danny Murtaugh	.20	.15	.06
142 John Bateman	.17	.13	.06
143 Bubba Philips	.17	.13	.06
144 Al Worthington	.17	.13	.06
145 Norm Siebern	.17	.13	.06
146 Rookies (Indians)	4.50	3.50	1.60
147 Ray Sadecki	.17	.13	.06
148 J. C. Martin	.17	.13	.06
149 Paul Foytack	.17	.13	.06
150 Willie Mays	12.50	9.00	4.00
151 Athletics Team	.30	.25	.10
152 Denver Lemaster	.17	.13	.06
153 Dick Williams	.25	.20	.08
154 Dick Tracewski	.17	.13	.06
155 Duke Snider	4.00	3.00	1.40
156 Bill Dailey	.17	.13	.06
157 Gene Mauch	.25	.20	.08
158 Ken Johnson	.17	.13	.06
159 Charlie Dees	.17	.13	.06
160 Ken Boyer	1.00	.70	.30
161 Dave McNally	.30	.25	.10
162 Hitting Area	.25	.20	.08
163 Donn Clendenon	.20	.15	.06
164 Bud Daley	.17	.13	.06
165 Jerry Lumpe	.17	.13	.06
166 Marty Keough	.17	.13	.06
167 Rookies (Senators)	1.00	.70	.30
168 Al Weis	.17	.13	.06
169 Del Crandall	.20	.15	.06
170 Dick Radatz	.17	.13	.06
171 Ty Cline	.17	.13	.06
172 Indians Team	.30	.25	.10
173 Ryne Duren	.20	.15	.06
174 Doc Edwards	.17	.13	.06
175 Billy Williams	.75	.55	.25
176 Tracy Stallard	.17	.13	.06
177 Harmon Killebrew	2.50	1.80	.80
178 Hank Bauer	.30	.25	.10
179 Carl Warwick	.17	.13	.06
180 Tommy Davis	.50	.40	.18
181 Dave Wickersham	.17	.13	.06
182 Sox Sockers	1.25	.90	.40
183 Ron Taylor	.17	.13	.06
184 Al Luplow	.17	.13	.06
185 Jim O'Toole	.17	.13	.06
186 Roman Mejias	.17	.13	.06
187 Ed Roebuck	.17	.13	.06
188 3rd Ser. Checklist	.17	.13	.06
189 Bob Hendley	.17	.13	.06
190 Bob Richardson	.30	.25	.10
191 Clay Dalrymple	.17	.13	.06
192 Rookies (Cubs)	.17	.13	.06
193 Jerry Lynch	.17	.13	.06
194 John Goryl	.17	.13	.06
195 Floyd Robinson	.17	.13	.06
196 Jim Gentile	.20	.15	.06
197 Frank Lary	.20	.15	.06
198 Len Gabrielson	.17	.13	.06
199 Joe Azcue	.17	.13	.06
200 Sandy Koufax	7.50	5.75	2.50
201 Rookies (Orioles)	.17	.13	.06
202 Galen Cisco	.17	.13	.06
203 John Kennedy	.20	.15	.06
204 Matty Alou	1.00	.70	.30
205 Nellie Fox	.17	.13	.06
206 Steve Hamilton	.30	.25	.10
207 Fred Hutchinson	.17	.13	.06
208 Wes Covington	.17	.13	.06
209 Bob Allen	10.00	7.00	3.00
210 Carl Yastrzemski			
211 Jim Coker	.17	.13	.06
212 Pete Lovrich	.17	.13	.06
213 Angels Team	.30	.25	.10
214 Ken McMullen	.17	.13	.06
215 Ray Herbert	.17	.13	.06

	MINT	VG-E	F-G
216 Mike De La Hoz	.17	.13	.06
217 Jim King	.17	.13	.06
218 Hank Fischer	.17	.13	.06
219 Young Aces	.40	.30	.13
220 Dick Ellsworth	.20	.15	.06
221 Bob Saverine	.17	.13	.06
222 Bill Pierce	.60	.45	.20
223 George Banks	.17	.13	.06
224 Tommie Sisk	.17	.13	.06
225 Roger Maris	3.00	2.25	1.00
226 Rookies (Colts)	.17	.13	.06
227 Barry Latman	.17	.13	.06
228 Felix Mantilla	.17	.13	.06
229 Charley Lau	.20	.15	.06
230 Brooks Robinson	4.50	3.50	1.60
231 Dick Calmus	.17	.13	.06
232 Al Lopez	1.00	.70	.30
233 Hal Smith	.17	.13	.06
234 Gary Bell	.17	.13	.06
235 Ron Hunt	.17	.13	.06
236 Bill Faul	.17	.13	.06
237 Cubs Team	.35	.27	.12
238 Roy McMillan	.17	.13	.06
239 Herm Starrette	.17	.13	.06
240 Bill White	.20	.15	.06
241 Jim Owens	.17	.13	.06
242 Harvey Kuenn	.30	.25	.10
243 Rookies (Phils)	2.50	1.80	.80
Richie Allen			
244 Tony LaRussa	.17	.13	.06
245 Dick Stigman	.17	.13	.06
246 Manny Mota	.25	.20	.08
247 Dave DeBusschere	1.25	.90	.40
248 Johnny Pesky	.20	.15	.06
249 Doug Camilli	.17	.13	.06
250 Al Kaline	3.50	2.50	1.20
251 Choo Choo Coleman	.17	.13	.06
252 Ken Aspromonte	.17	.13	.06
253 Wally Post	.17	.13	.06
254 Don Hoak	.17	.13	.06
255 Lee Thomas	.17	.13	.06
256 Johnny Weekly	.17	.13	.06
257 Giants Team	.35	.27	.12
258 Garry Roggenburk	.17	.13	.06
259 Harry Bright	.17	.13	.06
260 Frank Robinson	3.50	2.50	1.20
261 Jim Hannan	.17	.13	.06
262 Rookies (Cards)	.17	.13	.06
263 Chuck Estrada	.17	.13	.06
264 Jim Landis	.17	.13	.06
265 Jim Bunning	.50	.40	.18
266 Gene Freese	.17	.13	.06
267 Wilbur Wood	.20	.15	.06
268 Bill's Got It	.30	.25	.10
269 Ellis Burton	.17	.13	.06
270 Rich Rollins	.17	.13	.06
271 Bob Sadowski	.17	.13	.06
272 Jake Wood	.17	.13	.06
273 Mel Nelson	.17	.13	.06
274 4th Ser. Checklist	.17	.13	.06
275 John Tsitouris	.17	.13	.06
276 Jose Tartabull	.17	.13	.06
277 Ken Retzer	.17	.13	.06
278 Bobby Shantz	.25	.20	.08
279 Joe Koppe	.17	.13	.06
280 Juan Marichal	1.50	1.10	.50
281 Rookies (Yanks)	.17	.13	.06
282 Bob Bruce	.17	.13	.06
283 Tommy McCraw	.17	.13	.06
284 Dick Schofield	.17	.13	.06
285 Robin Roberts	2.50	1.80	.80
286 Don Landrum	.17	.13	.06
287 Rookies (R. Sox)	.17	.13	.06
288 Al Moran	.17	.13	.06
289 Frank Funk	.17	.13	.06
290 Bob Allison	.25	.20	.08
291 Phil Ortega	.17	.13	.06
292 Mike Roarke	.17	.13	.06
293 Phillies Team	.35	.27	.12
294 Kent Hunt	.17	.13	.06
295 Roger Craig	.20	.15	.06
296 Ed Kirkpatrick	.17	.13	.06
297 Ken MacKenzie	.17	.13	.06
298 Harry Craft	.17	.13	.06
299 Bill Stafford	.17	.13	.06
300 Hank Aaron	11.00	8.00	3.50
301 Larry Brown	.17	.13	.06
302 Dan Pfister	.17	.13	.06
303 Jim Campbell	.17	.13	.06
304 Bob Johnson	.17	.13	.06
305 Jack Lamabe	.17	.13	.06
306 Giant Gunners	2.25	1.65	.75
307 Joe Gibbon	.17	.13	.06

	MINT	VG-E	F-G
308 Gene Stephens	.17	.13	.06
309 Paul Toth	.17	.13	.06
310 Jim Gilliam	.75	.55	.25
311 Tom Brown	.17	.13	.06
312 Rookies (Tigers)	.17	.13	.06
313 Chuck Hiller	.17	.13	.06
314 Jerry Buchek	.17	.13	.06
315 Bo Belinski	.20	.15	.06
316 Gene Oliver	.17	.13	.06
317 Al Smith	.17	.13	.06
318 Twins Team	.30	.25	.10
319 Paul Brown	.17	.13	.06
320 Rocky Colavito	.70	.50	.20
321 Bob Lillis	.17	.13	.06
322 George Brunet	.17	.13	.06
323 John Buzhardt	.17	.13	.06
324 Casey Stengel	3.00	2.25	1.00
325 Hector Lopez	.17	.13	.06
326 Ron Brand	.17	.13	.06
327 Don Blasingame	.17.	.13	.06
328 Bob Shaw	.17	.13	.06
329 Russ Nixon	.17	.13	.06
330 Tommy Harper	.17	.13	.06
331 A. L. Bombers	2.50	1.80	.80
332 Ray Washburn	.17	.13	.06
333 Billy Moran	.17	.13	.06
334 Lew Krausse	.17	.13	.06
335 Don Mossi	.17	.13	.06
336 Andre Rodgers	.17	.13	.06
337 Rookies (Dodgers)	.17	.13	.06
338 Jack Kralick	.17	.13	.06
339 Walt Bond	.17	.13	.06
340 Joe Cunningham	.17	.13	.06
341 Jim Roland	.17	.13	.06
342 Willie Stargell	3.00	2.25	1.00
343 Senators Team	.30	.25	.10
344 Phil Linz	.17	.13	.06
345 Frank Thomas	.17	.13	.06
346 Joe Jay	.17	.13	.06
347 Bobby Wine	.17	.13	.06
348 Ed Lopat	.30	.25	.10
349 Art Fowler	.17	.13	.06
350 Willie McCovey	4.00	3.00	1.40
351 Dan Schneider	.17	.13	.06
352 Eddie Bressoud	.17	.13	.06
353 Wally Moon	.20	.15	.06
354 Dave Giusti	.17	.13	.06
355 Vic Power	.17	.13	.06
356 Rookies (Reds)	.17	.13	.06
357 Charley James	.17	.13	.06
358 Ron Kline	.17	.13	.06
359 Jim Schaffer	.17	.13	.06
360 Joe Pepitone	.25	.20	.08
361 Jay Hook	.17	.13	.06
362 5th Ser. Checklist	.17	.13	.06
363 Dick McAuliffe	.17	.13	.06
364 Joe Gaines	.17	.13	.06
365 Cal McLish	.17	.13	.06
366 Nelson Mathews	.17	.13	.06
367 Fred Whitfield	.17	.13	.06
368 Rookies (W. Sox)	.17	.13	.06
369 Jerry Zimmerman	.17	.13	.06
370 Hal Woodeshick	.17	.13	.06
371 Frank Howard	.60	.45	.20
372 Howie Koplitz	.17	.13	.06
373 Pirates Team	.35	.27	.12
374 Bobby Bolin	.17	.13	.06
375 Ron Santo	.50	.40	.18
376 Dave Morehead	.17	.13	.06
377 Bob Skinner	.17	.13	.06
378 Rookies (Braves)	.17	.13	.06
379 Tony Gonzalez	.17	.13	.06
380 Whitey Ford	4.00	3.00	1.40
381 Bob Taylor	.17	.13	.06
382 Wes Stock	.17	.13	.06
383 Bill Rigney	.17	.13	.06
384 Ron Hansen	.17	.13	.06
385 Curt Simmons	.20	.15	.06
386 Lenny Green	.17	.13	.06
387 Terry Fox	.17	.13	.06
388 Rookies (A's)	.17	.13	.06
389 Jim Umbricht	.17	.13	.06
390 Orlando Cepeda	1.50	1.10	.50
391 Sam McDowell	.30	.25	.10
392 Jim Pagliaroni	.17	.13	.06
393 Casey Teaches	1.25	.90	.40
394 Bob Miller	.17	.13	.06
395 Tom Tresh	.20	.15	.06
396 Dennis Bennett	.17	.13	.06
397 Chuck Cottier	.17	.13	.06
398 Rookies (Mets)	.17	.13	.06
399 Jackie Brandt	.17	.13	.06
400 Warren Spahn	3.00	2.25	1.00

	MINT	VG-E	F-G
401 Charlie Maxwell	.17	.13	.06
402 Tom Sturdivant	.17	.13	.06
403 Reds Team	.40	.30	.13
404 Tony Martinez	.17	.13	.05
405 Ken McBride	.17	.13	.06
406 Al Spangler	.17	.13	.06
407 Bill Freehan	.30	.25	.10
408 Rookies (Cubs)	.17	.13	.06
409 Bill Fischer	.17	.13	.06
410 Dick Stuart	.20	.15	.06
411 Lee Walls	.17	.13	.06
412 Ray Culp	.17	.13	.06
413 Johnny Keane	.17	.13	.06
414 Jack Sanford	.17	.13	.06
415 Tony Kubek	.50	.40	.18
416 Lee Maye	.17	.13	.06
417 Don Cardwell	.17	.13	.06
418 Rookies (Orio.)	.17	.13	.06
419 Ken Harrelson	.30	.25	.10
420 Jim Maloney	.25	.20	.08
421 Camilo Carreon	.17	.13	.06
422 Jack Fisher	.17	.13	.06
423 Tops in N. L.	3.50	2.50	1.20
424 Dick Bertell	.17	.13	.06
425 Norm Cash	.50	.40	.18
426 Bob Rodgers	.17	.13	.06
427 Don Rudolph	.17	.13	.06
428 Rookies (R. Sox)	.17	.13	.06
429 Tim McCarver	.17	.13	.06
430 Juan Pizarro	.22	.17	.07
431 George Alusik	.22	.17	.07
432 Ruben Amaro	.22	.17	.07
433 Yankees Team	.60	.45	.20
434 Don Nottebart	.22	.17	.07
435 Vic Davalillo	.22	.17	.07
436 Charlie Neal	.22	.17	.07
437 Ed Bailey	.22	.17	.07
438 6th Ser. Checklist	.22	.17	.07
439 Harvey Haddix	.22	.17	.07
440 Bob Clemente	7.50	5.75	2.50
441 Bob Duliba	.22	.17	.07
442 Pumpsie Green	.22	.17	.07
443 Chuck Dressen	.22	.17	.07
444 Larry Jackson	.22	.17	.07
445 Bill Skowron	.40	.30	.13
446 Julian Javier	.22	.17	.07
447 Ted Bowsfield	.22	.17	.07
448 Cookie Rojas	.22	.17	.07
449 Deron Johnson	.22	.17	.07
450 Steve Barber	.22	.17	.07
451 Joe Amalfitano	.22	.17	.07
452 Rookies (Giants)	.22	.17	.07
453 Frank Baumann	.22	.17	.07
454 Tommie Aaron	.22	.17	.07
455 Bernie Allen	.22	.17	.07
456 Rookies (Dodg.)	.50	.40	.18
457 Jesse Gonder	.22	.17	.07
458 Ralph Terry	.22	.17	.07
459 Rookies (R. Sox)	.22	.17	.07
460 Bob Gibson	3.50	2.50	1.20
461 George Thomas	.22	.17	.07
462 Birdie Tebbetts	.22	.17	.07
463 Don Leppert	.22	.17	.07
464 Dallas Green	.60	.45	.20
465 Mike Hershberger	.22	.17	.07
466 Rookies (A's)	.22	.17	.07
467 Bob Aspromonte	.22	.17	.07
468 Gaylord Perry	2.00	1.50	.60
469 Rookies (Cubs)	.22	.17	.07
470 Jim Bouton	.50	.40	.18
471 Gates Brown	.22	.17	.07
472 Vern Law	.22	.17	.07
473 Orioles Team	.50	.40	.18
474 Larry Sherry	.22	.17	.07
475 Ed Charles	.22	.17	.07
476 Rookies (Braves)	1.00	.70	.30
477 Mike Joyce	.22	.17	.07
478 Dick Howser	.50	.40	.18
479 Rookies (Cards)	.22	.17	.07
480 Bob Purkey	.22	.17	.07
481 Chuck Schilling	.22	.17	.07
482 Rookies (Phils)	.22	.17	.07
483 Fred Valentine	.22	.17	.07
484 Bill Pleis	.22	.17	.07
485 Tom Haller	.22	.17	.07
486 Bob Kennedy	.22	.17	.07
487 Mike McCormick	.22	.17	.07
488 Rookies (Yanks)	.22	.17	.07
489 Julio Navarro	.22	.17	.07
490 Ron Fairly	.22	.17	.07
491 Ed Rakow	.22	.17	.07
492 Rookies (Colts)	.22	.17	.07
493 Don Lee	.22	.17	.07
494 Al Jackson	.22	.17	.07

1964 TOPPS (CONTINUED)

	MINT	VG-E	F-G
495 Bill Virdon	1.00	.70	.30
496 White Sox Team	.50	.40	.18
497 Jeoff Long	.22	.17	.07
498 Dave Stenhouse	.22	.17	.07
499 Rookies (Ind.)	.22	.17	.07
500 Camilo Pascual	.22	.17	.07
501 Bob Veale	.22	.17	.07
502 Rookies (Angels)	.22	.17	.07
503 Earl Wilson	.22	.17	.07
504 Claude Raymond	.22	.17	.07
505 Stan Williams	.22	.17	.07
506 Bobby Bragan	.22	.17	.07
507 John Edwards	.22	.17	.07
508 Diego Segui	.22	.17	.07
509 Rookies (Pirates)	.22.	.17	.07
510 Lindy McDaniel	.22	.17	.07
511 Lou Jackson	.22	.17	.07
512 Rookies (Tigers)	.75	.55	.25
513 Don Larsen	.40	.30	.13
514 Jim Hickman	.22	.17	.07
515 Johnny Romano	.22	.17	.07
516 Rookies (Twins)	.22	.17	.07
517 7th Ser. Checklist	.22	.17	.07
518 Carl Bouldin	.22	.17	.07
519 Charlie Smith	.22	.17	.07
520 Jack Baldschun	.22	.17	.07
521 Tom Satriano	.22	.17	.07
522 Bob Tiefenauer	.22	.17	.07
523 Lou Burdette	.50	.40	.18
524 Rookies (Reds)	.35	.25	.10
525 Al McBean	.35	.25	.10
526 Lou Clinton	.35	.25	.10
527 Larry Bearnarth	.35	.25	.10
528 Rookies (A's)	.35	.25	.10
529 Al Dark	.50	.40	.18
530 Leon Wagner	.35	.25	.10
531 Dodgers Team	.75	.55	.25
532 Rookies (Twins)	.35	.25	.10
533 John Klippstein	.35	.25	.10
534 Gus Bell	.35	.25	.10
535 Phil Regan	.35	.25	.10
536 Rookies (Mets)	.35	.25	.10
537 Dan Osinski	.35	.25	.10
538 Minnie Minoso	1.00	.70	.30
539 Roy Face	.50	.40	.18
540 Luis Aparicio	1.50	1.10	.50

	MINT	VG-E	F-G
541 Rookies (Braves)	1.50	1.10	.50
542 Don Mincher	.35	.25	.10
543 Bob Uecker	1.00	.70	.30
544 Rookies (Colts)	.35	.25	.10
545 Max Alvis	.35	.25	.10
546 Joe Christopher	.35	.25	.10
547 Gil Hodges	2.50	1.80	.80
548 Rookies (N.L.)	.35	.25	.10
549 Joe Moeller	.35	.25	.10
550 Ken Hubbs	1.50	1.10	.50
551 Billy Hoeft	.35	.25	.10
552 Rookie Stars	.35	.25	.10
553 Jim Brewer	.35	.25	.10
554 Hank Foiles	.35	.25	.10
555 Lee Stange	.35	.25	.10
556 Rookies (Mets)	.35	.25	.10
557 Leo Burke	.35	.25	.10
558 Don Schwall	.35	.25	.10
559 Dick Phillips	.35	.25	.10
560 Dick Farrell	.35	.25	.10
561 Rookies (Phils)	.35	.25	.10
562 Pedro Ramos	.35	.25	.10
563 Dal Maxvill	.35	.25	.10
564 Rookies (A.L.)	.35	.25	.10
565 Stu Miller	.35	.25	.10
566 Ed Kranepool	.50	.40	.18
567 Jim Kaat	1.00	.70	.30
568 Rookies (N.L.)	.35	.25	.10
569 Fred Newman	.35	.25	.10
570 Bill Mazeroski	.50	.40	.18
571 Gene Conley	.35	.25	.10
572 Rookies(A.L.)	.35	.25	.10
573 Jim Duffalo	.35	.25	.10
574 Manny Jimenez	.35	.25	.10
575 Tony Cloninger	.35	.25	.10
576 Rookies (Mets)	.35	.25	.10
577 Gordy Coleman	.35	.25	.10
578 Glen Hobbie	.35	.25	.10
579 Red Sox Team	.75	.55	.25
580 Johnny Podres	.60	.45	.20
581 Rookies (Yanks)	.35	.25	.10
582 Rod Kanehl	.35	.25	.10
583 Tito Francona	.35	.25	.10
584 Joel Horlen	.35	.25	.10
585 Tony Taylor	.35	.25	.10
586 Jim Piersall	.75	.55	.25
587 Bennie Daniels	.50	.25	.10

1964 TOPPS STAND UPS (77) 2 1/2" X 3 1/2"

BOOG POWELL
BALT. ORIOLES   OUTFIELD

The 1964 Topps Stand-Ups
are green & yellow die-cut
cards issued separately from
the regular 1964 Topps issue.
Of 77 cards, 22 cards were
produced in limited quantities;
these cards are designated by
(*) on the checklist.

	MINT	VG-E	F-G
COMPLETE SET	450.00	350.00	140.00
COMMON PLAYER	1.00	.75	.30
SCARCE PLAYERS (*)	7.00	5.25	2.00
1 Hank Aaron	18.00	13.50	6.00
2 Hank Aguirre	1.00	.75	.30
3 George Altman	1.00	.75	.30
4 Max Alvis	1.00	.75	.30
5 Bob Aspromonte	1.00	.75	.30
6 Jack Baldschun*	7.00	5.25	2.00
7 Ernie Banks	5.00	3.75	1.75
8 Steve Barber	1.00	.75	.30
9 Earl Battey	1.00	.75	.30
10 Ken Boyer	1.50	1.10	.50
11 Ernie Broglio	1.00	.75	.30
12 John Callison	1.00	.75	.30
13 Norm Cash*	9.00	6.75	3.00

	MINT	VG-E	F-G
14 Wayne Causey	1.00	.75	.30
15 Orlando Cepeda	2.00	1.50	.60
16 Ed Charles	1.00	.75	.30
17 Bob Clemente	10.00	7.00	3.00
18 Donn Clendenon*	7.00	5.25	2.00
19 Rocky Colavito	1.50	1.10	.50
20 Ray Culp*	7.00	5.25	2.00
21 Tommy Davis	1.00	.75	.30
22 Don Drysdale*	18.00	13.50	6.00
23 Dick Ellsworth	1.00	.75	.30
24 Dick Farrell	1.00	.75	.30
25 Jim Fregosi	1.50	1.10	.50
26 Bob Friend	1.00	.75	.30
27 Jim Gentile	1.00	.75	.30
28 Jesse Gonder*	7.00	5.25	2.00
29 Tony Gonzalez*	7.00	5.25	2.00
30 Dick Groat	1.00	.75	.30
31 Woody Held	1.00	.75	.30

	MINT	VG-E	F-G			MINT	VG-E	F-G
32 Chuck Hinton	1.00	.75	.30	55 Albie Pearson *		7.00	5.25	2.00
32 Elston Howard	2.00	1.50	.60	56 Gary Peters		1.00	.75	.30
34 Frank Howard*	10.00	7.00	3.00	57 Vada Pinson		1.50	1.10	.50
35 Ron Hunt	1.00	.75	.30	58 Juan Pizarro		1.00	.75	.30
36 Al Jackson	1.00	.75	.30	59 Boog Powell		1.50	1.10	.50
37 Ken Johnson	1.00	.75	.30	60 Bobby Richardson		1.50	1.10	.50
38 Al Kaline	6.00	4.50	2.00	61 Brooks Robinson		5.00	3.75	1.75
39 Harmon Killebrew	3.50	2.50	1.20	62 Floyd Robinson		1.00	.75	.30
40 Sandy Koufax	10.00	7.00	3.00	63 Frank Robinson		5.00	3.75	1.75
41 Don Lock*	7.00	5.25	2.00	64 Ed Roebuck*		7.00	5.25	2.00
42 Jerry Lumpe *	7.00	5.25	2.00	65 Rich Rollins		1.00	.75	.30
43 Jim Maloney	1.00	.75	.30	66 John Romano		1.00	.75	.30
44 Frank Malzone	1.00	.75	.30	67 Ron Santo*		8.00	6.00	2.50
45 Mickey Mantle	30.00	22.50	10.50	68 Norm Siebern		1.00	.75	.30
46 Juan Marichal*	12.00	8.75	4.00	69 Warren Spahn*		15.00	11.00	5.00
47 Eddie Mathews*	15.00	11.00	5.00	70 Dick Stuart*		7.00	5.25	2.00
48 Willie Mays	18.00	13.50	6.00	71 I. Thomas		1.00	.75	.30
49 Bill Mazeroski	1.00	.75	.30	72 Joe Torre		1.50	1.10	.50
50 Ken McBride	1.00	.75	.30	73 P. Ward		1.00	.75	.30
51 Willie McCovey*	15.00	11.00	5.00	74 Bill White*		7.00	5.25	2.00
52 Claude Osteen	1.00	.75	.30	75 Billy Williams*		10.00	7.00	3.00
53 Jim O'Toole	1.00	.75	.30	76 Hal Woodeshick*		7.00	5.25	2.00
54 Camilo Pascual	1.00	.75	.30	77 Carl Yastrzemski*		30.00	22.50	10.50

1964 TOPPS GIANTS (60) 3 1/8" X 5 1/4"

Warren Spahn

The 1964 Topps Giants are large postcard-sized cards issued separately from the 1964 Topps regular issue. An uneven distribution of cards makes card nos. 3, 28, 42, 45, 47, 51, and 60 somewhat more difficult to obtain.

31 WARREN KEEPS ROLLING ON ⚫T.C.G. PRINTED IN U.S.A.

SPAHN WINS 350TH BALLGAME

Warren Spahn completed the 1963 campaign with a 23-7 record and won his 350th ballgame. The pitcher is the winningest lefthander in the history of baseball. The Braves' hurler appeared in his first big league game in 1942, before some of our current stars were even born. Thirteen times during his career Warren has won 20 games or better. At the end of 1963, Warren had pitched a total of 62 career shutouts vs. National League opposition. For four consecutive years, from 1949 through 1952, Warren led the N.L. in strikeouts. The biggest thrill of the fabulous lefty's career was in 1960 when he pitched a no-hitter vs. the Phillies for his 20th win of the year. Warren pitched another no-hit game vs. the Giants in 1961. In World Series competition, Warren has won four ballgames!

	MINT	VG-E	F-G			MINT	VG-E	F-G
COMPLETE SET	18.00	14.00	5.00	29 F. Robinson		1.00	.70	.30
COMMON PLAYERS	.12	.08	.03	30 B. Freehan		.12	.08	.03
				31 W. Spahn		.80	.60	.25
1 G. Peters	.12	.08	.03	32 C. Pascual		.12	.08	.03
2 K. Johnson	.12	.08	.03	33 P. Ward		.12	.08	.03
3 S. Koufax *	2.00	1.50	.60	34 J. Maloney		.12	.08	.03
4 B. Bailey	.12	.08	.03	35 D. Wickersham		.12	.08	.03
5 M. Pappas	.15	.11	.05	36 J. Callison		.12	.08	.03
6 R. Hunt	.12	.08	.03	37 J. Marichal		.40	.30	.13
7 W. Ford	.75	.55	.25	38 H. Killebrew		.50	.40	.18
8 R. McMillan	.12	.08	.03	39 L. Aparicio		.30	.25	.10
9 R. Colavito	.30	.25	.10	40 D. Radatz		.12	.08	.03
10 J. Bunning	.25	.20	.08	41 B. Gibson		.50	.40	.18
11 B. Clemente	1.50	1.10	.50	42 D. Stuart*		.50	.40	.18
12 A. Kaline	1.00	.70	.30	43 T. Davis		.20	.15	.06
13 N. Fox	.30	.25	.10	44 T. Oliva		.30	.25	.10
14 T. Gonzalez	.12	.08	.03	45 W. Causey*		.50	.40	.18
15 J. Gentile	.12	.08	.03	46 M. Alvis		.12	.08	.03
16 B. Chance	.12	.08	.03	47 G. Cisco*		.50	.40	.18
17 D. Ellsworth	.12	.08	.03	48 C. Yastrzemski		2.00	1.50	.60
18 J. Fregosi	.20	.15	.06	49 H. Aaron		2.00	1.50	.60
19 D. Groat	.20	.15	.06	50 B. Robinson		1.25	.90	.40
20 C. Hinton	.12	.08	.03	51 W. Mays*		3.00	2.25	1.00
21 E. Howard	.30	.25	.10	52 B. Williams		.40	.30	.13
22 D. Farrell	.12	.08	.03	53 J. Pizarro		.12	.08	.03
23 A. Pearson	.12	.08	.03	54 L. Wagner		.12	.08	.03
24 F. Howard	.25	.20	.08	55 O. Cepeda		.50	.40	.18
25 M. Mantle	2.50	1.80	.80	56 V. Pinson		.30	.25	.10
26 J. Torre	.20	.15	.06	57 K. Boyer		.30	.25	.10
27 E. Brinkman	.12	.08	.03	58 R. Santo		.20	.15	.06
28 B. Friend *	.50	.40	.18	59 J. Romano		.12	.08	.03
				60 B. Skowron *		.50	.40	.18

1965 TOPPS (598)   2 1/2" X 3 1/2"

The 1965 Topps set contains
high numbers 523-598 which
are somewhat more difficult
to obtain than the low numbers.

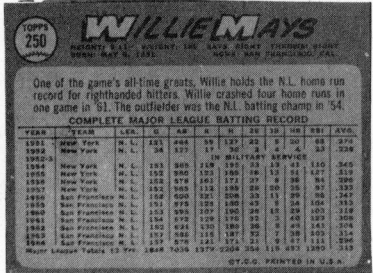

	MINT	VG-E	F-G
COMPLETE SET	270.00	200.00	90.00
COMMON PLAYER (1-446)	.17	.13	.06
COMMON PLAYER (447-522)	.22	.17	.07
COMMON PLAYER (523-598)	.35	.25	.10
1 A.L. Bat Leaders	.60	.45	.20
2 N.L. Bat Leaders	.50	.40	.18
3 A.L. H.R. Leaders	.50	.40	.18
4 N.L. H.R. Leaders	.50	.40	.18
5 A.L. R.B.I. Leaders	.50	.40	.18
6 N.L. R.B.I. Leaders	.50	.40	.18
7 A.L. E.R.A. Leaders	.50	.40	.18
8 N.L. E.R.A. Leaders	.50	.40	.18
9 A.L. Pitch. Leaders	.50	.40	.18
10 N.L. Pitch. Leaders	.50	.40	.18
11 A.L. S.O. Leaders	.50	.40	.18
12 N.L. S.O. Leaders	.50	.40	.18

	MINT	VG-E	F-G
13 Pedro Ramos	.17	.13	.06
14 Len Gabrielson	.17	.13	.06
15 Robin Roberts	2.50	1.80	.80
16 Rookies (Houston)	4.00	3.00	1.40
17 John Romano	.17	.13	.06
18 Bill McCool	.17	.13	.06
19 Gates Brown	.17	.13	.06
20 Jim Bunning	.60	.45	.20
21 Don Blasingame	.17	.13	.06
22 Charlie Smith	.17	.13	.06
23 Bob Tiefenauer	.17	.13	.06
24 Twins Team	.50	.40	.18
25 Al McBean	.17	.13	.06
26 Bob Knoop	.17	.13	.06
27 Dick Bertell	.17	.13	.06
28 Barney Schultz	.17	.13	.06

#	Player	MINT	VG-E	F-G
29	Felix Mantilla	.17	.13	.06
30	Jim Bouton	.40	.30	.13
31	Mike White	.17	.13	.06
32	Herman Franks	.20	.15	.06
33	Jackie Brandt	.17	.13	.06
34	Cal Koonce	.17	.13	.06
35	Ed Charles	.17	.13	.06
36	Bob Wine	.17	.13	.06
37	Fred Gladding	.17	.13	.06
38	Jim King	.17	.13	.06
39	Gerry Arrigo	.17	.13	.06
40	Frank Howard	.60	.45	.20
41	Rookies (W. Sox)	.17	.13	.06
42	Earl Wilson	.17	.13	.06
43	Mike Shannon	.17	.13	.06
44	Wade Blasingame	.17	.13	.06
45	Roy McMillan	.17	.13	.06
46	Bob Lee	.17	.13	.06
47	Tom Harper	.20	.15	.06
48	Claude Raymond	.17	.13	.06
49	Rookies (Orioles)	.17	.13	.06
50	Juan Marichal	1.25	.90	.40
51	Bill Bryan	.17	.13	.06
52	Ed Roebuck	.17	.13	.06
53	Dick McAuliffe	.17	.13	.06
54	Joe Gibbon	.17	.13	.06
55	Tony Conigliaro	.25	.20	.08
56	Ron Kline	.17	.13	.06
57	Cardinals Team	.35	.27	.12
58	Fred Talbot	.17	.13	.06
59	Nate Oliver	.17	.13	.06
60	Jim O'Toole	.17	.13	.06
61	Chris Cannizzaro	.17	.13	.06
62	Jim Kaat	.75	.55	.25
63	Ty Cline	.17	.13	.06
64	Lou Burdette	.35	.27	.12
65	Tony Kubek	.50	.40	.18
66	Bill Rigney	.17	.13	.06
67	Harvey Haddix	.20	.15	.06
68	Del Crandall	.20	.15	.06
69	Bill Virdon	.60	.45	.20
70	Bill Skowron	.30	.25	.10
71	John O'Donoghue	.17	.13	.06
72	Tony Gonzalez	.17	.13	.06
73	Dennis Ribant	.17	.13	.06
74	Rookies (R. Sox)	.30	.25	.10
75	Deron Johnson	.17	.13	.06
76	Sam McDowell	.30	.25	.10
77	Doug Camilli	.17	.13	.06
78	Dal Maxvill	.17	.13	.06
79	1st Ser. Checklist	.17	.13	.06
80	Turk Farrell	.17	.13	.06
81	Don Buford	.17	.13	.06
82	Rookies (Braves)	.17	.13	.06
83	George Thomas	.17	.13	.06
84	Ron Herbel	.17	.13	.06
85	Willie Smith	.17	.13	.06
86	Les Narum	.17	.13	.06
87	Nelson Mathews	.17	.13	.06
88	Jack Lamabe	.17	.13	.06
89	Mike Hershberger	.17	.13	.06
90	Rich Rollins	.17	.13	.06
91	Cubs Team	.35	.27	.12
92	Dick Howser	.30	.25	.10
93	Jack Fisher	.17	.13	.06
94	Charlie Lau	.20	.15	.06
95	Bill Mazeroski	.30	.25	.10
96	Sonny Siebert	.17	.13	.06
97	Pedro Gonzalez	.17	.13	.06
98	Bob Miller	.17	.13	.06
99	Gil Hodges	2.50	1.80	.80
100	Ken Boyer	.75	.55	.25
101	Fred Newman	.17	.13	.06
102	Steve Boros	.17	.13	.06
103	Harvey Kuenn	.35	.27	.12
104	2nd Ser. Checklist	.17	.13	.06
105	Chico Salmon	.17	.13	.06
106	Gene Oliver	.17	.13	.06
107	Rookies (Phils)	.17	.13	.06
108	Don Mincher	.17	.13	.06
109	Walt Bond	.17	.13	.06
110	Ron Santo	.40	.30	.13
111	Lee Thomas	.17	.13	.06
112	Derrell Griffith	.17	.13	.06
113	Steve Barber	.17	.13	.06
114	Jim Hickman	.17	.13	.06
115	Bob Richardson	.30	.25	.10
116	Rookies (Cards)	.17	.13	.06
117	Wes Stock	.17	.13	.06
118	Hal Lanier	.17	.13	.06
119	John Kennedy	.17	.13	.06
120	Frank Robinson	3.50	2.50	1.20
121	Gene Alley	.20	.15	.06
122	Bill Pleis	.17	.13	.06
123	Frank Thomas	.17	.13	.06
124	Tom Satriano	.17	.13	.06
125	Juan Pizarro	.17	.13	.06
126	Dodgers Team	.40	.30	.13
127	Frank Lary	.20	.15	.06
128	Vic Davalillo	.17	.13	.06
129	Bennie Daniels	.17	.13	.06
130	Al Kaline	3.50	2.50	1.20
131	John Keane	.17	.13	.06
132	World Series 1	.50	.40	.18
133	World Series 2	.50	.40	.18
134	World Series 3	.50	.40	.18
135	World Series 4	.50	.40	.18
136	World Series 5	.50	.40	.18
137	World Series 6	.50	.40	.18
138	World Series 7	.50	.40	.18
139	Cards Celebrate	.50	.40	.18
140	Dean Chance	.20	.15	.06
141	Charlie James	.17	.13	.06
142	Bill Monbouquette	.17	.13	.06
143	Rookies (Pirates)	.17	.13	.06
144	Ed Kranepool	.20	.15	.06
145	Luis Tiant	1.25	.90	.40
146	Ron Hansen	.17	.13	.06
147	Dennis Bennett	.17	.13	.06
148	Willie Kirkland	.17	.13	.06
149	Wayne Schurr	.17	.13	.06
150	Brooks Robinson	3.50	2.50	1.20
151	Athletics Team	.35	.27	.12
152	Phil Ortega	.17	.13	.06
153	Norm Cash	.50	.40	.18
154	Bob Humphreys	.17	.13	.06
155	Roger Maris	3.00	2.25	1.00
156	Bob Sadowski	.17	.13	.06
157	Zoilo Versalles	.50	.40	.18
158	Dick Sisler	.17	.13	.06
159	Jim Duffalo	.17	.13	.06
160	Bob Clemente	7.00	5.25	2.50
161	Frank Baumann	.17	.13	.06
162	Russ Nixon	.17	.13	.06
163	John Briggs	.17	.13	.06
164	Al Spangler	.17	.13	.06
165	Dick Ellsworth	.17	.13	.06
166	Rookies (Ind.)	.17	.13	.06
167	Bill Wakefield	.17	.13	.06
168	Dick Green	.17	.13	.06
169	Dave Vineyard	.17	.13	.06
170	Hank Aaron	10.00	7.00	3.00
171	Jim Roland	.17	.13	.06
172	Jim Piersall	.30	.25	.10
173	Tigers Team	.35	.27	.12
174	Joe Jay	.17	.13	.06
175	Bob Aspromonte	.17	.13	.06
176	Willie McCovey	3.50	2.50	1.20
177	Pete Mikkelsen	.17	.13	.06
178	Dalton Jones	.17	.13	.06
179	Hal Woodeshick	.17	.13	.06
180	Bob Allison	.25	.20	.08
181	Rookies (Wash.)	.17	.13	.06
182	Mike De La Hoz	.17	.13	.06
183	Dave Nicholson	.17	.13	.06
184	John Boozer	.17	.13	.06
185	Max Alvis	.17	.13	.06
186	Bill Cowan	.17	.13	.06
187	Casey Stengel	3.00	2.25	1.00
188	Sam Bowens	.17	.13	.06
189	3rd Ser. Checklist	.17	.13	.06
190	Bill White	.17	.13	.06
191	Phil Regan	.17	.13	.06
192	Jim Coker	.17	.13	.06
193	Gaylord Perry	1.50	1.10	.50
194	Rookies (Angels)	.17	.13	.06
195	Bob Veale	.17	.13	.06
196	Ron Fairly	.20	.15	.06
197	Diego Segui	.17	.13	.06
198	Smoky Burgess	.20	.15	.06
199	Bob Heffner	.17	.13	.06
200	Joe Torre	.60	.45	.20
201	Rookies (Twins)	.17	.13	.06
202	Leo Burke	.17	.13	.06
203	Dallas Green	.50	.40	.18
204	Russ Snyder	.17	.13	.06
205	Warren Spahn	3.00	2.25	1.00
206	Willie Horton	.20	.15	.06
207	Pete Rose	10.00	7.00	3.00
208	Tom John	1.00	.70	.30
209	Pirates Team	.35	.27	.12
210	Jim Fregosi	.30	.25	.10
211	Steve Ridzik	.17	.13	.06
212	Ron Brand	.17	.13	.06
213	Jim Davenport	.17	.13	.06

	MINT	VG-E	F-G		MINT	VG-E	F-G
214 Bob Purkey	.17	.13	.06	306 Bubba Phillips	.17	.13	.06
215 Pete Ward	.17	.13	.06	307 Barry Latman	.17	.13	.06
216 Al Worthington	.17	.13	.06	308 Rookies (Mets)	.17	.13	.06
217 Walt Alston	.25	.20	.08	309 Steve Hamilton	.17	.13	.06
218 Dick Schofield	.17	.13	.06	310 John Callison	.17	.13	.06
219 Bob Meyer	.17	.13	.06	311 Orlando Pena	.17	.13	.06
220 Bill Williams	.75	.55	.25	312 Joe Nuxhall	.20	.15	.06
221 John Tsitouris	.17	.13	.06	313 Jim Schaffer	.17	.13	.06
222 Bob Tillman	.17	.13	.06	314 Ster. Slaughter	.17	.13	.06
223 Dan Osinski	.17	.13	.06	315 Frank Malzone	.20	.15	.06
224 Bob Chance	.17	.13	.06	316 Reds Team	.40	.30	.13
225 Bo Belinsky	.20	.15	.06	317 Don McMahon	.17	.13	.06
226 Rookies (Yanks)	.17	.13	.06	318 Matty Alou	.25	.20	.08
227 Bob Klaus	.17	.13	.06	319 Ken McMullen	.17	.13	.06
228 Jack Sanford	.17	.13	.06	320 Bob Gibson	3.00	2.25	1.00
229 Lou Clinton	.17	.13	.06	321 Rusty Staub	.50	.40	.18
230 Ray Sadecki	.17	.13	.06	322 Rick Wise	.40	.30	.13
231 Jerry Adair	.17	.13	.06	323 Hank Bauer	.30	.25	.10
232 Steve Blass	.25	.20	.08	324 Bob Locke	.17	.13	.06
233 Don Zimmer	.30	.25	.10	325 Donn Clendenon	.17	.13	.06
234 White Sox Team	.35	.27	.12	326 Dwight Siebler	.17	.13	.06
235 Chuck Hinton	.17	.13	.06	327 Dennis Menke	.17	.13	.06
236 Dennis McLain	1.00	.70	.30	328 Eddie Fisher	.17	.13	.06
237 Bernie Allen	.17	.13	.06	329 Hawk Taylor	.17	.13	.06
238 Joe Moeller	.20	.15	.06	330 Whitey Ford	3.25	2.40	1.10
239 Doc Edwards	.17	.13	.06	331 Rookies (Dodg.)	.17	.13	.06
240 Bob Bruce	.17	.13	.06	332 Ted Abernathy	.17	.13	.06
241 Mack Jones	.17	.13	.06	333 Tom Reynolds	.17	.13	.06
242 George Brunet	.17	.13	.06	334 Vic Roznovsky	.17	.13	.06
243 Rookies (Reds)	.17	.13	.06	335 Mickey Lolich	.40	.30	.13
244 Lindy McDaniel	.20	.15	.06	336 Woody Held	.17	.13	.06
245 Joe Pepitone	.25	.20	.08	337 Mike Cuellar	.20	.15	.06
246 Tom Butters	.17	.13	.06	338 Phillies Team	.35	.27	.12
247 Wally Moon	.20	.15	.08	339 Ryne Duren	.20	.15	.06
248 Gus Triandos	.20	.15	.08	340 Tony Oliva	1.00	.70	.30
249 Dave McNally	.20	.15	.08	341 Bob Bolin	.17	.13	.06
250 Willie Mays	10.00	7.00	3.00	342 Bob Rodgers	.17	.13	.06
251 Billy Herman	.60	.45	.20	343 Mike McCormick	.17	.13	.06
252 Pete Richert	.17	.13	.06	344 Wes Parker	.50	.40	.18
253 Danny Cater	.17	.13	.06	345 Floyd Robinson	.17	.13	.06
254 Roland Sheldon	.17	.13	.06	346 Bob Bragan	.17	.13	.06
255 Camilo Pascual	.20	.15	.08	347 Roy Face	.20	.15	.06
256 Tito Francona	.17	.13	.06	348 George Banks	.17	.13	.06
257 Jim Wynn	.25	.20	.08	349 Larry Miller	.17	.13	.06
258 Larry Bearnarth	.17	.13	.06	350 Mickey Mantle	13.00	9.50	4.00
259 Rookies (Tigers)	.17	.13	.06	351 Jim Perry	.20	.15	.06
260 Don Drysdale	2.75	2.00	.90	352 Alex Johnson	.20	.15	.06
261 Duke Carmel	.17	.13	.06	353 Jerry Lumpe	.17	.13	.06
262 Bud Daley	.17	.13	.06	354 Rookies (Cubs)	.17	.13	.06
263 Marty Keough	.17	.13	.06	355 Vada Pinson	.60	.45	.20
264 Bob Buhl	.17	.13	.06	356 Bill Spanswick	.17	.13	.06
265 Jim Pagliaroni	.17	.13	.06	357 Carl Warwick	.17	.13	.06
266 Bert Campaneris	.50	.40	.18	358 Albie Pearson	.17	.13	.06
267 Senators Team	.30	.25	.10	359 Ken Johnson	.17	.13	.06
268 Ken McBride	.17	.13	.06	360 Orlando Cepeda	1.50	1.10	.50
269 Frank Bolling	.17	.13	.06	361 5th Ser. Checklist	.17	.13	.06
270 Milt Pappas	.20	.15	.06	362 Don Schwall	.17	.13	.06
271 Don Wert	.17	.13	.06	363 Bob Johnson	.17	.13	.06
272 Chuck Schilling	.17	.13	.06	364 Galen Cisco	.17	.13	.06
273 4th Ser. Checklist	.17	.13	.06	365 Jim Gentile	.17	.13	.06
274 Lum Harris	.17	.13	.06	366 Dan Schneider	.17	.13	.06
275 Dick Groat	.25	.20	.08	367 Leon Wagner	.17	.13	.06
276 Hoyt Wilhelm	.75	.55	.25	368 Rookies (W. Sox)	.17	.13	.06
277 John Lewis	.17	.13	.06	369 Phil Linz	.17	.13	.06
278 Ken Retzer	.17	.13	.06	370 Tom Davis	.30	.25	.10
279 Dick Tracewski	.17	.13	.06	371 Frank Kreutzer	.17	.13	.06
280 Dick Stuart	.20	.15	.06	372 Clay Dalrymple	.17	.13	.06
281 Bill Stafford	.17	.13	.06	373 Curt Simmons	.20	.15	.06
282 Rookies (Giants)	.20	.15	.06	374 Rookies (Angels)	.17	.13	.06
283 Fred Whitfield	.17	.13	.06	375 Dave Wickersham	.17	.13	.06
284 Nick Willhite	.17	.13	.06	376 Jim Landis	.17	.13	.06
285 Ron Hunt	.17	.13	.06	377 Willie Stargell	2.25	1.65	.75
286 Rookies (A's)	.17	.13	.06	378 Chuck Estrada	.17	.13	.06
287 Gary Kolb	.17	.13	.06	379 Giants Team	.35	.27	.12
288 Jack Hamilton	.17	.13	.06	380 Rocky Colavito	.50	.40	.18
289 Gordy Coleman	.17	.13	.06	381 Al Jackson	.17	.13	.06
290 Wally Bunker	.17	.13	.06	382 J. C. Martin	.17	.13	.06
291 Jerry Lynch	.17	.13	.06	383 Felipe Alou	.20	.15	.06
292 Larry Yellen	.17	.13	.06	384 John Klippstein	.17	.13	.06
293 Angels Team	.30	.25	.10	385 C. Yastrzemski	9.00	6.75	3.00
294 Tim McCarver	.20	.15	.06	386 Rookies (Cubs)	.17	.13	.06
295 Dick Radatz	.20	.15	.06	387 John Podres	.25	.20	.08
296 Tony Taylor	.17	.13	.06	388 John Blanchard	.17	.13	.06
297 Dave Debusschere	1.00	.70	.30	389 Don Larson	.20	.15	.06
298 Jim Stewart	.17	.13	.06	390 Bill Freehan	.25	.20	.08
299 Jerry Zimmerman	.17	.13	.06	391 Mel McGaha	.17	.13	.06
300 Sandy Koufax	7.00	5.25	2.50	392 Bob Friend	.20	.15	.06
301 Birdie Tebbetts	.17	.13	.06	393 Ed Kirkpatrick	.17	.13	.06
302 Al Stanek	.17	.13	.06	394 Jim Hannan	.17	.13	.06
303 John Orsino	.17	.13	.06	395 Jim Hart	.17	.13	.06
304 Dave Stenhouse	.17	.13	.06	396 Frank Bertaina	.17	.13	.06
305 Rico Carty	.40	.30	.13	397 Jerry Buchek	.17	.13	.06
				398 Rookies (Reds)	.17	.13	.06

	MINT	VG-E	F-G			MINT	VG-E	F-G
399 Ray Herbert	.17	.13	.06	491 Tracy Stallard	.22	.17	.07
400 Harmon Killebrew	2.50	1.80	.80	492 Gene Freese	.22	.17	.07
401 Carl Willey	.17	.13	.06	493 Rookies (Tigers)	.22	.17	.07
402 Joe Amalfitano	.17	.13	.06	494 Jay Ritchie	.22	.17	.07
403 Red Sox Team	.40	.30	.13	495 Joe Christopher	.22	.17	.07
404 Stan Williams	.17	.17	.06	496 Joe Cunningham	.22	.17	.07
405 John Roseboro	.17	.13	.06	497 Rookies (Giants)	.22	.17	.07
406 Ralph Terry	.17	.13	.06	498 Gene Stephens	.22	.17	.07
407 Lee Maye	.17	.13	.06	499 Stu Miller	.22	.17	.07
408 Larry Sherry	.17	.13	.06	500 Ed Mathews	4.00	3.00	1.40
409 Rookies (Houston)	.17	.13	.06	501 Rookies (Ind.)	.22	.17	.07
410 Luis Aparicio	.80	.60	.25	502 Don Cardwell	.22	.17	.07
411 Roger Craig	.17	.13	.06	503 Phil Gagliano	.22	.17	.07
412 Bob Bailey	.17	.13	.06	504 Jerry Grote	.22	.17	.07
413 Hal Reniff	.17	.13	.06	505 Ray Culp	.22	.17	.07
414 Al Lopez	.80	.60	.25	506 Sam Mele	.22	.17	.07
415 Curt Flood	.30	.25	.10	507 Sam Ellis	.22	.17	.07
416 Jim Brewer	.17	.13	.06	508 7th Ser. Checklist	.22	.17	.07
417 Ed Brinkman	.17	.13	.06	509 Rookies (R. Sox)	.22	.17	.07
418 John Edwards	.17	.13	.06	510 Ernie Banks	8.00	6.00	2.50
419 Ruben Amaro	.17	.13	.06	511 Ron Locke	.22	.17	.07
420 Larry Jackson	.17	.13	.06	512 Cap Peterson	.22	.17	.07
421 Rookies (Twins)	.17	.13	.06	513 Yankees Team	.75	.55	.25
422 Aubrey Gatewood	.17	.13	.06	514 Joe Azcue	.22	.17	.07
423 Jesse Gonder	.17	.13	.06	515 Vern Law	.30	.25	.10
424 Gary Bell	.17	.13	.06	516 Al Weis	.22	.17	.07
425 Wayne Causey	.17	.13	.06	517 Rookies (Angels)	.22	.17	.07
426 Braves Team	.35	.27	.12	518 Ken Rowe	.22	.17	.07
427 Bob Saverine	.17	.13	.06	519 Bob Uecker	.75	.55	.25
428 Bob Shaw	.17	.13	.06	520 Tony Cloninger	.22	.17	.07
429 Don Demeter	.17	.13	.06	521 Rookies (Phils)	.22	.17	.07
430 Gary Peters	.17	.13	.06	522 Hank Aguirre	.22	.17	.07
431 Rookies (Cards)	.17	.13	.06	523 Mike Brumley	.35	.25	.10
432 Jim Grant	.17	.13	.06	524 Dave Giusti	.35	.25	.10
433 John Bateman	.17	.13	.06	525 Ed Bressoud	.35	.25	.10
434 Dave Morehead	.17	.13	.06	526 Rookies (A's)	5.00	3.75	1.75
435 Willie Davis	.30	.25	.10	527 Jeff Torborg	.35	.25	.10
436 Don Elston	.17	.13	.06	528 George Altman	.35	.25	.10
437 Chico Cardenas	.17	.13	.06	529 Jerry Fosnow	.35	.25	.10
438 Harry Walker	.17	.13	.06	530 Jim Maloney	.40	.30	.13
439 Moe Drabowski	.17	.13	.06	531 Chuck Hiller	.35	.25	.10
440 Tom Tresh	.30	.25	.10	532 Hector Lopez	.35	.25	.10
441 Denny Lemaster	.17	.13	.06	533 Rookies (Mets)	1.00	.70	.30
442 Vic Power	.17	.13	.06	534 John Herrnstein	.35	.25	.10
443 6th Ser. Checklist	.17	.13	.06	535 Jack Kralick	.35	.25	.10
444 Bob Hendley	.17	.13	.06	536 Andre Rodgers	.35	.25	.10
445 Don Lock	.17	.13	.06	537 Rookies (Angels)	.35	.25	.10
446 Art Mahaffey	.17	.13	.06	538 Chuck Dressen	.35	.25	.10
447 Julian Javier	.22	.17	.07	539 Herm Starrette	.35	.25	.10
448 Lee Stange	.22	.17	.07	540 Lou Brock	8.00	6.00	2.50
449 Rookies (Mets)	.22	.17	.07	541 Rookies (W. Sox)	.35	.25	.10
450 Elston Howard	1.25	.90	.40	542 Lou Klimchock	.35	.25	.10
451 Jim Owens	.22	.17	.07	543 Ed Connolly	.35	.25	.10
452 Gary Geiger	.22	.17	.07	544 Howie Reed	.35	.25	.10
453 Rookies (Dodg.)	.22	.17	.07	545 Jesus Alou	.35	.25	.10
454 Ed Rakow	.22	.17	.07	546 Rookies (Ind.)	.35	.25	.10
455 Norm Siebern	.22	.17	.07	547 Jake Wood	.35	.25	.10
456 Bill Henry	.22	.17	.07	548 Dick Stigman	.35	.25	.10
457 Bob Kennedy	.22	.17	.07	549 Rookies (Cubs)	.35	.25	.10
458 John Buzhardt	.22	.17	.07	550 Mel Stottlemyre	.40	.30	.13
459 Frank Kostro	.22	.17	.07	551 Mets Team	.75	.55	.25
460 Richie Allen	1.25	.90	.40	552 Julio Gotay	.35	.25	.10
461 Rookies (Braves)	.60	.45	.20	553 Rookies (Astros)	.35	.25	.10
462 Lew Krausse	.22	.17	.07	554 Chico Ruiz	.35	.25	.10
463 Manny Mota	.40	.30	.13	555 Jack Baldschun	.35	.25	.10
464 Ron Piche	.22	.17	.07	556 Red Schoendienst	1.00	.70	.30
465 Tom Haller	.22	.17	.07	557 Jose Santiago	.35	.25	.10
466 Rookies (Wash.)	.22	.17	.07	558 Tom Sisk	.35	.25	.10
467 Ray Washburn	.22	.17	.07	559 Ed Bailey	.35	.25	.10
468 Larry Brown	.22	.17	.07	560 Boog Powell	1.00	.70	.30
469 Don Nottebart	.22	.17	.07	561 Rookies (Dodg.)	.35	.25	.10
470 Yogi Berra	4.50	3.50	1.60	562 Bill Moran	.35	.25	.10
471 Bill Hoeft	.22	.17	.07	563 Julio Navarro	.35	.25	.10
472 Don Pavletich	.22	.17	.07	564 Mel Nelson	.35	.25	.10
473 Rookies (Orioles)	.22	.17	.07	565 Ernie Broglio	.35	.25	.10
474 Cookie Rojas	.22	.17	.07	566 Rookies (Yanks)	.35	.25	.10
475 Clete Boyer	.22	.17	.07	567 Tom Aaron	.35	.25	.10
476 Billy O'Dell	.22	.17	.07	568 Ron Taylor	.35	.25	.10
477 Rookies (Cards)	5.00	3.75	1.75	569 Gino Cimoli	.35	.25	.10
478 Wilbur Wood	.30	.25	.10	570 Claude Osteen	.35	.25	.10
479 Ken Harrelson	.40	.30	.13	571 Ossie Virgil	.35	.25	.10
480 Joel Horlen	.22	.17	.07	572 Orioles Team	.60	.45	.20
481 Indians Team	.40	.30	.13	573 Rookies (R. Sox)	.35	.25	.10
482 Bob Priddy	.22	.17	.07	574 Roy Sievers	.40	.30	.13
483 George Smith	.22	.17	.07	575 Jose Pagan	.35	.25	.10
484 Ron Perranoski	.22	.17	.07	576 Terry Fox	.35	.25	.10
485 Nellie Fox	1.00	.70	.30	577 Rookies (A.L.)	.35	.25	.10
486 Rookies (Angels)	.22	.17	.07	578 Cam Carreon	.35	.25	.10
487 Woody Woodward	.22	.17	.07	579 Dick Smith	.35	.25	.10
488 Ted Wills	.22	.17	.07	580 Jim Hall	.35	.25	.10
489 Gene Mauch	.30	.25	.10	581 Rookies (N.L.)	4.00	3.00	1.40
490 Earl Battey	.22	.17	.07	582 Bob Schmidt	.35	.25	.10
				583 Wes Covington	.35	.25	.10

	MINT	VG-E	F-G
584 Harry Bright	.35	.25	.10
585 Hank Fischer	.35	.25	.10
586 Tom McGraw	.35	.25	.10
587 Joe Sparma	.35	.25	.10
588 Len Green	.35	.25	.10
589 Rookies (Giants)	.35	.25	.10
590 John Wyatt	.35	.25	.10

	MINT	VG-E	F-G
591 Bob Skinner	.35	.25	.10
592 Frank Bork	.35	.25	.10
593 Rookies (Tigers)	.35	.25	.10
594 Joe Gaines	.35	.25	.10
595 Don Lee	.35	.25	.10
596 Don Landrum	.35	.25	.10
597 Rookies (Twins)	.35	.25	.10
598 Al Downing	.35	.25	.10

1965 TOPPS EMBOSSED (72)　　　　2 1/8" X 3 1/2"

The 1965 Topps Embossed set contains 33 gold cameo portraits on blue (A.L.) and red (N.L.) backgrounds. These cards were issued as inserts with the regular Topps cards in 1965.

	MINT	VG-E	F-G
COMPLETE SET	32.00	26.00	10.00
COMMON PLAYER	.27	.20	.08
1 Carl Yastrzemski	2.00	1.50	.60
2 Ron Fairly	.35	.27	.12
3 Max Alvis	.27	.20	.08
4 Jim Hart	.27	.20	.08
5 Bill Skowron	.35	.27	.12
6 Ed Kranepool	.35	.27	.12
7 Tim McCarver	.35	.27	.12
8 Sandy Koufax	2.00	1.50	.60
9 Donn Clendenon	.27	.20	.08
10 John Romano	.27	.20	.08
11 Mickey Mantle	3.00	2.25	1.00
12 Joe Torre	.35	.27	.12
13 Al Kaline	1.50	1.10	.50
14 Al McBean	.27	.20	.08
15 Don Drysdale	1.25	.90	.40
16 Brooks Robinson	1.50	1.10	.50
17 Jim Bunning	.35	.27	.12
18 Gary Peters	.27	.20	.08
19 Bob Clemente	2.00	1.50	.60
20 Milt Pappas	.35	.25	.12
21 Wayne Causey	.27	.20	.08
22 Frank Robinson	1.50	1.10	.60
23 Bill Mazeroski	.35	.25	.12
24 Diego Segui	.27	.20	.08
25 Jim Bouton	.35	.27	.12
26 Ed Mathews	1.25	.90	.40
27 Willie Mays	2.00	1.50	.60
28 Ron Santo	.35	.27	.12
29 Boog Powell	.35	.27	.12
30 Ken McBride	.27	.20	.08
31 Leon Wagner	.27	.20	.08
32 John Callison	.27	.20	.08
33 Zoilo Versalles	.35	.27	.12
34 Jack Baldschun	.27	.20	.08

	MINT	VG-E	F-G
35 Ron Hunt	.27	.20	.08
36 Richie Allen	.40	.30	.13
37 Frank Malzone	.30	.25	.10
38 Bob Allison	.30	.25	.10
39 Jim Fregosi	.35	.27	.12
40 Billy Williams	.50	.40	.18
41 Bill Freehan	.35	.27	.12
42 Vada Pinson	.35	.27	.12
43 Bill White	.27	.20	.08
44 Roy McMillan	.27	.20	.08
45 Orlando Cepeda	.60	.45	.20
46 Rocky Colavito	.50	.40	.18
47 Ken Boyer	.40	.30	.13
48 Dick Radatz	.27	.20	.08
49 Tommy Davis	.35	.27	.12
50 Walt Bond	.27	.20	.08
51 John Orsino	.27	.20	.08
52 Joe Christopher	.27	.20	.08
53 Al Spangler	.27	.20	.08
54 Jim King	.27	.20	.08
55 Mickey Lolich	.35	.27	.12
46 Harmon Killebrew	1.25	.90	.40
57 Bob Shaw	.27	.20	.08
58 Ernie Banks	1.50	1.10	.50
59 Hank Aaron	2.00	1.50	.60
60 Chuck Hinton	.27	.20	.08
61 Bob Aspromonte	.27	.20	.08
62 Lee Maye	.27	.20	.08
63 Joe Cunningham	.27	.20	.08
64 Pete Ward	.27	.20	.08
65 Bobby Richardson	.35	.27	.12
66 Dean Chance	.27	.20	.08
67 Dick Ellsworth	.27	.20	.08
68 Jim Maloney	.27	.20	.08
69 Bob Gibson	1.25	.90	.40
70 Earl Battey	.27	.20	.08
71 Tony Kubek	.35	.27	.12
72 Jack Kralick	.27	.20	.08

Watch the hobby papers and your local bookstores for the release later this year of the Sport Americana Baseball Memorabilia Price Guide. This book will contain prices and descriptions of baseball memorabilia other than the popular baseball card issues — yearbooks, baseball coins, programs, press pins, uniforms, statues, postcards, etc.

Little Buc Sports, Inc

MINT SETS
Baseball

1981 FLEER	$16.00
1981 DONRUSS	$16.00
1981 Topps	$17.00
1980 Topps	$20.00
1979 Topps	$24.00
1978 Topps	$28.00

+ $1.50 postage

UNOPENED CASES

1981 Fleer (12,000)	140.00
1981 Topps (12,000)	140.00
1980 Topps (9,000)	135.00
1979 Topps (6,480)	135.00

Plus $10.00 postage per case

Indestructo Boxes

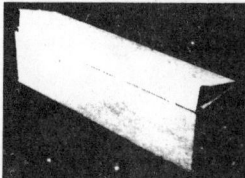

The ideal way to store and protect your cards. Boxes stack without crushing. Each holds 800 cards.

10 boxes	.60 each	$ 6.00
25 boxes	.50 each	$12.50
50 boxes	.40 each	$20.00
100 boxes	.35 each	$35.00

Add 15% for postage

TCMA CARD SETS

Stars of the Fifties	$13.00
Stars of the Sixties	$13.00
Japanese Set	$7.00
Hall of Fame Set	$12.00

$1.50 postage

Team Name	# of cards	
1890 Brooklyn Club	16	1.50
1910-14 Philadelphia Athletics	12	1.00
1914 Miracle Braves	32	3.00
1919 Chicago White Sox	28	3.00
1920 Cleveland Indians	22	2.00
1924-25 Washington Senators	41	4.00
1927 N.Y. Yankees	33	3.00
1929-31 Philadelphia Athletics	28	3.00
1934-35 Detroit Tigers	32	3.50
1934 St. Louis Cardinals	31	3.00
1938 Chicago Cubs	33	3.50
1936-39 N.Y. Yankees	54	5.50
1941 Btroo Dodgers	42	4.00
1950 Philadelphia Phillies	31	3.50
1939-40 Cincinnati Reds	45	4.00
1946 Boston Red Sox	43	4.50
1942-46 St. Louis Cardinals	69	6.00
1951 N.Y. Giants	34	3.50
1952 Brooklyn Dodgers	40	4.00
1954 Cleveland Indians	39	4.00
1957 Braves	43	4.00
1959 L.A. Dodgers	42	4.00
1960 Pittsburgh Pirates	41	4.00
1961 Cincinnati Reds	41	4.00

Add 15% for postage

2107 East 18th Street
dept. PG3
Brooklyn, New York 11229

295

1966 TOPPS (598)   2 1/2" X 3 1/2"

The 1966 Topps set contains high numbers 523-598 which are more difficult to obtain than the low numbers.

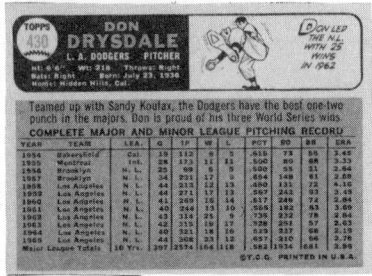

	MINT	VG-E	F-G
COMPLETE SET	400.00	300.00	140.00
COMMON PLAYER (1-446)	.16	.12	.05
COMMON PLAYER (447-522)	.21	.16	.06
COMMON PLAYER (523-598)	1.85	1.25	.50

	MINT	VG-E	F-G
1 Willie Mays	15.00	9.00	4.00
2 Ted Abernathy	.16	.12	.05
3 Sam Mele	.16	.12	.05
4 Ray Culp	.16	.12	.06
5 Jim Fregosi	.30	.25	.10
6 Chuck Schilling	.16	.12	.05
7 Tracy Stallard	.16	.12	.05
8 Floyd Robinson	.16	.12	.05
9 Clete Boyer	.16	.12	.05
10 Tony Cloninger	.16	.12	.05
11 Senators Rookies	.16	.12	.05
12 John Tsitouris	.16	.12	.05
13 Lou Johnson	.16	.12	.05
14 Norm Siebern	.16	.12	.05
15 Vern Law	.20	.15	.06
16 Larry Brown	.16	.12	.05
17 John Stephenson	.16	.12	.05
18 Roland Sheldon	.16	.12	.05
19 Giants Team	.35	.27	.12
20 Willie Horton	.20	.15	.06
21 Don Nottebart	.16	.12	.05
22 Joe Nossek	.16	.12	.05
23 Jack Sanford	.16	.12	.05
24 Don Kessinger	.25	.20	.08
25 Pete Ward	.16	.12	.05
26 Ray Sadecki	.16	.12	.05
27 Orioles Rookies	.16	.12	.05
28 Phil Niekro	.50	.40	.18
29 Mike Brumley	.16	.12	.05
30 Pete Rose	8.00	6.00	2.50
31 Jack Cullen	.16	.12	.05
32 Adolfo Phillips	.16	.12	.05
33 Jim Pagliaroni	.16	.12	.05
34 1st Ser. Checklist	.16	.12	.05
35 Ron Swoboda	.16	.12	.05
36 Jim Hunter	2.00	1.50	.60
37 Billy Herman	.75	.55	.25
38 Ron Nischwitz	.16	.12	.05
39 Ken Henderson	.16	.12	.05
40 Jim Grant	.16	.12	.05
41 Don Le John	.16	.12	.05
42 Aubrey Gatewood	.16	.12	.05
43 Don Landrum	.16	.12	.05
44 Indians Rookies	.16	.12	.05
45 Jim Gentile	.20	.15	.06
46 Howie Koplitz	.16	.12	.05
47 J. C. Martin	.16	.12	.05
48 Paul Blair	.20	.15	.06
49 Woody Woodward	.16	.12	.05
50 Mickey Mantle	12.00	8.75	4.00
51 Gordon Richardson	.16	.12	.05

	MINT	VG-E	F-G
52 Power Plus	.20	.15	.06
53 Bob Duliba	.16	.12	.05
54 Jose Pagan	.16	.12	.05
55 Ken Harrelson	.25	.20	.08
56 Sandy Valdespino	.16	.12	.05
57 Jim Lefebvre	.20	.15	.06
58 Dave Wickersham	.16	.12	.05
59 Reds Team	.35	.27	.12
60 Curt Flood	.25	.20	.08
61 Bob Bolin	.16	.12	.05
62 Merritt Ranew	.16	.12	.05
63 Jim Stewart	.16	.12	.05
64 Bob Bruce	.16	.12	.05
65 Leon Wagner	.16	.12	.05
66 Al Weis	.16	.12	.05
67 Mets Rookies	.16	.12	.05
68 Hal Reniff	.16	.12	.05
69 Ken Hamlin	.16	.12	.05
70 Carl Yastrzemski	8.00	6.00	2.50
71 Frank Carpin	.16	.12	.05
72 Tony Perez	.75	.55	.25
73 Jerry Zimmerman	.16	.12	.05
74 Don Mossi	.16	.12	.05
75 Tommy Davis	.25	.20	.08
76 Red Schoendienst	.30	.25	.10
77 Johnny Orsino	.16	.12	.05
78 Frank Linzy	.16	.12	.05
79 Joe Pepitone	.20	.15	.06
80 Richie Allen	.50	.40	.18
81 Ray Oyler	.16	.12	.05
82 Bob Hendley	.16	.12	.05
83 Albie Pearson	.16	.12	.05
84 Braves Rookies	.16	.12	.05
85 Eddie Fisher	.16	.12	.05
86 John Bateman	.16	.12	.05
87 Dan Napoleon	.16	.12	.05
88 Fred Whitfield	.16	.12	.05
89 Ted Davidson	.16	.12	.05
90 Luis Aparicio	.80	.60	.25
91 Bob Uecker	.70	.50	.20
92 Yankees Team	.40	.30	.13
93 Jim Lonborg	.25	.20	.08
94 Matty Alou	.20	.15	.06
95 Pete Richert	.16	.12	.05
96 Felipe Alou	.20	.15	.06
97 Jim Merritt	.16	.12	.05
98 Don Demeter	.16	.12	.05
99 Buc Belters	.50	.40	.18
100 Sandy Koufax	6.50	5.00	2.25
101 2nd Ser. Checklist	.16	.12	.05
102 Ed Kirkpatrick	.16	.12	.05
103 Dick Groat	.25	.20	.08
104 Alex Johnson	.16	.12	.05
105 Milt Pappas	.20	.15	.06
106 Rusty Staub	.40	.30	.13

	MINT	VG-E	F-G
107 A's Rookies	.16	.12	.05
108 Bobby Klaus	.16	.12	.05
109 Ralph Terry	.16	.12	.05
110 Ernie Banks	3.50	2.50	1.20
111 Gary Peters	.16	.12	.05
112 Manny Mota	.20	.15	.06
113 Hank Aguirre	.16	.12	.05
114 Jim Gosger	.16	.12	.05
115 Bill Henry	.16	.12	.05
116 Walt Alston	.25	.20	.08
117 Jake Gibbs	.16	.12	.05
118 Mike McCormick	.16	.12	.05
119 Art Shamsky	.16	.12	.05
120 H. Killebrew	2.50	1.80	.80
121 Ray Herbert	.16	.12	.05
122 Joe Gaines	.16	.12	.05
123 Pirates Rookies	.16	.12	.05
124 Tug McGraw	.30	.25	.10
125 Lou Brock	4.00	3.00	1.40
126 Jim Palmer	5.00	3.75	1.75
127 Ken Berry	.16	.12	.05
128 Jim Landis	.16	.12	.05
129 Jack Kralick	.16	.12	.05
130 Joe Torre	.50	.40	.18
131 Angels Team	.30	.25	.10
132 Orlando Cepeda	1.25	.90	.40
133 Don McMahon	.16	.12	.05
134 Wes Parker	.30	.25	.10
135 Dave Morehead	.16	.12	.05
136 Woody Held	.16	.12	.05
137 Pat Corrales	.16	.12	.05
138 Roger Repoz	.16	.12	.05
139 Cubs Rookies	.16	.12	.05
140 Jim Maloney	.20	.15	.06
141 Tom McCraw	.16	.12	.05
142 Don Dennis	.16	.12	.05
143 Jose Tartabull	.16	.12	.05
144 Don Schwall	.16	.12	.05
145 Bill Freehan	.20	.15	.06
146 George Altman	.16	.12	.05
147 Lum Harris	.16	.12	.05
148 Bob Johnson	.16	.12	.05
149 Dick Nen	.16	.12	.05
150 Rocky Colavito	.60	.45	.20
151 Gary Wagner	.16	.12	.05
152 Frank Malzone	.20	.15	.06
153 Rico Carty	.30	.25	.10
154 Chuck Hiller	.16	.12	.05
155 Marcelino Lopez	.16	.12	.05
156 D. P. Combo	.20	.15	.06
157 Rene Lachemann	.16	.12	.05
158 Jim Brewer	.16	.12	.05
159 Chico Ruiz	.16	.12	.05
160 Whitey Ford	3.50	2.50	1.20
161 Jerry Lumpe	.16	.12	.05
162 Lee Maye	.16	.12	.05
163 Tito Francona	.16	.12	.05
164 W. Sox Rookies	.16	.12	.05
165 Don Lock	.16	.12	.05
166 Chris Krug	.16	.12	.05
167 Boog Powell	.50	.40	.18
168 Dan Osinski	.16	.12	.05
169 Duke Sims	.16	.12	.05
170 Cookie Rojas	.16	.12	.05
171 Nick Willhite	.16	.12	.05
172 Mets Team	.35	.27	.12
173 Al Spangler	.16	.12	.05
174 Ron Taylor	.16	.12	.05
175 Bert Campaneris	.25	.20	.08
176 Jim Davenport	.16	.12	.05
177 Hector Lopez	.16	.12	.05
178 Bob Tillman	.16	.12	.05
179 Cards Rookies	.16	.12	.05
180 Vada Pinson	.50	.40	.18
181 Al Worthington	.16	.12	.05
182 Jerry Lynch	.16	.12	.05
183 3rd Ser. Checklist	.16	.12	.05
184 Denis Menke	.16	.12	.05
185 Bob Buhl	.16	.12	.05
186 Ruben Amaro	.16	.12	.05
187 Chuck Dressen	.20	.15	.06
188 Al Luplow	.16	.12	.05
189 John Roseboro	.16	.12	.05
190 Jimmie Hall	.16	.12	.05
191 Darrell Sutherland	.16	.12	.05
192 Vic Power	.16	.12	.05
193 Dave McNally	.25	.20	.08
194 Senators Team	.30	.25	.10
195 Joe Morgan	2.25	1.65	.75
196 Don Pavletich	.16	.12	.05
197 Sonny Siebert	.16	.12	.05
198 Mickey Stanley	.16	.12	.05
199 Chisox Clubbers	.20	.15	.06
200 Ed Mathews	2.75	2.00	.90
201 Jim Dickson	.16	.12	.05
202 Clay Dalrymple	.16	.12	.05
203 Jose Santiago	.16	.12	.05
204 Cubs Team	.30	.25	.10
205 Tom Tresh	.20	.15	.06
206 Alvin Jackson	.16	.12	.05
207 Frank Quilici	.16	.12	.05
208 Bob Miller	.16	.12	.05
209 Tigers Rookies	.16	.12	.05
210 Bill Mazeroski	.25	.20	.08
211 Frank Kreutzer	.16	.12	.05
212 Ed Kranepool	.20	.15	.06
213 Fred Newman	.16	.12	.05
214 Tommy Harper	.16	.12	.05
215 N.L. Batting	.50	.40	.18
216 A.L. Batting	.50	.40	.18
217 N.L. Home Run	.50	.40	.18
218 A.L. Home Run	.60	.45	.20
219 N.L. R.B.I.	.50	.40	.18
220 A.L. R.B.I.	.60	.45	.20
221 N.L. E.R.A.	.50	.40	.18
222 A.L. E.R.A.	.50	.40	.18
223 N.L. Pitching	.50	.40	.18
224 A.L. Pitching	.50	.40	.18
225 N.L. Strikeout	.50	.40	.18
226 A.L. Strikeout	.50	.40	.18
227 Russ Nixon	.16	.12	.05
228 Larry Dierker	.16	.12	.05
229 Hank Bauer	.25	.20	.08
230 John Callison	.16	.12	.05
231 Floyd Weaver	.16	.12	.05
232 Glenn Beckert	.16	.12	.05
233 Dom Zanni	.16	.12	.05
234 Yankees Rookies	.16	.12	.05
235 Don Cardwell	.16	.12	.05
236 M. Hershberger	.16	.12	.05
237 Billy O'Dell	.16	.12	.05
238 Dodgers Team	.40	.30	.13
239 Orlando Pena	.16	.12	.05
240 Earl Battey	.16	.12	.05
241 Dennis Ribant	.16	.12	.05
242 Jesus Alou	.16	.12	.05
243 Nelson Briles	.16	.12	.05
244 Astros Rookies	.16	.12	.05
245 John Buzhardt	.16	.12	.05
246 Ed Bailey	.16	.12	.05
247 Carl Warwick	.16	.12	.05
248 Pete Mickelsen	.16	.12	.05
249 Bill Rigney	.16	.12	.05
250 Sam Ellis	.16	.12	.05
251 Ed Brinkman	.16	.12	.05
252 D. Lemaster	.16	.12	.05
253 Don Wert	.16	.12	.05
254 Phillies Rookies	2.50	1.80	.80
255 Willie Stargell	2.50	1.80	.80
256 Lew Krausse	.16	.12	.05
257 Jeff Torborg	.16	.12	.05
258 Dave Giusti	.16	.12	.05
259 Red Sox Team	.35	.27	.12
260 Bob Shaw	.16	.12	.05
261 Ron Hansen	.16	.12	.05
262 Jack Hamilton	.16	.12	.05
263 Tom Egan	.16	.12	.05
264 Twins Rookies	.16	.12	.05
265 Stu Miller	.16	.12	.05
266 Pedro Gonzalez	.16	.12	.05
267 Joe Sparma	.16	.12	.05
268 John Blanchard	.16	.12	.05
269 Don Heffner	.16	.12	.05
270 Claude Osteen	.16	.12	.05
271 Hal Lanier	.16	.12	.05
272 Jack Baldschun	.16	.12	.05
273 Astro Aces	.25	.20	.08
274 Buster Narum	.16	.12	.05
275 Tim McCarver	.20	.15	.06
276 Jim Bouton	.25	.20	.08
277 George Thomas	.16	.12	.05
278 Calvin Koonce	.16	.12	.05
279 4th Ser. Checklist	.16	.12	.05
280 Bobby Knoop	.16	.12	.05
281 Bruce Howard	.16	.12	.05
282 Johnny Lewis	.16	.12	.05
283 Jim Perry	.20	.15	.08
284 Bobby Wine	.16	.12	.05
285 Luis Tiant	.50	.40	.18
286 Gary Geiger	.16	.12	.05
287 Jack Aker	.16	.12	.05
288 Dodgers Rookies	2.00	1.50	.60
289 Larry Sherry	.20	.15	.08
290 Ron Santo	.40	.30	.13
291 Moe Drabowsky	.16	.12	.05

	MINT	VG-E	F-G
292 Jim Coker	.16	.12	.05
293 Mike Shannon	.20	.15	.06
294 Steve Ridzik	.16	.12	.05
295 Jim Hart	.16	.12	.05
296 John Keane	.16	.12	.05
297 Jim Owens	.16	.12	.05
298 Rico Petrocelli	.20	.15	.06
299 Lou Burdette	.30	.25	.10
300 Bob Clemente	6.50	5.00	2.25
301 Greg Bollo	.16	.12	.05
302 Ernie Bowman	.16	.12	.05
303 Indians Team	.30	.25	.10
304 John Herrnstein	.16	.12	.05
305 Camilo Pascual	·.20	.15	.06
306 Ty Cline	.16	.12	.05
307 Clay Carroll	.16	.12	.05
308 Tom Haller	.16	.12	.05
309 Diego Segui	.16	.12	.05
310 Frank Robinson	5.00	3.75	1.75
311 Reds Rookies	.16	.12	.05
312 Bob Saverine	.16	.12	.05
313 Chris Zachary	.16	.12	.05
314 Hector Valle	.16	.12	.05
315 Norm Cash	.40	.30	.13
316 Jack Fisher	.16	.12	.05
317 Dalton Jones	.16	.12	.05
318 Harry Walker	.16	.12	.05
319 Gene Freese	.16	.12	.05
320 Bob Gibson	2.75	2.00	.90
321 Rick Reichardt	.16	.12	.05
322 Bill Faul	.16	.12	.05
323 Ray Barker	.16	.12	.05
324 J. Boozer	.16	.12	.05
325 Vic Davalillo	.16	.12	.05
326 Braves Team	.30	.25	.10
327 Bernie Allen	.16	.12	.05
328 Jerry Grote	.16	.12	.05
329 Pete Charlton	.16	.12	.05
330 Ron Fairly	.20	.15	.06
331 Ron Herbel	.16	.12	.05
332 Billy Bryan	.16	.12	.05
333 Senators Rookies	.16	.12	.05
334 Marty Keough	.16	.12	.05
335 Juan Pizarro	.16	.12	.05
336 Gene Alley	.16	.12	.05
337 Fred Gladding	.16	.12	.05
338 Dal Maxvill	.16	.12	.05
339 Del Crandall	.20	.15	.06
340 Dean Chance	.20	.15	.06
341 Wes Westrum	.16	.12	.05
342 Bob Humphreys	.16	.12	.05
343 Joe Christopher	.16	.12	.05
344 Steve Blass	.25	.20	.08
345 Bob Allison	.20	.15	.06
346 Mike De La Hoz	.16	.12	.05
347 Phil Regan	.16	.12	.05
348 Orioles Team	.35	.27	.12
349 Cap Peterson	.16	.12	.05
350 Mel Stottlemyre	.20	.15	.06
351 Fred Valentine	.16	.12	.05
352 Bob Aspromonte	.16	.12	.05
353 Al McBean	.16	.12	.05
354 Smoky Burgess	.20	.15	.06
355 Wade Blasingame	.16	.12	.05
356 Red Sox Rookies	.16	.12	.05
357 Gerry Arrigo	.16	.12	.05
358 Charlie Smith	.16	.12	.05
359 Johnny Briggs	.16	.12	.05
360 Ron Hunt	.16	.12	.05
361 Tom Satriano	.16	.12	.05
362 Gates Brown	.16	.12	.05
363 5th Ser. Checklist	.16	.12	.05
364 Nate Oliver	.16	.12	.05
365 Roger Maris	3.00	2.25	1.00
366 Wayne Causey	.16	.12	.05
367 Mel Nelson	.16	.12	.05
368 Charlie Lau	.20	.15	.06
369 Jim King	.16	.12	.05
370 Chico Cardenas	.16	.12	.05
371 Lee Stange	.16	.12	.05
372 Harvey Kuenn	.30	.25	.10
373 Giants Rookies	.16	.12	.05
374 Bob Locker	.16	.12	.05
375 Donn Clendenon	.16	.12	.05
376 Paul Schaal	.16	.12	.05
377 Turk Farrell	.16	.12	.05
378 Dick Tracewski	.16	.12	.05
379 Cardinal Team	.30	.25	.10
380 Tony Conigliaro	.25	.20	.08
381 Hank Fischer	.16	.12	.05
382 Phil Roof	.16	.12	.05
383 Jack Brandt	.16	.12	.05
384 Al Downing	.16	.12	.05

	MINT	VG-E	F-G
385 Ken Boyer	.60	.45	.20
386 Gil Hodges	2.25	1.65	.75
387 Howie Reed	.16	.12	.05
388 Don Mincher	.16	.12	.05
389 Jim O'Toole	.20	.15	.06
390 Brooks Robinson	3.75	2.75	1.25
391 Chuck Hinton	.16	.12	.05
392 Cubs Rookies	.16	.12	.05
393 George Brunet	.16	.12	.05
394 Ron Brand	.16	.12	.05
395 Len Gabrielson	.16	.12	.05
396 J. Stephenson	.16	.12	.05
397 Bill White	.20	.15	.06
398 Danny Cater	.16	.12	.05
399 Ray Washburn	.16	.12	.05
400 Zoilo Versalles	.20	.15	.06
401 Ken McMullen	.16	.12	.05
402 Jim Hickman	.16	.12	.05
403 Fred Talbot	.16	.12	.05
404 Pirates Team	.30	.25	.10
405 Elston Howard	.75	.55	.25
406 Joe Jay	.16	.12	.05
407 John Kennedy	.16	.12	.05
408 Lee Thomas	.16	.12	.05
409 Billy Hoeft	.16	.12	.05
410 Al Kaline	3.50	2.50	1.20
411 Gene Mauch	.30	.25	.10
412 Sam Bowens	.16	.12	.05
413 John Romano	.16	.12	.05
414 Dan Coombs	.16	.12	.05
415 Max Alvis	.16	.12	.05
416 Phil Ortega	.16	.12	.05
417 Angels Rookies	.16	.12	.05
418 Phil Gagliano	.16	.12	.05
419 Mike Ryan	.16	.12	.05
420 Juan Marichal	1.25	.90	.40
421 Roy McMillan	.16	.12	.05
422 Ed Charles	.16	.12	.05
423 Ernie Broglio	.16	.12	.05
424 Reds Rookies	.16	.12	.05
425 Bob Veale	.16	.12	.05
426 White Sox Team	.30	.25	.10
427 John Miller	.16	.12	.05
428 Sandy Alomar	.16	.12	.05
429 B. Monbouquette	.16	.12	.05
430 Don Drysdale	2.75	2.00	.90
431 Walt Bond	.16	.12	.05
432 Bob Heffner	.16	.12	.05
433 Alvin Dark	.20	.15	.06
434 Willie Kirkland	.16	.12	.05
435 Jim Bunning	.40	.30	.13
436 Julian Javier	.16	.12	.05
437 Al Stanek	.16	.12	.05
438 Willie Smith	.16	.12	.05
439 Pedro Ramos	.16	.12	.05
440 Deron Johnson	.16	.12	.05
441 Tommie Sisk	.16	.12	.05
442 Orioles Rookies	.16	.12	.05
443 Bill Wakefield	.16	.12	.05
444 6th Ser. Checklist	.16	.12	.05
445 Jim Kaat	.50	.40	.18
446 Mack Jones	.16	.12	.05
447 Dick Ellsworth	.30	.25	.10
448 Eddie Stanky	.30	.25	.10
449 Joe Moeller	.30	.25	.10
450 Tony Oliva	1.00	.70	.30
451 Barry Latman	.21	.16	.06
452 Joe Azcue	.21	.16	.06
453 Ron Kline	.21	.16	.06
454 Jerry Buchek	.21	.16	.06
455 Mickey Lolich	.40	.30	.13
456 Red Sox Rookies	.21	.16	.06
457 Joe Gibbon	.21	.16	.06
458 Manny Jiminez	.21	.16	.06
459 Bill McCool	.30	.25	.10
460 Curt Blefary	.21	.16	.06
461 Roy Face	.30	.25	.10
462 Bob Rodgers	.21	.16	.06
463 Phillies Team	.35	.27	.12
464 Larry Bearnarth	.21	.16	.06
465 Don Buford	.21	.16	.06
466 Ken Johnson	.21	.16	.06
467 Vic Roznovsky	.21	.16	.06
468 Johnny Podres	.30	.25	.10
469 Yankees Rookies	1.25	.90	.40
470 Sam McDowell	.30	.25	.10
471 Bob Skinner	.21	.16	.06
472 Terry Fox	.21	.16	.06
473 Rich Rollins	.21	.16	.06
474 Dick Schofield	.21	.16	.06
475 Dick Radatz	.21	.16	.06
476 Bobby Bragan	.21	.16	.06
477 Steve Barber	.21	.16	.06

	MINT	VG-E	F-G
478 Tony Gonzalez	.21	.16	.06
479 Jim Hannan	.21	.16	.06
480 Dick Stuart	.30	.25	.10
481 Bob Lee	.21	.16	.06
482 Cubs Rookies	.21	.16	.06
483 Joe Nuxhall	.30	.25	.10
484 Wes Covington	.21	.16	.06
485 Bob Bailey	.21	.16	.06
486 Tommy John	1.00	.70	.30
487 Al Ferrara	.21	.16	.06
488 George Banks	.21	.16	.06
489 Curt Simmons	.30	.25	.10
490 Bobby Richardson	.40	.30	.13
491 Dennis Bennett	.21	.16	.06
492 Athletics Team	.30	.25	.10
493 John Klippstein	.21	.16	.06
494 Gordon Coleman	.21	.16	.06
495 Dick McAuliffe	.21	.16	.06
496 Lindy McDaniel	.30	.25	.10
497 Chris Cannizzaro	.21	.16	.06
498 Pirates Rookies	.21	.16	.06
499 Wally Bunker	.21	.16	.06
500 Hank Aaron	12.00	8.75	4.00
501 John O'Donoghue	.21	.16	.06
502 Lenny Green	.21	.16	.06
503 Steve Hamilton	.21	.16	.06
504 Grady Hatton	.21	.16	.06
505 Jose Cardenal	.21	.16	.06
506 Bo Belinsky	.25	.20	.08
507 John Edwards	.21	.16	.06
508 Steve Hargan	.21	.16	.06
509 Jake Wood	.21	.16	.06
510 Hoyt Wilhelm	1.25	.90	.40
511 Giants Rookies	.21	.16	.06
512 Dick Stigman	.21	.16	.06
513 Camilo Carreon	.21	.16	.06
514 Hal Woodeshick	.21	.16	.06
515 Frank Howard	1.00	.70	.30
516 Eddie Bressoud	.21	.16	.06
517 7th Ser. Checklist	.21	.16	.06
518 Braves Rookies	.21	.16	.06
519 Bob Friend	.30	.25	.10
520 Jim Wynn	.40	.30	.13
521 John Wyatt	.21	.16	.06
522 Phil Linz	.21	.16	.06
523 Bob Sadowski	1.85	1.25	.50
524 Giants Rookies	1.85	1.25	.50
525 Gary Bell	1.85	1.25	.50
526 Twins Team	3.00	2.25	1.00
527 Julio Navarro	1.85	1.25	.50
528 Jesse Gonder	1.85	1.25	.50
529 White Sox Rookies	1.85	1.25	.50
530 Robin Roberts	10.00	7.00	3.00
531 Joe Cunningham	1.85	1.25	.50
532 A. Monteagudo	1.85	1.25	.50
533 Jerry Adair	1.85	1.25	.50
534 Mets Rookies	1.85	1.25	.50
535 Willie Davis	3.00	2.25	1.00
536 Dick Egan	1.85	1.25	.50
537 Herman Franks	1.85	1.25	.50

	MINT	VG-E	F-G
538 Bob Allen	1.85	1.25	.50
539 Astros Rookies	1.85	1.25	.50
540 Denny McLain	12.00	8.75	4.00
541 Gene Oliver	1.85	1.25	.50
542 George Smith	1.05	1.25	.50
543 Roger Craig	2.00	1.50	.60
544 Cardinals Rookies	1.85	1.25	.50
545 Dick Green	1.85	1.25	.50
546 Dwight Siebler	1.85	1.25	.50
547 Horace Clarke	1.85	1.25	.50
548 Gary Kroll	1.85	1.25	.50
549 Senators Rookies	1.85	1.25	.50
550 Willie McCovey	28.00	21.00	10.00
551 Bob Purkey	1.85	1.25	.50
552 Birdie Tebbetts	1.85	1.25	.50
553 Rookie Stars	1.85	1.25	.50
554 Jim Northrup	1.85	1.25	.50
555 Ron Perranoski	1.85	1.25	.50
556 Mel Queen	1.85	1.25	.50
557 Felix Mantilla	1.85	1.25	.50
558 Red Sox Rookies	3.00	2.25	1.10
559 Roberto Pena	1.85	1.25	.50
560 Joel Horlen	1.85	1.25	.50
561 Choo Choo Coleman	1.85	1.25	.50
562 Russ Snyder	1.85	1.25	.50
563 Twins Rookies	1.85	1.25	.50
564 Bob Chance	1.85	1.25	.50
565 Jimmy Piersall	3.00	2.25	1.10
566 Mike Cuellar	2.00	1.50	.60
567 Dick Howser	2.00	1.50	.60
568 Athletics Rookies	1.85	1.25	.50
569 Orlando McFarlane	1.85	1.25	.50
570 Art Mahaffey	1.85	1.25	.50
571 Dave Roberts	1.85	1.25	.50
572 Bob Priddy	1.85	1.25	.50
573 Derrell Griffith	1.85	1.25	.50
574 Mets Rookies	1.85	1.25	.50
575 Earl Wilson	1.85	1.25	.50
576 Dave Nicholson	1.85	1.25	.50
577 Jack Lamabe	1.85	1.25	.50
578 Chi Chi Olivo	1.85	1.25	.50
579 Orioles Rookies	1.85	1.25	.50
580 Billy Williams	5.00	3.75	1.75
581 Tony Martinez	1.85	1.25	.50
582 Garry Roggenburk	1.85	1.25	.50
583 Tigers Team	3.00	2.25	1.00
584 Yankees Rookies	1.85	1.25	.50
585 Tony Taylor	1.85	1.25	.50
586 Claude Raymond	1.85	1.25	.50
587 Dick Bertell	1.85	1.25	.50
588 Athletics Rookies	1.85	1.25	.50
589 Lou Klimchock	1.85	1.25	.50
590 Bill Skowron	3.00	2.25	1.00
591 Rookies Stars	1.85	1.25	.50
592 Andre Rodgers	1.85	1.25	.50
593 Doug Camilli	1.85	1.25	.50
594 Chico Salmon	1.85	1.25	.50
595 Larry Jackson	1.85	1.25	.50
596 Astros Rookies	1.85	1.25	.50
597 John Sullivan	1.85	1.25	.50
598 Gaylord Perry	50.00	38.00	17.00

1967 TOPPS (609)

2 1/2" X 3 1/2"

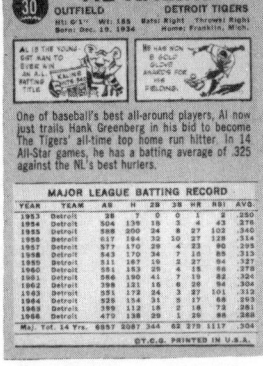

The 1967 Topps set contains high numbers 534-609 which are more difficult to obtain than the low numbers. Due to the strange distribution of this last series, certain of the high numbers are difficult to obtain in parts of the country.

	MINT	VG-E	F-G
COMPLETE SET	530.00	400.00	150.00
COMMON PLAYER (1-457)	.16	.12	.05
COMMON PLAYER (458-533)	.21	.16	.06
COMMON PLAYER (534-609)	1.60	1.25	.50
1 The Champs	1.25	.80	.35

	MINT	VG-E	F-G
2 Jack Hamilton	.16	.12	.05
3 Duke Sims	.16	.12	.05
4 Hal Lanier	.16	.12	.05
5 Whitey Ford	2.75	2.00	.90
6 Dick Simpson	.16	.12	.05

	MINT	VG-E	F-G
7 Don McMahon	.16	.12	.05
8 Chuck Harrison	.16	.12	.05
9 Ron Hansen	.16	.12	.05
10 Matty Alou	.20	.15	.06
11 Barry Moore	.16	.12	.05
12 Dodgers Rookies	.16	.12	.05
13 Joe Sparma	.16	.12	.05
14 Phil Linz	.16	.12	.05
15 Earl Battey	.16	.12	.05
16 Bill Hands	.16	.12	.05
17 Jim Gosger	.16	.12	.05
18 Gene Oliver	.16	.12	.05
19 Jim McGlothlin	.16	.12	.05
20 Orlando Cepeda	1.50	1.10	.50
21 Dave Bristol	.16	.12	.05
22 Gene Brabender	.16	.12	.05
23 Larry Elliot	.16	.12	.05
24 Bob Allen	.16	.12	.05
25 Elston Howard	.80	.60	.25
26 Bob Priddy	.16	.12	.05
27 Bob Saverine	.16	.12	.05
28 Barry Latman	.16	.12	.05
29 Tommy McCraw	.16	.12	.05
30 Al Kaline	3.00	2.25	1.00
31 Jim Brewer	.16	.12	.05
32 Bob Bailey	.16	.12	.05
33 K.C.A. Rookies	.16	.12	.05
34 Pete Cimino	.16	.12	.05
35 Rico Carty	.25	.20	.08
36 Bob Tillman	.16	.12	.05
37 Rick Wise	.20	.15	.06
38 Bob Johnson	.16	.12	.05
39 Curt Simmons	.20	.15	.06
40 Rick Reichardt	.16	.12	.05
41 Joe Hoerner	.16	.12	.05
42 Mets Team	.30	.25	.10
43 Chico Salmon	.16	.12	.05
44 Joe Nuxhall	.20	.15	.06
45 Roger Maris	3.00	2.25	1.00
46 Lindy McDaniel	.20	.15	.06
47 Ken McMullen	.16	.12	.05
48 Bill Freehan	.20	.15	.06
49 Roy Face	.20	.15	.06
50 Tony Oliva	.80	.60	.25
51 Astros Rookies	.16	.12	.05
52 Dennis Higgins	.16	.12	.05
53 Clay Dalrymple	.16	.12	.05
54 Dick Green	.16	.12	.05
55 Don Drysdale	2.50	1.80	.80
56 Jose Tartabull	.16	.12	.05
57 Pat Jarvis	.16	.12	.05
58 Paul Schaal	.16	.12	.05
59 Ralph Terry	.16	.12	.05
60 Luis Aparicio	1.00	.70	.30
61 Gordy Coleman	.16	.12	.05
62 1st Checklist	.16	.12	.05
63 Cards' Clubbers	1.00	.70	.30
64 Fred Valentine	.16	.12	.05
65 Tom Haller	.16	.12	.05
66 Manny Mota	.20	.15	.06
67 Ken Berry	.16	.12	.05
68 Bob Buhl	.16	.12	.05
69 Vic Davalillo	.16	.12	.05
70 Ron Santo	.30	.25	.10
71 Camilo Pascual	.20	.15	.06
72 Tigers Rookies	.16	.12	.05
73 Rusty Staub	.40	.30	.13
74 Wes Stock	.16	.12	.05
75 George Scott	.25	.20	.08
76 Jim Barbieri	.16	.12	.05
77 Dooley Womack	.16	.12	.05
78 Pat Corrales	.16	.12	.05
79 Bubba Morton	.16	.12	.05
80 Jim Maloney	.20	.15	.06
81 Eddie Stanky	.20	.15	.06
82 Steve Barber	.16	.12	.05
83 Ollie Brown	.16	.12	.05
84 Tommie Sisk	.16	.12	.05
85 Johnny Callison	.16	.12	.05
86 Mike McCormick	.16	.12	.05
87 George Altman	.16	.12	.05
88 Mickey Lolich	.30	.25	.10
89 Felix Millan	.16	.12	.05
90 Jim Nash	.16	.12	.05
91 Johnny Lewis	.16	.12	.05
92 Ray Washburn	.16	.12	.05
93 Yankees Rookies	.40	.30	.13
94 Ron Fairly	.20	.15	.06
95 Sonny Siebert	.16	.12	.05
96 Art Shamsky	.16	.12	.05
97 Mike Cuellar	.20	.15	.06
98 Rich Rollins	.16	.12	.05
99 Lee Stange	.16	.12	.05
100 Frank Robinson	3.25	2.40	1.10

	MINT	VG-E	F-G
101 Ken Johnson	.16	.12	.05
102 Phillies Team	.30	.25	.10
103 2nd Checklist	.16	.12	.05
104 Minnie Rojas	.16	.12	.05
105 Ken Boyer	.60	.45	.20
106 Randy Hundley	.16	.12	.05
107 Joel Horlen	.16	.12	.05
108 Alex Johnson	.16	.12	.05
109 Tribe Thumpers	.25	.20	.08
110 Jack Aker	.16	.12	.05
111 John Kennedy	.16	.12	.05
112 D. Wickersham	.16	.12	.05
113 Dave Nicholson	.16	.12	.05
114 Jack Baldschun	.16	.12	.05
115 Paul Casanova	.16	.12	.05
116 Herman Franks	.16	.12	.05
117 Darrell Brandon	.16	.12	.05
118 Bernie Allen	.16	.12	.05
119 W. Blasingame	.16	.12	.05
120 Floyd Robinson	.16	.12	.05
121 Ed Bressoud	.16	.12	.05
122 George Brunet	.16	.12	.05
123 Pirates Rookies	.16	.12	.05
124 Jim Stewart	.16	.12	.05
125 Moe Drabowsky	.16	.12	.05
126 Tony Taylor	.16	.12	.05
127 J. O'Donoghue	.16	.12	.05
128 Ed Spiezio	.16	.12	.05
129 Phil Roof	.16	.12	.05
130 Phil Regan	.16	.12	.05
131 Yankees Team	.35	.27	.12
132 Ozzie Virgil	.16	.12	.05
133 Ron Kline	.16	.12	.05
134 Gates Brown	.16	.12	.05
135 Deron Johnson	.16	.12	.05
136 C. Sembera	.16	.12	.05
137 Twins Rookies	.16	.12	.05
138 Dick Kelley	.16	.12	.05
139 Dalton Jones	.16	.12	.05
140 Willie Stargell	2.25	1.65	.75
141 John Miller	.16	.12	.05
142 Jackie Brandt	.16	.12	.05
143 Sox Sockers	.20	.15	.06
144 Bill Hepler	.16	.12	.05
145 Larry Brown	.16	.12	.05
146 Steve Carlton	2.00	1.50	.60
147 Tom Egan	.16	.12	.05
148 Adolfo Phillips	.16	.12	.05
149 Joe Moeller	.20	.15	.06
150 Mickey Mantle	12.00	8.75	4.00
151 World Series #1	.40	.30	.13
152 World Series #2	.40	.30	.13
153 World Series #3	.40	.30	.13
154 World Series #4	.40	.30	.13
155 World Series #5	.40	.30	.13
156 Ron Herbel	.16	.12	.05
157 Danny Cater	.16	.12	.05
158 Jimmie Coker	.16	.12	.05
159 Bruce Howard	.16	.12	.05
160 Willie Davis	.25	.20	.08
161 Dick Williams	.20	.15	.06
162 Billy O'Dell	.16	.12	.05
163 Vic Roznovsky	.16	.12	.05
164 Dwight Siebler	.16	.12	.05
165 Cleon Jones	.16	.12	.05
166 Ed Mathews	2.50	1.80	.80
167 Senators Rookies	.16	.12	.05
168 Ray Culp	.16	.12	.05
169 Horace Clarke	.16	.12	.05
170 D. McAuliffe	.16	.12	.05
171 Calvin Koonce	.16	.12	.05
172 Bill Heath	.16	.12	.05
173 Cardinals Team	.30	.25	.10
174 Dick Radatz	.16	.12	.05
175 Bobby Knoop	.16	.12	.05
176 Sammy Ellis	.16	.12	.05
177 Tito Fuentes	.16	.12	.05
178 John Buzhardt	.16	.12	.05
179 Braves Rookies	.16	.12	.05
180 Curt Blefary	.16	.12	.05
181 Terry Fox	.16	.12	.05
182 Ed Charles	.16	.12	.05
183 Jim Pagliaroni	.16	.12	.05
184 George Thomas	.16	.12	.05
185 Ken Holtzman	.20	.15	.06
186 Mets Maulers	.25	.20	.08
187 Pedro Ramos	.16	.12	.05
188 Ken Harrelson	.20	.15	.06
189 Chuck Hinton	.16	.12	.05
190 Turk Farrell	.16	.12	.05
191 3rd Series Checklist	.16	.12	.05
192 Fred Gladding	.16	.12	.05
193 Jose Cardenal	.16	.12	.05
194 Bob Allison	.20	.15	.06
195 Al Jackson	.16	.12	.05

	MINT	VG-E	F-G
196 Johnny Romano	.16	.12	.05
197 Ron Perranoski	.16	.12	.05
198 Chuck Hiller	.16	.12	.05
199 Billy Hitchcock	.16	.12	.05
200 Willie Mays	10.00	7.00	3.00
201 Hal Reniff	.16	.12	.05
202 Johnny Edwards	.16	.12	.05
203 Al McBean	.16	.12	.05
204 Orioles Rookies	.16	.12	.05
205 Dick Groat	.20	.15	.06
206 Dennis Bennett	.16	.12	.05
207 John Orsino	.16	.12	.05
208 Jack Lamabe	.16	.12	.05
209 Joe Nossek	.16	.12	.05
210 Bob Gibson	2.50	1.80	.80
211 Twins Team	.30	.25	.10
212 Chris Zachary	.16	.12	.05
213 Jay Johnstone	.16	.12	.05
214 Dick Kelley	.16	.12	.05
215 Ernie Banks	3.00	2.25	1.00
216 Bengal Belters	1.00	.70	.30
217 Rob Gardner	.16	.12	.05
218 Wes Parker	.25	.20	.08
219 Clay Carroll	.16	.12	.05
220 Jim Hart	.16	.12	.05
221 Woody Fryman	.16	.12	.05
222 Reds Rookies	.16	.12	.05
223 Mike Ryan	.16	.12	.05
224 Walt Bond	.16	.12	.05
225 Mel Stottlemyre	.20	.15	.06
226 Julian Javier	.16	.12	.05
227 Paul Lindblad	.16	.12	.05
228 Gil Hodges	2.00	1.50	.60
229 Larry Jackson	.16	.12	.05
230 Boog Powell	.50	.40	.18
231 John Bateman	.16	.12	.05
232 Don Buford	.16	.12	.05
233 A.L. E.R.A.	.40	.30	.13
234 N.L. E.R.A.	.40	.30	.13
235 A.L. Pitching	.40	.30	.13
236 N.L. Pitching	.40	.30	.13
237 A.L. Strikeout	.40	.30	.13
238 N.L. Strikeout	.40	.30	.13
239 A.L. Batting	.60	.45	.20
240 N.L. Batting	.40	.30	.13
241 A.L. R.B.I.	.60	.45	.20
242 N.L. R.B.I.	.40	.30	.13
243 A.L. Home Run	.60	.45	.20
244 N.L. Home Run	.40	.30	.13
245 Curt Flood	.25	.20	.08
246 Jim Perry	.20	.15	.06
247 Jerry Lumpe	.16	.12	.05
248 Gene Mauch	.20	.15	.06
249 Nick Willhite	.16	.12	.05
250 Hank Aaron	10.00	7.00	3.00
251 Woody Held	.16	.12	.05
252 Bob Bolin	.16	.12	.05
253 Indians Rookies	.16	.12	.05
254 Milt Pappas	.20	.15	.06
255 Frank Howard	.60	.45	.20
256 Bob Hendley	.16	.12	.05
257 C. Smith	.16	.12	.05
258 Lee Maye	.16	.12	.05
259 Don Dennis	.16	.12	.05
260 Jim Lefebvre	.20	.15	.06
261 John Wyatt	.16	.12	.05
262 Athletics Team	.30	.25	.10
263 Hank Aguirre	.16	.12	.05
264 Ron Swoboda	.16	.12	.05
265 Lou Burdette	.30	.25	.10
266 Pitt Power	.50	.40	.18
267 Don Schwall	.16	.12	.05
268 John Briggs	.16	.12	.05
269 Don Nottebart	.16	.12	.05
270 Zoilo Versalles	.16	.12	.05
271 Eddie Watt	.16	.12	.05
272 Cubs Rookies	.16	.12	.05
273 Dick Lines	.16	.12	.05
274 Bob Aspromonte	.16	.12	.05
275 Fred Whitfield	.16	.12	.05
276 Bruce Brubaker	.16	.12	.05
277 Steve Whitaker	.16	.12	.05
278 3rd Series Checklist	.16	.12	.05
279 Frank Linzy	.16	.12	.05
280 Tony Conigliaro	.20	.15	.06
281 Bob Rodgers	.16	.12	.05
282 Johnny Odom	.16	.12	.05
283 Gene Alley	.16	.12	.05
284 Johnny Podres	.20	.15	.06
285 Lou Brock	3.50	2.50	1.20
286 Wayne Causey	.16	.12	.05
287 Mets Rookies	.16	.12	.05
288 D. Lemaster	.16	.12	.05
289 Tom Tresh	.20	.15	.06

	MINT	VG-E	F-G
290 Bill White	.20	.15	.06
291 Jim Hannan	.16	.12	.05
292 Don Pavletich	.16	.12	.05
293 Ed Kirkpatrick	.16	.12	.05
294 Walt Alston	.20	.15	.06
295 Sam McDowell	.20	.15	.06
296 Glenn Beckert	.16	.12	.05
297 Dave Morehead	.16	.12	.05
298 Ron Davis	.16	.12	.05
299 Norm Siebern	.16	.12	.05
300 Jim Kaat	.50	.40	.18
301 Jesse Gonder	.16	.12	.05
302 Orioles Team	.35	.27	.12
303 Gil Blanco	.16	.12	.05
304 Phil Gagliano	.16	.12	.05
305 Earl Wilson	.16	.12	.05
306 Bud Harrelson	.16	.12	.05
307 Jim Beauchamp	.16	.12	.05
308 Al Downing	.16	.12	.05
309 Hurlers Beware	.25	.20	.08
310 Gary Peters	.20	.15	.06
311 Ed Brinkman	.16	.12	.05
312 Don Mincher	.16	.12	.05
313 Bob Lee	.16	.12	.05
314 Red Sox Rookies	1.25	.90	.40
315 Billy Williams	.90	.70	.30
316 Jack Kralick	.16	.12	.05
317 Cesar Tovar	.16	.12	.05
318 Dave Giusti	.16	.12	.05
319 Paul Blair	.16	.12	.05
320 Gaylord Perry	1.50	1.10	.50
321 Mayo Smith	.16	.12	.05
322 Jose Pagan	.16	.12	.05
323 M. Hershberger	.16	.12	.05
324 Hal Woodeshick	.16	.12	.05
325 Chico Cardenas	.16	.12	.05
326 Bob Uecker	.60	.45	.20
327 Angels Team	.30	.25	.10
328 Clete Boyer	.16	.12	.05
329 Charlie Lau	.20	.16	.05
330 Claude Osteen	.16	.12	.05
331 Joe Foy	.16	.12	.05
332 Jesus Alou	.16	.12	.05
333 F. Jenkins	.40	.30	.13
334 Twin Terrors	.80	.60	.25
335 Bob Veale	.16	.12	.05
336 Joe Azcue	.16	.12	.05
337 Joe Morgan	2.00	1.50	.60
338 Bob Locker	.16	.12	.05
339 Chico Ruiz	.16	.12	.05
340 Joe Pepitone	.20	.15	.06
341 Giants Rookies	.16	.12	.05
342 Hank Fischer	.16	.12	.05
343 Tom Satriano	.16	.12	.05
344 O. Chavarria	.16	.12	.05
345 Stu Miller	.16	.12	.05
346 Jim Hickman	.16	.12	.05
347 Grady Hatton	.16	.12	.05
348 Tug McGraw	.25	.20	.08
349 Bob Chance	.16	.12	.05
350 Joe Torre	.50	.40	.18
351 Vern Law	.20	.15	.06
352 Ray Oyler	.16	.12	.05
353 Bill McCool	.16	.12	.05
354 Cubs Team	.30	.25	.10
355 Carl Yastrzemski	10.00	7.00	3.00
356 Larry Jaster	.16	.12	.05
357 Bill Skowron	.20	.15	.06
358 Ruben Amaro	.16	.12	.05
359 Dick Ellsworth	.16	.12	.05
360 Leon Wagner	.16	.12	.05
361 5th Series Checklist	.16	.12	.05
362 Darold Knowles	.16	.12	.05
363 Dave Johnson	.16	.12	.05
364 Claude Raymond	.16	.12	.05
365 John Roseboro	.16	.12	.05
366 Andy Kosco	.16	.12	.05
367 Angels Rookies	.16	.12	.05
368 Jack Hiatt	.16	.12	.05
369 Jim Hunter	2.00	1.50	.60
370 Tommy Davis	.25	.20	.08
371 Jim Lonborg	.20	.15	.06
372 Mike De La Hoz	.16	.12	.05
373 White Sox Rookies	.16	.12	.05
374 Mel Queen	.16	.12	.05
375 Jake Gibbs	.16	.12	.05
376 Don Lock	.16	.12	.05
377 Luis Tiant	.40	.30	.13
378 Tigers Team	.30	.25	.10
379 Jerry May	.16	.12	.05
380 Dean Chance	.16	.12	.05
381 Dick Schofield	.16	.12	.05
382 Dave McNally	.20	.15	.06
383 Ken Henderson	.16	.12	.05
384 Cardinals Rookies	.16	.12	.05

	MINT	VG-E	F-G
385 Jim Fregosi	.25	.20	.08
386 Dick Selma	.16	.12	.05
387 Cap Peterson	.16	.12	.05
388 Arnold Earley	.16	.12	.05
389 Al Dark	.20	.15	.06
390 Jim Wynn	.20	.15	.06
391 Wilbur Wood	.20	.15	.06
392 Tommy Harper	.16	.12	.05
393 Jim Bouton	.30	.25	.10
394 Jake Wood	.16	.12	.05
395 Chris Short	.16	.12	.05
396 Atlanta Aces	.20	.15	.06
397 Willie Smith	.16	.12	.05
398 Jeff Torborg	.16	.12	.05
399 Al Worthington	.16	.12	.05
400 Bob Clemente	7.00	5.25	2.50
401 Jim Coates	.16	.12	.05
402 Phillies Rookies	.16	.12	.05
403 Dick Nen	.16	.12	.05
404 Nelson Briles	.16	.12	.05
405 Russ Snyder	.16	.12	.05
406 Lee Elia	.16	.12	.05
407 Reds Team	.35	.27	.12
408 Jim Northrup	.16	.12	.05
409 Ray Sadecki	.16	.12	.05
410 Lou Johnson	.16	.12	.05
411 Dick Howser	.25	.20	.08
412 Astros Rookies	.16	.12	.05
413 Jerry Grote	.16	.12	.05
414 Casey Cox	.16	.12	.05
415 Sonny Jackson	.16	.12	.05
416 Roger Repoz	.16	.12	.05
417 Bob Bruce	.16	.12	.05
418 Same Mele	.16	.12	.05
419 Don Kessinger	.20	.15	.06
420 Denny McLain	.75	.55	.25
421 Dal Maxvill	.16	.12	.05
422 Hoyt Wilhelm	.75	.55	.25
423 Fence Busters	3.00	2.25	1.00
424 Pedro Gonzales	.16	.12	.05
425 Pete Mikkelsen	.16	.12	.05
426 Lou Clinton	.16	.12	.05
427 Ruben Gomez	.16	.12	.05
428 Dodgers Rookies	.16	.12	.05
429 Garry Roggenburk	.16	.12	.05
430 Pete Rose	8.00	6.00	2.50
431 T. Uhlaender	.16	.12	.05
432 Jimmie Hall	.16	.12	.05
433 Al Luplow	.16	.12	.05
434 Eddie Fisher	.16	.12	.05
435 Mack Jones	.16	.12	.05
436 Pete Ward	.16	.12	.05
437 Senators Team	.30	.25	.10
438 Chuck Dobson	.16	.12	.05
439 Byron Browne	.16	.12	.05
440 Steve Hargan	.16	.12	.05
441 Jim Davenport	.16	.12	.05
442 Yankees Rookies	.16	.12	.05
443 Tito Francona	.16	.12	.05
444 George Smith	.16	.12	.05
445 Don Sutton	.75	.55	.25
446 Russ Nixon	.16	.12	.05
447 Bo Belinsky	.20	.15	.06
448 Harry Walker	.16	.12	.05
449 Orlando Pena	.16	.12	.05
450 Richie Allen	.75	.55	.25
451 Fred Newman	.16	.12	.05
452 Ed Kranepool	.20	.15	.06
453 A. Monteagudo	.16	.12	.05
454 6th Series Checklist	.16	.12	.05
455 Tommie Agee	.16	.12	.05
456 Phil Niekro	.50	.40	.18
457 Andy Etchebarren	.16	.12	.05
458 Lee Thomas	.21	.16	.06
459 Senators Rookies	.21	.16	.06
460 H. Killebrew	3.00	2.25	1.00
461 Bob Miller	.21	.16	.06
462 Bob Barton	.21	.16	.06
463 Tribe Hill Aces	.21	.16	.06
464 Dan Coombs	.21	.16	.06
465 Willie Horton	.21	.16	.06
466 Bobby Wine	.21	.16	.06
467 Jim O'Toole	.21	.16	.06
468 Ralph Houk	.30	.25	.10
469 Len Gabrielson	.21	.16	.06
470 Bob Shaw	.21	.16	.06
471 Rene Lachemann	.21	.16	.06
472 Pirates Rookies	.21	.16	.06
473 Jose Santiago	.21	.16	.06
474 Bob Tolan	.21	.16	.06
475 Jim Palmer	3.00	2.25	1.00
476 Tony Perez	1.25	.90	.40
477 Braves Team	.35	.27	.12
478 Bob Humphreys	.21	.16	.06

	MINT	VG-E	F-G
479 Gary Bell	.21	.16	.06
480 Willie McCovey	4.00	3.00	1.40
481 Leo Durocher	.40	.30	.13
482 B. Monbouquette	.21	.16	.06
483 Jim Landis	.21	.16	.06
484 Jerry Adair	.21	.16	.06
485 Tim McCarver	.21	.16	.06
486 Twins Rookies	.21	.16	.06
487 Tommie Reynolds	.21	.16	.06
488 Gerry Arrigo	.21	.16	.06
489 Doug Clemens	.21	.16	.06
490 Tony Cloninger	.21	.16	.06
491 Sam Bowens	.21	.16	.06
492 Pirates Team	.35	.27	.12
493 Phil Ortega	.21	.16	.06
494 Bill Rigney	.21	.16	.06
495 Fritz Peterson	.21	.16	.06
496 O. McFarlane	.21	.16	.06
497 Ron Campbell	.21	.16	.06
498 Larry Dierker	.21	.16	.06
499 Indians Rookies	.21	.16	.06
500 Juan Marichal	2.00	1.50	.60
501 J. Zimmerman	.21	.16	.06
502 Derrell Griffith	.21	.16	.06
503 Dodgers Team	.35	.27	.12
504 O. Martinez	.21	.16	.06
505 Tommy Helms	.21	.16	.06
506 Smoky Burgess	.21	.16	.06
507 Orioles Rookies	.21	.16	.06
508 Dick Hall	.21	.16	.06
509 Jim King	.21	.16	.06
510 Bill Mazeroski	.40	.30	.13
511 Don Wert	.21	.16	.06
512 Red Schoendienst	.40	.30	.13
513 Marcelino Lopez	.21	.16	.06
514 John Werhas	.21	.16	.06
515 Bert Campaneris	.40	.30	.13
516 Giants Team	.35	.27	.12
517 Fred Talbot	.40	.30	.13
518 Denis Menke	.21	.16	.06
519 Ted Davidson	.21	.16	.06
520 Max Alvis	.21	.16	.06
521 Bird Bombers	.40	.30	.13
522 John Stephenson	.21	.16	.06
523 Jim Merritt	.21	.16	.06
524 Felix Mantilla	.21	.16	.06
525 Ron Hunt	.21	.16	.06
526 Tigers Rookies	.21	.16	.06
527 Dennis Ribant	.21	.16	.06
528 Rico Petrocelli	.30	.25	.10
529 Gary Wagner	.21	.16	.06
530 Felipe Alou	.30	.25	.10
531 7th Checklist	.21	.16	.06
532 Jim Hicks	.21	.16	.06
533 Jack Fisher	.21	.16	.06
534 Hank Bauer	2.50	1.80	.80
535 Donn Clendenon	1.60	1.25	.50
536 Cubs Rookies	2.00	1.50	.60
537 Chuck Estrada	1.60	1.25	.50
538 J. C. Martin	1.60	1.25	.50
539 Dick Egan	1.60	1.25	.50
540 Norm Cash	5.00	3.75	1.75
541 Joe Gibbon	1.60	1.25	.50
542 Athletics Rookies	1.60	1.25	.50
543 Dan Schneider	1.60	1.25	.50
544 Indians Team	2.50	1.80	.80
545 Jim Grant	1.60	1.25	.50
546 Woody Woodward	1.60	1.25	.50
547 Red Sox Rookies	1.60	1.25	.50
548 Tony Gonzalez	1.60	1.25	.50
549 Jack Sanford	1.60	1.25	.50
550 Vada Pinson	2.00	1.50	.60
551 Doug Camilli	1.60	1.25	.50
552 Ted Savage	1.60	1.25	.50
553 Yankees Rookies	1.60	1.25	.50
554 Andre Rogers	1.60	1.25	.50
555 Don Cardwell	1.60	1.25	.50
556 Al Weis	1.60	1.25	.50
557 Al Ferrara	1.60	1.25	.50
558 Orioles Rookies	1.60	1.25	.50
559 Dick Tracewski	1.60	1.25	.50
560 Jim Bunning	5.00	3.75	1.75
561 Sandy Alomar	1.60	1.25	.50
562 Steve Blass	1.60	1.25	.50
563 Joe Adcock	2.00	1.50	.60
564 Astros Rookies	1.60	1.25	.50
565 Lew Krausse	1.60	1.25	.50
566 Gary Geiger	1.60	1.25	.50
567 Steve Hamilton	1.60	1.25	.50
568 John Sullivan	1.60	1.25	.50
569 AL Rookies Carew	32.00	24.00	11.00
570 Maury Wills	60.00	45.00	20.00
571 Larry Sherry	1.60	1.25	.50
572 Don Demeter	1.60	1.25	.50
573 White Sox Team	2.50	1.80	.80

1967 TOPPS (CONTINUED)

	MINT	VG-E	F-G
574 Jerry Buchek	1.60	1.25	.50
575 Dave Boswell	1.60	1.25	.50
576 Nat. L. Rookies	1.60	1.25	.50
577 Bill Short	1.60	1.25	.50
578 John Boccabella	1.60	1.25	.50
579 Bill Henry	1.60	1.25	.50
580 Rocky Colavito	8.00	6.00	2.50
581 Mets Rookies	70.00	50.00	23.00
582 Jim Owens	1.60	1.25	.50
583 Ray Barker	1.60	1.25	.50
584 Jim Piersall	5.00	3.75	1.75
585 Wally Bunker	1.60	1.25	.50
586 Manny Jimenez	1.60	1.25	.50
587 Nat. L. Rookies	1.60	1.25	.50
588 J. Klippstein	1.60	1.25	.50
589 Dave Ricketts	1.60	1.25	.50
590 Pete Richert	1.60	1.25	.50
591 Ty Cline	1.60	1.25	.50

	MINT	VG-E	F-G
592 Nat. L. Rookies	1.60	1.25	.50
593 Wes Westrum	1.60	1.25	.50
594 Dan Osinski	1.60	1.25	.50
595 Cookie Rojas	1.60	1.25	.50
596 Galen Cisco	1.60	1.25	.50
597 Ted Abernathy	1.60	1.25	.50
598 White Sox Rookies	1.60	1.25	.50
599 Bob Duliba	1.60	1.25	.50
600 Brooks Robinson	90.00	70.00	30.00
601 Bill Bryan	1.60	1.25	.50
602 Juan Pizarro	1.60	1.25	.50
603 A's Rookies	1.60	1.25	.50
604 Red Sox Team	4.00	3.00	1.40
605 Mike Shannon	1.60	1.25	.50
606 Ron Taylor	1.60	1.25	.50
607 Mickey Stanley	1.60	1.25	.50
608 Cubs Rookies	1.60	1.25	.50
609 Tommy John	21.00	15.50	7.00

1968 TOPPS (598)

2 1/2" X 3 1/2"

GIL HODGES
(New York Mets — Manager)

The newly appointed manager of the New York Mets is a veteran of 25 years in the major leagues! Gil put on his first professional uniform in 1943 when he appeared in one game for the Brooklyn Dodgers. He spent the next two years fulfilling his military obligations. In 1946, Gil returned to the baseball wars playing for Newport News in the Piedmont League. The next year, he was promoted to the Brooklyn Dodgers where he became their regular first sacker until 1961. One of Gil's mightiest feats came in 1950, when he tied the major league record for total bases in one game. That day, Gil singled and blasted four home runs in five appearances at the plate. In 1962, he joined the Mets. In May 1963, Gil launched a new career as he took over as manager of the Washington Senators.

ⒸT.C.G. PRINTED IN U.S.A.

The 1968 Topps set includes The Sporting News All-Star selections as card numbers 361-380. High numbers 534-598 are slightly more difficult to obtain.

	MINT	VG-E	F-G
COMPLETE SET	190.00	140.00	60.00
COMMON PLAYERS (1-533)	.13	.10	.04
COMMON PLAYERS(534-598)	.20	.15	.06
1 N.L. Bat Leaders	.50	.30	.12
2 A.L. Bat Leaders	.50	.30	.12
3 N.L. R.B.I. Leaders	.35	.27	.12
4 A.L. R.B.I. Leaders	.50	.30	.12
5 N.L. H.R. Leaders	.35	.27	.12
6 A.L. H.R. Leaders	.50	.30	.12
7 N.L. E.R.A. Leaders	.35	.27	.12
8 A.L. E.R.A. Leaders	.35	.27	.12
9 N.L. Pitch Leaders	.35	.27	.12
10 A.L. Pitch Leaders	.35	.27	.12
11 N.L. S.O. Leaders	.35	.27	.12
12 A.L. S.O. Leaders	.35	.27	.12
13 C. Hartenstein	.13	.10	.04
14 Jerry McNertney	.13	.10	.04
15 Ron Hunt	.13	.10	.04
16 Indians Rookies	.13	.10	.04
17 Dick Hall	.13	.10	.04
18 M. Hershberger	.13	.10	.04
19 Juan Pizarro	.13	.10	.04
20 B. Robinson	3.00	2.25	1.00
21 Ron Davis	.13	.10	.04
22 Pat Dobson	.13	.10	.04
23 Chico Cardenas	.13	.10	.04
24 Bobby Locke	.13	.10	.04
25 Julian Javier	.13	.10	.04
26 Darrell Brandon	.13	.10	.04
27 Gil Hodges	1.75	1.25	.55
28 T. Uhlaender	.13	.10	.04
29 Joe Verbanic	.13	.10	.04
30 Joe Torre	.40	.30	.13
31 Ed Stroud	.13	.10	.04
32 Joe Gibbon	.13	.10	.04
33 Pete Ward	.13	.10	.04
34 Al Ferrara	.13	.10	.04
35 Steve Hargan	.13	.10	.04
36 Pirates Rookies	.13	.10	.04
37 Billy Williams	.50	.40	.18
38 Tony Pierce	.13	.10	.04
39 Cookie Rojas	.13	.10	.04
40 Denny McLain	.75	.55	.25
41 Julio Gotay	.13	.10	.04

	MINT	VG-E	F-G
42 Larry Haney	.13	.10	.04
43 Gary Bell	.13	.10	.04
44 Frank Kostro	.13	.10	.04
45 Tom Seaver	5.50	4.25	2.00
46 Dave Ricketts	.13	.10	.04
47 Ralph Houk	.20	.15	.06
48 Ted Davidson	.13	.10	.04
49 Ed Brinkman	.13	.10	.04
50 Willie Mays	8.00	6.00	2.50
51 Bob Locker	.13	.10	.04
52 Hawk Taylor	.13	.10	.04
53 Gene Alley	.13	.10	.04
54 Stan Williams	.13	.10	.04
55 Felipe Alou	.15	.11	.05
56 Orioles Rookies	.13	.10	.04
57 Dan Schneider	.13	.10	.04
58 Ed Mathews	2.25	1.65	.75
59 Don Lock	.13	.10	.04
60 Ken Holtzman	.15	.11	.05
61 Reggie Smith	.50	.40	.18
62 Chuck Dobson	.13	.10	.04
63 Dick Kenworthy	.13	.10	.04
64 Jim Merritt	.13	.10	.04
65 John Roseboro	.13	.10	.04
66 Casey Cox	.13	.10	.04
67 1st Checklist	.13	.10	.04
68 Ron Willis	.13	.10	.04
69 Tom Tresh	.15	.11	.05
70 Bob Veale	.13	.10	.04
71 Vern Fuller	.13	.10	.04
72 Tommy John	.50	.40	.18
73 Jim Hart	.13	.10	.04
74 Milt Pappas	.20	.15	.06
75 Don Mincher	.13	.10	.04
76 Braves Rookies	.13	.10	.04
77 Don Wilson	.13	.10	.04
78 Jim Northrup	.13	.10	.04
79 Ted Kubiak	.13	.10	.04
80 Rod Carew	5.50	4.25	2.00
81 Larry Jackson	.13	.10	.04
82 Sam Bowens	.13	.10	.04
83 J. Stephenson	.13	.10	.04
84 Bob Tolan	.13	.10	.04
85 Gaylord Perry	1.50	1.10	.50

	MINT	VG-E	F-G
86 Willie Stargell	1.50	1.10	.50
87 Dick Williams	.15	.11	.05
88 Phil Regan	.13	.10	.04
89 Jake Gibbs	.13	.10	.04
90 Vada Pinson	.40	.30	.13
91 Jim Ollom	.13	.10	.04
92 Ed Kranepool	.15	.11	.05
93 Tony Cloninger	.13	.10	.04
94 Lee Maye	.13	.10	.04
95 B. Aspromonte	.13	.10	.04
96 Sen. Rookies	.13	.10	.04
97 Tom Phoebus	.13	.10	.04
98 Gary Sutherland	.13	.10	.04
99 Rocky Colavito	.50	.40	.18
100 Bob Gibson	2.50	1.80	.80
101 Glenn Beckert	.13	.10	.04
102 Jose Cardenal	.13	.10	.04
103 Don Sutton	.60	.45	.20
104 Dick Dietz	.13	.10	.04
105 Al Downing	.13	.10	.04
106 Dalton Jones	.13	.10	.04
107 2nd Checklist	.13	.10	.04
108 Don Pavletich	.13	.10	.04
109 Bert Campaneris	.15	.11	.05
110 Hank Aaron	7.00	5.25	2.50
111 Rich Reese	.13	.10	.04
112 Woody Fryman	.13	.10	.04
113 Tigers Rookies	.13	.10	.04
114 Ron Swoboda	.13	.10	.04
115 Sam McDowell	.15	.11	.05
116 Ken McMullen	.13	.10	.04
117 Larry Jaster	.13	.10	.04
118 Mark Belanger	.15	.11	.05
119 Ted Savage	.13	.10	.04
120 M. Stottlemyre	.15	.11	.05
121 Jimmie Hall	.13	.10	.04
122 Gene Mauch	.20	.15	.06
123 Jose Santiago	.13	.10	.04
124 Nate Oliver	.13	.10	.04
125 Joe Horlen	.13	.10	.04
126 B. Etheridge	.13	.10	.04
127 P. Lindblad	.13	.10	.04
128 Hous. Rookies	.13	.10	.04
129 M. Stanley	.15	.11	.05
130 Tony Perez	.50	.40	.18
131 F. Bertaina	.13	.10	.04
132 B. Harrelson	.13	.10	.04
133 F. Whitfield	.13	.10	.04
134 Pat Jarvis	.13	.10	.04
135 Paul Blair	.13	.10	.04
136 R. Hundley	.13	.10	.04
137 Twins Team	.25	.20	.08
138 R. Amaro	.13	.10	.04
139 Chris Short	.13	.10	.04
140 T. Conigliaro	.20	.15	.06
141 Dal Maxvill	.13	.10	.04
142 W. S. Rookies	.13	.10	.04
143 Pete Cimino	.13	.10	.04
144 Joe Morgan	1.75	1.25	.55
145 Don Drysdale	2.25	1.65	.75
146 Sal Bando	.30	.25	.10
147 Frank Linzy	.13	.10	.04
148 Dave Bristol	.13	.10	.04
149 Bob Saverine	.13	.10	.04
150 Bob Clemente	6.00	4.50	2.00
151 World Series #1	.35	.27	.12
152 World Series #2	.35	.27	.12
153 World Series #3	.35	.27	.12
154 World Series #4	.35	.27	.12
155 World Series #5	.35	.27	.12
156 World Series #6	.35	.27	.12
157 World Series #7	.35	.27	.12
158 World Series Conc.	.35	.27	.12
159 Don Kessinger	.20	.15	.06
160 Earl Wilson	.13	.10	.04
161 Norm Miller	.13	.10	.04
162 Cards Rookies	.40	.30	.13
163 G. Brabender	.13	.10	.04
164 Ramon Webster	.13	.10	.04
165 Tony Oliva	.75	.55	.25
166 C. Raymond	.13	.10	.04
167 Elston Howard	.75	.55	.25
168 Dodgers Team	.30	.25	.10
169 Bob Bolin	.13	.10	.04
170 J. Fregosi	.25	.20	.08
171 D. Nottebart	.13	.10	.04
172 Walt Williams	.13	.10	.04
173 John Boozer	.13	.10	.04
174 Bob Tillman	.13	.10	.04
175 Maury Wills	.80	.60	.25
176 Bob Allen	.13	.10	.04
177 Mets Rookies	7.50	5.75	2.50

	MINT	VG-E	F-G
178 Don Wert	.13	.10	.04
179 Bill Stoneman	.13	.10	.04
180 Curt Flood	.25	.20	.08
181 J. Zimmerman	.13	.10	.04
182 Dave Giusti	.13	.10	.04
183 Bob Kennedy	.13	.10	.04
184 Lou Johnson	.13	.10	.04
185 Tom Haller	.13	.10	.04
186 Eddie Watt	.13	.10	.04
187 Sonny Jackson	.13	.10	.04
188 Cap Peterson	.13	.10	.04
189 Bill Landis	.13	.10	.04
190 Bill White	.15	.11	.05
191 Dan Frisella	.13	.10	.04
192 3rd Checklist	.13	.10	.04
193 J. Hamilton	.13	.10	.04
194 Don Buford	.13	.10	.04
195 Joe Pepitone	.15	.11	.05
196 Gary Nolan	.13	.10	.04
197 Larry Brown	.13	.10	.04
198 Roy Face	.15	.11	.05
199 A's Rookies	.13	.10	.04
200 Orlando Cepeda	1.00	.70	.30
201 Mike Marshall	.40	.30	.13
202 Adolfo Phillips	.13	.10	.04
203 Dick Kelley	.13	.10	.04
204 A. Etchebarren	.13	.10	.04
205 Juan Marichal	1.00	.70	.30
206 Cal Ermer	.13	.10	.04
207 Carroll Sembera	.13	.10	.04
208 Willie Davis	.15	.11	.05
209 Tim Cullen	.13	.10	.04
210 Gary Peters	.15	.11	.05
211 J. C. Martin	.13	.10	.04
212 Dave Morehead	.13	.10	.04
213 Chico Ruiz	.13	.10	.04
214 Yanks Rookies	.13	.10	.04
215 Jim Bunning	.50	.40	.18
216 Bubba Morton	.13	.10	.04
217 Turk Farrell	.13	.10	.04
218 Ken Suarez	.13	.10	.04
219 Rob Gardner	.13	.10	.04
220 H. Killebrew	2.00	1.50	.60
221 Braves Team	.30	.25	.10
222 Jim Hardin	.13	.10	.04
223 Ollie Brown	.13	.10	.04
224 Jack Aker	.13	.10	.04
225 Richie Allen	.50	.40	.18
226 Jimmie Price	.13	.10	.04
227 Joe Hoerner	.13	.10	.04
228 Dodgers Rookies	.13	.10	.04
229 Fred Klages	.13	.10	.04
230 Pete Rose	6.50	5.00	2.25
231 Dave Baldwin	.13	.10	.04
232 Denis Menke	.13	.10	.04
233 George Scott	.25	.20	.08
234 B. Monbouquette	.13	.10	.04
235 Ron Santo	.25	.20	.08
236 Tug McGraw	.20	.15	.06
237 Alvin Dark	.15	.11	.05
238 Tom Satriano	.13	.10	.04
239 Bill Henry	.13	.10	.04
240 Al Kaline	2.50	1.80	.80
241 Felix Millan	.13	.10	.04
242 M. Drabowsky	.13	.10	.04
243 Rich Rollins	.13	.10	.04
244 J. Donaldson	.13	.10	.04
245 Tony Gonzalez	.13	.10	.04
246 Fritz Peterson	.13	.10	.04
247 Reds Rookies Bench	8.00	6.00	2.50
248 Fred Valentine	.13	.10	.04
249 Bill Singer	.13	.10	.04
250 C. Yastrzemski	6.50	5.00	2.25
251 M. Sanguillen	.13	.10	.04
252 Angels Team	.25	.20	.08
253 Dick Hughes	.13	.10	.04
254 Cleon Jones	.13	.10	.04
255 Dean Chance	.13	.10	.04
256 Norm Cash	.40	.30	.13
257 Phil Niekro	.40	.30	.13
258 Cubs Rookies	.13	.10	.04
259 Ken Boyer	.40	.30	.13
260 Jim Wynn	.15	.11	.05
261 Dave Duncan	.13	.10	.04
262 Rick Wise	.20	.15	.06
263 Horace Clarke	.13	.10	.04
264 Ted Abernathy	.13	.10	.04
265 Tommy Davis	.20	.15	.06
266 Paul Popovich	.13	.10	.04
267 Herman Franks	.13	.10	.04
268 B. Humphreys	.13	.10	.04
269 B. Tiefenauer	.13	.10	.04
270 Matty Alou	.15	.11	.05

	MINT	VG-E	F-G
271 Bobby Knoop	.13	.10	.04
272 Ray Culp	.13	.10	.04
273 Dave Johnson	.13	.10	.04
274 Mike Cuellar	.15	.11	.05
275 Tim McCarver	.15	.11	.05
276 Jim Roland	.13	.10	.04
277 Jerry Buchek	.13	.10	.04
278 4th Checklist	.13	.10	.04
279 Bill Hands	.13	.10	.04
280 Mickey Mantle	10.00	7.00	3.00
281 Jim Campanis	.13	.10	.04
282 Rick Monday	.20	.15	.06
283 Mel Queen	.13	.10	.04
284 John Briggs	.13	.10	.04
285 Dick McAuliffe	.13	.10	.04
286 Cecil Upshaw	.13	.10	.04
287 W. Sox Rookies	.13	.10	.04
288 D. Wickersham	.13	.10	.04
289 Woody Held	.13	.10	.04
290 Willie McCovey	3.00	2.25	1.00
291 Dick Lines	.13	.10	.04
292 Art Shamsky	.13	.10	.04
293 Bruce Howard	.13	.10	.04
294 R. Schoendienst	.25	.20	.08
295 Sonny Siebert	.13	.10	.04
296 Byron Browne	.13	.10	.04
297 Russ Gibson	.13	.10	.04
298 Jim Brewer	.13	.10	.04
299 Gene Michael	.25	.20	.08
300 Rusty Staub	.30	.25	.10
301 Twins Rookies	.13	.10	.04
302 Gerry Arrigo	.13	.10	.04
303 Dick Green	.13	.10	.04
304 S. Valdespino	.13	.10	.04
305 Minnie Rojas	.13	.10	.04
306 Mike Ryan	.13	.10	.04
307 John Hiller	.20	.15	.06
308 Pirates Team	.25	.20	.08
309 Ken Henderson	.13	.10	.04
310 Luis Aparicio	.60	.45	.20
311 Jack Lamabe	.13	.10	.04
312 Curt Blefary	.13	.10	.04
313 Al Weis	.13	.10	.04
314 R. Sox Rookies	.13	.10	.04
315 Zoilo Versalles	.13	.10	.04
316 Steve Barber	.13	.10	.04
317 Ron Brand	.13	.10	.04
318 Chico Salmon	.13	.10	.04
319 George Culver	.13	.10	.04
320 Frank Howard	.50	.40	.18
321 Leo Durocher	.30	.25	.10
322 Dave Boswell	.13	.10	.04
323 Deron Johnson	.13	.10	.04
324 Jim Nash	.13	.10	.04
325 Manny Mota	.15	.11	.05
326 Denny Ribant	.13	.10	.04
327 Tony Taylor	.13	.10	.04
328 Angels Rookies	.13	.10	.04
329 D. Josephson	.13	.10	.04
330 Roger Maris	2.00	1.50	.60
331 Dan Osinski	.13	.10	.04
332 Doug Rader	.13	.10	.04
333 Ron Herbel	.13	.10	.04
334 Orioles Team	.25	.20	.08
335 Bob Allison	.20	.15	.06
336 John Purdin	.13	.10	.04
337 Bill Robinson	.13	.10	.04
338 Bob Johnson	.13	.10	.04
339 Rich Nye	.13	.10	.04
340 Max Alvis	.13	.10	.04
341 Jim Lemon	.13	.10	.04
342 Ken Johnson	.13	.10	.04
343 Jim Gosger	.13	.10	.04
344 D. Clendenon	.13	.10	.04
345 Bob Hendley	.13	.10	.04
346 Jerry Adair	.13	.10	.04
347 George Brunet	.13	.10	.04
348 Phillies Rookies	.13	.10	.04
349 Ed Spiezio	.13	.10	.04
350 Hoyt Wilhelm	.60	.45	.20
351 Bob Barton	.13	.10	.04
352 J. Hernandez	.13	.10	.04
353 Mack Jones	.13	.10	.04
354 Pete Richert	.13	.10	.04
355 Ernie Banks	3.00	2.25	1.00
356 5th Checklist	.13	.10	.04
357 Len Gabrielson	.13	.10	.04
358 Mike Epstein	.13	.10	.04
359 Joe Moeller	.15	.11	.05
360 Willie Horton	.20	.15	.06
361 H. Killebrew, AS	1.00	.70	.30
362 Orlando Cepeda, AS	.50	.40	.18

	MINT	VG-E	F-G
363 Rod Carew, AS	1.75	1.25	.55
364 Joe Morgan, AS	.75	.55	.25
365 B. Robinson, AS	1.75	1.25	.55
366 Ron Santo, AS	.25	.20	.08
367 Jim Fregosi, AS	.25	.20	.08
368 Gene Alley, AS	.20	.15	.06
369 C. Yastrzemski, AS	2.00	1.50	.60
370 Hank Aaron, AS	2.50	1.80	.80
371 Tony Oliva, AS	.50	.40	.18
372 Lou Brock, AS	1.75	1.25	.55
373 Frank Robinson, AS	1.50	1.10	.50
374 Bob Clemente, AS	2.00	1.50	.60
375 Bill Freehan, AS	.20	.15	.06
376 Tim McCarver, AS	.20	.15	.06
377 Joe Horlen, AS	.20	.15	.06
378 Bob Gibson, AS	1.25	.90	.40
379 Gary Peters, AS	.20	.15	.06
380 Ken Holtzman, AS	.20	.15	.06
381 Boog Powell	.30	.25	.10
382 R. Hernandez	.13	.10	.04
383 Steve Whitaker	.13	.10	.04
384 Reds Rookies	.13	.10	.04
385 Jim Hunter	1.50	1.10	.50
386 Greg Goossen	.13	.10	.04
387 Joe Foy	.13	.10	.04
388 Ray Washburn	.13	.10	.04
389 Jay Johnstone	.13	.10	.04
390 Bill Mazeroski	.20	.15	.06
391 Bob Priddy	.13	.10	.04
392 Grady Hatton	.13	.10	.04
393 Jim Perry	.15	.11	.05
394 Tommie Aaron	.15	.11	.05
395 Camilo Pascual	.15	.11	.05
396 Bobby Wine	.13	.10	.04
397 Vic Davalillo	.13	.10	.04
398 Jim Grant	.13	.10	.04
399 Ray Oyler	.13	.10	.04
400 Mike McCormick	.13	.10	.04
401 Mets Team	.30	.25	.10
402 Mike Hegan	.13	.10	.04
403 John Buzhardt	.13	.10	.04
404 Floyd Robinson	.13	.10	.04
405 Tommy Helms	.13	.10	.04
406 Dick Ellsworth	.15	.11	.05
407 Gary Kolb	.13	.10	.04
408 Steve Carlton	1.50	1.10	.50
409 Orioles Rookies	.13	.10	.04
410 F. Jenkins	.50	.40	.18
411 Ron Hansen	.13	.10	.04
412 Clay Carroll	.13	.10	.04
413 Tommy McCraw	.13	.10	.04
414 Mickey Lolich	.30	.25	.10
415 Johnny Callison	.13	.10	.04
416 Bill Rigney	.13	.10	.04
417 Willie Crawford	.13	.10	.04
418 Eddie Fisher	.13	.10	.04
419 Jack Hiatt	.13	.10	.04
420 Cesar Tovar	.13	.10	.04
421 Ron Taylor	.13	.10	.04
422 R. Lachemann	.13	.10	.04
423 Fred Gladding	.13	.10	.04
424 White Sox Team	.25	.20	.08
425 Jim Maloney	.15	.11	.05
426 Hank Allen	.13	.10	.04
427 Dick Calmus	.13	.10	.04
428 Vic Roznovsky	.13	.10	.04
429 Tommie Sisk	.13	.10	.04
430 Rico Petrocelli	.15	.11	.05
431 Dooley Womack	.13	.10	.04
432 Indians Rookies	.13	.10	.04
433 Bob Rodgers	.13	.10	.04
434 Ricardo Joseph	.13	.10	.04
435 Ron Perranoski	.13	.10	.04
436 Hal Lanier	.13	.10	.04
437 Don Cardwell	.13	.10	.04
438 Lee Thomas	.13	.10	.04
439 Luman Harris	.13	.10	.04
440 Claude Osteen	.13	.10	.04
441 Alex Johnson	.13	.10	.04
442 Dick Bosman	.13	.10	.04
443 Joe Azcue	.13	.10	.04
444 Jack Fisher	.13	.10	.04
445 Mike Shannon	.15	.11	.05
446 Ron Kline	.13	.10	.04
447 Tigers Rookies	.13	.10	.04
448 Gary Wagner	.13	.10	.04
449 Gene Oliver	.13	.10	.04
450 Jim Kaat	.40	.30	.13
451 Al Spangler	.13	.10	.04
452 Jesus Alou	.13	.10	.04
453 Sammy Ellis	.13	.10	.04
454 6th Checklist	.13	.10	.04
455 Rico Carty	.30	.25	.10

	MINT	VG-E	F-G
456 J. O'Donoghue	.13	.10	.04
457 Jim Lefebvre	.15	.11	.05
458 Lew Krausse	.13	.10	.04
459 Dick Simpson	.13	.10	.04
460 Jim Lonborg	.15	.11	.05
461 Chuck Hiller	.13	.10	.04
462 Barry Moore	.13	.10	.04
463 Jim Schaffer	.13	.10	.04
464 Don McMahon	.13	.10	.04
465 Tommie Agee	.13	.10	.04
466 Bill Dillman	.13	.10	.04
467 Dick Howser	.25	.20	.08
468 Larry Sherry	.15	.11	.05
469 Ty Cline	.13	.10	.04
470 Bill Freehan	.15	.11	.05
471 Orlando Pena	.13	.10	.04
472 Walt Alston	.15	.11	.05
473 Al Worthington	.13	.10	.04
474 Paul Schaal	.13	.10	.04
475 Joe Niekro	.25	.20	.08
476 W. Woodward	.13	.10	.04
477 Phillies Team	.25	.20	.08
478 Dave McNally	.20	.15	.06
479 Phil Gagliano	.13	.10	.04
480 Mgr's Dream	1.50	1.10	.50
481 John Wyatt	.13	.10	.04
482 Jose Pagan	.13	.10	.04
483 Darold Knowles	.13	.10	.04
484 Phil Roof	.13	.10	.04
485 Ken Berry	.13	.10	.04
486 Cal Koonce	.13	.10	.04
487 Lee May	.13	.10	.04
488 Dick Tracewski	.13	.10	.04
489 Wally Bunker	.13	.10	.04
490 Super-Stars	3.00	2.25	1.00
491 Denny LeMaster	.13	.10	.04
492 Jeff Torborg	.13	.10	.04
493 Jim McGlothlin	.13	.10	.04
494 Ray Sadecki	.13	.10	.04
495 Leon Wagner	.13	.10	.04
496 Steve Hamilton	.13	.10	.04
497 Cards Team	.30	.25	.10
498 Bill Bryan	.13	.10	.04
499 Steve Blass	.15	.11	.05
500 Frank Robinson	3.00	2.25	1.00
501 John Odom	.13	.10	.04
502 Mike Andrews	.13	.10	.04
503 Al Jackson	.13	.10	.04
504 Russ Snyder	.13	.10	.04
505 Joe Sparma	.13	.10	.04
506 Clarence Jones	.13	.10	.04
507 W. Blasingame	.13	.10	.04
508 Duke Sims	.13	.10	.04
509 Dennis Higgins	.13	.10	.04
510 Ron Fairly	.15	.11	.05
511 Bill Kelso	.13	.10	.04
512 Grant Jackson	.13	.10	.04
513 Hank Bauer	.15	.11	.05
514 Al McBean	.13	.10	.04
515 Russ Nixon	.13	.10	.04
516 Pete Mikkelsen	.13	.10	.04
517 Diego Segui	.13	.10	.04
518 7th Checklist	.13	.10	.04
519 J. Stephenson	.13	.10	.04
520 Lou Brock	3.00	2.25	1.00
521 Don Shaw	.13	.10	.04
522 Wayne Causey	.13	.10	.04
523 John Tsitouris	.13	.10	.04
524 Andy Kosco	.13	.10	.04
525 Jim Davenport	.13	.10	.04
526 Bill Denehy	.13	.10	.04

	MINT	VG-E	F-G
527 Tito Francona	.13	.10	.04
528 Tigers Team	.50	.40	.18
529 Bruce Von Hoff	.13	.10	.04
530 Bird Belters	1.50	1.10	.50
531 Chuck Hinton	.13	.10	.04
532 Luis Tiant	.40	.30	.13
533 Wes Parker	.25	.20	.08
534 Bob Miller	.20	.15	.06
535 Danny Cater	.20	.15	.06
536 Bill Short	.20	.15	.06
537 Norm Siebern	.20	.15	.06
538 Manny Jimenez	.20	.15	.06
539 Maj. L. Rookies	.20	.15	.06
540 Nelson Briles	.20	.15	.06
541 Sandy Alomar	.20	.15	.06
542 J. Boccabella	.20	.15	.06
543 Bob Lee	.20	.15	.06
544 Mayo Smith	.20	.15	.06
545 Lindy McDaniel	.25	.20	.08
546 Roy White	.25	.20	.08
547 Dan Coombs	.20	.15	.06
548 Bernie Allen	.20	.15	.06
549 Orioles Rookies	.20	.15	.06
550 Clete Boyer	.20	.15	.06
551 D. Sutherland	.20	.15	.06
552 Ed Kirkpatrick	.20	.15	.06
553 Hank Aguirre	.20	.15	.06
554 A's Team	.35	.27	.12
555 Jose Tartabull	.20	.15	.06
556 Dick Selma	.20	.15	.06
557 Frank Quilici	.20	.15	.06
558 John Edwards	.20	.15	.06
559 Pirates Rookies	.20	.15	.06
560 Paul Casanova	.20	.15	.06
561 Lee Elia	.20	.15	.06
562 Jim Bouton	.40	.30	.13
563 Ed Charles	.20	.15	.06
564 Ed Stanky	.25	.20	.08
565 Larry Dierker	.20	.15	.06
566 Larry Harrelson	.20	.15	.06
567 Clay Dalrymple	.20	.15	.06
568 Willie Smith	.20	.15	.06
569 Nat. L. Rookies	.20	.15	.06
570 Rick Reichardt	.20	.15	.06
571 Tony LaRussa	.20	.15	.06
572 Don Bosch	.20	.15	.06
573 Joe Coleman	.20	.15	.06
574 Reds Team	.35	.27	.12
575 Jim Palmer	2.50	1.80	.80
576 Dave Adlesh	.20	.15	.06
577 Fred Talbot	.20	.15	.06
578 O. Martinez	.20	.15	.06
579 Nat. L. Rookies	.60	.45	.20
580 Bob Bailey	.20	.15	.06
581 G. Roggenburk	.20	.15	.06
582 Jerry Grote	.20	.15	.06
583 Gates Brown	.20	.15	.06
584 Larry Shepard	.20	.15	.06
585 Wilbur Wood	.20	.15	.06
586 Jim Pagliaroni	.20	.15	.06
587 Roger Repoz	.20	.15	.06
588 Dick Schofield	.20	.15	.06
589 Twins Rookies	.20	.15	.06
590 Tommy Harper	.20	.15	.06
591 Dick Nen	.20	.15	.06
592 John Bateman	.20	.15	.06
593 Lee Stange	.20	.15	.06
594 Phil Linz	.20	.15	.06
595 Phil Ortega	.20	.15	.06
596 Charlie Smith	.20	.15	.06
597 Bill McCool	.20	.15	.06
598 Jerry May	.20	.15	.06

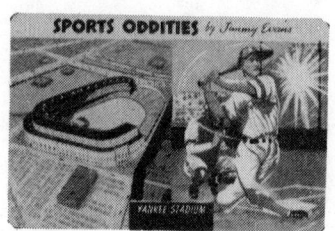

F279-20 SPORTS ODDITIES

1968 TOPPS GAME (33)   2 1/4″ X 3 1/4″

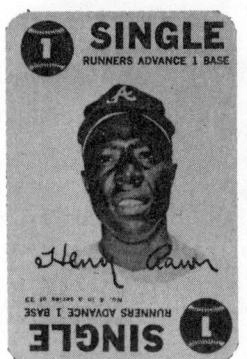

The 1968 Topps Game set contains 33 small game cards with blue backs. They were issued with the regular 1968 Topps cards as inserts.

	MINT	VG-E	F-G			MINT	VG-E	F-G
COMPLETE SET	14.00	10.00	4.00	16	Dean Chance	.22	.16	.06
COMMON PLAYER	.22	.16	.06	17	Mike McCormick	.22	.16	.06
				18	Tim McCarver	.22	.16	.06
1 Matty Alou	.22	.16	.06	19	Ron Santo	.25	.20	.08
2 Mickey Mantle	2.00	1.50	.60	20	Tony Gonzalez	.22	.16	.06
3 Carl Yastrzemski	1.50	1.10	.50	21	Frank Howard	.35	.27	.12
4 Hank Aaron	1.50	1.10	.50	22	George Scott	.25	.20	.08
5 Harmon Killebrew	.75	.55	.25	23	Rich Allen	.35	.27	.12
6 Roberto Clemente	1.25	.90	.40	24	Jim Wynn	.25	.20	.08
7 Frank Robinson	1.00	.70	.30	25	Gene Alley	.22	.16	.06
8 Willie Mays	1.00	.70	.30	26	Rick Monday	.25	.20	.08
9 Brooks Robinson	1.00	.70	.30	27	Al Kaline	1.00	.70	.30
10 Tommy Davis	.25	.20	.08	28	Rusty Staub	.30	.25	.10
11 Bill Freehan	.22	.16	.06	29	Rod Carew	1.00	.70	.30
12 Claude Osteen	.22	.16	.06	30	Pete Rose	1.50	1.10	.50
13 Gary Peters	.22	.16	.06	31	Joe Torre	.35	.27	.12
14 Jim Lonborg	.22	.16	.06	32	Orlando Cepeda	.50	.40	.18
15 Steve Hargan	.22	.16	.06	33	Jim Fregosi	.25	.20	.08

1968 TOPPS 3—D (12)   2 1/4″ X 3 1/2″

The 1968 Topps 3—D set contains 12 unnumbered cards which give the impression of being three dimensional. The set and all cards in the set are quite scarce.

	MINT	VG-E	F-G			MINT	VG-E	F-G
COMPLETE SET	2500.00	2000.00	700.00					
COMMON PLAYER	200.00	150.00	65.00					
				7	Tony Perez	250.00	180.00	80.00
1 Bob Clemente	500.00	375.00	175.00	8	Boog Powell	250.00	180.00	80.00
2 Willie Davis	225.00	165.00	75.00	9	Bill Robinson	200.00	150.00	65.00
3 Ron Fairly	200.00	150.00	65.00	10	Rusty Staub	250.00	180.00	80.00
4 Curt Flood	225.00	165.00	75.00	11	Mel Stottlemyre	200.00	150.00	65.00
5 Jim Lonborg	200.00	150.00	65.00	12	Ron Swoboda	200.00	150.00	65.00
6 Jim Maloney	200.00	150.00	65.00					

Most serious collectors subscribe to at least one of the hobby papers. Read the ads in this Guide for The Trader Speaks (for advanced collectors), Sports Collectors Digest, and Baseball Hobby News to determine which one or more appeal to you.

308

1969 TOPPS (664)

2 1/2" X 3 1/4"

The 1969 Topps set includes The Sporting News All-Star selections as card nos. 416-435. The fifth series contains several variations; the difficult variety consists of cards with the player's whole name in white letters. Two different poses of Dalrymple and Clendennon exist as indicated in the checklist.

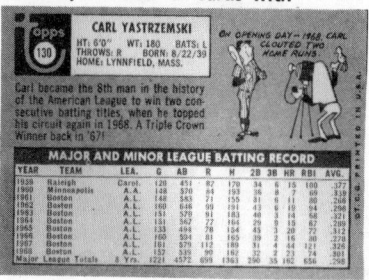

	MINT	VG-E	F-G
COMPLETE SET	200.00	140.00	60.00
COMMON PLAYERS (1-512)	.13	.10	.04
COMMON PLAYERS (513-664)	.15	.12	.05
1 A.L. Bat Leaders	.40	.30	.13
2 N.L. Bat Leaders	.40	.30	.13
3 A.L. R.B.I. Leaders	.30	.25	.10
4 N.L. R.B.I. Leaders	.30	.25	.10
5 A.L. H.R. Leaders	.30	.25	.10
6 N.L. H.R. Leaders	.40	.30	.13
7 A.L. E.R.A. Leaders	.30	.25	.10
8 N.L. E.R.A. Leaders	.30	.25	.10
9 A.L. Pitch Leaders	.30	.25	.10
10 N.L. Pitch Leaders	.40	.30	.13
11 A.L. S.O. Leaders	.30	.25	.10
12 N.L. S.O. Leaders	.30	.25	.10
13 Mickey Stanley	.15	.11	.05
14 Al McBean	.13	.10	.04
15 Boog Powell	.40	.30	.13
16 Giants Rookies	.13	.10	.04
17 Mike Marshall	.25	.20	.08
18 Dick Schofield	.13	.10	.04
19 Ken Suarez	.13	.10	.04
20 Ernie Banks	2.75	2.00	.90
21 Jose Santiago	.13	.10	.04
22 Jesus Alou	.13	.10	.04
23 Lew Krausse	.13	.10	.04
24 Walt Alston	.20	.15	.06
25 Roy White	.15	.11	.05
26 Clay Carroll	.13	.10	.04
27 Bernie Allen	.13	.10	.04
28 Mike Ryan	.13	.10	.04
29 Dave Morehead	.13	.10	.04
30 Bob Allison	.20	.15	.06
31 Mets Rookies (Otis)	1.00	.70	.30
32 Sammy Ellis	.13	.10	.04
33 Wayne Causey	.13	.10	.04
34 Gary Peters	.15	.11	.05
35 Joe Morgan	1.75	1.25	.55
36 Luke Walker	.13	.10	.04
37 Curt Motton	.13	.10	.04
38 Zoilo Versalles	.13	.10	.04
39 Dick Hughes	.13	.10	.04
40 Mayo Smith	.13	.10	.04
41 Bob Barton	.13	.10	.04
42 Tommy Harper	.13	.10	.04
43 Joe Niekro	.15	.11	.05
44 Danny Cater	.13	.10	.04
45 Maury Wills	.75	.55	.25
46 Fritz Peterson	.13	.10	.04
47 Paul Popovich	.13	.10	.04
48 Brant Alyea	.13	.10	.04
49A Royals Rookies (g)	.15	.11	.05
49B Royals Rookies (q)	5.00	3.75	1.75
50 Bob Clemente	4.25	3.25	1.50
51 Woody Fryman	.13	.10	.04
52 Mike Andrews	.13	.10	.04
53 Sonny Jackson	.13	.10	.04
54 Cisco Carlos	.13	.10	.04
55 Jerry Grote	.13	.10	.04
56 Rich Reese	.13	.10	.04
57 1st Checklist	.13	.10	.04
58 Fred Gladding	.13	.10	.04
59 Jay Johnstone	.13	.10	.04

	MINT	VG-E	F-G
60 Nelson Briles	.13	.10	.04
61 Jimmie Hall	.13	.10	.04
62 Chico Salmon	.13	.10	.04
63 Jim Hickman	.13	.10	.04
64 B. Monbouquette	.13	.10	.04
65 Willie Davis	.15	.11	.05
66 Orioles Rookies	.13	.10	.04
67 Bill Stoneman	.13	.10	.04
68 Dave Duncan	.13	.10	.04
69 Steve Hamilton	.13	.10	.04
70 Tommy Helms	.13	.10	.04
71 Steve Whitaker	.13	.10	.04
72 Ron Taylor	.13	.10	.04
73 Johnny Briggs	.13	.10	.04
74 Preston Gomez	.13	.10	.04
75 Luis Aparicio	.60	.45	.20
76 Norm Miller	.13	.10	.04
77 Ron Perranoski	.13	.10	.04
78 Tom Satriano	.13	.10	.04
79 Milt Pappas	.15	.11	.05
80 Norm Cash	.30	.25	.10
81 Mel Queen	.13	.10	.04
82 Pirates Rookies	2.00	1.50	.60
83 Mike Ferraro	.13	.10	.04
84 Bob Humphreys	.13	.10	.04
85 Lou Brock	3.00	2.25	1.00
86 Pete Richert	.13	.10	.04
87 Horace Clarke	.13	.10	.04
88 Rich Nye	.13	.10	.04
89 Russ Gibson	.13	.10	.04
90 Jerry Koosman	.75	.55	.25
91 Al Dark	.15	.11	.05
92 J. Billingham	.13	.10	.04
93 Joe Foy	.13	.10	.04
94 Hank Aguirre	.13	.10	.04
95 Johnny Bench	6.00	4.50	2.00
96 Denver LeMaster	.13	.10	.04
97 Buddy Bradford	.13	.10	.04
98 Dave Giusti	.13	.10	.04
99 Twins Rookies	1.50	1.10	.50
100 Hank Aaron	7.00	5.25	2.50
101 Daryl Patterson	.13	.10	.04
102 Jim Davenport	.13	.10	.04
103 Roger Repoz	.13	.10	.04
104 Steve Blass	.15	.11	.05
105 Rick Monday	.20	.15	.06
106 Jim Hannan	.13	.10	.04
107 2nd Checklist	.13	.10	.04
108 Tony Taylor	.13	.10	.04
109 Jim Lonborg	.15	.11	.05
110 Mike Shannon	.15	.11	.05
111 Johnny Morris	.13	.10	.04
112 J.C. Martin	.13	.10	.04
113 Dave May	.13	.10	.04
114 Yanks Rookies	.13	.10	.04
115 Bill Hands	.13	.10	.04
116 Chuck Harrison	.13	.10	.04
117 Jim Fairey	.13	.10	.04
118 Stan Williams	.13	.10	.04
119 Doug Rader	.13	.10	.04
120 Pete Rose	6.00	4.50	2.00
121 Joe Grzenda	.13	.10	.04
122 Ron Fairly	.15	.11	.05
123 Wilbur Wood	.15	.11	.05

	MINT	VG-E	F-G
124 Hank Bauer	.20	.15	.06
125 Ray Sadecki	.13	.10	.04
126 Dick Tracewski	.13	.10	.04
127 Kevin Collins	.13	.10	.04
128 Tommie Aaron	.15	.11	.05
129 Bill McCool	.13	.10	.04
130 Carl Yastrzemski	6.00	4.50	2.00
131 Chris Cannizzaro	.13	.10	.04
132 Dave Baldwin	.13	.10	.04
133 Johnny Callison	.13	.10	.04
134 Jim Weaver	.13	.10	.04
135 Tommy Davis	.20	.15	.06
136 Cards Rookies	.20	.15	.06
137 Wally Bunker	.13	.10	.04
138 John Bateman	.13	.10	.04
139 Andy Kosco	.13	.10	.04
140 Jim LeFebvre	.15	.11	.05
141 Bill Dillman	.13	.10	.04
142 Woody Woodward	.13	.10	.04
143 Joe Nossek	.13	.10	.04
144 Bob Hendley	.13	.10	.04
145 Max Alvis	.13	.10	.04
146 Jim Perry	.20	.15	.06
147 Leo Durocher	.30	.25	.10
148 Lee Stange	.13	.10	.04
149 Ollie Brown	.13	.10	.04
150 Denny McLain	.75	.55	.25
151A Clay Dalrymple (Port)	.13	.10	.04
151B Clay Dalrymple (Phil)	5.00	3.75	1.75
153 Ed Brinkman	.13	.10	.04
154 Jim Britton	.13	.10	.04
155 Pete Ward	.13	.10	.04
156 Houston Rookies	.13	.10	.04
157 Bob Rodgers	.13	.10	.04
158 Joe Gibbon	.13	.10	.04
159 Jerry Adair	.13	.10	.04
160 Vada Pinson	.50	.40	.18
161 John Purdin	.13	.10	.04
162 World Series #1	.40	.30	.13
163 World Series #2	.40	.30	.13
164 World Series #3	.40	.30	.13
165 World Series #4	.40	.30	.13
166 World Series #5	.40	.30	.13
167 World Series #6	.40	.30	.13
168 World Series #7	.40	.30	.13
169 World Series Conc.	.40	.30	.13
170 Frank Howard	.50	.40	.18
171 Glenn Beckert	.13	.10	.04
172 Jerry Stephenson	.13	.10	.04
173 Rookies (Chi)	.13	.10	.04
174 Grant Jackson	.13	.10	.04
175 Jim Bunning	.40	.30	.13
176 Joe Azcue	.13	.10	.04
177 Ron Reed	.13	.10	.04
178 Ray Oyler	.13	.10	.04
179 Don Pavletich	.13	.10	.04
180 Willie Horton	.15	.11	.05
181 Mel Nelson	.13	.10	.04
182 Bill Rigney	.13	.10	.04
183 Don Shaw	.13	.10	.04
184 Roberto Pena	.13	.10	.04
185 Tom Phoebus	.13	.10	.04
186 John Edwards	.13	.10	.04
187 Leon Wagner	.13	.10	.04
188 Rick Wise	.20	.15	.06
189 Rookies (Bost)	.13	.10	.04
190 Willie Mays	8.00	6.00	2.50
191 Lindy McDaniel	.15	.11	.05
192 Jose Pagan	.13	.10	.04
193 Don Cardwell	.13	.10	.04
194 Ted Uhlaender	.13	.10	.04
195 John Odom	.13	.10	.04
196 Lum Harris	.13	.10	.04
197 Dick Selma	.13	.10	.04
198 Willie Smith	.13	.10	.04
199 Jim French	.13	.10	.04
200 Bob Gibson	2.25	1.65	.75
201 Russ Snyder	.13	.10	.04
202 Don Wilson	.13	.10	.04
203 Dave Johnson	.13	.10	.04
204 Jack Hiatt	.13	.10	.04
205 Rick Reichardt	.13	.10	.04
206 Rookies (Phi)	.20	.15	.06
207 Roy Face	.20	.15	.06
208A Donn Clendenon (Hous)	.13	.10	.04
208B Donn Clendenon (Expo)	5.00	3.75	1.75
209 Larry Haney	.13	.10	.04
210 Felix Millan	.13	.10	.04
211 Galen Cisco	.13	.10	.04
212 Tom Tresh	.15	.11	.05
213 Gerry Arrigo	.13	.10	.04
214 3rd Checklist	.13	.10	.04

	MINT	VG-E	F-G
215 Rico Petrocelli	.15	.11	.05
216 Don Sutton	.75	.55	.25
217 John Donaldson	.13	.10	.04
218 John Roseboro	.13	.10	.04
219 Freddie Patek	.20	.15	.06
220 Sam McDowell	.20	.15	.06
221 Art Shamsky	.13	.10	.04
222 Duane Josephson	.13	.10	.04
223 Tom Dukes	.13	.10	.04
224 Rookies (Cal)	.13	.10	.04
225 Don Kessinger	.20	.15	.06
226 Bruce Howard	.13	.10	.04
227 Frank Johnson	.13	.10	.04
228 Dave Leonhard	.13	.10	.04
229 Don Lock	.13	.10	.04
230 Rusty Staub	.30	.25	.10
231 Pat Dobson	.13	.10	.04
232 Dave Ricketts	.13	.10	.04
233 Steve Barber	.13	.10	.04
234 Dave Bristol	.13	.10	.04
235 Jim Hunter	1.75	1.25	.55
236 Manny Mota	.15	.11	.05
237 Bobby Cox	.13	.10	.04
238 Ken Johnson	.13	.10	.04
239 Bob Taylor	.13	.10	.04
240 Ken Harrelson	.20	.15	.06
241 Jim Brewer	.13	.10	.04
242 Frank Kostro	.13	.10	.04
243 Ron Kline	.13	.10	.04
244 Indians Rookies	.13	.10	.04
245 Ed Charles	.13	.10	.04
246 Joe Coleman	.13	.10	.04
247 Gene Oliver	.13	.10	.04
248 Bob Priddy	.13	.10	.04
249 Ed Spiezio	.13	.10	.04
250 Frank Robinson	4.00	3.00	1.40
251 Ron Herbel	.13	.10	.04
252 Chuck Cottier	.13	.10	.04
253 Jerry Johnson	.13	.10	.04
254 Joe Schultz	.13	.10	.04
255 Steve Carlton	1.50	1.10	.50
256 Gates Brown	.13	.10	.04
257 Jim Ray	.13	.10	.04
258 J. Hernandez	.13	.10	.04
259 Bill Short	.13	.10	.04
260 Reggie Jackson	9.00	6.75	3.00
261 Bob Johnson	.13	.10	.04
262 Mike Kekich	.13	.10	.04
263 Jerry May	.13	.10	.04
264 Bill Landis	.13	.10	.04
265 Chico Cardenas	.13	.10	.04
266 Dodger Rookies	.13	.10	.04
267 Vicente Romo	.13	.10	.04
268 Al Spangler	.13	.10	.04
269 Al Weis	.13	.10	.04
270 Mickey Lolich	.30	.25	.10
271 Larry Stahl	.13	.10	.04
272 Ed Stroud	.13	.10	.04
273 Ron Willis	.13	.10	.04
274 Clyde King	.13	.10	.04
275 Vic Davalillo	.13	.10	.04
276 Gary Wagner	.13	.10	.04
277 Rod Hendricks	.13	.10	.04
278 Gary Geiger	.13	.10	.04
279 Roger Nelson	.13	.10	.04
280 Alex Johnson	.13	.10	.04
281 Ted Kubiak	.13	.10	.04
282 Pat Jarvis	.13	.10	.04
283 Sandy Alomar	.13	.10	.04
284 Expo Rookies	.13	.10	.04
285 Don Mincher	.13	.10	.04
286 Dock Ellis	.13	.10	.04
287 Jose Tartabull	.13	.10	.04
288 Ken Holtzman	.15	.11	.05
289 Bart Shirley	.13	.10	.04
290 Jim Kaat	.40	.30	.13
291 Vern Fuller	.13	.10	.04
292 Al Downing	.13	.10	.04
293 Dick Dietz	.13	.10	.04
294 Jim Lemon	.13	.10	.04
295 Tony Perez	.60	.45	.20
296 A. Messersmith	.20	.15	.06
297 Deron Johnson	.13	.10	.04
298 Dave Nicholson	.13	.10	.04
299 Mark Belanger	.20	.15	.06
300 Felipe Alou	.15	.11	.05
301 Darrell Brandon	.13	.10	.04
302 Jim Pagliaroni	.13	.10	.04
303 Cal Koonce	.13	.10	.04
304 Padres Rookies	.13	.10	.04
305 Dick McAuliffe	.13	.10	.04
306 Jim Grant	.13	.10	.04
307 Gary Kolb	.13	.10	.04
308 Wade Blasingame	.13	.10	.04

	MINT	VG-E	F-G		MINT	VG-E	F-G
309 Walt Williams	.13	.10	.04	402 Ken Boswell	.13	.10	.04
310 Tom Haller	.13	.10	.04	403 Bob Miller	.13	.10	.04
311 Sparky Lyle	.75	.55	.25	404 Cubs Rookies	.13	.10	.04
312 Lee Elia	.13	.10	.04	405 Lee May	.13	.10	.04
313 Bill Robinson	.13	.10	.04	406 Phil Ortega	.13	.10	.04
314 4th Checklist	.13	.10	.04	407 Tom Egan	.13	.10	.04
315 Eddie Fisher	.13	.10	.04	408 Nate Colbert	.13	.10	.04
316 Hal Lanier	.13	.10	.04	409 Bob Moose	.13	.10	.04
317 Bruce Look	.13	.10	.04	410 Al Kaline	2.50	1.80	.80
318 Jack Fisher	.13	.10	.04	411 Larry Dierker	.13	.10	.04
319 Ken McMullen	.13	.10	.04	412 5th Checklist	.13	.10	.04
320 Dal Maxvill	.13	.10	.04	413 Roland Sheldon	.13	.10	.04
321 Jim McAndrew	.13	.10	.04	414 Duke Sims	.13	.10	.04
322 Jose Vidal	.13	.10	.04	415 Ray Washburn	.13	.10	.04
323 Larry Miller	.13	.10	.04	416 Willie McCovey, AS	1.50	1.10	.50
324 Tiger Rookies	.13	.10	.04	417 Ken Harrelson, AS	.25	.20	.08
325 Jose Cardenal	.13	.10	.04	418 Tommy Helms, AS	.15	.11	.05
326 Gary Sutherland	.13	.10	.04	419 Rod Carew, AS	1.75	1.25	.55
327 Willie Crawford	.13	.10	.04	420 Ron Santo, AS	.30	.25	.10
328 Joe Horlen	.13	.10	.04	421 Brooks Robinson, AS	1.50	1.10	.50
329 Rick Joseph	.13	.10	.04	422 Don Kessinger, AS	.20	.15	.06
330 Tony Conigliaro	.15	.11	.05	423 Bert Campaneris, AS	.20	.15	.06
331 Braves Rookies	.13	.10	.04	424 Pete Rose, AS	2.00	1.50	.60
332 Fred Talbot	.13	.10	.04	425 Carl Yastrzemski, AS	2.00	1.50	.60
333 Ivan Murrell	.13	.10	.04	426 Curt Flood, AS	.20	.15	.06
334 Phil Roof	.13	.10	.04	427 Tony Oliva, AS	.40	.30	.13
335 Bill Mazeroski	.20	.15	.06	428 Lou Brock, AS	1.50	1.10	.50
336 Jim Roland	.13	.10	.04	429 Willie Horton, AS	.20	.15	.06
337 Marty Martinez	.13	.10	.04	430 Johnny Bench, AS	2.00	1.50	.60
338 Del Unser	.13	.10	.04	431 Bill Freehan, AS	.20	.15	.06
339 Reds Rookies	.13	.10	.04	432 Bob Gibson, AS	1.25	.90	.40
340 Dave McNally	.15	.11	.05	433 Denny McLain, AS	.50	.40	.18
341 Dave Adlesh	.13	.10	.04	434 Jerry Koosman, AS	.30	.25	.10
342 Bubba Morton	.13	.10	.04	435 Sam McDowell, AS	.30	.15	.06
343 Dan Frisella	.13	.10	.04	436 Gene Alley	.13	.10	.04
344 Tom Matchick	.13	.10	.04	437 Luis Alcaraz	.13	.10	.04
345 Frank Linzy	.13	.10	.04	438 Gary Waslewski	.13	.10	.04
346 Wayne Comer	.13	.10	.04	439 White Sox Rookies	.13	.10	.04
347 Randy Hundley	.13	.10	.04	440A Willie McCovey	4.00	3.00	1.40
348 Steve Hargan	.13	.10	.04	440B Willie McCovey(White)	25.00	18.50	8.75
349 Dick Williams	.20	.15	.06	441A Dennis Higgins	.13	.10	.04
350 Richie Allen	.60	.45	.20	441B Dennis Higgins(White)	3.00	2.25	1.00
351 Carroll Sembera	.13	.10	.04	442 Ty Cline	.13	.10	.04
352 Paul Schaal	.13	.10	.04	443 Don Wert	.13	.10	.04
353 Jeff Torborg	.13	.10	.04	444A Joe Moeller	.13	.10	.04
354 Nate Oliver	.13	.10	.04	444B Joe Moeller(White)	3.00	2.25	1.00
355 Phil Niekro	.50	.40	.18	445 Bobby Knoop	.13	.10	.04
356 Frank Quilici	.13	.10	.04	446 Claude Raymond	.13	.10	.04
357 Carl Taylor	.13	.10	.04	447A Ralph Houk	.30	.25	.10
358 Rookies (Athletics)	.13	.10	.04	447B Ralph Houk(White)	4.00	3.00	1.50
359 Dick Kelley	.13	.10	.04	448 Bob Tolan	.13	.10	.04
360 Jim Wynn	.15	.11	.05	449 Paul Lindblad	.13	.10	.04
361 Gary Holman	.13	.10	.04	450 Billy Williams	.50	.40	.18
362 Jim Maloney	.15	.11	.05	451A Rich Rollins	.13	.10	.04
363 Russ Nixon	.13	.10	.04	451B Rich Rollins(White)	3.00	2.25	1.00
364 Tommie Agee	.13	.10	.04	452A Al Ferrara	.13	.10	.04
365 Jim Fregosi	.25	.20	.08	452B Al Ferrara(White)	3.00	2.25	1.00
366 Bo Belinsky	.15	.11	.05	453 Mike Cuellar	.30	.25	.10
367 Lou Johnson	.13	.10	.04	454A Phillies Rookies	.13	.10	.04
368 Vic Roznovsky	.13	.10	.04	454B Phillies Rookies(White)	3.00	2.25	1.00
369 Bob Skinner	.13	.10	.04	455 Sonny Siebert	.13	.10	.04
370 Juan Marichal	1.25	.90	.40	456 Bud Harrelson	.13	.10	.04
371 Sal Bando	.30	.25	.10	457 Dalton Jones	.13	.10	.04
372 Adolfo Phillips	.13	.10	.04	458 Curt Blefary	.13	.10	.04
373 Fred Lasher	.13	.10	.04	459 Dave Boswell	.13	.10	.04
374 Bob Tillman	.13	.10	.04	460 Joe Torre	.50	.40	.18
375 Harmon Killebrew	2.50	1.80	.80	461A Mike Epstein	.13	.10	.04
376 Rookies (Royals)	.13	.10	.04	461B Mike Epstein(White)	3.00	2.25	1.00
377 Gary Bell	.13	.10	.04	462 Red Schoendienst	.25	.20	.08
378 Jose Herrera	.13	.10	.04	463 Dennis Ribant	.13	.10	.04
379 Ken Boyer	.50	.40	.18	464A Dave Marshall	.13	.10	.04
380 Stan Bahnsen	.13	.10	.04	464B Dave Marshall(White)	3.00	2.25	1.00
381 Ed Kranepool	.15	.11	.05	465 Tommy John	.75	.55	.25
382 Pat Corrales	.13	.10	.04	466 John Boccabella	.13	.10	.04
383 Casey Cox	.13	.10	.04	467 Tom Reynolds	.13	.10	.04
384 Larry Shepard	.13	.10	.04	468A Pirates Rookies	.13	.10	.04
385 Orlando Cepeda	1.00	.70	.30	468B Pirates Rookies(White)	3.00	2.25	1.00
386 Jim McGlothlin	.13	.10	.04	469 Chico Ruiz	.13	.10	.04
387 Bobby Klaus	.13	.10	.04	470A Mel Stottlemyre	.20	.15	.06
388 Tom McCraw	.13	.10	.04	470B Mel Stottlemyre(White)	4.00	3.00	1.50
389 Dan Coombs	.13	.10	.04	471A Ted Savage	.13	.10	.04
390 Bill Freehan	.15	.11	.05	471B Ted Savage(White)	3.00	2.25	1.00
391 Ray Culp	.13	.10	.04	472 Jim Price	.13	.10	.04
392 Bob Burda	.13	.10	.04	473A Jose Arcia	.13	.10	.04
393 Gene Brabender	.13	.10	.04	473B Jose Arcia(White)	3.00	2.25	1.00
394 Rookies (Pilots)	.13	.10	.04	474 Tom Murphy	.13	.10	.04
395 Chris Short	.13	.10	.04	475 Tim McCarver	.15	.11	.05
396 Jim Campanis	.13	.10	.04	476A Boston Rookies	.13	.10	.04
397 Chuck Dobson	.13	.10	.04	476B Boston Rookies(White)	3.00	2.25	1.00
398 Tito Francona	.13	.10	.04	477 Jeff James	.13	.10	.04
399 Bob Bailey	.13	.10	.04	478 Don Buford	.13	.10	.04
400 Don Drysdale	2.25	1.65	.75	479 Richie Scheinblum	.13	.10	.04
401 Jake Gibbs	.13	.10	.04	480 Tom Seaver	7.50	5.75	2.50
				481 Bell Melton	.13	.10	.04
				482A Jim Gosger	.13	.10	.04

	MINT	VG-E	F-G
482B Jim Gosger(White)	3.00	2.25	1.00
483 Joe Gordon	.13	.10	.04
485A Gaylord Perry	1.75	1.25	.55
485B Gaylord Perry(White)	15.00	11.00	5.00
486A Paul Casanova	.13	.10	.04
486B Paul Casanova(White)	3.00	2.25	1.00
487 Denis Menke	.13	.10	.04
488 Joe Sparma	.13	.10	.04
489 Clete Boyer	.13	.10	.04
490 Matty Alou	.15	.11	.05
491A Twins Rookies	.13	.10	.04
491B Twins Rookies(White)	3.00	2.25	1.00
492 Tony Cloninger	.13	.10	.04
493A Wes Parker	.20	.15	.06
493B Wes Parker(White)	4.00	3.00	1.40
494 Ken Berry	.13	.10	.04
495 Bert Campaneris	.15	.11	.05
496 Larry Jaster	.13	.10	.04
497 Julian Javier	.13	.10	.04
498 Juan Pizarro	.13	.10	.04
499 Astro Rookies	.13	.10	.04
500A Mickey Mantle	15.00	11.00	5.00
500B Mickey Mantle(White)	60.00	45.00	20.00
501A Tony Gonzalez	.13	.10	.04
501B Tony Gonzalez(White)	3.00	2.25	1.00
502 Minnie Rojas	.13	.10	.04
503 Lary Brown	.13	.10	.04
504 6th Checklist	.13	.10	.04
505A Bobby Bolin	.13	.10	.04
505B Bobby Bolin(White)	3.00	2.25	1.00
506 Paul Blair	.15	.11	.05
587 Cookie Rojas	.13	.10	.04
508 Moe Drabowsky	.13	.10	.04
509 Manny Sanguillen	.15	.11	.05
510 Rod Carew	6.00	4.50	2.00
511A Diego Segui	.13	.10	.04
511B Diego Segui(White)	3.00	2.25	1.00
512 Cleon Jones	.13	.10	.04
513 Camilo Pascual	.15	.12	.05
514 Mike Lum	.15	.12	.05
515 Dick Green	.15	.12	.05
516 Earl Weaver	.25	.20	.08
517 Mike McCormick	.15	.12	.05
518 Fred Whitfield	.15	.12	.05
519 Yankees Rookies	.15	.12	.05
520 Bob Veale	.16	.12	.05
521 George Thomas	.15	.12	.05
522 Joe Hoerner	.15	.12	.05
523 Bob Chance	.15	.12	.05
524 Expos Rookies	.15	.12	.05
525 Earl Wilson	.15	.12	.05
526 Hector Torres	.15	.12	.05
527 Al Lopez	.75	.55	.25
528 Claude Osteen	.15	.12	.05
529 Ed Kirkpatrick	.15	.12	.05
530 Cesar Tovar	.15	.12	.05
531 Dick Farrell	.15	.12	.05
532 Bird Hill Aces	.40	.30	.13
533 Nolan Ryan	4.50	3.50	1.60
534 Jerry McNertney	.15	.12	.05
535 Phil Regan	.15	.12	.05
537 Padres Rookies	.15	.12	.05
538 Charlie Smith	.15	.12	.05
539 Ted Shows How	1.00	.70	.30
540 Curt Flood	.25	.20	.08
541 Joe Verbanic	.15	.12	.05
542 Bob Aspromonte	.15	.12	.05
543 Fred Newman	.15	.12	.05
544 Tigers Rookies	.15	.12	.05
545 Willie Stargell	2.25	1.65	.75
546 Jim Nash	.15	.12	.05
547 Billy Martin	.50	.40	.18
548 Bob Locker	.15	.12	.05
549 Ron Brand	.15	.12	.05
550 Brooks Robinson	4.00	3.00	1.40
551 Wayne Granger	.15	.12	.05
552 Dodgers Rookies	.15	.12	.05
553 Ron Davis	.15	.12	.05
554 Frank Bertaina	.15	.12	.05
555 Jim Hart	.15	.12	.05
556 A's Stars	.40	.30	.13
557 Frank Fernandez	.15	.12	.05
558 Tom Burgmeier	.15	.12	.05
559 Cardinals Rookies	.15	.12	.05
560 Luis Tiant	.40	.30	.13
561 Ron Clark	.15	.12	.05
562 Bob Watson	.75	.55	.25
563 Marty Pattin	.15	.12	.05
564 Gil Hodges	1.75	1.25	.55
565 Hoyt Wilhelm	.60	.45	.20
566 Ron Hansen	.15	.12	.05
567 Pirates Rookies	.15	.12	.05
568 Cecil Upshaw	.15	.12	.05
569 Billy Harris	.15	.12	.05
570 Ron Santo	.40	.30	.13

	MINT	VG-E	F-
571 Cap Peterson	.15	.12	.05
572 Giants Heroes	1.25	.90	.40
573 Jim Palmer	2.50	1.80	.80
574 George Scott	.20	.15	.06
575 Bill Singer	.15	.12	.05
576 Phillies Rookies	.15	.12	.05
577 Mike Hegan	.15	.12	.05
578 Don Bosch	.15	.12	.05
579 Dave Nelson	.15	.12	.05
580 Jim Northrup	.15	.12	.05
581 Gary Nolan	.15	.12	.05
582 7th Checklist	.15	.12	.05
583 Clyde Wright	.15	.12	.05
584 Don Mason	.15	.12	.05
585 Ron Swoboda	.15	.12	.05
586 Tim Cullen	.15	.12	.05
587 Joe Rudi	.25	.20	.08
588 Bill White	.20	.15	.06
589 Joe Pepitone	.20	.15	.06
590 Rico Carty	.30	.25	.10
591 Mike Hedlund	.15	.12	.05
592 Padres Rookies	.15	.12	.05
593 Duane Josephson	.15	.12	.05
594 Dooley Womack	.15	.12	.05
595 Lee Maye	.15	.12	.05
596 Chuck Hartenstein	.15	.12	.05
597 A. L. Rookies	1.25	.90	.40
598 Ruben Amaro	.15	.12	.05
599 John Boozer	.15	.12	.05
600 Tony Oliva	.80	.60	.25
601 Tug McGraw	.40	.30	.13
602 Cubs Rookies	.15	.12	.05
603 Joe Keough	.15	.12	.05
604 Bobby Etheridge	.15	.12	.05
605 Dick Ellsworth	.15	.12	.05
606 Gene Mauch	.20	.15	.06
607 Dick Bosman	.15	.12	.05
608 Dick Simpson	.15	.12	.05
609 Phil Gagliano	.15	.12	.05
610 Jim Hardin	.15	.12	.05
611 Braves Rookies	.15	.12	.05
612 Jack Aker	.15	.12	.05
613 Jim Beauchamp	.15	.12	.05
614 Houston Rookies	.15	.12	.05
615 Len Gabrielson	.15	.12	.05
616 Don McMahon	.15	.12	.05
617 Jesse Gonder	.15	.12	.05
618 Ramon Webster	.15	.12	.05
619 Royals Rookies	.15	.12	.05
620 Dean Chance	.15	.12	.05
621 Bill Voss	.15	.12	.05
622 Dan Osinski	.15	.12	.05
623 Hank Allen	.15	.12	.05
624 N. L. Rookies	.15	.12	.05
625 Mack Jones	.15	.12	.05
626 Gene Michael	.30	.25	.10
627 George Stone	.15	.12	.05
628 Red Sox Rookies	.15	.12	.05
629 Jack Hamilton	.15	.12	.05
630 Bobby Bonds	1.50	1.10	.50
631 John Kennedy	.15	.12	.05
632 Jon Warden	.15	.12	.05
633 Harry Walker	.15	.12	.05
634 Andy Etchebarren	.15	.12	.05
635 George Culver	.15	.12	.05
636 Woodie Held	.15	.12	.05
637 Padres Rookies	.15	.12	.05
638 Ed Sprague	.15	.12	.05
639 Barry Moore	.15	.12	.05
640 Fergie Jenkins	.60	.45	.20
641 N. L. Rookies	.15	.12	.05
642 John Hiller	.15	.12	.05
643 Billy Cowan	.15	.12	.05
644 Chuck Hinton	.15	.12	.05
645 George Brunet	.15	.12	.05
646 Expos Rookies	.15	.12	.05
647 Dave Wickersham	.15	.12	.05
648 Bobby Wine	.15	.12	.05
649 Al Jackson	.15	.12	.05
650 Ted Williams	2.00	1.50	.60
651 Gus Gil	.15	.12	.05
652 Eddie Watt	.15	.12	.05
653 Aurelio Rodriguez	1.00	.70	.30
654 White Sox Rookies	.15	.12	.05
655 Mike Hershberger	.15	.12	.05
656 Dan Schneider	.15	.12	.05
657 Bobby Murcer	.40	.30	.13
658 Rookie Stars (AL)	.15	.12	.05
659 Johnny Podres	.20	.15	.06
660 Reggie Smith	.75	.55	.25
661 Jim Merritt	.15	.12	.05
662 Royals Rookies	.15	.12	.05
663 Dick Radatz	.15	.12	.05
664 Ron Hunt	.15	.12	.05

1969 TOPPS SUPER (66)   2 1/4" X 3 1/4"

BOB CLEMENTE
Pittsburgh Pirates   Outfield

No. 58 of 66 Super Baseball Cards
T.C.G.   PRNTD. IN U.S.A.

The 1969 Topps Super set is a beautiful 66 card set released in 1969 as a separate issue from Topps regular 1969 set. Although it is called "Super", the card size is not postcard size as are the 1970 & 1971 Topps Super cards.

	MINT	VG-E	F-G
COMPLETE SET	1500.00	1100.00	400.00
COMMON PLAYER	7.50	6.00	2.00
1 Dave McNally	10.00	7.00	3.00
2 Frank Robinson	60.00	4.50	2.00
3 Brooks Robinson	75.00	55.00	24.00
4 Ken Harrelson	9.00	6.75	3.00
5 Carl Yastrzemski	150.00	110.00	50.00
6 Ray Culp	7.50	6.00	2.00
7 Jim Fregosi	9.00	6.75	3.00
8 Rick Reichardt	7.50	6.00	2.00
9 Vic Davalillo	7.50	6.00	2.00
10 Luis Aparicio	10.00	7.00	3.00
11 Pete Ward	7.50	6.00	2.00
12 Joe Horlen	7.50	6.00	2.00
13 Luis Tiant	10.00	7.00	3.00
14 Sam McDowell	9.00	6.75	3.00
15 Jose Cardenal	7.50	6.00	2.00
16 Willie Horton	9.00	6.75	3.00
17 Denny McLain	12.00	8.75	4.00
18 Bill Freehan	9.00	6.75	3.00
19 Harmon Killebrew	40.00	30.00	13.00
20 Tony Oliva	12.00	8.75	4.00
21 Dean Chance	7.50	6.00	2.00
22 Joe Foy	7.50	6.00	2.00
23 Roger Nelson	7.50	6.00	2.00
24 Mickey Mantle	400.00	300.00	125.00
25 Mel Stottlemyre	9.00	6.75	3.00
26 Roy White	7.50	6.00	2.00
27 Rick Monday	9.00	6.75	3.00
28 Reggie Jackson	75.00	55.00	24.00
29 Bert Campaneris	9.00	6.75	3.00
30 Frank Howard	10.00	7.00	3.00
31 Camilo Pascual	7.50	6.00	2.00
32 Tommy Davis	9.00	6.75	3.00
33 Don Mincher	7.50	6.00	2.00
34 Hank Aaron	200.00	150.00	65.00
35 Felipe Alou	7.50	6.00	2.00
36 Joe Torre	10.00	7.00	3.00
37 Fergie Jenkins	10.00	7.00	3.00
38 Ron Santo	10.00	7.00	3.00
39 Billy Williams	10.00	7.00	3.00
40 Tommy Helms	7.50	6.00	2.00
41 Pete Rose	150.00	110.00	50.00
42 Joe Morgan	25.00	18.50	8.75
43 Jim Wynn	7.50	6.00	2.00
44 Curt Blefary	7.50	6.00	2.00
45 Willie Davis	7.50	6.00	2.00
46 Don Drysdale	25.00	18.50	8.75
47 Tom Haller	7.50	6.00	2.00
48 Rusty Staub	10.00	7.00	3.00
49 Maury Wills	12.00	8.75	4.00
50 Cleon Jones	7.50	6.00	2.00
51 Jerry Koosman	10.00	7.00	3.00
52 Tom Seaver	75.00	55.00	24.00
53 Richie Allen	10.00	7.00	3.00
54 Chris Short	7.50	6.00	2.00
55 Cookie Rojas	7.50	6.00	2.00
56 Matty Alou	7.50	6.00	2.00
57 Steve Blass	7.50	6.00	2.00
58 Bob Clemente	100.00	70.00	30.00
59 Curt Flood	9.00	6.75	3.00
60 Bob Gibson	40.00	30.00	13.00
61 Tim McCarver	7.50	6.00	2.00
62 Dick Selma	7.50	6.00	2.00
63 Ollie Brown	7.50	6.00	2.00
64 Juan Marichal	20.00	15.00	6.50
65 Willie Mays	250.00	185.00	87.50
66 Willie McCovey	70.00	50.00	23.00

1969 TOPPS DECKLE EDGE (33)   2 1/4" X 3 1/4"

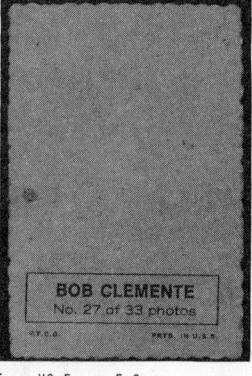

BOB CLEMENTE
No. 27 of 33 photos
T.C.G.   PRNTD. IN U.S.A.

The 1969 Topps Deckle Edge set is a serated border black & white set included as inserts with the 1969 Topps regular issue. There are two different numbers 11 and 22.

	MINT	VG-E	F-G
COMPLETE SET	20.00	15.00	6.00
COMMON PLAYER	.20	.15	.06
1 Brooks Robinson	1.25	.90	.40
2 Boog Powell	.30	.25	.10
3 Ken Harrelson	.25	.20	.08
4 Carl Yastrzemski	1.75	1.25	.55
5 Jim Fregosi	.25	.20	.08
6 Luis Aparicio	.30	.25	.10
7 Luis Tiant	.25	.20	.08
8 Denny McLain	.30	.25	.10
9 Willie Horton	.20	.15	.06
10 Bill Freehan	.20	.15	.06
11 Hoyt Wilhelm	1.00	.70	.30

1969 TOPPS DECKLE (CONTINUED)

	MINT	VG-E	F-G			MINT	VG-E	F-G
11 Jim Wynn	4.00	3.00	1.40	22 Joe Foy	4.00	3.00	1.40
12 Rod Carew	1.25	.90	.40	23 Tom Haller	.20	.15	.06
13 Mel Stottlemyre	.20	.15	.06	24 Maury Wills	.40	.30	.13
14 Rick Monday	.20	.15	.06	25 Jerry Koosman	.25	.20	.08
15 Tommy Davis	.25	.20	.08	26 Richie Allen	.30	.25	.10
16 Frank Howard	.30	.25	.10	27 Bob Clemente	1.50	1.10	.50
17 Felipe Alou	.20	.15	.06	28 Curt Flood	.75	.55	.25
18 Don Kessinger	.20	.15	.06	29 Bob Gibson	.75	.55	.25
19 Ron Santo	.25	.20	.08	30 Al Ferrara	.20	.15	.06
20 Tommy Helms	.20	.15	.06	31 Willie McCovey	.75	.55	.25
21 Pete Rose	1.75	1.25	.55	32 Juan Marichal	.50	.40	.18
22 Rusty Staub	1.00	.70	.30	33 Willie Mays	2.00	1.50	.60

1969 TOPPS DECAL INSERTS (48)   1 1/2" X 1 1/2"

The 1969 Topps Decal Inserts are a set of 48 un-numbered decals issues as inserts in packages of 1969 Topps regular issue cards. The decals appear to be miniature versions of the Topps regular issue of that year. Most of the players on the decals are stars.

	MINT	VG-E	F-G
COMPLETE SET	100.00	70.00	30.00
COMMON PLAYER	1.00	.75	.30

	MINT	VG-E	F-G			MINT	VG-E	F-G
1 Hank Aaron	10.00	7.00	3.00	25 Denny McLain	1.50	1.10	.50
2 Richie Allen	1.50	1.10	.50	26 Dave McNally	1.25	.90	.40
3 Felipe Alou	1.00	.75	.30	27 Mickey Mantle	15.00	11.00	5.00
4 Matty Alou	1.00	.75	.30	28 Willie Mays	10.00	7.00	3.00
5 Luis Aparicio	1.50	1.10	.50	29 Reggie Jackson	8.00	6.00	2.50
6 Bob Clemente	10.00	7.00	3.00	30 Don Mincher	1.00	.75	.30
7 Donn Clendenon	1.00	.75	.30	31 Rick Monday	1.25	.90	.40
8 Tommy Davis	1.25	.90	.40	32 Tony Oliva	1.50	1.10	.50
9 Don Drysdale	4.00	3.00	1.40	33 Camilo Pascual	1.25	.90	.40
10 Joe Foy	1.00	.75	.30	34 Rick Reichardt	1.00	.75	.30
11 Jim Fregosi	1.50	.75	.30	35 Pete Rose	10.00	7.00	3.00
12 Bob Gibson	4.00	3.00	1.40	36 Frank Robinson	5.00	3.75	1.75
13 Tony Gonzalez	1.00	.75	.30	37 Ron Santo	1.50	1.10	.50
14 Tom Haller	1.00	.75	.30	38 Dick Selma	1.00	.75	.30
15 Ken Harrelson	1.00	.75	.30	39 Tom Seaver	8.00	6.00	2.50
16 Tommy Helms	1.00	.75	.30	40 Chris Short	1.00	.75	.30
17 Willie Horton	1.00	.75	.30	41 Rusty Staub	1.50	1.10	.50
18 Frank Howard	1.50	1.10	.50	42 Mel Stottlemyre	1.00	.75	.30
19 Fergie Jenkins	1.50	1.10	.50	43 Luis Tiant	1.50	1.10	.50
20 Harmon Killebrew	4.00	3.00	1.40	44 Pete Ward	1.00	.75	.30
21 Jerry Koosman	1.25	.90	.40	45 Hoyt Wilhelm	2.00	1.50	.60
22 Tim McCarver	1.00	.75	.30	46 Maury Wills	2.00	1.50	.60
23 Willie McCovey	5.00	3.75	1.75	47 Jim Wynn	1.00	.75	.30
24 Sam McDowell	1.25	.90	.40	48 Carl Yastrzemski	10.00	7.00	3.00

1969 POSE AND TEAM VARIATION

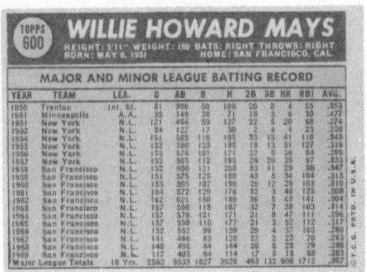

The 1970 Topps set includes The Sporting News All-Star selections as card nos. 450-469. High numbers 637-720 are somewhat more difficult to obtain. The next to last series contains cards which are also, but to a lesser extent, more difficult to obtain.

	MINT	VG-E	F-G
COMPLETE SET	200.00	150.00	60.00
COMMON PLAYER (1-552)	.12	.09	.04
COMMON PLAYER (553-636)	.18	.14	.05
COMMON PLAYER (637-720)	.45	.32	.13
1 Worlds Champions	.50	.30	.12
2 Diego Segui	.12	.09	.04
3 Darrel Chaney	.12	.09	.04
4 Tom Egan	.12	.09	.04
5 Wes Parker	.15	.11	.05
6 Grant Jackson	.12	.09	.04
7 Indians Rookies	.12	.09	.04
8 Jose Martinez	.12	.09	.04
9 1st Checklist	.12	.09	.04
10 Carl Yastrzemski	4.00	3.00	1.40
11 Nate Colbert	.12	.09	.04
12 John Hiller	.12	.09	.04
13 Jack Hiatt	.12	.09	.04
14 Hank Allen	.12	.09	.04
15 Larry Dierker	.12	.09	.04
16 Charlie Metro	.12	.09	.04
17 Hoyt Wilhelm	.40	.30	.13
18 Carlos May	.12	.09	.04
19 John Boccabella	.12	.09	.04
20 Dave McNally	.15	.11	.05
21 Oakland Rookies (Blue)	1.75	1.25	.55
22 Ray Washburn	.12	.09	.04
23 Bill Robinson	.12	.09	.04
24 Dick Selma	.12	.09	.04
25 Cesar Tovar	.12	.09	.04
26 Tug McGraw	.20	.15	.06
27 Chuck Hinton	.12	.09	.04
28 Billy Wilson	.12	.09	.04
29 Sandy Alomar	.12	.09	.04
30 Matty Alou	.15	.11	.05
31 Marty Pattin	.12	.09	.04
32 Harry Walker	.12	.09	.04
33 Don Wert	.12	.09	.04
34 Willie Crawford	.12	.09	.04
35 Joe Horlen	.12	.09	.04
36 Red Rookies	.12	.09	.04
37 Dick Drago	.12	.09	.04
38 Mack Jones	.12	.09	.04
39 Mike Nagy	.12	.09	.04
40 Rich Allen	.40	.30	.13
41 G. Lauzerique	.12	.09	.04
42 Tito Fuentes	.12	.09	.04
43 Jack Aker	.12	.09	.04
44 Roberto Pena	.12	.09	.04
45 Dave Johnson	.12	.09	.04
46 Ken Rudolph	.12	.09	.04
47 Bob Miller	.12	.09	.04
48 Gil Garrido	.12	.09	.04
49 Tim Cullen	.12	.09	.04
50 Tommie Agee	.12	.09	.04
51 Bob Christian	.12	.09	.04
52 Bruce Dal Canton	.12	.09	.04
53 John Kennedy	.12	.09	.04
54 Jeff Torborg	.12	.09	.04
55 John Odom	.12	.09	.04
56 Phillies Rookies	.12	.09	.04
57 Pat Kelly	.12	.09	.04
58 Dave Marshall	.12	.09	.04
59 Dick Ellsworth	.12	.09	.04

	MINT	VG-E	F-G
60 Jim Wynn	.15	.11	.05
61 N.L. Bat Leaders	.25	.20	.08
62 A.L. Bat Leaders	.25	.20	.08
63 N.L. R.B.I. Leaders	.25	.20	.08
64 A.L. R.B.I. Leaders	.25	.20	.08
65 N.L. H.R. Leaders	.25	.20	.08
66 A.L. H.R. Leaders	.25	.20	.08
67 N.L. E.R.A. Leaders	.25	.20	.08
68 A.L. E.R.A. Leaders	.25	.20	.08
69 N.L. Pitch Leaders	.25	.20	.08
70 A.L. Pitch Leaders	.25	.20	.08
71 N.L. S.O. Leaders	.25	.20	.08
72 A.L. S.O. Leaders	.25	.20	.08
73 Wayne Granger	.12	.09	.04
74 Angels Rookies	.12	.09	.04
75 Jim Kaat	.30	.25	.10
76 Carl Taylor	.12	.09	.04
77 Frank Linzy	.12	.09	.04
78 Joe Lahoud	.12	.09	.04
79 Clay Kirby	.12	.09	.04
80 Don Kessinger	.15	.11	.05
81 Dave May	.12	.09	.04
82 Frank Fernandez	.12	.09	.04
83 Don Cardwell	.12	.09	.04
84 Paul Casanova	.12	.09	.04
85 Max Alvis	.12	.09	.04
86 Lum Harris	.12	.09	.04
87 Steve Renko	.12	.09	.04
88 Pilots Rookies	.12	.09	.04
89 Juan Rios	.12	.09	.04
90 Tim McCarver	.15	.11	.05
91 Rich Morales	.12	.09	.04
92 George Culver	.12	.09	.04
93 Rick Renick	.12	.09	.04
94 Fred Patek	.15	.11	.05
95 Earl Wilson	.12	.09	.04
96 Cardinals Rookies	.30	.25	.10
97 Joe Moeller	.12	.09	.04
98 Gates Brown	.12	.09	.04
99 Bobby Pfeil	.12	.09	.04
100 Mel Stottlemyre	.15	.11	.05
101 Bobby Floyd	.12	.09	.04
102 Joe Rudi	.15	.11	.05
103 Frank Reberger	.12	.09	.04
104 Gerry Moses	.12	.09	.04
105 Tony Gonzalez	.12	.09	.04
106 Darold Knowles	.12	.09	.04
107 Bobby Etheridge	.12	.09	.04
108 Tom Burgmeier	.12	.09	.04
109 Expos Rookies	.12	.09	.04
110 Bob Moose	.12	.09	.04
111 Mike Hegan	.12	.09	.04
112 Dave Nelson	.12	.09	.04
113 Jim Ray	.12	.09	.04
114 Gene Michael	.20	.15	.06
115 Alex Johnson	.12	.09	.04
116 Sparky Lyle	.20	.15	.06
117 Don Young	.12	.09	.04
118 George Mitterwald	.12	.09	.04
119 Chuck Taylor	.12	.09	.04
120 Sal Bando	.20	.15	.06
121 Orioles Rookies	.12	.09	.04
122 George Stone	.12	.09	.04

	MINT	VG-E	F-G
123 Don Gutteridge	.12	.09	.04
124 Larry Jaster	.12	.09	.04
125 Deron Johnson	.12	.09	.04
126 Marty Martinez	.12	.09	.04
127 Joe Coleman	.12	.09	.04
128 2nd Checklist	.12	.09	.04
129 Jimmie Price	.12	.09	.04
130 Ollie Brown	.12	.09	.04
131 Dodgers Rookies	.12	.09	.04
132 Jim McGlothlin	.12	.09	.04
133 Clay Carroll	.12	.09	.04
134 Danny Walton	.12	.09	.04
135 Dick Dietz	.12	.09	.04
136 Steve Hargan	.12	.09	.04
137 Art Shamsky	.12	.09	.04
138 Joe Foy	.12	.09	.04
139 Rich Nye	.12	.09	.04
140 Reggie Jackson	3.00	2.25	1.00
141 Pirates Rookies	.12	.09	.04
142 Fritz Peterson	.12	.09	.04
143 Phil Gagliano	.12	.09	.04
144 Ray Culp	.12	.09	.04
145 Rico Carty	.20	.15	.06
146 Danny Murphy	.12	.09	.04
147 Angel Hermoso	.12	.09	.04
148 Earl Weaver	.20	.15	.06
149 Billy Champion	.12	.09	.04
150 Harmon Killebrew	1.75	1.25	.55
151 Dave Roberts	.12	.09	.04
152 Ike Brown	.12	.09	.04
153 Gary Gentry	.12	.09	.04
154 Senators Rookies	.12	.09	.04
155 Denis Menke	.12	.09	.04
156 Eddie Fisher	.12	.09	.04
157 Manny Mota	.15	.11	.05
158 Jerry McNertney	.12	.09	.04
159 Tommy Helms	.12	.09	.04
160 Phil Niekro	.30	.25	.10
161 Richie Scheinblum	.12	.09	.04
162 Jerry Johnson	.12	.09	.04
163 Syd O'Brien	.12	.09	.04
164 Ty Cline	.12	.09	.04
165 Ed Kirkpatrick	.12	.09	.04
166 Al Oliver	.50	.40	.18
167 Bill Burbach	.12	.09	.04
168 Dave Watkins	.12	.09	.04
169 Tom Hall	.12	.09	.04
170 Billy Williams	.50	.40	.18
171 Jim Nash	.12	.09	.04
172 Braves Rookies	.12	.09	.04
173 Jim Hicks	.12	.09	.04
174 Ted Sizemore	.12	.09	.04
175 Dick Bosman	.12	.09	.04
176 Jim Hart	.12	.09	.04
177 Jim Northrup	.12	.09	.04
178 Denny Lemaster	.12	.09	.04
179 Ivan Murrell	.12	.09	.04
180 Tommy John	1.00	.70	.30
181 Sparky Anderson	.30	.25	.10
182 Dick Hall	.12	.09	.04
183 Jerry Grote	.12	.09	.04
184 Ray Fosse	.12	.09	.04
185 Don Mincher	.12	.09	.04
186 Rick Joseph	.12	.09	.04
187 Mike Hedlund	.12	.09	.04
188 Manny Sanguillen	.15	.11	.05
189 Yankees Rookies Munson	7.50	5.75	2.50
190 Joe Torre	.30	.25	.10
191 Vicente Romo	.12	.09	.04
192 Jim Qualls	.12	.09	.04
193 Mike Wegener	.12	.09	.04
194 Chuck Manuel	.12	.09	.04
195 N.L. Playoff #1	.25	.20	.08
196 N.L. Playoff #2	.25	.20	.08
197 N.L. Playoff #3	.25	.20	.08
198 Mets Celebrate	.25	.20	.08
199 A.L. Playoff #1	.25	.20	.08
200 A.L. Playoff #2	.25	.20	.08
201 A.L. Playoff #3	.25	.20	.08
202 Orioles Celebrate	.25	.20	.08
203 Rudy May	.15	.11	.05
204 Len Gabrielson	.12	.09	.04
205 Bert Campaneris	.15	.11	.05
206 Clete Boyer	.12	.09	.04
207 Tigers Rookies	.12	.09	.04
208 Fred Gladding	.12	.09	.04
209 Ken Suarez	.12	.09	.04
210 Juan Marichal	.80	.60	.25
211 Ted Williams	2.00	1.50	.60
212 Al Santorini	.12	.09	.04
213 Andy Etchebarren	.12	.09	.04
214 Ken Boswell	.12	.09	.04

	MINT	VG-E	F-G
215 Reggie Smith	.50	.40	.18
216 C. Hartenstein	.12	.09	.04
217 Ron Hansen	.12	.09	.04
218 Ron Stone	.12	.09	.04
219 Jerry Kenney	.12	.09	.04
220 Steve Carlton	1.25	.90	.40
221 Ron Brand	.12	.09	.04
222 Jim Rooker	.12	.09	.04
223 Nate Oliver	.12	.09	.04
224 Steve Barber	.12	.09	.04
225 Lee May	.12	.09	.04
226 Ron Perranoski	.12	.09	.04
227 Astros Rookies	.30	.25	.10
228 Aurelio Rodriguez	.12	.09	.04
229 Rich Robertson	.12	.09	.04
230 Brooks Robinson	2.50	1.80	.80
231 Luis Tiant	.40	.30	.13
232 Bob Didier	.12	.09	.04
233 Lew Krausse	.12	.09	.04
234 Tommy Dean	.12	.09	.04
235 Mike Epstein	.12	.09	.04
236 Bob Veale	.12	.09	.04
237 Russ Gibson	.12	.09	.04
238 Jose Laboy	.12	.09	.04
239 Ken Berry	.12	.09	.04
240 Fergie Jenkins	.35	.27	.12
241 Royals Rookies	.12	.09	.04
242 Walter Alston	.15	.11	.05
243 Joe Sparma	.12	.09	.04
244 3rd Checklist	.12	.09	.04
245 Leo Cardenas	.12	.09	.04
246 Jim McAndrew	.12	.09	.04
247 Lou Klimchock	.12	.09	.04
248 Jesus Alou	.12	.09	.04
249 Bob Locker	.12	.09	.04
250 Willie McCovey	2.50	1.80	.80
251 Dick Schofield	.12	.09	.04
252 Lowell Palmer	.12	.09	.04
253 Ron Woods	.12	.09	.04
254 Camilo Pascual	.15	.11	.05
255 Jim Spencer	.12	.09	.04
256 Vic Davalillo	.12	.09	.04
257 Dennis Higgins	.12	.09	.04
258 Paul Popovich	.12	.09	.04
259 Tommie Reynolds	.12	.09	.04
260 Claude Osteen	.12	.09	.04
261 Curt Motton	.12	.09	.04
262 Padres Rookies	.12	.09	.04
263 Duane Josephson	.12	.09	.04
264 Rich Hebner	.15	.11	.05
265 Randy Hundley	.12	.09	.04
266 Wally Bunker	.12	.09	.04
267 Twins Rookies	.12	.09	.04
268 Claude Raymond	.12	.09	.04
269 Cesar Gutierrez	.12	.09	.04
270 Chris Short	.12	.09	.04
271 Greg Goossen	.12	.09	.04
272 Hector Torres	.12	.09	.04
273 Ralph Houk	.20	.15	.06
274 Gerry Arrigo	.12	.09	.04
275 Duke Sims	.12	.09	.04
276 Ron Hunt	.12	.09	.04
277 Paul Doyle	.12	.09	.04
278 Tommie Aaron	.15	.11	.05
279 Bill Lee	.25	.20	.09
280 Donn Clendenon	.12	.09	.04
281 Casey Cox	.12	.09	.04
282 Steve Huntz	.12	.09	.04
283 Angel Bravo	.12	.09	.04
284 Jack Baldschun	.12	.09	.04
285 Paul Blair	.15	.11	.05
286 Dodgers Rookies	.50	.40	.18
287 Fred Talbot	.12	.09	.04
288 Larry Hisle	.25	.20	.09
289 Gene Brabender	.12	.09	.04
290 Rod Carew	3.50	2.50	1.20
291 Leo Durocher	.30	.25	.10
292 Eddie Leon	.12	.09	.04
293 Bob Bailey	.12	.09	.04
294 Jose Azcue	.12	.09	.04
295 Cecil Upshaw	.12	.09	.04
296 Woody Woodward	.12	.09	.04
297 Curt Blefary	.12	.09	.04
298 Ken Henderson	.12	.09	.04
299 Buddy Bradford	.12	.09	.04
300 Tom Seaver	4.50	3.50	1.60
301 Chico Salmon	.12	.09	.04
302 Jeff James	.12	.09	.04
303 Brant Alyea	.12	.09	.04
304 Bill Russell	.25	.20	.08
305 World Series #1	.25	.20	.08
306 World Series #2	.25	.20	.08
307 World Series #3	.25	.20	.08

		MINT	VG-E	F-G
308	World Series #4	.25	.20	.08
309	World Series #5	.25	.20	.08
310	World Series Celeb.	.25	.20	.08
311	Dick Green	.12	.09	.04
312	Mike Torrez	.15	.11	.05
313	Mayo Smith	.12	.09	.04
314	Bill McCool	.12	.09	.04
315	Luis Aparicio	.50	.40	.18
316	Skip Guinn	.12	.09	.04
317	Red Sox Rookies	.12	.09	.04
318	Willie Smith	.12	.09	.04
319	Clay Dalrymple	.12	.09	.04
320	Jim Maloney	.15	.11	.05
321	Lou Piniella	.20	.15	.06
322	Luke Walker	.12	.09	.04
323	Wayne Comer	.12	.09	.04
324	Tony Taylor	.12	.09	.04
325	Dave Boswell	.12	.09	.04
326	Bill Voss	.12	.09	.04
327	Hal King	.12	.09	.04
328	Ron Law	.12	.09	.04
329	Chris Cannizzaro	.12	.09	.04
330	Lou Brock	2.25	1.65	.75
331	Chuck Dobson	.12	.09	.04
332	Bobby Wine	.12	.09	.04
333	Bobby Murcer	.30	.25	.10
334	Phil Regan	.12	.09	.04
335	Bill Freehan	.15	.11	.05
336	Del Unser	.12	.09	.04
337	Mike McCormick	.12	.09	.04
338	Paul Schaal	.12	.09	.04
339	Johnny Edwards	.12	.09	.04
340	Tony Conigliaro	.15	.11	.05
341	Bill Sudakis	.12	.09	.04
342	Wilbur Wood	.15	.11	.05
343	4th Checklist	.12	.09	.04
344	Marcelino Lopez	.12	.09	.04
345	Al Ferrara	.12	.09	.04
346	Red Schoendienst	.20	.15	.06
347	Russ Snyder	.12	.09	.04
348	Mets Rookies	.12	.09	.04
349	Steve Hamilton	.12	.09	.04
350	Roberto Clemente	4.00	3.00	1.40
351	Tom Murphy	.12	.09	.04
352	Bob Barton	.12	.09	.04
353	Bill Zepp	.12	.09	.04
354	Amos Otis	.25	.20	.08
355	Doug Rader	.12	.09	.04
356	Fred Lasher	.12	.09	.04
357	Bob Burda	.12	.09	.04
358	Pedro Borbon	.12	.09	.04
359	Phil Roof	.12	.09	.04
360	Curt Flood	.20	.15	.06
361	Ray Jarvis	.12	.09	.04
362	Joe Hague	.12	.09	.04
363	Tom Shopay	.12	.09	.04
364	Dan McGinn	.12	.09	.04
365	Zoilo Versalles	.12	.09	.04
366	Barry Moore	.12	.09	.04
367	Mike Lum	.12	.09	.04
368	Ed Herrmann	.12	.09	.04
369	Alan Foster	.12	.09	.04
370	Tommy Harper	.12	.09	.04
371	Rod Gaspar	.12	.09	.04
372	Dave Giusti	.12	.09	.04
373	Roy White	.15	.11	.05
374	Tommie Sisk	.12	.09	.04
375	Johnny Callison	.12	.09	.04
376	Lefty Phillips	.12	.09	.04
377	Bill Butler	.12	.09	.04
378	Jim Davenport	.12	.09	.04
379	Tom Tischinski	.12	.09	.04
380	Tony Perez	.40	.30	.13
381	Oakland Rookies	.12	.09	.04
382	Jack DiLauro	.12	.09	.04
383	Mickey Stanley	.15	.11	.05
384	Gary Neibauer	.12	.09	.04
385	George Scott	.20	.15	.05
386	Bill Dillman	.12	.09	.04
387	Orioles Team	.30	.25	.10
388	Byron Browne	.12	.09	.04
389	Jim Shellenback	.12	.09	.04
390	Willie Davis	.15	.11	.05
391	Larry Brown	.12	.09	.04
392	Walt Hriniak	.12	.09	.04
393	John Gelnar	.12	.09	.04
394	Gil Hodges	1.50	1.10	.50
395	Walt Williams	.12	.09	.04
396	Steve Blass	.15	.11	.05
397	Roger Repoz	.12	.09	.04
398	Bill Stoneman	.12	.09	.04
399	Yankees Team	.30	.25	.10

		MINT	VG-E	F-G
400	Denny McLain	.40	.30	.13
401	Giants Rookies	.12	.09	.04
402	Ellie Rodriquez	.12	.09	.04
403	Jim Bunning	.30	.25	.10
404	Rich Reese	.12	.09	.04
405	Bill Hands	.12	.09	.04
406	Mike Andrews	.12	.09	.04
407	Bob Watson	.20	.15	.06
408	Paul Lindblad	.12	.09	.04
409	Bob Tolan	.12	.09	.04
410	Boog Powell	.60	.45	.20
411	Dodgers Team	.30	.25	.10
412	Larry Burchart	.12	.09	.04
413	Sonny Jackson	.12	.09	.04
414	Paul Edmondson	.15	.11	.05
415	Julian Javier	.12	.09	.04
416	Joe Verbanic	.12	.09	.04
417	John Bateman	.12	.09	.04
418	John Donaldson	.12	.09	.04
419	Ron Taylor	.12	.09	.04
420	Ken McMullen	.12	.09	.04
421	Pat Dobson	.12	.09	.04
422	Royals Team	.25	.20	.08
423	Jerry May	.12	.09	.04
424	Mike Kilkenny	.12	.09	.04
425	Bobby Bonds	.35	.27	.12
426	Bill Rigney	.12	.09	.04
427	Fred Norman	.12	.09	.04
428	Don Buford	.12	.09	.04
429	Cubs Rookies	.12	.09	.04
430	Andy Messersmith	.20	.15	.06
431	Ron Swoboda	.12	.09	.04
432	5th Checklist	.12	.09	.04
433	Ron Bryant	.12	.09	.04
434	Felipe Alou	.15	.11	.05
435	Nelson Briles	.12	.09	.04
436	Phillies Team	.25	.20	.08
437	Danny Cater	.12	.09	.04
438	Pat Jarvis	.12	.09	.04
439	Lee Maye	.12	.09	.04
440	Bill Mazeroski	.20	.15	.06
441	John O'Donoghue	.12	.09	.04
442	Gene Mauch	.20	.15	.06
443	Al Jackson	.12	.09	.04
444	White Sox Rookies	.12	.09	.04
445	Vada Pinson	.35	.27	.12
446	Billy Grabarkewitz	.12	.09	.04
447	Lee Stange	.12	.09	.04
448	Astros Team	.25	.20	.08
449	Jim Palmer	1.75	1.25	.55
450	Willie McCovey, AS	1.50	1.10	.50
451	Boog Powell, AS	.25	.20	.08
452	Felix Millan, AS	.15	.11	.05
453	Rod Carew, AS	2.00	1.50	.60
454	Ron Santo, AS	.20	.15	.06
455	B. Robinson, AS	1.50	1.10	.50
456	D. Kessinger, AS	.15	.11	.05
457	R. Petrocelli, AS	.15	.11	.05
458	Pete Rose, AS	2.00	1.50	.60
459	Reggie Jackson, AS	1.50	1.10	.50
460	Matty Alou, AS	.15	.11	.04
461	C. Yastrzemski, AS	2.00	1.50	.60
462	Hank Aaron, AS	2.00	1.50	.60
463	Frank Robinson, AS	1.25	.90	.40
464	Johnny Bench, AS	2.00	1.50	.60
465	Bill Freehan, AS	.15	.11	.05
466	Juan Marichal, AS	.60	.45	.20
467	Denny McLain, AS	.25	.20	.08
468	Jerry Koosman, AS	.20	.15	.06
469	Sam McDowell, AS	.15	.11	.05
470	Willie Stargell	2.00	1.50	.60
471	Chris Zachary	.12	.09	.04
472	Braves Team	.25	.20	.08
473	Don Bryant	.12	.09	.04
474	Dick Kelley	.12	.09	.04
475	Dick McAuliffe	.12	.09	.04
476	Don Shaw	.12	.09	.04
477	Orioles Rookies	.12	.09	.04
478	Bob Heise	.12	.09	.04
479	Dick Woodson	.12	.09	.04
480	Glen Beckert	.12	.09	.04
481	Jose Tartabull	.12	.09	.04
482	Tom Hilgendorf	.12	.09	.04
483	Gail Hopkins	.12	.09	.04
484	Gary Nolan	.12	.09	.04
485	Jay Johnstone	.12	.09	.04
486	Terry Harmon	.12	.09	.04
487	Cisco Carlos	.12	.09	.04
488	J. C. Martin	.12	.09	.04
489	Eddie Kasko	.12	.09	.04
490	Bill Singer	.12	.09	.04
491	Graig Nettles	.50	.40	.18
492	Astros Rookies	.12	.09	.04

	MINT	VG-E	F-G			MINT	VG-E	F-G
493 Lindy McDaniel	.15	.11	.05		585 Rusty Staub	.40	.30	.13
494 Larry Stahl	.12	.09	.04		586 Rickey Clark	.18	.14	.05
495 Dave Morehead	.12	.09	.04		587 Jose Arcia	.18	.14	.05
496 Steve Whitaker	.12	.09	.04		588 7th Checklist	.18	.14	.05
497 Eddie Watt	.12	.09	.04		589 Joe Keough	.18	.14	.05
498 Al Weis	.12	.09	.04		590 Mike Cuellar	.18	.14	.05
499 Skip Lockwood	.12	.09	.04		591 Mike Ryan	.18	.14	.05
500 Hank Aaron	6.50	5.00	2.25		592 Daryl Patterson	.18	.14	.05
501 White Sox Team	.25	.20	.08		593 Cubs Team	.30	.25	.10
502 Rollie Fingers	.25	.20	.08		594 Jake Gibbs	.18	.14	.05
503 Dal Maxvill	.12	.09	.04		595 Maury Wills	1.00	.70	.30
504 Don Pavletich	.12	.09	.04		596 Mike Hershberger	.18	.14	.05
505 Ken Holtzman	.15	.11	.05		597 Sonny Siebert	.18	.14	.05
506 Ed Stroud	.12	.09	.04		598 Joe Pepitone	.25	.20	.08
507 Pat Corrales	.12	.09	.04		599 Senators Rookies	.18	.14	.05
508 Joe Niekro	.15	.11	.05		600 Willie Mays	7.50	5.75	2.50
509 Expos Team	.25	.20	.08		601 Pete Richert	.18	.14	.05
510 Tony Oliva	.60	.45	.20		602 Ted Savage	.18	.14	.05
511 Joe Hoerner	.12	.09	.04		603 Ray Oyler	.18	.14	.05
512 Billy Harris	.12	.09	.04		604 Clarence Gaston	.18	.14	.05
513 Preston Gomez	.12	.09	.04		605 Rick Wise	.25	.20	.08
514 Steve Hovley	.12	.09	.04		606 Chico Ruiz	.18	.14	.05
515 Don Wilson	.12	.09	.04		607 Gary Waslewski	.18	.14	.05
516 Yankees Rookies	.12	.09	.04		608 Pirates Team	.30	.25	.10
517 Joe Gibbon	.12	.09	.04		609 Buck Martinez	.18	.14	.05
518 Bill Melton	.12	.09	.04		610 Jerry Koosman	.50	.40	.18
519 Don McMahon	.12	.09	.04		611 Norm Cash	.50	.40	.18
520 Willie Horton	.15	.11	.05		612 Jim Hickman	.18	.14	.05
521 Cal Koonce	.12	.09	.04		613 Dave Baldwin	.18	.14	.05
522 Angels Team	.25	.20	.08		614 Mike Shannon	.18	.14	.05
523 Jose Pena	.12	.09	.04		615 Mark Belanger	.25	.20	.08
524 Alvin Dark	.15	.11	.05		616 Jim Merritt	.18	.14	.05
525 Jerry Adair	.12	.09	.04		617 Jim French	.18	.14	.05
526 Ron Herbel	.12	.09	.04		618 Billy Wynne	.18	.14	.05
527 Don Bosch	.12	.09	.04		619 Norm Miller	.18	.14	.05
528 Elrod Hendricks	.12	.09	.04		620 Jim Perry	.50	.40	.18
529 Bob Aspromonte	.12	.09	.04		621 Braves Rookies	.18	.14	.05
530 Bob Gibson	2.00	1.50	.60		622 Don Sutton	1.00	.70	.30
531 Ron Clark	.12	.09	.04		623 Horace Clarke	.18	.14	.05
532 Danny Murtaugh	.12	.09	.04		624 Clyde King	.18	.14	.05
533 Buzz Stephen	.12	.09	.04		625 Dean Chance	.18	.14	.05
534 Twins Team	.25	.20	.08		626 Dave Ricketts	.18	.14	.05
535 Andy Kosco	.12	.09	.04		627 Gary Wagner	.18	.14	.05
536 Mike Kekich	.12	.09	.04		628 Wayne Garrett	.18	.14	.05
537 Joe Morgan	1.75	1.25	.55		629 Merv Rettenmund	.18	.14	.05
538 Bob Humphreys	.12	.09	.04		630 Ernie Banks	4.00	3.00	1.40
539 Phillies Rookies	1.25	.90	.40		631 Athletics Team	.30	.25	.10
540 Gary Peters	.12	.09	.04		632 Gary Sutherland	.18	.14	.05
541 Bill Heath	.12	.09	.04		633 Roger Nelson	.18	.14	.05
542 6th Checklist	.12	.09	.04		634 Bud Harrelson	.18	.14	.05
543 Clyde Wright	.12	.09	.04		635 Bob Allison	.18	.14	.05
544 Reds Team	.30	.25	.10		636 Jim Stewart	.18	.14	.05
545 Ken Harrelson	.15	.11	.05		637 Indians Team	.60	.45	.20
546 Ron Reed	.12	.09	.04		638 Frank Bertaina	.45	.32	.13
547 Rick Monday	.15	.11	.05		639 Dave Campbell	.45	.32	.13
548 Howie Reed	.12	.09	.04		640 Al Kaline	7.50	5.75	2.50
549 Cardinals Team	.25	.20	.08		641 Al McBean	.45	.32	.13
550 Frank Howard	.50	.40	.18		642 Angels Rookies	.45	.32	.13
551 Dock Ellis	.12	.09	.04		643 Jose Pagan	.45	.32	.13
552 Royals Rookies	.12	.09	.04		644 Gerry Nyman	.45	.32	.13
553 Jim LeFebvre	.18	.14	.05		645 Don Money	.60	.45	.20
554 Tom Timmermann	.18	.14	.05		646 Jim Britton	.45	.32	.13
555 Orlando Cepeda	1.00	.70	.30		647 Tom Matchick	.45	.32	.13
556 Dave Bristol	.18	.14	.05		648 Larry Haney	.45	.32	.13
557 Ed Kranepool	.18	.14	.05		649 Jimmie Hall	.45	.32	.13
558 Vern Fuller	.18	.14	.05		650 Sam McDowell	.60	.45	.20
559 Tommy Davis	.25	.20	.08		651 Jim Gosger	.45	.32	.13
560 Gaylord Perry	1.50	1.10	.50		652 Rich Rollins	.45	.32	.13
561 Tom McCraw	.18	.14	.05		653 Moe Drabowsky	.45	.32	.13
562 Ted Abernathy	.18	.14	.05		654 N. L. Rookies	.60	.45	.20
563 Red Sox	.30	.25	.10		655 John Roseboro	.45	.32	.13
564 Johnny Briggs	.18	.14	.05		656 Jim Hardin	.45	.32	.13
565 Jim Hunter	1.75	1.25	.55		657 Padres Team	.60	.45	.20
566 Gene Alley	.18	.14	.05		658 Ken Tatum	.45	.32	.13
567 Bob Oliver	.18	.14	.05		659 Pete Ward	.45	.32	.13
568 Stan Bahnsen	.18	.14	.05		660 *Johnny Bench*	32.00	24.00	11.00
569 Cookie Rojas	.18	.14	.05		661 Jerry Robertson	.45	.32	.13
570 Jim Fregosi	.25	.20	.08		662 Frank Lucchesi	.45	.32	.13
571 Jim Brewer	.18	.14	.05		663 Tito Francona	.45	.32	.13
572 Frank Quilici	.18	.14	.05		664 Bob Robertson	.45	.32	.13
573 Padres Rookies	.18	.14	.05		665 Jim Lonborg	.60	.45	.20
574 Bobby Bolin	.18	.14	.05		666 Adolpho Phillips	.45	.32	.13
575 Cleon Jones	.18	.14	.05		667 Bob Meyer	.45	.32	.13
576 Milt Pappas	.25	.20	.08		668 Bob Tillman	.45	.32	.13
577 Bernie Allen	.18	.14	.05		669 White Sox Rookies	.45	.32	.13
578 Tom Griffin	.18	.14	.05		670 Ron Santo	1.00	.70	.30
579 Tigers Team	.35	.27	.12		671 Jim Campanis	.45	.32	.13
580 Pete Rose	6.50	5.00	2.25		672 Leon McFadden	.45	.32	.13
581 Tom Satriano	.18	.14	.05		673 Ted Uhlaender	.45	.32	.13
582 Mike Paul	.18	.14	.05		674 Dave Leonhard	.45	.32	.13
583 Hal Lanier	.18	.14	.05		675 Jose Cardenal	.45	.32	.13
584 Al Downing	.18	.14	.05		676 Senators Team	.65	.50	.20
					677 Woodie Fryman	.45	.32	.13

	MINT	VG-E	F-G
678 Dave Duncan	.45	.32	.13
679 Ray Sadecki	.45	.32	.13
680 Rico Petrocelli	.60	.45	.20
681 Bob Garibaldi	.45	.32	.13
682 Dalton Jones	.45	.32	.13
683 Reds Rookies	.45	.32	.13
684 Jack Fisher	.45	.32	.13
685 Tom Haller	.45	.32	.13
686 Jackie Hernandez	.45	.32	.13
687 Bob Priddy	.45	.32	.13
688 Ted Kubiak	.45	.32	.13
689 Frank Tepedino	.45	.32	.13
690 Ron Fairly	.60	.45	.20
691 Joe Grzenda	.45	.32	.13
692 Duffy Dyer	.45	.32	.13
693 Bob Johnson	.45	.32	.13
694 Gary Ross	.45	.32	.13
695 Bobby Knoop	.45	.32	.13
696 Giants Team	.60	.45	.20
697 Jim Hannan	.45	.32	.13
698 Tom Tresh	.60	.45	.20

	MINT	VG-E	F-G
699 Hank Aguirre	.45	.32	.13
700 Frank Robinson	7.50	5.75	2.50
701 Jack Billingham	.45	.32	.13
702 A. L. Rookies	.45	.32	.13
703 Lou Marone	.45	.32	.13
704 Frank Baker	.45	.32	.13
705 Tony Cloninger	.45	.32	.13
706 John McNamara	.45	.32	.13
707 Kevin Collins	.45	.32	.13
708 Jose Santiago	.45	.32	.13
709 Mike Fiore	.45	.32	.13
710 Felix Millan	.45	.32	.13
711 Ed Brinkman	.45	.32	.13
712 Nolan Ryan	7.50	5.75	2.50
713 Pilots Team	1.00	.70	.30
714 Al Spangler	.45	.32	.13
715 Mickey Lolich	1.50	1.10	.50
716 Cardinals Rookies	.45	.32	.13
717 Tom Phoebus	.45	.32	.13
718 Ed Spiezio	.45	.32	.13
719 Jim Roland	.45	.32	.13
720 Rick Reichardt	.45	.32	.13

Watch the hobby papers and your local bookstores for the release later this year of the Sport Americana Baseball Memorabilia Price Guide. This book will contain prices and descriptions of baseball memorabilia other than the popular baseball card issues — yearbooks, baseball coins, programs, press pins, uniforms, statues, postcards, etc.

1970 TOPPS SUPER (42)   3 1/8" X 5 1/4"

The 1970 Topps Super set is separate Topps issue printed on heavy stock. The yellow backs have write-ups identical to the 1970 Topps regular issue. Card nos. 36—37 are somewhat more difficult to obtain and no. 38' Powell is by far the scarcest card in the set.

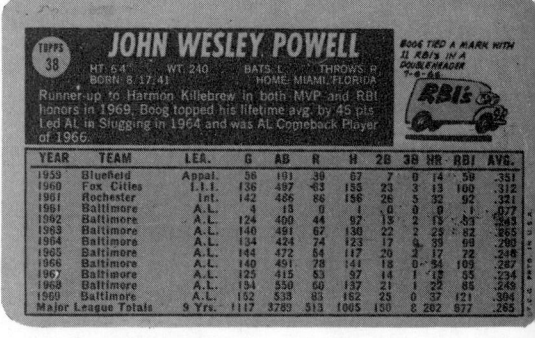

	MINT	VG-E	F-G
COMPLETE SET	60.00	45.00	18.00
COMMON PLAYER	.40	.30	.12
1 Claude Osteen	.40	.30	.12
2 Sal Bando	.50	.40	.18
3 Luis Aparicio	.60	.45	.20
4 Harmon Killebrew	.75	.55	.25
5 Tom Seaver	1.50	1.10	.50
6 Larry Dierker	.40	.30	.12
7 Bill Freehan	.40	.30	.12
8 Johnny Bench	1.50	1.10	.50
9 Tommy Harper	.40	.30	.12
10 Sam McDowell	.40	.30	.12
11 Lou Brock	1.50	1.10	.50
12 Bob Clemente	2.00	1.50	.60

	MINT	VG-E	F-G
13 Willie McCovey	1.00	.70	.30
14 Rico Petrocelli	.40	.30	.12
15 Phil Niekro	.50	.40	.18
16 Frank Howard	.60	.45	.20
17 Denny McLain	.60	.45	.20
18 Willie Mays	3.00	2.25	1.00
19 Willie Stargell	1.00	.70	.30
20 Joel Horlen	.40	.30	.12
21 Ron Santo	.50	.40	.18
22 Dick Bosman	.40	.30	.12
23 Tim McCarver	.40	.30	.12
24 Hank Aaron	3.00	2.25	1.00
25 A. Messersmith	.50	.40	.18
26 Tony Oliva	.60	.45	.20
27 Mel Stottlemyre	.40	.30	.12

	MINT	VG-E	F-G
28 Reggie Jackson	1.50	1.10	.50
29 Carl Yastrzemski	2.00	1.50	.60
30 Jim Fregosi	.30	.25	.10
31 Vada Pinson	.50	.40	.18
32 Lou Piniella	.40	.30	.12
33 Bob Gibson	.75	.55	.25
34 Pete Rose	2.00	1.50	.60
35 Jim Wynn	.40	.30	.12

	MINT	VG-E	F-G
36 Ollie Brown	2.00	1.50	.60
37 Frank Robinson	7.00	5.25	2.50
38 *Boog Powell*	35.00	26.00	12.00
39 Willie Davis	.40	.30	.12
40 Billy Williams	.60	.45	.20
41 Rusty Staub	.50	.40	.18
42 Tommie Agee	.40	.30	.12

1971 TOPPS (752)

2 1/2" X 3 1/2"

The 1971 Topps set includes high numbers 644-752 which are somewhat more difficult to obtain. The next to last series cards (524-643) are also, but to a lesser extent, more difficult to obtain. These cards chip on the black border quite easily and are becoming increasingly difficult to obtain in mint condition.

	MINT	VG-E	F-G
COMPLETE SET	190.00	140.00	60.00
COMMON PLAYER (1-523)	.12	.08	.04
COMMON PLAYER (524-643)	.18	.13	.05
COMMON PLAYER (644-752)	.45	.30	.13

	MINT	VG-E	F-G
1 World Champions	.50	.30	.13
2 Dock Ellis	.12	.08	.04
3 Dick McAuliffe	.12	.08	.04
4 Vic Davalillo	.12	.08	.04
5 Thurman Munson	3.50	2.50	1.20
6 Ed Spiezio	.12	.08	.04
7 Jim Holt	.12	.08	.04
8 Mike McQueen	.12	.08	.04
9 George Scott	.15	.11	.05
10 Claude Osteen	.12	.08	.04
11 Elliott Maddox	.12	.08	.04
12 Johnny Callison	.12	.08	.04
13 White Sox Rookies	.12	.08	.04
14 Dave Concepcion	.75	.55	.25
15 Andy Messersmith	.15	.11	.05
16 Ken Singleton	1.00	.70	.30
17 Billy Sorrell	.12	.08	.04
18 Norm Miller	.12	.08	.04
19 Skip Pitlock	.12	.08	.04
20 Reggie Jackson	2.50	1.80	.80
21 Dan McGinn	.12	.08	.04
22 Phil Roof	.12	.08	.04
23 Oscar Gamble	.15	.11	.05
24 Rich Hand	.12	.08	.04
25 Clarence Gaston	.12	.08	.04
26 Bert Blyleven	.50	.40	.18
27 Pirates Rookies	.12	.08	.04
28 Ron Klimkowski	.12	.08	.04
29 Don Buford	.12	.08	.04
30 Phil Niekro	.30	.25	.10
31 Eddie Kasko	.12	.08	.04
32 Jerry Davanon	.12	.08	.04
33 Del Unser	.12	.08	.04
34 Sandy Vance	.12	.08	.04
35 Lou Piniella	.20	.15	.06
36 Dean Chance	.12	.08	.04
37 Rich McKinney	.12	.08	.04
38 Jim Colborn	.12	.08	.04
39 Tiger Rookies	.12	.08	.04

	MINT	VG-E	F-G
40 Lee May	.15	.11	.05
41 Rick Austin	.12	.08	.04
42 Boots Day	.12	.08	.04
43 Steve Kealey	.12	.08	.04
44 Johnny Edwards	.12	.08	.04
45 Jim Hunter	1.50	1.10	.50
46 Dave Campbell	.12	.08	.04
47 Johnny Jeter	.12	.08	.04
48 Dave Baldwin	.12	.08	.04
49 Don Money	.15	.11	.05
50 Willie McCovey	2.25	1.65	.75
51 Steve Kline	.12	.08	.04
52 Braves Rookies	.12	.08	.04
53 Paul Blair	.12	.08	.04
54 Checklist 1st Ser.	.12	.08	.04
55 Steve Carlton	1.25	.90	.40
56 Duane Josephson	.12	.08	.04
57 Von Joshua	.12	.08	.04
58 Bill Lee	.15	.11	.05
59 Gene Mauch	.15	.11	.05
60 Dick Bosman	.12	.08	.04
61 A.L. Batting Ldrs.	.25	.20	.08
62 N.L. Batting Ldrs.	.25	.20	.08
63 A.L. R.B.I. Ldrs.	.25	.20	.08
64 N.L. R.B.I. Ldrs.	.25	.20	.08
65 A.L. H.R. Ldrs.	.25	.20	.08
66 N.L. H.R. Ldrs.	.25	.20	.08
67 A.L. ERA Ldrs.	.25	.20	.08
68 N.L. ERA Ldrs.	.25	.20	.08
69 A.L. Pitch. Ldrs.	.25	.20	.08
70 N.L. Pitch. Ldrs.	.25	.20	.08
71 A.L. So Ldrs.	.25	.20	.08
72 N.L. So Ldrs.	.25	.20	.08
73 George Brunet	.12	.08	.04
74 Twins Rookies	.12	.08	.04
75 Gary Nolan	.12	.08	.04
76 Ted Savage	.12	.08	.04
77 Mike Compton	.12	.08	.04
78 Jim Spencer	.12	.08	.04
79 W. Blasingame	.12	.08	.04
80 Bill Melton	.12	.08	.04
81 Felix Millan	.12	.08	.04

	MINT	VG-E	F-G
82 Casey Cox	.12	.08	.04
83 Met Rookies	.12	.08	.04
84 M. Lachemann	.12	.08	.04
85 Bill Grabarkewitz	.12	.08	.04
86 Mike Kilkenny	.12	.08	.04
87 Jack Heidemann	.12	.08	.04
88 Hal King	.12	.08	.04
89 Ken Brett	.12	.08	.04
90 Joe Pepitone	.15	.11	.05
91 Bob Lemon	.75	.55	.25
92 Fred Wenz	.12	.08	.04
93 Senators Rookies	.12	.08	.04
94 Don Hahn	.12	.08	.04
95 Luis Tiant	.40	.30	.13
96 Joe Hague	.12	.08	.04
97 Floyd Wicker	.12	.08	.04
98 Joe Decker	.12	.08	.04
99 Mark Belanger	.15	.11	.05
100 Pete Rose	4.00	3.00	1.40
101 Les Cain	.12	.08	.04
102 Astros Rookies	.12	.08	.04
103 Rich Severson	.12	.08	.04
104 Dan Frisella	.12	.08	.04
105 Tony Conigliaro	.15	.11	.05
106 Tom Dukes	.12	.08	.04
107 Roy Foster	.12	.08	.04
108 J. Cumberland	.12	.08	.04
109 Steve Hovley	.12	.08	.04
110 Bill Mazeroski	.15	.11	.05
111 Yankee Rookies	.12	.08	.04
112 Manny Mota	.15	.11	.05
113 Jerry Crider	.12	.08	.04
114 Billy Conigliaro	.15	.11	.05
115 Donn Clendenon	.12	.08	.04
116 Ken Sanders	.12	.08	.04
117 Ted Simmons	1.50	1.10	.50
118 Cookie Rojas	.12	.08	.04
119 Frank Lucchesi	.12	.08	.04
120 Willie Horton	.15	.11	.05
121 Cubs Rookies	.12	.08	.04
122 Eddie Watt	.12	.08	.04
123 List - 2nd Ser.	.12	.08	.04
124 Don Gullett	.15	.11	.05
125 Ray Fosse	.12	.08	.04
126 Danny Coombs	.12	.08	.04
127 Danny Thompson	.12	.08	.04
128 Frank Johnson	.12	.08	.04
129 A. Monteagudo	.12	.08	.04
130 Denis Menke	.12	.08	.04
131 Curt Blefary	.12	.08	.04
132 Jose Laboy	.12	.08	.04
133 Mickey Lolich	.20	.15	.06
134 Jose Arcia	.12	.08	.04
135 Rick Monday	.15	.11	.05
136 Duffy Dyer	.12	.08	.04
137 Marcelino Lopez	.12	.08	.04
138 Phillies Rookies	.12	.08	.04
139 Paul Casanova	.12	.08	.04
140 Gaylord Perry	1.50	1.10	.50
141 Frank Quilici	.12	.08	.04
142 Mack Jones	.12	.08	.04
143 Steve Blass	.15	.11	.05
144 J. Hernandez	.12	.08	.04
145 Bill Singer	.12	.08	.04
146 Ralph Houk	.15	.11	.05
147 Bob Priddy	.12	.08	.04
148 John Mayberry	.15	.11	.05
149 M. Hershberger	.12	.08	.04
150 Sam McDowell	.15	.11	.05
151 Tommy Davis	.20	.15	.06
152 Angels Rookies	.12	.08	.04
153 Gary Ross	.12	.08	.04
154 Cesar Gutierrez	.12	.08	.04
155 Ken Henderson	.12	.08	.04
156 Bart Johnson	.12	.08	.04
157 Bob Bailey	.12	.08	.04
158 Jerry Reuss	.20	.15	.06
159 Jarvis Tatum	.12	.08	.04
160 Tom Seaver	3.00	2.25	1.00
161 Base. Coin List	.15	.11	.05
162 J. Billingham	.12	.08	.04
163 Buck Martinez	.12	.08	.04
164 Red Rookies	.12	.08	.04
165 Cesar Tovar	.12	.08	.04
166 Joe Hoerner	.12	.08	.04
167 Tom Grieve	.12	.08	.04
168 Bruce Dal Canton	.12	.08	.04
169 Ed Herrmann	.12	.08	.04
170 Mike Cuellar	.12	.08	.04
171 Bobby Wine	.12	.08	.04
172 Duke Sims	.12	.08	.04
173 Gil Garrido	.12	.08	

	MINT	VG-E	F-G
174 Dave LaRoche	.12	.08	.04
175 Jim Hickman	.12	.08	.04
176 Red Sox Rookies	.12	.08	.04
177 Hal McRae	.12	.08	.04
178 Dave Duncan	.12	.08	.04
179 Mike Corkins	.12	.08	.04
180 Al Kaline	2.50	1.80	.80
181 Hal Lanier	.12	.08	.04
182 Al Downing	.12	.08	.04
183 Gil Hodges	1.50	1.10	.50
184 Stan Bahnsen	.12	.08	.04
185 Julian Javier	.12	.08	.04
186 Bob Spence	.12	.08	.04
187 Ted Abernathy	.12	.08	.04
188 Dodgers Rookies	.12	.08	.04
189 Geo. Mitterwald	.12	.08	.04
190 Bob Tolan	.12	.08	.04
191 Mike Andrews	.12	.08	.04
192 Billy Wilson	.12	.08	.04
193 Bob Grich	.20	.15	.06
194 Mike Lum	.12	.08	.04
195 A.L. Playoff #1	.25	.20	.08
196 A.L. Playoff #2	.25	.20	.08
197 A.L. Playoff #3	.25	.20	.08
198 Orioles Celebrate	.25	.20	.08
199 N.L. Playoff #1	.25	.20	.08
200 N.L. Playoff #2	.25	.20	.08
201 N.L. Playoff #3	.25	.20	.08
202 Reds Celebrate	.25	.20	.08
203 Larry Gura	.20	.15	.06
204 Brewers Rookies	.12	.08	.04
205 Gerry Moses	.12	.08	.04
206 Checklist 3rd Ser.	.12	.08	.04
207 Alan Foster	.12	.08	.04
208 Billy Martin	.50	.40	.18
209 Steve Renko	.12	.08	.04
210 Rod Carew	3.50	2.50	1.20
211 Phil Hennigan	.12	.08	.04
212 Rich Hebner	.12	.08	.04
213 Frank Baker	.12	.08	.04
214 Al Ferrara	.12	.08	.04
215 Diego Segui	.12	.08	.04
216 Cards Rookies	.12	.08	.04
217 Ed Stroud	.12	.08	.04
218 Tony Cloninger	.12	.08	.04
219 Elrod Hendricks	.12	.08	.04
220 Ron Santo	.25	.20	.00
221 Dave Morehead	.12	.08	.04
222 Bob Watson	.20	.15	.06
223 Cecil Upshaw	.12	.08	.04
224 Alan Gallagher	.12	.08	.04
225 Gary Peters	.12	.08	.04
226 Bill Russell	.12	.08	.04
227 Floyd Weaver	.12	.08	.04
228 Wayne Garrett	.12	.08	.04
229 Jim Hannan	.12	.08	.04
230 Willie Stargell	2.00	1.50	.60
231 Indians Rookies	.12	.08	.04
232 John Strohmayer	.12	.08	.04
233 Larry Bowa	.60	.45	.20
234 Jim Lyttle	.12	.08	.04
235 Nate Colbert	.12	.08	.04
236 Bob Humphreys	.12	.08	.04
237 Cesar Cedeno	1.25	.90	.40
238 Chuck Dobson	.12	.08	.04
239 Red Schoendienst	.20	.15	.06
240 Clyde Wright	.12	.08	.04
241 Dave Nelson	.12	.08	.04
242 Jim Ray	.12	.08	.04
243 Carlos May	.12	.08	.04
244 Bob Tillman	.12	.08	.04
245 Jim Kaat	.35	.27	.12
246 Tony Taylor	.12	.08	.04
247 Royals Rookies	.12	.08	.04
248 Hoyt Wilhelm	.35	.27	.12
249 Chico Salmon	.12	.08	.04
250 Johnny Bench	3.00	2.25	1.00
251 Frank Reberger	.12	.08	.04
252 Eddie Leon	.12	.08	.04
253 Bill Sudakis	.12	.08	.04
254 Cal Koonce	.12	.08	.04
255 Bob Robertson	.12	.08	.04
256 Tony Gonzalez	.12	.08	.04
257 Nelson Briles	.12	.08	.04
258 Dick Green	.12	.08	.04
259 Dave Marshall	.12	.08	.04
260 Tommy Harper	.12	.08	.04
261 Darold Knowles	.12	.08	.04
262 Padres Rookies	.12	.08	.04
263 John Ellis	.12	.08	.04
264 Joe Morgan	1.50	1.10	.50
265 Jim Northrup	.12	.08	.04
266 Bill Stoneman	.12	.08	.04

	MINT	VG-E	F-G		MINT	VG-E	F-G
267 Rich Morales	.12	.08	.04	359 Ron Reed	.12	.08	.04
268 Phillies Team	.25	.20	.08	360 Jim Fregosi	.20	.15	.06
269 Gail Hopkins	.12	.08	.04	361 Don Sutton	.75	.55	.25
270 Rico Carty	.25	.20	.08	362 Orioles Rookies	.12	.08	.04
271 Bill Zepp	.12	.08	.04	363 Mike Nagy	.12	.08	.04
272 Tommy Helms	.12	.08	.04	364 Tommy Dean	.12	.08	.04
273 Pete Richert	.12	.08	.04	365 Bob Johnson	.12	.08	.04
274 Ron Slocum	.12	.08	.04	366 Ron Stone	.12	.08	.04
275 Vada Pinson	.25	.20	.08	367 Dalton Jones	.12	.08	.04
276 Giants Rookies Foster	3.00	2.25	1.00	368 Bob Veale	.12	.08	.04
277 Gary Waslewski	.12	.08	.04	369 Checklist 4th Ser.	.12	.08	.04
278 Jerry Grote	.12	.08	.04	370 Joe Torre	.75	.55	.25
279 Lefty Phillips	.12	.08	.04	371 Jack Hiatt	.12	.08	.04
280 Fergie Jenkins	.60	.45	.20	372 Lew Krausse	.12	.08	.04
281 Danny Walton	.12	.08	.04	373 Tom McCraw	.12	.08	.04
282 Jose Pagan	.12	.08	.04	374 Clete Boyer	.12	.08	.04
283 Dick Such	.12	.08	.04	375 Steve Hargan	.12	.08	.04
284 Jim Gosger	.12	.08	.04	376 Expos Rookies	.12	.08	.04
285 Sal Bando	.20	.15	.06	377 Steve Hargan	.12	.08	.04
286 Jerry McNertney	.12	.08	.04	378 Tito Fuentes	.12	.08	.04
287 Mike Fiore	.12	.08	.04	379 Wayne Granger	.12	.08	.04
288 Joe Moeller	.12	.08	.04	380 Ted Williams	2.00	1.50	.60
289 White Sox Team	.25	.20	.08	381 Fred Gladding	.12	.08	.04
290 Tony Oliva	.50	.40	.18	382 Jake Gibbs	.12	.08	.04
291 George Culver	.12	.08	.04	383 Rod Gaspar	.12	.08	.04
292 Jay Johnstone	.12	.08	.04	384 Rollie Fingers	.20	.15	.06
293 Pat Corrales	.12	.08	.04	385 Maury Wills	.30	.25	.10
294 Steve Dunning	.12	.08	.04	386 Red Sox Team	.30	.25	.10
295 Bobby Bonds	.50	.40	.18	387 Ron Herbel	.12	.08	.04
296 Tom Timmermann	.12	.08	.04	388 Al Oliver	.50	.40	.18
297 Johnny Briggs	.12	.08	.04	389 Ed Brinkman	.12	.08	.04
298 Jim Nelson	.12	.08	.04	390 Glenn Beckert	.12	.08	.04
299 Ed Kirkpatrick	.12	.08	.04	391 Twins Rookies	.12	.08	.04
300 Brooks Robinson	2.50	1.80	.80	392 Grant Jackson	.12	.08	.04
301 Earl Wilson	.12	.08	.04	393 M. Rettenmund	.12	.08	.04
302 Phil Gagliano	.12	.08	.04	394 Clay Carroll	.12	.08	.04
303 Lindy McDaniel	.12	.08	.04	395 Roy White	.12	.08	.04
304 Ron Brand	.12	.08	.04	396 Dick Schofield	.12	.08	.04
305 Reggie Smith	.50	.40	.18	397 Alvin Dark	.15	.11	.05
306 Jim Nash	.12	.08	.04	398 Howie Reed	.12	.08	.04
307 Don Wert	.12	.08	.04	399 Jim French	.12	.08	.04
308 Cardinals Team	.25	.20	.08	400 Hank Aaron	6.00	4.50	2.00
309 Dick Ellsworth	.12	.08	.04	401 Tom Murphy	.12	.08	.04
310 Tommie Agee	.12	.08	.04	402 Dodgers Team	.30	.25	.10
311 Lee Stange	.12	.08	.04	403 Joe Coleman	.12	.08	.04
312 Harry Walker	.12	.08	.04	404 Astros Rookies	.12	.08	.04
313 Tom Hall	.12	.08	.04	405 Leo Cardenas	.12	.08	.04
314 Jeff Torborg	.12	.08	.04	406 Ray Sadecki	.12	.08	.04
315 Ron Fairly	.15	.11	.05	407 Joe Rudi	.15	.11	.05
316 Fred Scherman	.12	.08	.04	408 Rafael Robles	.12	.08	.04
317 Athletic Rookies	.12	.08	.04	409 Don Pavletich	.12	.08	.04
318 Rudy May	.15	.11	.05	410 Ken Holtzman	.15	.11	.05
319 Ty Cline	.12	.08	.04	412 Jerry Johnson	.12	.08	.04
320 Dave McNally	.15	.11	.05	413 Pat Kelly	.12	.08	.04
321 Tom Matchick	.12	.08	.04	414 Woodie Fryman	.12	.08	.04
322 Jim Beauchamp	.12	.08	.04	415 Mike Hegan	.12	.08	.04
323 Billy Champion	.12	.08	.04	416 Gene Alley	.12	.08	.04
324 Graig Nettles	.30	.25	.10	417 Dick Hall	.12	.08	.04
325 Juan Marichal	.80	.60	.25	418 Adolfo Phillips	.12	.08	.04
326 Richie Scheinblum	.12	.08	.04	419 Ron Hansen	.12	.08	.04
327 World Series #1	.25	.20	.08	420 Jim Merritt	.12	.08	.04
328 World Series #2	.25	.20	.08	421 John Stephenson	.12	.08	.04
329 World Series #3	.25	.20	.08	422 Frank Bertaina	.12	.08	.04
330 World Series #4	.25	.20	.08	423 Tigers Rookies	.12	.08	.04
331 World Series #5	.25	.20	.08	424 R. Rodriguez	.12	.08	.04
332 World Series Celeb.	.25	.20	.08	425 Doug Rader	.12	.08	.04
333 Clay Kirby	.12	.08	.04	426 Chris Cannizzaro	.12	.08	.04
334 Roberto Pena	.12	.08	.04	427 Bernie Allen	.12	.08	.04
335 Jerry Koosman	.25	.20	.08	428 Jim McAndrew	.12	.08	.04
336 Tigers Team	.25	.20	.08	429 Chuck Hinton	.12	.08	.04
337 Jesus Alou	.12	.08	.04	430 Wes Parker	.15	.11	.05
338 Gene Tenace	.15	.11	.05	431 Tom Burgmeier	.12	.08	.04
339 Wayne Simpson	.12	.08	.04	432 Bob Didier	.12	.08	.04
340 Rico Petrocelli	.15	.11	.05	433 Skip Lockwood	.12	.08	.04
341 Steve Garvey	6.50	5.00	2.25	434 Gary Sutherland	.12	.08	.04
342 Frank Tepedino	.12	.08	.04	435 Jose Cardenal	.12	.08	.04
343 Pirates Rookies	.12	.08	.04	436 Wilbur Wood	.15	.11	.05
344 Ellie Rodriguez	.12	.08	.04	437 Danny Murtaugh	.12	.08	.04
345 Joe Horlen	.12	.08	.04	438 Mike McCormick	.12	.08	.04
346 Lum Harris	.12	.08	.04	439 Phillies Rookies	1.75	1.25	.55
347 Ted Uhlaender	.12	.08	.04	440 Bert Campaneris	.15	.11	.05
348 Fred Norman	.12	.08	.04	441 Milt Pappas	.15	.11	.05
349 Rich Reese	.12	.08	.04	442 Angels Team	.25	.20	.08
350 Billy Williams	.50	.40	.18	443 Rich Robertson	.12	.08	.04
351 Jim Shellenback	.12	.08	.04	444 Jimmie Price	.12	.08	.04
352 Denny Doyle	.12	.08	.04	445 Art Shamsky	.12	.08	.04
353 Carl Taylor	.12	.08	.04	446 Bobby Bolin	.12	.08	.04
354 Don McMahon	.12	.08	.04	447 Cesar Geronimo	.12	.08	.04
355 Bud Harrelson	.12	.08	.04	448 Dave Roberts	.12	.08	.04
356 Bob Locker	.12	.08	.04	449 Brant Alyea	.12	.08	.04
357 Reds Team	.25	.20	.08	450 Bob Gibson	2.25	1.65	.75
358 Danny Cater	.12	.08	.04	451 Joe Keough	.12	.08	.04
				452 John Boccabella	.12	.08	.04

	MINT	VG-E	F-G
453 Terry Crowley	.12	.08	.04
454 Mike Paul	.12	.08	.04
455 Don Kessinger	.20	.15	.06
456 Bob Meyer	.12	.08	.04
457 Willie Smith	.12	.08	.04
458 White Sox Rookies	.12	.08	.04
459 Jim LeFebvre	.15	.11	.05
460 Fritz Peterson	.12	.08	.04
461 Jim Hart	.12	.08	.04
462 Senators Team	.25	.20	.08
463 Tom Kelley	.12	.08	.04
464 Aurelio Rodriguez	.12	.08	.04
465 Tim McCarver	.12	.08	.04
466 Ken Berry	.12	.08	.04
467 Al Santorini	.12	.08	.04
468 Frank Fernandez	.12	.08	.04
469 Bob Aspromonte	.12	.08	.04
470 Bob Oliver	.12	.08	.04
471 Tom Griffin	.12	.08	.04
472 Ken Rudolph	.12	.08	.04
473 Gary Wagner	.12	.08	.04
474 Jim Fairey	.12	.08	.04
475 Ron Perranoski	.12	.08	.04
476 Dal Maxvill	.12	.08	.04
477 Earl Weaver	.15	.11	.05
478 Bernie Carbo	.12	.08	.04
479 Dennis Higgins	.12	.08	.04
480 Manny Sanguillen	.15	.11	.05
481 Daryl Patterson	.12	.08	.04
482 Padres Team	.25	.20	.08
483 Gene Michael	.25	.20	.08
484 Don Wilson	.12	.08	.04
485 Ken McMullen	.12	.08	.04
486 Steve Huntz	.12	.08	.04
487 Paul Schaal	.12	.08	.04
488 Jer. Stephenson	.12	.08	.04
489 Luis Alvarado	.12	.08	.04
490 Deron Johnson	.12	.08	.04
491 Jim Hardin	.12	.08	.04
492 Ken Boswell	.12	.08	.04
493 Dave May	.12	.08	.04
494 Braves Rookies	.12	.08	.04
495 Felipe Alou	.15	.11	.05
496 W. Woodward	.12	.08	.04
497 Horacio Pina	.12	.08	.04
498 John Kennedy	.12	.08	.04
499 Checklist 5th Ser.	.12	.08	.04
500 Jim Perry	.20	.15	.06
501 A. Etchebarren	.12	.08	.04
502 Cubs Team	.25	.20	.08
503 Gates Brown	.12	.08	.04
504 Ken Wright	.12	.08	.04
505 Ollie Brown	.12	.08	.04
506 Bobby Knoop	.12	.08	.04
507 George Stone	.12	.08	.04
508 Roger Repoz	.12	.08	.04
509 Jim Grant	.12	.08	.04
510 Ken Harrelson	.15	.11	.05
511 Chris Short	.12	.08	.04
512 Red Sox Rookies	.12	.08	.04
513 Nolan Ryan	2.50	1.80	.80
514 Ron Woods	.12	.08	.04
515 Carl Morton	.12	.08	.04
516 Ted Kubiak	.12	.08	.04
517 Charlie Fox	.12	.08	.04
518 Joe Grzenda	.12	.08	.04
519 Willy Crawford	.12	.08	.04
520 Tommy John	1.25	.90	.40
521 Leron Lee	.12	.08	.04
522 Twins Team	.25	.20	.08
523 John Odom	.12	.08	.04
524 Mickey Stanley	.18	.13	.05
525 Ernie Banks	3.50	2.50	1.20
526 Ray Jarvis	.18	.13	.05
527 Cleon Jones	.18	.13	.05
528 Wally Bunker	.18	.13	.05
529 N.L. Rookie Inf.	.18	.13	.05
530 Carl Yastrzemski	5.00	2.75	1.75
531 Mike Torrez	.25	.20	.08
532 Bill Rigney	.18	.13	.05
533 Mike Ryan	.18	.13	.05
534 Luke Walker	.18	.13	.05
535 Curt Flood	.25	.20	.08
536 Claude Raymond	.18	.13	.05
537 Tom Egan	.18	.13	.05
538 Angel Bravo	.18	.13	.05
539 Larry Brown	.18	.13	.05
540 Larry Dierker	.18	.13	.05
541 Bob Burda	.18	.13	.05
542 Bob Miller	.18	.13	.05
543 Yankees Team	.40	.30	.13
544 Vida Blue	2.00	1.50	.60

	MINT	VG-E	F-G
545 Dick Dietz	.18	.13	.05
546 John Matias	.18	.13	.05
547 Pat Dobson	.18	.13	.05
548 Don Mason	.18	.13	.05
549 Jim Brewer	.18	.13	.05
550 Harmon Killebrew	2.50	1.80	.80
551 Frank Linzy	.18	.13	.05
552 Buddy Bradford	.18	.13	.05
553 Kevin Collins	.18	.13	.05
554 Lowell Palmer	.18	.13	.05
555 Walt Williams	.18	.13	.05
556 Jim McGlothlin	.18	.13	.05
557 Tom Satriano	.18	.13	.05
558 Hector Torres	.18	.13	.05
559 A.L. Rookie Pitcher	.18	.13	.05
560 Rusty Staub	.40	.30	.13
561 Syd O'Brien	.18	.13	.05
562 Dave Giusti	.18	.13	.05
563 Giants Team	.35	.27	.12
564 Al Fitzmorris	.18	.13	.05
565 Jim Wynn	.25	.20	.08
566 Tim Cullen	.18	.13	.05
567 Walt Alston	.25	.20	.08
568 Sal Campisi	.18	.13	.05
569 Ivan Murrel	.18	.13	.05
570 Jim Palmer	2.00	1.50	.60
571 Ted Sizemore	.18	.13	.05
572 Jerry Kenney	.18	.13	.05
573 Ed Kranepool	.25	.20	.08
574 Jim Bunning	.40	.30	.13
575 Bill Freehan	.25	.20	.08
576 Cubs Rookies	.18	.13	.05
577 Jim Lonborg	.25	.20	.08
578 Ron Hunt	.18	.13	.05
579 Marty Pattin	.18	.13	.05
580 Tony Perez	.40	.30	.13
581 Roger Nelson	.18	.13	.05
582 Dave Cash	.18	.13	.05
583 Ron Cook	.18	.13	.05
584 Indians Team	.30	.25	.10
585 Willie Davis	.25	.20	.08
586 Dick Woodson	.18	.13	.05
587 Sonny Jackson	.18	.13	.05
588 Tom Bradley	.18	.13	.05
589 Bob Barton	.18	.13	.05
590 Alex Johnson	.18	.13	.05
591 Jackie Brown	.18	.13	.05
592 Randy Hundley	.18	.13	.05
593 Jack Aker	.18	.13	.05
594 Cards Rookies	.18	.13	.05
595 Dave Johnson	.18	.13	.05
596 Mike Jorgensen	.18	.13	.05
597 Ken Suarez	.18	.13	.05
598 Rick Wise	.25	.20	.08
599 Norm Cash	.30	.25	.10
600 Willie Mays	7.00	5.25	2.50
601 Ken Tatum	.18	.13	.05
602 Marty Martinez	.18	.13	.05
603 Pirates Team	.30	.25	.10
604 John Gelnar	.18	.13	.05
605 Orlando Cepeda	1.00	.70	.30
606 Chuck Taylor	.18	.13	.05
607 Paul Ratliff	.18	.13	.05
608 Mike Wegener	.18	.13	.05
609 Leo Durocher	.40	.30	.13
610 Amos Otis	.40	.30	.13
611 Tom Phoebus	.18	.13	.05
612 Indians Rookies	.18	.13	.05
613 Pedro Borbon	.18	.13	.05
614 Billy Cowan	.18	.13	.05
615 Mel Stottlemyre	.25	.20	.08
616 Larry Hisle	.30	.25	.10
617 Clay Dalrymple	.18	.13	.05
618 Tug McGraw	.30	.25	.10
619 List 6th Ser.	.13	.13	.05
620 Frank Howard	.40	.30	.13
621 Ron Bryant	.18	.13	.05
622 Joe LaHoud	.18	.13	.05
623 Pat Jarvis	.18	.13	.05
624 Athletics Team	.30	.25	.10
625 Lou Brock	3.00	2.25	1.00
626 Freddie Patek	.18	.13	.05
627 Steve Hamilton	.18	.13	.05
628 John Bateman	.18	.13	.05
629 John Hiller	.18	.13	.05
630 Roberto Clemente	5.50	4.25	2.00
631 Eddie Fisher	.18	.13	.05
632 Darrel Chaney	.18	.13	.05
633 A.L. Rookies OF's	.18	.13	.05
634 Phil Regan	.18	.13	.05
635 Bobby Murcer	.40	.30	.13
636 Denny LeMaster	.18	.13	.05
637 Dave Bristol	.18	.13	.05

	MINT	VG-E	F-G		MINT	VG-E	F-G
638 Stan Williams	.18	.13	.05	695 Joe Niekro	.60	.45	.20
639 Tom Haller	.18	.13	.05	696 Jerry Morales	.45	.30	.13
640 Frank Robinson	3.50	2.50	1.20	697 Rickey Clark	.45	.30	.13
641 Mets Team	.50	.40	.18	698 Brewers Team	.60	.45	.20
642 Jim Roland	.18	.13	.05	699 Jim Britton	.45	.30	.13
643 Rick Reichardt	.18	.13	.05	700 Boog Powell	1.00	.70	.30
644 Jim Stewart	.45	.30	.13	701 Bob Garibaldi	.45	.20	.13
645 Jim Maloney	.60	.45	.20	702 Milt Ramirez	.45	.30	.13
646 Bobby Floyd	.45	.30	.13	703 Mike Kekich	.45	.30	.13
647 Juan Pizarro	.45	.30	.13	704 J. C. Martin	.45	.30	.13
648 Mets Rookies	1.25	.90	.40	705 Dick Selma	.45	.30	.13
649 Sparky Lyle	.75	.55	.25	706 Joe Foy	.45	.30	.13
650 Rich Allen	1.25	.90	.40	707 Fred Lasher	.45	.30	.13
651 Jerry Robertson	.45	.30	.13	708 Russ Nagelson	.45	.30	.13
652 Braves Team	.60	.45	.20	709 Rookie Outfielders	2.50	1.80	.80
653 Russ Snyder	.45	.30	.13	710 Sonny Siebert	.45	.30	.13
654 Don Shaw	.45	.30	.13	711 Larry Stahl	.45	.30	.13
655 Mike Epstein	.45	.30	.13	712 Jose Martinez	.45	.30	.13
656 Gerry Nyman	.45	.30	.13	713 Mike Marshall	.60	.45	.20
657 Jose Azcue	.45	.30	.13	714 Dick Williams	.60	.45	.20
658 Paul Lindblad	.45	.30	.13	715 Horace Clarke	.45	.30	.13
659 Byron Browne	.45	.30	.13	716 Dave Leonhard	.45	.30	.13
660 Ray Culp	.45	.30	.13	717 Tommie Aaron	.45	.30	.13
661 Chuck Tanner	.60	.45	.20	718 Billy Wynne	.45	.30	.13
662 Mike Hedlund	.45	.30	.13	719 Jerry May	.45	.30	.13
663 Marv Staehle	.45	.30	.13	720 Matty Alou	.60	.45	.20
664 Rookie Pitchers	.45	.30	.13	721 John Morris	.45	.30	.13
665 Ron Swoboda	.45	.30	.13	722 Astros Team	.60	.45	.20
666 Gene Brabender	.45	.30	.13	723 Vicente Romo	.45	.30	.13
667 Pete Ward	.45	.30	.13	724 Tom Tischinski	.45	.30	.13
668 Gary Neibauer	.45	.30	.13	725 Gary Gentry	.45	.30	.13
669 Ike Brown	.45	.30	.13	726 Paul Popovich	.45	.30	.13
670 Bill Hands	.45	.30	.13	727 Ray Lamb	.45	.30	.13
671 Bill Voss	.45	.30	.13	728 N.L. Rookies OF's	.45	.30	.13
672 Ed Crosby	.45	.30	.13	729 Dick Billings	.45	.30	.13
673 Gerry Janeski	.45	.30	.13	730 Jim Rooker	.45	.30	.13
674 Expos Team	.60	.45	.20	731 Jim Qualls	.45	.30	.13
675 Dave Boswell	.45	.30	.13	732 Bob Reed	.45	.30	.13
676 Tommie Reynolds	.45	.30	.13	733 Lee Maye	.45	.30	.13
677 Jack DiLauro	.45	.30	.13	734 Rob Gardner	.45	.30	.13
678 George Thomas	.45	.30	.13	735 Mike Shannon	.45	.30	.13
679 Don O'Riley	.45	.30	.13	736 Mel Queen	.45	.30	.13
680 Don Mincher	.45	.30	.13	737 Preston Gomez	.45	.30	.13
681 Bill Butler	.45	.30	.13	738 Russ Gibson	.45	.30	.13
682 Terry Harmon	.45	.30	.13	739 Barry Lersch	.45	.30	.13
683 Bill Burbach	.45	.30	.13	740 Luis Aparicio	1.25	.90	.40
684 Curt Motton	.45	.30	.13	741 Skip Guinn	.45	.30	.13
685 Moe Drabowsky	.45	.30	.13	742 Royals Team	.60	.45	.20
686 Chico Ruiz	.45	.30	.13	743 John O'Donoghue	.45	.30	.13
687 Ron Taylor	.45	.30	.13	744 Chuck Manuel	.45	.30	.13
688 Sparky Anderson	.75	.55	.25	745 Sandy Alomar	.45	.30	.13
689 Frank Baker	.45	.30	.13	746 Andy Kosco	.45	.30	.13
690 Bob Moose	.45	.30	.13	747 N.L. Rookie Pitchers	.45	.30	.13
691 Bob Heise	.45	.30	.13	748 John Purdin	.45	.30	.13
692 A.L. Rookie Pitchers	.45	.30	.13	749 Ken Szotkiewicz	.45	.30	.13
693 Jose Pena	.45	.30	.13	750 Denny McLain	1.50	1.10	.50
694 Rick Renick	.45	.30	.13	751 Al Weis	.45	.30	.13
				752 Dick Drago	.45	.30	.13

1960 PIRATE TAG—ONS

The 1971 Topps Greatest Moments set contains 55 numbered cards portraying some of the feats of current players. The set features the player's portrait and an action shot of his accomplishment.

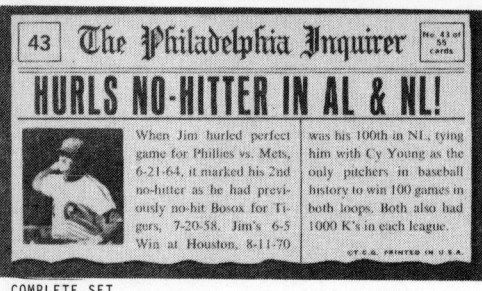

	MINT	VG-E	F-G
COMPLETE SET	300.00	225.00	90.00
COMMON CARD	2.50	1.75	.75
1 Thurman Munson-Named Al Rookie of the Year for 1970.	12.00	8.75	4.00
2 Hoyt Wilhelm-Hurls in 1000th Game.	3.00	2.25	1.00
3 Rico Carty-Leads Majors with .366 Avg. 1970.	2.50	1.75	.75
4 Carl Morton-Named NL Rookie of the Year for 1970.	2.50	1.75	.75
5 Sal Bando-Plays All A's Games, 1st 2 years in Oakland.	2.50	1.75	.75
6 Bert Campaneris-Hits 2 Homers in First Major League Game.	2.50	1.75	.75
7 Jim Kaat-Named to Gold Glove Team 9 Straight Years.	3.00	2.25	1.00
8 Harmon Killebrew-Tops 40 Homers for 8th Time, 1970.	6.00	4.50	2.00
9 Brooks Robinson-Named Outstanding Player of 1970 World Series.	10.00	7.00	3.00
10 Jim Perry-Wins AL Cy Young Award 1970.	2.50	1.75	.75
11 Tony Oliva-Leads AL in Batting His 1st 2 Full Years in Majors.	3.00	2.25	1.00
12 Vada Pinson-Tops 200 Hits His 1st Full Year in Majors.	3.00	2.25	1.00
13 Johnny Bench-Named Major League Player of the Year for 1970.	10.00	7.00	3.00
14 Tony Perez-Hits 15th Inning Homer to win All-Star Game.	3.00	2.25	1.00
15 Pete Rose-Leads Majors in Batting 2nd Consecutive year.	15.00	11.00	5.00
16 Jim Fregosi-Hits for cycle twice.	3.00	2.25	1.00
17 Alex Johnson-Leads AL in battings his 1st year in league.	2.50	1.75	.75
18 Clyde Wright-Hurls no-hitter vs. A's.	2.50	1.75	.75
19 Al Kaline-Becomes youngest player to win AL batting crown.	10.00	7.00	3.00
20 Denny McLain-Becomes 1st AL hurler to win 30 games in 37 years.	3.00	2.25	1.00
21 Jim Northrup-Hits 3 Grand-Slammers in 1 week.	2.50	1.75	.75
22 Bill Freehan-Leads AL catchers in fielding 6 consecutive years.	2.50	1.75	.75
23 Mickey Lolich-Wins 3 games in 1968 world series.	3.00	2.25	1.00
24 Bob Gibson-Has lowest ERA in history for 300 or more innings.	7.00	5.25	2.50
25 Tim McCarver-Becomes 1st catcher to lead majors in triples	2.50	1.75	.75
26 Orlando Cepeda-Voted NL player of the year for 1967.	3.00	2.25	1.00
27 Lou Brock-Tops 50 stolen bases for 6th straight year, 1970	10.00	7.00	3.00
28 Nate Colbert-Sets New Club Mark with 38 Homers, 1970.	2.50	1.75	.75
29 Maury Wills-Sets Modern Mark with 104 Stolen Bases.	4.00	3.00	1.40
30 Wes Parker-Leads Major Leagues With 47 Doubles.	2.50	1.75	.75
31 Jim Wynn-Hits One of Two Astro Grand-Slammers in Same Inning.	2.50	1.75	.75
32 Larry Dierker-Makes Major League Debut on 18th Birthday.	2.50	1.75	.75
33 Bill Melton-Becomes 1st Chisox Batter in History to Hit 30 Homers.	2.50	1.75	.75
34 Joe Morgan-Ties Record with 6 Hits in 6 at Bats.	5.00	3.75	1.75
35 Rusty Staub-Leads Major Leagues with 44 Doubles	3.00	2.25	1.00
36 Ernie Banks-Sets Major League Record with 5 Grand-Slammers.	10.00	7.00	3.00
37 Billy Williams-Plays in 1,117th Consecutive Game	3.00	2.25	1.00
38 Lou Piniella-Wins Al Rookie of the Year Award for 1969.	3.00	2.25	1.00
39 Rico Petrocelli-Sets Al Homer Mark for Shortstops.	2.50	1.75	.75
40 Carl Yastrzemski-Wins Al Triple Crown	10.00	7.00	3.00
41 Willie Mays-Gets 3000th Hit of Career	15.00	11.00	5.00
42 Tommy Harper-Leads Major Leagues with 73 Stolen Bases.	2.50	1.75	.75
43 Jim Bunning-Hurls No-Hitter in Both Al and NL.	3.00	2.25	1.00
44 Fritz Peterson-Wins 20th Game on Last Day of 1970.	2.50	1.75	.75
45 Roy White-Hits Homers Lefty & Righty.	2.50	1.75	.75
46 Bobby Murcer-Hits 4 Consecutive Homers in a Twinbill.	2.50	1.75	.75
47 Reggie Jackson-Gets 10 Runs Batted in in One Game	10.00	7.00	3.00
48 Frank Howard-Sets New Record with 10 Homers in One Week.	4.00	3.00	1.40
49 Dick Bosman-Wins Al in Earned Run.	2.50	1.75	.75
50 Sam McDowell-Hurls Two Consecutive One-Hitters.	2.50	1.75	.75
51 Luis Aparicio - Leads AL in steals 9 consecutive years	3.00	2.25	1.00
52 Willie McCovey-Gets 4 Hits in First Game.	6.00	4.50	2.00
53 Joe Pepitone-Hits 2 Homers in One Inning.	3.00	2.25	1.00
54 Jerry Grote-Registers 20 Putouts in a 9-Inning Game.	2.50	1.75	.75
55 Bud Harrelson-Plays 54 Consecutive Errorless Games at Shortstop.	2.50	1.75	.75

The 1971 Topps Super set is a separate Topps issue printed on heavy stock. Cards have green backs with write-ups identical to the 1971 Topps regular issue.

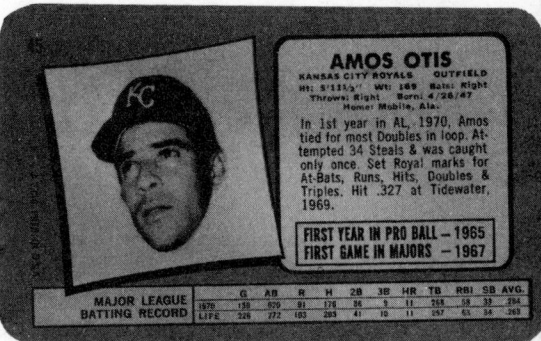

	MINT	VG-E	F-G
COMPLETE SET	38.00	30.00	12.00
COMMON PLAYER	.35	.25	.10
1 Reggie Smith	.50	.40	.18
2 Gaylord Perry	.75	.55	.25
3 Ted Savage	.35	.25	.10
4 Donn Clendenon	.35	.25	.10
5 Boog Powell	.50	.40	.18
6 Tony Perez	.50	.40	.18
7 Dick Bosman	.35	.25	.10
8 Alex Johnson	.35	.25	.10
9 Rusty Staub	.50	.40	.18
10 Mel Stottlemyre	.35	.25	.10
11 Tony Oliva	.60	.45	.20
12 Bill Freehan	.35	.25	.10
13 Fritz Peterson	.35	.25	.10
14 Wes Parker	.35	.25	.10
15 Cesar Cedeno	.50	.40	.18
16 Sam McDowell	.35	.25	.10
17 Frank Howard	.60	.45	.20
18 Dave McNally	.35	.25	.10
19 Rico Petrocelli	.35	.25	.10
20 Pete Rose	2.00	1.50	.60
21 Luke Walker	.35	.25	.10
22 Nate Colbert	.35	.25	.10
23 Luis Aparicio	.60	.45	.20
24 Jim Perry	.35	.25	.10
25 Lou Brock	1.50	1.10	.50
26 Roy White	.35	.25	.10
27 Claude Osteen	.35	.25	.10
28 Carl Morton	.35	.25	.10
29 Rico Carty	.50	.40	.18
30 Larry Dierker	.35	.25	.10

	MINT	VG-E	F-G
31 B. Campaneris	.35	.25	.10
32 Johnny Bench	1.75	1.25	.55
33 Felix Millan	.35	.25	.10
34 Tim McCarver	.35	.25	.10
35 Ron Santo	.50	.40	.18
36 Tommie Agee	.35	.25	.10
37 Bob Clemente	2.00	1.50	.60
38 Reggie Jackson	1.50	1.10	.50
39 Clyde Wright	.35	.25	.10
40 Rich Allen	.50	.40	.18
41 Curt Flood	.35	.25	.10
42 Fergie Jenkins	.50	.40	.18
43 Willie Stargell	1.00	.70	.30
44 Hank Aaron	2.50	1.80	.80
45 Amos Otis	.50	.40	.18
46 Willie McCovey	1.00	.70	.30
47 Bill Melton	.35	.25	.10
48 Bob Gibson	.75	.55	.25
49 Carl Yastremski	2.00	1.50	.60
50 Glenn Beckert	.35	.25	.10
51 Ray Fosse	.35	.25	.10
52 Cito Gaston	.35	.25	.10
53 Tom Seaver	1.75	1.25	.55
54 Al Kaline	1.75	1.25	.55
55 Jim Northrup	.35	.25	.10
56 Willie Mays	2.50	1.80	.80
57 Sal Bando	.50	.40	.18
58 Deron Johnson	.35	.25	.10
59 Brooks Robinson	1.50	1.10	.50
60 Harmon Killebrew	1.00	.70	.30
61 Joe Torre	.50	.40	.18
62 Lou Piniella	.35	.25	.10
63 Tommy Harper	.35	.25	.10

JERSEY SHORE BASEBALL CARDS

123 W. Front Street
Box 684 Dept. PG-3
Red Bank, New Jersey 07701

Phone Numbers
Store: 201-747-7766
Home: 201-544-1635

STORE HOURS:

Tuesday Night . . . . 6 - 9 P.M.
Friday Night . . . . 6 - 9 P.M.
Saturday . . . . 10 A.M. - 4 P.M.

STOP IN AND SEE OUR ENORMOUS INVENTORY OF:

Baseball Cards . . . Sets • Superstars • Singles
Yearbooks • Glossy Photographs • Autographs • Football Cards
Hartland Statues • Non-sports Cards • Hobby Supplies

OR ORDER BY MAIL

"IF WE DON'T HAVE IT . . . WE KNOW WHERE TO GET IT!"

BUY — SELL — TRADE — APPRAISE

"TOP DOLLAR PAID FOR BASEBALL CARDS 1880-1980"

Steve Moore, Proprietor
In the hobby since 1967

1972 TOPPS (787)   2 1/2" X 3 1/2"

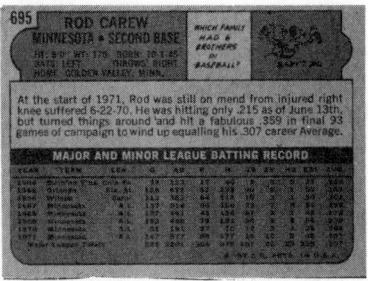

The 1972 Topps set include
high numbers 657-787 whic
are somewhat more difficul
to obtain. The next to las
series cards (526-656) ar
also, but to a lesser exten
more difficult to obtain

	MINT	VG-E	F-G
COMPLETE SET	200.00	150.00	60.00
COMMON PLAYER (1-525)	.11	.08	.03
COMMON PLAYER (526-656)	.16	.12	.04
COMMON PLAYER (657-787)	.40	.30	.12
1 Pirates Team	.50	.30	.12
2 Ray Culp	.11	.08	.03
3 Bob Tolan	.11	.08	.03
4 Checklist-1st Ser.	.11	.08	.03
5 John Bateman	.11	.08	.03
6 Fred Scherman	.11	.08	.03

	MINT	VG-E	F-G
7 Enzo Hernandez	.11	.08	.03
8 Ron Swoboda	.11	.08	.03
9 Stan Williams	.11	.08	.03
10 Amos Otis	.20	.15	.06
11 Bobby Valentine	.11	.08	.03
12 Jose Cardenal	.11	.08	.03
13 Joe Grzenda	.11	.08	.03
14 Phillies Rookies	.11	.08	.03
15 Walt Williams	.11	.08	.03

	MINT	VG-E	F-G
16 Mike Jorgensen	.11	.08	.03
17 Dave Duncan	.11	.08	.03
18 Juan Pizarro	.11	.08	.03
19 Billy Cowan	.11	.08	.03
20 Don Wilson	.11	.08	.03
21 Braves Team	.20	.15	.06
22 Rob Gardner	.11	.08	.03
23 Ted Kubiak	.11	.08	.03
24 Ted Ford	.11	.08	.03
25 Bill Singer	.11	.08	.03
26 Andy Etchebarren	.11	.08	.03
27 Bob Johnson	.11	.08	.03
28 Twins Rookies	.11	.08	.03
29 Bill Bonham	.11	.08	.03
30 Rico Petrocelli	.11	.08	.03
31 Cleon Jones	.11	.08	.03
32 Jones In Action	.11	.08	.03
33 Billy Martin	.40	.30	.13
34 Martin In Action	.25	.20	.08
35 Jerry Johnson	.11	.08	.03
36 Johnson In Action	.11	.08	.03
37 Carl Yastrzemski	3.25	2.40	1.10
38 Yastrzemski In Act	1.50	1.10	.50
39 Bob Barton	.11	.08	.03
40 Barton In Action	.11	.08	.03
41 Tommy Davis	.15	.11	.05
42 Davis In Action	.11	.08	.03
43 Rick Wise	.15	.11	.05
44 Wise In Action	.11	.08	.03
45 Glenn Beckert	.11	.08	.03
46 Beckert In Action	.11	.08	.03
47 John Ellis	.11	.08	.03
48 Ellis In Action	.11	.08	.03
49 Willie Mays	3.75	2.75	1.25
50 Mays In Action	2.00	1.50	.60
51 Harmon Killebrew	1.50	1.10	.50
52 Killebrew In Action	.80	.60	.25
53 Bud Harrelson	.11	.08	.03
54 Harrelson In Action	.11	.08	.03
55 Clyde Wright	.11	.08	.03
56 Rich Chiles	.11	.08	.03
57 Bob Oliver	.11	.08	.03
58 Ernie McAnally	.11	.08	.03
59 Fred Stanley	.11	.08	.03
60 Manny Sanguillen	.11	.08	.03
61 Cubs Rookies	.40	.30	.13
62 Angel Mangual	.11	.08	.03
63 Duke Sims	.11	.08	.03
64 Pete Broberg	.11	.08	.03
65 Cesar Cedeno	.40	.30	.13
66 Ray Corbin	.11	.08	.03
67 Red Schoendienst	.15	.11	.05
68 Jim York	.11	.08	.03
69 Roger Freed	.11	.08	.03
70 Mike Cuellar	.11	.08	.03
71 Angels Team	.20	.15	.06
72 Bruce Kison	.11	.08	.03
73 Steve Huntz	.11	.08	.03
74 Cecil Upshaw	.11	.08	.03
75 Bert Campaneris	.15	.11	.05
76 Don Carrithers	.11	.08	.03
77 Ron Theobald	.11	.08	.03
78 Steve Arlin	.11	.08	.03
79 Red Sox Rookies	2.25	1.65	.75
80 Tony Perez	.30	.25	.10
81 Mike Hedlund	.11	.08	.03
82 Ron Woods	.11	.08	.03
83 Dalton Jones	.11	.08	.03
84 Vince Colbert	.11	.08	.03
85 N.L. Batting Ldrs.	.20	.15	.06
86 A.L. Batting Ldrs.	.20	.15	.06
87 N.L. R.B.I. Ldrs.	.20	.15	.06
88 A.L. R.B.I. Ldrs.	.20	.15	.06
89 N.L. H.R. Ldrs.	.20	.15	.06
90 A.L. H.R. Ldrs.	.20	.15	.06
91 N.L. E.R.A. Ldrs.	.20	.15	.06
92 A.L. E.R.A. Ldrs.	.20	.15	.06
93 N.L. Pitching Ldrs.	.20	.15	.06
94 A.L. Pitching Ldrs.	.20	.15	.06
95 N.L. S.O. Ldrs.	.20	.15	.06
96 A.L. S.O. Ldrs.	.20	.15	.06
97 Tom Kelley	.11	.08	.03
98 Chuck Tanner	.15	.11	.05
99 Ross Grimsley	.11	.08	.03
100 Frank Robinson	2.00	1.50	.60
101 Astros Rookies	2.25	1.65	.75
102 Lloyd Allen	.11	.08	.03
103 Checklist-2nd Ser.	.11	.08	.03
104 Toby Harrah	.15	.11	.05
105 Gary Gentry	.11	.08	.03
106 Brewers Team	.20	.15	.06
107 Jose Cruz	.25	.20	.08

	MINT	VG-E	F-G
108 Gary Waslewski	.11	.08	.03
109 Jerry May	.11	.08	.03
110 Ron Hunt	.11	.08	.03
111 Jim Grant	.11	.08	.03
112 Greg Luzinski	1.00	.70	.30
113 Rogelio Moret	.11	.08	.03
114 Bill Buckner	.25	.20	.08
115 Jim Fregosi	.15	.11	.05
116 Ed Farmer	.11	.08	.03
117 Cleo James	.11	.08	.03
118 Skip Lockwood	.11	.08	.03
119 Marty Perez	.11	.08	.03
120 Bill Freehan	.15	.11	.05
121 Ed Sprague	.11	.08	.03
122 Larry Bittner	.11	.08	.03
123 Ed Acosta	.11	.08	.03
124 Yankees Rookies	.11	.08	.03
125 Dave Cash	.11	.08	.03
126 Bart Johnson	.11	.08	.03
127 Duffy Dyer	.11	.08	.03
128 Eddie Watt	.11	.08	.03
129 Charlie Fox	.11	.08	.03
130 Bob Gibson	1.50	1.10	.50
131 Jim Nettles	.11	.08	.03
132 Joe Morgan	1.00	.70	.30
133 Joe Keough	.11	.08	.03
134 Carl Morton	.11	.08	.03
135 Vada Pinson	.25	.20	.08
136 Darrel Chaney	.11	.08	.03
137 Dick Williams	.15	.11	.05
138 Mike Kekich	.11	.08	.03
139 Tim McCarver	.11	.08	.03
140 Pat Dobson	.11	.08	.03
141 Mets Rookies	.11	.08	.03
142 Chris Chambliss	.50	.40	.18
143 Garry Jestadt	.11	.08	.03
144 Marty Pattin	.11	.08	.03
145 Don Kessinger	.15	.11	.05
146 Steve Kealey	.11	.08	.03
147 Dave Kingman	1.50	1.10	.50
148 Dick Billings	.11	.08	.03
149 Gary Neibauer	.11	.08	.03
150 Norm Cash	.20	.15	.06
151 Jim Brewer	.11	.08	.03
152 Gene Clines	.11	.08	.03
153 Rick Auerbach	.11	.08	.03
154 Ted Simmons	.75	.55	.25
155 Larry Dierker	.11	.08	.03
156 Twins Team	.20	.15	.06
157 Don Gullett	.15	.11	.05
158 Jerry Kenney	.11	.08	.03
159 John Boccabella	.11	.08	.03
160 Andy Messersmith	.15	.11	.05
161 Brock Davis	.11	.08	.03
162 Brewers Rookies	.50	.40	.18
163 Tug McGraw	.20	.15	.06
164 McGraw In Action	.15	.11	.05
165 Chris Speier	.11	.08	.03
166 Speier In Action	.11	.08	.03
167 Deron Johnson	.11	.08	.03
168 Johnson In Action	.11	.08	.03
169 Vida Blue	.80	.60	.25
170 Blue In Action	.40	.30	.13
171 Darrell Evans	.11	.08	.03
172 Evans In Action	.11	.08	.03
173 Clay Kirby	.11	.08	.03
174 Kirby In Action	.11	.08	.03
175 Tom Haller	.11	.08	.03
176 Haller In Action	.11	.08	.03
177 Paul Schaal	.11	.08	.03
178 Schaal In Action	.11	.08	.03
179 Dock Ellis	.11	.08	.03
180 Ellis In Action	.11	.08	.03
181 Ed Kranepool	.11	.08	.03
182 Kranepool In Action	.11	.08	.03
183 Bill Melton	.11	.08	.03
184 Melton In Action	.11	.08	.03
185 Ron Bryant	.11	.08	.03
186 Bryant In Action	.11	.08	.03
187 Gates Brown	.11	.08	.03
188 Frank Lucchesi	.11	.08	.03
189 Gene Tenace	.15	.11	.05
190 Dave Giusti	.11	.08	.03
191 Jeff Burroughs	.40	.30	.13
192 Cubs Team	.20	.15	.06
193 Kurt Bevacqua	.11	.08	.03
194 Fred Norman	.11	.08	.03
195 Orlando Cepeda	.50	.40	.18
196 Mel Queen	.11	.08	.03
197 Johnny Briggs	.11	.08	.03
198 Dodgers Rookies	.11	.08	.03
199 Mike Fiore	.11	.08	.03
200 Lou Brock	2.00	1.50	.60

	MINT	VG-E	F-G
201 Phil Roof	.11	.08	.03
202 Scipio Spinks	.11	.08	.03
203 Ron Blomberg	.11	.08	.03
204 Tommy Helms	.11	.08	.03
205 Dick Drago	.11	.08	.03
206 Dal Maxvill	.11	.08	.03
207 Tom Egan	.11	.08	.03
208 Milt Pappas	.15	.11	.05
209 Joe Rudi	.15	.11	.05
210 Denny McLain	.25	.20	.08
211 Gary Sutherland	.11	.08	.03
212 Grant Jackson	.11	.08	.03
213 Angels Rookies	.11	.08	.03
214 Mike McQueen	.11	.08	.03
215 Alex Johnson	.11	.08	.03
216 Joe Niekro	.15	.11	.05
217 Roger Metzger	.11	.08	.03
218 Eddie Kasko	.11	.08	.03
219 Rennie Stennett	.15	.11	.05
220 Jim Perry	.15	.11	.05
221 N.L. Playoff	.20	.15	.06
222 A.L. Playoff	.20	.15	.06
223 World Series #1	.20	.15	.06
224 World Series #2	.20	.15	.06
225 World Series #3	.20	.15	.06
226 World Series #4	.20	.15	.06
227 World Series #5	.20	.15	.06
228 World Series #6	.20	.15	.06
229 World Series #7	.20	.15	.06
230 Series Celeb.	.20	.15	.06
231 Casey Cox	.11	.08	.03
232 Giants Rookies	.11	.08	.03
223 Jay Johnstone	.11	.08	.03
234 Ron Taylor	.11	.08	.03
235 M. Rettenmund	.11	.08	.03
236 Jim McGlothlin	.11	.08	.03
237 Yankees Team	.25	.20	.08
238 Leron Lee	.11	.08	.03
239 T. Timmermann	.11	.08	.03
240 Rich Allen	.30	.25	.10
241 Rollie Fingers	.20	.15	.06
242 Don Mincher	.11	.08	.03
243 Frank Linzy	.11	.08	.03
244 Steve Braun	.11	.08	.03
245 Tommie Agee	.11	.08	.03
246 Tom Burgmeier	.11	.08	.03
247 Milt May	.11	.08	.03
248 Tom Bradley	.11	.08	.03
249 Garry Walker	.11	.08	.03
250 Boog Powell	.20	.15	.06
251 Checklist 3	.11	.08	.03
252 Ken Reynolds	.11	.08	.03
253 Sandy Alomar	.11	.08	.03
254 Boots Day	.11	.08	.03
255 Jim Lonborg	.15	.11	.05
256 George Foster	1.25	.90	.40
257 Tigers Rookies	.11	.08	.03
258 Randy Hundley	.11	.08	.03
259 Sparky Lyle	.20	.15	.06
260 Ralph Garr	.15	.11	.05
261 Steve Mingori	.11	.08	.03
262 Padres Team	.20	.15	.06
263 Felipe Alou	.15	.11	.05
264 Tommy John	.90	.70	.30
265 Wes Parker	.15	.11	.05
266 Bobby Bolin	.11	.08	.03
267 Dave Concepcion	.30	.25	.10
268 A's Rookies	.11	.08	.03
269 Don Hahn	.11	.08	.03
270 Jim Palmer	1.25	.90	.40
271 Ken Rudolph	.11	.08	.03
272 Mickey Rivers	.50	.40	.18
273 Bobby Floyd	.11	.08	.03
274 Al Severinsen	.11	.08	.03
275 Cesar Tovar	.11	.08	.03
276 Gene Mauch	.15	.11	.05
277 Elliott Maddox	.11	.08	.03
278 Dennis Higgins	.11	.08	.03
279 Larry Brown	.11	.08	.03
280 Willie McCovey	2.00	1.50	.60
281 Bill Parsons	.11	.08	.03
282 Astros Team	.20	.15	.06
283 Darrell Brandon	.11	.08	.03
284 Ike Brown	.11	.08	.03
285 Gaylord Perry	1.25	.90	.40
286 Gene Alley	.11	.08	.03
287 Jim Hardin	.11	.08	.03
288 Johnny Jeter	.11	.08	.03
289 Syd O'Brien	.11	.08	.03
290 Sonny Siebert	.11	.08	.03
291 Hal McRae	.11	.08	.03
292 McRae In Action	.11	.08	.03

	MINT	VG-E	F-G
293 Danny Frisella	.11	.08	.03
294 Frisella In Action	.11	.08	.03
295 Dick Dietz	.11	.08	.03
296 Dietz In Action	.11	.08	.03
297 Claude Osteen	.11	.08	.03
298 Osteen In Action	.11	.08	.03
299 Hank Aaron	4.25	3.25	1.50
300 Aaron In Action	2.25	1.65	.75
301 George Mitterwald	.11	.08	.03
302 Mitterwald In Action	.11	.08	.03
303 Joe Pepitone	.15	.11	.05
304 Pepitone In Action	.11	.08	.03
305 Ken Boswell	.11	.08	.03
306 Boswell In Action	.11	.08	.03
307 Steve Renko	.11	.08	.03
308 Renko In Action	.11	.08	.03
309 Roberto Clemente	3.25	2.40	1.10
310 Clemente In Action	2.00	1.50	.60
311 Clay Carroll	.11	.08	.03
312 Carroll In Action	.11	.08	.03
313 Luis Aparicio	.40	.30	.13
314 Aparicio In Action	.20	.15	.06
315 Paul Splittorff	.11	.08	.03
316 Cardinals Rookies	.11	.08	.03
317 Rich Hand	.11	.08	.03
318 Sonny Jackson	.11	.08	.03
319 Aurelio Rodriguez	.11	.08	.03
320 Steve Blass	.15	.11	.05
321 Joe LaHoud	.11	.08	.03
322 Jose Pena	.11	.08	.03
323 Earl Weaver	.15	.11	.05
324 Mike Ryan	.11	.08	.03
325 Mel Stottlemyre	.15	.11	.05
326 Pat Kelly	.11	.08	.03
327 Steve Stone	.50	.40	.18
328 Red Sox Team	.25	.20	.06
329 Roy Foster	.11	.08	.03
330 Jim Hunter	1.00	.70	.30
331 Stan Swanson	.11	.08	.06
332 Buck Martinez	.11	.08	.03
333 Steve Barber	.11	.08	.03
334 Rangers Rookies	.11	.08	.03
335 Bill Hands	.11	.08	.03
336 Marty Martinez	.11	.08	.03
337 Mike Kilkenny	.11	.08	.03
338 Bob Grich	.15	.11	.05
339 Ron Cook	.11	.08	.03
340 Roy White	.15	.11	.05
341 Kid Pix-J. Torre	.15	.11	.05
342 Kid Pix-W. Wood	.11	.08	.03
343 Kid Pix-Stargell	.30	.25	.10
344 Kid Pix-McNally	.11	.08	.03
345 Kid Pix-R. Wise	.11	.08	.03
346 Kid Pix-J. Fregosi	.15	.11	.05
347 Kid Pix-T. Seaver	.40	.30	.13
348 Kid Pix-S. Bando	.15	.11	.05
349 Al Fitzmorris	.11	.08	.03
350 Frank Howard	.40	.30	.13
351 Braves Rookies	.11	.08	.03
352 Dave LaRoche	.11	.08	.03
353 Art Shamsky	.11	.08	.03
354 Tom Murphy	.11	.08	.03
355 Bob Watson	.20	.15	.06
356 Gerry Moses	.11	.08	.03
357 Woodie Fryman	.11	.08	.03
358 Sparky Anderson	.25	.20	.06
359 Don Pavletich	.11	.08	.03
360 Dave Roberts	.11	.08	.03
361 Mike Andrews	.11	.08	.03
362 Mets Team	.25	.20	.08
363 Ron Klimkowski	.11	.08	.03
364 Johnny Callison	.11	.08	.03
365 Dick Bosman	.11	.08	.03
366 Jimmy Rosario	.11	.08	.03
367 Ron Perranoski	.11	.08	.03
368 Danny Thompson	.11	.08	.03
369 Jim LeFebvre	.11	.08	.03
370 Don Buford	.11	.08	.03
371 Denny LeMaster	.11	.08	.03
372 Royals Rookies	.11	.08	.03
373 John Mayberry	.15	.11	.05
374 Jack Heidemann	.11	.08	.03
375 Reggie Cleveland	.11	.08	.03
376 Andy Kosco	.11	.08	.03
377 Terry Harmon	.11	.08	.03
378 Checklist-4th Ser.	.11	.08	.03
379 Ken Berry	.11	.08	.03
380 Earl Williams	.11	.08	.03
381 White Sox Team	.20	.15	.06
382 Joe Gibbon	.11	.08	.03
383 Brant Alyea	.11	.08	.03
384 Dave Campbell	.11	.08	.03
385 Mickey Stanley	.11	.08	.03

	MINT	VG-E	F-G			MINT	VG-E	F-G
386 Jim Colborn	.11	.08	.03	478 Checklist-5th Ser.		.11	.08	.03
387 Horace Clarke	.11	.08	.03	479 Don Shaw		.11	.08	.03
388 Charlie Williams	.11	.08	.03	480 Lee May		.11	.08	.03
389 Bill Rigney	.11	.08	.03	481 Billy Conigliaro		.11	.08	.03
390 Willie Davis	.15	.11	.05	482 Bob Hoerner		.11	.08	.03
391 Ken Sanders	.11	.08	.03	483 Ken Suarez		.11	.08	.03
392 Pirates Rookies	.60	.45	.20	484 Lum Harris		.11	.08	.03
393 Curt Motton	.11	.08	.03	485 Phil Regan		.11	.08	.03
394 Ken Forsch	.15	.11	.05	486 J. Lowenstein		.11	.08	.03
395 Matty Alou	.11	.08	.03	487 Tigers Team		.25	.20	.08
396 Paul Lindblad	.20	.15	.06	488 Mike Nagy		.11	.08	.03
397 Phillies Team	.20	.15	.06	489 Expos Rookies		.11	.08	.03
398 Larry Hisle	.15	.11	.05	490 Dave McNally		.15	.11	.05
399 Milt Wilcox	.11	.08	.03	491 Kid Pix-L. Piniella		.11	.08	.03
400 Tony Oliva	.40	.30	.13	492 Kid Pix-Stottlemyre		.11	.08	.03
401 Jim Nash	.11	.08	.03	493 Kid Pix-B. Bailey		.11	.08	.03
402 Bobby Heise	.11	.08	.03	494 Kid Pix-W. Horton		.11	.08	.03
403 John Cumberland	.11	.08	.03	495 Kid Pix-B. Melton		.11	.08	.03
404 Jeff Torborg	.11	.08	.03	496 Kid Pix-B. Harrelson		.11	.08	.03
405 Ron Fairly	.15	.11	.05	497 Kid Pix-J. Perry		.11	.08	.03
406 George Hendrick	.40	.30	.13	498 Kid Pix-B. Robinson		.40	.30	.13
407 Chuck Taylor	.11	.08	.03	499 Vicente Romo		.11	.08	.03
408 Jim Northrup	.11	.08	.03	500 Joe Torre		.40	.30	.13
409 Frank Baker	.11	.08	.03	501 Pete Hamm		.11	.08	.03
410 Fergie Jenkins	.40	.30	.13	502 Jackie Hernandez		.11	.08	.03
411 Bob Montgomery	.11	.08	.03	503 Gary Peters		.11	.08	.03
412 Dick Kelley	.11	.08	.03	504 Ed Spiezio		.11	.08	.03
413 White Sox Rookies	.11	.08	.03	505 Mike Marshall		.20	.15	.06
414 Bob Miller	.11	.08	.03	506 Indians Rookies		.11	.08	.03
415 Cookie Rojas	.11	.08	.03	507 Fred Gladding		.11	.08	.03
416 Johnny Edwards	.11	.08	.03	508 Ellie Hendricks		.11	.08	.03
417 Tom Hall	.11	.08	.03	509 Don McMahon		.11	.08	.03
418 Tom Shopay	.11	.08	.03	510 Ted Williams	2.00	1.50	.60
419 Jim Spencer	.11	.08	.03	511 Tony Taylor		.11	.08	.03
420 Steve Carlton	1.00	.70	.30	512 Paul Popovich		.11	.08	.03
421 Ellie Rodriguez	.11	.08	.03	513 Lindy McDaniel		.11	.08	.03
422 Ray Lamb	.11	.08	.03	514 Ted Sizemore		.11	.08	.03
423 Oscar Gamble	.15	.11	.05	515 Bert Blyleven		.20	.15	.06
424 Bill Gogolewski	.11	.08	.03	516 Oscar Brown		.11	.08	.03
425 Ken Singleton	.60	.45	.20	517 Ken Brett		.11	.08	.03
426 Singleton In Action	.30	.25	.10	518 Wayne Garrett		.11	.08	.03
427 Tito Fuentes	.11	.08	.03	519 Ted Abernathy		.11	.08	.03
428 Fuentes In Action	.11	.08	.03	520 Larry Bowa		.40	.30	.13
429 Bob Robertson	.11	.08	.03	521 Alan Foster		.11	.08	.03
430 Robertson In Action	.11	.08	.03	522 Dodgers Team		.25	.20	.08
431 Clarence Gaston	.11	.08	.03	523 Chuck Dobson		.11	.08	.03
432 Gaston In Action	.11	.08	.03	524 Reds Rookies		.11	.08	.03
433 Johnny Bench	3.00	2.25	1.00	525 Carlos May		.11	.08	.03
434 Bench In Action	1.75	1.25	.55	526 Bob Bailey		.16	.12	.04
435 Reggie Jackson	2.50	1.80	.80	527 Dave Leonhard		.16	.12	.04
436 Jackson In Action	1.50	1.10	.50	528 Ron Stone		.16	.12	.04
437 Maury Wills	.40	.30	.13	529 Dave Nelson		.16	.12	.04
438 Wills In Action	.25	.20	.08	530 Don Sutton		.75	.55	.25
439 Billy Williams	.40	.30	.13	531 Freddie Patek		.20	.15	.06
440 Williams In Action	.25	.20	.08	532 Fred Kendall		.16	.12	.04
441 Thurman Munson	2.50	1.80	.80	533 Ralph Houk		.25	.20	.08
442 Munson In Action	1.50	1.10	.50	534 Jim Hickman		.16	.12	.04
443 Ken Henderson	.11	.08	.03	535 Ed Brinkman		.16	.12	.04
444 Henderson In Action	.11	.08	.03	536 Doug Rader		.16	.12	.04
445 Tom Seaver	2.50	1.80	.80	537 Bob Locker		.16	.12	.04
446 Seaver In Action	1.50	1.10	.50	538 Charlie Sands		.16	.12	.04
447 Willie Stargell	1.50	1.10	.50	539 Terry Forster		.50	.40	.18
448 Stargell In Action	.80	.60	.25	540 Felix Milan		.16	.12	.04
449 Bob Lemon	.75	.55	.25	541 Roger Repoz		.16	.12	.04
450 Mickey Lolich	.30	.25	.10	542 Jack Billingham		.16	.12	.04
451 Tony LaRussa	.11	.08	.03	543 Duane Josephson		.16	.12	.04
452 Ed Herrmann	.11	.08	.03	544 Ted Martinez		.16	.12	.04
453 Barry Lerch	.11	.08	.03	545 Wayne Granger		.16	.12	.04
454 A's Team	.25	.20	.08	546 Joe Hague		.16	.12	.04
455 Tommy Harper	.11	.08	.03	547 Indians Team		.25	.20	.08
456 Mark Belanger	.15	.11	.05	548 Frank Reberger		.16	.12	.04
457 Padres Rookies	.11	.08	.03	549 Dave Marr		.16	.12	.04
458 A. Monteagudo	.11	.08	.03	550 Brooks Robinson	3.00	2.25	1.00
459 Rick Renick	.11	.08	.03	551 Ollie Brown		.16	.12	.04
460 Al Downing	.11	.08	.03	552 Brown In Action		.16	.12	.04
461 Tim Cullen	.11	.08	.03	553 Wilbur Wood		.16	.12	.04
462 Rickey Clark	.11	.08	.03	554 Wood In Action		.16	.12	.04
463 Bernie Carbo	.11	.08	.03	555 Ron Santo		.30	.25	.10
464 Jim Roland	.11	.08	.03	556 Santo In Action		.20	.15	.06
465 Gil Hodges	1.00	.70	.30	557 John Odom		.16	.12	.04
466 Norm Miller	.11	.08	.03	558 Odom In Action		.16	.12	.04
467 Steve Kline	.11	.08	.03	559 Pete Rose	4.25	3.25	1.50
468 R. Scheinblum	.11	.08	.03	560 Rose In Action	2.25	1.65	.75
469 Ron Herbel	.11	.08	.03	561 Leo Cardenas		.16	.12	.04
470 Ray Fosse	.11	.08	.03	562 Cardenas In Action		.16	.12	.04
471 Luke Walker	.11	.08	.03	563 Ray Sadecki		.16	.12	.04
472 Phil Gagliano	.11	.08	.03	564 Sadecki In Action		.16	.12	.04
473 Dan McGinn	.11	.08	.03	565 Reggie Smith		.50	.40	.18
474 Orioles Rookies	.50	.40	.18	566 Smith In Action		.25	.20	.08
475 Gary Nolan	.11	.08	.03	567 Juan Marichal	1.00	.70	.30
476 Lee Richard	.11	.08	.03	568 Marichal In Action		.50	.40	.18
477 Tom Phoebus	.11	.08	.03	569 Ed Kirkpatrick		.16	.12	.04
				570 Kirkpatrick In Act		.16	.12	.04

	MINT	VG-E	F-G
571 Nate Colbert	.16	.12	.04
572 Colbert In Action	.16	.12	.04
573 Fritz Peterson	.16	.12	.04
574 Peterson In Action	.16	.12	.04
575 Al Oliver	.50	.40	.18
576 Leo Durocher	.30	.25	.10
577 Mike Paul	.16	.12	.04
578 Billy Grabarkewitz	.16	.12	.04
579 Doyle Alexander	.16	.12	.04
580 Lou Piniella	.30	.25	.10
581 Wade Blasingame	.16	.12	.04
582 Expos Team	.25	.20	.08
583 Darold Knowles	.16	.12	.04
584 Jerry McNertney	.16	.12	.04
585 George Scott	.25	.20	.08
586 Denis Menke	.16	.12	.04
587 Billy Wilson	.16	.12	.04
588 Jim Holt	.16	.12	.04
589 Hal Lanier	.16	.12	.04
590 Graig Nettles	.40	.30	.13
591 Paul Casanova	.16	.12	.04
592 Lew Krausse	.16	.12	.04
593 Rich Morales	.16	.12	.04
594 Jim Beauchamp	.16	.12	.04
595 Nolan Ryan	2.50	1.80	.80
596 Manny Mota	.25	.20	.08
597 Jim Magnuson	.16	.12	.04
598 Hal King	.16	.12	.04
599 Billy Champion	.16	.12	.04
600 Al Kaline	3.25	2.40	1.10
601 George Stone	.16	.12	.04
602 Dave Bristol	.16	.12	.04
603 Jim Ray	.16	.12	.04
604 Checklist-6th Ser.	.16	.12	.04
605 Nelson Briles	.16	.12	.04
606 Luis Melendez	.16	.12	.04
607 Frank Duffy	.16	.12	.04
608 Mike Corkins	.16	.12	.04
609 Tom Grieve	.16	.12	.04
610 Bill Stoneman	.16	.12	.04
611 Rich Reese	.16	.12	.04
612 Joe Decker	.16	.12	.04
613 Mike Ferraro	.16	.12	.04
614 Ted Uhlaender	.16	.12	.04
615 Steve Hargan	.16	.12	.04
616 Joe Ferguson	.16	.12	.04
617 Royals Team	.25	.20	.08
618 Rich Robertson	.16	.12	.04
619 Rich McKinney	.16	.12	.04
620 Phil Niekro	.40	.30	.13
621 Comm. Award	.30	.25	.10
622 M.V.P. Award	.40	.30	.13
623 Cy Young Award	.40	.30	.13
624 Min. Lea. Plyr.	.30	.25	.10
625 Rookie Award	.30	.25	.10
626 Ruth Award	.50	.40	.18
627 Moe Drabowsky	.16	.12	.04
628 Terry Crowley	.16	.12	.04
629 Paul Doyle	.16	.12	.04
630 Rich Hebner	.20	.15	.06
631 John Strohmayer	.16	.12	.04
632 Mike Hegan	.16	.12	.04
633 Jack Hiatt	.16	.12	.04
634 Dick Woodson	.16	.12	.04
635 Don Money	.20	.15	.06
636 Bill Lee	.20	.15	.06
637 Preston Gomez	.16	.12	.04
638 Ken Wright	.16	.12	.04
639 J. C. Martin	.16	.12	.04
640 Joe Coleman	.16	.12	.04
641 Mike Lum	.16	.12	.04
642 D. Riddleberger	.16	.12	.04
643 Russ Gibson	.16	.12	.04
644 Bernie Allen	.16	.12	.04
645 Jim Maloney	.20	.15	.06
646 Chico Salmon	.16	.12	.04
647 Bob Moose	.16	.12	.04
648 Jim Lyttle	.16	.12	.04
649 Pete Richert	.16	.12	.04
650 Sal Bando	.25	.20	.08
651 Reds Team	.30	.25	.10
652 Marcelino Lopez	.16	.12	.04
653 Jim Fairey	.16	.12	.04
654 Horacio Pina	.16	.12	.04
655 Jerry Grote	.16	.12	.04
656 Rudy May	.25	.20	.08
657 Bobby Wine	.40	.30	.12
658 Steve Dunning	.40	.30	.12
659 Bob Aspromonte	.40	.30	.12
660 Paul Blair	.40	.30	.12
661 Bill Virdon	1.00	.70	.30
662 Stan Bahnsen	.40	.30	.12

	MINT	VG-E	F-G
663 Fran Healy	.40	.30	.12
664 Bobby Knoop	.40	.30	.12
665 Chris Short	.40	.30	.12
666 Hector Torres	.40	.30	.12
667 Ray Newman	.40	.30	.12
668 Rangers Team	.60	.45	.20
669 Willie Crawford	.40	.30	.12
670 Ken Holtzman	.60	.45	.20
671 Donn Clendenon	.40	.30	.12
672 Archie Reynolds	.40	.30	.12
673 Dave Marshall	.40	.30	.12
674 John Kennedy	.40	.30	.12
675 Pat Jarvis	.40	.30	.12
676 Danny Cater	.40	.30	.12
677 Ivan Murrell	.40	.30	.12
678 Steve Luebber	.40	.30	.12
679 Astros Rookies	.40	.30	.12
680 Dave Johnson	.40	.30	.12
681 Bobby Pfeil	.40	.30	.12
682 Mike McCormick	.40	.30	.12
683 Steve Hovley	.40	.30	.12
684 Hal Breeden	.40	.30	.12
685 Joe Horlen	.40	.30	.12
686 Steve Garvey	22.00	16.50	7.50
687 Del Unser	.40	.30	.12
688 Cardinals Team	.60	.45	.20
689 Eddie Fisher	.40	.30	.12
690 Willie Montanez	.40	.30	.12
691 Curt Blefary	.40	.30	.12
692 Blefary In Action	.40	.30	.12
693 Alan Gallagher	.40	.30	.12
694 Gallagher In Action	.40	.30	.12
695 Rod Carew	28.00	21.00	10.00
696 Carew In Action	12.50	9.00	4.00
697 Jerry Koosman	1.50	1.10	.50
698 Koosman In Action	1.00	.70	.30
699 Bobby Murcer	1.00	.70	.30
700 Murcer In Action	.75	.55	.25
701 Jose Pagan	.40	.30	.12
702 Pagan In Action	.40	.30	.12
703 Doug Griffin	.40	.30	.12
704 Griffin In Action	.40	.30	.12
705 Pat Corrales	.40	.30	.12
706 Corrales In Action	.40	.30	.12
707 Tim Foli	.40	.30	.12
708 Foli In Action	.40	.30	.12
709 Jim Kaat	1.00	.70	.30
710 Kaat In Action	.75	.55	.25
711 Bobby Bonds	2.00	1.50	.60
712 Bonds In Action	1.25	.90	.40
713 Gene Michael	.75	.55	.25
714 Michael In Action	.50	.40	.18
715 Mike Epstein	.40	.30	.12
716 Jesus Alou	.40	.30	.12
717 Bruce Dal Canton	.40	.30	.12
718 Del Rice	.40	.30	.12
719 Cesar Geronimo	.40	.30	.12
720 Sam McDowell	.60	.45	.20
721 Eddie Leon	.40	.30	.12
722 Bill Sudakis	.40	.30	.12
723 Al Santorini	.40	.30	.12
724 '72 Rookies-P	.40	.30	.12
725 Dick McAuliffe	.40	.30	.12
726 Dick Selma	.40	.30	.12
727 Jose LaBoy	.40	.30	.12
728 Gail Hopkins	.40	.30	.12
729 Bob Veale	.40	.30	.12
730 Rick Monday	.60	.45	.20
731 Orioles Team	.60	.45	.20
732 George Culver	.40	.30	.12
733 Jim Hart	.40	.30	.12
734 Bob Burda	.40	.30	.12
735 Diego Segui	.40	.30	.12
736 Bill Russell	.40	.30	.12
737 Lenny Randle	.40	.30	.12
738 Jim Merritt	.40	.30	.12
739 Don Mason	.40	.30	.12
740 Rico Carty	.75	.55	.25
741 '72 Rookies-1B	.40	.30	.12
742 Jim Rooker	.40	.30	.12
743 Cesar Guitierrez	.40	.30	.12
744 Jim Slaton	.40	.30	.12
745 Julian Javier	.40	.30	.12
746 Lowell Palmer	.40	.30	.12
747 Jim Stewart	.40	.30	.12
748 Phil Hennigan	.40	.30	.12
749 Walter Alston	.75	.55	.25
750 Willie Horton	.60	.45	.20
751 Steve Carlton(traded)	5.00	3.75	1.75
752 Joe Morgan(traded)	3.50	2.50	1.20
753 Denny McLain(traded)	2.00	1.50	.60
754 Frank Robinson(traded	4.00	3.00	1.40
755 Jim Fregosi(traded)	1.00	.70	.30

1972 TOPPS (CONTINUED)

	MINT	VG-E	F-G
756 Rick Wise(traded)	.75	.55	.25
757 Jose Cardenal(traded)	.40	.30	.12
758 Gil Garrido	.40	.30	.12
759 Chris Cannizzaro	.40	.30	.12
760 Bill Mazeroski	.75	.55	.25
761 '72 Rookies-OF	2.00	1.50	.60
762 Wayne Simpson	.40	.30	.12
763 Ron Hansen	.40	.30	.12
764 Dusty Baker	1.00	.70	.30
765 Ken McMullen	.40	.30	.12
766 Steve Hamilton	.40	.30	.12
767 Tom McCraw	.40	.30	.12
768 Denny Doyle	.40	.30	.12
769 Jack Aker	.40	.30	.12
770 Jim Wynn	.60	.45	.20

	MINT	VG-E	F-G
771 Giants Team	.60	.45	.20
772 Ken Tatum	.40	.30	.12
773 Ron Brand	.40	.30	.12
774 Luis Alvarado	.40	.30	.12
775 Jerry Reuss	.75	.55	.25
776 Bill Voss	.40	.30	.12
777 Hoyt Wilhelm	1.25	.90	.40
778 Twins Rookies	.40	.30	.12
779 Tony Cloninger	.40	.30	.12
780 Dick Green	.40	.30	.12
781 Jim McAndrew	.40	.30	.12
782 Larry Stahl	.40	.30	.12
783 Les Cain	.40	.30	.12
784 Ken Aspromonte	.40	.30	.12
785 Vic Davalillo	.40	.30	.12
786 Chuck Brinkman	.40	.30	.12
787 Ron Reed	.40	.30	.12

1973 TOPPS (660)   2 1/2" X 3 1/2"

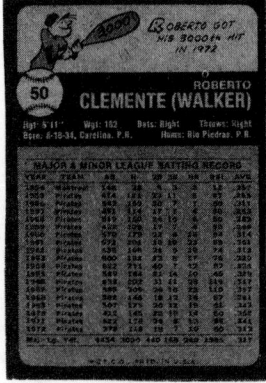

The 1973 Topps set is the last to be issued in series. The higher numbers are slightly more difficult to obtain.

	MINT	VG-E	F-G
COMPLETE SET	110.00	85.00	30.00
COMMON PLAYER (1-528)	.10	.07	.03
COMMON PLAYER (529-660)	.20	.15	.06
1 All-Time Home Run	2.50	1.80	.80
2 Rich Hebner	.10	.07	.03
3 Jim Lonborg	.10	.07	.03
4 John Milner	.10	.07	.03
5 Ed Brinkman	.10	.07	.03
6 Mac Scarce	.10	.07	.03
7 Texas Rangers Team	.20	.15	.06
8 Tom Hall	.10	.07	.03
9 Johnny Oates	.10	.07	.03
10 Don Sutton	.50	.40	.18
11 Chris Chambliss	.15	.11	.05
12 San Diego Padres Mgr.	.15	.11	.05
13 George Hendrick	.20	.15	.06
14 Sonny Siebert	.10	.07	.03
15 Ralph Garr	.10	.07	.03
16 Steve Braun	.10	.07	.03
17 Fred Gladding	.10	.07	.03
18 Leroy Stanton	.10	.07	.03
19 Tim Foli	.10	.07	.03
20 Stan Bahnsen	.10	.07	.03
21 Randy Hundley	.10	.07	.03
22 Ted Abernathy	.10	.07	.03
23 Dave Kingman	.60	.45	.20
24 Al Santorini	.10	.07	.03
25 Roy White	.10	.07	.03
26 Pirates Team	.20	.16	.06
27 Bill Gogolewski	.10	.07	.03
28 Hal McRae	.10	.07	.03
29 Tony Taylor	.10	.07	.03
30 Tug McGraw	.15	.11	.05
31 Buddy Bell	.50	.40	.18
32 Fred Norman	.10	.07	.03
33 Jim Breazeale	.10	.07	.03
34 Pat Dobson	.10	.07	.03
35 Willie Davis	.15	.11	.05
36 Steve Barber	.10	.07	.03
37 Bill Robinson	.10	.07	.03
38 Mike Epstein	.10	.07	.03
39 Dave Roberts	.10	.07	.03
40 Reggie Smith	.40	.30	.13
41 Tom Walker	.10	.07	.03
42 Mike Andrews	.10	.07	.03
43 Randy Moffitt	.10	.07	.03

	MINT	VG-E	F-G
44 Rick Monday	.15	.11	.05
45 Ellie Rodriguez	.10	.07	.03
46 Lindy McDaniel	.10	.07	.03
47 Luis Melendez	.10	.07	.03
48 Paul Splittorff	.15	.11	.05
49 Minn. Twins Mgr.	.10	.07	.03
50 Roberto Clemente	2.75	2.00	.90
51 Chuck Seelbach	.10	.07	.03
52 Denis Menke	.10	.07	.03
53 Steve Dunning	.10	.07	.03
54 Checklist-1st Ser.	.10	.07	.03
55 John Matlack	.15	.11	.05
56 Merv Rettenmund	.10	.07	.03
57 Derrel Thomas	.10	.07	.03
58 Mike Paul	.10	.07	.03
59 Steve Yeager	.10	.07	.03
60 Ken Holtzman	.12	.08	.04
61 1972 Batting Ldrs.	.20	.15	.06
62 1972 HR Ldrs.	.20	.15	.06
63 1972 RBI Ldrs.	.20	.15	.06
64 1972 SB Ldrs.	.20	.15	.06
65 1972 Era Ldrs.	.20	.15	.06
66 1972 Vic. Ldrs.	.20	.15	.06
67 1972 SO Ldrs.	.20	.15	.06
68 1972 Lead. Firemen	.20	.15	.06
69 Phil Gagliano	.10	.07	.03
70 Milt Pappas	.15	.11	.05
71 Johnny Briggs	.10	.07	.03
72 Ron Reed	.10	.07	.03
73 Ed Herrmann	.10	.07	.03
74 Billy Champion	.10	.07	.03
75 Vada Pinson	.25	.20	.08
76 Doug Rader	.10	.07	.03
77 Mike Torrez	.15	.11	.05
78 Richie Scheinblum	.10	.07	.03
79 Jim Willoughby	.10	.07	.03
80 Tony Oliva	.40	.30	.13
81 Chicago Cubs Mgr.	.10	.07	.03
82 Fritz Peterson	.10	.07	.03
83 Leron Lee	.10	.07	.03
84 Rollie Fingers	.20	.15	.06
85 Ted Simmons	.50	.40	.13
86 Tom McCraw	.10	.07	.03
87 Ken Boswell	.10	.07	.03
88 Mickey Stanley	.10	.07	.03
89 Jack Billingham	.10	.07	.03

1973 TOPPS (CONTINUED)

	MINT	VG-E	F-G			MINT	VG-E	F-G
90 Brooks Robinson	1.50	1.10	.50	184 Jerry Koosman	.20	.15	.06
91 Dodgers Team	.25	.20	.08	185 Jim Wynn	.15	.11	.05
92 Jerry Bell	.10	.07	.03	186 Bill Fahey	.10	.07	.03
93 Jesus Alou	.10	.07	.03	187 Luke Walker	.10	.07	.03
94 Dick Billings	.10	.07	.03	188 Cookie Rojas	.10	.07	.03
95 Steve Blass	.12	.08	.04	189 Greg Luzinski	1.00	.70	.30
96 Doug Griffin	.10	.07	.03	190 Bob Gibson	1.25	.90	.40
97 Willie Montanez	.15	.11	.05	191 Tigers Team	.20	.15	.06
98 Dick Woodson	.10	.07	.03	192 Pat Jarvis	.10	.07	.03
99 Carl Taylor	.10	.07	.03	193 Carlton Fisk	.80	.60	.25
100 Hank Aaron	3.00	2.25	1.00	194 Jorge Orta	.10	.07	.03
101 Ken Henderson	.10	.07	.03	195 Clay Carroll	.10	.07	.03
102 Rudy May	.15	.11	.05	196 Ken McMullen	.10	.07	.03
103 Celerino Sanchez	.10	.07	.03	197 Ed Goodson	.10	.07	.03
104 Reggie Cleveland	.10	.07	.03	198 Horace Clarke	.10	.07	.03
105 Carlos May	.10	.07	.03	199 Bert Blyleven	.15	.11	.05
106 Terry Humphrey	.10	.07	.03	200 Billy Williams	.35	.27	.12
107 Phil Hennigan	.10	.07	.03	201 1972 AL Champ Series	.20	.15	.06
108 Bill Russell	.10	.07	.03	202 1972 NL Champ Series	.20	.15	.06
109 Doyle Alexander	.10	.07	.03	203 World Series Game #1	.20	.15	.06
110 Bob Watson	.15	.11	.05	204 World Series Game #2	.20	.15	.06
111 Dave Nelson	.10	.07	.03	205 World Series Game #3	.20	.15	.06
112 Gary Ross	.10	.07	.03	206 World Series Game #4	.20	.15	.06
113 Jerry Grote	.10	.07	.03	207 World Series Game #5	.20	.15	.06
114 Lynn McGlothen	.10	.07	.03	208 World Series Game #6	.20	.15	.06
115 Ron Santo	.20	.15	.06	209 World Series Game #7	.20	.15	.06
116 Yankees Manager	.15	.11	.05	210 World Series Celebr.	.20	.15	.06
117 Ramon Hernandez	.10	.07	.03	211 Balor Moore	.10	.07	.03
118 John Mayberry	.15	.11	.05	212 Joe LaHoud	.10	.07	.03
119 Larry Bowa	.40	.30	.13	213 Steve Garvey	2.00	1.50	.60
120 Joe Coleman	.10	.07	.03	214 Dave Hamilton	.10	.07	.03
121 Dave Rader	.10	.07	.03	215 Dusty Baker	.20	.15	.06
122 Jim Strickland	.10	.07	.03	216 Toby Harrah	.10	.07	.03
123 Sandy Alomar	.10	.07	.03	217 Don Wilson	.10	.07	.03
124 Jim Hardin	.10	.07	.03	218 Aurelio Rodriguez	.10	.07	.03
125 Ron Fairly	.12	.08	.04	219 St. Louis Cards	.20	.15	.06
126 Jim Brewer	.10	.07	.03	220 Nolan Ryan	1.50	1.10	.50
127 Milwaukee Brewers	.20	.15	.06	221 Fred Kendall	.10	.07	.03
128 Ted Sizemore	.10	.07	.03	222 Rob Gardner	.10	.07	.03
129 Terry Forster	.15	.11	.05	223 Bud Harrelson	.10	.07	.03
130 Pete Rose	2.50	1.80	.80	224 Bill Lee	.12	.08	.04
131 Redsox Manager	.10	.07	.03	225 Al Oliver	.30	.25	.10
132 Matty Alou	.12	.08	.04	226 Ray Fosse	.10	.07	.03
133 Dave Roberts	.10	.07	.03	227 Wayne Twitchell	.10	.07	.03
134 Milt Wilcox	.10	.07	.03	228 Bobby Darwin	.10	.07	.03
135 Lee May	.12	.08	.04	229 Roric Harrison	.10	.07	.03
136 Orioles Manager	.12	.08	.04	230 Joe Morgan	1.00	.70	.30
137 Jim Beauchamp	.10	.07	.03	231 Bill Parsons	.10	.07	.03
138 Horacio Pina	.10	.07	.03	232 Ken Singleton	.30	.25	.10
139 Carmen Fanzone	.10	.07	.03	233 Ed Kirkpatrick	.10	.07	.03
140 Lou Piniella	.15	.11	.05	234 Bill North	.10	.07	.03
141 Bruce Kison	.10	.07	.03	235 Jim Hunter	.75	.55	.25
142 Thurman Munson	2.25	1.65	.75	236 Tito Fuentes	.10	.07	.03
143 John Curtis	.10	.07	.03	237 Braves Manager	.40	.30	.13
144 Marty Perez	.10	.07	.03	238 Tony Muser	.10	.07	.03
145 Bobby Bonds	.30	.25	.10	239 Pete Richert	.10	.07	.03
146 Woodie Fryman	.10	.07	.03	240 Bobby Murcer	.25	.20	.08
147 Mike Anderson	.10	.07	.03	241 Dwain Anderson	.10	.07	.03
148 Dave Goltz	.12	.08	.04	242 George Culver	.10	.07	.03
149 Ron Hunt	.10	.07	.03	243 Angels Team	.20	.15	.06
150 Wilbur Wood	.12	.08	.04	244 Ed Acosta	.10	.07	.03
151 Wes Parker	.12	.08	.04	245 Carl Yastrzemski	2.50	1.80	.80
152 Dave May	.10	.07	.03	246 Ken Sanders	.10	.07	.03
153 Al Hrabosky	.20	.15	.06	247 Del Unser	.10	.07	.03
154 Jeff Torborg	.10	.07	.03	248 Jerry Johnson	.10	.07	.03
155 Sal Bando	.15	.11	.05	249 Larry Bittner	.10	.07	.03
156 Cesar Geronimo	.10	.07	.03	250 Manny Sanguillen	.10	.07	.03
157 Denny Riddleberger	.10	.07	.03	251 Roger Nelson	.10	.07	.03
158 Astros Team	.20	.15	.06	252 Charlie Fox	.10	.07	.03
159 Clarence Gaston	.10	.07	.03	253 Mark Belanger	.15	.11	.05
160 Jim Palmer	1.25	.90	.40	254 Bill Stoneman	.10	.07	.03
161 Ted Martinez	.10	.07	.03	255 Reggie Jackson	2.25	1.65	.75
162 Pete Broberg	.10	.07	.03	256 Chris Zachary	.10	.07	.03
163 Vic Davalillo	.10	.07	.03	257 Mets Manager	.50	.40	.18
164 Monty Montgomery	.10	.07	.03	258 Tommy John	.70	.50	.20
165 Luis Aparicio	.30	.25	.10	259 Jim Holt	.10	.07	.03
166 Terry Harmon	.10	.07	.03	260 Gary Nolan	.10	.07	.03
167 Steve Stone	.20	.15	.06	261 Pat Kelly	.10	.07	.03
168 Jim Northrup	.10	.07	.03	262 Jack Aker	.10	.07	.03
169 Ron Schueler	.10	.07	.03	263 George Scott	.15	.11	.05
170 Harmon Killebrew	1.00	.70	.30	264 Checklist - 2nd Ser.	.10	.07	.03
171 Bernie Carbo	.10	.07	.03	265 Gene Michael	.20	.15	.06
172 Steve Kline	.10	.07	.03	266 Mike Lum	.10	.07	.03
173 Hal Breeden	.10	.07	.03	267 Lloyd Allen	.10	.07	.03
174 Rich Gossage	1.25	.90	.40	268 Jerry Morales	.10	.07	.03
175 Frank Robinson	1.50	1.10	.50	269 Tim McCarver	.10	.07	.03
176 Chuck Taylor	.10	.07	.03	270 Luis Tiant	.20	.15	.06
177 Bill Plummer	.10	.07	.03	271 Tom Hutton	.10	.07	.03
178 Don Rose	.10	.07	.03	272 Ed Farmer	.10	.07	.03
179 Oakland A's Manager	.10	.07	.03	273 Chris Speier	.10	.07	.03
180 Fergie Jenkins	.25	.20	.08	274 Darold Knowles	.10	.07	.03
181 Jack Brohamer	.10	.07	.03	275 Tony Perez	.25	.20	.08
182 Mike Caldwell	.15	.11	.05	276 Joe Lovitto	.10	.07	.03
183 Don Buford	.10	.07	.03	277 Bob Miller	.10	.07	.03
				278 Orioles Team	.20	.15	.06

	MINT	VG-E	F-G			MINT	VG-E	F-G
279 Mike Strahler	.10	.07	.03	373 Clyde Wright		.10	.07	.03
280 Al Kaline	2.25	1.65	.75	374 Darrell Evans		.10	.07	.03
281 Mike Jorgensen	.10	.07	.03	375 Larry Dierker		.10	.07	.03
282 Steve Hovley	.10	.07	.03	376 Frank Duffy		.10	.07	.03
283 Ray Sadecki	.10	.07	.03	377 Expos Manager		.10	.07	.03
284 Glenn Borgmann	.10	.07	.03	378 Lenny Randle		.10	.07	.03
285 Don Kessinger	.12	.08	.04	379 Cy Acosta		.10	.07	.03
286 Frank Linzy	.10	.07	.03	380 Johnny Bench		2.50	1.80	.80
287 Eddie Leon	.10	.07	.03	381 Vicente Romo		.10	.07	.03
288 Gary Gentry	.10	.07	.03	382 Mike Hegan		.10	.07	.03
289 Bob Oliver	.10	.07	.03	383 Diego Sequi		.10	.07	.03
290 Cesar Cedeno	.30	.25	.10	384 Don Baylor		.30	.25	.10
291 Rogelio Moret	.10	.07	.03	385 Jim Perry		.15	.11	.05
292 Jose Cruz	.12	.08	.04	386 Don Money		.15	.11	.05
293 Bernie Allen	.10	.07	.03	387 Jim Barr		.10	.07	.03
294 Steve Arlin	.10	.07	.03	388 Ben Oglivie		.20	.15	.06
295 Bert Campaneris	.12	.08	.04	389 Mets Team		.25	.20	.08
296 Cincinnati Reds Mgr.	.25	.20	.08	390 Mickey Lolich		.20	.15	.06
297 Walt Williams	.10	.07	.03	391 Lee Lacy		.10	.07	.03
298 Ron Bryant	.10	.07	.03	392 Dick Drago		.10	.07	.03
299 Ted Ford	.10	.07	.03	393 Jose Cardenal		.10	.07	.03
300 Steve Carlton	1.00	.70	.30	394 Sparky Lyle		.20	.15	.06
301 Billy Grabarkewitz	.10	.07	.03	395 Roger Metzger		.10	.07	.03
302 Terry Crowley	.10	.07	.03	396 Grant Jackson		.10	.07	.03
303 Nelson Briles	.10	.07	.03	397 Dave Cash		.10	.07	.03
304 Duke Sims	.10	.07	.03	398 Rich Hand		.10	.07	.03
305 Willie Mays	4.00	3.00	1.40	399 George Foster		1.00	.70	.30
306 Tom Burgmeier	.10	.07	.03	400 Gaylord Perry		1.00	.70	.30
307 Boots Day	.10	.07	.03	401 Clyde Mashore		.10	.07	.03
308 Skip Lockwood	.10	.07	.03	402 Jack Hiatt		.10	.07	.03
309 Paul Popovich	.10	.07	.03	403 Sonny Jackson		.10	.07	.03
310 Dick Allen	.25	.20	.08	404 Chuck Brinkman		.10	.07	.03
311 Joe Decker	.10	.07	.03	405 Cesar Tovar		.10	.07	.03
312 Oscar Brown	.10	.07	.03	406 Paul Lindblad		.10	.07	.03
313 Jim Ray	.10	.07	.03	407 Felix Millan		.10	.07	.03
314 Ron Swoboda	.10	.07	.03	408 Jim Colborn		.10	.07	.03
315 John Odom	.10	.07	.03	409 Ivan Murrell		.10	.07	.03
316 Padres Team	.20	.15	.06	410 Willie McCovey		1.50	1.10	.50
317 Danny Cater	.10	.07	.03	411 Ray Corbin		.10	.07	.03
318 Jim McGlothlin	.10	.07	.03	412 Manny Mota		.15	.11	.05
319 Jim Spencer	.10	.07	.03	413 Tom Timmerman		.10	.07	.03
320 Lou Brock	2.00	1.50	.60	414 Ken Rudolph		.10	.07	.03
321 Rich Hinton	.10	.07	.03	415 Marty Pattin		.10	.07	.03
322 Garry Maddox	.40	.30	.13	416 Paul Schaal		.10	.07	.03
323 Detroit Tigers Mgr.	.20	.15	.06	417 Scipio Spinks		.10	.07	.03
324 Al Downing	.10	.07	.03	418 Bobby Grich		.12	.08	.04
325 Boog Powell	.20	.15	.06	419 Casey Cox		.10	.07	.03
326 Darrell Brandon	.10	.07	.03	420 Tommie Agee		.10	.07	.03
327 John Lowenstein	.10	.07	.03	421 Angels Manager		.10	.07	.03
328 Bill Bonham	.10	.07	.03	422 Bob Robertson		.10	.07	.03
329 Ed Kranepool	.12	.08	.04	423 Johnny Jeter		.10	.07	.03
330 Rod Carew	2.50	1.80	.80	424 Denny Doyle		.10	.07	.03
331 Carl Morton	.10	.07	.03	425 Alex Johnson		.10	.07	.03
332 John Felske	.10	.07	.03	426 Dave Laroche		.10	.07	.03
333 Gene Clines	.10	.07	.03	427 Rick Auerbach		.10	.07	.03
334 Freddie Patek	.10	.07	.03	428 Wayne Simpson		.10	.07	.03
335 Bob Tolan	.10	.07	.03	429 Jim Fairey		.10	.07	.03
336 Tom Bradley	.10	.07	.03	430 Vida Blue		.50	.40	.18
337 Dave Duncan	.10	.07	.03	431 Gerry Moses		.10	.07	.03
338 Checklist - 3rd Ser.	.10	.07	.03	432 Dan Frisella		.10	.07	.03
339 Dick Tidrow	.10	.07	.03	433 Willie Horton		.12	.08	.04
340 Nate Colbert	.10	.07	.03	434 Giants Team		.20	.15	.06
341 Kid. Pic. Palmer	.35	.27	.12	435 Rico Carty		.20	.15	.06
342 Kid. Pic. McDowell	.10	.07	.03	436 Jim McAndrew		.10	.07	.03
343 Kid. Pic. Murcer	.12	.08	.04	437 John Kennedy		.10	.07	.03
344 Kid. Pic. Hunter	.25	.20	.08	438 Enzo Hernandez		.10	.07	.03
345 Kid. Pic. Speier	.10	.07	.03	439 Eddie Fisher		.10	.07	.03
346 Kid. Pic. Perry	.25	.20	.08	440 Glenn Beckert		.10	.07	.03
347 Royals Team	.20	.15	.06	441 Gail Hopkins		.10	.07	.03
348 Rennie Stennett	.10	.07	.03	442 Dick Dietz		.10	.07	.03
349 Dick McAuliffe	.10	.07	.03	443 Danny Thompson		.10	.07	.03
350 Tom Seaver	2.75	2.00	.90	444 Ken Brett		.10	.07	.03
351 Jimmy Stewart	.10	.07	.03	445 Ken Berry		.10	.07	.03
352 Don Stanhouse	.12	.08	.04	446 Jerry Reuss		.20	.15	.06
353 Steve Brye	.10	.07	.03	447 Joe Hague		.10	.07	.03
354 Billy Parker	.10	.07	.03	448 John Hiller		.12	.08	.04
355 Mike Marshall	.15	.11	.05	449 Indians Manager		.10	.07	.03
356 White Sox Manager	.10	.07	.03	450 Joe Torre		.25	.20	.08
357 Ross Grimsley	.10	.07	.03	451 John Vukovich		.10	.07	.03
358 Jim Nettles	.10	.07	.03	452 Paul Casanova		.10	.07	.03
359 Cecil Upshaw	.10	.07	.03	453 Checklist - 4th Ser		.10	.07	.03
360 Joe Rudi	.15	.11	.05	454 Tom Haller		.10	.07	.03
361 Fran Healy	.10	.07	.03	455 Bill Melton		.10	.07	.03
362 Eddie Watt	.10	.07	.03	456 Dick Green		.10	.07	.03
363 Jackie Hernandez	.10	.07	.03	457 John Strohmayer		.10	.07	.03
364 Rick Wise	.15	.11	.05	458 Jim Mason		.10	.07	.03
365 Rico Petrocelli	.12	.08	.04	459 Jimmy Howarth		.10	.07	.03
366 Brock Davis	.10	.07	.03	460 Bill Freehan		.12	.08	.04
367 Burt Hooton	.20	.15	.06	461 Mike Corkins		.10	.07	.03
368 Bill Buckner	.20	.15	.06	462 Ron Blomberg		.10	.07	.03
369 Lerrin LaGrow	.10	.07	.03	463 Ken Tatum		.10	.07	.03
370 Willie Stargell	1.50	1.10	.50	464 Chicago Cubs Team		.20	.15	.06
371 Mike Kekich	.10	.07	.03	465 Dave Giusti		.10	.07	.03
372 Oscar Gamble	.15	.11	.05	466 Jose Arcia		.10	.07	.03
				467 Mike Ryan		.10	.07	.03

	MINT	VG-E	F-G
468 Tom Griffin	.10	.07	.03
469 Dan Monzon	.10	.07	.03
470 Mike Cuellar	.12	.08	.04
471 All-Time Hit Leaders	1.00	.70	.30
472 All-Time Grand Sl. Ldrs	1.00	.70	.30
473 All-Time Total Ba. Ldrs	1.25	.90	.40
474 All-Time RBI Leaders	1.25	.90	.40
475 All-Time Batting Ldrs	1.00	.70	.30
476 All-Time Shutout Ldrs	.50	.40	.18
477 All-Time Vic. Ldrs.	.50	.40	.18
478 All-Time Strikeout Ldr	1.00	.70	.30
479 Hal Lanier	.10	.07	.03
480 Juan Marichal	.50	.40	.18
481 White Sox Team	.20	.15	.06
482 Rick Reuschel	.50	.40	.18
483 Dal Maxvill	.10	.07	.03
484 Ernie McAnally	.10	.07	.03
485 Norm Cash	.20	.15	.06
486 Phillies Manager	.10	.07	.03
487 Bruce Dal Canton	.10	.07	.03
488 Dave Campbell	.10	.07	.03
489 Jeff Burroughs	.20	.15	.06
490 Claude Osteen	.10	.07	.03
491 Bob Montgomery	.10	.07	.03
492 Pedro Borbon	.10	.07	.03
493 Duffy Dyer	.10	.07	.03
494 Rich Morales	.10	.07	.03
495 Tommy Helms	.10	.07	.03
496 Ray Lamb	.10	.07	.03
497 Cardinals Manager	.15	.11	.05
498 Graig Nettles	.25	.20	.08
499 Bob Moose	.10	.07	.03
500 Oakland A's Team	.20	.15	.06
501 Larry Gura	.20	.15	.06
502 Bobby Valentine	.10	.07	.03
503 Phil Niekro	.25	.20	.08
504 Earl Williams	.10	.07	.03
505 Bob Bailey	.10	.07	.03
506 Bart Johnson	.10	.07	.03
507 Darrel Chaney	.10	.07	.03
508 Gates Brown	.10	.07	.03
509 Jim Nash	.10	.07	.03
510 Amos Otis	.20	.15	.06
511 Sam McDowell	.12	.08	.04
512 Dalton Jones	.10	.07	.03
513 Dave Marshall	.10	.07	.03
514 Jerry Kenney	.10	.07	.03
515 Andy Messersmith	.15	.11	.05
516 Danny Walton	.10	.07	.03
517 Pirates Manager	.10	.07	.03
518 Bob Veale	.10	.07	.03
519 John Edwards	.10	.07	.03
520 Mel Stottlemyre	.12	.08	.04
521 Atlanta Braves	.20	.15	.06
522 Leo Cardenas	.10	.07	.03
523 Wayne Granger	.10	.07	.03
524 Gene Tenace	.12	.08	.04
525 Jim Fregosi	.15	.11	.05
526 Ollie Brown	.10	.07	.03
527 Dan McGinn	.10	.07	.03
528 Paul Blair	.10	.07	.03
529 Milt May	.20	.15	.06
530 Jim Kaat	.40	.30	.13
531 Ron Woods	.20	.15	.06
532 Steve Mingori	.20	.15	.06
533 Larry Stahl	.20	.15	.06
534 Dave Lemonds	.20	.15	.06
535 John Callison	.20	.15	.06
536 Phillies Team	.30	.25	.10
537 Bill Slayback	.20	.15	.06
538 Jim Hart	.20	.15	.06
539 Tom Murphy	.20	.15	.06
540 Cleon Jones	.20	.15	.06
541 Bob Bolin	.20	.15	.06
542 Pat Corrales	.20	.15	.06
543 Alan Foster	.20	.15	.06
544 Von Joshua	.20	.15	.06
545 Orlando Cepeda	.50	.40	.18
546 Jim York	.20	.15	.06
547 Bobby Heise	.20	.15	.06
548 Don Durham	.20	.15	.06
549 Rangers Manager	.20	.15	.06
550 Dave Johnson	.20	.15	.06
551 Mike Kilkenny	.20	.15	.06
552 J. C. Martin	.20	.15	.06
553 Mickey Scott	.20	.15	.06
554 Dave Concepcion	.30	.25	.10
555 Bill Hands	.20	.15	.06
556 Yankees Team	.30	.25	.10
557 Bernie Williams	.20	.15	.06
558 Jerry May	.20	.15	.06
559 Barry Lersch	.20	.15	.06
560 Frank Howard	.50	.40	.18
561 Jim Geddes	.20	.15	.06

	MINT	VG-E	F-G
562 Wayne Garrett	.20	.15	.06
563 Larry Haney	.20	.15	.06
564 Mike Thompson	.20	.15	.06
565 Jim Hickman	.20	.15	.06
566 Lew Krausse	.20	.15	.06
567 Bob Fenwick	.20	.15	.06
568 Ray Newman	.20	.15	.06
569 Dodgers Manager	.30	.25	.10
570 Bill Singer	.20	.15	.06
571 Rusty Torres	.20	.15	.06
572 Gary Sutherland	.20	.15	.06
573 Fred Beene	.20	.15	.06
574 Bob Didier	.20	.15	.06
575 Dock Ellis	.20	.15	.06
576 Expos Team	.30	.25	.10
577 Eric Soderholm	.20	.15	.06
578 Ken Wright	.20	.15	.06
579 Tom Grieve	.20	.15	.06
580 Joe Pepitone	.25	.20	.08
581 Steve Kealey	.20	.15	.06
582 Darrell Porter	.60	.45	.20
583 Bill Grief	.20	.15	.06
584 Chris Arnold	.20	.15	.06
585 Joe Niekro	.30	.25	.10
586 Bill Sudakis	.20	.15	.06
587 Rich McKinney	.20	.15	.06
588 Checklist - 5th Ser	.20	.15	.06
589 Ken Forsch	.20	.15	.06
590 Deron Johnson	.20	.15	.06
591 Mike Hedlund	.20	.15	.06
592 John Boccabella	.20	.15	.06
593 Royals Manager	.20	.15	.06
594 Vic Harris	.20	.15	.06
595 Don Gullett	.25	.20	.08
596 Red Sox Team	.30	.25	.10
597 Mickey Rivers	.50	.40	.18
598 Phil Roof	.20	.15	.06
599 Ed Crosby	.20	.15	.06
600 Dave McNally	.30	.25	.10
601 73 Rookie Catchers	.20	.15	.06
602 73 Rookie Pitchers	.20	.15	.06
603 73 Rookie 3rd Baseman	.20	.15	.06
604 73 Rookie Pitchers	.20	.15	.06
605 73 Rookie 1st Baseman	.20	.15	.06
606 73 Rookie Outfielders	.20	.15	.06
607 73 Rookie Shortstops	.20	.15	.06
608 73 Rookie Pitchers	.20	.15	.06
609 73 Rookie 2nd Base	.60	.45	.20
610 73 Rookie Pitchers	.20	.15	.06
611 73 Rookie Outfielders	.40	.30	.13
612 73 Rookie Pitchers	.20	.15	.06
613 73 Rookie Catchers	.20	.15	.06
614 73 Rookie Outfielders	.20	.15	.06
615 73 Rookie Third Base	7.00	5.25	2.50
616 73 Rookie Pitchers	.20	.15	.06
617 Rich Chiles	.20	.15	.06
518 Andy Etchebarren	.20	.15	.06
619 Billy Wilson	.20	.15	.06
620 Tommy Harper	.20	.15	.06
621 Joe Ferguson	.20	.15	.06
622 Larry Hisle	.35	.27	.12
623 Steve Renko	.20	.15	.06
624 Astros Manager	.20	.15	.06
625 Angel Mangual	.20	.15	.06
626 Bob Barton	.20	.15	.06
627 Luis Alvarado	.20	.15	.06
628 Jim Slaton	.20	.15	.06
629 Indians Team	.30	.25	.10
630 Denny McLain	.35	.27	.12
631 Tom Matchick	.20	.15	.06
632 Dick Selma	.20	.15	.06
633 Ike Brown	.20	.15	.06
634 Alan Closter	.20	.15	.06
635 Gene Alley	.20	.15	.06
636 Rickey Clark	.20	.15	.06
637 Norm Miller	.20	.15	.06
638 Ken Reynolds	.20	.15	.06
639 Willie Crawford	.20	.15	.06
640 Dick Bosman	.20	.15	.06
641 Reds Team	.30	.25	.10
642 Jose LaBoy	.20	.15	.06
643 Al Fitzmorris	.20	.15	.06
644 Jack Heidemann	.20	.15	.06
645 Bob Locker	.20	.15	.06
646 Brewers Manager	.20	.15	.06
647 George Stone	.20	.15	.06
648 Tom Egan	.20	.15	.06
649 Rich Folkers	.20	.15	.06
650 Felipe Alou	.25	.20	.08
651 Don Carrithers	.20	.15	.06
652 Ted Kubiak	.20	.15	.06
653 Joe Hoerner	.20	.15	.06
654 Twins Team	.30	.25	.10
655 Clay Kirby	.20	.15	.06
656 John Ellis	.20	.15	.06

	MINT	VG-E	F-G		MINT	VG-E	F-G
657 Bob Johnson	.20	.15	.06	659 Jose Pagan	.20	.15	.06
658 Elliott Maddox	.20	.15	.06	660 Fred Scherman	20	.15	.06

1974 TOPPS (660)

2 1/2" X 3 1/2"

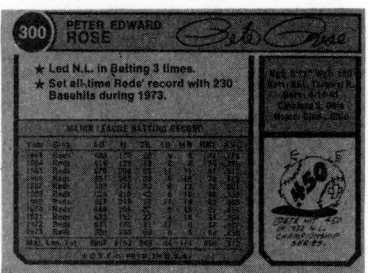

The 1974 Topps set includes at least two variations for all cards portraying San Diego Padre players. These 15 cards, including the team card and the rookie card no. 599, exist with both San Diego Padres designation and the Washington Nat'l League designation on the front. The Washington Nat'l League cards are considered the scarcer variety. This set is considered complete without the Washington Nat'l League cards and the set price below does not include these cards. This year marked the first time Topps issued all cards at the same time rather than in series.

	MINT	VG-E	F-G
COMPLETE SET	70.00	54.00	22.00
COMMON PLAYERS	.08	.06	.02
WASHINGTON N.L. COMMON	1.60	1.20	.50
1 Hank Aaron	4.00	2.00	.80
2 Aaron Special(54-57)	.90	.70	.30
3 Aaron Special(58-61)	.90	.70	.30
4 Aaron Special(62-65)	.90	.70	.30
5 Aaron Special(66-69)	.90	.70	.30
6 Aaron Special(70-73)	.90	.70	.30
7 Jim Hunter	.65	.50	.20
8 George Theodore	.08	.06	.02
9 Mickey Lolich	.15	.11	.05
10 Johnny Bench	1.50	1.10	.50
11 Jim Bibby	.12	.09	.04
12 D. May	.08	.06	.02
13 T. Hilgendorf	.08	.06	.02
14 Paul Popovich	.08	.06	.02
15 Joe Torre	.20	.15	.06
16 Orioles	.15	.11	.05
17 Doug Bird	.08	.06	.02
18 Gary Thomasson	.08	.06	.02
19 G. Moses	.08	.06	.02
20 Nolan Ryan	1.00	.70	.30
21 B. Gallagher	.08	.06	.02
22 C. Acosta	.08	.06	.02
23 C. Robinson	.08	.06	.02
24 John Hiller	.08	.06	.02
25 Ken Singleton	.20	.15	.06
26 Bill Campbell	.10	.07	.03
27 George Scott	.10	.07	.03
28 Manny Sanguillen	.10	.07	.03
29 Phil Niekro	.20	.15	.06
30 Bobby Bonds	.25	.20	.08
31 P. Gomez	.08	.06	.02
32a J. Grubb(Padres)	.10	.07	.03
32b J. Grubb(WashNL)	1.60	1.20	.60
33 D. Newhauser	.08	.06	.02
34 Andy Kosco	.08	.06	.02
35 Gaylord Perry	.70	.50	.20
36 Cardinals	.15	.11	.05
37 D. Sells	.08	.06	.02
38 Don Kessinger	.10	.07	.03
39 Ken Suarez	.08	.06	.02
40 Jim Palmer	1.00	.70	.30
41 Bobby Floyd	.08	.06	.02
42 Claude Osteen	.08	.06	.02
43 Jim Wynn	.10	.07	.03
44 Mel Stottlemyre	.10	.07	.03
45 Dave Johnson	.08	.06	.02
46 Pat Kelly	.08	.06	.02
47 Dick Ruthven	.08	.06	.02
48 Dick Sharon	.08	.06	.02
49 Steve Renko	.08	.06	.02
50 Rod Carew	1.50	1.10	.50
51 Bob Heise	.08	.06	.02
52 Al Oliver	.30	.25	.10
53a Fred Kendall(Padres)	.10	.07	.03
53b Fred Kendall(WashNL)	1.60	1.20	.60
54 Elias Sosa	.08	.06	.02

	MINT	VG-E	F-G
55 Frank Robinson	1.00	.70	.30
56 Mets	.15	.11	.05
57 Darold Knowles	.08	.06	.02
58 Charlie Spikes	.08	.06	.02
59 Ross Grimsley	.08	.06	.02
60 Lou Brock	1.25	.90	.40
61 Luis Aparicio	.25	.20	.08
62 Bob Locker	.08	.06	.02
63 Bill Sudakis	.08	.06	.02
64 Doug Rau	.08	.06	.02
65 Amos Otis	.15	.11	.05
66 Sparky Lyle	.15	.11	.05
67 Tommy Helms	.08	.06	.02
68 Grant Jackson	.08	.06	.02
69 Del Unser	.08	.06	.02
70 Dick Allen	.20	.15	.06
71 Dan Frisella	.08	.06	.02
72 Aurelio Rodriguez	.08	.06	.02
73 Mike Marshall	.25	.20	.08
74 Twins	.15	.11	.05
75 Jim Colborn	.08	.06	.02
76 Mickey Rivers	.20	.15	.06
77a R. Troedson(Padres)	.10	.07	.03
77b R. Troedson(WashNL)	1.60	1.20	.60
78 C. Fox	.08	.06	.02
79 Gene Tenace	.10	.07	.03
80 Tom Seaver	1.50	1.10	.50
81 Frank Duffy	.08	.06	.02
82 Dave Giusti	.08	.06	.02
83 Orlando Cepeda	.30	.25	.10
84 Rick Wise	.15	.11	.05
85 Joe Morgan	.75	.55	.25
86 Joe Ferguson	.08	.06	.02
87 Fergie Jenkins	.20	.15	.06
88 Fred Patek	.10	.07	.03
89 J. Brown	.08	.06	.02
90 Bobby Murcer	.20	.15	.06
91 Ken Forsch	.08	.06	.02
92 Paul Blair	.08	.06	.02
93 R. Gilbreath	.08	.06	.02
94 Tigers	.15	.11	.05
95 Steve Carlton	.80	.60	.25
96 J. Hairston	.08	.06	.02
97 Bob Bailey	.08	.06	.02
98 Bert Blyleven	.15	.11	.05
99 Del Crandall	.10	.07	.03
100 Willie Stargell	1.00	.70	.30
101 Bobby Valentine	.08	.06	.02
102a B. Greif(Padres)	.10	.07	.03
102b B. Greif(WashNL)	1.60	1.20	.60
103 Sal Bando	.15	.11	.05
104 R. Bryant	.08	.06	.02
105 Carlton Fisk	.60	.45	.20
106 H. Parker	.08	.06	.02
107 A. Johnson	.08	.06	.02
108 Al Hrabosky	.15	.11	.05
109 Bob Grich	.10	.07	.03
110 Billy Williams	.40	.30	.13
111 Clay Carroll	.08	.06	.02
112 Dave Lopes	.15	.11	.04

#	Player	MINT	VG-E	F-G
113	Dick Drago	.08	.06	.02
114	Angels	.15	.11	.05
115	Willie Horton	.10	.07	.03
116	Jerry Reuss	.15	.11	.05
117	Ron Blomberg	.08	.06	.02
118	Bill Lee	.10	.07	.03
119	Danny Ozark	.08	.06	.02
120	Wilbur Wood	.10	07	.03
121	Larry Lintz	.08	.06	.02
122	Jim Holt	.08	.06	.02
123	Nellie Briles	.08	.06	.02
124	B. Coluccio	.08	.06	.02
125a	Nate Colbert(Padres)	.10	.07	.03
125b	Nate Colbert(WashNL)	1.60	1.20	.60
126	Checklist 1	.08	.06	.02
127	Tom Paciorek	.08	.06	.02
128	J. Ellis	.08	.06	.02
129	Chris Speier	.08	.06	.02
130	Reggie Jackson	1.50	1.10	.50
131	Bob Boone	.08	.06	.02
132	Felix Millan	.08	.06	.02
133	David Clyde	.10	.07	.03
134	Dennis Menke	.08	.06	.02
135	Roy White	.10	.07	.03
136	Rick Reuschel	.20	.15	.06
137	Al Bumbry	.08	.06	.02
138	Eddie Brinkman	.08	.06	.02
139	A. Monteagudo	.08	.06	.02
140	D. Evans	.08	.06	.02
141	Pat Bourque	.08	.06	.02
142	P. Garcia	.08	.06	.02
143	D. Woodson	.08	.06	.02
144	Walt Alston	.10	.07	.03
145	D. Ellis	.08	.06	.02
146	Ron Fairly	.10	.07	.03
147	Bart Johnson	.08	.06	.02
148a	D. Hilton(Padres)	.10	.07	.03
148b	D. Hilton(WashNL)	1.60	1.20	.60
149	Mac Scarce	.08	.06	.02
150	John Mayberry	.15	.11	.05
151	Diego Sequi	.08	.06	.02
152	Oscar Gamble	.10	.07	.03
153	Jon Matlack	.15	.11	.05
154	Astros	.15	.11	.05
155	Bert Campaneris	.10	.07	.03
156	R. Moffitt	.08	.06	.02
157	Vic Harris	.00	.00	.02
158	Jack Billingham	.08	.06	.02
159	J. Hart	.08	.06	.02
160	Brooks Robinson	1.25	.90	.40
161	Ray Burris	.08	.06	.02
162	Bill Freehan	.10	.07	.03
163	Ken Berry	.08	.06	.02
164	Tom House	.08	.06	.02
165	Willie Davis	.10	.07	.03
166	Jack McKeon	.08	.06	.02
167	Luis Tiant	.15	.11	.05
168	Danny Thompson	.08	.06	.02
169	Steve Rogers	.20	.15	.06
170	Bill Melton	.08	.06	.02
171	Ed. Rodriguez	.08	.06	.02
172	Gene Clines	.08	.06	.02
173a	Randy Jones(Padres)	.50	.40	.18
173b	Randy Jones(WashNL)	2.50	1.80	.80
174	Bill Robinson	.08	.06	.02
175	Reggie Cleveland	.08	.06	.02
176	John Lowenstein	.08	.06	.02
177	D. Roberts	.08	.06	.02
178	Garry Maddox	.15	.11	.05
179	Yogi Berra	.60	.45	.20
180	Ken Holtzman	.10	.07	.03
181	Cesar Geronimo	.08	.06	.02
182	Lindy McDaniel	.08	.06	.02
183	Johnny Oates	.08	.06	.02
184	Rangers	.15	.11	.05
185	Jose Cardenal	.08	.06	.02
186	Fred Scherman	.08	.06	.02
187	Don Baylor	.30	.25	.10
188	Rudy Meoli	.08	.06	.02
189	J. Brewer	.08	.06	.02
190	Tony Oliva	.30	.25	.10
191	Al Fitzmorris	.08	.06	.02
192	Mario Guerrero	.08	.06	.02
193	T. Walker	.08	.06	.02
194	Darrell Porter	.25	.20	.08
195	C. May	.08	.06	.02
196	Jim Fregosi	.15	.11	.05
197a	V. Romo(Padres)	.10	.07	.03
197b	V. Romo(WashNL)	1.60	1.20	.60
198	Dave Cash	.10	.07	.03
199	Mike Kekich	.08	.06	.02
200	Cesar Cedeno	.30	.25	.10

#	Player	MINT	VG-E	F-G
201	'73 Bat Led	.20	.15	.06
202	'73 HR Led	.20	.15	.06
203	'73 RBI Led	.20	.15	.06
204	'73 SB Led	.20	.15	.06
205	'73 Vic Led	.15	.11	.05
206	'73 ERA Led	.20	.15	.06
207	'73 SO Led	.20	.15	.06
208	'73 Fireman	.15	.11	.05
209	Ted Sizemore	.08	.06	.02
210	Bill Singer	.08	.06	.02
211	Cubs	.15	.11	.05
212	Rollie Fingers	.20	.15	.06
213	Dave Rader	.08	.06	.02
214	Bill Grabarkewitz	.08	.06	.02
215	Al Kaline	1.25	.90	.40
216	Ray Sadecki	.08	.06	.02
217	Tim Foli	.08	.06	.02
218	J. Briggs	.08	.06	.02
219	D. Griffin	.08	.06	.02
220	Don Sutton	.50	.40	.18
221	Chuck Tanner	.15	.11	.05
222	R. Hernandez	.08	.06	.02
223	Jeff Burroughs	.50	.40	.18
224	Roger Metzger	.08	.06	.02
225	Paul Splittorff	.10	.07	.03
226a	Padres	.25	.20	.08
226b	Padres(Wash NL)	2.50	1.80	.80
227	Mike Lum	.08	.06	.02
228	Ted Kubiak	.08	.06	.02
229	Fritz Peterson	.08	.06	.02
230	Tony Perez	.20	.15	.06
231	Dick Tidrow	.08	.06	.02
232	Steve Brye	.08	.06	.02
233	Jim Barr	.08	.06	.02
234	John Milner	.08	.06	.02
235	Dave McNally	.10	.07	.03
236	Red Schoendienst	.10	.07	.03
237	Ken Brett	.08	.06	.02
238	Fran Healy	.08	.06	.02
239	Bill Russell	.08	.06	.02
240	Joe Coleman	.08	.06	.02
241a	Glenn Beckert(Padres)	.10	.07	.03
241b	Glenn Beckert(WashNL)	1.60	1.20	.60
242	B. Gogolewski	.08	.06	.02
243	Bob Oliver	.08	.06	.02
244	Carl Morton	.08	.06	.02
245	C. Jones	.08	.06	.02
246	Athletics	.15	.11	.05
247	R. Miller	.08	.06	.02
248	Tom Hall	.08	.06	.02
249	George Mitterwald	.08	.06	.02
250a	Willie McCovey(Padres)	1.50	1.10	.50
250b	Willie McCovey(WashNL)	7.00	5.25	2.50
251	Graig Nettles	.20	.15	.06
252	Dave Parker	3.00	2.25	1.00
253	John Boccabella	.08	.06	.02
254	Stan Bahnsen	.08	.06	.02
255	Larry Bowa	.20	.15	.06
256	T. Griffin	.08	.06	.02
257	Buddy Bell	.20	.15	.06
258	J. Morales	.08	.06	.02
259	B. Reynolds	.08	.06	.02
260	Ted Simmons	.50	.40	.18
261	J. Bell	.08	.06	.02
262	Ed Kirkpatrick	.08	.06	.02
263	Checklist 2	.08	.06	.02
264	Joe Rudi	.10	.07	.03
265	Tug McGraw	.15	.11	.05
266	Jim Northrup	.08	.06	.02
267	Andy Messersmith	.10	.07	.03
268	Tom Grieve	.08	.06	.02
269	Bob Johnson	.08	.06	.02
270	Ron Santo	.20	.15	.06
271	Bill Hands	.08	.06	.02
272	Paul Casanova	.08	.06	.02
273	Checklist 3	.08	.06	.02
274	Fred Beene	.08	.06	.02
275	Ron Hunt	.08	.06	.02
276	Bobby Winkles	.08	.06	.02
277	Gary Nolan	.08	.06	.02
278	Cookie Rojas	.08	.06	.02
279	J. Crawford	.08	.06	.02
280	Carl Yastrzemski	2.00	1.50	.60
281	Giants	.15	.11	.05
282	Doyle Alexander	.08	.06	.02
283	Mike Schmidt	1.50	1.10	.50
284	Dave Duncan	.08	.06	.02
285	Reggie Smith	.30	.25	.10
286	Tony Muser	.08	.06	.02
287	Clay Kirby	.08	.06	.02
288	Gorman Thomas	.60	.45	.20
289	R. Auerbach	.08	.06	.02
290	Vida Blue	.40	.30	.13

	MINT	VG-E	F-G			MINT	VG-E	F-G
291 D. Hahn	.08	.06	.02	381 C. Sands	.08	.06	.02
292 Chuck Seelbach	.08	.06	.02	382 Bob Moose	.08	.06	.02
293 Milt May	.08	.06	.02	383 Phillies	.15	.11	.05
294 Steve Foucault	.08	.06	.02	384 Chris Chambliss	.10	.07	.03
295 Rick Monday	.10	.07	.03	385 Don Gullett	.10	.07	.03
296 Ray Corbin	.08	.06	.02	386 Gary Matthews	.15	.11	.05
297 Hal Breeden	.08	.06	.02	387a R. Morales (Padres)	.10	.07	.03
298 R. Harrison	.08	.06	.02	387b R. Morales (WashNL)	1.60	1.20	.60
299 Gene Michael	.15	.11	.05	388 Phil Roof	.08	.06	.02
300 Pete Rose	2.00	1.50	.60	389 Gates Brown	.08	.06	.02
301 Bob Montgomery	.08	.06	.02	390 Lou Piniella	.15	.11	.05
302 Rudy May	.10	.07	.03	391 B. Champion	.08	.06	.02
303 George Hendrick	.15	.11	.05	392 D. Green	.08	.06	.02
304 D. Wilson	.08	.06	.02	393 O. Pena	.08	.06	.02
305 Tito Fuentes	.08	.06	.02	394 Ken Henderson	.08	.06	.02
306 Earl Weaver	.10	.07	.03	395 Doug Rader	.08	.06	.02
307 Luis Melendez	.08	.06	.02	396 Tommy Davis	.10	.07	.03
308 Bruck Dal Canton	.08	.06	.02	397 G. Stone	.08	.06	.02
309a D.Roberts (Padres)	.10	.07	.03	398 Duke Sims	.08	.06	.02
309b D.Roberts (WashNL)	1.60	1.20	.60	399 Mike Paul	.08	.06	.02
310 Terry Forster	.15	.11	.05	400 Harmon Killebrew	.80	.60	.25
311 Jerry Grote	.08	.06	.02	401 Elliot Maddox	.08	.06	.02
312 De. Johnson	.08	.06	.02	402 Jim Rooker	.08	.06	.02
313 B. Lersch	.08	.06	.02	403 Darrell Johnson	.08	.06	.02
314 Brewers	.15	.11	.05	404 J. Howarth	.08	.06	.02
315 Ron Cey	.30	.25	.10	405 El. Rodriguez	.08	.06	.02
316 Jim Perry	.10	.07	.03	406 S. Arlin	.08	.06	.02
317 Richie Zisk	.20	.15	.06	407 J. Wohlford	.08	.06	.02
318 Jim Merritt	.08	.06	.02	408 Charlie Hough	.08	.06	.02
319 Randy Hundley	.08	.06	.02	409 I. Brown	.08	.06	.02
320 Dusty Baker	.20	.15	.06	410 Pedro Borbon	.08	.06	.02
321 S. Braun	.08	.06	.02	411 F. Baker	.08	.06	.02
322 Ernie McAnally	.08	.06	.02	412 C. Taylor	.08	.06	.02
323 Richie Scheinblum	.08	.06	.02	413 Don Money	.10	.07	.03
324 Steve Kline	.08	.06	.02	414 Checklist 4	.08	.06	.02
325 Tommy Harper	.08	.06	.02	415 Gary Gentry	.08	.06	.02
326 Sparky Anderson	.10	.07	.03	416 White Sox	.15	.11	.05
327 Timmermann	.08	.06	.02	417 Rich Folkers	.08	.06	.02
328 Skip Jutze	.08	.06	.02	418 Walt Williams	.08	.06	.02
329 Mark Belanger	.10	.07	.03	419 Wayne Twitchell	.08	.06	.02
330 Juan Marichal	.40	.30	.13	420 Ray Fosse	.08	.06	.02
331 All-Star C	.40	.30	.13	421 D. Fife	.08	.06	.02
332 All-Star 1B	.40	.30	.13	422 Gonzalo Marquez	.08	.06	.02
333 All-Star 2B	.40	.30	.13	423 Fred Stanley	.08	.06	.02
334 All-Star 3B	.40	.30	.13	424 J. Beauchamp	.08	.06	.02
335 All-Star SS	.15	.11	.05	425 Pete Broberg	.08	.06	.02
336 All-Star LF	.40	.30	.13	426 Rennie Stennett	.08	.06	.02
337 All-Star CF	.15	.11	.05	427 B. Bolin	.08	.06	.02
338 All-Star RF	.40	.30	.13	428 Gary Sutherland	.08	.06	.02
339 All-Star P	.15	.11	.05	429 D. Lange	.08	.06	.02
340 Thurman Munson	1.50	1.10	.50	430 Matty Alou	.10	.07	.03
341 Dan Driessen	.10	.07	.03	431 Gene Garber	.08	.06	.02
342 Jim Lonborg	.10	.07	.03	432 C. Arnold	.08	.06	.02
343 Royals	.15	.11	.05	433 L. LaGrow	.08	.06	.02
344 Mike Caldwell	.10	.07	.03	434 Ken McMullen	.08	.06	.02
345 Bill North	.08	.06	.02	435 Dave Concepcion	.20	.15	.06
346 Ron Reed	.08	.06	.02	436 D. Hood	.08	.06	.02
347 Sandy Alomar	.08	.06	.02	437 J. Lyttle	.08	.06	.02
348 Pete Richert	.08	.06	.02	438 Ed Herrmann	.08	.06	.02
349 J. Vukovich	.08	.06	.02	439 N. Miller	.08	.06	.02
350 Bob Gibson	1.00	.80	.30	440 Jim Kaat	.20	.15	.06
351 D. Evans	.08	.06	.02	441 T. Ragland	.08	.06	.02
352 B. Stoneman	.08	.06	.02	442 A. Foster	.08	.06	.02
353 Rich Coggins	.08	.06	.02	443 Tom Hutton	.08	.06	.02
354 Whitey Lockman	.08	.06	.02	444 Vic Davalillo	.08	.06	.02
355 D. Nelson	.08	.06	.02	445 George Medich	.08	.06	.02
356 Jerry Koosman	.15	.11	.05	446 Len Randle	.08	.06	.02
357 B. Bradford	.08	.06	.02	447 Frank Quilici	.08	.06	.02
358 Dal Maxvill	.08	.06	.02	448 R. Hodges	.08	.06	.02
359 Brent Strom	.08	.06	.02	449 Tom McCraw	.08	.06	.02
360 Greg Luzinski	.65	.50	.20	450 Rich Hebner	.10	.07	.03
361 D. Carrithers	.08	.06	.02	451 Tommy John	.60	.45	.20
362 Hal King	.08	.06	.02	452 G. Hiser	.08	.06	.02
363 Yankees	.15	.11	.05	453 B. Moore	.08	.06	.02
364a C. Gaston (Padres)	.10	.07	.03	454 Kurt Bevacqua	.08	.06	.02
364b C. Gaston (WashNL)	1.60	1.20	.60	455 T. Bradley	.08	.06	.02
365 Steve Busby	.08	.06	.02	456 Dave Winfield	3.00	2.25	1.00
366 Larry Hisle	.20	.15	.06	457 Chuck Goggin	.08	.06	.02
367 Norm Cash	.15	.11	.05	458 J. Ray	.08	.06	.02
368 Manny Mota	.10	.07	.03	459 Reds	.15	.11	.05
369 Paul Lindblad	.08	.06	.02	460 Boog Powell	.15	.11	.05
370 Bob Watson	.10	.07	.03	461 John Odom	.08	.06	.02
371 Jim Slaton	.08	.06	.02	462 L. Alvarado	.08	.06	.02
372 Ken Reitz	.10	.07	.03	463 Pat Dobson	.08	.06	.02
373 John Curtis	.10	.07	.03	464 J. Cruz	.08	.06	.02
374 Marty Perez	.08	.06	.02	465 Dick Bosman	.08	.06	.02
375 E. Williams	.08	.06	.02	466 Dick Billings	.08	.06	.02
376 J. Orta	.08	.06	.02	467 Winston Llenas	.08	.06	.02
377 R. Woods	.08	.06	.02	468 Pepe Frias	.08	.06	.02
378 Burt Hooton	.15	.11	.05	469 Joe Decker	.08	.06	.02
379 Billy Martin	.20	.15	.06	470 AL Champ Ser.	.15	.11	.05
380 Bud Harrelson	.08	.06	.02	471 NL Champ Ser.	.15	.11	.05
				472 World Series #1	.15	.11	.05
				473 World Series #2	.15	.11	.05

	MINT	VG-E	F-G
474 World Series #3	.15	.11	.05
475 World Series #4	.15	.11	.05
476 World Series #5	.15	.11	.05
477 World Series #6	.15	.11	.05
478 World Series #7	.15	.11	.05
479 A's Celebrate	.15	.11	.05
480 Willie Crawford	.08	.06	.02
481 Jerry Terrell	.08	.06	.02
482 Bob Didier	.08	.06	.02
483 Braves	.15	.11	.05
484 Carmen Fanzone	.08	.06	.02
485 Felipe Alou	.10	.07	.03
486 Steve Stone	.20	.15	.06
487 T. Martinez	.08	.06	.02
488 Andy Etchebarren	.08	.06	.02
489 Danny Murtaugh	.08	.06	.02
490 Vada Pinson	.20	.15	.06
491 R. Nelson	.08	.06	.02
492 Rogodzinski	.08	.06	.02
493 Joe Hoerner	.08	.06	.02
494 Ed Goodson	.08	.06	.02
495 Dick McAuliffe	.08	.06	.02
496 T. Murphy	.08	.06	.02
497 B. Mitchell	.08	.06	.02
498 Pat Corrales	.08	.06	.02
499 R. Torres	.08	.06	.02
500 Lee May	.10	.07	.03
501 Eddie Leon	.08	.06	.02
502 Dave LaRoche	.08	.06	.02
503 Eric Soderholm	.08	.06	.02
504 Joe Niekro	.10	.07	.03
505 Bill Buckner	.20	.15	.06
506 Ed Farmer	.08	.06	.02
507 L. Stahl	.08	.06	.02
508 Expos	.15	.11	.05
509 Jesse Jefferson	.08	.06	.02
510 Wayne Garrett	.08	.06	.02
511 Toby Harrah	.10	.07	.03
512 Joe Lahoud	.08	.06	.02
513 J. Campanis	.08	.06	.02
514 Paul Schaal	.08	.06	.02
515 Willie Montanez	.10	.07	.03
516 H. Pina	.08	.06	.02
517 Mike Hegan	.08	.06	.02
518 D. Thomas	.08	.06	.02
519 B. Sharp	.08	.06	.02
520 Tim McCarver	.08	.06	.02
521 Ken Aspromonte	.08	.06	.02
522 J. R. Richard	.60	.45	.20
523 Cecil Cooper	.30	.25	.10
524 Bill Plummer	.08	.06	.02
525 Clyde Wright	.08	.06	.02
526 Frank Tepedino	.08	.06	.02
527 Bobby Darwin	.08	.06	.02
528 Bill Bonham	.08	.06	.02
529 Horace Clarke	.08	.06	.02
530 Mickey Stanley	.10	.07	.03
531 Gene Mauch	.10	.07	.03
532 Skip Lockwood	.08	.06	.02
533 M. Phillips	.08	.06	.02
534 Eddie Watt	.08	.06	.02
535 Bob Tolan	.08	.06	.02
536 Duffy Dyer	.08	.06	.02
537 Steve Mingori	.08	.06	.02
538 Cesar Tovar	.08	.06	.02
539 Lloyd Allen	.08	.06	.02
540 Bob Robertson	.08	.06	.02
541 Indians	.15	.11	.05
542 Rick Gossage	.40	.30	.13
543 Danny Cater	.08	.06	.02
544 Ron Schueler	.08	.06	.02
545 B. Conigliaro	.08	.06	.02
546 M. Corkins	.08	.06	.02
547 Glenn Borgmann	.08	.06	.02
548 Sonny Siebert	.08	.06	.02
549 Mike Jorgensen	.08	.06	.02
550 Sam McDowell	.10	.07	.03
551 Von Joshua	.08	.06	.02
552 Denny Doyle	.08	.06	.02
553 Jim Willoughby	.08	.06	.02
554 T. Johnson	.08	.06	.02
555 Woody Fryman	.08	.06	.02
556 D. Campbell	.08	.06	.02
557 J. McGlothlin	.08	.06	.02
558 Bill Fahey	.08	.06	.02
559 Darrell Chaney	.08	.06	.02
560 Mike Cuellar	.10	.07	.03
561 Ed Kranepool	.10	.07	.03
562 J. Aker	.08	.06	.02
563 Hal McRae	.08	.06	.02
564 Mike Ryan	.08	.06	.02
565 Milt Wilcox	.08	.06	.02
566 J. Hernandez	.08	.06	.02
567 Red Sox	.15	.11	.05
568 Mike Torrez	.15	.11	.05
569 Rick Dempsey	.08	.06	.02
570 Ralph Garr	.10	.07	.03
571 R. Hand	.08	.06	.02
572 E. Hernandez	.08	.06	.02
573 M. Adams	.08	.06	.02
574 B. Parsons	.08	.06	.02
575 Steve Garvey	1.50	1.10	.50
576 S. Spinks	.08	.06	.02
577 Mike Sadek	.08	.06	.02
578 Ralph Houk	.15	.11	.05
579 Cecil Upshaw	.08	.06	.02
580 Jim Spencer	.08	.06	.02
581 Fred Norman	.08	.06	.02
582 Bucky Dent	.15	.11	.05
583 Marty Pattin	.08	.06	.02
584 Ken Rudolph	.08	.06	.02
585 Merv Rettenmund	.08	.06	.02
586 Jack Brohamer	.08	.06	.02
587 Larry Christenson	.08	.06	.02
588 Hal Lanier	.08	.06	.02
589 B. Day	.08	.06	.02
590 Roger Moret	.08	.06	.02
591 S. Jackson	.08	.06	.02
592 Ed Bane	.08	.06	.02
593 Steve Yeager	.08	.06	.02
594 L. Stanton	.08	.06	.02
595 Steve Blass	.10	.07	.03
596 Rookie P	.08	.06	.02
597 Rookie SS	.08	.06	.02
598 Rookie OF	.80	.60	.25
599a Rookie P (Wash. NL)	.50	.40	.18
599b Rookie P (San Diego)	1.00	.70	.30
600 Rookie INF	.80	.60	.25
601 Rookie OF	.80	.60	.25
602 Rookie P	.30	.25	.10
603 Rookie C	.08	.06	.02
604 Rookie INF	.08	.06	.02
605 Rookie P	.30	.25	.10
606 Rookie OF	.08	.06	.02
607 Rookie SS	.08	.06	.02
608A Rookie P (Apodaca)	.10	.07	.03
608B Rookie P (Apodaco)	1.00	.70	.30
610 Dave Kingman	.50	.40	.18
611 Rich Stelmaszek	.08	.06	.02
612 Luke Walker	.00	.06	.02
613 D. Monzon	.08	.06	.02
614 Adrian Devine	.08	.06	.02
615 J. Jeter	.08	.06	.02
616 Larry Gura	.12	.09	.04
617 T. Ford	.08	.06	.02
618 Jim Mason	.08	.06	.02
619 M. Anderson	.08	.06	.02
620 Al Downing	.08	.06	.02
621 Bernie Carbo	.08	.06	.02
622 Phil Gagliano	.08	.06	.02
623 C. Sanchez	.08	.06	.02
624 Bob Miller	.08	.06	.02
625 Ollie Brown	.08	.06	.02
626 Pirates	.15	.11	.05
627 C. Taylor	.08	.06	.02
628 Ivan Murrell	.08	.06	.02
629 Rusty Staub	.15	.11	.05
630 Tommy Agee	.08	.06	.02
631 Steve Barber	.08	.06	.02
632 George Culver	.08	.06	.02
633 D. Hamilton	.08	.06	.02
634 Eddie Mathews	.50	.40	.18
635 J. Edwards	.08	.06	.02
636 Dave Goltz	.10	.07	.03
637 Checklist 5	.08	.06	.02
638 Ken Sanders	.08	.06	.02
639 Joe Lovitto	.08	.06	.02
640 Milt Pappas	.10	.07	.03
641 C. Brinkman	.08	.06	.02
642 T. Harmon	.08	.06	.02
643 Dodgers	.15	.11	.05
644 Wayne Granger	.08	.06	.02
645 Ken Boswell	.08	.06	.02
646 George Foster	.90	.70	.30
647 Juan Beniquez	.08	.06	.02
648 Terry Crowley	.08	.06	.02
649 Fernando Gonzalez	.08	.06	.02
650 Mike Epstein	.08	.06	.02
651 L. Lee	.08	.06	.02
652 Gail Hopkins	.08	.06	.02
653 Bob Stinson	.08	.06	.02
654a Jesus Alou (outfield)	.15	.11	.05
654b Jesus Alou (no pos.)	2.00	1.50	.60
655 Mike Tyson	.08	.06	.02
656 A. Garrett	.08	.06	.02

	MINT	VG-E	F-G
657 Jim Shellenback	.08	.06	.02
658 Lee Lacy	.08	.06	.02

	MINT	VG-E	F-G
659 Joe Lis	.08	.06	.02
660 Larry Dierker	.08	.06	.02

1974 TOPPS TRADED (44)　　2 1/2" X 3 1/2"

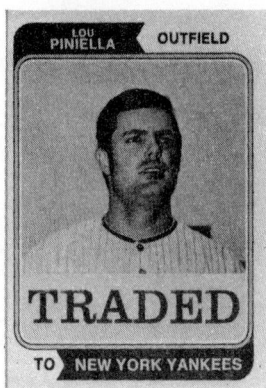

The 1974 Topps Traded set consists of 44 cards, including a Traded set checklist card, portraying players who were Traded after Topps' regular set was printed. Players are portrayed with their new teams, and the card number for the Traded cards are the same as the player's card in the regular set with a "T" following the number.

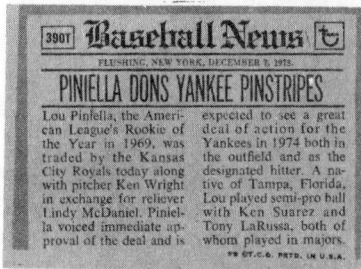

	MINT	VG-E	F-G
COMPLETE SET	2.50	2.00	.80
COMMON PLAYER	.06	.04	.02

	MINT	VG-E	F-G
Trade Checklist	.10	.07	.03
23T Craig Robinson	.06	.04	.02
42T Claude Osteen	.06	.04	.02
43T Jim Wynn	.10	.07	.03
51T Bobby Heise	.06	.04	.02
59T Ross Grimsley	.06	.04	.02
62T Bob Locker	.06	.04	.02
63T Bill Sudakis	.06	.04	.02
73T Mike Marshall	.10	.07	.03
123T Nelson Briles	.06	.04	.02
139T A. Monteagudo	.06	.04	.02
151T Diego Segui	.06	.04	.02
165T Willie Davis	.10	.07	.03
175T Reg Cleveland	.06	.04	.02
182T Lindy McDaniel	.06	.04	.02
186T Fred Scherman	.06	.04	.02
249T Geo. Mitterwald	.06	.04	.02
262T Ed Kirkpatrick	.06	.04	.02
269T Bob Johnson	.06	.04	.02
270T Ron Santo	.10	.07	.03
313T Barry Lersch	.06	.04	.02
319T Randy Hundley	.06	.04	.02

	MINT	VG-E	F-G
330T Juan Marichal	.25	.20	.08
348T Pete Richert	.06	.04	.02
373T John Curtis	.06	.04	.02
390T Lou Piniella	.10	.07	.03
428T G. Sutherland	.06	.04	.02
454T Kurt Bevacqua	.06	.04	.02
458T Jim Ray	.06	.04	.02
485T Felipe Alou	.10	.07	.03
486T Steve Stone	.10	.07	.03
496T Tom Murphy	.06	.04	.02
516T Horacio Pina	.06	.04	.02
534T Eddie Watt	.06	.04	.02
538T Cesar Tovar	.06	.04	.02
544T Ron Schueler	.06	.04	.02
579T Cecil Upshaw	.06	.04	.02
585T M. Rettenmund	.06	.04	.02
612T Luke Walker	.06	.04	.02
616T Larry Gura	.10	.07	.03
618T Jim Mason	.06	.04	.02
630T Tommie Agee	.06	.04	.02
648T Terry Crowley	.06	.04	.02
649T F. Gonzalez	.06	.04	.02

EARLY EXHIBIT

NON-BASEBALL EXHIBITS

1974 TOPPS DECKLE—EDGE (72)   2 7/8" X 5"

The 1974 Topps Deckle-Edge set of 72 black and white, numbered cards was of limited distribution. The cards have serrated borders with only a blue facsimile autograph on the front to mar the photo. The backs include a small news clipping of one of the career highlights of the player.

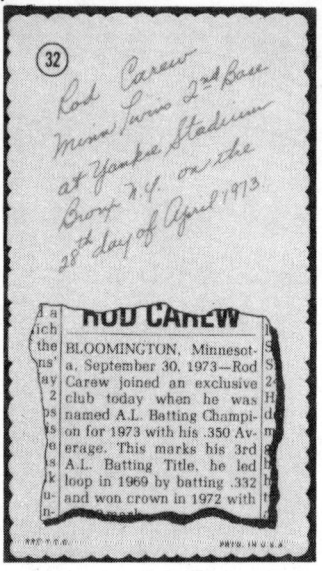

	MINT	VG-E	F-G			MINT	VG-E	F-G
COMPLETE SET	600.00	450.00	200.00	36	Rod Carew	18.00	13.50	6.00
COMMON PLAYER	8.00	6.00	2.50	37	Buddy Bell	10.00	7.00	3.00
				38	Claude Osteen	8.00	6.00	2.50
1 Amos Otis	10.00	7.00	3.00	39	Dick Allen	10.00	7.00	3.00
2 Darrell Evans	8.00	6.00	2.50	40	Bill Russell	8.00	6.00	2.50
3 Bob Gibson	15.00	11.00	5.00	41	Nolan Ryan	15.00	11.00	5.00
4 Dave Nelson	8.00	6.00	2.50	42	Willie Davis	8.00	6.00	2.50
5 Steve Carlton	15.00	11.00	5.00	43	Carl Yastrzemski	25.00	18.50	8.75
6 Jim Hunter	15.00	11.00	5.00	44	Jon Matlack	8.00	6.00	2.50
7 Thurman Munson	20.00	15.00	6.50	45	Jim Palmer	15.00	11.00	5.00
8 Bob Grich	8.00	6.00	2.50	46	Bert Campaneris	8.00	6.00	2.50
9 Tom Seaver	20.00	15.00	6.50	47	Bert Blyleven	10.00	7.00	3.00
10 Ted Simmons	12.50	9.00	4.00	48	Jeff Burroughs	10.00	7.00	3.00
11 Bob Valentine	8.00	6.00	2.50	49	Jim Colborn	8.00	6.00	2.50
12 Don Sutton	12.50	9.00	4.00	50	Dave Johnson	8.00	6.00	2.50
13 Wilbur Wood	8.00	6.00	2.50	51	John Mayberry	8.00	6.00	2.50
14 Doug Rader	8.00	6.00	2.50	52	Don Kessinger	8.00	6.00	2.50
15 Chris Chambliss	8.00	6.00	2.50	53	Joe Coleman	8.00	6.00	2.50
16 Pete Rose	25.00	18.50	8.75	54	Tony Perez	12.50	9.00	4.00
17 John Hiller	8.00	6.00	2.50	55	Jose Cardenal	8.00	6.00	2.50
18 Burt Hooton	8.00	6.00	2.50	56	Paul Splittorff	8.00	6.00	2.50
19 Tim Foli	8.00	6.00	2.50	57	Hank Aaron	25.00	18.50	8.75
20 Lou Brock	18.00	13.50	6.00	58	Dave May	8.00	6.00	2.50
21 Ron Bryant	8.00	6.00	2.50	59	Fergie Jenkins	10.00	7.00	3.00
22 Manny Sanguillen	8.00	6.00	2.50	60	Ron Blomberg	8.00	6.00	2.50
23 Bob Tolan	8.00	6.00	2.50	61	Reggie Jackson	18.00	13.50	6.00
24 Greg Luzinski	12.50	9.00	4.00	62	Tony Oliva	10.00	7.00	3.00
25 Brooks Robinson	20.00	15.00	6.50	63	Bobby Murcer	10.00	7.00	3.00
26 Felix Millan	8.00	6.00	2.50	64	Carlton Fisk	12.50	9.00	4.00
27 Luis Tiant	10.00	7.00	3.00	65	Steve Rogers	10.00	7.00	3.00
28 Willie McCovey	15.00	11.00	5.00	66	Frank Robinson	15.00	11.00	5.00
29 Chris Speier	8.00	6.00	2.50	67	Joe Ferguson	8.00	6.00	2.50
30 George Scott	8.00	6.00	2.50	68	Bill Melton	8.00	6.00	2.50
31 Willie Stargell	15.00	11.00	5.00	69	Bob Watson	10.00	7.00	3.00
32 Rod Carew	18.00	13.50	6.00	70	Larry Bowa	10.00	7.00	3.00
33 Charlie Spikes	8.00	6.00	2.50	71	Johnny Bench	20.00	15.00	6.50
34 Nate Colbert	8.00	6.00	2.50	72	Willie Horton	8.00	6.00	2.50
35 Rich Hebner	8.00	6.00	2.50					

REMEMBER THE NATIONAL CONVENTION IS BEING HELD JULY 9 - 12, 1981, IN PLYMOUTH, MICHIGAN

342

1975 TOPPS (660)
1975 TOPPS MINIS (660)

2 1/2" X 3 1/2"
2 1/4" X 3 1/8"

The 1975 Topps regular set features 1951-1974 most valuable players as cards nos. 189-212. In 1975 Topps also issued a "mini" set which contains the exact same cards as the regular issue but the size of the card is smaller (2 1/4 x 3 1/8). The minis were of lim-ited distribution; hence they are scarcer than the regular issue cards. Both the regular issue and mini issue are borderless.

	REGULAR			MINI'S		
	MINT	VG-E	F-G	MINT	VG-E	F-G
REGULAR COMPLETE SET	70.00	55.00	20.00	xxx	xxx	xxx
REGULAR COMMON PLAYERS	.06	.04	.02	xxx	xxx	xxx
MINI COMPLETE SET	xxx	xxx	xxx	175.00	130.00	50.00
MINI COMMON PLAYERS	xx	xx	xx	.15	.11	.05
1 Aaron: Record	2.00	1.50	.60	4.00	3.00	1.40
2 Brock: Record	.60	.45	.20	1.25	.90	.40
3 Gibson: Record	.50	.40	.18	1.00	.70	.30
4 Kaline: Record	.60	.45	.20	1.25	.90	.40
5 Ryan: Record	.50	.40	.18	1.00	.70	.30
6 Marshall: Record	.10	.07	.03	.20	.15	.06
7 No Hitters	.10	.07	.03	.20	.15	.06
8 Rogelio Moret	.06	.04	.02	.15	.11	.05
9 Frank Tepedino	.06	.04	.02	.15	.11	.05
10 Willie Davis	.10	.07	.03	.20	.15	.06
11 Bill Melton	.06	.04	.02	.15	.11	.05
12 David Clyde	.06	.04	.02	.15	.11	.05
13 Gene Locklear	.06	.04	.02	.15	.11	.05
14 Milt Wilcox	.06	.04	.02	.15	.11	.05
15 Jose Cardenal	.06	.04	.02	.15	.11	.05
16 Frank Tanana	.10	.07	.03	.20	.15	.06
17 Dave Concepcion	.15	.11	.05	.30	.25	.10
18 Tigers: Team/Mgr	.10	.07	.03	.25	.20	.08
19 Jerry Koosman	.10	.07	.03	.20	.15	.06
20 Thurman Munson	1.50	1.10	.50	3.00	2.25	1.00
21 Rollie Fingers	.15	.11	.05	.30	.25	.10
22 Dave Cash	.06	.04	.02	.15	.11	.05
23 Bill Russell	.06	.04	.02	.15	.11	.05
24 Al Fitzmorris	.06	.04	.02	.15	.11	.05
25 Lee May	.06	.04	.02	.15	.11	.05
26 Dave McNally	.08	.06	.02	.20	.15	.06
27 Ken Reitz	.06	.04	.02	.15	.11	.05
28 Tom Murphy	.06	.04	.02	.15	.11	.05
29 Dave Parker	1.25	.90	.40	2.75	2.00	.90
30 Bert Blyleven	.10	.07	.03	.20	.15	.06
31 Dave Rader	.06	.04	.02	.15	.11	.05
32 Reggie Cleveland	.06	.04	.02	.15	.11	.05
33 Dusty Baker	.12	.08	.04	.30	.25	.10
34 Steve Renko	.06	.04	.02	.15	.11	.05
35 Ron Santo	.10	.07	.03	.20	.15	.06
36 Joe Lovitto	.06	.04	.02	.15	.11	.05
37 Dave Freisleben	.06	.04	.02	.15	.11	.05
38 Buddy Bell	.12	.08	.04	.30	.25	.10
39 Andy Thornton	.10	.07	.03	.20	.15	.06
40 Bill Singer	.06	.04	.02	.15	.11	.05

	REGULAR			MINI'S		
	MINT	VG-E	F-G	MINT	VG-E	F-G
41 Cesar Geronimo	.06	.04	.02	.15	.11	.05
42 Joe Coleman	.06	.04	.02	.15	.11	.05
43 Cleon Jones	.06	.04	.02	.15	.11	.05
44 Pat Dobson	.06	.04	.02	.15	.11	.05
45 Joe Rudi	.10	.07	.03	.20	.15	.05
46 Phillies: Team/Mgr	.10	.07	.03	.25	.20	.08
47 Tommy John	.60	.45	.20	1.25	.90	.40
48 Freddie Patek	.06	.04	.02	.15	.11	.05
49 Larry Dierker	.06	.04	.02	.15	.11	.05
50 Brooks Robinson	1.00	.70	.30	2.50	1.80	.80
51 Bob Forsch	.06	.04	.02	.15	.11	.05
52 Darrell Porter	.15	.11	.05	.35	.27	.12
53 Dave Giusti	.06	.04	.02	.15	.11	.05
54 Eric Soderholm	.06	.04	.02	.15	.11	.05
55 Bobby Bonds	.20	.15	.06	.40	.30	.13
56 Rick Wise	.10	.07	.03	.20	.15	.06
57 Dave Johnson	.06	.04	.02	.15	.11	.05
58 Chuck Taylor	.06	.04	.02	.15	.11	.05
59 Ken Henderson	.06	.04	.02	.15	.11	.05
60 Fergie Jenkins	.15	.11	.05	.30	.25	.10
61 Dave Winfield	1.25	.90	.40	2.75	2.00	.90
62 Fritz Peterson	.06	.04	.02	.15	.11	.05
63 Steve Swisher	.06	.04	.02	.15	.11	.05
64 Dave Chalk	.06	.04	.02	.15	.11	.05
65 Don Gullett	.06	.04	.02	.15	.11	.05
66 Willie Horton	.10	.07	.03	.20	.15	.06
67 Tug McGraw	.12	.08	.04	.30	.25	.10
68 Ron Blomberg	.06	.04	.02	.15	.11	.05
69 John Odom	.06	.04	.02	.15	.11	.05
70 Mike Schmidt	1.25	.90	.40	2.75	2.00	.90
71 Charlie Hough	.06	.04	.02	.15	.11	.05
72 Royals: Team/Mgr	.10	.07	.03	.25	.20	.08
73 J. R. Richard	.60	.45	.20	1.25	.90	.40
74 Mark Belanger	.10	.07	.03	.20	.15	.06
75 Ted Simmons	.40	.30	.13	1.00	.70	.30
76 Ed Sprague	.06	.04	.02	.15	.11	.05
77 Richie Zisk	.12	.08	.04	.30	.25	.10
78 Ray Corbin	.06	.04	.02	.15	.11	.05
79 Gary Matthews	.12	.08	.04	.30	.25	.10
80 Carlton Fisk	.40	.30	.13	1.00	.70	.30
81 Ron Reed	.06	.04	.02	.15	.11	.05
82 Pat Kelly	.06	.04	.02	.15	.11	.05
83 Jim Merritt	.06	.04	.02	.15	.11	.05
84 Enzo Hernandez	.06	.04	.02	.15	.11	.05
85 Bill Bonham	.06	.04	.02	.15	.11	.05

MICKEY MANTLE
NEW YORK YANKEES

HOME RUN DERBY

		REGULAR			MINI'S		
		MINT	VG-E	F-G	MINT	VG-E	F-G
86	Joe Lis	.06	.04	.02	.15	.11	.05
87	George Foster	.60	.45	.20	1.25	.90	.40
88	Tom Egan	.06	.04	.02	.15	.11	.05
89	Jim Ray	.06	.04	.02	.15	.11	.05
90	Rusty Staub	.12	.08	.04	.30	.25	.10
91	Dick Green	.06	.04	.02	.15	.11	.05
92	Cecil Upshaw	.06	.04	.02	.15	.11	.05
93	Dave Lopes	.12	.08	.04	.30	.25	.10
94	Jim Lonborg	.10	.07	.03	.20	.15	.06
95	John Mayberry	.10	.07	.03	.20	.15	.06
96	Mike Cosgrove	.06	.04	.03	.20	.15	.06
97	Earl Williams	.06	.04	.02	.15	.11	.05
98	Rich Folkers	.06	.04	.02	.15	.11	.05
99	Mike Hegan	.06	.04	.02	.15	.11	.05
100	Willie Stargell	.75	.55	.25	1.50	1.10	.50
101	Expos: Team/Mgr	.10	.07	.03	.25	.20	.08
102	Joe Decker	.06	.04	.02	.15	.11	.05
103	Rick Miller	.06	.04	.02	.15	.11	.05
104	Bill Madlock	.15	.11	.05	.35	.27	.12
105	Buzz Capra	.06	.04	.02	.15	.11	.05
106	Mike Hargrove	.06	.04	.02	.15	.11	.05
107	Jim Barr	.06	.04	.02	.15	.11	.05
108	Tom Hall	.06	.04	.02	.15	.11	.05
109	George Hendrick	.12	.08	.04	.30	.25	.11
110	Wilbur Wood	.06	.04	.02	.15	.11	.05
111	Wayne Garrett	.06	.04	.02	.15	.11	.05
112	Larry Hardy	.06	.04	.02	.15	.11	.05
113	Elliott Maddox	.06	.04	.02	.15	.11	.05
114	Dick Lange	.06	.04	.02	.15	.11	.05
115	Joe Ferguson	.06	.04	.02	.15	.11	.05
116	Lerrin LaGrow	.06	.04	.02	.15	.11	.05
117	Orioles: Team/Mgr	.10	.07	.03	.25	.20	.08
118	Mike Anderson	.06	.04	.02	.15	.11	.05
119	Tommy Helms	.06	.04	.02	.15	.11	.05
120	Steve Busby	.06	.04	.02	.15	.11	.05
121	Bill North	.06	.04	.02	.15	.11	.05
122	Al Hrabosky	.12	.08	.04	.30	.25	.11
123	Johnny Briggs	.06	.04	.02	.15	.11	.05
124	Jerry Reuss	.10	.07	.03	.20	.15	.06
125	Ken Singleton	.30	.25	.12	.75	.55	.25
126	Checklist: 1-132	.06	.04	.02	.15	.11	.05
127	Glenn Borgmann	.06	.04	.02	.15	.11	.05
128	Bill Lee	.06	.04	.02	.15	.11	.05
129	Rick Monday	.10	.07	.03	.20	.15	.06
130	Phil Niekro	.15	.11	.05	.35	.27	.12
131	Toby Harrah	.06	.04	.02	.15	.11	.05
132	Randy Moffitt	.06	.04	.02	.15	.11	.05
133	Dan Driessen	.06	.04	.02	.15	.11	.05
134	Ron Hodges	.06	.04	.02	.15	.11	.05
135	Charlie Spikes	.06	.04	.02	.15	.11	.05
136	Jim Mason	.06	.04	.02	.15	.11	.05
137	Terry Forster	.12	.08	.04	.30	.25	.11
138	Del Unser	.06	.04	.02	.15	.11	.05
139	Horacio Pina	.06	.04	.02	.15	.11	.05
140	Steve Garvey	1.25	.90	.40	2.75	2.00	.90
141	Mickey Stanley	.06	.04	.02	.15	.11	.05
142	Bob Reynolds	.06	.04	.02	.15	.11	.05
143	Cliff Johnson	.06	.04	.02	.15	.11	.05
144	Jim Wohlford	.06	.04	.02	.15	.11	.05
145	Ken Holtzman	.10	.07	.03	.20	.15	.06
146	Padres: Team/Mgr	.10	.07	.03	.25	.20	.08
147	Pedro Garcia	.06	.04	.02	.15	.11	.05
148	Jim Rooker	.06	.04	.02	.15	.11	.05
149	Tim Foli	.06	.04	.02	.15	.11	.05
150	Bob Gibson	.75	.55	.25	1.50	1.10	.50
151	Steve Brye	.06	.04	.02	.15	.11	.05
152	Mario Guerrero	.06	.04	.02	.15	.11	.05
153	Rick Reuschel	.15	.11	.05	.35	.27	.12
154	Mike Lum	.06	.04	.02	.15	.11	.05
155	Jim Bibby	.10	.07	.03	.20	.15	.06
156	Dave Kingman	.50	.40	.18	1.00	.70	.30
157	Pedro Borbon	.06	.04	.02	.15	.11	.05
158	Jerry Grote	.06	.04	.02	.15	.11	.05
159	Steve Arlin	.06	.04	.02	.15	.11	.05
160	Graig Nettles	.15	.11	.05	.35	.27	.12
161	Stan Bahnsen	.06	.04	.02	.15	.11	.05
162	Willie Montanez	.10	.07	.03	.20	.15	.06
163	Jim Brewer	.06	.04	.02	.15	.11	.05
164	Mickey Rivers	.15	.11	.05	.35	.27	.12
165	Doug Rader	.06	.04	.02	.15	.11	.05
166	Woodie Fryman	.06	.04	.02	.15	.11	.05
167	Rich Coggins	.06	.04	.02	.15	.11	.05
168	Bill Greif	.06	.04	.02	.15	.11	.05
169	Cookie Rojas	.06	.04	.02	.15	.11	.05
170	Bert Campaneris	.10	.07	.03	.20	.15	.05
171	Ed Kirkpatrick	.06	.04	.02	.15	.11	.05
172	Red Sox: Team/Mgr	.12	.08	.04	.20	.15	.06
173	Steve Rogers	.10	.07	.03	.20	.15	.06
174	Bake McBride	.10	.07	.03	.20	.15	.06
175	Don Money	.10	.07	.03	.20	.15	.06
176	Burt Hooton	.10	.07	.03	.20	.15	.06
177	Vic Correll	.06	.04	.02	.15	.11	.05

	REGULAR			MINI'S		
	MINT	VG-E	F-G	MINT	VG-E	F-G
178 Cesar Tovar	.06	.04	.02	.15	.11	.05
179 Tom Bradley	.06	.04	.02	.15	.11	.05
180 Joe Morgan	.60	.45	.20	1.25	.90	.40
181 Fred Beene	.06	.04	.02	.15	.11	.05
182 Don Hahn	.06	.04	.02	.15	.11	.05
183 Mel Stottlemyre	.10	.07	.03	.20	.15	.06
184 Jorge Orta	.06	.04	.02	.15	.11	.05
185 Steve Carlton	.75	.55	.25	1.50	1.10	.50
186 Willie Crawford	.06	.04	.02	.15	.11	.05
187 Denny Doyle	.06	.04	.02	.15	.11	.05
188 Tom Griffin	.06	.04	.02	.15	.11	.05
189 1951 MVP's	.40	.30	.13	1.25	.90	.40
190 1952 MVP's	.20	.15	.06	.50	.40	.18
191 1953 MVP's	.30	.25	.10	1.00	.70	.30
192 1954 MVP's	.40	.30	.13	1.00	.70	.30
193 1955 MVP's	.40	.30	.13	1.25	.90	.40
194 1956 MVP's	.40	.30	.13	1.25	.90	.40
195 1957 MVP's	.40	.30	.13	1.25	.90	.40
196 1958 MVP's	.20	.15	.06	.50	.40	.18
197 1959 MVP's	.20	.15	.06	.50	.40	.18
198 1960 MVP's	.20	.15	.06	.50	.40	.18
199 1961 MVP's	.30	.25	.10	1.00	.70	.30
200 1962 MVP's	.25	.20	.08	.75	.55	.25
201 1963 MVP's	.25	.20	.08	.75	.55	.25
202 1964 MVP's	.20	.15	.06	.50	.40	.18
203 1965 MVP's	.20	.15	.06	.50	.40	.18
204 1966 MVP's	.25	.20	.08	.75	.55	.25
205 1967 MVP's	.20	.15	.06	.50	.40	.18
206 1968 MVP's	.20	.15	.06	.50	.40	.18
207 1969 MVP's	.20	.15	.06	.50	.40	.18
208 1970 MVP's	.25	.20	.08	.25	.20	.08
209 1971 MVP's	.20	.15	.06	.50	.40	.18
210 1972 MVP's	.20	.15	.06	.50	.40	.18
211 1973 MVP's	.20	.15	.06	.50	.40	.18
212 1974 MVP's	.20	.15	.06	.50	.40	.18
213 Oscar Gamble	.10	.07	.03	.20	.15	.06
214 Harry Parker	.06	.04	.02	.15	.11	.05
215 Bobby Valentine	.06	.04	.02	.15	.11	.05
216 Giants: Team/Mgr	.10	.07	.03	.25	.20	.08
217 Lou Piniella	.10	.07	.03	.20	.15	.06
218 Jerry Johnson	.06	.04	.02	.15	.11	.05
219 Ed Herrmann	.06	.04	.02	.15	.11	.05
220 Don Sutton	.40	.30	.13	.80	.60	.25
221 Aurelio Rodriguez	.06	.04	.02	.15	.11	.05
222 Dan Spillner	.06	.04	.02	.15	.11	.05
223 Robin Yount	.50	.40	.18	1.00	.70	.30
224 Ramon Hernandez	.06	.04	.02	.15	.11	.05
225 Bob Grich	.10	.07	.03	.20	.15	.06
226 Bill Campbell	.06	.04	.02	.15	.11	.05
227 Bob Watson	.10	.07	.03	.20	.15	.06
228 George Brett	6.00	4.50	2.00	12.00	8.75	4.00
229 Barry Foote	.06	.04	.02	.15	.11	.05
230 Jim Hunter	.40	.30	.13	.80	.60	.25
231 Mike Tyson	.06	.04	.02	.15	.11	.05
232 Diego Segui	.06	.04	.02	.15	.11	.05
233 Billy Grabarkewitz	.06	.04	.02	.15	.11	.05
234 Tom Grieve	.06	.04	.02	.15	.11	.05
235 Jack Billingham	.06	.04	.02	.15	.11	.05
236 Angels: Team/Mgr	.10	.07	.03	.25	.20	.08
237 Carl Morton	.06	.04	.02	.15	.11	.05
238 Dave Duncan	.06	.04	.02	.15	.11	.05
239 George Stone	.06	.04	.02	.15	.11	.05
240 Garry Maddox	.10	.07	.03	.20	.15	.06
241 Dick Tidrow	.06	.04	.02	.15	.11	.05
242 Jay Johnstone	.06	.04	.02	.15	.11	.05
243 Jim Kaat	.12	.08	.04	.40	.30	.13
244 Bill Buckner	.12	.08	.04	.30	.25	.10
245 Mickey Lolich	.10	.07	.03	.20	.15	.06
246 Cardinals: Team/Mgr	.10	.07	.03	.25	.20	.08
247 Enos Cabell	.06	.04	.02	.15	.11	.05
248 Randy Jones	.10	.07	.03	.20	.15	.06
249 Danny Thompson	.06	.04	.02	.15	.11	.05
250 Ken Brett	.06	.04	.02	.15	.11	.05
251 Fran Healy	.06	.04	.02	.15	.11	.05
252 Fred Scherman	.06	.04	.02	.15	.11	.05
253 Jesus Alou	.06	.04	.02	.15	.11	.05
254 Mike Torrez	.10	.07	.03	.20	.15	.06
255 Dwight Evans	.06	.04	.02	.15	.11	.05
256 Billy Champion	.06	.04	.02	.15	.11	.05
257 Checklist: 133-264	.06	.04	.02	.15	.11	.05
258 Dave LaRoche	.06	.04	.02	.15	.11	.05
259 Len Randle	.06	.04	.02	.15	.11	.05
260 Johnny Bench	1.25	.90	.40	2.75	2.00	.90
261 Andy Hassler	.06	.04	.02	.15	.11	.05
262 Rowland Office	.06	.04	.02	.15	.11	.05
263 Jim Perry	.06	.04	.02	.15	.11	.05
264 John Milner	.06	.04	.02	.15	.11	.05
265 Ron Bryant	.06	.04	.02	.15	.11	.05
266 Sandy Alomar	.06	.04	.02	.15	.11	.05
267 Dick Ruthven	.06	.04	.02	.15	.11	.05
268 Hal McRae	.06	.04	.02	.15	.11	.05
269 Doug Rau	.06	.04	.02	.15	.11	.05
270 Ron Fairly	.06	.04	.02	.15	.11	.05

		REGULAR		MINI'S		
	MINT	VG-E	F-G	MINT	VG-E	F-G
271 Jerry Moses	.06	.04	.02	.15	.11	.05
272 Lynn McGlothen	.06	.04	.02	.15	.11	.05
273 Steve Braun	.06	.04	.02	.15	.11	.05
274 Vincente Romo	.06	.04	.02	.15	.11	.05
275 Paul Blair	.06	.04	.02	.15	.11	.05
276 Chisox: Team/Mgr	.10	.07	.03	.25	.20	.08
277 Frank Taveras	.06	.04	.02	.15	.11	.08
278 Paul Lindblad	.06	.04	.02	.15	.11	.05
279 Milt May	.06	.04	.02	.15	.11	.05
280 Carl Yastrzemski	1.50	1.10	.50	3.50	2.50	1.20
281 Jim Slaton	.06	.04	.02	.15	.11	.05
282 Jerry Morales	.06	.04	.02	.15	.11	.05
283 Steve Foucault	.06	.04	.02	.15	.11	.05
284 Ken Griffey	.12	.08	.04	.30	.25	.10
285 Ellie Rodriguez	.06	.04	.02	.15	.11	.05
286 Mike Jorgensen	.06	.04	.02	.15	.11	.05
287 Roric Harrison	.06	.04	.02	.15	.11	.05
288 Bruce Ellingsen	.06	.04	.02	.15	.11	.05
289 Ken Rudolph	.06	.04	.02	.15	.11	.05
290 Jon Matlack	.10	.07	.03	.20	.15	.06
291 Bill Sudakis	.06	.04	.02	.15	.11	.05
292 Ron Schueler	.06	.04	.02	.15	.11	.05
293 Dick Sharon	.06	.04	.02	.15	.11	.05
294 Geoff Zahn	.06	.04	.02	.15	.11	.05
295 Vada Pinson	.15	.11	.05	.35	.27	.12
296 Alan Foster	.06	.04	.02	.15	.11	.05
297 Craig Kusick	.06	.04	.02	.15	.11	.05
298 Johnny Grubb	.06	.04	.02	.15	.11	.05
299 Bucky Dent	.12	.08	.04	.30	.25	.10
300 Reggie Jackson	1.25	.90	.40	2.75	2.00	.90
301 Dave Roberts	.06	.04	.02	.15	.11	.05
302 Rick Burleson	.35	.27	.12	.75	.55	.25
303 Grant Jackson	.06	.04	.02	.15	.11	.05
304 Pirates: Team/Mgr	.10	.07	.03	.25	.20	.08
305 Jim Colborn	.06	.04	.02	.15	.11	.05
306 '74 Batting Ldrs.	.15	.11	.05	.35	.27	.12
307 '74 HR Leaders	.15	.11	.05	.35	.27	.12
308 '74 RBI Leaders	.15	.11	.05	.35	.27	.12
309 '74 SB Leaders	.15	.11	.05	.35	.27	.12
310 '74 Victory Ldrs.	.15	.11	.05	.35	.27	.12
311 '74 ERA Leaders	.15	.11	.05	.35	.27	.12
312 '74 Strikeout Ldrs.	.15	.11	.05	.35	.27	.12
313 '74 Lead Firemen	.15	.11	.05	.35	.27	.12
314 Buck Martinez	.06	.04	.02	.15	.11	.05
315 Don Kessinger	.10	.07	.03	.20	.15	.06
316 Jackie Brown	.06	.04	.02	.15	.11	.05
317 Joe Lahoud	.06	.04	.02	.15	.11	.05
318 Ernie McAnally	.06	.04	.02	.15	.11	.05
319 Johnny Oates	.06	.04	.02	.15	.11	.05
320 Pete Rose	1.75	1.25	.55	4.00	3.00	1.40
321 Rudy May	.10	.07	.03	.20	.15	.06
322 Ed Goodson	.06	.04	.02	.15	.11	.05
323 Fred Holdsworth	.06	.04	.02	.15	.11	.05
324 Ed Kranepool	.10	.07	.03	.20	.15	.06
325 Tony Oliva	.25	.20	.08	.60	.45	.20
326 Wayne Twitchell	.06	.04	.02	.15	.11	.05
327 Jerry Hairston	.06	.04	.02	.15	.11	.05
328 Sonny Siebert	.06	.04	.02	.15	.11	.05
329 Ted Kubiak	.06	.04	.02	.15	.11	.05
330 Mike Marshall	.12	.08	.04	.30	.25	.10
331 Indians: Team/Mgr	.10	.07	.03	.25	.20	.08
332 Fred Kendall	.06	.04	.02	.15	.11	.05
333 Dick Drago	.06	.04	.02	.15	.11	.05
334 Greg Gross	.06	.04	.02	.15	.11	.05
335 Jim Palmer	.75	.55	.25	2.00	1.50	.50
336 Rennie Stennett	.06	.04	.02	.15	.11	.05
337 Kevin Kobel	.06	.04	.02	.15	.11	.05
338 Rick Stelmaszek	.06	.04	.02	.15	.11	.05
339 Jim Fregosi	.10	.07	.03	.20	.15	.06
340 Paul Splittorff	.06	.04	.02	.15	.11	.05
341 Hal Breeden	.06	.04	.02	.15	.11	.05
342 Leroy Stanton	.06	.04	.02	.15	.11	.05
343 Danny Frisella	.06	.04	.02	.15	.11	.05
344 Ben Oglivie	.12	.08	.04	.30	.25	.10
345 Clay Carroll	.06	.04	.02	.15	.11	.05
346 Bobby Darwin	.06	.04	.02	.15	.11	.05
347 Mike Caldwell	.10	.07	.03	.20	.15	.06
348 Tony Muser	.06	.04	.02	.15	.11	.05
349 Ray Sadecki	.06	.04	.02	.15	.11	.05
350 Bobby Murcer	.12	.08	.04	.30	.25	.10
351 Bob Boone	.06	.04	.02	.15	.11	.05
352 Darold Knowles	.06	.04	.02	.15	.11	.05
353 Luis Melendez	.06	.04	.02	.15	.11	.05
354 Dick Bosman	.06	.04	.02	.15	.11	.05
355 Chris Cannizzaro	.06	.04	.02	.15	.11	.05
356 Rico Petrocelli	.10	.07	.03	.20	.15	.06
357 Ken Forsch	.06	.04	.02	.15	.11	.05
358 Al Bumbry	.06	.04	.02	.15	.11	.05
359 Paul Popovich	.06	.04	.02	.15	.11	.05
360 George Scott	.10	.07	.03	.20	.15	.06
361 Dodgers: Team/Mgr	.10	.07	.03	.25	.20	.06
362 Steve Hargan	.06	.04	.02	.15	.11	.05

	REGULAR			MINI'S		
	MINT	VG-E	F-G	MINT	VG-E	F-G
363 Carmen Fanzone	.06	.04	.02	.15	.11	.05
364 Doug Bird	.06	.04	.02	.15	.11	.05
365 Bob Bailey	.06	.04	.02	.15	.11	.05
366 Ken Sanders	.06	.04	.02	.15	.11	.05
367 Craig Robinson	.06	.04	.02	.15	.11	.05
368 Vic Albury	.06	.04	.02	.15	.11	.05
369 Merv Rettenmund	.06	.04	.02	.15	.11	.05
370 Tom Seaver	1.25	.90	.40	2.75	2.00	.90
371 Gates Brown	.06	.04	.02	.15	.11	.05
372 John D'Acquisto	.06	.04	.02	.15	.11	.05
373 Bill Sharp	.06	.04	.02	.15	.11	.05
374 Eddie Watt	.06	.04	.02	.15	.11	.05
375 Roy White	.06	.04	.02	.15	.11	.05
376 Steve Yeager	.06	.04	.02	.15	.11	.05
377 Tom Hilgendorf	.06	.04	.02	.15	.11	.05
378 Derrel Thomas	.06	.04	.02	.15	.11	.05
379 Bernie Carbo	.06	.04	.02	.15	.11	.05
380 Sal Bando	.10	.07	.03	.20	.15	.06
381 John Curtis	.06	.04	.02	.15	.11	.05
382 Don Baylor	.30	.25	.10	1.00	.70	.30
383 Jim York	.06	.04	.02	.15	.11	.05
384 Brewers: Team/Mgr	.10	.07	.03	.25	.20	.08
385 Dock Ellis	.06	.04	.02	.15	.11	.05
386 Check List: 265-396	.06	.04	.02	.15	.11	.05
387 Jim Spencer	.06	.04	.02	.15	.11	.05
388 Steve Stone	.10	.07	.03	.20	.15	.06
389 Tony Solaita	.06	.04	.02	.15	.11	.06
390 Ron Cey	.12	.08	.04	.30	.25	.10
391 Don DeMola	.06	.04	.02	.15	.11	.05
392 Bruce Bochte	.06	.04	.02	.15	.11	.05
393 Gary Gentry	.06	.04	.02	.15	.11	.05
394 Larvell Blanks	.06	.04	.02	.15	.11	.05
395 Bud Harrelson	.06	.04	.02	.15	.11	.05
396 Fred Norman	.06	.04	.02	.15	.11	.05
397 Bill Freehan	.10	.07	.03	.20	.15	.06
398 Elias Sosa	.06	.04	.02	.15	.11	.05
399 Terry Harmon	.06	.04	.02	.15	.11	.05
400 Dick Allen	.20	.15	.06	.50	.40	.18
401 Mike Wallace	.06	.04	.02	.15	.11	.05
402 Bob Tolan	.06	.04	.02	.15	.11	.05
403 Tom Buskey	.06	.04	.02	.15	.11	.05
404 Ted Sizemore	.06	.04	.02	.15	.11	.05
405 John Montague	.06	.04	.02	.15	.11	.05
406 Bob Gallagher	.06	.04	.02	.15	.11	.05
407 Herb Washington	.06	.04	.02	.15	.11	.05
408 Clyde Wright	.06	.04	.02	.15	.11	.05
409 Bob Robertson	.06	.04	.02	.15	.11	.05
410 Mike Cuellar	.06	.04	.02	.15	.11	.05
411 George Mitterwald	.06	.04	.02	.15	.11	.05
412 Bill Hands	.06	.04	.02	.15	.11	.05
413 Marty Pattin	.06	.04	.02	.15	.11	.05
414 Manny Mota	.10	.07	.03	.20	.15	.06
415 John Hiller	.06	.04	.02	.15	.11	.05
416 Larry Lintz	.06	.04	.02	.15	.11	.05
417 Skip Lockwood	.06	.04	.02	.15	.11	.05
418 Leo Foster	.06	.04	.02	.15	.11	.05
419 Dave Goltz	.10	.07	.03	.20	.15	.06
420 Larry Bowa	.30	.25	.10	.75	.55	.25
421 Mets: Team/Mgr	.10	.07	.03	.25	.20	.08
422 Brian Downing	.06	.04	.02	.15	.11	.05
423 Clay Kirby	.06	.04	.02	.15	.11	.05
424 John Lowenstein	.06	.04	.02	.15	.11	.05
425 Tito Fuentes	.06	.04	.02	.15	.11	.05
426 George Medich	.06	.04	.02	.15	.11	.05
427 Clarence Gaston	.06	.04	.02	.15	.11	.05
428 Dave Hamilton	.06	.04	.02	.15	.11	.05
429 Jim Dwyer	.06	.04	.02	.15	.11	.05
430 Luis Tiant	.12	.08	.04	.30	.25	.10
431 Rod Gilbreath	.06	.04	.02	.15	.11	.05
432 Ken Berry	.06	.04	.02	.15	.11	.05
433 Larry Demery	.06	.04	.02	.15	.11	.05
434 Bob Locker	.06	.04	.02	.15	.11	.05
435 Dave Nelson	.06	.04	.02	.15	.11	.05
436 Ken Frailing	.06	.04	.02	.15	.11	.05
437 Al Cowens	.06	.04	.02	.15	.11	.05
438 Don Carrithers	.06	.04	.02	.15	.11	.05
439 Ed Brinkman	.06	.04	.02	.15	.11	.05
440 A. Messersmith	.10	.07	.03	.20	.15	.06
441 Bobby Heise	.06	.04	.02	.15	.11	.05
442 Maximino Leon	.06	.04	.02	.15	.11	.05
443 Twins: Team/Mgr	.10	.07	.03	.25	.20	.08
444 Gene Garber	.06	.04	.02	.15	.11	.05
445 Felix Millan	.06	.04	.02	.15	.11	.05
446 Bart Johnson	.06	.04	.02	.15	.11	.05
447 Terry Crowley	.06	.04	.02	.15	.11	.05
448 Frank Duffy	.06	.04	.02	.15	.11	.05
449 Charlie Williams	.06	.04	.02	.15	.11	.05
450 Willie McCovey	.80	.60	.25	2.00	1.50	.60
451 Rick Dempsey	.06	.04	.02	.15	.11	.05
452 Angel Mangual	.06	.04	.02	.15	.11	.05
453 Claude Osteen	.06	.04	.02	.15	.11	.05
454 Doug Griffin	.06	.04	.02	.15	.11	.05
455 Don Wilson	.06	.04	.02	.15	.11	.05

1980 TOPPS SUPERSTAR PHOTO

1939 PLAY BALL

1940 PLAY BALL

1938—39 W711-1

1950 DRAKE

W517 (NOTE DIFFERENT COLORS)

1937 GOUDEY
KNOT HOLE

1981 TOPPS

1981 FLEER

1981 DONRUSS

1977 PEPSI GLOVE & DISC

1928 YUENGLINGS

M116

1932 R337 SERIES OF 24

1963 PEPSI COLT 45's

1966 PEPSI TULSA OILERS

1980 SSPC HOF

1949 R302-2 MP & CO

E90-1

E91 FAKE DESIGNS

E92

E93

E94

E95

E96

E97 COLOR

E97 B&W

E98

E101

E102

E103

E107

E120

E121

E135

1961 NU-CARD
SCOOPS

1961 GOLDEN
PRESS

1941 DOUBLE PLAY

1937 GOUDEY
FLIP MOVIES

1934—36 BATTER UP

1950 TEAM EXHIBIT CARD

1960 NU-CARD HI-LITES

1948 EXHIBIT
HALL OF FAME

1953 CANADIAN EXHIBITS

SALUTATION EXHIBITS

1947-66 EXHIBIT

1954 WILSON

1953 STAHL-MEYER

1954 STAHL-MEYER

1954 GLENDALE

1953 JOHNSTON COOKIES

1968 TOPPS 3-D

1954 JOHNSTON COOKIES

1954 DAN DEE

1955 RODEO

1949-51 ROYAL

1950 WORLD WIDE GUM

1960 MORRELL

1958 SAN FRAN CALL-BULLETIN

1960 LAKE TO LAKE

1961 BELL BRAND

1952 MOTHERS COOKIES

1953 HUNTERS

1961 PETER'S MEATS

1958 HIRES TEST SET

1934 GOUDEY

1934-36 DIAMOND STARS

1933 GOUDEY

"JOE" DI MAGGIO
1941 PLAY BALL

1948-49 LEAF

1933 DE LONG

1935 GOUDEY

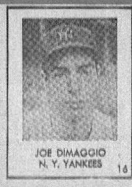
1947 R346/W518

1938 GOUDEY

1952 BERK ROSS

1933 TATOO ORBIT

1909-T204 RAMLY

1949 BOWMAN PCL

1933 SPORT KINGS

1941 GOUDEY

1912 C-46

T-205

T-207

1911 T201 MECCA

1936 R-312

1933 SPORT KINGS

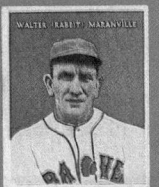
CRACKER JACK

1933 GEO. C. MILLER

1932 U.S. CARAMEL

T-206

1912 T202 TRIPLE FOLDER

1948 BOWMAN

1949 BOWMAN

1950 BOWMAN

1951 BOWMAN

1952 BOWMAN

1954 BOWMAN

**1953 BOWMAN
BLACK & WHITE**

**1951 TOPPS—
BLUE BACK**

**1951 TOPPS—
RED BACK**

**1953 BOWMAN
COLOR**

1952 WHEATIES

1953 TOPPS

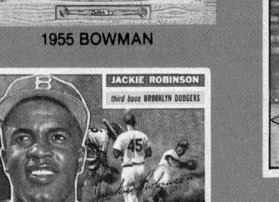

1955 BOWMAN

1956 TOPPS

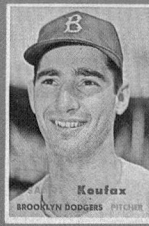

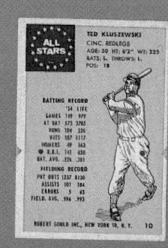

1952 TOPPS

**1951 TOPPS
CONNIE MACK A·S**

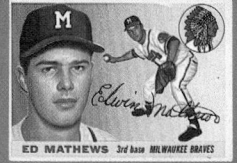

1954 TOPPS

1957 TOPPS

1955 ROBERT GOULD

**1955 TOPPS
DOUBLEHEADER**

1955 TOPPS

1958 HIRES

1951 TOPPS TEAM CARD

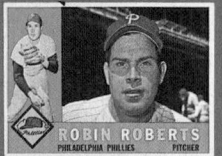
1960 TOPPS

1959 FLEER

1963 BAZOOKA
ALL TIME GREATS

1961 POST

1961 TOPPS

1962 TOPPS

1961 UNION OIL

1962 POST

1962 CANADIAN POST

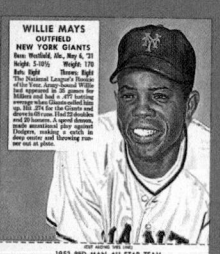
1952 RED MAN

1958 TOPPS

1960 FLEER

1962 JELLO

1953 RED MAN

1954 RED HEART

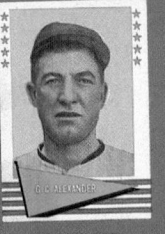
1961 FLEER

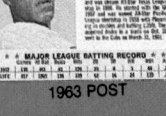
1963 POST

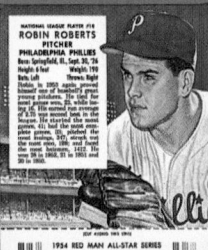
1954 RED MAN

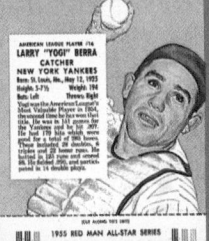
1955 RED MAN

1959 TOPPS

1964 TOPPS GIANTS

1963 TOPPS

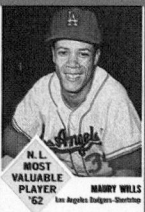
1963 FLEER

1964 TOPPS

1965 TOPPS

1965 TOPPS
EMBOSSED

1966 TOPPS

1967 TOPPS

1968 TOPPS

1968 TOPPS
GAME

1978 TCMA
THE 60'S

1964 BAZOOKA

1975 HOSTESS PANEL

KAHN'S 1966-68

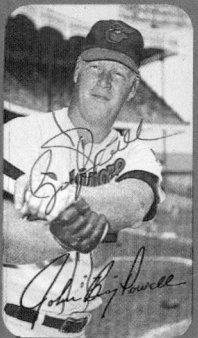
1970 TOPPS SUPER

1959 BAZOOKA

1911 T-3 TURKEY RED

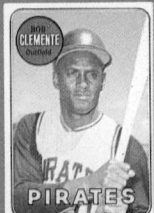

1969 TOPPS

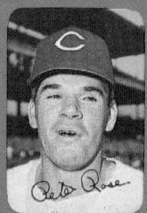

**1969 TOPPS
SUPER**

**1969 TOPPS
DECAL
INSERT**

**1969 NABISCO
TEAM FLAKES**

1970 TOPPS

1971 TOPPS

1971 KELLOGG

1972 TOPPS

**1972 KELLOGG
ALL-TIME GREATS**

1972 KELLOGG

1973 TOPPS

1973 KELLOGG

1974 TOPPS

1974 KELLOGG

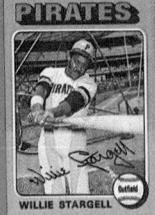

1975 TOPPS

1977 TOPPS

1976 KELLOGG

1976 SSPC

1976 TOPPS

1977 KELLOGG

1978 TOPPS

1978 KELLOGG

1979 TOPPS

1979 KELLOGG

1980 TOPPS

	REGULAR			MINI'S		
	MINT	VG-E	F-G	MINT	VG-E	F-G
456 Bob Coluccio	.06	.04	.02	.15	.11	.05
457 Mario Mendoza	.06	.04	.02	.15	.11	.05
458 Ross Grimsley	.06	.04	.02	.15	.11	.05
459 1974 A.L. Champs	.12	.08	.04	.30	.25	.10
460 1974 N.L. Champs	.12	.08	.04	.30	.25	.10
461 1974 W.S. Game #1	.12	.08	.04	.30	.25	.10
462 1974 W.S. Game #2	.12	.08	.04	.30	.25	.10
463 1974 W.S. Game #3	.12	.08	.04	.20	.15	.06
464 1974 W.S. Game #4	.12	.08	.04	.30	.25	.10
465 1974 W.S. Game #5	.12	.08	.04	.30	.25	.10
466 A's Celebrate	.12	.08	.04	.30	.25	.10
467 Ed Halicki	.06	.04	.02	.15	.11	.05
468 Bobby Mitchell	.06	.04	.02	.15	.11	.05
469 Tom Dettore	.06	.04	.02	.15	.11	.05
470 Jeff Burroughs	.20	.15	.06	.50	.40	.18
471 Bob Stinson	.06	.04	.02	.15	.11	.05
472 Bruce Dal Canton	.06	.04	.02	.15	.11	.05
473 Ken McMullen	.06	.04	.02	.15	.11	.05
474 Luke Walker	.06	.04	.02	.15	.11	.05
475 Darrell Evans	.06	.04	.02	.15	.11	.05
476 Eduardo Figueroa	.06	.04	.02	.15	.11	.05
477 Tom Hutton	.06	.04	.02	.15	.11	.05
478 Tom Burgmeier	.06	.04	.02	.15	.11	.05
479 Ken Boswell	.06	.04	.02	.15	.11	.05
480 Carlos May	.06	.04	.02	.15	.11	.05
481 Will McEnaney	.06	.04	.02	.15	.11	.05
482 Tom McCraw	.06	.04	.02	.15	.11	.05
438 Steve Ontiveros	.06	.04	.02	.15	.11	.05
484 Glenn Beckert	.06	.04	.02	.15	.11	.05
485 Sparky Lyle	.12	.08	.04	.30	.25	.10
486 Ray Fosse	.06	.04	.02	.15	.11	.05
487 Astros: Team/Mgr	.10	.07	.03	.25	.20	.08
488 Bill Travers	.06	.04	.02	.15	.11	.05
489 Cecil Cooper	.20	.15	.06	.50	.40	.18
490 Reggie Smith	.25	.20	.08	.60	.45	.20
491 Doyle Alexander	.06	.04	.02	.15	.11	.05
492 Rich Hebner	.06	.04	.02	.15	.11	.05
493 Don Stanhouse	.06	.04	.02	.15	.11	.05
494 Pete LaCock	.06	.04	.02	.15	.11	.05
495 Nelson Briles	.06	.04	.02	.15	.11	.05
496 Pepe Frias	.06	.04	.02	.15	.11	.05
497 Jim Nettles	.06	.04	.02	.15	.11	.05
498 Al Downing	.06	.04	.02	.15	.11	.05
499 Marty Perez	.06	.04	.02	.15	.11	.05
500 Nolan Ryan	.75	.55	.25	1.50	1.10	.50
501 Bill Robinson	.06	.04	.02	.15	.11	.05
502 Pat Bourque	.06	.04	.02	.15	.11	.05
503 Fred Stanley	.06	.04	.02	.15	.11	.05
504 Buddy Bradford	.06	.04	.02	.15	.11	.05
505 Chris Speier	.06	.04	.02	.15	.11	.05
506 Leron Lee	.06	.04	.02	.15	.11	.05
507 Tom Carroll	.06	.04	.02	.15	.11	.05
508 Bob Hansen	.06	.04	.02	.15	.11	.05
509 Dave Hilton	.06	.04	.02	.15	.11	.05
510 Vida Blue	.30	.25	.10	.75	.55	.25
511 Rangers: Team/Mgr	.10	.07	.03	.25	.20	.08
512 Larry Milbourne	.06	.04	.02	.15	.11	.05
513 Dick Pole	.06	.04	.02	.15	.11	.05
514 Jose Cruz	.10	.07	.03	.20	.15	.06
515 Manny Sanguillen	.06	.04	.02	.15	.11	.05
516 Don Hood	.06	.04	.02	.15	.11	.05
517 Check List: 397-528	.06	.04	.02	.15	.11	.05
518 Leo Cardenas	.06	.04	.02	.15	.11	.05
519 Jim Todd	.06	.04	.02	.15	.11	.05
520 Amos Otis	.10	.07	.03	.20	.15	.06
521 Dennis Blair	.06	.04	.02	.15	.11	.05
522 Gary Sutherland	.06	.04	.02	.15	.11	.05
523 Tom Paciorek	.06	.04	.02	.15	.11	.05
524 John Doherty	.06	.04	.02	.15	.11	.05
525 Tom House	.06	.04	.02	.15	.11	.05
526 Larry Hisle	.15	.11	.05	.35	.27	.12
527 Mac Scarce	.06	.04	.02	.15	.11	.05
528 Eddie Leon	.06	.04	.02	.15	.11	.05
529 Gary Thomasson	.06	.04	.02	.15	.11	.05
530 Gaylord Perry	.60	.45	.02	1.25	.90	.40
531 Reds: Team/Mgr	.15	.11	.05	.35	.27	.12
532 Gorman Thomas	.15	.11	.04	.35	.27	.12
533 Rudy Meoli	.06	.04	.02	.15	.11	.05
534 Alex Johnson	.06	.04	.02	.15	.11	.05
535 Gene Tenace	.06	.04	.02	.15	.11	.05
536 Bob Moose	.06	.04	.02	.15	.11	.05
537 Tommy Harper	.06	.04	.02	.15	.11	.05
538 Duffy Dyer	.06	.04	.02	.15	.11	.05
539 Jesse Jefferson	.06	.04	.02	.15	.11	.05
540 Lou Brock	1.00	.70	.30	2.25	1.65	.75
541 Roger Metzger	.06	.04	.02	.15	.11	.05
542 Pete Broberg	.06	.04	.02	.15	.11	.05
543 Larry Biittner	.06	.04	.02	.15	.11	.05
544 Steve Mingori	.06	.04	.02	.15	.11	.05
545 Billy Williams	.25	.20	.08	.60	.45	.20
546 John Knox	.06	.04	.02	.15	.11	.05
547 Von Joshua	.06	.04	.02	.15	.11	.05

	REGULAR			MINI'S		
	MINT	VG-E	F-G	MINT	VG-E	F-G
548 Charlie Sands	.06	.04	.02	.15	.11	.05
549 Bill Butler	.06	.04	.02	.15	.11	.05
550 Ralph Garr	.06	.04	.02	.15	.11	.05
551 Larry Christenson	.06	.04	.02	.15	.11	.05
552 Jack Brohamer	.06	.04	.02	.15	.11	.05
553 John Boccabella	.06	.04	.02	.15	.11	.05
554 Rich Gossage	.20	.15	.06	.50	.40	.18
555 Al Oliver	.20	.15	.06	.50	.40	.18
556 Tim Johnson	.06	.04	.02	.15	.11	.05
557 Larry Gura	.10	.07	.03	.20	.15	.06
558 Dave Roberts	.06	.04	.02	.15	.11	.05
559 Bob Montgomery	.06	.04	.02	.15	.11	.05
560 Tony Perez	.20	.15	.06	.50	.40	.18
561 A's: Team/Mgr	.10	.07	.03	.20	.15	.06
562 Gary Nolan	.06	.04	.02	.15	.11	.05
563 Wilbur Howard	.06	.04	.02	.15	.11	.05
564 Tommy Davis	.10	.07	.03	.20	.15	.06
565 Joe Torre	.20	.15	.06	.50	.40	.18
566 Ray Burris	.06	.04	.02	.15	.11	.05
567 Jim Sundberg	.12	.08	.04	.30	.25	.10
568 Dale Murray	.06	.04	.02	.15	.11	.05
569 Frank White	.10	.07	.03	.20	.15	.06
570 Jim Wynn	.10	.07	.03	.20	.15	.06
571 Dave Lemanczyk	.06	.04	.02	.15	.11	.05
572 Roger Nelson	.06	.04	.02	.15	.11	.05
573 Orlando Pena	.06	.04	.02	.15	.11	.05
574 Tony Taylor	.06	.04	.02	.15	.11	.05
575 Gene Clines	.06	.04	.02	.15	.11	.05
576 Phil Roof	.06	.04	.02	.15	.11	.05
577 John Morris	.06	.04	.02	.15	.11	.05
578 Dave Tomlin	.06	.04	.02	.15	.11	.05
579 Skip Pitlock	.06	.04	.02	.15	.11	.05
580 Frank Robinson	.75	.55	.25	1.50	1.10	.50
581 Darrel Chaney	.06	.04	.02	.15	.11	.05
582 Eduardo Rodriguez	.06	.04	.02	.15	.11	.05
583 Andy Etchebarren	.06	.04	.02	.15	.11	.05
584 Mike Garman	.06	.04	.02	.15	.11	.05
585 Chris Chambliss	.10	.07	.03	.20	.15	.06
586 Tim McCarver	.06	.04	.02	.15	.11	.05
587 Chris Ward	.06	.04	.02	.15	.11	.05
588 Rick Auerbach	.06	.04	.02	.15	.11	.05
589 Braves: Team/Mgr	.10	.07	.03	.25	.20	.08
590 Cesar Cedeno	.30	.25	.10	.75	.55	.25
591 Glenn Abbott	.06	.04	.02	.15	.11	.05
592 Balor Moore	.06	.04	.02	.15	.11	.05
593 Gene Lamont	.06	.04	.02	.15	.11	.05
594 Jim Fuller	.06	.04	.02	.15	.11	.05
595 Joe Niekro	.10	.07	.03	.20	.15	.05
596 Ollie Brown	.06	.04	.02	.15	.11	.05
597 Winston Llenas	.06	.04	.02	.15	.11	.05
598 Bruce Kison	.06	.04	.02	.15	.11	.05
599 Nate Colbert	.06	.04	.02	.15	.11	.05
600 Rod Carew	1.25	.90	.40	2.75	2.20	.90
601 Juan Beniquez	.06	.04	.02	.15	.11	.05
602 John Vukovich	.06	.04	.02	.15	.11	.05
603 Lew Krausse	.06	.04	.02	.15	.11	.05
604 Oscar Zamora	.06	.04	.02	.15	.11	.05
605 John Ellis	.06	.04	.02	.15	.11	.05
606 Bruce Miller	.06	.04	.02	.15	.11	.05
607 Jim Holt	.06	.04	.02	.15	.11	.05
608 Gene Michael	.10	.07	.03	.20	.15	.06
609 Ellie Hendricks	.06	.04	.02	.15	.11	.05
610 Ron Hunt	.06	.04	.02	.15	.11	.05
611 Yankees: Team/Mgr	.10	.07	.03	.25	.20	.08
612 Terry Hughes	.06	.04	.02	.15	.11	.05
613 Bill Parsons	.06	.04	.02	.15	.11	.05
614 '75 Rookie Pitchers	.10	.07	.03	.25	.20	.08
615 '75 Rookie Pitchers	.30	.25	.10	.75	.55	.25
616 '75 Rookie Of's	6.00	4.50	2.00	12.00	8.75	4.00
617 '75 Rookie Inf's	.10	.07	.03	.25	.20	.08
618 '75 Rookie Pitchers	.10	.07	.03	.25	.20	.08
619 '75 Rookie Of's	.10	.07	.03	.25	.20	.08
620 '75 Rookie C's/Of's	1.25	.90	.40	2.50	1.80	.80
621 '75 Rookie Pitchers	.10	.07	.03	.25	.20	.08
622 '75 Rookie Of's	6.00	4.50	2.00	12.00	8.75	4.00
623 '75 Rookie Inf's	2.00	1.50	.60	4.00	3.00	1.40
624 '75 Rookie Pitchers	.10	.07	.03	.25	.20	.08
625 Boog Powell	.15	.11	.05	.35	.27	.12
626 Larry Haney(Duncan)	.10	.07	.03	.20	.15	.06
627 Tom Walker	.06	.04	.02	.15	.11	.05
628 Ron LeFlore	.75	.55	.25	1.50	1.10	.50
629 Joe Hoerner	.06	.04	.02	.15	.11	.05
630 Greg Luzinski	.40	.30	.13	1.00	.70	.30
631 Lee Lacy	.06	.04	.02	.15	.11	.05
632 Morris Nettles	.06	.04	.02	.15	.11	.05
633 Paul Casanova	.06	.04	.02	.15	.11	.05
634 Cy Acosta	.06	.04	.02	.15	.11	.05
635 Chuck Dobson	.06	.04	.02	.15	.11	.05
636 Charlie Moore	.06	.04	.02	.15	.11	.05
637 Ted Martinez	.06	.04	.02	.15	.11	.05
638 Cubs: Team/Mgr	.10	.07	.03	.25	.20	.08
639 Steve Kline	.06	.04	.02	.15	.11	.05
640 Harmon Killebrew	.60	.45	.20	1.25	.90	.40

	REGULAR			MINI'S		
	MINT	VG-E	F-G	MINT	VG-E	F-G
641 Jim Northrup	.06	.04	.02	.15	.11	.05
642 Mike Phillips	.06	.04	.02	.15	.11	.05
643 Brent Strom	.06	.04	.02	.15	.11	.05
644 Bill Fahey	.06	.04	.02	.15	.11	.05
645 Danny Cater	.06	.04	.02	.15	.11	.05
646 Checklist: 529-660	.06	.04	.02	.15	.11	.05
647 C. Washington	.10	.07	.03	.20	.15	.06
648 Dave Pagan	.06	.04	.02	.15	.11	.05
649 Jack Heidemann	.06	.04	.02	.15	.11	.05
650 Dave May	.06	.04	.02	.15	.11	.05
651 John Morlan	.06	.04	.02	.15	.11	.05
652 Lindy McDaniel	.06	.04	.02	.15	.11	.05
653 Lee Richard	.06	.04	.02	.15	.11	.05
654 Jerry Terrell	.06	.04	.02	.15	.11	.05
655 Rico Carty	.10	.07	.03	.20	.15	.06
656 Bill Plummer	.06	.04	.02	.15	.11	.05
657 Bob Oliver	.06	.04	.02	.15	.11	.05
658 Vic Harris	.06	.04	.02	.15	.11	.05
659 Bob Apodaca	.06	.04	.02	.15	.11	.05
660 Hank Aaron	2.50	1.80	.80	6.00	4.50	2.00

1976 TOPPS (660) 2 1/2″ X 3 1/2″

The 1976 Topps set features All Time All-Star card nos. 341—350 and Record breakers of 1975 as card nos. 1—6.

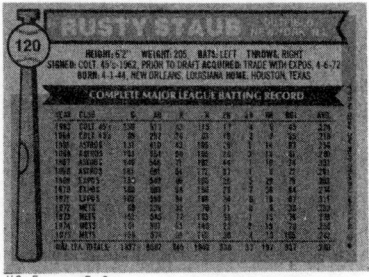

	MINT	VG-E	F-G		MINT	VG-E	F-G
COMPLETE SET	40.00	30.00	12.00	51 Ray Burris	.05	.03	.01
COMMON PLAYERS	.05	.03	.01	52 Dave Chalk	.05	.03	.01
				53 Mike Beard	.05	.03	.01
1 '75 Records: Aaron	2.00	1.25	.50	54 Dave Radar	.05	.03	.01
2 '75 Records: Bonds	.12	.08	.04	55 Gaylord Perry	.50	.40	.18
3 '75 Records: Lolich	.12	.08	.04	56 Bob Tolan	.05	.03	.01
4 '75 Record: Lopes	.10	.07	.03	57 Phil Garner	.05	.03	.01
5 '75 Record: Seaver	.60	.45	.20	58 Ron Reed	.05	.03	.01
6 '75 Rec: Stennett	.10	.07	.03	59 Larry Hisle	.10	.07	.03
7 Jim Umbarger	.05	.03	.01	60 Jerry Reuss	.10	.07	.03
8 Tito Fuentes	.05	.03	.01	61 Ron LeFlore	.20	.15	.06
9 Paul Lindblad	.05	.03	.01	62 Johnny Oates	.05	.03	.01
10 Lou Brock	.75	.55	.25	63 Bobby Darwin	.05	.03	.01
11 Jim Hughes	.05	.03	.01	64 Jerry Koosman	.10	.07	.03
12 Richie Zisk	.12	.08	.04	65 Chris Chambliss	.10	.07	.03
13 J. Wockenfuss	.05	.03	.01	66 Father & Son: Bell	.10	.07	.03
14 Gene Garber	.05	.03	.01	67 Father & Son: Boone	.10	.07	.03
15 George Scott	.08	.06	.02	68 Father & Son: Coleman	.05	.03	.01
16 Bob Apodaca	.05	.03	.01	69 Father & Son: Hegan	.05	.03	.01
17 Yankees--Team	.10	.07	.03	70 Father & Son: Smalley	.10	.07	.03
18 Dale Murray	.05	.03	.01	71 Steve Rogers	.10	.07	.03
19 George Brett	1.75	1.25	.55	72 Hal McRae	.08	.06	.02
20 Bob Watson	.10	.07	.03	73 Orioles--Team	.10	.07	.03
21 Dave LaRoche	.05	.03	.01	74 Oscar Gamble	.10	.07	.03
22 Bill Russell	.05	.03	.01	75 Larry Dierker	.05	.03	.01
23 Brian Downing	.05	.03	.01	76 Willie Crawford	.05	.03	.01
24 Cesar Geronimo	.05	.03	.01	77 Pedro Borbon	.05	.03	.01
25 Mike Torrez	.08	.06	.02	78 Cecil Cooper	.15	.11	.05
26 Andy Thornton	.08	.06	.02	79 Jerry Morales	.05	.03	.01
27 Ed Figueroa	.05	.03	.01	80 Jim Kaat	.15	.11	.05
28 Dusty Baker	.10	.07	.03	81 Darrell Evans	.05	.03	.01
29 Rick Burleson	.15	.11	.05	82 Von Joshua	.05	.03	.01
30 Bob Montefusco	.05	.03	.01	83 Jim Spencer	.05	.03	.01
31 Len Randle	.05	.03	.01	84 Brent Strom	.05	.03	.01
32 Danny Frisella	.05	.03	.01	85 Mickey Rivers	.12	.08	.04
33 Bill North	.05	.03	.01	86 Mike Tyson	.05	.03	.01
34 Mike Garman	.05	.03	.01	87 Tom Burgmeier	.05	.03	.01
35 Tony Oliva	.15	.11	.05	88 Duffy Dyer	.05	.03	.01
36 Frank Taveras	.05	.03	.01	89 Vern Ruhle	.05	.03	.01
37 John Hiller	.05	.03	.01	90 Sal Bando	.10	.07	.03
38 Garry Maddox	.10	.07	.03	91 Tom Hutton	.05	.03	.01
39 Pete Broberg	.05	.03	.01	92 Eduardo Rodriguez	.05	.03	.01
40 Dave Kingman	.35	.27	.12	93 Mike Phillips	.05	.03	.01
41 Tippy Martinez	.05	.03	.01	94 Jim Dwyer	.05	.03	.01
42 Barry Foote	.05	.03	.01	95 Brooks Robinson	.75	.55	.25
43 Paul Splittorff	.05	.03	.01	96 Doug Bird	.05	.03	.01
44 Doug Rader	.05	.03	.01	97 Wilbur Howard	.05	.03	.01
45 Boog Powell	.12	.08	.04	98 Dennis Eckersley	.12	.08	.04
46 Dodgers--Team	.10	.07	.03	99 Lee Lacy	.05	.03	.01
47 Jesse Jefferson	.05	.03	.01	100 Jim Hunter	.35	.27	.12
48 Dave Concepcion	.15	.11	.05	101 Pete LaCock	.05	.03	.01
49 Dave Duncan	.05	.03	.01	102 Jim Willoughby	.05	.03	.01
50 Fred Lynn	1.25	.90	.40	103 Biff Pocoroba	.05	.03	.01

	MINT	VG-E	F-G
104 Reds--Team	.12	.08	.04
105 Gary Lavelle	.05	.03	.01
106 Tom Grieve	.05	.03	.01
107 Dave Roberts	.05	.03	.01
108 Don Kirkwood	.05	.03	.01
109 Larry Lintz	.05	.03	.01
110 Carlos May	.05	.03	.01
111 Danny Thompson	.05	.03	.01
112 Kent Tekulve	.40	.30	.13
113 Gary Sutherland	.05	.03	.01
114 Jay Johnstone	.05	.03	.01
115 Ken Holtzman	.08	.06	.02
116 Charlie Moore	.05	.03	.01
117 Mike Jorgensen	.05	.03	.01
118 Red Sox--Team	.10	.07	.03
119 Checklist 1-132	.05	.03	.01
120 Rusty Staub	.12	.08	.04
121 Tony Solaita	.05	.03	.01
122 Mike Cosgrove	.05	.03	.01
123 Walt Williams	.05	.03	.01
124 Doug Rau	.05	.03	.01
125 Don Baylor	.20	.15	.06
126 Tom Dettore	.05	.03	.01
127 Larvell Blanks	.05	.03	.01
128 Ken Griffey	.10	.07	.03
129 Andy Etchebarren	.05	.03	.01
130 Luis Tiant	.12	.08	.04
131 Bill Stein	.05	.03	.01
132 Don Hood	.05	.03	.01
133 Gary Matthews	.10	.07	.03
134 Mike Ivie	.05	.03	.01
135 Bake McBride	.10	.07	.03
136 Dave Goltz	.05	.03	.01
137 Bill Robinson	.05	.03	.01
138 Lerrin LaGrow	.05	.03	.01
139 Gorman Thomas	.20	.15	.06
140 Vida Blue	.25	.20	.08
141 Larry Parrish	.20	.15	.06
142 Dick Drago	.05	.03	.01
143 Jerry Grote	.05	.03	.01
144 Al Fitzmorris	.05	.03	.01
145 Larry Bowa	.20	.15	.06
146 George Medich	.05	.03	.01
147 Astros Team	.10	.07	.03
148 Stan Thomas	.05	.03	.01
149 Tommy Davis	.10	.07	.03
150 Steve Garvey	1.00	.70	.30
151 Bill Bonham	.05	.03	.01
152 Leroy Stanton	.05	.03	.01
153 Buzz Capra	.05	.03	.01
154 Bucky Dent	.10	.07	.03
155 Jack Billingham	.05	.03	.01
156 Rico Carty	.10	.07	.03
157 Mike Caldwell	.08	.06	.02
158 Ken Reitz	.05	.03	.01
159 Jerry Terrell	.05	.03	.01
160 Dave Winfield	1.00	.70	.30
161 Bruce Kison	.05	.03	.01
162 Jack Pierce	.05	.03	.01
163 Jim Slaton	.05	.03	.01
164 Pepe Mangual	.05	.03	.01
165 Gene Tenace	.05	.03	.01
166 Skip Lockwood	.05	.03	.01
167 Freddie Patek	.05	.03	.01
168 Tom Hilgendorf	.05	.03	.01
169 Craig Nettles	.12	.08	.04
170 Rick Wise	.08	.06	.02
171 Greg Gross	.05	.03	.01
172 Rangers--Team	.10	.07	.03
173 Steve Swisher	.05	.03	.01
174 Charlie Hough	.05	.03	.01
175 Ken Singleton	.20	.15	.06
176 Dick Lange	.05	.03	.01
177 Marty Perez	.05	.03	.01
178 Tom Buskey	.05	.03	.01
179 George Foster	.50	.40	.18
180 Rich Gossage	.20	.15	.06
181 Willie Montanez	.05	.03	.01
182 Harry Rasmussen	.05	.03	.01
183 Steve Braun	.05	.03	.01
184 Bill Greif	.05	.03	.01
185 Dave Parker	1.00	.70	.30
186 Tom Walker	.05	.03	.01
187 Pedro Garcia	.05	.03	.01
188 Fred Scherman	.05	.03	.01
189 C. Washington	.05	.03	.01
190 Jon Matlack	.10	.07	.03
191 75 NL Batt & Ldrs	.12	.08	.04
192 75 AL Batt & Ldrs	.12	.08	.04
193 75 NL HR Leaders	.12	.08	.04
194 75 AL HR Leaders	.12	.08	.04
195 75 NL RBI Ldrs	.12	.08	.04

	MINT	VG-E	F-G
196 75 AL RBI Ldrs	.12	.08	.04
197 75 NL SB Leaders	.12	.08	.04
198 75 AL SB Leaders	.12	.08	.04
199 75 NL Vict Ldrs	.12	.08	.04
200 75 AL Vict Ldrs	.12	.08	.04
201 75 NL ERA Ldrs	.12	.08	.04
202 75 AL ERA Ldrs	.12	.08	.04
203 75 NL SO Ldrs	.12	.08	.04
204 75 AL SO Ldrs	.12	.08	.04
205 75 Top Firemen	.12	.08	.04
206 Manny Trillo	.10	.07	.03
207 Andy Hassler	.05	.03	.01
208 Mike Lum	.05	.03	.01
209 Alan Ashby	.05	.03	.01
210 Lee May	.05	.03	.01
211 Clay Carroll	.05	.03	.01
212 Pat Kelly	.05	.03	.01
213 Dave Heaverlo	.05	.03	.01
214 Eric Soderholm	.05	.03	.01
215 Reggie Smith	.20	.15	.06
216 Expos--Team	.10	.07	.03
217 Dave Freisleben	.05	.03	.01
218 John Knox	.05	.03	.01
219 Tom Murphy	.05	.03	.01
220 Manny Sanguillen	.05	.03	.01
221 Jim Todd	.05	.03	.01
222 Wayne Garrett	.05	.03	.01
223 Ollie Brown	.05	.03	.01
224 Jim York	.05	.03	.01
225 Roy White	.05	.03	.01
226 Jim Sundberg	.10	.07	.03
227 Oscar Zamora	.05	.03	.01
228 John Hale	.05	.03	.01
229 Jerry Remy	.05	.03	.01
230 Carl Yastrzemski	1.50	1.10	.50
231 Tom House	.05	.03	.01
232 Frank Duffy	.05	.03	.01
233 Grant Jackson	.05	.03	.01
234 Mike Sadek	.05	.03	.01
235 Bert Blyleven	.10	.07	.03
236 Royals--Team	.10	.07	.03
237 Dave Hamilton	.05	.03	.01
238 Larry Biittner	.05	.03	.01
239 John Curtis	.05	.03	.01
240 Pete Rose	1.50	1.10	.50
241 Hector Torres	.05	.03	.01
242 Dan Meyer	.05	.03	.01
243 Jim Rooker	.05	.03	.01
244 Bill Sharp	.05	.03	.01
245 Felix Millan	.05	.03	.01
246 Cesar Tovar	.05	.03	.01
247 Terry Harmon	.05	.03	.01
248 Dick Tidrow	.05	.03	.01
249 Cliff Johnson	.05	.03	.01
250 Fergie Jenkins	.15	.11	.05
251 Rick Monday	.10	.07	.03
252 Tim Nordbrook	.05	.03	.01
253 Bill Buckner	.10	.07	.03
254 Rudy Meoli	.05	.03	.01
255 Fritz Peterson	.05	.03	.01
256 Rowland Office	.05	.03	.01
257 Ross Grimsley	.05	.03	.01
258 Nyls Nyman	.05	.03	.01
259 Darrel Chaney	.05	.03	.01
260 Steve Busby	.05	.03	.01
261 Gary Thomasson	.05	.03	.01
262 Checklist: 133-264	.05	.03	.01
263 Lyman Bostock	.30	.25	.10
264 Steve Renko	.05	.03	.01
265 Willie Davis	.08	.06	.02
266 Alan Foster	.05	.03	.01
267 A. Rodriquez	.05	.03	.01
268 Del Unser	.05	.03	.01
269 Rick Austin	.05	.03	.01
270 Willie Stargell	.65	.50	.20
271 Jim Lonborg	.08	.06	.02
272 Rick Dempsey	.05	.03	.01
273 Joe Niekro	.10	.07	.03
274 Tommy Harper	.05	.03	.01
275 Rick Manning	.05	.03	.01
276 Mickey Scott	.05	.03	.01
277 Cubs Team	.10	.07	.03
278 Bernie Carbo	.05	.03	.01
279 Roy Howell	.05	.03	.01
280 Burt Hooton	.10	.07	.03
281 Dave May	.05	.03	.01
282 Dan Osborn	.05	.03	.01
283 Merv Rettenmund	.05	.03	.01
284 Steve Ontiveros	.05	.03	.01
285 Mike Cuellar	.05	.03	.01
286 Jim Wohlford	.05	.03	.01
287 Pete Mackanin	.05	.03	.01
288 Bill Campbell	.05	.03	.01
289 Enzo Hernandez	.05	.03	.01

	MINT	VG-E	F-G
290 Ted Simmons	.40	.30	.15
291 Ken Sanders	.05	.03	.01
292 Leon Roberts	.05	.03	.01
293 Bill Castro	.05	.03	.01
294 Ed Kirkpatrick	.05	.03	.01
295 Dave Cash	.05	.03	.01
296 Pat Dobson	.05	.03	.01
297 Roger Metzger	.05	.03	.01
298 Dick Bosman	.05	.03	.01
299 Champ Summers	.10	.07	.03
300 Johnny Bench	1.00	.70	.30
301 Jackie Brown	.05	.03	.01
302 Rick Miller	.05	.03	.01
303 Steve Foucault	.05	.03	.01
304 Angels--Team	.10	.07	.03
305 A. Messersmith	.08	.06	.02
306 Rod Gilbreath	.05	.03	.01
307 Al Bumbry	.05	.03	.01
308 Jim Barr	.05	.03	.01
309 Bill Melton	.05	.03	.01
310 Randy Jones	.10	.07	.03
311 Cookie Rojas	.05	.03	.01
312 Don Carrithers	.05	.03	.01
313 Dan Ford	.05	.03	.01
314 Ed Kranepool	.08	.06	.02
315 Al Hrabosky	.08	.06	.02
316 Robin Yount	.20	.15	.06
317 John Candelaria	.08	.06	.02
318 Bob Boone	.05	.03	.01
319 Larry Gura	.10	.07	.03
320 Willie Horton	.08	.06	.02
321 Jose Cruz	.10	.07	.03
322 Glenn Abbott	.05	.03	.01
323 Rob Sperring	.05	.03	.01
324 Jim Bibby	.10	.07	.03
325 Tony Perez	.20	.15	.06
326 Dick Pole	.05	.03	.01
327 Dave Moates	.05	.03	.01
328 Carl Morton	.05	.03	.01
329 Joe Ferguson	.05	.03	.01
330 Nolan Ryan	.65	.50	.20
331 Padres--Team	.10	.07	.03
332 Charlie Williams	.05	.03	.01
333 Bob Coluccio	.05	.03	.01
334 Dennis Leonard	.15	.11	.05
335 Bob Grich	.08	.06	.02
336 Vic Albury	.05	.03	.01
337 Bud Harrelson	.05	.03	.01
338 Bob Bailey	.05	.03	.01
339 John Denny	.05	.03	.01
340 Jim Rice	1.25	.90	.40
341 All-Time 1B	.60	.45	.20
342 All-Time 2B	.20	.15	.06
343 All-Time 3B	.20	.15	.06
344 All-Time SS	.20	.15	.06
345 All-Time OF	1.00	.70	.30
346 All-Time OF	.50	.40	.18
347 All-Time OF	.50	.40	.18
348 All Time C	.20	.15	.06
349 All-Time RHP	.20	.15	.06
350 All-Time LHP	.20	.15	.06
351 Randy Hundley	.05	.03	.01
352 Dave Giusti	.05	.03	.01
353 Sixto Lezcano	.12	.08	.04
354 Ron Blomberg	.05	.03	.01
355 Steve Carlton	.50	.40	.18
356 Ted Martinez	.05	.03	.01
357 Ken Forsch	.05	.03	.01
358 Buddy Bell	.12	.08	.04
359 Rick Reuschel	.12	.08	.04
360 Jeff Burroughs	.12	.08	.04
361 Tigers--Team	.10	.07	.03
362 Will McEnaney	.05	.03	.01
363 Dave Collins	.10	.07	.03
364 Elias Sosa	.05	.03	.01
365 Carlton Fisk	.30	.25	.10
366 Bobby Valentine	.05	.03	.01
367 Bruce Miller	.05	.03	.01
368 Wilbur Wood	.08	.06	.02
369 Frank White	.08	.06	.02
370 Ron Cey	.12	.08	.04
371 Ellie Hendricks	.05	.03	.01
372 Rick Baldwin	.05	.03	.01
373 Johnny Briggs	.05	.03	.01
374 Dan Warthen	.05	.03	.01
375 Ron Fairly	.08	.06	.02
376 Rich Hebner	.05	.03	.01
377 Mike Hegan	.05	.03	.01
378 Steve Stone	.12	.08	.04
379 Ken Boswell	.05	.03	.01
380 Bobby Bonds	.20	.15	.06
381 Denny Doyle	.05	.03	.01

	MINT	VG-E	F-G
382 Matt Alexander	.05	.03	.01
383 John Ellis	.05	.03	.01
384 Phillies Team	.10	.07	.03
385 Mickey Lolich	.10	.07	.03
386 Ed Goodson	.05	.03	.01
387 Mike Miley	.05	.03	.01
388 Stan Perzanowski	.05	.03	.01
389 Glenn Adams	.05	.03	.01
390 Don Gullett	.05	.03	.01
391 Jerry Hairston	.05	.03	.01
392 Checklist 265-396	.05	.03	.01
393 Paul Mitchell	.05	.03	.01
394 Fran Healy	.05	.03	.01
395 Jim Wynn	.08	.06	.02
396 Bill Lee	.08	.06	.02
397 Tim Foli	.05	.03	.01
398 Dave Tomlin	.05	.03	.01
399 Luis Melendez	.05	.03	.01
400 Rod Carew	1.00	.70	.30
401 Ken Brett	.05	.03	.01
402 Don Money	.08	.06	.02
403 Geoff Zahn	.05	.03	.01
404 Enos Cabell	.05	.03	.01
405 Rollie Fingers	.10	.07	.03
406 Ed Herrmann	.05	.03	.01
407 Tom Underwood	.05	.03	.01
408 Charlie Spikes	.05	.03	.01
409 Dave Lemanczyk	.05	.03	.01
410 Ralpy Garr	.05	.03	.01
411 Bill Singer	.05	.03	.01
412 Toby Harrah	.05	.03	.01
413 Pete Varney	.05	.03	.01
414 Wayne Garland	.05	.03	.01
415 Vada Pinson	.12	.08	.04
416 Tommy John	.50	.40	.18
417 Gene Clines	.05	.03	.01
418 Jose Morales	.05	.03	.01
419 Reggie Cleveland	.05	.03	.01
420 Joe Morgan	.40	.30	.13
421 A's--Team	.10	.07	.03
422 Johnny Grubb	.05	.03	.01
423 Ed Halicki	.05	.03	.01
424 Phil Roof	.05	.03	.01
425 Rennie Stennett	.05	.03	.01
426 Bob Forsch	.05	.03	.01
427 Kurt Bevacqua	.05	.03	.01
428 Jim Crawford	.05	.03	.01
429 Fred Stanley	.05	.03	.01
430 Jose Cardenal	.05	.03	.01
431 Dick Ruthven	.05	.03	.01
432 Tom Veryzer	.05	.03	.01
433 Rick Waits	.05	.03	.01
434 Morris Nettles	.05	.03	.01
435 Phil Niekro	.15	.11	.05
436 Bill Fahey	.05	.03	.01
437 Terry Forster	.10	.07	.03
438 Doug DeCinces	.05	.03	.01
439 Rick Rhoden	.05	.03	.01
440 John Mayberry	.08	.06	.02
441 Gary Carter	.25	.20	.08
442 Hank Webb	.05	.03	.01
443 Giants--Team	.10	.07	.03
444 Gary Nolan	.05	.03	.01
445 Rico Petrocelli	.08	.06	.02
446 Larry Haney	.05	.03	.01
447 Gene Locklear	.05	.03	.01
448 Tom Johnson	.05	.03	.01
449 Bob Robertson	.05	.03	.01
450 Jim Palmer	.60	.45	.20
451 Buddy Bradford	.05	.03	.01
452 Tom Hausman	.05	.03	.01
453 Lou Piniella	.10	.07	.03
454 Tom Griffin	.05	.03	.01
455 Dick Allen	.12	.08	.04
456 Joe Coleman	.05	.03	.01
457 Ed Crosby	.05	.03	.01
458 Earl Williams	.05	.03	.01
459 Jim Brewer	.05	.03	.01
460 Cesar Cedeno	.25	.20	.08
461 75 Playoffs	.12	.08	.04
462 75 Series	.12	.08	.04
463 Steve Hargan	.05	.03	.01
464 Ken Henderson	.05	.03	.01
465 Mike Marshall	.08	.06	.02
466 Bob Stinson	.05	.03	.01
467 Woodie Fryman	.05	.03	.01
468 Jesus Alou	.05	.03	.01
469 Rawly Eastwick	.05	.03	.01
470 Bobby Murcer	.10	.07	.03
471 Jim Burton	.05	.03	.01
472 Bob Davis	.05	.03	.01
473 Paul Blair	.05	.03	.01
474 Ray Corbin	.05	.03	.01
475 Joe Rudi	.08	.06	.02

		MINT	VG-E	F-G
476	Bob Moose	.05	.03	.01
477	Indians--Team	.10	.07	.03
478	Lynn McGlothen	.05	.03	.01
479	Bobby Mitchell	.05	.03	.01
480	Mike Schmidt	.80	.60	.25
481	Rudy May	.10	.07	.03
482	Tim Hosley	.05	.03	.01
483	Mickey Stanley	.05	.03	.01
484	Eric Raich	.05	.03	.01
485	Mike Hargrove	.05	.03	.01
486	Bruce Dal Canton	.05	.03	.01
487	Leron Lee	.05	.03	.01
488	Claude Osteen	.05	.03	.01
489	Skip Jutze	.05	.03	.01
490	Frank Tanana	.10	.07	.03
491	Terry Crowley	.05	.03	.01
492	Martin Pattin	.05	.03	.01
493	Derrel Thomas	.05	.03	.01
494	Craig Swan	.10	.07	.03
495	Nate Colbert	.05	.03	.01
496	Juan Beniquez	.05	.03	.01
497	Joe McIntosh	.05	.03	.01
498	Glenn Borgmann	.05	.03	.01
499	Mario Guerrero	.05	.03	.01
500	Reggie Jackson	1.00	.70	.30
501	Billy Champion	.05	.03	.01
502	Tim McCarver	.05	.03	.01
503	Elliott Maddox	.05	.03	.01
504	Pirates--Team	.10	.07	.03
505	Mark Belanger	.08	.06	.02
506	G. Mitterwald	.05	.03	.01
507	Ray Bare	.05	.03	.01
508	Duane Kuiper	.05	.03	.01
509	Bill Hands	.05	.03	.01
510	Amos Otis	.10	.07	.03
511	Jamie Easterly	.05	.03	.01
512	Ellie Rodriguez	.05	.03	.01
513	Bart Johnson	.05	.03	.01
514	Dan Driessen	.05	.03	.01
515	Steve Yeager	.05	.03	.01
516	Wayne Granger	.05	.03	.01
517	John Milner	.05	.03	.01
518	Doug Flynn	.05	.03	.01
519	Steve Brye	.05	.03	.01
520	Willie McCovey	.75	.55	.25
521	Jim Colborn	.05	.03	.01
522	Ted Sizemore	.05	.03	.01
523	Bob Montgomery	.05	.03	.01
524	Pete Falcone	.05	.03	.01
525	Billy Williams	.20	.15	.06
526	Checklist 397-528	.05	.03	.01
527	Mike Anderson	.05	.03	.01
528	Dock Ellis	.05	.03	.01
529	Deron Johnson	.05	.03	.01
530	Don Sutton	.40	.30	.13
531	Mets--Team	.10	.07	.03
532	Milt May	.05	.03	.01
533	Lee Richard	.05	.03	.01
534	Stan Bahnsen	.05	.03	.01
535	Dave Nelson	.05	.03	.01
536	Mike Thompson	.05	.03	.01
537	Tony Muser	.05	.03	.01
538	Pat Darcy	.05	.03	.01
539	John Balaz	.05	.03	.01
540	Bill Freehan	.08	.06	.02
541	Steve Mingori	.05	.03	.01
542	Keith Hernandez	.60	.45	.20
543	Wayne Twitchell	.05	.03	.01
544	Pepe Frias	.05	.03	.01
545	Sparky Lyle	.12	.08	.04
546	Dave Rosello	.05	.03	.01
547	Roric Harrison	.05	.03	.01
548	Manny Mota	.08	.06	.02
549	Randy Tate	.05	.03	.01
550	Hank Aaron	2.00	1.50	.60
551	Jerry DeVanon	.05	.03	.01
552	Terry Humphrey	.05	.03	.01
553	Randy Moffitt	.05	.03	.01
554	Ray Fosse	.05	.03	.01
555	Dyar Miller	.05	.03	.01
556	Twins Team	.10	.07	.03
557	Dan Spillner	.05	.03	.01
558	Clarence Gaston	.05	.03	.01
559	Clyde Wright	.05	.03	.01
560	Jorge Orta	.05	.03	.01
561	Tom Carroll	.05	.03	.01
562	Adrian Garrett	.05	.03	.01
563	Larry Demery	.05	.03	.01
564	Bubble Champ	.08	.06	.02
565	Tug McGraw	.10	.07	.03
566	Ken McMullen	.05	.03	.01
567	George Stone	.05	.03	.01

		MINT	VG-E	F-G
568	Rob Andrews	.05	.03	.01
569	Nelson Briles	.05	.03	.01
570	George Hendrick	.10	.07	.03
571	Don DeMola	.05	.03	.01
572	Rich Coggins	.05	.03	.01
573	Bill Travers	.05	.03	.01
574	Don Kessinger	.08	.06	.02
575	Dwight Evans	.05	.03	.01
576	Maximino Leon	.05	.03	.01
577	Marc Hill	.05	.03	.01
578	Ted Kubiak	.05	.03	.01
579	Clay Kirby	.05	.03	.01
580	Bert Campaneris	.08	.06	.02
581	Cardinals--Team	.10	.07	.03
582	Mike Kekich	.05	.03	.01
583	Tommy Helms	.05	.03	.01
584	Stan Wall	.05	.03	.01
585	Joe Torre	.15	.11	.05
586	Ron Schueler	.05	.03	.01
587	Leo Cardenas	.05	.03	.01
588	Kevin Kobel	.05	.03	.01
589	Rookie Pitchers	.50	.40	.18
590	Rookie Outfielders	.10	.07	.03
591	Rookie Pitchers	.10	.07	.03
592	Rookie Infielders	.50	.40	.18
593	Rookie Pitchers	.10	.07	.03
594	Catchers & OF's	.10	.07	.03
595	Rookie Pitchers	.10	.07	.03
596	Rookie Infielders	.10	.07	.03
597	Rookie Pitchers	.10	.07	.03
598	Rookie Outfielders	.10	.07	.03
599	Rookie Pitchers (Guidry)	2.00	1.50	.60
600	Tom Seaver	1.25	.90	.40
601	Ken Rudolph	.05	.03	.01
602	Doug Konieczny	.05	.03	.01
603	Jim Holt	.05	.03	.01
604	Joe Lovitto	.05	.03	.01
605	Al Downing	.05	.03	.01
606	Brewers--Team	.10	.07	.03
607	Rich Hinton	.05	.03	.01
608	Vic Correll	.05	.03	.01
609	Fred Norman	.05	.03	.01
610	Greg Luzinski	.30	.25	.10
611	Rich Folkers	.05	.03	.01
612	Joe Lahoud	.05	.03	.01
613	Tim Johnson	.05	.03	.01
614	Fernando Arroyo	.05	.03	.01
615	Mike Cubbage	.05	.03	.01
616	Buck Martinez	.05	.03	.01
617	Darold Knowles	.05	.03	.01
618	Jack Brohamer	.05	.03	.01
619	Bill Butler	.05	.03	.01
620	Al Oliver	.20	.15	.06
621	Tom Hall	.05	.03	.01
622	Rich Auerbach	.05	.03	.01
623	Bob Alletta	.05	.03	.01
624	Tony Taylor	.05	.03	.01
625	J. R. Richard	.30	.25	.10
626	Bob Sheldon	.05	.03	.01
627	Bill Plummer	.05	.03	.01
628	John D'Acquisto	.05	.03	.01
629	Sandy Alomar	.05	.03	.01
630	Chris Speier	.05	.03	.01
631	Braves-Team	.10	.07	.03
632	Rogelio Moret	.05	.03	.01
633	John Stearns	.10	.07	.03
634	Larry Christenson	.05	.03	.01
635	Jim Fregosi	.10	.07	.03
636	Joe Decker	.05	.03	.01
637	Bruce Bochte	.08	.06	.02
638	Doyle Alexander	.05	.03	.01
639	Fred Kendall	.05	.03	.01
640	Bill Madlock	.10	.07	.03
641	Tom Paciorek	.05	.03	.01
642	Dennis Blair	.05	.03	.01
643	Checklist 529-660	.05	.03	.01
644	Tom Bradley	.05	.03	.01
645	Darrell Porter	.10	.07	.03
646	John Lowenstein	.05	.03	.01
647	Ramon Hernandez	.05	.03	.01
648	Al Cowens	.05	.03	.01
649	Dave Roberts	.05	.03	.01
650	Thurman Munson	1.00	.70	.30
651	John Odom	.05	.03	.01
652	Ed Armbrister	.05	.03	.01
653	Mike Norris	.35	.27	.12
654	Doug Griffin	.05	.03	.01
655	Mike Vail	.05	.03	.01
656	White Sox--Team	.10	.07	.03
657	Roy Smalley	.08	.06	.02
658	Jerry Johnson	.05	.03	.01
659	Ben Oglivie	.15	.11	.05
660	Dave Lopes	.20	.15	.06

1976 TOPPS TRADED (44)   2 1/2" X 3 1/2"

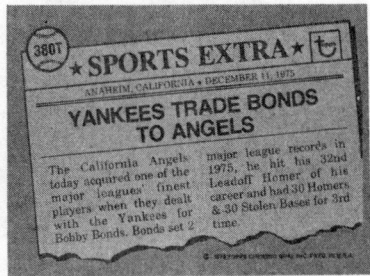

The 1976 Topps Traded set consists of 44 cards, including a Traded set checklist card, portraying players who were traded after Topps' regular set was printed. Players are portrayed with their new teams, and the card number for the Traded cards are the same as the player's card in the regular set with a "T" following the number.

	MINT	VG-E	F-G
COMPLETE SET	2.00	1.50	.50
COMMON PLAYER	.05	.03	.01
Checklist Card	.10	.07	.03
27T Ed Figueroa	.05	.03	.01
28T Dusty Baker	.10	.07	.03
44T Doug Rader	.05	.03	.01
58T Ron Reed	.05	.03	.01
74T Oscar Gamble	.05	.03	.01
80T Jim Kaat	.10	.07	.03
83T Jim Spencer	.05	.03	.01
85T Mickey Rivers	.10	.07	.03
99T Lee Lacy	.05	.03	.01
120T Rusty Staub	.10	.07	.03
127T Larvell Blanks	.05	.03	.01
146T George Medich	.05	.03	.01
158T Ken Reitz	.05	.03	.01
208T Mike Lum	.05	.03	.01
211T Clay Carroll	.05	.03	.01
231T Tom House	.05	.03	.01
250T Fergie Jenkins	.10	.07	.03
259T Darrel Chaney	.05	.03	.01
292T Leon Roberts	.05	.03	.01
296T Pat Dobson	.05	.03	.01

	MINT	VG-E	F-G
309T Bill Melton	.05	.03	.01
338T Bob Bailey	.05	.03	.01
380T Bobby Bonds	.10	.07	.03
383T John Ellis	.05	.03	.01
385T Mickey Lolich	.10	.07	.03
401T Ken Brett	.05	.03	.01
410T Ralph Garr	.05	.03	.01
411T Bill Singer	.05	.03	.01
428T Jim Crawford	.05	.03	.01
434T Morris Nettles	.05	.03	.01
464T Ken Henderson	.05	.03	.01
497T Joe McIntosh	.05	.03	.01
524T Pete Falcone	.05	.03	.01
527T Mike Anderson	.05	.03	.01
528T Dock Ellis	.05	.03	.01
532T Milt May	.05	.03	.01
554T Ray Fosse	.05	.03	.01
579T Clay Kirby	.05	.03	.01
583T Tommy Helms	.05	.03	.01
592T Willie Randolph	.10	.07	.03
618T Jack Brohamer	.05	.03	.01
632T Rogelio Moret	.05	.03	.01
649T Dave Roberts	.05	.03	.01

The 1977 Topps set features record breakers of the 1976 season as card nos. 231—234.

	MINT	VG-E	F-G		MINT	VG-E	F-G
COMPLETE SET	36.00	22.00	12.00	39 Tom Griffin	.05	.03	.01
COMMON PLAYERS	.05	.03	.01	40 Bobby Murcer	.10	.07	.03
				41 Jim Kern	.05	.03	.01
1 76 Bat Leaders	.15	.11	.05	42 Jose Cruz	.08	.06	.02
2 76 HR Leaders	.12	.08	.04	43 Ray Bare	.05	.03	.01
3 76 RBI Leaders	.12	.08	.04	44 Bud Harrelson	.05	.03	.01
4 76 SB Leaders	.12	.08	.04	45 Rawly Eastwick	.05	.03	.01
5 76 Victory Ldrs.	.10	.07	.03	46 Buck Martinez	.05	.03	.01
6 76 SO Leaders	.10	.07	.03	47 Lynn McGlothen	.05	.03	.01
7 76 ERA Leaders	.10	.07	.03	48 Tom Paciorek	.05	.03	.01
8 76 Best Firemen	.10	.07	.03	49 Grant Jackson	.05	.03	.01
9 Doug Rader	.05	.03	.01	50 Ron Cey	.10	.07	.03
10 Reggie Jackson	.75	.55	.25	51 Brewers Team	.10	.07	.03
11 Rob Dressler	.05	.03	.01	52 Ellis Valentine	.10	.07	.03
12 Larry Haney	.05	.03	.01	53 Paul Mitchell	.05	.03	.01
13 Luis Gomez	.05	.03	.01	54 Sandy Alomar	.05	.03	.01
14 Tommy Smith	.05	.03	.01	55 Jeff Burroughs	.10	.07	.03
15 Don Gullett	.05	.03	.01	56 Rudy May	.08	.06	.02
16 Bob Jones	.05	.03	.01	57 Marc Hill	.05	.03	.01
17 Steve Stone	.10	.07	.03	58 Chet Lemon	.10	.07	.03
18 Indians Team	.10	.07	.03	59 L. Christenson	.05	.03	.01
19 John D'Acquisto	.05	.03	.01	60 Jim Rice	.75	.55	.25
20 Graig Nettles	.12	.08	.04	61 M. Sanguillen	.05	.03	.01
21 Ken Forsch	.05	.03	.01	62 Eric Raich	.05	.03	.01
22 Bill Freehan	.08	.06	.02	63 Tito Fuentes	.05	.03	.01
23 Dan Driessen	.08	.06	.02	64 Larry Bittner	.05	.03	.01
24 Carl Morton	.05	.03	.01	65 Skip Lockwood	.05	.03	.01
25 Dwight Evans	.05	.03	.01	66 Roy Smalley	.06	.04	.02
26 Ray Sadecki	.05	.03	.01	67 Joaquin Andujar	.05	.03	.01
27 Bill Buckner	.10	.07	.03	68 Bruce Bochte	.05	.03	.01
28 Woodie Fryman	.05	.03	.01	69 Jim Crawford	.05	.03	.01
29 Bucky Dent	.10	.07	.03	70 Johnny Bench	.75	.55	.25
30 Greg Luzinski	.30	.25	.10	71 Dock Ellis	.05	.03	.01
31 Jim Todd	.05	.03	.01	72 Mike Anderson	.05	.03	.01
32 Checklist #1	.05	.03	.01	73 Charles Williams	.05	.03	.01
33 Wayne Garland	.05	.03	.01	74 A's Team	.10	.07	.03
34 Angels Team	.10	.07	.03	75 Dennis Leonard	.10	.07	.03
35 Rennie Stennett	.05	.03	.01	76 Tim Foli	.05	.03	.01
36 John Ellis	.05	.03	.01	77 Dyar Miller	.05	.03	.01
37 Steve Hargan	.05	.03	.01	78 Bob Davis	.05	.03	.01
38 Craig Kusick	.05	.03	.01	79 Don Money	.06	.04	.02

THE ACE CASE

The ACE CASE is an entirely new and patented device for single or multicard storage, display and shipping.

THE ACE CASE (PICTURED AT LEFT) IS A CLEAR, 20 MIL THICK, PLASTIC DISPLAY CASE DIMEN-SIONED TO HOLD ONE UP TO SIX STANDARD BASEBALL CARDS. BOTH 1952-1956 AND 1957-PRESENT SIZES ARE AVAILABLE. THE CASE OPENS IN AN INSTANT; NO LONGER ARE TIME CONSUMING SCREW POSTS NECESSARY. CARDS MAY BE SENT PROTECTED THROUGH THE MAILS IN THE ACE CASE; THE CASE IS LIGHT ENOUGH TO REQUIRE ONLY 15 CENTS POSTAGE. EACH CASE COMES WITH A LABEL WHICH CAN BE USED TO DESCRIBE AND PRICE THE CARD IN THE CASE.

ellow collectors and dealers have found ways to utilize THE ACE CASE : 1) It is ct for housing one card; it literally never o leave the case. 2) Placing two cards back ack creates an added dimension. 3) THE CASE will hold as many as six cards, ble for less valuable and duplicates. 4) A important feature is this: A large number of sactions in our hobby take place through mail. We have not found a safer, more ble way of mailing cards than THE ACE €*, and it is light enough to require only postage.

As the popularity of our hobby increases, the need for an effective and inexpensive way to display and mail cards has become apparent. Plastic sheets are fine but many people want more protection for their valuable cards. All of the new acrylic products are, in our opinion, too bulky, too hard to use, and at several dollars each, too expensive. The ACE CASE is the solution to this dilemma. It is a patented device for single or multi (up to 6) card shipping and display.

Here's how the ACE CASE works: it consists of two perfectly interlocking pieces of high quality transparent poly-vinyl, forming a rigid protective seal. Your cards are enclosed in a spill-proof, soil-proof, basically element-proof case that is only 3/16ths of an inch thick. It snaps shut solidly on all four edges yet opens easily. Both sides of the card (even the edges) are visible, and there is no excess space for the card to move around.

The ACE CASE
Is Yours For 25 Cents
plus postage and handling

Two sizes available - Please specify
A: 2½ x 3½ (57 Topps-present)
B: 2-5/8 x 3¾ (52-56 Topps, Bowman, etc)

ox of 100 at 20¢.................$20.00
ox of 300 at 18¢.................$48.00
ox of 500 at 16¢.................$80.00
uantity prices also available. Dealer inquiries
elcome.

POSTAGE & HANDLING SCHEDULE

$ .01 to $ 6.00 add $1.00
$ 6.01 to $19.00 add $1.50
$19.01 to $29.00 add $2.00
$29.01 and over add $2.50

		MINT	VG-E	F-G
80	A. Messersmith	.06	.04	.02
81	Juan Beniquez	.05	.03	.01
82	Jim Rooker	.05	.03	.01
83	Kevin Bell	.05	.03	.01
84	Ollie Brown	.05	.03	.01
85	Duane Kuiper	.05	.03	.01
86	Pat Zachry	.05	.03	.01
87	Glenn Borgmann	.05	.03	.01
88	Stan Wall	.05	.03	.01
89	Butch Hobson	.06	.04	.02
90	Cesar Cedeno	.20	.15	.06
91	John Verhoeven	.05	.03	.01
92	Dave Rosello	.05	.03	.01
93	Tom Poquette	.05	.03	.01
94	Craig Swan	.06	.04	.02
95	Keith Hernandez	.40	.30	.13
96	Lou Piniella	.10	.07	.03
97	Dave Heaverlo	.05	.03	.01
98	Milt May	.05	.03	.01
99	Tom Hausman	.05	.03	.01
100	Joe Morgan	.30	.25	.10
101	Dick Bosman	.05	.03	.01
102	Jose Morales	.05	.03	.01
103	Mike Bacsik	.05	.03	.01
104	Omar Moreno	.30	.25	.10
105	Steve Yeager	.05	.03	.01
106	Mike Flanagan	.15	.11	.05
107	Bill Melton	.05	.03	.01
108	Alan Foster	.05	.03	.01
109	Jorge Orta	.05	.03	.01
110	Steve Carlton	.50	.40	.18
111	Rico Petrocelli	.06	.04	.02
112	Bill Greif	.05	.03	.01
113	Blue Jays Team	.10	.07	.03
114	B. Dal Canton	.05	.03	.01
115	Rich Manning	.05	.03	.01
116	Joe Niekro	.06	.04	.02
117	Frank White	.06	.04	.02
118	Rick Jones	.05	.03	.01
119	John Stearns	.05	.03	.01
120	Rod Carew	.75	.55	.25
121	Gary Nolan	.05	.03	.01
122	Ben Oglivie	.08	.06	.02
123	Fred Stanley	.05	.03	.01
124	Geo. Mitterwald	.05	.03	.01
125	Bill Travers	.05	.03	.01
126	Rod Gilbreath	.05	.03	.01
127	Ron Fairly	.06	.04	.02
128	Tommy John	.40	.30	.13
129	Mike Sadek	.05	.03	.01
130	Al Oliver	.20	.15	.06
131	Orlando Ramirez	.05	.03	.01
132	Chip Lang	.05	.03	.01
133	Ralph Garr	.06	.04	.02
134	Padres Team	.10	.07	.03
135	Mark Belanger	.06	.04	.02
136	Jerry Humphrey	.05	.03	.01
137	Jeff Terpko	.05	.03	.01
138	Bob Stinson	.05	.03	.01
139	Fred Norman	.05	.03	.01
140	Mike Schmidt	.65	.50	.20
141	Mark Littell	.05	.03	.01
142	Steve Dillard	.05	.03	.01
143	Ed Herrmann	.05	.03	.01
144	Bruce Sutter	.60	.45	.20
145	Tom Veryzer	.05	.03	.01
146	Dusty Baker	.12	.08	.04
147	Jackie Brown	.05	.03	.01
148	Fran Healy	.05	.03	.01
149	Mike Cubbage	.05	.03	.01
150	Tom Seaver	.75	.55	.25
151	John LeMaster	.05	.03	.01
152	Gaylord Perry	.40	.30	.13
153	Ron Jackson	.05	.03	.01
154	Dave Giusti	.05	.03	.01
155	Joe Rudi	.06	.04	.02
156	Pete Mackanin	.05	.03	.01
157	Ken Brett	.05	.03	.01
158	Ted Kubiak	.05	.03	.01
159	Bernie Carbo	.05	.03	.01
160	Will McEnaney	.05	.03	.01
161	Garry Templeton	1.25	.90	.40
162	Mike Cuellar	.06	.04	.02
163	Dave Hilton	.05	.03	.01
164	Tug McGraw	.10	.07	.03
165	Jim Wynn	.06	.04	.02
166	Bill Campbell	.05	.03	.01
167	Rich Hebner	.05	.03	.01
168	Charlie Spikes	.05	.03	.01
169	Darold Knowles	.05	.03	.01
170	Thurman Munson	.75	.55	.25
171	Ken Sanders	.05	.03	.01

		MINT	VG-E	F-G
172	John Milner	.05	.03	.01
173	Chuck Scrivener	.05	.03	.01
174	Nelson Briles	.05	.03	.01
175	Butch Wynegar	.05	.03	.01
176	Bob Robertson	.05	.03	.01
177	Bart Johnson	.05	.03	.01
178	Bombo Rivera	.05	.03	.01
179	Paul Hartzell	.05	.03	.01
180	Dave Lopes	.10	.07	.03
181	Ken McMullen	.05	.03	.01
182	Dan Spillner	.05	.03	.01
183	Cardinals Team	.10	.07	.03
184	Bo McLaughlin	.05	.03	.01
185	Sixto Lezcano	.10	.07	.03
186	Doug Flynn	.05	.03	.01
187	Dick Pole	.05	.03	.01
188	Bob Tolan	.05	.03	.01
189	Rick Dempsey	.05	.03	.01
190	Ray Burris	.05	.03	.01
191	Doug Griffin	.05	.03	.01
192	Clarence Gaston	.05	.03	.01
193	Larry Gura	.08	.06	.02
194	Gary Matthews	.08	.06	.02
195	Ed Figueroa	.05	.03	.01
196	Len Randle	.05	.03	.01
197	Ed Ott	.05	.03	.01
198	Wilbur Wood	.05	.03	.01
199	Pepe Frias	.05	.03	.01
200	Frank Tanana	.10	.07	.03
201	Ed Kranepool	.06	.04	.02
202	Tom Johnson	.05	.03	.01
203	Ed Armbrister	.05	.03	.01
204	Jeff Newman	.05	.03	.01
205	Pete Falcone	.05	.03	.01
206	Boog Powell	.10	.07	.03
207	Glenn Abbott	.05	.03	.01
208	Checklist #2	.05	.03	.01
209	Rob Andrews	.05	.03	.01
210	Fred Lynn	.75	.55	.25
211	Giants Team	.10	.07	.03
212	Jim Mason	.05	.03	.01
213	Maximino Leon	.05	.03	.01
214	Darrell Porter	.10	.07	.03
215	Butch Metzger	.05	.03	.01
216	Doug DeCinces	.05	.03	.01
217	Tom Underwood	.05	.03	.01
218	John Wathan	.05	.03	.01
219	Joe Coleman	.05	.03	.01
220	Chris Chambliss	.06	.04	.02
221	Bob Bailey	.05	.03	.01
222	Fran Barrios	.05	.03	.01
223	Earl Williams	.05	.03	.01
224	Rusty Torres	.05	.03	.01
225	Bob Apodaca	.05	.03	.01
226	Leroy Stanton	.05	.03	.01
227	Joe Sambito	.10	.07	.03
228	Twins Team	.10	.07	.03
229	Don Kessinger	.06	.04	.02
230	Vida Blue	.25	.20	.08
231	Brett Record	.60	.45	.20
232	Minoso Record	.08	.06	.02
233	Morales Record	.05	.03	.01
234	Ryan Record	.20	.15	.06
235	Cecil Cooper	.15	.11	.05
236	Tom Buskey	.05	.03	.01
237	Gene Clines	.05	.03	.01
238	Tippy Martinez	.05	.03	.01
239	Bill Plummer	.05	.03	.01
240	Ron LeFlore	.25	.20	.08
241	Dave Tomlin	.05	.03	.01
242	Ken Henderson	.05	.03	.01
243	Ron Reed	.05	.03	.01
244	John Mayberry	.06	.04	.02
245	Rick Rhoden	.05	.03	.01
246	Mike Vail	.05	.03	.01
247	Chris Knapp	.05	.03	.01
248	Wilbur Howard	.05	.03	.01
249	Pete Redfern	.05	.03	.01
250	Bill Madlock	.10	.07	.03
251	Tony Muser	.05	.03	.01
252	Dale Murray	.05	.03	.01
253	John Hale	.05	.03	.01
254	Doyle Alexander	.05	.03	.01
255	George Scott	.06	.04	.02
256	Joe Hoerner	.05	.03	.01
257	Mike Miley	.05	.03	.01
258	Luis Tiant	.10	.07	.03
259	Mets Team	.10	.07	.03
260	J. R. Richard	.40	.30	.13
261	Phil Garner	.06	.04	.02
262	Al Cowens	.05	.03	.01
263	Mike Marshall	.06	.04	.02
264	Tom Hutton	.05	.03	.01

	MINT	VG-E	F-G
265 Mark Fidrych	.20	.15	.06
266 Derrel Thomas	.05	.03	.01
267 Ray Fosse	.05	.03	.01
268 Rick Sawyer	.05	.03	.01
269 Joe Lis	.05	.03	.01
270 Dave Parker	.75	.55	.25
271 Terry Forster	.10	.07	.03
272 Lee Lacy	.05	.03	.01
273 Eric Soderholm	.05	.03	.01
274 Don Stanhouse	.06	.04	.02
275 Mike Hargrove	.05	.03	.01
276 A.L. Playoffs	.10	.07	.03
277 N.L. Playoffs	.10	.07	.03
278 Danny Frisella	.05	.03	.01
279 Joe Wallis	.05	.03	.01
280 Jim Hunter	.25	.20	.08
281 Roy Staiger	.05	.03	.01
282 Sid Monge	.05	.03	.01
283 Jerry DaVanon	.05	.03	.01
284 Mike Norris	.10	.07	.03
285 Brooks Robinson	.65	.50	.20
286 Johnny Grubb	.05	.03	.01
287 Reds Team	.10	.07	.03
288 Bob Montgomery	.05	.03	.01
289 Gene Garber	.05	.03	.01
290 Amos Otis	.08	.06	.02
291 Jason Thompson	.08	.06	.02
292 Rogelio Moret	.05	.03	.01
293 Jack Brohamer	.05	.03	.01
294 George Medich	.05	.03	.01
295 Gary Carter	.12	.08	.04
296 Don Hood	.05	.03	.01
297 Ken Reitz	.05	.03	.01
298 Charlie Hough	.05	.03	.01
299 Otto Velez	.05	.03	.01
300 Jerry Koosman	.08	.06	.02
301 Toby Harrah	.05	.03	.01
302 Mike Garman	.05	.03	.01
303 Gene Tenace	.06	.04	.02
304 Jim Hughes	.05	.03	.01
305 Mickey Rivers	.10	.07	.03
306 Rick Waits	.05	.03	.01
307 Gary Sutherland	.05	.03	.01
308 Gene Pentz	.05	.03	.01
309 Red Sox Team	.10	.07	.03
310 Larry Bowa	.20	.15	.06
311 Vern Ruhle	.05	.03	.01
312 Rob Belloir	.05	.03	.01
313 Paul Blair	.05	.03	.01
314 Steve Mingori	.05	.03	.01
315 Dave Chalk	.05	.03	.01
316 Steve Rogers	.08	.06	.02
317 Kurt Bevacqua	.05	.03	.01
318 Duffy Dyer	.05	.03	.01
319 Rich Gossage	.15	.11	.05
320 Ken Griffey	.10	.07	.03
321 Dave Goltz	.05	.03	.01
322 Bill Russell	.05	.03	.01
323 Larry Lintz	.05	.03	.01
324 John Curtis	.05	.03	.01
325 Mike Ivie	.05	.03	.01
326 Jesse Jefferson	.05	.03	.01
327 Astros Team	.10	.07	.03
328 Tommy Boggs	.05	.03	.01
329 Ron Hodges	.05	.03	.01
330 George Hendrick	.10	.07	.03
331 Jim Colborn	.05	.03	.01
332 Elliott Maddox	.05	.03	.01
333 Paul Reuschel	.05	.03	.01
334 Bill Stein	.05	.03	.01
335 Bill Robinson	.05	.03	.01
336 Denny Doyle	.05	.03	.01
337 Ron Schueler	.05	.03	.01
338 Dave Duncan	.05	.03	.01
339 Adrian Devine	.05	.03	.01
340 Hal McRae	.05	.03	.01
341 Joe Kerrigan	.05	.03	.01
342 Jerry Remy	.05	.03	.01
343 Ed Halicki	.05	.03	.01
344 Brian Downing	.05	.03	.01
345 Reggie Smith	.15	.11	.05
346 Bill Singer	.05	.03	.01
347 George Foster	.50	.40	.18
348 Brent Strom	.05	.03	.01
349 Jim Holt	.05	.03	.01
350 Larry Dierker	.05	.03	.01
351 Jim Sundberg	.10	.07	.03
352 Mike Phillips	.05	.03	.01
353 Stan Thomas	.05	.03	.01
354 Pirates Team	.10	.07	.03
355 Lou Brock	.65	.50	.20
356 Checklist #3	.05	.03	.01

	MINT	VG-E	F-G
357 Tim McCarver	.05	.03	.01
358 Tom House	.05	.03	.01
359 Willie Randolph	.10	.07	.03
360 Rick Monday	.06	.04	.02
361 Ed Rodriguez	.05	.03	.01
362 Tommy Davis	.06	.04	.02
363 Dave Roberts	.05	.03	.01
364 Vic Correll	.05	.03	.01
365 Mike Torrez	.06	.04	.02
366 Ted Sizemore	.05	.03	.01
367 Dave Hamilton	.05	.03	.01
368 Mike Jorgensen	.05	.03	.01
369 Terry Humphrey	.05	.03	.01
370 John Montefusco	.05	.03	.01
371 Royals Team	.10	.07	.03
372 Rich Folkers	.05	.03	.01
373 Bert Campaneris	.06	.04	.02
374 Kent Tekulve	.10	.07	.03
375 Larry Hisle	.10	.07	.03
376 Nino Espinosa	.05	.03	.01
377 Dave McNally	.06	.04	.02
378 Jim Umbarger	.05	.03	.01
379 Larry Cox	.05	.03	.01
380 Lee May	.05	.03	.01
381 Bob Forsch	.05	.03	.01
382 Charlie Moore	.05	.03	.01
383 Stan Bahnsen	.05	.03	.01
384 Darrel Chaney	.05	.03	.01
385 Dave LaRoche	.06	.04	.02
386 Manny Mota	.10	.07	.03
387 Yankees Team	.05	.03	.01
388 Terry Harmon	.05	.03	.01
389 Ken Kravec	.05	.03	.01
390 Dave Winfield	.75	.55	.25
391 Dan Warthen	.05	.03	.01
392 Phil Roof	.05	.03	.01
393 John Lowenstein	.05	.03	.01
394 Bill Laxton	.05	.03	.01
395 Manny Trillo	.06	.04	.02
396 Tom Murphy	.05	.03	.01
397 Larry Herndon	.05	.03	.01
398 Tom Burgmeier	.05	.03	.01
399 Bruce Boisclair	.05	.03	.01
400 Steve Garvey	.75	.55	.25
401 Mickey Scott	.05	.03	.01
402 Tommy Helms	.05	.03	.01
403 Tom Grieve	.05	.03	.01
404 Eric Rasmussen	.05	.03	.01
405 C. Washington	.05	.03	.01
406 Tim Johnson	.05	.03	.01
407 D. Freisleben	.05	.03	.01
408 Cesar Tovar	.05	.03	.01
409 Pete Broberg	.05	.03	.01
410 Willie Montanez	.05	.03	.01
411 World Series	.10	.07	.03
412 World Series	.10	.07	.03
413 World Series	.10	.07	.03
414 Tommy Harper	.05	.03	.01
415 Jay Johnstone	.05	.03	.01
416 C. Hartenstein	.05	.03	.01
417 Wayne Garrett	.05	.03	.01
418 White Sox Team	.10	.07	.03
419 Steve Swisher	.05	.03	.01
420 Rusty Staub	.10	.07	.03
421 Doug Rau	.05	.03	.01
422 Freddie Patek	.06	.04	.02
423 Gary Lavelle	.05	.03	.01
424 Steve Brye	.05	.03	.01
425 Joe Torre	.10	.07	.03
426 Dick Drago	.05	.03	.01
427 Dave Rader	.05	.03	.01
428 Rangers Team	.10	.07	.03
429 Ken Boswell	.05	.03	.01
430 Fergie Jenkins	.15	.11	.04
431 Dave Collins	.06	.04	.02
432 Buzz Capra	.05	.03	.01
433 Clock: Colbert	.05	.03	.01
434 Clock: Yastrzemski	.30	.25	.10
435 Clock: Wills	.15	.11	.05
436 Clock: Keegan	.05	.03	.01
437 Clock: Kiner	.15	.11	.05
438 Marty Perez	.05	.03	.01
439 Gorman Thomas	.15	.11	.05
440 Jon Matlack	.06	.04	.02
441 Larvell Blanks	.05	.03	.01
442 Braves Team	.10	.07	.03
443 Lamar Johnson	.05	.03	.01
444 Wayne Twitchell	.05	.03	.01
445 Ken Singleton	.15	.11	.05
446 Bill Bonham	.05	.03	.01
447 Jerry Turner	.05	.03	.01
448 Ellie Rodriguez	.05	.03	.01
449 Al Fitzmorris	.05	.03	.01

		MINT	VG-E	F-G
450	Pete Rose	1.00	.70	.30
451	Checklist #4	.05	.03	.01
452	Mike Caldwell	.06	.04	.02
453	Pedro Garcia	.05	.03	.01
454	Andy Etchebarren	.05	.03	.01
455	Rick Wise	.06	.04	.02
456	Leon Roberts	.05	.03	.01
457	Steve Luebber	.05	.03	.01
458	Leo Foster	.05	.03	.01
459	Steve Foucault	.05	.03	.01
460	Willie Stargell	.65	.50	.20
461	Dick Tidrow	.05	.03	.01
462	Don Baylor	.20	.15	.06
463	Jamie Quirk	.05	.03	.01
464	Randy Moffitt	.05	.03	.01
465	Rico Carty	.08	.06	.02
466	Fred Holdsworth	.05	.03	.01
467	Phillies Team	.10	.07	.03
468	Ramon Hernandez	.05	.03	.01
469	Pat Kelly	.05	.03	.01
470	Ted Simmons	.25	.20	.08
471	Del Unser	.05	.03	.01
472	Rookie Pitchers	.05	.03	.01
473	Rookie Outfield	.40	.30	.13
474	Rookie SS	.05	.03	.01
475	Rookie Pitchers	.05	.03	.01
476	Rookie Catchers	.05	.03	.01
477	Rookie Infield	.50	.40	.18
478	Rookie Pitchers	.05	.03	.01
479	Rookie Outfield	.05	.03	.01
480	Carl Yastrzemski	1.00	.70	.30
481	Roger Metzger	.05	.03	.01
482	Tony Solaita	.05	.03	.01
483	Richie Zisk	.08	.06	.02
484	Burt Hooton	.08	.06	.02
485	Roy White	.05	.03	.01
486	Ed Bane	.05	.03	.01
487	Rookie Pitchers	.05	.03	.01
488	Rookie Outfield	1.00	.70	.30
489	Rookie Pitchers	.05	.03	.01
490	Rookie SS	.05	.03	.01
491	Rookie Pitchers	.05	.03	.01
492	Rookie Outfield	.50	.40	.18
493	Rookie Pitchers	.05	.03	.01
494	Rookie Infield	.05	.03	.01
495	Al Hrabosky	.06	.04	.02
496	Gary Thomasson	.05	.03	.01
497	Clay Carroll	.05	.03	.01
498	Sal Bando	.08	.06	.02
499	Pablo Torrealba	.05	.03	.01
500	Dave Kingman	.40	.30	.13
501	Jim Bibby	.06	.04	.02
502	Randy Hundley	.05	.03	.01
503	Bill Lee	.06	.04	.02
504	Dodgers Team	.10	.07	.03
505	Oscar Gamble	.06	.04	.02
506	Steve Grilli	.05	.03	.01
507	Mike Hegan	.05	.03	.01
508	Dave Pagan	.05	.03	.01
509	Cookie Rojas	.05	.03	.01
510	John Candelaria	.06	.04	.02
511	Bill Fahey	.05	.03	.01
512	Jack Billingham	.05	.03	.01
513	Jerry Terrell	.05	.03	.01
514	Cliff Johnson	.05	.03	.01
515	Chris Speier	.05	.03	.01
516	Bake McBride	.06	.04	.02
517	Pete Vuckovich	.05	.03	.01
518	Cubs Team	.10	.07	.03
519	Don Kirkwood	.05	.03	.01
520	Garry Maddox	.08	.06	.02
521	Bob Grich	.06	.04	.02
522	Enzo Hernandez	.05	.03	.01
523	Rollie Fingers	.08	.06	.02
524	Rowland Office	.05	.03	.01
525	Dennis Eckersley	.08	.06	.02
526	Larry Parrish	.06	.04	.02
527	Dan Meyer	.05	.03	.01
528	Bill Castro	.05	.03	.01
529	Jim Essian	.05	.03	.01
530	Rick Reuschel	.10	.07	.03
531	Lyman Bostock	.15	.11	.05
532	Jim Willoughby	.05	.03	.01
533	Mickey Stanley	.05	.03	.01
534	Paul Splittorff	.05	.03	.01
535	Cesar Geronimo	.05	.03	.01
536	Vic Albury	.05	.03	.01
537	Dave Roberts	.05	.03	.01
538	Frank Taveras	.05	.03	.01
539	Mike Wallace	.05	.03	.01
540	Bob Watson	.06	.04	.02
541	John Denny	.05	.03	.01

		MINT	VG-E	F-G
542	Frank Duffy	.05	.03	.01
543	Ron Blomberg	.05	.03	.01
544	Gary Ross	.05	.03	.01
545	Bob Boone	.05	.03	.01
546	Orioles Team	.10	.07	.03
547	Willie McCovey	.50	.40	.18
548	Joel Youngblood	.05	.03	.01
549	Jerry Royster	.05	.03	.01
550	Randy Jones	.12	.08	.04
551	Bill North	.05	.03	.01
552	Pepe Mangual	.05	.03	.01
553	Jack Heidemann	.05	.03	.01
554	Bruce Kimm	.05	.03	.01
555	Dan Ford	.06	.04	.02
556	Doug Bird	.05	.03	.01
557	Jerry White	.05	.03	.01
558	Elias Sosa	.05	.03	.01
559	Alan Bannister	.05	.03	.01
560	Dave Concepcion	.10	.07	.03
561	Pete LaCock	.05	.03	.01
562	Checklist #5	.05	.03	.01
563	Bruce Kison	.05	.03	.01
564	Alan Ashby	.05	.03	.01
565	Mickey Lolich	.08	.06	.02
566	Rick Miller	.05	.03	.01
567	Enos Cabell	.05	.03	.01
568	Carlos May	.05	.03	.01
569	Jim Lonborg	.06	.04	.02
570	Bobby Bonds	.12	.08	.04
571	Darrell Evans	.05	.03	.01
572	Ross Grimsley	.05	.03	.01
573	Joe Ferguson·	.05	.03	.01
574	Aurl. Rodriguez	.05	.03	.01
575	Dick Ruthven	.05	.03	.01
576	Fred Kendall	.05	.03	.01
577	Jerry Augustine	.05	.03	.01
578	Bob Randall	.05	.03	.01
579	Don Carrithers	.05	.03	.01
580	George Brett	1.00	.70	.30
581	Pedro Borbon	.05	.03	.01
582	Ed Kirkpatrick	.05	.03	.01
583	Paul Lindblad	.05	.03	.01
584	Ed Goodson	.05	.03	.01
585	Rick Burleson	.12	.08	.04
586	Steve Renko	.05	.03	.01
587	Rick Baldwin	.05	.03	.01
588	Dave Moates	.05	.03	.01
589	Mike Cosgrove	.05	.03	.01
590	Buddy Bell	.12	.08	.04
591	Chris Arnold	.05	.03	.01
592	Dan Briggs	.05	.03	.01
593	Dennis Blair	.05	.03	.01
594	Biff Pocoroba	.05	.03	.01
595	John Hiller	.06	.04	.02
596	Jerry Martin	.05	.03	.01
597	Mariners Team	.10	.07	.03
598	Sparky Lyle	.20	.15	.06
599	Mike Tyson	.05	.03	.01
600	Jim Palmer	.50	.40	.18
601	Mike Lum	.05	.03	.01
602	Andy Hassler	.05	.03	.01
603	Willie Davis	.06	.04	.02
604	Jim Slaton	.05	.03	.01
605	Felix Millan	.05	.03	.01
606	Steve Braun	.05	.03	.01
607	Larry Demery	.05	.03	.01
608	Roy Howell	.05	.03	.01
609	Jim Barr	.05	.03	.01
610	Jose Cardenal	.05	.03	.01
611	Dave Lemanczyk	.05	.03	.01
612	Barry Foote	.05	.03	.01
613	Reg Cleveland	.05	.03	.01
614	Greg Gross	.05	.03	.01
615	Phil Niekro	.12	.08	.04
616	Tommy Sandt	.05	.03	.01
617	Bobby Darwin	.05	.03	.01
618	Pat Dobson	.05	.03	.01
619	Johnny Oates	.05	.03	.01
620	Don Sutton	.30	.25	.10
621	Tigers Team	.10	.07	.03
622	Jim Wohlford	.05	.03	.01
623	Jack Kucek	.05	.03	.01
624	Hector Cruz	.05	.03	.01
625	Ken Holtzman	.06	.04	.02
626	Al Bumbry	.05	.03	.01
627	Bob Myrick	.05	.03	.01
268	Mario Guerrero	.05	.03	.01
629	Bob Valentine	.05	.03	.01
630	Bert Blyleven	.08	.06	.02
631	Brett Brothers	.50	.40	.18
632	Forsch Brothers	.06	.04	.02
633	May Brothers	.06	.04	.02
634	Reuschel Brothers	.06	.04	.02

	MINT	VG-E	F-G
635 Robin Yount	.20	.15	.06
636 Santo Alcala	.05	.03	.01
637 Alex Johnson	.05	.03	.01
638 Jim Kaat	.12	.08	.04
639 Jerry Morales	.05	.03	.01
640 Carlton Fisk	.30	.25	.10
641 Dan Larson	.05	.03	.01
642 Willie Crawford	.05	.03	.01
643 Mike Pazik	.05	.03	.01
644 Matt Alexander	.05	.03	.01
645 Jerry Reuss	.08	.06	.02
646 Andres Mora	.05	.03	.01

	MINT	VG-E	F-G
647 Expos Team	.10	.07	.03
648 Jim Spencer	.05	.03	.01
649 Dave Cash	.05	.03	.01
650 Nolan Ryan	.50	.40	.18
651 Von Joshua	.05	.03	.01
652 Tom Walker	.05	.03	.01
653 Diego Segui	.05	.03	.01
654 Ron Pruitt	.05	.03	.01
655 Tony Perez	.15	.11	.05
656 Ron Guidry	.75	.55	.25
657 Mick Kelleher	.05	.03	.01
658 Marty Pattin	.05	.03	.01
659 Merv Rettenmund	.05	.03	.01
660 Willie Horton	.08	.06	.02

1977 TOPPS CLOTH STICKERS (55&18) 2 1/2" X 3 1/2"

THURMAN MUNSON
NEW YORK YANKEES • CATCHER

- Was selected as American League Rookie of the Year for 1970, had .302 Average with 59 Runs Scored.

- Topped 100 Runs Batted In for 1st time in career, 1975, with 102 and Batting Average of .318.

- Was named American League Most Valuable Player in 1976 as he helped Yankees win A.L. Pennant. Hit .302 with 105 Runs Batted In.

FOLD CORNER ON DOTTED LINE
Slowly peel sticker from FRONT of card

COLLECT ALL 55 STICKERS
• • ©1977 TOPPS CHEWING GUM, INC. PRTD. IN U.S.A.

The 1977 Topps Cloth Sticker Card set, also known as the Cloth Patches set, is a separate issue from the regular Topps set of 1977. In addition to the 55 player cards, 18 different checklist cards whose puzzle backs form the 1976 American and National League All-Star teams were issued. The set is of limited tribution and the lower three puzzle parts to the American League All-Star puzzle are somewhat more difficult to obtain.

BASEBALL PATCHES
CHECKLIST

	MINT	VG-E	F-G
COMMPLETE SET	20.00	15.00	6.00
COMMON PLAYER	.22	.16	.06
1 Alan Ashby	.22	.16	.06
2 Buddy Bell	.30	.25	.10
3 Johnny Bench	1.00	.70	.30
4 Vida Blue	.40	.30	.13
5 Bert Blyleven	.30	.25	.10
6 Steve Braun	.22	.16	.06
7 George Brett	1.00	.70	.30
8 Lou Brock	1.00	.70	.30
9 Jose Cardenal	.22	.16	.06
10 Rod Carew	1.00	.70	.30
11 Steve Carlton	.75	.55	.25
12 Dave Cash	.22	.16	.06
13 Cesar Cedeno	.40	.30	.13
14 Ron Cey	.30	.25	.10
15 Mark Fidrych	.30	.25	.10
16 Dan Ford	.22	.16	.06
17 Wayne Garland	.22	.16	.06
18 Ralph Garr	.22	.16	.06
19 Steve Garvey	.75	.55	.25
20 Mike Hargrove	.22	.16	.06
21 Jim Hunter	.40	.30	.13
22 Reggie Jackson	.75	.55	.25
23 Randy Jones	.30	.25	.10
24 Dave Kingman	.50	.40	.18
25 Bill Madlock	.22	.16	.06
26 Lee May	.22	.16	.06

	MINT	VG-E	F-G
27 John Mayberry	.22	.16	.06
28 Andy Messersmith	.22	.16	.06
29 Willie Montanez	.22	.16	.06
30 John Montefusco	.22	.16	.06
31 Joe Morgan	.50	.40	.18
32 Thurman Munson	1.00	.70	.30
33 Bobby Murcer	.30	.25	.10
34 Al Oliver	.40	.30	.13
35 Dave Pagan	.22	.16	.06
36 Jim Palmer	.65	.50	.20
37 Tony Perez	.40	.30	.13
38 Pete Rose	1.00	.70	.30
39 Joe Rudi	.30	.25	.10
40 Nolan Ryan	.65	.50	.20
41 Mike Schmidt	.75	.55	.25
42 Tom Seaver	.75	.55	.25
43 Ted Simmons	.50	.40	.18
44 Bill Singer	.22	.16	.06
45 Willie Stargell	.65	.50	.20
46 Rusty Staub	.30	.25	.10
47 Don Sutton	.50	.40	.18
48 Luis Tiant	.30	.25	.10
49 Bill Travers	.22	.16	.06
50 Claud. Washington	.22	.16	.06
51 Bob Watson	.30	.25	.10
52 Dave Winfield	.75	.55	.25
53 Carl Yastrzemski	1.00	.70	.30
54 Robin Yount	.30	.25	.10
55 Richie Zisk	.30	.25	.10

JOHNNY BENCH

The 1978 Topps set saw an increase of 66 cards from the previous five regular issues. Cards 1-7 feature record breakers of the 1977 season.

While no scarcities exist, 66 ◄ the cards are more abunda▊ in supply. The 66 doub▊ printed cards are noted in t▊ checklist (dp).

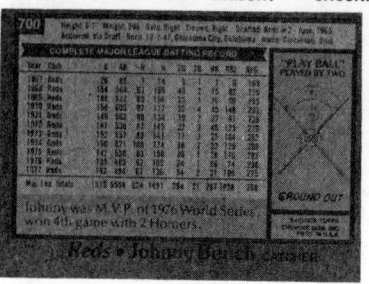

	MINT	VG-E	F-G
COMPLETE SET	30.00	23.00	10.00
COMMON PLAYERS	.04	.02	.01
1 Record: Lou Brock	.20	.15	.06
2 Record: Sparky Lyle	.08	.06	.02
3 Record: Willie McCovey	.15	.11	.05
4 Record: B. Robinson	.20	.15	.06
5 Record: Pete Rose	.40	.30	.13
6 Record: Nolan Ryan	.20	.15	.06
7 Record: Reggie Jackson	.30	.25	.10
8 Mike Sadek	.04	.02	.01
9 Doug DeCinces	.04	.02	.01
10 Phil Niekro	.10	.07	.03
11 Rick Manning	.04	.02	.01
12 Don Aase	.04	.02	.01
13 Art Howe	.04	.02	.01
14 Lerrin LaGrow	.04	.02	.01
15 Tony Perez (dp)	.05	.03	.01
16 Roy White	.04	.02	.01
17 Mike Krukow	.04	.02	.01
18 Bob Grich	.06	.04	.02
19 Darrell Porter	.08	.06	.02
20 Pete Rose (dp)	.65	.50	.20
21 Steve Kemp	.10	.07	.03
22 Charlie Hough	.04	.02	.01
23 Bump Wills	.06	.04	.02
24 Don Money (dp)	.04	.02	.01
25 Jon Matlack	.06	.04	.02
26 Rich Hebner	.04	.02	.01
27 Geoff Zahn	.04	.02	.01
28 Ed Ott	.04	.02	.01
29 Bob Lacey	.04	.02	.01
30 George Hendrick	.08	.06	.02
31 Glenn Abbott	.04	.02	.01
32 Garry Templeton	.35	.27	.12
33 Dave Lemanczyk	.04	.02	.01
34 Willie McCovey	.50	.40	.18
35 Sparky Lyle	.08	.06	.02
36 Eddie Murray	.50	.40	.18
37 Rick Waits	.04	.02	.01
38 Willie Montanez	.06	.04	.02
39 Floyd Bannister	.04	.02	.01
40 Carl Yastrzemski	.75	.55	.25
41 Burt Hooton	.08	.06	.02
42 Jorge Orta	.04	.02	.01
43 Bill Atkinson	.04	.02	.01
44 Toby Harrah	.04	.02	.01
45 Mark Fidrych	.15	.11	.05
46 Al Cowens	.04	.02	.01

	MINT	VG-E	F-G
47 Jack Billingham	.04	.02	.01
48 Don Baylor	.15	.11	.05
49 Ed Kranepool	.06	.04	.02
50 Rick Reuschel	.10	.07	.03
51 Charlie Moore (dp)	.03	.02	.01
52 Jim Lonborg	.04	.02	.01
53 Phil Garner (dp)	.03	.02	.01
54 Tom Johnson	.04	.02	.01
55 Mitchell Page	.25	.20	.08
56 Randy Jones	.08	.06	.02
57 Dan Meyer	.04	.02	.01
58 Bob Forsch	.04	.02	.01
59 Otto Velez	.06	.04	.02
60 Thurman Munson	.65	.50	.20
61 Larvell Blanks	.04	.02	.01
62 Jim Barr	.04	.02	.01
63 Don Zimmer	.06	.04	.02
64 Gene Pentz	.04	.02	.01
65 Ken Singleton	.12	.08	.04
66 White Sox Team	.10	.07	.03
67 C. Washington	.04	.02	.01
68 Steve Foucault (dp)	.03	.02	.01
69 Mike Vail	.04	.02	.01
70 Rich Gossage	.12	.08	.04
71 Terry Humphrey	.04	.02	.01
72 Andre Dawson	.10	.07	.03
73 Andy Hassler	.04	.02	.01
74 Checklist #1	.04	.02	.01
75 Dick Ruthven	.04	.02	.01
76 Steve Ontiveros	.04	.02	.01
77 Ed Kirkpatrick	.04	.02	.01
78 Pablo Torrealba	.04	.02	.01
79 Darrell Johnson (dp)	.03	.02	.01
80 Ken Griffey	.08	.06	.02
81 Pete Redfern	.04	.02	.01
82 Giants Team	.10	.07	.03
83 Bob Montgomery	.04	.02	.01
84 Ken Tekulve	.08	.06	.02
85 Ron Fairly	.06	.04	.02
86 Dave Tomlin	.04	.02	.01
87 John Lowenstein	.04	.02	.01
88 Mike Phillips	.04	.02	.01
89 Ken Clay	.04	.02	.01
90 Larry Bowa	.15	.11	.05
91 Oscar Zamora	.04	.02	.01
92 Adrian Devine	.04	.02	.01
93 Bobby Cox (dp)	.03	.02	.01
94 Chuck Scrivener	.04	.02	.01
95 Jamie Quirk	.04	.02	.01

	MINT	VG-E	F-G
96 Orioles Team	.08	.06	.02
97 Stan Bahnsen	.04	.02	.01
98 Jim Essian	.04	.02	.01
99 Willie Hernandez	.04	.02	.01
100 George Brett	.75	.55	.25
101 Sid Monge	.04	.02	.01
102 Matt Alexander	.04	.02	.01
103 Tom Murphy	.04	.02	.01
104 Lee Lacy	.04	.02	.01
105 Reg Cleveland	.04	.02	.01
106 Bill Plummer	.04	.02	.01
107 Ed Halicki	.04	.02	.01
108 Von Joshua	.10	.07	.03
109 Joe Torre	.08	.06	.02
110 Richie Zisk	.04	.02	.01
111 Mike Tyson	.08	.06	.02
112 Astros Team	.04	.02	.01
113 Dan Carrithers	.04	.02	.01
114 Paul Blair	.04	.02	.01
115 Gary Nolan	.04	.02	.01
116 Tucker Ashford	.04	.02	.01
117 John Montague	.04	.02	.01
118 Terry Harmon	.04	.02	.01
119 Denny Martinez	.10	.07	.03
120 Gary Carter	.04	.02	.01
121 Alvis Woods	.08	.06	.02
122 Dennis Eckersley	.06	.04	.02
123 Manny Trillo	.08	.06	.02
124 Dave Rozema	.06	.04	.02
125 George Scott	.04	.02	.01
126 Paul Moskau	.06	.04	.02
127 Chet Lemon	.04	.02	.01
128 Bill Russell	.04	.02	.01
129 Jim Colborn	.08	.06	.02
130 Jeff Burroughs	.08	.06	.02
131 Bert Blyleven	.04	.02	.01
132 Enos Cabell	.04	.02	.01
133 Jerry Augustine	.06	.04	.02
134 Steve Henderson	.50	.40	.18
135 Ron Guidry (dp)	.04	.02	.01
136 Ted Sizemore	.04	.02	.01
137 Craig Kusick	.04	.02	.01
138 Larry Demery	.04	.02	.01
139 Wayne Gross	.10	.07	.03
140 Rollie Fingers	.06	.04	.02
141 Ruppert Jones	.04	.02	.01
142 John Montefusco	.30	.25	.10
143 Keith Hernandez	.04	.02	.01
144 Jesse Jefferson	.06	.04	.02
145 Rick Monday	.04	.02	.01
146 Doyle Alexander	.15	.11	.05
147 Lee Mazzilli	.06	.04	.02
148 Andre Thornton	.04	.02	.01
149 Dale Murray	.15	.11	.05
150 Bobby Bonds	.04	.02	.01
151 Milt Wilcox	.04	.02	.01
152 Ivan DeJesus	.08	.06	.02
153 Steve Stone	.10	.07	.03
154 Cecil Cooper (dp)	.06	.04	.02
155 Butch Hobson	.06	.04	.02
156 A. Messersmith	.03	.02	.01
157 Pete LaCock (dp)	.04	.02	.01
158 Joaquin Andujar	.08	.06	.02
159 Lou Piniella	.45	.35	.15
160 Jim Palmer	.04	.02	.01
161 Bob Boone	.04	.02	.01
162 P. Thormodsgard	.04	.02	.01
163 Bill North	.04	.02	.01
164 Bob Owchinko	.04	.02	.01
165 Rennie Stennett	.04	.02	.01
166 Carlos Lopez	.04	.02	.01
167 Tim Foli	.15	.11	.05
168 Reggie Smith	.04	.02	.01
169 Jerry Johnson	.50	.40	.18
170 Lou Brock	.04	.02	.01
171 Pat Zachry	.04	.02	.01
172 Mike Hargrove	.10	.07	.03
173 Robin Yount	.04	.02	.01
174 Wayne Garland	.04	.02	.01
175 Jerry Morales	.04	.02	.01
176 Milt May	.03	.02	.01
177 Gene Garber (dp)	.04	.02	.01
178 Dave Chalk	.04	.02	.01
179 Dick Tidrow	.10	.07	.03
180 Dave Concepcion	.04	.02	.01
181 Ken Forsch	.04	.02	.01
182 Jim Spencer	.04	.02	.01
183 Doug Bird	.04	.02	.01
184 Checklist #2	.06	.04	.02
185 Ellis Valentine	.03	.02	.01
186 Bob Stanley (dp)	.03	.02	.01
187 Jerry Royster (dp)			

	MINT	VG-E	F-G
188 Al Bumbry	.04	.02	.01
189 Tom Lasorda	.06	.04	.02
190 John Candelaria	.06	.04	.02
191 Rodney Scott	.04	.02	.01
192 Padres Team	.08	.06	.02
193 Rich Chiles	.04	.02	.01
194 Derrel Thomas	.04	.02	.01
195 Larry Dierker	.04	.02	.01
196 Bob Bailor	.04	.02	.01
197 Nino Espinosa	.04	.02	.01
198 Ron Pruitt	.04	.02	.01
199 Craig Reynolds	.04	.02	.01
200 Reggie Jackson	.70	.50	.20
201 77 Bat Leaders	.25	.20	.08
202 77 HR Leaders (dp)	.06	.04	.02
203 77 RBI Leaders	.25	.20	.08
204 77 SB Leaders (dp)	.06	.04	.02
205 77 Victory Ldrs.	.10	.07	.03
206 77 SO Leaders (dp)	.05	.03	.01
207 77 ERA Leaders(dp)	.05	.03	.01
208 77 Top Firemen	.06	.04	.02
209 Dock Ellis	.04	.02	.01
210 Jose Cardenal	.04	.02	.01
211 Earl Weaver (dp)	.03	.02	.01
212 Mike Caldwell	.06	.04	.02
213 Alan Bannister	.04	.02	.01
214 Angels Team	.08	.06	.02
215 Darrell Evans	.04	.02	.01
216 Mike Paxton	.04	.02	.01
217 Rod Gilbreath	.04	.02	.01
218 Marty Pattin	.04	.02	.01
219 Mike Cubbage	.04	.02	.01
220 Pedro Borbon	.04	.02	.01
221 Chris Speier	.04	.02	.01
222 Jerry Martin	.04	.02	.01
223 Bruce Kison	.04	.02	.01
224 Jerry Tabb	.04	.02	.01
225 Don Gullett (dp)	.03	.02	.01
226 Joe Ferguson	.04	.02	.01
227 Al Fitzmorris	.04	.02	.01
228 Manny Mota (dp)	.03	.02	.01
229 Leo Foster	.04	.02	.01
230 Al Hrabosky	.04	.02	.01
231 Wayne Nordhagen	.04	.02	.01
232 Mickey Stanley	.04	.02	.01
233 Dick Pole	.04	.02	.01
234 Herman Franks	.04	.02	.01
235 Tim McCarver	.04	.02	.01
236 Terry Whitfield	.04	.02	.01
237 Rich Dauer	.04	.02	.01
238 Juan Beniquez	.04	.02	.01
239 Dyar Miller	.04	.02	.01
240 Gene Tenace	.04	.02	.01
241 Pete Vuckovich	.04	.02	.01
242 Barry Bonnell (dp)	.03	.02	.01
243 Bob McClure	.04	.02	.01
244 Expos Team (dp)	.03	.02	.01
245 Rick Burleson	.08	.06	.02
246 Dan Driessen	.04	.02	.01
247 L. Christenson	.04	.02	.01
248 Frank White (dp)	.03	.02	.01
249 Dave Goltz (dp)	.03	.02	.01
250 Graig Nettles (dp)	.05	.03	.01
251 Don Kirkwood	.04	.02	.01
252 Steve Swisher (dp)	.03	.02	.01
253 Jim Kern	.06	.04	.02
254 Dave Collins	.06	.04	.02
255 Jerry Reuss	.06	.04	.02
256 Joe Altobelli	.04	.02	.01
257 Hector Cruz	.04	.02	.01
258 John Hiller	.06	.04	.02
259 Dodgers Team	.10	.07	.03
260 B. Campaneris	.06	.04	.02
261 Tim Hosley	.04	.02	.01
262 Rudy May	.06	.04	.02
263 Danny Walton	.04	.02	.01
264 Jamie Easterly	.04	.02	.01
265 Sal Bando (dp)	.04	.02	.01
266 Bob Shirley	.04	.02	.01
267 Doug Ault	.04	.02	.01
268 Gil Flores	.04	.02	.01
269 Wayne Twitchell	.04	.02	.01
270 Carlton Fisk	.30	.25	.10
271 Randy Lerch (dp)	.03	.02	.01
272 Royle Stillman	.04	.02	.01
273 Fred Norman	.04	.02	.01
274 Freddie Patek	.04	.02	.01
275 Dan Ford	.04	.02	.01
276 Bill Bonham (dp)	.03	.02	.01
277 Bruce Boisclair	.04	.02	.01
278 Enrique Romo	.04	.02	.01
279 Bill Virdon	.10	.07	.03
280 Buddy Bell	.08	.06	.02

	MINT	VG-E	F-G
281 Eric Rasmussen (dp)	.03	.02	.01
282 Yankees Team	.10	.07	.03
283 Omar Moreno	.08	.06	.02
284 Randy Moffitt	.04	.02	.01
285 Steve Yeager (dp)	.03	.02	.01
286 Ben Oglivie	.08	.06	.02
287 Kiko Garcia	.04	.02	.01
288 Dave Hamilton	.04.	.02	.01
289 Checklist #3	.04	.02	.01
290 Willie Horton	.04	.02	.01
291 Gary Ross	.04	.02	.01
292 Gene Richards	.06	.04	.02
293 Mike Willis	.04	.02	.01
294 Larry Parrish	.06	.04	.02
295 Bill Lee	.06	.04	.02
296 Biff Pocoroba	.04	.02	.01
297 Warren Brusstar (dp)	.03	.02	.01
298 Tony Armas	.08	.06	.02
299 Whitey Herzog	.06	.04	.02
300 Joe Morgan	.30	.25	.10
301 Buddy Schultz	.04	.02	.01
302 Cubs Team	.08	.06	.02
303 Sam Hinds	.04	.02	.01
304 John Milner	.04	.02	.01
305 Rico Carty	.08	.06	.02
306 Joe Niekro	.06	.04	.02
307 Glenn Borgmann	.04	.02	.01
308 Jim Rooker	.04	.02	.01
309 Cliff Johnson	.04	.02	.01
310 Don Sutton	.25	.20	.08
311 Jose Baez (dp)	.03	.02	.01
312 Greg Minton	.04	.02	.01
313 Andy Etchebarren	.04	.02	.01
314 Paul Lindblad	.04	.02	.01
315 Mark Belanger	.04	.02	.01
316 Henry Cruz (dp)	.03	.02	.01
317 Dave Johnson	.04	.02	.01
318 Tom Griffin	.04	.02	.01
319 Alan Ashby	.04	.02	.01
320 Fred Lynn	.75	.55	.25
321 Santo Alcala	.04	.02	.01
322 Tom Paciorek	.04	.02	.01
323 Jim Fregosi (dp)	.03	.02	.01
324 Vern Rapp	.04	.02	.01
325 Bruce Sutter	.30	.25	.10
326 Mike Lum (dp)	.03	.02	.01
327 Rick Langford (dp)	.03	.02	.01
328 Brewers Team	.08	.06	.02
329 John Verhoeven	.04	.02	.01
330 Bob Watson	.06	.04	.02
331 Mark Littell	.04	.32	.01
332 Duane Kuiper	.04	.02	.01
333 Jim Todd	.04	.02	.01
334 John Stearns	.04	.02	.01
335 Bucky Dent	.08	.06	.02
336 Steve Busby	.04	.02	.01
337 Tom Grieve	.04	.02	.01
338 Dave Heaverlo	.04	.02	.01
339 Mario Guerrero	.04	.02	.01
340 Bake McBride	.06	.04	.02
341 Mike Flanagan	.10	.07	.03
342 A. Rodriguez	.04	.02	.01
343 John Wathan (dp)	.03	.02	.01
344 Sam Ewing	.04	.02	.01
345 Luis Tiant	.08	.06	.02
346 Larry Biittner	.04	.02	.01
347 Terry Forster	.08	.06	.02
348 Del Unser	.04	.02	.01
349 Rick Camp (dp)	.03	.02	.01
350 Steve Garvey	.75	.55	.25
351 Jeff Torborg	.04	.02	.01
352 Tony Scott	.04	.02	.01
353 Doug Bair	.04	.02	.01
354 Cesar Geronimo	.04	.02	.01
355 Bill Travers	.04	.02	.01
356 Mets Team	.08	.06	.02
357 Tom Poquette	.04	.02	.01
358 M. Lemongello	.04	.02	.01
359 Marc Hill	.04	.02	.01
360 Mike Schmidt	.60	.45	.20
361 Chris Knapp	.04	.02	.01
362 Dave May	.04	.02	.01
363 Bob Randall	.04	.02	.01
364 Jerry Turner	.04	.02	.01
365 Ed Figueroa	.04	.02	.01
366 Larry Milbourne(dp)	.03	.02	.01
367 Rick Dempsey	.04	.02	.01
368 Balor Moore	.04	.02	.01
369 Tim Nordbrook	.04	.02	.01
370 Rusty Staub	.10	.07	.03
371 Ray Burris	.04	.02	.01
372 E. Asseltine	.04	.02	.01
373 Jim Willoughby	.04	.02	.01
374 Jose Morales	.04	.02	.01
375 Tommy John	.40	.30	.13
376 Jim Wohlford	.04	.02	.01
377 Manny Sarmiento	.04	.02	.01
378 Bobby Winkles	.04	.02	.01
379 Skip Lockwood	.04	.02	.01
380 Ted Simmons	.25	.20	.08
381 Phillies Team	.08	.06	.02
382 Joe Lahoud	.04	.02	.01
383 Mario Mendoza	.04	.02	.01
384 Jack Clark	.15	.11	.05
385 Tito Fuentes	.04	.02	.01
386 Bob Gorinski	.04	.02	.01
387 Ken Holtzman	.06	.04	.02
388 Bill Fahey (dp)	.03	.02	.01
389 Julio Gonzalez	.04	.02	.01
390 Oscar Gamble	.06	.04	.02
391 Larry Haney	.04	.02	.01
392 Billy Almon	.04	.02	.01
393 Tippy Martinez	.04	.02	.01
394 Roy Howell (dp)	.03	.02	.01
395 Jim Hughes	.04	.02	.01
396 Bob Stinson (dp)	.03	.02	.01
397 Greg Gross	.04	.02	.01
398 Don Hood	.04	.02	.01
399 Pete Mackanin	.04	.02	.01
400 Nolan Ryan	.50	.40	.18
401 Sparky Anderson	.06	.04	.02
402 Dave Campbell	.04	.02	.01
403 Bud Harrelson	.04	.02	.01
404 Tigers Team	.08	.06	.02
405 Rawly Eastwick	.04	.02	.01
406 Mike Jorgensen	.04	.02	.01
407 Odell Jones	.04	.02	.01
408 Joe Zdeb	.04	.02	.01
409 Ron Schueler	.04	.02	.01
410 Bill Madlock	.06	.04	.02
411 A.L. Playoffs	.10	.07	.03
412 N.L. Playoffs	.10	.07	.03
413 World Series	.10	.07	.03
414 Darold Knowles (dp)	.03	.02	.01
415 Ray Fosse	.04	.02	.01
416 Jack Brohamer	.04	.02	.01
417 Mike Garman (dp)	.03	.02	.01
418 Tony Muser	.04	.02	.01
419 Jerry Garvin	.04	.02	.01
420 Greg Luzinski	.25	.20	.08
421 Junior Moore	.04	.02	.01
422 Steve Braun	.04	.02	.01
423 Dave Rosello	.04	.02	.01
424 Red Sox Team	.10	.07	.03
425 Steve Rogers (dp)	.04	.02	.01
426 Fred Kendall	.04	.02	.01
427 Mario Soto	.04	.02	.01
428 Joel Youngblood	.04	.02	.01
429 Mike Barlow	.04	.02	.01
430 Al Oliver	.15	.11	.05
431 Butch Metzger	.04	.02	.01
432 Terry Bulling	.04	.02	.01
433 Fernando Gonzalez	.04	.02	.01
434 Mike Norris	.08	.06	.02
435 Checklist #4	.04	.02	.01
436 Vic Harris (dp)	.03	.02	.01
437 Bo McLaughlin	.04	.02	.01
438 John Ellis	.04	.02	.01
439 Ken Kravec	.04	.02	.01
440 Dave Lopes	.08	.06	.02
441 Larry Gura	.08	.06	.02
442 Elliott Maddox	.04	.02	.01
443 Darrel Chaney	.04	.02	.01
444 Roy Hartsfield	.04	.02	.01
445 Mike Ivie	.04	.02	.01
446 Tug McGraw	.08	.06	.02
447 Leroy Stanton	.04	.02	.01
448 Bill Castro	.04	.02	.01
449 Tim Blackwell (dp)	.03	.02	.01
450 Tom Seaver	.65	.50	.20
451 Twins Team	.08	.06	.02
452 Jerry Mumphrey	.04	.02	.01
453 Doug Flynn	.04	.02	.01
454 Dave LaRoche	.04	.02	.01
455 Bill Robinson	.04	.02	.01
456 Vern Ruhle	.04	.02	.01
457 Bob Bailey	.04	.02	.01
458 Jeff Newman	.04	.02	.01
459 Charlie Spikes	.04	.02	.01
460 Jim Hunter	.25	.20	.08
461 Rob Andrews (dp)	.03	.02	.01
462 Rogelio Moret	.04	.02	.01
463 Kevin Bell	.04	.02	.01
464 Jerry Grote	.04	.02	.01
465 Hal McRae	.04	.02	.01

	MINT	VG-E	F-G		MINT	VG-E	F-G
466 Dennis Blair	.04	.02	.01	559 Phil Mankowski	.04	.02	.01
467 Alvin Dark	.04	.02	.01	560 Dave Parker	.60	.45	.20
468 Warren Cromartie	.06	.04	.02	561 Charlie Williams	.04	.02	.01
469 Rick Cerone	.08	.06	.02	562 Glenn Burke	.04	.02	.01
470 J. R. Richard	.35	.27	.12	563 Dave Rader	.04	.02	.01
471 Roy Smalley	.06	.04	.02	564 Mick Kelleher	.04	.02	.01
472 Ron Reed	.04	.02	.01	565 Jerry Koosman	.06	.04	.02
473 Bill Buckner	.06	.04	.02	566 Merv Rettenmund	.04	.02	.01
474 Jim Slaton	.04	.02	.01	567 Dick Drago	.04	.02	.01
475 Gary Matthews	.06	.04	.02	568 Tom Hutton	.04	.02	.01
476 Bill Stein	.04	.02	.01	569 Lary Sorensen	.06	.04	.02
477 Doug Capilla	.04	.02	.01	570 Dave Kingman	.30	.25	.10
478 Jerry Remy	.04	.02	.01	571 Buck Martinez	.04	.02	.01
479 Cardinals Team	.08	.06	.02	572 Rick Wise	.06	.04	.02
480 Ron LeFlore	.20	.15	.06	573 Luis Gomez	.04	.02	.01
481 Jackson Todd	.04	.02	.01	574 Bob Lemon	.20	.15	.06
482 Rick Miller	.04	.02	.01	575 Pat Dobson	.04	.02	.01
483 Ken Macha	.04	.02	.01	576 Sam Mejias	.04	.02	.01
484 Jim Norris	.04	.02	.01	577 A's Team	.08	.06	.02
485 Chris Chambliss	.06	.04	.02	578 Buzz Capra	.04	.02	.01
486 John Curtis	.04	.02	.01	579 Rance Mulliniks	.04	.02	.01
487 Jim Tyrone	.04	.02	.01	580 Rod Carew	.70	.50	.20
488 Dan Spillner	.04	.02	.01	581 Lynn McGlothen	.04	.02	.01
489 Rudy Meoli	.04	.02	.01	582 Fran Healy	.04	.02	.01
490 Amos Otis	.08	.06	.02	583 George Medich	.04	.02	.01
491 Scott McGregor	.08	.06	.02	584 John Hale	.04	.02	.01
492 Jim Sundberg	.10	.07	.03	585 Woodie Fryman (dp)	.03	.02	.01
493 Steve Renko	.04	.02	.01	586 Ed Goodson	.04	.02	.01
494 Chuck Tanner	.06	.04	.02	587 John Urrea	.04	.02	.01
495 Dave Cash	.04	.02	.01	588 Jim Mason	.04	.02	.01
496 Jim Clancy (dp)	.03	.02	.01	589 Bob Knepper	.06	.04	.02
497 Glenn Adams	.04	.02	.01	590 Bobby Murcer	.08	.06	.02
498 Joe Sambito	.06	.04	.02	591 George Zeber	.04	.02	.01
499 Mariners Team	.08	.06	.02	592 Bob Apodaca	.04	.02	.01
500 George Foster	.40	.30	.13	593 Dave Skaggs	.04	.02	.01
501 Dave Roberts	.04	.02	.01	594 Dave Freisleben	.04	.02	.01
502 Pat Rockett	.04	.02	.01	595 Sixto Lezcano	.08	.06	.02
503 Ike Hampton	.04	.02	.01	596 Gary Wheelock	.04	.02	.01
504 Roger Freed	.04	.02	.01	597 Steve Dillard	.04	.02	.01
505 Felix Millan	.04	.02	.01	598 Eddie Solomon	.04	.02	.01
506 Ron Blomberg	.04	.02	.01	599 Gary Woods	.04	.02	.01
507 Willie Crawford	.04	.02	.01	600 Frank Tanana	.08	.06	.02
508 Johnny Oates	.04	.02	.01	601 Gene Mauch	.06	.04	.02
509 Brent Strom	.04	.02	.01	602 Eric Soderholm	.04	.02	.01
510 Willie Stargell	.50	.40	.18	603 Will McEnaney	.04	.02	.01
511 Frank Duffy	.04	.02	.01	604 Earl Williams	.04	.02	.01
512 Larry Herndon	.04	.02	.01	605 Rick Rhoden	.04	.02	.01
513 Barry Foote	.04	.02	.01	606 Pirates Team	.08	.06	.02
514 Rob Sperring	.04	.02	.01	607 Fernando Arroyo	.04	.02	.01
515 Tim Corcoran	.04	.02	.01	608 Johnny Grubb	.04	.02	.01
516 Gary Beare	.04	.02	.01	609 John Denny	.04	.02	.01
517 Andres Mora	.04	.02	.01	610 Garry Maddox	.06	.04	.02
518 Tommy Boggs (dp)	.03	.02	.01	611 Pat Scanlon	.04	.02	.01
519 Brian Downing	.04	.02	.01	612 Ken Henderson	.04	.02	.01
520 Larry Hisle	.08	.06	.02	613 Marty Perez	.04	.02	.01
521 Steve Staggs	.04	.02	.01	614 Joe Wallis	.04	.02	.01
522 Dick Williams	.06	.04	.02	615 Clay Carroll	.04	.02	.01
523 Donnie Moore	.04	.02	.01	616 Pat Kelly	.04	.02	.01
524 Bernie Carbo	.04	.02	.01	617 Joe Nolan	.04	.02	.01
525 Jerry Terrell	.04	.02	.01	618 Tommy Helms	.04	.02	.01
526 Reds Team	.10	.07	.03	619 Thad Bosley (dp)	.03	.02	.01
527 Vic Correll	.04	.02	.01	620 Willie Randolph	.08	.06	.02
528 Rob Picciolo	.04	.02	.01	621 Craig Swan (dp)	.03	.02	.01
529 Paul Hartzell	.04	.02	.01	622 Champ Summers	.04	.02	.01
530 Dave Winfield	.65	.50	.20	623 Ed Rodriguez	.04	.02	.01
531 Tom Underwood	.04	.02	.01	624 Gary Alexander (dp)	.03	.02	.01
532 Skip Jutze	.04	.02	.01	625 Jose Cruz	.06	.04	.02
533 Sandy Alomar	.04	.02	.01	626 Blue Jays Team (dp)	.03	.02	.01
534 Wilbur Howard	.04	.02	.01	627 Dave Johnson	.04	.02	.01
535 Checklist #5	.04	.02	.01	628 Ralph Garr	.06	.04	.02
536 Roric Harrison	.04	.02	.01	629 Don Stanhouse	.06	.04	.02
537 Bruce Bochte	.04	.02	.01	630 Ron Cey	.10	.07	.03
538 John LeMaster	.04	.02	.01	631 Danny Ozark	.04	.02	.01
539 Vic Davalillo (dp)	.03	.02	.01	632 Rowland Office	.04	.02	.01
540 Steve Carlton	.45	.35	.15	633 Tom Veryzer	.04	.02	.01
541 Larry Cox	.04	.02	.01	634 Len Barker	.06	.04	.02
542 Tim Johnson	.04	.02	.01	635 Joe Rudi	.06	.04	.02
543 Larry Harlow (dp)	.03	.02	.01	636 Jim Bibby	.06	.04	.02
544 Len Randle (dp)	.03	.02	.01	637 Duffy Dyer	.04	.02	.01
545 Bill Campbell	.04	.02	.01	638 Paul Splittorff	.06	.04	.02
546 Ted Martinez	.04	.02	.01	639 Gene Clines	.04	.02	.01
547 John Scott	.04	.02	.01	640 Lee May (dp)	.03	.02	.01
548 Billy Hunter (dp)	.03	.02	.01	641 Doug Rau	.04	.02	.01
549 Joe Kerrigan	.04	.02	.01	642 Denny Doyle	.04	.02	.01
550 John Mayberry	.06	.04	.02	643 Tom House	.04	.02	.01
551 Braves Team	.08	.06	.02	644 Jim Dwyer	.04	.02	.01
552 Fran Barrios	.04	.02	.01	645 Mike Torrez	.06	.04	.02
553 Terry Puhl	.10	.07	.03	646 Rick Auerbach (dp)	.03	.02	.01
554 Joe Coleman	.04	.02	.01	647 Steve Dunning	.04	.02	.01
555 Butch Wynegar	.08	.06	.02	648 Gary Thomasson	.04	.02	.01
556 Ed Armbrister	.04	.02	.01	649 Moose Haas	.04	.02	.01
557 Tony Solaita	.04	.02	.01	650 Cesar Cedeno	.20	.15	.06
558 Paul Mitchell	.04	.02	.01	651 Doug Rader	.06	.04	.02
				652 Checklist #6	.04	.02	.01

1978 TOPPS (CONTINUED)

	MINT	VG-E	F-G
653 Ron Hodges (dp)	.03	.02	.01
654 Pepe Frias	.04	.02	.01
655 Lyman Bostock	.15	.11	.05
656 Dave Garcia	.04	.02	.01
657 Bombo Rivera	.04	.02	.01
658 Manny Sanguillen	.04	.02	.01
659 Rangers Team	.08	.06	.02
660 Jason Thompson	.08	.06	.02
661 Grant Jackson	.04	.02	.01
662 Paul Dade	.04	.02	.01
663 Paul Reuschel	.04	.02	.01
664 Fred Stanley	.04	.02	.01
665 Dennis Leonard	.08	.06	.02
666 Billy Smith	.04	.02	.01
667 Jeff Byrd	.04	.02	.01
668 Dusty Baker	.10	.07	.03
669 Pete Falcone	.04	.02	.01
670 Jim Rice	.75	.55	.25
671 Gary Lavelle	.06	.04	.02
672 Don Kessinger	.06	.04	.02
673 Steve Brye	.04	.02	.01
674 Ray Knight	.08	.06	.02
675 Jay Johnstone	.04	.02	.01
676 Bob Myrick	.04	.02	.01
677 Ed Herrmann	.04	.02	.01
678 Tom Burgmeier	.04	.02	.01
679 Wayne Garrett	.04	.02	.01
680 Vida Blue	.20	.15	.06
681 Rob Belloir	.04	.02	.01
682 Ken Brett	.04	.02	.01
683 Mike Champion	.04	.02	.01
684 Ralph Houk	.06	.04	.02
685 Frank Taveras	.04	.02	.01
686 Gaylord Perry	.30	.25	.10
687 Julio Cruz	.04	.02	.01
688 George Mitterwald	.04	.02	.01

	MINT	VG-E	F-G
689 Indians Team	.08	.06	.02
690 Mickey Rivers	.08	.06	.02
691 Ross Grimsley	.04	.02	.01
692 Ken Reitz	.04	.02	.01
693 Lamar Johnson	.04	.02	.01
694 Elias Sosa	.04	.02	.01
695 Dwight Evans	.04	.02	.01
696 Steve Mingori	.04	.02	.01
697 Roger Metzger	.04	.02	.01
698 Juan Bernhardt	.04	.02	.01
699 Jackie Brown	.04	.02	.01
700 Johnny Bench	.65	.50	.20
701 Rookie Pitchers	.04	.02	.01
702 Rookie Catchers	.04	.02	.01
703 Rookie Pitchers(dp)	.03	.02	.01
704 Rookie 2nd Base	.25	.20	.08
705 Rookie Outfield	.04	.02	.01
706 Rookie 1st Base	.04	.02	.01
707 Rookie Shortstops	.75	.55	.25
708 Rookie Catchers	.20	.15	.06
709 Rookie Pitchers	.04	.02	.01
710 Rookie Outfield	.04	.02	.01
711 Rookie Pitchers(dp)	.03	.02	.01
712 Bobby Valentine	.04	.02	.01
713 Bob Davis	.04	.02	.01
714 Mike Anderson	.04	.02	.01
715 Jim Kaat	.10	.07	.03
716 Clarence Gaston	.04	.02	.01
717 Nelson Briles	.04	.02	.01
718 Ron Jackson	.04	.02	.01
719 Randy Elliott	.04	.02	.01
720 Fergie Jenkins	.15	.11	.05
721 Billy Martin	.20	.15	.06
722 Pete Broberg	.04	.02	.01
723 John Wockenfuss	.04	.02	.01
724 Royals Team	.08	.06	.02
725 Kurt Bevacqua	.04	.02	.01
726 Wilbur Wood	.04	.02	.01

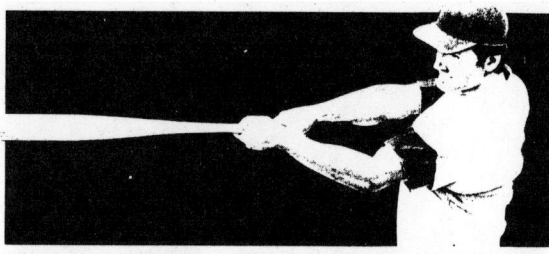

1979 TOPPS (726)

2 1/2" X 3 1/2"

DENNIS LEONARD P
ROYALS

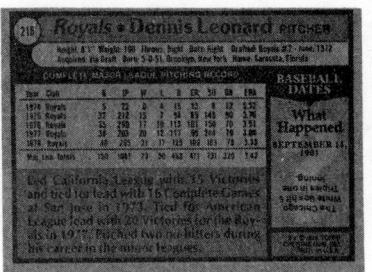

The 1979 Topps set contains Record Breakers of the 1978 season as card numbers 201-206. The 66 double printed cards are noted in the checklist by (dp). Bump Wills was printed initially as a Blue Jay and corrected in later printings. The set price does not include the Wills Ranger card.

	MINT	VG-E	F-G
COMPLETE SET	25.00	20.00	8.00
COMMON PLAYER	.03	.02	.01
1 Batting Leaders	.10	.07	.03
2 Home Run Leaders	.10	.07	.03
3 RBI Leaders	.10	.07	.03
4 Stolen Base Leaders	.08	.06	.02
5 Victory Leaders	.06	.04	.02
6 Strikeout Leaders	.06	.04	.02
7 ERA Leaders	.06	.04	.02
8 Leading Firemen	.06	.04	.02
9 Dave Campbell	.03	.02	.01
10 Lee May	.03	.02	.01
11 Marc Hill	.03	.02	.01
12 Dick Drago	.03	.02	.01
13 Paul Dade	.03	.02	.01
14 Rafael Landestoy	.03	.02	.01
15 Ross Grimsley	.03	.02	.01
16 Fred Stanley	.03	.02	.01
17 Donnie Moore	.03	.02	.01
18 Tony Solaita	.03	.02	.01
19 Larry Gura (dp)	.03	.02	.01
20 Joe Morgan (dp)	.15	.11	.05
21 Kevin Kobel	.03	.02	.01
22 Mike Jorgensen	.03	.02	.01
23 Terry Forster	.05	.03	.01
24 Paul Molitor	.15	.11	.05
25 Steve Carlton	.40	.30	.13
26 Jamie Quirk	.03	.02	.01
27 Dave Goltz	.03	.02	.01
28 Steve Brye	.03	.02	.01
29 Rick Langford	.03	.02	.01
30 Dave Winfield	.60	.45	.20
31 Tom House (dp)	.02	.01	.01½
32 Jerry Mumphrey	.03	.02	.01
33 Dave Rozema	.05	.03	.01
34 Rob Andrews	.03	.02	.01
35 Ed Figueroa	.03	.02	.01
36 Alan Ashby	.03	.02	.01
37 Joe Kerrigan (dp)	.02	.01	.01½
38 Bernie Carbo	.03	.02	.01
39 Dale Murphy	.05	.03	.01
40 Dennis Eckersley	.06	.04	.02
41 Twins Team	.07	.05	.02
42 Ron Blomberg	.03	.02	.01
43 Wayne Twitchell	.03	.02	.01
44 Kurt Bevacqua	.03	.02	.01
45 Al Hrabosky	.03	.02	.01
46 Ron Hodges	.03	.02	.01
47 Fred Norman	.03	.02	.01
48 Merv Rettenmund	.03	.02	.01
49 Vern Ruhle	.03	.02	.01
50 Steve Garvey (dp)	.40	.30	.13
51 Ray Fosse (dp)	.02	.01	.01½
52 Randy Lerch	.03	.02	.01
53 Mick Kelleher	.03	.02	.01
54 Dell Alston (dp)	.02	.01	.01½
55 Willie Stargell	.50	.40	.18
56 John Hale	.03	.02	.01
57 Eric Rasmussen	.03	.02	.01
58 Bob Randall (dp)	.02	.01	.01½
59 John Denny (dp)	.02	.01	.01½
60 Mickey Rivers	.06	.04	.02
61 Bo Diaz	.03	.02	.01

	MINT	VG-E	F-G
62 Randy Moffitt	.03	.02	.01
63 Jack Brohamer	.03	.02	.01
64 Tom Underwood	.03	.02	.01
65 Mark Belanger	.05	.03	.01
66 Detroit Tigers	.07	.05	.02
67 Jim Mason (dp)	.02	.01	.01½
68 Joe Niekro (dp)	.03	.02	.01
69 Elliott Maddox	.03	.02	.01
70 John Candelaria	.05	.03	.01
71 Brian Downing	.05	.03	.01
72 Steve Mingori	.03	.02	.01
73 Ken Henderson	.03	.02	.01
74 Shane Rawley	.03	.02	.01
75 Steve Yeager	.03	.02	.01
76 Warren Cromartie	.03	.02	.01
77 Dan Briggs (dp)	.02	.01	.01½
78 Elias Sosa	.03	.02	.01
79 Ted Cox	.03	.02	.01
80 Jason Thompson	.05	.03	.01
81 Roger Erickson	.03	.02	.01
82 New York Mets	.08	.06	.02
83 Fred Kendall	.03	.02	.01
84 Greg Minton	.03	.02	.01
85 Gary Matthews	.07	.05	.02
86 Rodney Scott	.03	.02	.01
87 Pete Falcone	.03	.02	.01
88 Bob Molinaro	.03	.02	.01
89 Dick Tidrow	.03	.02	.01
90 Bob Boone	.03	.02	.01
91 Terry Crowley	.03	.02	.01
92 Jim Bibby	.06	.04	.02
93 Phil Mankowski	.03	.02	.01
94 Len Barker	.05	.03	.01
95 Robin Yount	.12	.08	.04
96 Indians Team	.07	.05	.02
97 Sam Mejias	.03	.02	.01
98 Ray Burris	.03	.02	.01
99 John Wathan	.03	.02	.01
100 Tom Seaver (dp)	.40	.30	.13
101 Roy Howell	.03	.02	.01
102 Mike Anderson	.03	.02	.01
103 Jim Todd	.03	.02	.01
104 Johnny Oates (dp)	.02	.01	.01½
105 Rick Camp (dp)	.02	.01	.01½
106 Frank Duffy	.03	.02	.01
107 Jesus Alou (dp)	.02	.01	.01½
108 Eduardo Rodriguez	.03	.02	.01
109 Joel Youngblood	.03	.02	.01
110 Vida Blue	.15	.11	.05
111 Roger Freed	.03	.02	.01
112 Phillies Team	.08	.06	.02
113 Pete Redfern	.03	.02	.01
114 Cliff Johnson	.03	.02	.01
115 Nolan Ryan	.40	.30	.13
116 Ozzie Smith	.03	.02	.01
117 Grant Jackson	.03	.02	.01
118 Bud Harrelson	.03	.02	.01
119 Don Stanhouse	.05	.03	.01
120 Jim Sundberg	.08	.06	.02
121 Checklist 1 (dp)	.02	.01	.01½
122 Mike Paxton	.03	.02	.01
123 Lou Whitaker	.08	.06	.02
124 Dan Schatzeder	.03	.02	.01
125 Rick Burleson	.08	.06	.02

	MINT	VG-E	F-G			MINT	VG-E	F-G
126 Doug Bair	.03	.02	.01		219 Roy Smalley	.05	.03	.01
127 Thad Bosley	.03	.02	.01		220 Cesar Geronimo	.03	.02	.01
128 Ted Martinez	.03	.02	.01		221 Jesse Jefferson	.03	.02	.01
129 Marty Pattin (dp)	.02	.01	.01½		222 Bob Beall	.03	.02	.01
130 Bob Watson (dp)	.02	.01	.01½		223 Kent Tekulve	.07	.05	.02
131 Jim Clancy	.03	.02	.01		224 Dave Revering	.03	.02	.01
132 Rowland Office	.03	.02	.01		225 Rich Gossage	.08	.06	.02
133 Bill Castro	.03	.02	.01		226 Ron Pruitt	.03	.02	.01
134 Alan Bannister	.03	.02	.01		227 Steve Stone	.08	.06	.02
135 Bobby Murcer	.06	.04	.02		228 Vic Davalillo	.03	.02	.01
136 Jim Kaat	.08	.06	.02		229 Doug Flynn	.03	.02	.01
137 Larry Wolfe (dp)	.02	.01	.01½		230 Bob Forsch	.03	.02	.01
138 Mark Lee	.03	.02	.01		231 Johnny Wockenfuss	.03	.02	.01
139 Luis Pujols	.03	.02	.01		232 Jimmy Sexton	.03	.02	.01
140 Don Gullett	.03	.02	.01		233 Paul Mitchell	.03	.02	.01
141 Tom Paciorek	.03	.02	.01		234 Toby Harrah	.03	.02	.01
142 Charlie Williams	.03	.02	.01		235 Steve Rogers	.06	.04	.02
143 Tony Scott	.03	.02	.01		236 Jim Dwyer	.03	.02	.01
144 Sandy Alomar	.03	.02	.01		237 Billy Smith	.03	.02	.01
145 Rick Rhoden	.03	.02	.01		238 Balor Moore	.03	.02	.01
146 Duane Kuiper	.03	.02	.01		239 Willie Horton	.03	.02	.01
147 Dave Hamilton	.03	.02	.01		240 Rick Reuschel	.08	.06	.02
148 Bruce Boisclair	.03	.02	.01		241 Checklist 2 (dp)	.02	.01	.01½
149 Manny Sarmiento	.03	.02	.01		242 Pablo Torrealba	.03	.02	.01
150 Wayne Cage	.03	.02	.01		243 Buck Martinez (dp)	.02	.01	.01½
151 John Hiller	.03	.02	.01		244 Pirates Team	.08	.06	.02
152 Rick Cerone	.08	.06	.02		245 Jeff Burroughs	.06	.04	.02
153 Dennis Lamp	.03	.02	.01		246 Darrell Jackson	.03	.02	.01
154 Jim Gantner (dp)	.02	.01	.01½		247 Tucker Ashford (dp)	.02	.01	.01½
155 Dwight Evans	.03	.02	.01		248 Pete LaCock	.03	.02	.01
156 Buddy Solomon	.03	.02	.01		249 Paul Thormodsgard	.03	.02	.01
157 U.L. Washington	.03	.02	.01		250 Willie Randolph	.06	.04	.02
158 Joe Sambito	.05	.03	.01		251 Jack Morris	.05	.03	.01
159 Roy White	.03	.02	.01		252 Bob Stinson	.03	.02	.01
160 Mike Flanagan	.07	.05	.02		253 Rick Wise	.06	.04	.02
161 Barry Foote	.03	.02	.01		254 Luis Gomez	.03	.02	.01
162 Tom Johnson	.03	.02	.01		255 Tommy John	.25	.20	.08
163 Glenn Burke	.03	.02	.01		256 Mike Sadek	.03	.02	.01
164 Mickey Lolich	.05	.03	.01		257 Adrian Devine	.03	.02	.01
165 Frank Taveras	.03	.02	.01		258 Mike Phillips	.03	.02	.01
166 Leon Roberts	.03	.02	.01		259 Cincinnati Reds	.08	.06	.02
167 Roger Metzger (dp)	.02	.01	.01½		260 Richie Zisk	.07	.05	.02
168 Dave Freisleben	.03	.02	.01		261 Mario Guerrero	.03	.02	.01
169 Bill Nahorodny	.03	.02	.01		262 Nelson Briles	.03	.02	.01
170 Don Sutton	.20	.15	.06		263 Oscar Gamble	.05	.03	.01
171 Gene Clines	.03	.02	.01		264 Don Robinson	.03	.02	.01
172 Mike Druhert	.03	.02	.01		265 Don Money	.05	.03	.01
173 John Lowenstein	.03	.02	.01		266 Jim Willoughby	.03	.02	.01
174 Rick Auerbach	.03	.02	.01		267 Joe Rudi	.05	.03	.01
175 George Hendrick	.07	.05	.02		268 Julio Gonzalez	.03	.02	.01
176 Aurelio Rodriguez	.03	.02	.01		269 Woodie Fryman	.03	.02	.01
177 Ron Reed	.03	.02	.01		270 Butch Hobson	.05	.03	.01
178 Alvis Woods	.03	.02	.01		271 Rawly Eastwick	.03	.02	.01
179 Jim Beattie (dp)	.02	.01	.01½		272 Tim Corcoran	.03	.02	.01
180 Larry Hisle	.08	.06	.02		273 Jerry Terrell	.03	.02	.01
181 Mike Garman	.03	.02	.01		274 Willie Norwood	.03	.02	.01
182 Tim Johnson	.03	.02	.01		275 Junior Moore	.03	.02	.01
183 Paul Splittorff	.05	.03	.01		276 Jim Colborn	.03	.02	.01
184 Darrel Chaney	.03	.02	.01		277 Tom Grieve	.03	.02	.01
185 Mike Torrez	.06	.04	.02		278 Andy Messersmith	.05	.03	.01
186 Eric Soderholm	.03	.02	.01		279 Jerry Grote (dp)	.02	.01	.01½
187 Mark Lemongello	.03	.02	.01		280 Andre Thornton	.05	.03	.01
188 Pat Kelly	.03	.02	.01		281 Vic Correll (dp)	.02	.01	.01½
189 Eddie Whitson	.03	.02	.01		282 Toronto Blue Jays	.07	.05	.02
190 Ron Cey	.08	.06	.02		283 Ken Kravec	.03	.02	.01
191 Mike Norris	.05	.03	.01		284 Johnnie LeMaster	.03	.02	.01
192 Cardinals Team	.07	.05	.02		285 Bobby Bonds	.10	.07	.03
193 Glenn Adams	.03	.02	.01		286 Duffy Dyer	.03	.02	.01
194 Randy Jones	.08	.06	.02		287 Andres Mora	.03	.02	.01
195 Bill Madlock	.08	.06	.02		288 Milt Wilcox	.03	.02	.01
196 Steve Kemp (dp)	.05	.03	.01		289 Jose Cruz	.05	.03	.01
197 Bob Apodaca	.03	.02	.01		290 Dave Lopes	.07	.05	.02
198 Johnny Grubb	.03	.02	.01		291 Tom Griffin	.03	.02	.01
199 Larry Milbourne	.03	.02	.01		292 Don Reynolds	.03	.02	.01
200 Johnny Bench (dp)	.40	.30	.13		293 Jerry Garvin	.03	.02	.01
201 Record:Mike Edwards	.03	.02	.01		294 Pepe Frias	.03	.02	.01
202 Record:Ron Guidry	.25	.20	.08		295 Mitchell Page	.05	.03	.01
203 Record:J.R. Richard	.20	.15	.06		296 Preston Hanna	.03	.02	.01
204 Record:Pete Rose	.30	.25	.10		297 Ted Sizemore	.03	.02	.01
205 Record:John Stearns	.03	.02	.01		298 Rich Gale	.05	.03	.01
206 Record:Sam Stewart	.03	.02	.01		299 Steve Ontiveros	.03	.02	.01
207 Dave Lemanczyk	.03	.02	.01		300 Rod Carew	.50	.40	.18
208 Clarence Gaston	.03	.02	.01		301 Tom Hume	.03	.02	.01
209 Reggie Cleveland	.03	.02	.01		302 Atlanta Braves	.07	.05	.02
210 Larry Bowa	.15	.11	.05		303 Lary Sorensen	.05	.03	.01
211 Denny Martinez	.03	.02	.01		304 Steve Swisher	.03	.02	.01
212 Carney Lansford	.10	.07	.03		305 Willie Montanez	.03	.02	.01
213 Bill Travers	.03	.02	.01		306 Floyd Bannister	.03	.02	.01
214 Boston Red Sox	.08	.06	.02		307 Larvell Blanks	.03	.02	.01
215 Willie McCovey	.50	.40	.18		308 Bert Blyleven	.07	.05	.02
216 Wilbur Wood	.03	.02	.01		309 Ralph Garr	.05	.03	.01
217 Steve Dillard	.03	.02	.01		310 Thurman Munson	.75	.55	.25
218 Dennis Leonard	.08	.06	.02		311 Gary Lavelle	.05	.03	.01

	MINT	VG-E	F-G
312 Bob Robertson	.03	.02	.01
313 Dyar Miller	.03	.02	.01
314 Larry Harlow	.03	.02	.01
315 Jon Matlack	.05	.03	.01
316 Milt May	.03	.02	.01
317 Jose Cardenal	.03	.02	.01
318 Bob Welch	.03	.02	.01
319 Wayne Garrett	.03	.02	.01
320 Carl Yastrzemski	.75	.55	.25
321 Gaylord Perry	.35	.27	.12
322 Danny Goodwin	.03	.02	.01
323 Lynn McGlothen	.03	.02	.01
324 Mike Tyson	.03	.02	.01
325 Cecil Cooper	.15	.11	.05
326 Pedro Borbon	.03	.02	.01
327 Art Howe	.03	.02	.01
328 Oakland A's	.07	.05	.02
329 Joe Coleman	.03	.02	.01
330 George Brett	.75	.55	.25
331 Mickey Mahler	.03	.02	.01
332 Gary Alexander	.03	.02	.01
333 Chet Lemon	.07	.05	.02
334 Craig Swan	.06	.04	.02
335 Chris Chambliss	.05	.03	.01
336 Bobby Thompson	.03	.02	.01
337 John Montague	.03	.02	.01
338 Vic Harris	.03	.02	.01
339 Ron Jackson	.03	.02	.01
340 Jim Palmer	.35	.27	.12
341 Willie Upshaw	.03	.02	.01
342 Dave Roberts	.03	.02	.01
343 Ed Glynn	.03	.02	.01
344 Jerry Royster	.03	.02	.01
345 Tug McGraw	.07	.05	.02
346 Bill Buckner	.06	.04	.02
347 Doug Rau	.03	.02	.01
348 Andre Dawson	.06	.04	.02
349 Jim Wright	.03	.02	.01
350 Garry Templeton	.20	.15	.06
351 Wayne Nordhagen	.03	.02	.01
352 Steve Renko	.03	.02	.01
353 Checklist 3	.03	.02	.01
354 Bill Bonham	.03	.02	.01
355 Lee Mazzilli	.15	.11	.05
356 Giants Team	.07	.05	.02
357 Jerry Augustine	.03	.02	.01
358 Alan Trammell	.10	.07	.03
359 Dan Spillner (dp)	.02	.01	.01½
360 Amos Otis	.07	.05	.02
361 Tom Dixon	.03	.02	.01
362 Mike Cubbage	.03	.02	.01
363 Craig Skok	.03	.02	.01
364 Gene Richards	.03	.02	.01
365 Sparky Lyle	.03	.02	.01
366 Juan Bernhardt	.03	.02	.01
367 Dave Skaggs	.03	.02	.01
368 Don Aase	.03	.02	.01
369a Bump Wills (error)	3.00	2.25	1.00
369b Bump Wills(correct)	6.00	4.50	2.00
370 Dave Kingman	.25	.20	.08
371 Jeff Holly	.03	.02	.01
372 Lamar Johnson	.03	.02	.01
373 Lance Rautzham	.03	.02	.01
374 Ed Herrmann	.03	.02	.01
375 Bill Campbell	.05	.03	.01
376 Gorman Thomas	.08	.06	.02
377 Paul Moskau	.03	.02	.01
378 Rob Picciolo (dp)	.02	.01	.01½
379 Dale Murray	.03	.02	.01
380 John Mayberry	.06	.04	.02
381 Houston Astros	.07	.05	.02
382 Jerry Martin	.03	.02	.01
383 Phil Garner	.03	.02	.01
384 Tommy Boggs	.03	.02	.01
385 Dan Ford	.03	.02	.01
386 Francisco Barrios	.03	.02	.01
387 Gary Thomasson	.03	.02	.01
388 Jack Billingham	.03	.02	.01
389 Joe Zdeb	.03	.02	.01
390 Rollie Fingers	.08	.06	.02
391 Al Oliver	.12	.08	.04
392 Doug Ault	.03	.02	.01
393 Scott McGregor	.07	.05	.02
394 Randy Stein	.03	.02	.01
395 Dave Cash	.03	.02	.01
396 Bill Plummer	.03	.02	.01
397 Sergio Ferrer	.03	.02	.01
398 Ivan DeJesus	.03	.02	.01
399 David Clyde	.03	.02	.01
400 Jim Rice	.75	.55	.25
401 Ray Knight	.07	.05	.02
402 Paul Hartzell	.03	.02	.01
403 Tim Foli	.03	.02	.01

	MINT	VG-E	F-G
404 White Sox Team	.07	.05	.02
405 Butch Wynegar (dp)	.02	.01	.01½
406 Joe Wallis (dp)	.02	.01	.01½
407 Pete Vuckovich	.03	.02	.01
408 Charlie Moore (dp)	.02	.01	.01½
409 Willie Wilson	.90	.70	.30
410 Darrell Evans	.03	.02	.01
411 Hits Record	.10	.07	.03
412 RBI Record	.10	.07	.03
413 Home Run Record	.12	.08	.04
414 Batting Record	.10	.07	.03
415 Steals Record	.08	.06	.02
416 Wins Record	.06	.04	.02
417 Strikeout Record (dp)	.03	.02	.01
418 ERA Record (dp)	.03	.02	.01
419 Dick Ruthven	.03	.02	.01
420 Ken Griffey	.07	.05	.02
421 Doug DeCinces	.03	.02	.01
422 Ruppert Jones	.05	.03	.01
423 Bob Montgomery	.03	.02	.01
424 Angels Team	.07	.05	.02
425 Rick Manning	.03	.02	.01
426 Chris Speier	.03	.02	.01
427 Andy Replogle	.03	.02	.01
428 Bobby Valentine	.03	.02	.01
429 John Urrea (dp)	.02	.01	.01½
430 Dave Parker	.50	.40	.18
431 Glenn Borgmann	.03	.02	.01
432 Dave Heaverlo	.03	.02	.01
433 Larry Biittner	.03	.02	.01
434 Ken Clay	.03	.02	.01
435 Gene Tenace	.05	.03	.01
436 Hector Cruz	.03	.02	.01
437 Rick Williams	.03	.02	.01
438 Horace Speed	.03	.02	.01
439 Frank White	.05	.03	.01
440 Rusty Staub	.07	.05	.02
441 Lee Lacy	.03	.02	.01
442 Doyle Alexander	.03	.02	.01
443 Bruce Bochte	.03	.02	.01
444 Aurelio Lopez	.03	.02	.01
445 Steve Henderson	.05	.03	.01
446 Jim Lonborg	.05	.03	.01
447 Manny Sanguillen	.03	.02	.01
448 Moose Haas	.03	.02	.01
449 Bombo Rivera	.03	.02	.01
450 Dave Concepcion	.08	.06	.02
451 Kansas City Team	.07	.05	.02
452 Jerry Morales	.03	.02	.01
453 Chris Knapp	.03	.02	.01
454 Len Randle	.03	.02	.01
455 Bill Lee (dp)	.02	.01	.01½
456 Chuck Baker	.03	.02	.01
457 Bruce Sutter	.25	.20	.08
458 Jim Essian	.03	.02	.01
459 Sid Monge	.03	.02	.01
460 Graig Nettles	.10	.07	.03
461 Jim Barr (dp)	.02	.01	.01½
462 Otto Velez	.03	.02	.01
463 Steve Comer	.03	.02	.01
464 Joe Nolan	.03	.02	.01
465 Reggie Smith	.08	.06	.02
466 Mark Littell	.03	.02	.01
467 Don Kessinger (dp)	.02	.01	.01½
468 Stan Bahnsen (dp)	.02	.01	.01½
469 Lance Parrish	.07	.05	.02
470 Garry Maddox (dp)	.03	.02	.01
471 Joaquin Andujar	.03	.02	.01
472 Craig Kusick	.03	.02	.01
473 Dave Roberts	.03	.02	.01
474 Dick Davis	.03	.02	.01
475 Dan Driessen	.05	.03	.01
476 Tom Poquette	.03	.02	.01
477 Bob Grich	.05	.03	.01
478 Juan Beniquez	.03	.02	.01
479 San Diego Padres	.07	.05	.02
480 Fred Lynn	.75	.55	.25
481 Skip Lockwood	.03	.02	.01
482 Craig Reynolds	.03	.02	.01
483 Checklist 4 (dp)	.02	.01	.01½
484 Rick Waits	.03	.02	.01
485 Bucky Dent	.07	.05	.02
486 Bob Knepper	.03	.02	.01
487 Miguel Dilone	.05	.03	.01
488 Bob Owchinko	.03	.02	.01
489 Larry Cox	.03	.02	.01
490 Al Cowens	.03	.02	.01
491 Tippy Martinez	.03	.02	.01
492 Bob Bailor	.03	.02	.01
493 Larry Christenson	.03	.02	.01
494 Jerry White	.03	.02	.01
495 Tony Perez	.08	.06	.02
496 Barry Bonnell(dp)	.02	.01	.01½
497 Glenn Abbott	.03	.02	.01

	MINT	VG-E	F-G
498 Rich Chiles	.03	.02	.01
499 Texas Rangers	.07	.05	.02
500 Ron Guidry	.50	.40	.18
501 Junior Kennedy	.03	.02	.01
502 Steve Braun	.03	.02	.01
503 Terry Humphrey	.03	.02	.01
504 Larry McWilliams	.03	.02	.01
505 Ed Kranepool	.03	.02	.01
506 John D'Acquisto	.03	.02	.01
507 Tony Armas	.05	.03	.01
508 Charlie Hough	.03	.02	.01
509 Mario Mendoza	.03	.02	.01
510 Ted Simmons	.20	.15	.06
511 Paul Reuschel (dp)	.02	.01	.01½
512 Jack Clark	.08	.06	.02
513 Dave Johnson	.03	.02	.01
514 Mike Proly	.03	.02	.01
515 Enos Cabell	.03	.02	.01
516 Champ Summers (dp)	.02	.01	.01½
517 Al Bumbry	.03	.02	.01
518 Jim Umbarger	.03	.02	.01
519 Ben Oglivie	.07	.05	.02
520 Gary Carter	.10	.07	.03
521 Sam Ewing	.03	.02	.01
522 Ken Holtzman	.05	.03	.01
523 John Milner	.03	.02	.01
524 Tom Burgmeier	.03	.02	.01
525 Freddie Patek	.05	.03	.01
526 Dodgers Team	.08	.06	.02
527 Lerrin LaGrow	.03	.02	.01
528 Wayne Gross (dp)	.02	.01	.01½
529 Brian Asselstine	.03	.02	.01
530 Frank Tanana	.05	.03	.01
531 Fernando Gonzalez	.03	.02	.01
532 Buddy Schultz	.03	.02	.01
533 Leroy Stanton	.03	.02	.01
534 Ken Forsch	.03	.02	.01
535 Ellis Valentine	.05	.03	.01
536 Jerry Reuss	.07	.05	.02
537 Tom Veryzer	.03	.02	.01
538 Mike Ivie (dp)	.02	.01	.01½
539 John Ellis	.03	.02	.01
540 Greg Luzinski	.20	.15	.06
541 Jim Slaton	.03	.02	.01
542 Rick Bosetti	.03	.02	.01
543 Kiko Garcia	.03	.02	.01
544 Fergie Jenkins	.15	.11	.05
545 John Stearns	.03	.02	.01
546 Bill Russell	.03	.02	.01
547 Clint Hurdle	.05	.03	.01
548 Enrique Romo	.03	.02	.01
549 Bob Bailey	.03	.02	.01
550 Sal Bando	.06	.04	.02
551 Chicago Cubs	.07	.05	.02
552 Jose Morales	.03	.02	.01
553 Denny Walling	.03	.02	.01
554 Matt Keough	.03	.02	.01
555 Biff Pocoroba	.03	.02	.01
556 Mike Lum	.03	.02	.01
557 Ken Brett	.03	.02	.01
558 Jay Johnstone	.03	.02	.01
559 Greg Pryor	.03	.02	.01
560 John Montefusco	.03	.02	.01
561 Ed Ott	.03	.02	.01
562 Dusty Baker	.07	.05	.02
563 Roy Thomas	.03	.02	.01
564 Jerry Turner	.03	.02	.01
565 Rico Carty	.05	.03	.01
566 Nino Espinosa	.03	.02	.01
567 Rich Hebner	.03	.02	.01
568 Carlos Lopez	.03	.02	.01
569 Bob Sykes	.03	.02	.01
570 Cesar Cedeno	.15	.11	.05
571 Darrell Porter	.07	.05	.02
572 Rod Gilbreath	.03	.02	.01
573 Jim Kern	.05	.03	.01
574 Claudell Washington	.05	.03	.01
575 Luis Tiant	.07	.05	.02
576 Mike Parrott	.03	.02	.01
577 Milwaukee Brewers	.07	.05	.02
578 Pete Broberg	.03	.02	.01
579 Greg Gross	.03	.02	.01
580 Ron Fairly	.05	.03	.01
581 Darold Knowles	.03	.02	.01
582 Paul Blair	.03	.02	.01
583 Julio Cruz	.03	.02	.01
584 Jim Rooker	.03	.02	.01
585 Hal McRae	.03	.02	.01
586 Bob Horner	1.50	1.10	.50
587 Ken Reitz	.03	.02	.01
588 Tom Murphy	.03	.02	.01
589 Terry Whitfield	.03	.02	.01
590 J.R. Richard	.25	.20	.08

	MINT	VG-E	F-G
591 Mike Hargrove	.03	.02	.01
592 Mike Krukow	.03	.02	.01
593 Rick Dempsey	.03	.02	.01
594 Bob Shirley	.03	.02	.01
595 Phil Niekro	.10	.07	.03
596 Jim Wohlford	.03	.02	.01
597 Bob Stanley	.03	.02	.01
598 Mark Wagner	.03	.02	.01
599 Jim Spencer	.03	.02	.01
600 George Foster	.30	.25	.10
601 Dave LaRoche	.03	.02	.01
602 Checklist 5	.03	.02	.01
603 Rudy May	.06	.04	.02
604 Jeff Newman	.03	.02	.01
605 Rick Monday (dp)	.03	.02	.01
606 Montreal Expos	.07	.05	.02
607 Omar Moreno	.08	.06	.02
608 Dave McKay	.03	.02	.01
609 Silvio Martinez	.03	.02	.01
610 Mike Schmidt	.50	.40	.18
611 Jim Norris	.03	.02	.01
612 Rick Honeycutt	.03	.02	.01
613 Mike Edwards	.03	.02	.01
614 Willie Hernandez	.03	.02	.01
615 Ken Singleton	.15	.11	.05
616 Billy Almon	.03	.02	.01
617 Terry Puhl	.07	.05	.02
618 Jerry Remy	.03	.02	.01
619 Ken Landreaux	.06	.04	.02
620 Bert Campaneris	.05	.03	.01
621 Pat Zachry	.03	.02	.01
622 Dave Collins	.05	.03	.01
623 Bob McClure	.03	.02	.01
624 Larry Herndon	.03	.02	.01
625 Mark Fidrych	.10	.07	.03
626 New York Yankees	.08	.06	.02
627 Gary Serum	.03	.02	.01
628 Del Unser	.03	.02	.01
629 Gene Garber	.03	.02	.01
630 Bake McBride	.05	.03	.01
631 Jorge Orta	.03	.02	.01
632 Don Kirkwood	.03	.02	.01
633 Rob Wilfong (dp)	.02	.01	.01½
634 Paul Lindblad	.03	.02	.01
635 Don Baylor	.25	.20	.08
636 Wayne Garland	.03	.02	.01
637 Bill Robinson	.03	.02	.01
638 Al Fitzmorris	.03	.02	.01
639 Manny Trillo	.05	.03	.01
640 Eddie Murray	.10	.07	.03
641 Bobby Castillo	.03	.02	.01
642 Wilbur Howard (dp)	.02	.01	.01½
643 Tom Hausman	.03	.02	.01
644 Manny Mota	.05	.03	.01
645 George Scott (dp)	.03	.02	.01
646 Rick Sweet	.03	.02	.01
647 Bob Lacey	.03	.02	.01
648 Lou Piniella	.06	.04	.02
649 John Curtis	.03	.02	.01
650 Pete Rose	.75	.55	.25
651 Mike Caldwell	.05	.03	.01
652 Stan Papi	.03	.02	.01
653 Warren Brusstar(dp)	.02	.01	.01½
654 Rick Miller	.03	.02	.01
655 Jerry Koosman	.05	.03	.01
656 Hosken Powell	.03	.02	.01
657 George Medich	.03	.02	.01
658 Taylor Duncan	.03	.02	.01
659 Seattle Mariners	.07	.05	.02
660 Ron Leflore (dp)	.10	.07	.03
661 Bruce Kison	.03	.02	.01
662 Kevin Bell	.03	.02	.01
663 Mike Vail	.03	.02	.01
664 Doug Bird	.03	.02	.01
665 Lou Brock	.50	.40	.18
666 Rich Dauer	.03	.02	.01
667 Don Hood	.03	.02	.01
668 Bill North	.03	.02	.01
669 Checklist 6	.03	.02	.01
670 Jim Hunter (dp)	.15	.11	.05
671 Joe Ferguson(dp)	.02	.01	.01½
672 Ed Halicki	.03	.02	.01
673 Tom Hutton	.03	.02	.01
674 Dave Tomlin	.03	.02	.01
675 Tim McCarver	.03	.02	.01
676 Johnny Sutton	.03	.02	.01
677 Larry Parrish	.06	.04	.02
678 Geoff Zahn	.03	.02	.01
679 Derrel Thomas	.03	.02	.01
680 Carlton Fisk	.20	.15	.06
681 John Henry Johnson	.03	.02	.01
682 Dave Chalk	.03	.02	.01
683 Dan Meyer (dp)	.02	.01	.01½

1979 TOPPS (CONTINUED)

	MINT	VG-E	F-G
684 Jamie Easterly (dp)	.03	.02	.01
685 Sixto Lezcano	.07	.05	.02
686 Ron Schueler (dp)	.03	.02	.01
687 Rennie Stennett	.03	.02	.01
688 Mike Willis	.03	.02	.01
689 Baltimore Orioles	.07	.05	.02
690 Buddy Bell (dp)	.05	.03	.01
691 Dock Ellis (dp)	.02	.01	.0½
692 Mickey Stanley	.03	.02	.01
693 Dave Rader	.03	.02	.01
694 Burt Hooton	.06	.04	.02
695 Keith Hernandez	.25	.20	.08
696 Andy Hassler	.03	.02	.01
697 Dave Bergman	.03	.02	.01
698 Bill Stein	.03	.02	.01
699 Hal Dues	.03	.02	.01
700 Reggie Jackson (dp)	.40	.30	.13
701 Orioles Prsopects	.03	.02	.01
702 Red Sox Prospects	.03	.02	.01
703 Angels Prospects	.03	.02	.01
704 White Sox Prospects	.03	.02	.01

	MINT	VG-E	F-G
705 Indians Prospects	.03	.02	.01
706 Tigers Prospects	.03	.02	.01
707 Royals Prospects	.03	.02	.01
708 Brewers Prospects	.03	.02	.01
709 Twins Prospects	.03	.02	.01
710 Yankees Prospects	.03	.02	.01
711 Oakland Prospects	.20	.15	.06
712 Mariners Prospects	.03	.02	.01
713 Rangers Prospects	.03	.02	.01
714 Blue Jays Prospects	.03	.02	.01
715 Braves Prospects	.03	.02	.01
716 Cubs Prospects	.03	.02	.01
717 Reds Prospects	.03	.02	.01
718 Astros Prospects	.03	.02	.01
719 Dodgers Prospects	.03	.02	.01
720 Expos Prospects	.03	.02	.01
721 Mets Prospects	.03	.02	.01
722 Phillies Prospects	.03	.02	.01
723 Pirates Prospects	.03	.02	.01
724 Cardinals Prospects	.03	.02	.01
725 Padres Prospects	.03	.02	.01
726 Giants Prospects	.03	.02	.01

1980 TOPPS (726)

2 1/2" X 3 1/2"

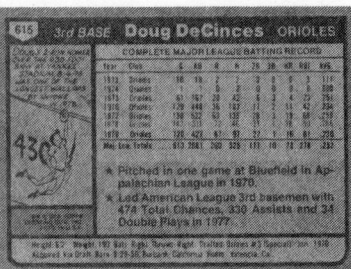

The 1980 Topps set contains 726 numbered cards. Card nos. 1 to 6 feature 1979 highlights while card nos. 659 to 686 feature the American and National League rookie prospects.

	MINT	VG-E	F-G
COMPLETE SET	18.00	13.00	6.00
COMMON PLAYER	.03	.02	.01
1 1979 Highlight	.10	.07	.03
2 1979 Highlight	.06	.04	.02
3 1979 Highlight	.06	.04	.02
4 1979 Highlight	.06	.04	.02
5 1979 Highlight	.06	.04	.02
6 1979 Highlight	.06	.04	.02
7 Mike Lum	.03	.02	.01
8 Craig Swan	.06	.04	.02
9 Steve Braun	.03	.02	.01
10 Denny Martinez	.03	.02	.01
11 Jimmy Sexton	.03	.02	.01
12 John Curtis (dp)	.02	.01	.0½
13 Ron Pruitt	.03	.02	.01
14 Dave Cash	.03	.02	.01
15 Bill Campbell (dp)	.02	.01	.0½
16 Jerry Narron	.03	.02	.01
17 Bruce Sutter	.20	.15	.06
18 Ron Jackson	.03	.02	.01
19 Balor Moore	.03	.02	.01
20 Dan Ford	.03	.02	.01
21 Manny Sarmiento	.03	.02	.01
22 Pat Putnam	.03	.02	.01
23 Derrel Thomas	.03	.02	.01
24 Jim Slaton	.03	.02	.01
25 Lee Mazzilli	.10	.07	.03
26 Marty Pattin	.03	.02	.01
27 Del Unser	.03	.02	.01
28 Bruce Kison	.03	.02	.01
29 Mark Wagner	.03	.02	.01
30 Vida Blue	.12	.08	.04
31 Jay Johnstone	.03	.02	.01
32 Julio Cruz (dp)	.02	.01	.0½
33 Tony Scott	.03	.02	.01
34 Jeff Newman (dp)	.02	.01	.0½
35 Luis Tiant	.08	.06	.02
36 Rusty Torres	.03	.02	.01
37 Kiko Garcia	.03	.02	.01
38 Dan Spillner (dp)	.02	.01	.0½

	MINT	VG-E	F-G
39 Rowland Office	.03	.02	.01
40 Carlton Fisk	.12	.08	.04
41 Texas Rangers Team / Pat Corrales,Mgr.	.06	.04	.02
42 Dave Palmer	.03	.02	.01
43 Bombo Rivera	.03	.02	.01
44 Bill Fahey	.03	.02	.01
45 Frank White	.05	.03	.01
46 Rico Carty	.05	.03	.01
47 Bill Bonham (dp)	.02	.01	.0½
48 Rick Miller	.03	.02	.01
49 Mario Guerrero	.03	.02	.01
50 J.R. Richard	.15	.11	.05
51 Joe Ferguson (dp)	.02	.01	.0½
52 Warren Brusstar	.03	.02	.01
53 Ben Oglivie	.08	.06	.02
54 Dennis Lamp	.03	.02	.01
55 Bill Madlock	.05	.03	.01
56 Bobby Valentine	.03	.02	.01
57 Pete Vuckovich	.03	.02	.01
58 Doug Flynn	.03	.02	.01
59 Eddy Putman	.03	.02	.01
60 Bucky Dent	.05	.03	.01
61 Gary Serum	.03	.02	.01
62 Mike Ivie	.03	.02	.01
63 Bob Stanley	.03	.02	.01
64 Joe Nolan	.03	.02	.01
65 Al Bumbry	.03	.02	.01
66 Kansas City Royals / Jim Frey, Mgr.	.06	.04	.02
67 Doyle Alexander	.03	.02	.01
68 Larry Harlow	.03	.02	.01
69 Rick Williams	.03	.02	.01
70 Gary Carter	.07	.05	.02
71 John Milner (dp)	.02	.01	.0½
72 Fred Howard (dp)	.02	.01	.0½
73 Dave Collins	.05	.03	.01
74 Sid Monge	.03	.02	.01
75 Bill Russell	.03	.02	.01
76 John Stearns	.03	.02	.01
77 Dave Stieb	.03	.02	.01

#	Player	MINT	VG-E	F-G
78	Ruppert Jones	.03	.02	.01
79	Bob Owchinko	.03	.02	.01
80	Ron LeFlore	.10	.07	.03
81	Ted Sizemore	.03	.02	.01
82	Houston Astros Team	.08	.06	.02
	Bill Virdon, Mgr.			
83	Steve Trout	.03	.02	.01
84	Gary Lavelle	.03	.02	.01
85	Ted Simmons	.12	.08	.04
86	Dave Hamilton	.03	.02	.01
87	Pepe Frias	.03	.02	.01
88	Ken Landreaux	.05	.03	.01
89	Don Hood	.03	.02	.01
90	Manny Trillo	.05	.03	.01
91	Rick Dempsey	.03	.02	.01
92	Rick Rhoden	.03	.02	.01
93	Dave Roberts (dp)	.02	.01	.01½
94	Neil Allen	.03	.02	.01
95	Cecil Cooper	.12	.08	.04
96	Oakland A's Team	.06	.04	.02
	Jim Marshall, Mgr.			
97	Bill Lee	.03	.02	.01
98	Jerry Terrell	.03	.02	.01
99	Victor Cruz	.03	.02	.01
100	Johnny Bench	.40	.30	.13
101	Aurelio Lopez	.03	.02	.01
102	Rich Dauer	.03	.02	.01
103	Bill Caudill	.03	.02	.01
104	Manny Mota	.05	.03	.01
105	Frank Tanana	.05	.03	.01
106	Jeff Leonard	.03	.02	.01
107	Francisco Barrios	.03	.02	.01
108	Bob Horner	.30	.25	.10
109	Bill Travers	.03	.02	.01
110	Fred Lynn (dp)	.30	.25	.10
111	Bob Knepper	.03	.02	.01
112	Chicago White Sox	.06	.04	.02
	Tony LaRussa, Mgr.			
113	Geoff Zahn	.03	.02	.01
114	Juan Beniquez	.03	.02	.01
115	Sparky Lyle	.06	.04	.02
116	Larry Cox	.03	.02	.01
117	Dock Ellis	.03	.02	.01
118	Phil Garner	.03	.02	.01
119	Sammy Stewart	.03	.02	.01
120	Greg Luzinski	.20	.15	.06
121	Check List 1	.03	.02	.01
122	Dave Rosello (dp)	.02	.01	.01½
123	Lynn Jones	.03	.02	.01
124	Dave Lemanczyk	.03	.02	.01
125	Tony Perez	.10	.07	.03
126	Dave Tomlin	.03	.02	.01
127	Gary Thomasson	.03	.02	.01
128	Tom Burgmeier	.03	.02	.01
129	Craig Reynolds	.03	.02	.01
130	Amos Otis	.07	.05	.02
131	Paul Mitchell	.03	.02	.01
132	Biff Pocoroba	.03	.02	.01
133	Jerry Turner	.03	.02	.01
134	Matt Keough	.03	.02	.01
135	Bill Buckner	.10	.07	.03
136	Dick Ruthven	.03	.02	.01
137	John Castino	.03	.02	.01
138	Ross Baumgarten	.03	.02	.01
139	Dane Iorg	.03	.02	.01
140	Rich Gossage	.08	.06	.02
141	Gary Alexander	.03	.02	.01
142	Phil Huffman	.03	.02	.01
143	Bruce Bochte (dp)	.03	.02	.01
144	Steve Comer	.03	.02	.01
145	Darrell Evans	.03	.02	.01
146	Bob Welch	.03	.02	.01
147	Terry Puhl	.07	.05	.02
148	Manny Sanguillen	.03	.02	.01
149	Tom Hume	.03	.02	.01
150	Jason Thompson	.05	.03	.01
151	Tom Hausman (dp)	.02	.01	.01½
152	John Fulgham	.03	.02	.01
153	Tim Blackwell	.03	.02	.01
154	Lary Sorensen	.03	.02	.01
155	Jerry Remy	.03	.02	.01
156	Tony Brizzolara	.03	.02	.01
157	Willie Wilson (dp)	.20	.15	.06
158	Rob Picciolo (dp)	.02	.01	.01½
159	Ken Clay	.03	.02	.01
160	Eddie Murray	.10	.07	.03
161	Larry Christenson	.03	.02	.01
162	Bob Randall	.03	.02	.01
163	Steve Swisher	.03	.02	.01
164	Greg Pryor	.03	.02	.01
165	Omar Moreno	.07	.05	.02
166	Glenn Abbott	.03	.02	.01
167	Jack Clark	.08	.06	.02
168	Rick Waits	.03	.02	.01
169	Luis Gomez	.03	.02	.01
170	Burt Hooton	.07	.05	.02
171	Fernando Gonzalez	.03	.02	.01
172	Ron Hodges	.03	.02	.01
173	John Henry Johnson	.03	.02	.01
174	Ray Knight	.06	.04	.02
175	Rick Reuschel	.07	.05	.02
176	Champ Summers	.03	.02	.01
177	Dave Heaverlo	.03	.02	.01
178	Tim McCarver	.03	.02	.01
179	Ron Davis	.03	.02	.01
180	Warren Cromartie	.03	.02	.01
181	Moose Haas	.03	.02	.01
182	Ken Reitz	.03	.02	.01
183	Jim Anderson (dp)	.02	.01	.01½
184	Steve Renko (dp)	.02	.01	.01½
185	Hal McRae	.03	.02	.01
186	Junior Moore	.03	.02	.01
187	Alan Ashby	.03	.02	.01
188	Terry Crowley	.03	.02	.01
189	Kevin Kobel	.03	.02	.01
190	Buddy Bell	.07	.05	.02
191	Ted Martinez	.03	.02	.01
192	Atlanta Braves Team	.06	.04	.02
	Bobby Cox, Mgr.			
193	Dave Goltz	.05	.03	.01
194	Mike Easler	.03	.02	.01
195	John Montefusco	.03	.02	.01
196	Lance Parrish	.06	.04	.02
197	Byron McLaughlin	.03	.02	.01
198	Dell Alston (dp)	.02	.01	.01½
199	Mike LaCoss	.03	.02	.01
200	Jim Rice	.50	.40	.18
201	Batting Leaders	.07	.05	.02
202	Home Run Leaders	.07	.05	.02
203	RBI leaders	.07	.05	.02
204	Stolen Base Leaders	.06	.04	.02
205	Victory Leaders	.06	.04	.02
206	Strikeout Leaders	.06	.04	.02
207	ERA Leaders	.06	.04	.02
208	Wayne Cage	.03	.02	.01
209	Von Joshua	.03	.02	.01
210	Steve Carlton	.35	.27	.12
211	Dave Skaggs (dp)	.02	.01	.01½
212	Dave Roberts	.03	.02	.01
213	Mike Jorgensen (dp)	.02	.01	.01½
214	California Angels	.06	.04	.02
	Jim Fregosi, Mgr.			
215	Sixto Lezcano	.06	.04	.02
216	Phil Mankowski	.03	.02	.01
217	Ed Halicki	.03	.02	.01
218	Jose Morales	.03	.02	.01
219	Steve Mingori	.03	.02	.01
220	Dave Concepcion	.07	.05	.02
221	Joe Cannon	.03	.02	.01
222	Ron Hassey	.03	.02	.01
223	Bob Sykes	.03	.02	.01
224	Willie Montanez	.05	.03	.01
225	Lou Piniella	.06	.04	.02
226	Bill Stein	.03	.02	.01
227	Len Barker	.05	.03	.01
228	Johnny Oates	.03	.02	.01
229	Jim Bibby	.05	.03	.01
230	Dave Winfield	.40	.30	.13
231	Steve McCatty	.03	.02	.01
323	Alan Trammell	.06	.04	.02
233	LaRue Washington	.03	.02	.01
234	Vern Ruhle	.03	.02	.01
235	Andre Dawson	.05	.03	.01
236	Marc Hill	.03	.02	.01
237	Scott McGregor	.06	.04	.02
238	Rob Wilfong	.03	.02	.01
239	Don Aase	.03	.02	.01
240	Dave Kingman	.20	.15	.06
241	Check List 2	.03	.02	.01
242	Lamar Johnson	.03	.02	.01
243	Jerry Augustine	.03	.02	.01
244	St. Louis Cardinals	.06	.04	.02
	Ken Boyer, Mgr.			
245	Phil Niekro	.08	.06	.02
246	Tim Foli (dp)	.02	.01	.01½
247	Frank Riccelli	.03	.02	.01
248	Jamie Quirk	.03	.02	.01
249	Jim Clancy	.03	.02	.01
250	Jim Kaat	.08	.06	.02
251	Kip Young	.03	.02	.01
252	Ted Cox	.03	.02	.01
253	John Montague	.03	.02	.01
254	Paul Dade (dp)	.02	.01	.01½
255	Dusty Baker (dp)	.05	.03	.01

	MINT	VG-E	F-G
256 Roger Erickson	.03	.02	.01
257 Larry Herndon	.03	.02	.01
258 Paul Moskau	.03	.02	.01
259 New York Mets Team	.07	.05	.02
Joe Torre, Mgr.			
260 Al Oliver	.10	.07	.03
261 Dave Chalk	.03	.02	.01
262 Benny Ayala	.03	.02	.01
263 Dave LaRoche (dp)	.02	.01	.01½
264 Bill Robinson	.03	.02	.01
265 Robin Yount	.08	.06	.02
266 Bernie Carbo	.03	.02	.01
267 Dan Schatzeder	.03	.02	.01
268 Rafael Landestoy	.03	.02	.01
269 Dave Tobik	.03	.02	.01
270 Mike Schmidt (dp)	.30	.25	.10
271 Dick Drago (dp)	.02	.01	.01½
272 Ralph Garr	.03	.02	.01
273 Eduardo Rodriguez	.03	.02	.01
274 Dale Murphy	.03	.02	.01
275 Jerry Koosman	.05	.03	.01
276 Tom Veryzer	.03	.02	.01
277 Rick Bosetti	.03	.02	.01
278 Jim Spencer	.03	.02	.01
279 Rob Andrews	.03	.02	.01
280 Gaylord Perry	.25	.20	.08
281 Paul Blair	.03	.02	.01
282 Seattle Mariners	.06	.04	.02
Darrell Johnson			
283 John Ellis	.03	.02	.01
284 Larry Murray (dp)	.02	.01	.01½
285 Don Baylor	.15	.11	.05
286 Darold Knowles (dp)	.02	.01	.01½
287 John Lowenstein	.03	.02	.01
288 Dave Rozema	.03	.02	.01
289 Bruce Bochy	.03	.02	.01
290 Steve Garvey	.40	.30	.13
291 Randy Scarbery	.03	.02	.01
292 Dale Berra	.05	.03	.01
293 Elias Sosa	.03	.02	.01
294 Charlie Spikes	.03	.02	.01
295 Larry Gura	.05	.03	.01
296 Dave Rader	.03	.02	.01
297 Tim Johnson	.03	.02	.01
298 Ken Holtzman	.05	.03	.01
299 Steve Henderson	.05	.03	.01
300 Ron Guidry	.30	.25	.10
301 Mike Edwards	.03	.02	.01
302 Los Angeles Dodgers	.07	.05	.02
Tom Lasorda			
303 Bill Castro	.03	.02	.01
304 Butch Wynegar	.03	.02	.01
305 Randy Jones	.05	.03	.01
306 Denny Walling	.03	.02	.01
307 Rick Honeycutt	.03	.02	.01
308 Mike Hargrove	.03	.02	.01
309 Larry McWilliams	.03	.02	.01
310 Dave Parker	.40	.30	.13
311 Roger Metzger	.03	.02	.01
312 Mike Barlow	.03	.02	.01
313 Johnny Grubb	.03	.02	.01
314 Tim Stoddard	.03	.02	.01
315 Steve Kemp	.10	.07	.03
316 Bob Lacey	.03	.02	.01
317 Mike Anderson (dp)	.02	.01	.01½
318 Jerry Reuss	.07	.05	.02
319 Chris Speier	.03	.02	.01
320 Dennis Eckersley	.06	.04	.02
321 Keith Hernandez	.25	.20	.08
322 Claudell Washington	.05	.03	.01
323 Mick Kelleher	.03	.02	.01
324 Tom Underwood	.03	.02	.01
325 Dan Driessen	.03	.02	.01
326 Bo McLaughlin	.03	.02	.01
327 Ray Fosse (dp)	.02	.01	.01½
328 Minnesota Twins Team	.06	.04	.02
Gene Mauch			
329 Bert Roberge	.03	.02	.01
330 Al Cowens	.03	.02	.01
331 Rich Hebner	.03	.02	.01
332 Enrique Romo	.03	.02	.01
333 Jim Norris (dp)	.02	.01	.01½
334 Jim Beattie	.03	.02	.01
335 Willie McCovey	.35	.27	.12
336 George Medich	.03	.02	.01
337 Carney Lansford	.07	.05	.02
338 Johnny Wockenfuss	.03	.02	.01
339 John D'Acquisto	.03	.02	.01
340 Ken Singleton	.10	.07	.03
341 Jim Essian	.03	.02	.01
342 Odell Jones	.03	.02	.01
343 Mike Vail	.03	.02	.01

	MINT	VG-E	F-G
344 Randy Lerch	.03	.02	.01
345 Larry Parrish	.05	.03	.01
346 Buddy Solomon	.03	.02	.01
347 Harry Chappas	.03	.02	.01
348 Checklist 3	.03	.02	.01
349 Jack Brohamer	.03	.02	.01
350 George Hendrick	.06	.04	.02
351 Bob Davis	.03	.02	.01
352 Dan Briggs	.03	.02	.01
353 Andy Hassler	.03	.02	.01
354 Rick Auerbach	.03	.02	.01
355 Gary Matthews	.05	.03	.01
356 San Diego Padres	.07	.05	.02
Jerry Coleman,Mgr.			
357 Bob McClure	.03	.02	.01
358 Lou Whitaker	.06	.04	.02
359 Randy Moffitt	.03	.02	.01
360 Darrell Porter (dp)	.03	.02	.01
361 Wayne Garland	.03	.02	.01
362 Danny Goodwin	.03	.02	.01
363 Wayne Gross	.03	.02	.01
364 Ray Burris	.03	.02	.01
365 Bobby Murcer	.06	.04	.02
366 Rob Dressler	.03	.02	.01
367 Billy Smith	.03	.02	.01
368 Willie Aikens	.10	.07	.03
369 Jim Kern	.03	.02	.01
370 Cesar Cedeno	.12	.08	.04
371 Jack Morris	.05	.03	.01
372 Joel Youngblood	.03	.02	.01
373 Dan Petry (dp)	.02	.01	.01½
374 Jim Gantner	.03	.02	.01
375 Ross Grimsley	.03	.02	.01
376 Gary Allenson	.03	.02	.01
377 Junior Kennedy	.03	.02	.01
378 Jerry Mumphrey	.03	.02	.01
379 Kevin Bell	.03	.02	.01
380 Garry Maddox	.05	.03	.01
381 Chicago Cubs Team	.07	.05	.02
Preston Gomez			
382 Dave Freisleben	.03	.02	.01
383 Ed Ott	.03	.02	.01
384 Joey McLaughlin	.03	.02	.01
385 Enos Cabell	.03	.02	.01
386 Darrell Jackson	.03	.02	.01
387 Fred Stanley	.03	.02	.01
388 Mike Paxton	.03	.02	.01
389 Pete LaCock	.03	.02	.01
390 Fergie Jenkins	.12	.08	.04
391 Tony Armas (dp)	.03	.02	.01
392 Milt Wilcox	.03	.02	.01
393 Ozzie Smith	.05	.03	.01
394 Reggie Cleveland	.03	.02	.01
395 Ellis Valentine	.06	.04	.02
396 Dan Meyer	.03	.02	.01
397 Roy Thomas (dp)	.02	.01	.01½
398 Barry Foote	.03	.02	.01
399 Mike Proly (dp)	.02	.01	.01½
400 George Foster	.30	.25	.10
401 Pete Falcone	.03	.02	.01
402 Merv Rettenmund	.03	.02	.01
403 Pete Redfern (dp)	.02	.01	.01½
404 Baltimore Orioles	.07	.05	.02
Earl Weaver			
405 Dwight Evans	.03	.02	.01
406 Paul Molitor	.10	.07	.03
407 Tony Solaita	.03	.02	.01
408 Bill North	.03	.02	.01
409 Paul Splittorff	.03	.02	.01
410 Bobby Bonds	.10	.07	.03
411 Frank LaCorte	.03	.02	.01
412 Thad Bosley	.03	.02	.01
413 Allen Ripley	.03	.02	.01
414 George Scott	.05	.03	.01
415 Bill Atkinson	.03	.02	.01
416 Tom Brookens	.03	.02	.01
417 Craig Chamberlain(dp)	.02	.01	.01½
418 Roger Freed(dp)	.02	.01	.01½
419 Vic Correll	.03	.02	.01
420 Butch Hobson	.05	.03	.01
421 Doug Bird	.03	.02	.01
422 Larry Milbourne	.03	.02	.01
423 Dave Frost	.03	.02	.01
424 New York Yankees	.07	.05	.02
Dick Howser			
425 Mark Belanger	.05	.03	.01
426 Grant Jackson	.03	.02	.01
427 Tom Hutton (dp)	.02	.01	.01½
428 Pat Zachry	.03	.02	.01
429 Duane Kuiper	.03	.02	.01
430 Larry Hisle (dp)	.03	.02	.01
431 Mike Krukow	.03	.02	.01

	MINT	VG-E	F-G
432 Willie Norwood	.03	.02	.01
433 Rich Gale	.03	.02	.01
434 Johnnie LeMaster	.03	.02	.01
435 Don Gullett	.03	.02	.01
436 Billy Almon	.03	.02	.01
437 Joe Niekro	.05	.03	.01
438 Dave Revering	.03	.02	.01
439 Mike Phillips	.03	.02	.01
440 Don Sutton	.15	.11	.05
441 Eric Soderholm	.03	.02	.01
442 Jorge Orta	.03	.02	.01
443 Mike Parrott	.03	.02	.01
444 Alvis Woods	.03	.02	.01
445 Mark Fidrych	.06	.04	.02
446 Duffy Dyer	.03	.02	.01
447 Nino Espinosa	.03	.02	.01
448 Jim Wohlford	.03	.02	.01
449 Doug Bair	.03	.02	.01
450 George Brett	.50	.40	.18
451 Cleveland Indians Dave Garcia	.06	.04	.02
452 Steve Dillard	.03	.02	.01
453 Mike Bacsik	.03	.02	.01
454 Tom Donohue	.03	.02	.01
455 Mike Torrez	.05	.03	.01
456 Frank Taveras	.03	.02	.01
457 Bert Blyleven	.06	.04	.02
458 Billy Sample	.03	.02	.01
459 Mickey Lolich (dp)	.03	.02	.01
460 Willie Randolph	.06	.04	.02
461 Dwayne Murphy	.05	.03	.01
462 Mike Sadek (dp)	.02	.01	.01½
463 Jerry Royster	.03	.02	.01
464 John Denny	.03	.02	.01
465 Rick Monday	.05	.03	.01
466 Mike Squires	.03	.02	.01
467 Jesse Jefferson	.03	.02	.01
468 Aurelio Rodriguez	.03	.02	.01
469 Randy Niemann (dp)	.02	.01	.01½
470 Bob Boone	.03	.02	.01
471 Hosken Powell (dp)	.02	.01	.01½
472 Willie Hernandez	.03	.02	.01
473 Bump Wills	.05	.03	.01
474 Steve Busby	.03	.02	.01
475 Cesar Geronimo	.03	.02	.01
476 Bob Shirley	.03	.02	.01
477 Buck Martinez	.03	.02	.01
478 Gil Flores	.03	.02	.01
479 Montreal Expos Team Dick Williams	.06	.04	.02
480 Bob Watson	.06	.04	.02
481 Tom Paciorek	.03	.02	.01
482 Rickey Henderson	.30	.25	.10
483 Bo Diaz	.03	.02	.01
484 Checklist 4	.03	.02	.01
485 Mickey Rivers	.06	.04	.02
486 Mike Tyson (dp)	.02	.01	.01½
487 Wayne Nordhagen	.03	.02	.01
488 Roy Howell	.03	.02	.01
489 Preston Hanna (dp)	.02	.01	.01½
490 Lee May	.03	.02	.01
491 Steve Mura (dp)	.02	.01	.01½
492 Todd Cruz	.03	.02	.01
493 Jerry Martin	.03	.02	.01
494 Craig Minetto	.03	.02	.01
495 Bake McBride	.05	.03	.01
496 Silvio Martinez	.03	.02	.01
497 Jim Mason	.03	.02	.01
498 Danny Darwin	.03	.02	.01
499 San Francisco Giants Dave Bristol	.06	.04	.02
500 Tom Seaver	.40	.30	.13
501 Rennie Stennett	.03	.02	.01
502 Rich Wortham (dp)	.02	.01	.01½
503 Mike Cubbage	.03	.02	.01
504 Gene Garber	.03	.02	.01
505 Bert Campaneris	.05	.03	.01
506 Tom Buskey	.03	.02	.01
507 Leon Roberts	.03	.02	.01
508 U. L. Washington	.05	.03	.01
509 Ed Glynn	.03	.02	.01
510 Ron Cey	.07	.05	.02
511 Eric Wilkins	.03	.02	.01
512 Jose Cardenal	.03	.02	.01
513 Tom Dixon (dp)	.02	.01	.01½
514 Steve Ontiveros	.03	.02	.01
515 Mike Caldwell	.05	.03	.01
516 Hector Cruz	.03	.02	.01
517 Don Stanhouse	.05	.03	.01
518 Nelson Norman	.03	.02	.01
519 Steve Nicosia	.03	.02	.01
520 Steve Rogers	.05	.03	.01

	MINT	VG-E	F-G
521 Ken Brett	.03	.02	.01
522 Jim Morrison	.03	.02	.01
523 Ken Henderson	.03	.02	.01
524 Jim Wright (dp)	.02	.01	.01½
525 Clint Hurdle	.03	.02	.01
526 Philadelphia Phillies Dallas Green	.08	.06	.02
527 Doug Rau (dp)	.02	.01	.01½
528 Adrian Devine	.03	.02	.01
529 Jim Barr	.03	.02	.01
530 Jim Sundberg (dp)	.03	.02	.01
531 Eric Rasmussen	.03	.02	.01
532 Willie Horton	.05	.03	.01
533 Checklist 5	.03	.02	.01
534 Andre Thornton	.05	.03	.01
535 Bob Forsch	.03	.02	.01
536 Lee Lacy	.03	.02	.01
537 Alex Trevino	.03	.02	.01
538 Joe Strain	.03	.02	.01
539 Rudy May	.05	.03	.01
540 Pete Rose	.50	.40	.18
541 Miguel Dilone	.05	.03	.01
542 Joe Coleman	.03	.02	.01
543 Pat Kelly	.03	.02	.01
544 Rick Sutcliffe	.03	.02	.01
545 Jeff Burroughs	.05	.03	.01
546 Rick Langford	.05	.03	.01
547 John Wathan	.03	.02	.01
548 Dave Rajsich	.03	.02	.01
549 Larry Wolfe	.06	.04	.02
550 Ken Griffey	.07	.05	.02
551 Pittsburgh Pirates	.03	.02	.01
552 Bill Nahorodny	.03	.02	.01
553 Dick Davis	.03	.02	.01
554 Art Howe	.03	.02	.01
555 Ed Figueroa	.03	.02	.01
556 Joe Rudi	.05	.03	.01
557 Mark Lee	.03	.02	.01
558 Alfredo Griffin	.03	.02	.01
559 Dale Murray	.03	.02	.01
560 Dave Lopes	.05	.03	.01
561 Eddie Whitson	.03	.02	.01
562 Joe Wallis	.03	.02	.01
563 Will McEnaney	.03	.02	.01
564 Rick Manning	.06	.04	.02
565 Dennis Leonard	.03	.02	.01
566 Bud Harrelson	.03	.02	.01
567 Skip Lockwood	.03	.02	.01
568 Gary Roenicke	.03	.02	.01
569 Terry Kennedy	.05	.03	.01
570 Roy Smalley	.05	.03	.01
571 Joe Sambito	.05	.03	.01
572 Jerry Morales(dp)	.02	.01	.01½
573 Kent Tekulve	.06	.04	.02
574 Scot Thompson	.03	.02	.01
575 Ken Kravec	.03	.02	.01
576 Jim Dwyer	.03	.02	.01
577 Toronto Blue Jays Bobby Mattick	.06	.04	.02
578 Scott Sanderson	.03	.02	.01
579 Charlie Moore	.03	.02	.01
580 Nolan Ryan	.35	.27	.12
581 Bob Bailor	.03	.02	.01
582 Brian Doyle	.03	.02	.01
583 Bob Stinson	.03	.02	.01
584 Kurt Bevacqua	.03	.02	.01
585 Al Hrabosky	.05	.03	.01
586 Mitchell Page	.05	.03	.01
587 Garry Templeton	.15	.11	.05
588 Greg Minton	.03	.02	.01
589 Chet Lemon	.06	.04	.02
590 Jim Palmer	.35	.27	.12
591 Rick Cerone	.07	.05	.02
592 Jon Matlack	.05	.03	.01
593 Jesus Alou	.03	.02	.01
594 Dick Tidrow	.03	.02	.01
595 Don Money	.05	.03	.01
596 Rick Matula	.03	.02	.01
597 Tom Poquette	.03	.02	.01
598 Fred Kendall (dp)	.02	.01	.01½
599 Mike Norris	.07	.05	.02
600 Reggie Jackson	.50	.40	.18
601 Buddy Schultz	.03	.02	.01
602 Brian Downing	.03	.02	.01
603 Jack Billingham(dp)	.02	.01	.01½
604 Glenn Adams	.03	.02	.01
605 Terry Forster	.05	.03	.01
606 Cincinnati Reds John McNamara	.06	.04	.02
607 Woodie Fryman	.03	.02	.01
608 Alan Bannister	.03	.02	.01
609 Ron Reed	.03	.02	.01

	MINT	VG-E	F-G			MINT	VG-E	F-G
610 Willie Stargell	.30	.25	.10	669 Twins Prospects		.03	.02	.01
611 Jerry Garvin (dp)	.02	.01	.0½	670 Yankees Prospects		.03	.02	.01
612 Cliff Johnson	.03	.02	.01	671 Oakland Prospects		.03	.02	.01
613 Randy Stein	.03	.02	.01	672 Mariners Prospects		.03	.02	.01
614 John Hiller	.03	.02	.01	673 Rangers Prospects		.03	.02	.01
615 Doug DeCinces	.03	.02	.01	674 Blue Jays Prospects		.03	.02	.01
616 Gene Richards	.03	.02	.01	675 Braves Prospects		.03	.02	.01
617 Joaquin Andujar	.03	.02	.01	676 Cubs Prospects		.03	.02	.01
618 Bob Montgomery (dp)	.02	.01	.0½	677 Reds Prospects		.03	.02	.01
619 Sergio Ferrer	.03	.02	.01	678 Astros Prospects		.03	.02	.01
620 Richie Zisk	.06	.04	.02	679 Dodgers Prospects		.03	.02	.01
621 Bob Grich	.05	.03	.01	680 Expos Prospects		.03	.02	.01
622 Mario Soto	.03	.02	.01	681 Mets Prospects		.03	.02	.01
623 Gorman Thomas	.10	.07	.03	682 Phillies Prospects		.03	.02	.01
624 Lerrin LaGrow	.03	.02	.01	683 Pirates Prospects		.03	.02	.01
625 Chris Chambliss	.05	.03	.01	684 Cardinals Prospects		.03	.02	.01
626 Detroit Tigers Team	.07	.05	.02	685 Padres Prospects		.03	.02	.01
627 Pedro Borbon	.03	.02	.01	686 Giants Prospects		.03	.02	.01
628 Doug Capilla	.03	.02	.01	687 Mike Heath (dp)		.02	.01	.0½
629 Jim Todd	.03	.02	.01	688 Steve Stone		.12	.08	.04
630 Larry Bowa	.10	.07	.03	689 Boston Red Sox		.07	.05	.02
631 Mark Littell	.03	.02	.01	Don Zimmer, Mgr.				
632 Barry Bonnell	.03	.02	.01	690 Tommy John		.25	.20	.08
633 Bob Apodaca	.03	.02	.01	691 Ivan DeJesus		.03	.02	.01
634 Glenn Borgmann(dp)	.02	.01	.0½	692 Rawly Eastwick (dp)		.02	.01	.0½
635 John Candelaria	.05	.03	.01	693 Craig Kusick		.03	.02	.01
636 Toby Harrah	.03	.02	.01	694 Jim Rooker		.03	.02	.01
637 Joe Simpson	.03	.02	.01	695 Reggie Smith		.10	.07	.03
638 Mark Clear	.03	.02	.01	696 Julio Gonzalez		.03	.02	.01
639 Larry Biittner	.03	.02	.01	697 David Clyde		.03	.02	.01
640 Mike Flanagan	.07	.05	.02	698 Oscar Gamble		.05	.03	.01
641 Ed Kranepool	.03	.02	.01	699 Floyd Bannister		.03	.02	.01
642 Ken Forsch (dp)	.02	.01	.0½	700 Rod Carew (dp)		.30	.25	.10
643 John Mayberry	.05	.03	.01	701 Ken Oberkfell		.03	.02	.01
644 Charlie Hough	.03	.02	.01	702 Ed Farmer		.03	.02	.01
645 Rick Burleson	.08	.06	.02	703 Otto Velez		.03	.02	.01
646 Checklist 6	.03	.02	.01	704 Gene Tenace		.03	.02	.01
647 Milt May	.03	.02	.01	705 Freddie Patek		.03	.02	.01
648 Roy White	.03	.02	.01	706 Tippy Martinez		.03	.02	.01
649 Tom Griffin	.03	.02	.01	707 Elliott Maddox		.03	.02	.01
650 Joe Morgan	.20	.15	.06	708 Bob Tolan		.03	.02	.01
651 Rollie Fingers	.10	.07	.03	709 Pat Underwood		.03	.02	.01
652 Mario Mendoza	.03	.02	.01	710 Graig Nettles		.07	.05	.02
653 Stan Bahnsen	.03	.02	.01	711 Bob Galasso		.03	.02	.01
654 Bruce Boisclair (dp)	.02	.01	.0½	712 Rodney Scott		.03	.02	.01
655 Tug McGraw	.10	.07	.03	713 Terry Whitfield		.03	.02	.01
656 Larvell Blanks	.03	.02	.01	714 Fred Norman		.03	.02	.01
657 Dave Edwards	.03	.02	.01	715 Sal Bando		.05	.03	.01
658 Chris Knapp	.03	.02	.01	716 Lynn McGlothen		.03	.02	.01
659 Milwaukee Brewers	.06	.04	.02	717 Mickey Klutts (dp)		.02	.01	.0½
George Bamberger				718 Greg Gross		.03	.02	.01
660 Rusty Staub	.07	.05	.02	719 Don Robinson		.03	.02	.01
661 Orioles Prospects	.03	.02	.01	720 Carl Yastrzemski (dp)		.30	.25	.10
662 Red Sox Prospects	.03	.02	.01	721 Paul Hartzell		.03	.02	.01
663 Angels Prospects	.03	.02	.01	722 Jose Cruz		.03	.02	.01
664 White Sox Prospects	.03	.02	.01	723 Shane Rawley		.03	.02	.01
665 Indians Prospects	.03	.02	.01	724 Jerry White		.03	.02	.01
666 Tigers Prospects	.03	.02	.01	725 Rick Wise		.05	.03	.01
667 Royals Prospects	.40	.30	.13	726 Steve Yeager		.03	.02	.01
668 Brewers Prospects	.03	.02	.01					

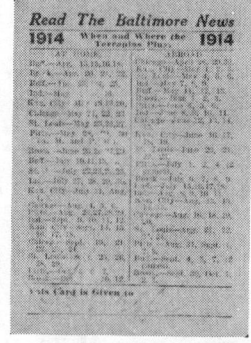

BALTIMORE NEWS

The 1980 Topps Superstar Photo set was issued in two different varieties. Both sets have the same fronts. One set is on thick, white stock and is commonly called the "white back" set. The other set is on thinner, gray-colored stock and is commonly called the "gray back" set. The white back set is thought to have been issued in lesser quantities than the gray back set. The gray back set features triple printings of cards numbered 2, 6, 12, 13, 14 and 17. Presumably, the white back set has similar triple printings of these same numbers; however, because of the method of distribution of the white back set, these triple printings have not as yet been verified. The prices in the checklist below refer to the cards in the gray back set. Cards in the white back set are worth three times as much as cards in the gray back set.

	MINT	VG-E	F-G
COMPLETE SET	13.00	10.00	4.00
COMMON PLAYER	.15	.11	.05

	MINT	VG-E	F-G
1 Willie Stargell	.50	.40	.18
2 Mike Schmidt (ftp)	.25	.20	.08
3 Johnny Bench	.60	.45	.20
4 Jim Palmer	.50	.40	.18
5 Jim Rice	.60	.45	.20
6 Reggie Jackson (tp)	.25	.20	.08
7 Ron Guidry	.50	.40	.18
8 Lee Mazzilli	.20	.15	.06
9 Don Baylor	.20	.15	.06
10 Fred Lynn	.60	.45	.20
11 Ken Singleton	.20	.15	.06
12 Rod Carew (tp)	.25	.20	.08
13 Steve Garvey (tp)	.25	.20	.08
14 George Brett (tp)	.25	.20	.08
15 Tom Seaver	.60	.45	.20
16 Dave Kingman	.40	.30	.13
17 Dave Parker (tp)	.25	.20	.08
18 Dave Winfield	.50	.40	.18
19 Pete Rose	.65	.50	.20
20 Nolan Ryan	.50	.40	.18
21 Graig Nettles	.15	.11	.05
22 Carl Yastrzemski	.65	.50	.20
23 Tommy John	.40	.30	.13
24 George Foster	.40	.30	.13
25 J. R. Richard	.30	.25	.10
26 Keith Hernandez	.30	.25	.10
27 Bob Horner	.40	.30	.13
28 Eddie Murray	.30	.25	.10
29 Steve Kemp	.20	.15	.06
30 Gorman Thomas	.20	.15	.06

	MINT	VG-E	F-G
31 Sixto Lezcano	.20	.15	.05
32 Bruce Sutter	.30	.25	.10
33 Cecil Cooper	.25	.20	.08
34 Larry Bowa	.25	.20	.08
35 Al Oliver	.25	.20	.08
36 Ted Simmons	.30	.25	.10
37 Garry Templeton	.30	.25	.10
38 Jerry Koosman	.15	.11	.05
39 Darrell Porter	.15	.11	.05
40 Roy Smalley	.15	.11	.05
41 Craig Swan	.15	.11	.05
42 Jason Thompson	.15	.11	.05
43 Andre Thornton	.15	.11	.05
44 Rick Manning	.15	.11	.05
45 Kent Tekulve	.15	.11	.05
46 Phil Niekro	.20	.15	.06
47 Buddy Bell	.20	.15	.06
48 Randy Jones	.15	.11	.05
49 Brian Downing	.15	.11	.05
50 Amos Otis	.20	.15	.06
51 Rick Bosetti	.15	.11	.05
52 Gary Carter	.20	.15	.06
53 Larry Parrish	.15	.11	.05
54 Jack Clark	.20	.15	.06
55 Bruce Bochte	.15	.11	.05
56 Cesar Cedeno	.25	.20	.08
57 Chet Lemon	.15	.11	.05
58 Dave Revering	.15	.11	.05
59 Vida Blue	.25	.20	.08
60 Davey Lopes	.15	.11	.05

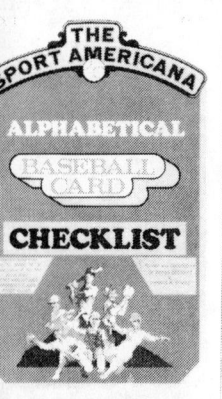

This 726 card set contains 66 doubly printed cards. These cards are marked with a (dp) in the checklist.

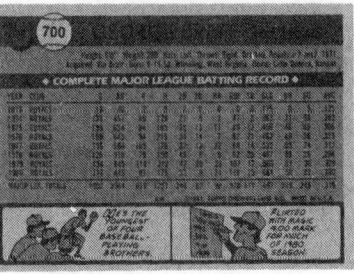

	MINT	VG-E	F-G
COMPLETE SET	16.50	12.00	5.00
COMMON PLAYER	.03	.02	.01
1 Batting Leaders: George Brett, Bill Buckner	.10	.17	.03
2 Home Run Leaders: Reggie Jackson, Ben Oglivie, Mike Schmidt	.08	.06	.02
3 Runs Batted in Leaders: Cecil Cooper, Mike Schmidt	.06	.04	.02
4 Stolen Base Leaders: Rickey Henderson, Ron LeFlore	.06	.04	.02
5 Victory Leaders: Steve Stone, Steve Carlton	.06	.04	.02
6 Strikeout Leaders: Len Barker, Steve Carlton	.06	.04	.02
7 Earned Run Average Leaders: Rudy May, Don Sutton	.06	.04	.02
8 Leading Firemen: Dan Quisenberry, Rollie Fingers, Tom Hume	.06	.04	.02
9 Pete LaCock (dp)	.02	.01	.01½
10 Mike Flanagan	.07	.05	.02
11 Jim Wohlford(dp)	.02	.01	.01½
12 Mark Clear	.03	.02	.01
13 Joe Charboneau	.15	.11	.05
14 John Tudor	.03	.02	.01
15 Larry Parrish	.06	.04	.02
16 Ron Davis	.03	.02	.01
17 Cliff Johnson	.03	.02	.01
18 Glenn Adams	.03	.02	.01
19 Jim Clancy	.03	.02	.01
20 Jeff Burroughs	.06	.04	.02
21 Ron Oester	.03	.02	.01
22 Danny Darwin	.03	.02	.01
23 Alex Trevino	.03	.02	.01
24 Don Stanhouse	.05	.03	.01
25 Sixto Lezcano	.06	.04	.02
26 U. L. Washington	.03	.02	.01
27 Champ Summers (dp)	.02	.01	.01½
28 Enrique Romo	.03	.02	.01
29 Gene Tenace	.03	.02	.01
30 Jack Clark	.07	.05	.02
31 Check List 1-121 (dp)	.02	.01	.01½
32 Ken Oberkfell	.03	.02	.01
33 Rick Honeycutt	.03	.02	.01
34 Aurelio Rodriguez	.03	.02	.01
35 Mitchell Page	.03	.02	.01
36 Ed Farmer	.03	.02	.01
37 Gary Roenicke	.03	.02	.01
38 Win Remmerswaal	.03	.02	.01
39 Tom Veryzer	.03	.02	.01
40 Tug McGraw	.06	.04	.02
41 Rangers Future Stars	.03	.02	.01
42 Jerry White (dp)	.02	.01	.01½
43 Jose Morales	.03	.02	.01
44 Larry McWilliams	.03	.02	.01
45 Enos Cabell	.03	.02	.01
46 Rick Bosetti	.03	.02	.01
47 Ken Brett	.03	.02	.01
48 Dave Skaggs	.03	.02	.01

	MINT	VG-E	F-G
49 Bob Shirley	.03	.02	.01
50 Dave Lopes	.05	.03	.01
51 Bill Robinson(dp)	.02	.01	.01½
52 Hector Cruz	.03	.02	.01
53 Kevin Saucier	.03	.02	.01
54 Ivan DeJesus	.03	.02	.01
55 Mike Norris	.07	.05	.02
56 Buck Martinez	.03	.02	.01
57 Dave Roberts	.03	.02	.01
58 Joel Youngblood	.03	.02	.01
59 Dan Petry	.03	.02	.01
60 Willie Randolph	.06	.04	.02
61 Butch Wynegar	.03	.02	.01
62 Joe Pettini	.03	.02	.01
63 Steve Renko(dp)	.02	.01	.01½
64 Brian Asselstine	.03	.02	.01
65 Scott McGregor	.06	.04	.02
66 Royals Future Stars	.03	.02	.01
67 Ken Kravec	.03	.02	.01
68 Matt Alexander(dp)	.02	.01	.01½
69 Ed Halicki	.03	.02	.01
70 Al Oliver (dp)	.05	.03	.01
71 Hal Dues	.03	.02	.01
72 Barry Evans (dp)	.02	.01	.01½
73 Doug Bair	.03	.02	.01
74 Mike Hargrove	.03	.02	.01
75 Reggie Smith	.07	.05	.02
76 Mario Mendoza	.03	.02	.01
77 Mike Barlow	.03	.02	.01
78 Steve Dillard	.03	.02	.01
79 Bruce Robbins	.03	.02	.01
80 Rusty Staub	.07	.05	.02
81 Dave Stapleton	.03	.02	.01
82 Astros Future Stars(dp)	.02	.01	.01½
83 Mike Proly	.03	.02	.01
84 Johnnie LeMaster	.03	.02	.01
85 Mike Caldwell	.04	.02	.01
86 Wayne Gross	.03	.02	.01
87 Rick Camp	.03	.02	.01
88 Joe Lefebvre	.03	.02	.01
89 Darrell Jackson	.03	.02	.01
90 Bake McBride	.04	.02	.01
91 Tim Stoddard (dp)	.02	.01	.01½
92 Mike Easler	.03	.02	.01
93 Ed Glynn (dp)	.02	.01	.01½
94 Harry Spilman(dp)	.02	.01	.01½
95 Jim Sundberg	.06	.04	.02
96 A's Future Stars	.03	.02	.01
97 Chris Speier	.03	.02	.01
98 Clint Hurdle	.03	.02	.01
99 Eric Wilkins	.03	.02	.01
100 Rod Carew	.30	.25	.10
101 Benny Ayala	.03	.02	.01
102 Dave Tobik	.03	.02	.01
103 Jerry Martin	.03	.02	.01
104 Terry Forster	.05	.03	.01
105 Jose Cruz	.05	.03	.01
106 Don Money	.05	.03	.01
107 Rich Wortham	.03	.02	.01
108 Bruce Benedict	.03	.02	.01
109 Mike Scott	.03	.02	.01
110 Carl Yastrzemski	.40	.30	.13
111 Greg Minton	.03	.02	.01
112 White Sox Future Stars	.03	.02	.01
113 Mike Phillips	.03	.02	.01
114 Tom Underwood	.03	.02	.01
115 Roy Smalley	.04	.02	.01
116 Joe Simpson	.03	.02	.01
117 Pete Falcone	.03	.02	.01

	MINT	VG-E	F-G
118 Kurt Bevacqua	.03	.02	.01
119 Tippy Martinez	.03	.02	.01
120 Larry Bowa	.10	.07	.03
121 Larry Harlow	.03	.02	.01
122 John Denny	.03	.02	.01
123 Al Cowens	.03	.02	.01
124 Jerry Garvin	.03	.02	.01
125 Andre Dawson	.06	.04	.02
126 Charlie Leibrandt	.03	.02	.01
127 Rudy Law	.03	.02	.01
128 Garry Allenson(dp)	.02	.01	.0½
129 Art Howe	.03	.02	.01
130 Larry Gura	.05	.03	.01
131 Keith Moreland	.03	.02	.01
132 Tommy Boggs	.03	.02	.01
133 Jeff Cox	.03	.02	.01
134 Steve Mura	.03	.02	.01
135 Gorman Thomas	.08	.06	.02
136 Doug Capilla	.03	.02	.01
137 Hosken Powell	.03	.02	.01
138 Rich Dotson(dp)	.02	.01	.0½
139 Oscar Gamble	.05	.03	.01
140 Bob Forsch	.03	.02	.01
141 Miguel Dilone	.04	.02	.01
142 Jackson Todd	.03	.02	.01
143 Dan Meyer	.03	.02	.01
144 Allen Ripley	.03	.02	.01
145 Mickey Rivers	.05	.03	.01
146 Bobby Castillo	.03	.02	.01
147 Dale Berra	.04	.02	.01
148 Randy Niemann	.03	.02	.01
149 Joe Nolan	.03	.02	.01
150 Mark Fidrych	.05	.03	.01
151 Claudell Washington	.04	.02	.01
152 John Urrea	.03	.02	.01
153 Tom Poquette	.03	.02	.01
154 Rick Langford	.04	.02	.01
155 Chris Chambliss	.04	.02	.01
156 Bob McClure	.03	.02	.01
157 John Wathan	.03	.02	.01
158 Fergie Jenkins	.08	.06	.02
159 Brian Doyle	.03	.02	.01
160 Garry Maddox	.06	.04	.02
161 Dan Graham	.03	.02	.01
162 Doug Corbett	.03	.02	.01
163 Billy Almon	.03	.02	.01
164 Lamarr Hoyt	.03	.02	.01
165 Tony Scott	.03	.02	.01
166 Floyd Bannister	.03	.02	.01
167 Terry Whitfield	.03	.02	.01
168 Don Robinson(dp)	.02	.01	.0½
169 John Mayberry	.05	.03	.01
170 Ross Grimsley	.03	.02	.01
171 Gene Richards	.03	.02	.01
172 Gary Woods	.03	.02	.01
173 Bump Wills	.04	.02	.01
174 Doug Rau	.03	.02	.01
175 Dave Collins	.04	.02	.01
176 Mike Krukow	.03	.02	.01
177 Rick Peters	.03	.02	.01
178 Jim Essian(dp)	.02	.01	.0½
179 Rudy May	.05	.03	.01
180 Pete Rose	.40	.30	.13
181 Elias Sosa	.03	.02	.01
182 Bob Grich	.04	.02	.01
183 Dick Davis(dp)	.02	.01	.0½
184 Jim Dwyer	.03	.02	.01
185 Dennis Leonard	.06	.04	.02
186 Wayne Nordhagen	.03	.02	.01
187 Mike Parrott	.03	.02	.01
188 Doug DeCinces	.03	.02	.01
189 Craig Swan	.04	.02	.01
190 Cesar Cedeno	.10	.07	.03
191 Rick Sutcliffe	.03	.02	.01
192 Braves Future Stars	.03	.02	.01
193 Pete Vuckovich	.03	.02	.01
194 Rod Scurry	.03	.02	.01
195 Rich Murray	.03	.02	.01
196 Duffy Dyer	.03	.02	.01
197 Jim Kern	.03	.02	.01
198 Jerry Dybzinski	.03	.02	.01
199 Chuck Rainey	.03	.02	.01
200 George Foster	.20	.15	.06
201 Record Breaker:	.10	.07	.03
Johnny Bench, Most			
Home Runs, Catcher,			
Lifetime			
202 Record Breaker:	.10	.07	.03
Steve Carlton, Most			
Strikeouts, Left-			
hander, Lifetime			

	MINT	VG-E	F-G
203 Record Breaker:	.03	.02	.01
Bill Gullickson,			
Most Strikeouts,			
Game Rookie			
204 Record Breaker:	.05	.03	.01
Ron LeFlore &			
Rodney Scott, Most			
Stolen Bases, Team-			
mates, Season			
205 Record Breaker:	.10	.07	.03
Pete Rose, Most			
Consecutive Seasons,			
600-or-more At-Bats			
206 Record Breaker:	.10	.07	.03
Mike Schmidt, Most			
Home Runs, Third			
Baseman, Season			
207 Record Breaker:	.03	.02	.01
Ozzie Smith, Most			
Assists, Shortstop,			
Season			
208 Record Breaker:	.05	.03	.01
Willie Wilson, Most-			
At-Bats, Season			
209 Dickie Thon(dp)	.02	.01	.0½
210 Jim Palmer	.30	.25	.10
211 Derrell Thomas	.03	.02	.01
212 Steve Nicosia	.03	.02	.01
213 Al Holland	.03	.02	.01
214 Angels Future Stars	.03	.02	.01
215 Larry Hisle	.07	.05	.02
216 John Henry Johnson	.03	.02	.01
217 Rich Hebner	.03	.02	.01
218 Paul Splittorff	.04	.02	.01
219 Ken Landreaux	.04	.02	.01
220 Tom Seaver	.35	.27	.12
221 Bob Davis	.03	.02	.01
222 Jorge Orta	.03	.02	.01
223 Roy Lee Jackson	.03	.02	.01
224 Pat Zachry	.03	.02	.01
225 Ruppert Jones	.04	.02	.01
226 Manny Sanguillen(dp)	.02	.01	.0½
227 Fred Martinez	.03	.02	.01
228 Tom Paciorek	.03	.02	.01
229 Rollie Fingers	.08	.06	.02
230 George Hendrick	.07	.05	.02
231 Joe Beckwith	.03	.02	.01
232 Mickey Klutts	.03	.02	.01
233 Skip Lockwood	.03	.02	.01
234 Lou Whitaker	.05	.03	.01
235 Scott Sanderson	.03	.02	.01
236 Mike Ivie	.03	.02	.01
237 Charlie Moore	.03	.02	.01
238 Willie Hernandez	.03	.02	.01
239 Rick Miller (dp)	.03	.02	.01
240 Nolan Ryan	.30	.25	.10
241 Checklist 122-242(dp)	.02	.01	.0½
242 Chet Lemon	.05	.03	.01
243 Sal Butera	.03	.02	.01
244 St. Louis Cardinals	.03	.02	.01
Future Stars			
245 Ed Figueroa	.03	.02	.01
246 Ed Ott (dp)	.02	.01	.0½
247 Glen Hubbard(dp)	.02	.01	.0½
248 Joey McLaughlin	.03	.02	.01
249 Larry Cox	.03	.02	.01
250 Ron Guidry	.25	.20	.08
251 Tom Brookens	.03	.02	.01
252 Victor Cruz	.03	.02	.01
253 Dave Bergman	.03	.02	.01
254 Ozzie Smith	.05	.03	.01
255 Mark Littell	.03	.02	.01
256 Bombo Rivera	.03	.02	.01
257 Rennie Stennett	.03	.02	.01
258 Joe Price	.03	.02	.01
259 Mets Future Stars	.03	.02	.01
260 Ron Cey	.08	.06	.02
261 Rickey Henderson	.12	.08	.04
262 Sammy Stewart	.03	.02	.01
263 Brian Downing	.04	.02	.01
264 Jim Norris	.03	.02	.01
265 John Candelaria	.05	.03	.01
266 Tom Herr	.03	.02	.01
267 Stan Bahnsen	.03	.02	.01
268 Jerry Royster	.03	.02	.01
269 Ken Forsch	.03	.02	.01
270 Greg Luzinski	.15	.11	.05
271 Bill Castro	.03	.02	.01
272 Bruce Kimm	.03	.02	.01
273 Stan Papi	.03	.02	.01
274 Craig Chamberlain	.03	.02	.01

	MINT	VG-E	F-G			MINT	VG-E	F-G
275 Dwight Evans	.03	.02	.01		367 Denny Martinez	.03	.02	.01
276 Dan Spillner	.03	.02	.01		368 Leon Roberts	.03	.02	.01
277 Alfredo Griffin	.03	.02	.01		369 Frank Tanana	.04	.02	.01
278 Rick Sofield	.03	.02	.01		370 Dave Winfield	.35	.27	.12
279 Bob Knepper	.03	.02	.01		371 Charlie Hough	.03	.02	.01
280 Ken Griffey	.05	.03	.01		372 Jay Johnstone	.03	.02	.01
281 Fred Stanley	.03	.02	.01		373 Pat Underwood	.03	.02	.01
282 Mariners Future Stars	.03	.02	.01		374 Tom Hutton	.03	.02	.01
283 Billy Sample	.03	.02	.01		375 Dave Concepcion	.06	.04	.02
284 Brian Kingman	.03	.02	.01		376 Ron Reed	.03	.02	.01
285 Jerry Turner	.03	.02	.01		377 Jerry Morales	.03	.02	.01
286 Dave Frost	.03	.02	.01		378 Dave Rader	.03	.02	.01
287 Lenn Sakata	.03	.02	.01		379 Lary Sorensen	.04	.02	.01
288 Bob Clark	.03	.02	.01		380 Willie Stargell	.25	.20	.08
289 Mickey Hatcher	.03	.02	.01		381 Cubs Future Stars	.03	.02	.01
290 Bob Boone (dp)	.02	.01	.01½		382 Paul Mirabella	.03	.02	.01
291 Aurelio Lopez	.03	.02	.01		383 Eric Soderholm (dp)	.02	.01	.01½
292 Mike Squires	.03	.02	.01		384 Mike Sadek	.03	.02	.01
293 Charlie Lea	.03	.02	.01		385 Joe Sambito	.04	.02	.01
294 Mike Tyson (dp)	.02	.01	.01½		386 Dave Edwards	.03	.02	.01
295 Hal McRae	.03	.02	.01		387 Phil Niekro	.06	.04	.02
296 Bill Nahorodny (dp)	.02	.01	.01½		388 Andre Thornton	.04	.02	.01
297 Bob Bailor	.03	.02	.01		389 Marty Pattin	.03	.02	.01
298 Buddy Solomon	.03	.02	.01		390 Cesar Geronimo	.03	.02	.01
299 Elliott Maddox	.03	.02	.01		391 Dave Lemanczyk (dp)	.02	.01	.01½
300 Paul Molitor	.10	.07	.03		392 Lance Parrish	.04	.02	.01
301 Matt Keough	.03	.02	.01		393 Broderick Perkins	.03	.02	.01
302 Dodgers Future Stars	.03	.02	.01		394 Woodie Fryman	.03	.02	.01
303 Johnny Oates	.03	.02	.01		395 Scot Thompson	.03	.02	.01
304 John Castino	.03	.02	.01		396 Bill Campbell	.03	.02	.01
305 Ken Clay	.03	.02	.01		397 Julio Cruz	.03	.02	.01
306 Juan Beniquez (dp)	.02	.01	.01½		398 Ross Baumgarten	.03	.02	.01
307 Gene Garber	.03	.02	.01		399 Orioles Future Stars	.03	.02	.01
308 Rick Manning	.03	.02	.01		400 Reggie Jackson	.35	.27	.12
309 Luis Salazar	.03	.02	.01		401 AL Playoffs	.06	.04	.02
310 Vida Blue (dp)	.06	.04	.02		402 NL Playoffs	.06	.04	.02
311 Freddie Patek	.03	.02	.01		403 1980 World Series	.06	.04	.02
312 Rick Rhoden	.03	.02	.01		404 1980 World Series	.06	.04	.02
313 Luis Pujols	.03	.02	.01		405 Nino Espinosa	.03	.02	.01
314 Rich Dauer	.03	.02	.01		406 Dickie Noles	.03	.02	.01
315 Kirk Gibson	.06	.04	.02		407 Ernie Whitt	.03	.02	.01
316 Craig Minetto	.03	.02	.01		408 Fernando Arroyo	.03	.02	.01
317 Lonnie Smith	.03	.02	.01		409 Larry Herndon	.03	.02	.01
318 Steve Yeager	.03	.02	.01		410 Bert Campaneris	.04	.02	.01
319 Rowland Office	.03	.02	.01		411 Terry Puhl	.05	.03	.01
320 Tom Burgmeier	.03	.02	.01		412 Britt Burns	.03	.02	.01
321 Leon Durham	.03	.02	.01		413 Tony Bernazard	.03	.02	.01
322 Neil Allen	.03	.02	.01		414 John Pacella (dp)	.02	.01	.01½
323 Jim Morrison (dp)	.02	.01	.01½		415 Ben Oglivie	.06	.04	.02
324 Mike Willis	.03	.02	.01		416 Gary Alexander	.03	.02	.01
325 Ray Knight	.04	.02	.01		417 Dan Schatzeder	.03	.02	.01
326 Biff Pocoroba	.03	.02	.01		418 Bobby Brown	.03	.02	.01
327 Moose Haas	.03	.02	.01		419 Tom Hume	.03	.02	.01
328 Twins Future Stars	.03	.02	.01		420 Keith Hernandez	.20	.15	.06
329 Joaquin Andujar	.03	.02	.01		421 Bob Stanley	.03	.02	.01
330 Frank White	.04	.02	.01		422 Dan Ford	.03	.02	.01
331 Dennis Lamp	.03	.02	.01		423 Shane Rawley	.03	.02	.01
332 Lee Lacy (dp)	.02	.01	.01½		424 Yankees Future Stars	.03	.02	.01
333 Sid Monge	.03	.02	.01		425 Al Bumbry	.03	.02	.01
334 Dane Iorg	.03	.02	.01		426 Warren Brusstar	.03	.02	.01
335 Rick Cerone	.05	.03	.01		427 John D'Acquisto	.03	.02	.01
336 Eddie Whitson	.03	.02	.01		428 John Stearns	.03	.02	.01
337 Lynn Jones	.03	.02	.01		429 Mick Kelleher	.03	.02	.01
338 Checklist 243-363	.03	.02	.01		430 Jim Bibby	.05	.03	.01
339 John Ellis	.03	.02	.01		431 Dave Roberts	.03	.02	.01
340 Bruce Kison	.03	.02	.01		432 Len Barker	.04	.02	.01
341 Dwayne Murphy	.06	.04	.02		433 Rance Mulliniks	.03	.02	.01
342 Eric Rasmussen (dp)	.02	.01	.01½		434 Roger Erickson	.03	.02	.01
343 Frank Taveras	.03	.02	.01		435 Jim Spencer	.03	.02	.01
344 Byron McLaughlin	.03	.02	.01		436 Gary Lucas	.03	.02	.01
345 Warren Cromartie	.03	.02	.01		437 Mike Heath (dp)	.02	.01	.01½
346 Larry Christenson(dp)	.02	.01	.01½		438 John Montefusco	.03	.02	.01
347 Harold Baines	.03	.02	.01		439 Denny Walling	.03	.02	.01
348 Bob Sykes	.03	.02	.01		440 Jerry Reuss	.05	.03	.01
349 Glenn Hoffman	.03	.02	.01		441 Ken Reitz	.03	.02	.01
350 J. R. Richard	.20	.15	.06		442 Ron Pruitt	.03	.02	.01
351 Otto Velez	.03	.02	.01		443 Jim Beattie (dp)	.02	.01	.01½
352 Dick Tidrow (dp)	.02	.01	.01½		444 Garth Iorg	.03	.02	.01
353 Terry Kennedy	.03	.02	.01		445 Ellis Valentine	.04	.02	.01
354 Mario Soto	.03	.02	.01		446 Checklist 364-484	.03	.02	.01½
355 Bob Horner	.25	.20	.08		447 Junior Kennedy (dp)	.02	.01	.01½
356 Padres Future Stars	.03	.02	.01		448 Tim Corcoran	.03	.02	.01
357 Jim Slaton	.03	.02	.01		449 Paul Mitchell	.03	.02	.01
358 Mark Wagner	.03	.02	.01		450 Dave Kingman (dp)	.06	.04	.02
359 Tom Hausman	.03	.02	.01		451 Indians Future Stars	.03	.02	.01
360 Willie Wilson	.15	.11	.05		452 Renie Martin	.03	.02	.01
361 Joe Strain	.03	.02	.01		453 Rob Wilfong (dp)	.02	.01	.01½
362 Bo Diaz	.03	.02	.01		454 Andy Hassler	.03	.02	.01
363 Geoff Zahn	.03	.02	.01		455 Rick Burleson	.07	.05	.02
364 Mike Davis	.03	.02	.01		456 Jeff Reardon	.03	.02	.01
365 Graig Nettles (dp)	.04	.02	.01		457 Mike Lum	.03	.02	.01
366 Mike Ramsey	.03	.02	.01		458 Randy Jones	.05	.03	.01

Baseball Card Collectors

Have you read the ultimate source of news for collectors? Each giant issue of Baseball Hobby News contains:

- Current card prices
- Hobby show calendar
- Buy, sell and trade advertising
- Collecting tips
- Timely stories
- News about old and new cards

"BHN features timely and interesting articles on collecting. My advice is to use the hobby periodicals, and Baseball Hobby News is as helpful a publication as you will find."
—Bill Madden, The Sporting News

Only $13.95 brings you 12 double issues

Clip coupon and mail with payment (U.S. funds only) to:

Baseball Hobby News
P.O. Box 128-D
Glen Cove, NY 11542

1981--A Choice Year for Card Collectors

Enclosed is my payment of $13.95 (US funds) for a full year's subscription to Baseball Hobby News.   [ ] Sample - - $1.25

Name _____

Address _____

City _____ State _____ Zip _____

	MINT	VG-E	F-G			MINT	VG-E	F-G
459 Greg Gross	.03	.02	.01	551 Pirates Future Stars		.03	.02	.01
460 Rich Gossage	.08	.06	.02	552 Steve Trout		.03	.02	.01
461 Dave McKay	.03	.02	.01	553 Tim Blackwell		.03	.02	.01
462 Jack Brohamer	.03	.02	.01	554 Bert Blyleven		.05	.03	.01
463 Milt May	.03	.02	.01	555 Cecil Cooper		.10	.07	.03
464 Adrian Devine	.03	.02	.01	556 Jerry Mumphrey		.03	.02	.01
465 Bill Russell	.03	.02	.01	557 Chris Knapp		.03	.02	.01
466 Bob Molinaro	.03	.02	.01	558 Barry Bonnell		.03	.02	.01
467 Dave Stieb	.03	.02	.01	559 Willie Montanez		.04	.02	.01
468 Johnny Wockenfuss	.03	.02	.01	560 Joe Morgan		.15	.11	.05
469 Jeff Leonard	.03	.02	.01	561 Dennis Littlejohn		.03	.02	.01
470 Manny Trillo	.04	.02	.01	562 Checklist 485-605		.03	.02	.01
471 Mike Vail	.03	.02	.01	563 Jim Kaat		.07	.05	.02
472 Dyar Miller (dp)	.02	.01	.01½	564 Ron Hassey (dp)		.02	.01	.01½
473 Jose Cardenal	.03	.02	.01	565 Burt Hooton		.05	.03	.01
474 Mike LaCoss	.03	.02	.01	566 Del Unser		.03	.02	.01
475 Buddy Bell	.08	.06	.02	567 Mark Bomback		.03	.02	.01
476 Jerry Koosman	.04	.02	.01	568 Dave Revering		.03	.02	.01
477 Luis Gomez	.03	.02	.01	569 Al Williams (dp)		.02	.01	.01½
478 Juan Eichelberger	.03	.02	.01	570 Ken Singleton		.07	.05	.02
479 Expos Future Stars	.03	.02	.01	571 Tod Cruz		.03	.02	.01
480 Carlton Fisk	.12	.08	.04	572 Jack Morris		.04	.02	.01
481 Bob Lacey (dp)	.02	.01	.01½	573 Phil Garner		.03	.02	.01
482 Jim Gantner	.03	.02	.01	574 Bill Caudill		.03	.02	.01
483 Mike Griffin	.03	.02	.01	575 Tony Perez		.08	.06	.02
484 Max Venable (dp)	.02	.01	.01½	576 Reggie Cleveland		.03	.02	.01
485 Garry Templeton	.15	.11	.05	577 Blue Jays Future Stars		.03	.02	.01
486 Marc Hill	.03	.02	.01	578 Bill Gullickson		.03	.02	.01
487 Dewey Robinson	.03	.02	.01	579 Tim Flannery		.03	.02	.01
488 Damaso Garcia	.03	.02	.01	580 Don Baylor		.10	.07	.03
489 John Littlefield	.03	.02	.01	581 Roy Howell		.03	.02	.01
490 Eddie Murray	.08	.06	.02	582 Gaylord Perry		.15	.11	.05
491 Gordy Pladson	.03	.02	.01	583 Larry Milbourne		.03	.02	.01
492 Barry Foote	.03	.02	.01	584 Randy Lerch		.03	.02	.01
493 Dan Quisenberry	.15	.11	.05	585 Amos Otis		.07	.05	.02
494 Bob Walk	.03	.02	.01	586 Silvio Martinez		.03	.02	.01
495 Dusty Baker	.08	.06	.02	587 Jeff Newman		.03	.02	.01
496 Paul Dade	.03	.02	.01	588 Gary Lavelle		.03	.02	.01
497 Fred Norman	.03	.02	.01	589 Lamar Johnson		.03	.02	.01
498 Pat Putnam	.03	.02	.01	590 Bruce Sutter		.15	.11	.05
499 Frank Pastore	.03	.02	.01	591 John Lowenstein		.03	.02	.01
500 Jim Rice	.40	.30	.13	592 Steve Comer		.03	.02	.01
501 Tim Foli (dp)	.02	.01	.01½	593 Steve Kemp		.06	.04	.02
502 Giants Future Stars	.03	.02	.01	594 Preston Hanna (dp)		.02	.01	.01½
503 Steve McCatty	.03	.02	.01	595 Butch Hobson		.04	.02	.01
504 Dale Murphy	.04	.02	.01	596 Jerry Augustine		.03	.02	.01
505 Jason Thompson	.04	.02	.01	597 Rafael Landestoy		.03	.02	.01
506 Phil Huffman	.03	.02	.01	598 George Vukovich (dp)		.02	.01	.01½
507 Jamie Quirk	.03	.02	.01	599 Dennis Kinney		.03	.02	.01
508 Rob Dressler	.03	.02	.01	600 Johnny Bench		.35	.27	.12
509 Pete Mackanin	.03	.02	.01	601 Don Aase		.03	.02	.01
510 Lee Mazzilli	.08	.06	.02	602 Bobby Murcer		.05	.03	.01
511 Wayne Garland	.03	.02	.01	603 John Verhoeven		.03	.02	.01
512 Gary Thomasson	.03	.02	.01	604 Rob Picciolo		.03	.02	.01
513 Frank LaCorte	.03	.02	.01	605 Don Sutton		.15	.11	.05
514 George Riley	.03	.02	.01	606 Reds Future Stars(dp)		.02	.01	.01½
515 Robin Yount	.10	.07	.03	607 Dave Palmer		.03	.02	.01
516 Doug Bird	.03	.02	.01	608 Greg Pryor		.03	.02	.01
517 Richie Zisk	.07	.05	.02	609 Lynn McGlothen		.03	.02	.01
518 Grant Jackson	.03	.02	.01	610 Darrell Porter		.05	.03	.01
519 John Tamargo(dp)	.03	.02	.01	611 Rick Matula (dp)		.03	.02	.01
520 Steve Stone	.10	.07	.03	612 Duane Kuiper		.03	.02	.01
521 Sam Mejias	.03	.02	.01	613 Jim Anderson		.03	.02	.01
522 Mike Colbern	.03	.02	.01	614 Dave Rozema		.03	.02	.01
523 John Fulgham	.03	.02	.01	615 Rick Dempsey		.03	.02	.01
524 Willie Aikens	.10	.07	.03	616 Rick Wise		.04	.02	.01
525 Mike Torrez	.03	.02	.01	617 Craig Reynolds		.03	.02	.01
526 Phillies Future Stars	.03	.02	.01	618 John Milner		.03	.02	.01
527 Danny Goodwin	.03	.02	.01	619 Steve Henderson		.04	.02	.01
528 Gary Matthews	.06	.04	.02	620 Dennis Eckersley		.04	.02	.01
529 Dave LaRoche	.03	.02	.01	621 Tom Donohue		.03	.02	.01
530 Steve Garvey	.35	.27	.12	622 Randy Moffitt		.03	.02	.01
531 John Curtis	.03	.02	.01	623 Sal Bando		.04	.02	.01
532 Bill Stein	.03	.02	.01	624 Bob Welch		.03	.02	.01
533 Jesus Figueroa	.03	.02	.01	625 Bill Buckner		.07	.05	.02
534 Dave Smith	.03	.02	.01	626 Tigers Future Stars		.03	.02	.01
535 Omar Moreno	.07	.05	.02	627 Luis Tiant		.06	.04	.02
536 Bob Owchinko(dp)	.02	.01	.01½	628 Vic Correll		.03	.02	.01
537 Ron Hodges	.03	.02	.01	629 Tony Armas		.04	.02	.01
538 Tom Griffin	.03	.02	.01	630 Steve Carlton		.25	.20	.08
539 Rodney Scott	.03	.02	.01	631 Ron Jackson		.03	.02	.01
540 Mike Schmidt (dp)	.20	.15	.06	632 Alan Bannister		.03	.02	.01
541 Steve Swisher	.03	.02	.01	633 Bill Lee		.03	.02	.01
542 Larry Bradford (dp)	.02	.01	.01½	634 Doug Flynn		.03	.02	.01
543 Terry Crowley	.03	.02	.01	635 Bobby Bonds		.07	.05	.02
544 Rich Gale	.03	.02	.01	636 Al Hrabosky		.06	.04	.02
545 Johnny Grubb	.03	.02	.01	637 Jerry Narron		.03	.02	.01
546 Paul Moskau	.03	.02	.01	638 Checklist 606-726		.03	.02	.01
547 Mario Guerrero	.03	.02	.01	639 Carney Lansford		.07	.05	.02
548 Dave Goltz	.03	.02	.01	640 Dave Parker		.30	.25	.10
549 Jerry Remy	.03	.02	.01	641 Mark Belanger		.04	.02	.01
550 Tommy John	.20	.15	.06	642 Vern Ruhle		.03	.02	.01
				643 Lloyd Moseby		.03	.02	.01

1981 TOPPS BB (CONTINUED)

	MINT	VG-E	F-G
644 Ramon Aviles (dp)	.02	.01	.0½
645 Rick Reuschel	.07	.05	.02
646 Marvis Foley	.03	.02	.01
647 Dick Drago	.03	.02	.01
648 Darrell Evans	.03	.02	.01
649 Manny Sarmiento	.03	.02	.01
650 Bucky Dent	.06	.04	.02
641 Pedro Guerrero	.03	.02	.01
652 John Montague	.03	.02	.01
653 Bill Fahey	.03	.02	.01
654 Ray Burris	.03	.02	.01
644 Dan Driessen	.03	.02	.01
656 Jon Matlack	.04	.02	.01
657 Mike Cubbage (dp)	.02	.01	.0½
658 Milt Wilcox	.03	.02	.01
659 Brewers Future Stars	.03	.02	.01
660 Gary Carter	.08	.06	.02
661 Baltimore Orioles	.06	.04	.02
662 Boston Red Sox Team	.06	.04	.02
663 California Angels	.06	.04	.02
664 Chicago White Sox	.06	.04	.02
665 Cleveland Indians	.06	.04	.02
666 Detroit Tigers Team	.06	.04	.02
667 K. C. Royals Team	.07	.05	.02
668 Milwaukee Brewers	.06	.04	.02
669 Minnesota Twins Team	.06	.04	.02
670 New York Yankees Team	.07	.05	.02
671 Oakland A's Team	.06	.04	.02
672 Seattle Mariners Team	.06	.04	.02
673 Texas Rangers Team	.06	.04	.02
674 Toronto Blue Jays	.06	.04	.02
675 Atlanta Braves Team	.06	.04	.02
676 Chicago Cubs Team	.06	.04	.02
677 Cincinnati Reds Team	.06	.04	.02
678 Houston Astros Team	.06	.04	.02
679 L. A. Dodgers Team	.07	.05	.02
680 Montreal Expos Team	.06	.04	.02
681 New York Mets Team	.06	.04	.02
682 Phil. Phillies Team	.08	.06	.02
683 Pitt. Pirates Team	.06	.04	.02
684 St. L. Cardinals Team	.06	.04	.02

	MINT	VG-E	F-G
685 San Diego Padres	.06	.04	.02
686 S. F. Giants Team	.06	.04	.02
687 Jeff Jones	.03	.02	.01
688 Kiko Garcia	.03	.02	.01
689 Red Sox Future Stars	.03	.02	.01
690 Bob Watson	.05	.03	.01
691 Dick Ruthven	.03	.02	.01
692 Lenny Randle	.03	.02	.01
693 Steve Howe	.03	.02	.01
694 Bud Harrelson (dp)	.02	.01	.0½
695 Kent Tekulve	.04	.02	.01
696 Alan Ashby	.03	.02	.01
697 Rick Waits	.03	.02	.01
698 Mike Jorgensen	.03	.02	.01
699 Glen Abbott	.03	.02	.01
700 George Brett	.45	.35	.15
701 Joe Rudi	.04	.02	.01
702 George Medich	.03	.02	.01
703 Alvis Woods	.03	.02	.01
704 Bill Travers(dp)	.02	.01	.0½
705 Ted Simmons	.10	.07	.03
706 Dave Ford	.03	.02	.01
707 Dave Cash	.03	.02	.01
708 Doyle Alexander	.03	.02	.01
709 Alan Trammell(dp)	.03	.02	.01
710 Ron LeFlore (dp)	.05	.03	.01
711 Joe Ferguson	.03	.02	.01
712 Bill Bonham	.03	.02	.01
713 Bill North	.03	.02	.01
714 Pete Redfern	.03	.02	.01
715 Bill Madlock	.05	.03	.01
716 Glenn Borgmann	.03	.02	.01
717 Jim Barr (dp)	.02	.01	.0½
718 Larry Biittner	.03	.02	.01
719 Sparky Lyle	.07	.05	.02
720 Fred Lynn	.40	.30	.13
721 Toby Harrah	.03	.02	.01
722 Joe Niekro	.04	.02	.01
723 Bruce Bochte	.03	.02	.01
724 Lou Piniella	.05	.03	.01
725 Steve Rogers	.05	.03	.01
726 Rick Monday	.05	.03	.01

1963 TOPPS STICK—ON INSERTS (46)   1 3/4" X 2 3/4"

SANDY KOUFAX
L. A. DODGERS   PITCHER

Stick-on inserts were found in several series of the 1963 Topps cards. They are found either with blank backs or with instructions on the reverse.

	MINT	VG-E	F-G
COMPLETE SET	40.00	30.00	12.00
COMMON PLAYER	.50	.35	.15

	MINT	VG-E	F-G
1 Hank Aaron	4.00	3.00	1.40
2 Luis Aparicio	.75	.55	.25
3 Richie Ashburn	.75	.55	.25
4 Bob Aspromonte	.50	.35	.15
5 Ernie Banks	2.50	1.80	.80
6 Ken Boyer	.75	.55	.25
7 Jim Bunning	.75	.55	.25
8 Johnny Callison	.50	.35	.15
9 Bob Clemente	3.50	2.50	1.20
10 Orlando Cepeda	.75	.55	.25
11 Rocky Colavito	.75	.55	.25
12 Tommy Davis	.50	.35	.15
13 Dick Donovan	.50	.35	.15
14 Don Drysdale	2.00	1.50	.60
15 Dick Farrell	.50	.35	.15
16 Jim Gentile	.50	.35	.15
17 Ray Herbert	.50	.35	.15
18 Chuck Hinton	.50	.35	.15
19 Ken Hubbs	.75	.55	.25
20 Al Jackson	.50	.35	.15
21 Al Kaline	2.50	1.80	.80
22 Harmon Killebrew	2.00	1.50	.60
23 Sandy Koufax	3.50	2.50	1.20

	MINT	VG-E	F-G
24 Jerry Lumpe	.50	.35	.15
25 Art Mahaffey	.50	.35	.15
26 Mickey Mantle	5.00	3.75	1.75
27 Willie Mays	4.00	3.00	1.40
28 Bill Mazeroski	.75	.55	.25
29 Bill Monbouquette	.50	.35	.15
30 Stan Musial	3.50	2.50	1.20
31 Camilo Pascual	.50	.35	.15
32 Bob Purkey	.50	.35	.15
33 Bobby Richardson	.75	.55	.25
34 Brooks Robinson	2.50	1.80	.80
35 Floyd Robinson	.50	.35	.15
36 Frank Robinson	2.50	1.80	.80
37 Bob Rodgers	.50	.35	.15
38 Johnny Romano	.50	.35	.15
39 Jack Sanford	.50	.35	.15
40 Norm Siebern	.50	.35	.15
41 Warren Spahn	2.00	1.50	.60
42 Dave Stenhouse	.50	.35	.15
43 Ralph Terry	.50	.35	.15
44 Lee Thomas	.50	.35	.15
45 Bill White	.50	.35	.15
46 Carl Yastrzemski	3.50	2.50	1.20

1967 TOPPS PAPER INSERT (32)   5" X 7"

BERT CAMPANERIS

The wrappers of the 1967 Topps cards have the set advertised as follows: "Extra! All Star Pin-up inside." Printed on paper in full color, the "All Star" inserts have fold lines which are generally not noticeable when stored carefully. They are numbered and carry a facsimile autograph.

	MINT	VG-E	F-G
COMPLETE SET	15.00	12.00	4.00
COMMON PLAYER	.25	.20	.08

	MINT	VG-E	F-G
1 Boog Powell	.35	.27	.12
2 Bert Campaneris	.25	.20	.08
3 Brooks Robinson	1.50	1.10	.50
4 Tommie Agee	.25	.20	.08
5 Carl Yastrzemski	2.00	1.50	.60
6 Mickey Mantle	3.00	2.25	1.00
7 Frank Howard	.50	.40	.18
8 Sam McDowell	.35	.27	.12
9 Orlando Cepeda	.50	.40	.18
10 Chico Cardenas	.25	.20	.08
11 Bob Clemente	1.50	1.10	.50
12 Willie Mays	2.00	1.50	.60
13 Cleon Jones	.25	.20	.08
14 John Callison	.25	.20	.08
15 Hank Aaron	2.00	1.50	.50

	MINT	VG-E	F-G
16 Don Drysdale	1.00	.70	.30
17 Bobby Knoop	.25	.20	.08
18 Tony Oliva	.50	.40	.18
19 Frank Robinson	1.25	.90	.40
20 Denny McLain	.35	.27	.12
21 Al Kaline	1.50	1.10	.50
22 Joe Pepitone	.35	.27	.12
23 Harmon Killebrew	1.00	.70	.30
24 Leon Wagner	.25	.20	.08
25 Joe Morgan	.50	.40	.18
26 Ron Santo	.35	.27	.12
27 Joe Torre	.50	.40	.18
28 Juan Marichal	.50	.40	.18
29 Matty Alou	.35	.27	.12
30 Felipe Alou	.35	.27	.12
31 Ron Hunt	.25	.20	.08
32 Willie McCovey	1.00	.70	.30

1968 TOPPS BASEBALL POSTERS (24)   9 3/4" X 18 1/8"

This 1968 color poster set is not an "insert" but was issued separately with a piece of gum and in its own wrapper (see IWC). The posters are numbered at the lower left and the player's name and team appear in a large star. The poster was folded six times to fit into the package, so fold lines are a factor in grading.

	MINT	VG-E	F-G
COMPLETE SET	50.00	35.00	12.00
COMMON PLAYER	1.00	.70	.30
1 Dean Chance	1.00	.70	.30
2 Max Alvis	1.00	.70	.30
3 Frank Howard	1.50	1.10	.50
4 Jim Fregosi	1.50	1.10	.50
5 Jim Hunter	1.50	1.10	.50
6 Bob Clemente	6.00	4.50	2.00
7 Don Drysdale	2.50	1.80	.80
8 Jim Wynn	1.25	.90	.40
9 Al Kaline	4.00	3.00	1.40
10 Harmon Killibrew	2.50	1.80	.80
11 Jim Lonborg	1.25	.90	.40

	MINT	VG-E	F-G
12 Orlando Cepeda	1.25	.90	.40
13 Gary Peters	1.00	.70	.30
14 Hank Aaron	8.00	6.00	2.50
15 Richie Allen	1.25	.90	.40
16 Carl Yastrzemski	6.00	4.50	2.00
17 Ron Swoboda	1.00	.70	.30
18 Mickey Mantle	10.00	7.00	3.00
19 Tim McCarver	1.00	.70	.30
20 Willie Mays	8.00	6.00	2.50
21 Ron Santo	1.25	.90	.40
22 Rusty Staub	1.50	1.10	.50
23 Pete Rose	8.00	6.00	2.50
24 Frank Robinson	4.00	3.00	1.40

1970 TOPPS PAPER INSERT (24)   8 11/16" X 9 5/8"

1970 marked the year that Topps raised its price per package of cards to ten cents, and a series of 24 color posters was included as a bonus to the collector. The thin-paper poster is numbered and features a large portrait and a smaller, black & white action pose. It was folded five times to fit the packaging.

	MINT	VG-E	F-G
COMPLETE SET	30.00	23.00	9.00
COMMON PLAYER	.80	.60	.25
1 Joe Horlen	.80	.60	.25
2 Phil Niekro	1.00	.70	.30
3 Willie Davis	.80	.60	.25
4 Lou Brock	3.00	2.25	1.00
5 Ron Santo	1.00	.70	.30
6 Ken Harrelson	1.00	.70	.30
7 Willie McCovey	3.00	2.25	1.00
8 Rick Wise	.80	.60	.25
9 Andy Messersmith	1.00	.70	.30
10 Ron Fairly	.80	.60	.25
11 Johnny Bench	4.00	3.00	1.40

	MINT	VG-E	F-G
12 Frank Robinson	3.00	2.25	1.00
13 Tommie Agee	.80	.60	.25
14 Roy White	.80	.60	.25
15 Larry Dierker	.80	.60	.25
16 Rod Carew	4.00	3.00	1.40
17 Don Mincher	.80	.60	.25
18 Ollie Brown	.80	.60	.25
19 Ed Kirkpatrick	.80	.60	.25
20 Reggie Smith	1.50	1.10	.50
21 Bob Clemente	4.00	3.00	1.40
22 Frank Howard	1.50	1.10	.60
23 Bert Campaneris	.80	.60	.25
24 Denny McLain	1.25	.90	.40

1970 TOPPS STORY BOOKLETS (24)   2 1/2" X 3 7/16"

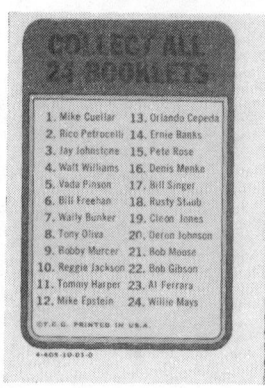

Inserted into packages of the 1970 Topps regular issue of cards, there are 24 miniature biographies of ballplayers in the set. Each numbered paper booklet contains 6 pages of comic-book-style story and a checklist of the booklet is available on the back page.

	MINT	VG-E	F-G
COMPLETE SET	10.00	7.00	3.00
COMMON PLAYER	.25	.20	.08
1 Mike Cuellar	.25	.20	.08
2 Rico Petrocelli	.25	.20	.08
3 Jay Johnstone	.25	.20	.08
4 Walt Williams	.25	.20	.08
5 Vada Pinson	.40	.30	.13
6 Bill Freehan	.30	.25	.10
7 Wally Bunker	.25	.20	.08
8 Tony Oliva	.50	.40	.18
9 Bobby Murcer	.50	.40	.18
10 Reggie Jackson	1.50	1.10	.50
11 Tommy Harper	.25	.20	.08
12 Mike Epstein	.25	.20	.08

	MINT	VG-E	F-G
13 Orlando Cepeda	.75	.55	.25
14 Ernie Banks	1.50	1.10	.50
15 Pete Rose	2.00	1.50	.60
16 Denis Menke	.25	.20	.08
17 Bill Singer	.25	.20	.08
18 Rusty Staub	.50	.40	.18
19 Cleon Jones	.25	.20	.08
20 Deron Johnson	.25	.20	.08
21 Bob Moose	.25	.20	.08
22 Bob Gibson	1.00	.70	.30
23 Al Ferrara	.25	.20	.08
24 Willie Mays	2.00	1.50	.60

1970-71 TOPPS SCRATCH-OFF INSERTS (24)   3 3/8" X 5"

The 1970-71 Topps Scratch-off inserts are heavy cardboard, folded inserts issued with the regular card series of those years. Unfolded, they form a game board upon which a baseball game is played by means of rubbing off black ink from the playing squares to reveal moves. Inserts with white centers were issued in 1970 and inserts with red centers in 1971.

	MINT	VG-E	F-G
COMPLETE SET	12.00	9.00	3.50
COMMON PLAYER	.25	.20	.08

	MINT	VG-E	F-G
1 Hank Aaron	2.00	1.50	.60
2 Rich Allen	.50	.40	.18
3 Luis Aparicio	.50	.40	.18
4 Sal Bando	.40	.30	.13
5 Glenn Beckert	.25	.20	.08
6 Dick Bosman	.25	.20	.08
7 Nate Colbert	.25	.20	.08
8 Mike Hegan	.25	.20	.08
9 Mack Jones	.25	.20	.08
10 Al Kaline	1.50	1.10	.50
11 Harmon Killebrew	1.00	.70	.30
12 Juan Marichal	.75	.55	.25

	MINT	VG-E	F-G
13 Tim McCarver	.25	.20	.08
14 Sam McDowell	.40	.30	.13
15 Claude Osteen	.25	.20	.08
16 Tony Perez	.50	.40	.18
17 Lou Piniella	.40	.30	.13
18 Boog Powell	.50	.40	.18
19 Tom Seaver	1.50	1.10	.50
20 Jim Spencer	.25	.20	.08
21 Willie Stargell	1.00	.70	.30
22 Mel Stottlemyre	.25	.20	.08
23 Jim Wynn	.25	.20	.08
24 Carl Yastrzemski	2.00	1.50	.60

1972 TOPPS BASEBALL POSTERS (24)   9 7/16" X 18"

Tom Seaver
METS   PITCHER

This giant, full-color series of 24 was issued as a separate set in 1972. The posters are individually numbered and, unlike other Topps posters described in this book, are borderless. They are printed on thin paper and were folded 5 times to facilitate packaging.

	MINT	VG-E	F-G
COMPLETE SET	50.00	35.00	12.00
COMMON PLAYER	1.00	.70	.30
1 Dave McNally	1.00	.70	.30
2 Carl Yastrzemski	6.00	4.50	2.00
3 Bill Melton	1.00	.70	.30
4 Ray Fosse	1.00	.70	.30
5 Mickey Lolich	1.50	1.10	.50
6 Amos Otis	1.50	1.10	.50
7 Tony Oliva	1.50	1.10	.50
8 Vida Blue	2.50	1.80	.80
9 Hank Aaron	8.00	6.00	2.50
10 Fergie Jenkins	1.50	1.10	.50
11 Pete Rose	8.00	6.00	2.50
12 Willie Davis	1.00	.70	.30
13 Tom Seaver	5.00	3.75	1.75
14 Rick Wise	1.00	.70	.30
15 Willie Stargell	4.00	3.00	1.40
16 Joe Torre	2.00	1.50	.60
17 Willie Mays	8.00	6.00	2.50
18 Andy Messersmith	1.25	.90	.40
19 Wilbur Wood	1.00	.70	.30
20 Harmon Killibrew	3.00	2.25	1.00
21 Billy Williams	2.00	1.50	.50
22 Bud Harrelson	1.00	.70	.30
23 Roberto Clemente	6.00	4.50	2.00
24 Willie McCovey	3.00	2.25	1.00

1969 TRANSOGRAM (60)

2 1/2'' X 3 1/2''

WILLIE HORTON

OUTFIELD — DETROIT TIGERS
Ht: 5'11" Wt: 190 Bats: Right Throws: Right
Born: October 18, 1942 Home: Arno, Virginia

This first Transogram set contains 60 full-color, blank-back cards issued as the back of the box of individual player statues. The cards are of slightly different dimensions than the 1970 set, and the Callison photo is reversed. A complete box with cards is worth 50% more than the price listed below.

	MINT	VG-E	F-G
COMPLETE SET	180.00	135.00	60.00
COMMON PLAYER	1.50	1.10	.50

		MINT	VG-E	F-G
1	Joe Azcue	1.50	1.10	.50
2	Willie Horton	1.50	1.10	.50
3	Luis Tiant	2.00	1.50	.60
4	Denny McLain	2.00	1.50	.60
5	Jose Cardenal	1.50	1.10	.50
6	Al Kaline	8.00	6.00	2.50
7	Tony Oliva	2.50	1.80	.80
8	Blue Moon Odom	1.50	1.10	.50
9	Cesar Tovar	1.50	1.10	.50
10	Rick Monday	1.50	1.10	.50
11	Harmon Killebrew	5.50	4.25	2.00
12	Danny Cater	1.50	1.10	.50
13	Brooks Robinson	8.00	6.00	2.50
14	Jim Fregosi	2.50	1.80	.80
15	Dave McNally	1.50	1.10	.50
16	Frank Robinson	7.00	5.25	2.50
17	Bobby Knoop	1.50	1.10	.50
18	Rick Reichardt	1.50	1.10	.50
19	Carl Yastrzemski	15.00	11.00	5.00
20	Pete Ward	1.50	1.10	.50
21	Rico Petrocelli	1.50	1.10	.50
22	Tommy John	3.00	2.25	1.00
23	Ken Harrelson	1.50	1.10	.50
24	Luis Aparicio	2.50	1.80	.80
25	Mike Epstein	1.50	1.10	.50
26	Roy White	1.50	1.10	.50
27	Camilo Pascual	1.50	1.10	.50
28	Mel Stottlemyre	1.50	1.10	.50
29	Frank Howard	2.50	1.80	.80
30	Mickey Mantle	25.00	18.50	8.75

		MINT	VG-E	F-G
31	Lou Brock	7.00	5.25	2.50
32	Juan Marichal	3.00	2.00	1.00
33	Bob Gibson	5.50	4.25	2.00
34	Willie Mays	1.50	1.10	.50
35	Tim McCarver	1.50	1.10	.50
36	Willie McCovey	5.50	4.25	2.00
37	Don Wilson	1.50	1.10	.50
38	Billy Williams	3.00	2.00	1.00
39	Rusty Staub	2.50	1.80	.80
40	Ernie Banks	8.00	6.00	2.50
41	Jim Wynn	1.50	1.10	.50
42	Ron Santo	2.00	2.00	1.00
43	Tom Haller	1.50	1.10	.50
44	Ron Swoboda	1.50	1.10	.50
45	Willie Davis	1.50	1.10	.50
46	Jerry Koosman	1.50	1.10	.50
47	Jim Lefebvre	1.50	1.10	.50
48	Tom Seaver	10.00	7.00	3.00
49	Joe Torre	2.50	1.80	.80
50	Tony Perez	2.50	1.80	.80
51	Felipe Alou	1.50	1.10	.50
52	Lee May	1.50	1.10	.50
53	Hank Aaron	18.00	13.50	6.00
54	Pete Rose	18.00	13.50	6.00
55	Cookie Rojas	1.50	1.10	.50
56	Bob Clemente	15.00	11.00	5.00
57	Richie Allen	2.00	1.50	.60
58	Matty Alou	1.50	1.10	.50
59	John Callison	1.50	1.10	.50
60	Bill Mazeroski	2.00	1.50	.60

1970 TRANSOGRAM (45)

2 9/16'' X 3 1/2''

ERNIE BANKS

1st BASE — CHICAGO CUBS
Ht: 6'1" Wt: 180 Bats: Right Throws: Right
Born: January 31, 1931 Home: Dallas, Texas

Similar to the 1969 set, these blank-back cards were issued as the back of a box containing three small plastic player statues. The cards have yellow borders with the player's name in red, and the pictures, with the exception of Torre and a reversal of the Callison photo, are identical to those in the 1969 set.

	AS INDIVIDUALS			AS PANELS		
	MINT	VG-E	F-G	MINT	VG-E	F-G
COMPLETE SET	140.00	100.00	45.00	150.00	110.00	50.00
COMMON PLAYER	1.50	1.10	.60	xxx	xxx	xxx
COMMON PANEL	xxx	xxx	xxx	5.00	3.75	1.75

1 Pete Rose	18.00	13.50	6.00	
Willie Mays	18.00	13.50	6.00	40.00	30.00	13.00
Cleon Jones	1.50	1.10	.60	

2 Ron Santo	2.00	1.50	.60			
Willie Davis	1.50	1.10	.60	10.00	7.00	3.00
Willie McCovey	5.50	4.25	2.00			
3 Juan Marichal	3.00	2.25	1.00			
Joe Torre	2.50	1.80	.80	14.00	10.50	4.75
Ernie Banks	8.00	6.00	2.50			
4 Hank Aaron	18.00	13.50	6.00			
Jim Wynn	1.50	1.10	.60	30.00	22.50	10.50
Tom Seaver	10.00	7.00	3.00			
5 Bob Gibson	5.50	4.25	2.00			
Roberto Clemente	15.00	11.00	5.00	22.00	16.50	7.50
Jerry Koosman	1.50	1.10	.60			
11 Denny McLain	2.00	1.50	.60			
Reggie Jackson	10.00	7.00	3.00	14.00	10.50	4.75
Boog Powell	2.00	1.50	.60			
12 Frank Robinson	7.00	5.25	2.50			
Frank Howard	2.50	1.80	.80	11.00	8.00	3.50
Rick Reichardt	1.50	1.10	.60			
13 Carl Yastrzemski	15.00	11.00	5.00			
Tony Oliva	2.50	1.80	.80	20.00	15.00	6.50
Mel Stottlemyre	1.50	1.10	.60			
14 Al Kaline	8.00	6.00	2.50			
Jim Fregosi	2.50	1.80	.80	14.00	10.50	4.75
Sam McDowell	2.00	1.50	.60			
15 Blue Moon Odom	1.50	1.10	.60			
Harmon Killebrew	6.00	4.50	2.00	9.00	6.75	3.00
Rico Petrocelli	1.50	1.10	.60			

NATIONAL LEAGUE SERIES 3

JUAN MARICHAL • SAN FRANCISCO GIANTS
• JOE TORRE • ST. LOUIS CARDINALS
ERNIE BANKS • CHICAGO CUBS

NATIONAL LEAGUE
ALL STAR COLLECTOR PLAY FIGURES

1970 TRANSOGRAM METS (15) 2 9/16" X 3 1/2"

The 1970 Transogram Mets are a set of 15 blank-back cards issued as the back of a box containing three small, plastic statues honoring the 1969 Mets.

ED KRANEPOOL
1st BASE N.Y. METS
Ht: 6'3" Wt: 210 Bats: Left Throws: Left
Born: Nov. 8, 1944 Home: Bronx, N.Y.

AL WEIS
2nd BASE N.Y. METS
Ht: 6' Wt: 165 Bats: Right Throws: Right
Born: April 2, 1938 Home: Franklin Sq., N.Y.

TOM SEAVER
PITCHER N.Y. METS
Ht: 6 1" Wt: 200 Bats: Right Throws: Right
Born: Nov. 17, 1944 Home: Fresno, Cal.

	AS INDIVIDUALS			AS PANELS		
	MINT	VG-E	F-G	MINT	VG-E	F-G
COMPLETE SET	45.00	35.00	15.00	50.00	38.00	17.00
COMMON PLAYER	1.50	1.10	.50	xxx	xxx	xxx
COMMON PANEL	xxx	xxx	xxx	5.00	3.75	1.75
21 Ed Kranepool	1.50	1.10	.50			
Al Weis	1.50	1.10	.50	20.00	15.00	6.50
Tom Seaver	15.00	11.00	5.00			
22 Ken Boswell	1.50	1.10	.50			
Jerry Koosman	2.00	1.50	.60	5.00	3.75	1.75
Jerry Grote	1.50	1.10	.50			
23 Art Shamsky	1.50	1.10	.50			
Gary Gentry	1.50	1.10	.50	5.00	3.75	1.75
Tommie Agee	1.50	1.10	.50			
24 Nolan Ryan	13.00	7.00	3.00			
Tug McGraw	5.00	3.75	1.75	20.00	15.00	6.50
Cleon Jones	1.50	1.10	.50			
25 Ron Swoboda	1.50	1.10	.50			
Bud Harrelson	1.50	1.10	.50	5.00	3.75	1.75
Donn Clendenon	1.50	1.10	.50			

Few players of top caliber have managed to achieve the anonymity of Harry Stovey. A solid batsman and base-stealer extraordinaire, Stovey was one of the most feared offensive threats of his time. Perhaps he has been overshadowed by the "legends" who were his contemporaries: Anson, Comiskey, Ward, Kelly, etc. Perhaps he was not "colorful" or popular among his teammates. But although he remains unknown to modern-day fans and, apparently, to the Old Timer's Committee of the Hall of Fame, both the fans and the ballplayers of the 1880's knew him well. Combining speed-of-foot with smashing power at the plate, Harry Stovey always seemed to be standing on 2nd or 3rd, or crossing home with a run.

Born Harry Stow on December 20, 1856, Stovey played in the "major leagues" for the first time in 1880, with Worcester of the National League. Why he changed his name is a matter of conjecture; perhaps his friends and family considered baseball disreputable; possibly he used the "extra" name to pick up cash as a "ringer." Or it simply may have resulted from an uncorrected oversight or error during his career. Whatever the cause, his baseball cards can be found with both spellings, "Stovey" in the Old Judge (N172) set, and "Stowe" [sic] in the Kalamazoo bats (N690) series.

Stovey "broke in" with a bang with the 1880 Worcester team, tying for the league lead in home runs. He and pitcher Lee Richmond (32-32) were the stars among an otherwise mediocre club. Despite their efforts during the next three years, Worcester became the doormat of the National League.

In 1883, Stovey signed on with the Philadelphia Athletic Club of the American Association, a team which nosed out St. Louis for the league championship. No one can say how low Philadelphia might have finished had not Stovey been playing first base for them in '83. His contributions were spectacular: he led the Association in home runs, home run percentage, slugging percentage, total bases, runs, and doubles. Two categories — rbi's and stolen bases — are not available for that year, but surely the Athletic's first-sacker was near the top in these. It was a dream come true for the Philadelphia-born Stovey to perform so gloriously for the hometown fans.

During his seven-year stay in the Quaker City, Harry Stovey led the American Association in home runs four times and finished second twice. He was always near the top in home run percentage, slugging percentage and total bases. He topped the league in runs scored three years in succession, 1883-1885, and again led in 1889, and he also took honors for most two— and three—base hits on several occasions. During a period of the National Pastime when the stolen base was a primary offensive weapon, Harry Stovey was among the best at pilfering that extra sack. Baseball writer Hugh Fullerton credited him with inventing the "delayed steal," and called him ". . . a wonderful base runner. . ." Stovey stole 87 bases in 1888 and 97 in 1890.

Harry Stovey jumped to the Boston entry in the Players League in 1890 at age 33. Playing in right field for the first time in his career (having played first base and center field previously), Stovey was a vital part of the championship Boston crew, taking a league 2nd in home runs, 3rd in runs scored, and 1st in stolen bases. Joining the National League's Boston club in 1891, he again led his team to top honors in this, his last full season as a regular. Even at age 34, Harry Stovey was a formidible player, as his statistics for '91 demonstrate: 2nd in home runs, home run percentage, and slugging average; 1st in total bases; 3rd in rbi's; 3rd in doubles; 1st in triples; and 6th in stolen bases. He played in 112 games for Boston and Baltimore in 1892, and closed out his career in '93 as a utility outfielder for Baltimore and Brooklyn.

Stovey, Stow or Stowe: Whichever name he used or favored he was "trouble" for opposing ball teams. He participated in 1486 games and averaged more than one run scored per game, compared to Ty Cobb's average of .739. He led his league in home runs five times; Willie Mays accomplished it on four occasions. Stovey stole 441 bases in the seven years of his career for which we have records; the "Fordam Flash," Frankie Frisch played in 825 more games and pilfered but 419. Stovey led in triples four times; DiMaggio only once. Cobb, Mays, Frisch and DiMaggio are counted among baseball's immortal players while Harry Stovey is one of its forgotten sons.

We pay tribute to Harry Stovey and his baseball accomplishments with the following display of momentos from his personal estate, including his 1891 Championship medal and his silver-plated lifetime baseball pass. The player cards with no advertising are photographs taken in a private Philadelphia studio from which the Goodwin Company selected the poses to be used in its "Old Judge" (N172) series of tobacco insert cards. The card with the obverse advertising comes from the latter. Stovey appears on each of the team cards shown with his contemporaries, two of whom — Wilbert Robinson & King Kelly — are now enshrined in the Hall of Fame.

STUDIO PHOTOGRAPH

1891 CHAMPIONSHIP MEDAL

STUDIO PHOTOGRAPH

1880 WORCESTER
NATIONAL LEAGUE

N172 OLD JUDGE

STUDIO PHOTOGRAPH

1891 BOSTON
NATIONAL LEAGUE

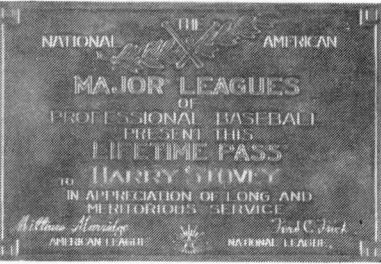

SILVER—PLATED LIFETIME PASS

1886 PHILADELPHIA
AMERICAN ASSOCIATION

1911 T−3 TURKEY RED (126)

5 3/4" X 8"

The 1911 T3 Turkey Red set contains 126 full color, cabinet type cards. Card nos. 1 to 50 and nos. 77 to 126 portray baseball players. Card nos. 51 to 76 portray boxers. The backs of card nos. 77 to 126 contain either a checklist or an ad for Turkey Red cigarettes. The ACC designation for the baseball players is T3. The ACC designation for the boxers is T9.

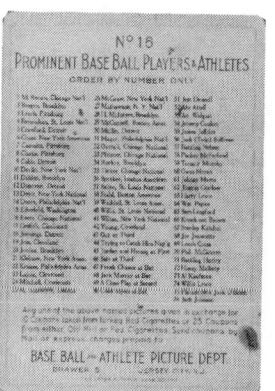

	MINT	VG-E	F-G
COMPLETE SET	6500.00	5000.00	2000.00
COMMON PLAYER (1-50, 77-126)	50.00	38.00	16.00
COMMON BOXERS (51-76)	20.00	15.00	6.00
1 M. Brown, Chicago Nat	90.00	70.00	30.00
2 Bergen, Brooklyn	50.00	38.00	16.00
3 Leach, Pittsburg	50.00	38.00	16.00
4 Bresnahan, St. Louis N.	80.00	60.00	25.00
5 Crawford, Detroit	80.00	60.00	25.00
6 Chase, New York Amer.	50.00	39.99	16.00
7 Camnitz, Pittsburg	50.00	38.00	16.00
8 Clarke, Pittsburg	80.00	60.00	25.00
9 Cobb, Detroit	350.00	260.00	120.00
10 Devlin, New York Nat'l	50.00	38.00	16.00
11 Dahlen, Brooklyn	50.00	38.00	16.00
12 Donovan, Detroit	50.00	38.00	16.00
13 Doyle, New York Nat'l	50.00	38.00	16.00
14 Dooin, Phila. Nat'l	50.00	38.00	16.00
15 Elberfeld, Washington	50.00	38.00	16.00
16 Evers, Chicago Nat'l	90.00	70.00	30.00
17 Griffith, Cincinnati	90.00	70.00	30.00
18 Jennings, Detroit	90.00	70.00	30.00
19 Joss, Cleveland	100.00	70.00	30.00
20 Jordan, Brooklyn	50.00	38.00	16.00
21 Kleinow, New York Nat.	50.00	38.00	16.00
22 Krause, Phila. Amer.	50.00	38.00	16.00
23 Lajoie, Cleveland	150.00	110.00	50.00
24 Mitchell, Cincinnati	50.00	38.00	16.00
25 M. McIntyre, Detroit	50.00	38.00	16.00
26 McGraw, New York Nat.	100.00	70.00	30.00
27 Mathewson, N. Y. Nat.	200.00	150.00	65.00
28 H. McIntyre, Brooklyn	50.00	38.00	16.00
29 McConnell, Boston Amer.	50.00	38.00	16.00
30 Mullin, Detroit	50.00	38.00	16.00
31 Magee, Phila. Nat'l	50.00	38.00	16.00
32 Overall, Chicago Nat.	50.00	38.00	16.00
33 Pfeister, Chicago Nat.	50.00	38.00	16.00
34 Rucker, Brooklyn	50.00	38.00	16.00
35 Tinker, Chicago Nat.	90.00	70.00	30.00
36 Speaker, Boston Amer.	125.00	90.00	40.00
37 Sallee, St. Louis Nat.	50.00	38.00	16.00
38 Stahl, Boston Amer.	50.00	38.00	16.00
39 Waddell, St. Louis Am.	90.00	70.00	30.00
40 Willis, St. Louis Nat.	50.00	38.00	16.00
41 Wiltse, New York Nat.	50.00	38.00	16.00
42 Young, Cleveland	125.00	90.00	40.00
43 Out At Third	50.00	38.00	16.00
44 Trying to Catch Him Napping	50.00	38.00	16.00
45 Jordan and Herzog at First	50.00	38.00	16.00
46 Safe At Third	50.00	38.00	16.00
47 Frank Chance At Bat	100.00	70.00	30.00
48 Jack Murray At Bat	50.00	38.00	16.00
49 A Close Play At Second	50.00	38.00	16.00
50 Chief Myers At Bat	50.00	38.00	16.00
51 Jim Driscoll	20.00	15.00	6.00
52 Abe Attell	20.00	15.00	6.00
53 Ad. Walgast	20.00	15.00	6.00
54 Johnny Coulon	20.00	15.00	6.00
55 James Jeffries	40.00	30.00	13.00
56 Jack (Twin) Sullivan	20.00	15.00	6.00
57 Battling Nelson	20.00	15.00	6.00
58 Packey McFarland	20.00	15.00	6.00
59 Tommy Murphy	20.00	15.00	6.00
60 Owen Moran	20.00	15.00	6.00
61 Johnny Marto	20.00	15.00	6.00
62 Jimmie Gardner	20.00	15.00	6.00
63 Harry Lewis	20.00	15.00	6.00
64 Wm. Papke	20.00	15.00	6.00
65 Sam Langford	20.00	15.00	6.00
66 Knock-out Brown	20.00	15.00	6.00
67 Stanley Ketchel	30.00	22.50	10.50
68 Joe Jeannette	20.00	15.00	6.00
69 Leach Cross	20.00	15.00	6.00
70 Phil. McGovern	20.00	15.00	6.00
71 Battling Hurley	20.00	15.00	6.00
72 Honey Mellody	20.00	15.00	6.00
73 Al Kaufman	20.00	15.00	6.00

T3 TURKEY REDS (CONT'D)

	MINT	VG-E	F-G
74 Willie Lewis	20.00	15.00	6.00
75 Phila. Jack O'Brien	20.00	15.00	6.00
76 Jack Johnson	40.00	30.00	13.00
77 Ames, New York Nat	50.00	38.00	16.00
78 Baker, Phila. Amer	90.00	70.00	30.00
79 Bell, Brooklyn	50.00	38.00	16.00
80 Bender, Phila. Amer	90.00	70.00	30.00
81 Bescher, Cincinnati	50.00	38.00	16.00
82 Bransfield, Phila. N	50.00	38.00	16.00
83 Bridwell, Phila. Nat	50.00	38.00	16.00
84 Browne, Wash and Chi	50.00	38.00	16.00
85 Burns, Chi. and Cin.	50.00	38.00	16.00
86 Carrigan, Boston Am.	50.00	38.00	16.00
87 Collins, Phila. Am.	90.00	70.00	30.00
88 Coveleski, Cin.	50.00	38.00	16.00
89 Criger, New York Am	50.00	38.00	16.00
90 Doolan, Phila. Nat.	50.00	38.00	16.00
91 Downey, Cincinnati	50.00	38.00	16.00
92 Dygert, Phila. Am.	50.00	38.00	16.00
93 Fromme, Cincinnati	50.00	38.00	16.00
94 Gibson, Pittsburg	50.00	38.00	16.00
95 Graham, Boston Nat.	50.00	38.00	16.00
96 Groom, Washington	50.00	38.00	16.00
97 Hoblitzell, Cin.	50.00	38.00	16.00
98 Hofman, Chicago Nat	50.00	38.00	16.00
99 Johnson, Washington	200.00	150.00	65.00
100 D. Jones, Detroit	50.00	38.00	16.00

	MINT	VG-E	F-G
101 Keeler, New York Nat.	125.00	90.00	38.00
102 Kling, Chicago Nat.	50.00	38.00	16.00
103 Konetchy, St. Louis N	50.00	38.00	16.00
104 Lennox, Brooklyn	50.00	38.00	16.00
105 Lobert, Cincinnati	50.00	38.00	16.00
106 Lord, Bos. and Chi.	50.00	38.00	16.00
107 Manning, N. Y. Amer.	50.00	38.00	16.00
108 Merkle, New York Nat.	50.00	38.00	16.00
109 Moran, Chi. and Phila.	50.00	38.00	16.00
110 McBride, Washington	50.00	38.00	16.00
111 Niles, Bos. and Cleve.	50.00	38.00	16.00
112 Paskert, Cincinnati	50.00	38.00	16.00
113 Raymond, N. Y. Nat.	50.00	38.00	16.00
114 Rhoades, Cleveland	50.00	38.00	16.00
115 Schlei, New York Nat.	50.00	38.00	16.00
116 Schmidt, Detroit	50.00	38.00	16.00
117 Schulte, Chicago Nat.	50.00	38.00	16.00
118 Smith, Chi. and Bos.	50.00	38.00	16.00
119 Stone, St. Louis Am.	50.00	38.00	16.00
120 Street, Washington	50.00	38.00	16.00
121 Sullivan, Chi. Amer.	50.00	38.00	16.00
122 Tenney, New York Nat.	50.00	38.00	16.00
123 Thomas, Phila. Amer.	50.00	38.00	16.00
124 Wallace, St. Louis Am	80.00	60.00	25.00
125 Walsh, Chicago Amer.	90.00	70.00	30.00
126 Wilson, Pittsburg	50.00	38.00	16.00

1913 T–200 FATIMA (16)   2 5/8"X 5 13/16"

The 1913 Fatima Cigarettes issue contains 16 unnumbered glossy surface team cards.Both St. Louis team cards are considered difficult to obtain. A 13" X 21" unnumbered, heavy cardboard premium issue is also known to exist and is quite scarce.

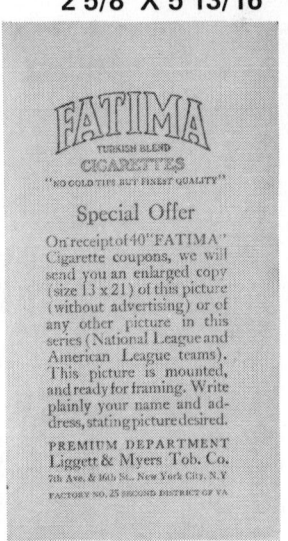

FATIMA
TURKISH BLEND
CIGARETTES
"NO COLD TIPS BUT FINEST QUALITY"

Special Offer

On receipt of 40 "FATIMA" Cigarette coupons, we will send you an enlarged copy (size 13 x 21) of this picture (without advertising) or of any other picture in this series (National League and American League teams). This picture is mounted, and ready for framing. Write plainly your name and address, stating picture desired.

PREMIUM DEPARTMENT
Liggett & Myers Tob. Co.
7th Ave. & 16th St., New York City, N.Y.
FACTORY NO. 25 SECOND DISTRICT OF VA

	MINT	VG-E	F-G
COMPLETE SET	800.00	600.00	200.00
COMMON TEAM	36.00	27.00	11.00
Boston, A. L.	60.00	45.00	20.00
Chicago, A. L.	50.00	38.00	17.00
Cleveland, A. L.	36.00	27.00	11.00
Detroit, A. L.	100.00	70.00	30.00
New York, A. L.	125.00	90.00	40.00
Philadelphia, A. L.	36.00	27.00	11.00
St. Louis, A. L.	150.00	110.00	50.00
Washington, A. L.	36.00	27.00	11.00

	MINT	VG-E	F-G
Boston, N. L.	100.00	70.00	30.00
Brooklyn, N. L.	40.00	30.00	13.00
Chicago, N. L.	50.00	38.00	17.00
Cincinnati, N. L.	36.00	27.00	11.00
New York, N. L.	50.00	38.00	17.00
Philadelphia, N. L.	36.00	27.00	11.00
Pittsburg, N. L.	36.00	27.00	11.00
St. Louis, N. L.	80.00	60.00	25.00

> Attend a Sports Memorabilia Show or Convention in your area sometime this year. They are both interesting and enjoyable to all members of the family.

1911 T201 MECCA

2 1/4″ X 4 11/16″

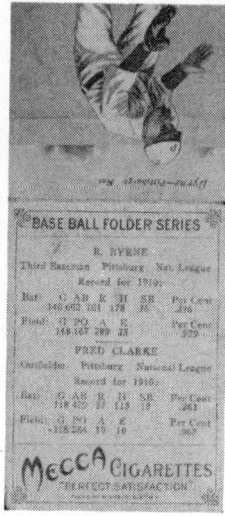

The 1911 Mecca Double Folder issue contains 50 unnumbered cards. This issue was one of the first to list statistics of players portrayed on the cards. Each card portrays two players—one when the card is folded, another when the card is unfolded. The card of Dougherty and Lord is considered scarce.

	MINT	VG-E	F-G
COMPLETE SET	350.00	275.00	120.00
COMMON PAIR	6.00	4.50	2.00
1 Baker and Collins	15.00	11.00	5.00
2 Barry and Lapp	6.00	4.50	2.00
3 Bergen and Wheat	10.00	7.00	3.00
4 Blair and Hartzell	6.00	4.50	2.00
5 Bresnahan and Huggins	15.00	11.00	5.00
6 Bridwell and Mathewson	15.00	11.00	5.00
7 Butler and Abstein	6.00	4.50	2.00
8 Byrne and Clark	6.00	4.50	2.00
9 Chance and Evers	20.00	15.00	6.50
10 Clarke and Gaspar	10.00	7.00	3.00
11 Cobb and Crawford	60.00	45.00	20.00
12 Cole and Kling	6.00	4.50	2.00
13 Coombs and Thomas	6.00	4.50	2.00
14 Daubert and Rucker	6.00	4.50	2.00
15 Dougherty and Lord	50.00	38.00	17.00
16 Dooin and Titus	6.00	4.90	2.00
17 Downie and Baker	6.00	4.50	2.00
18 Dygert and Seymour	6.00	4.50	2.00
19 Elberfeld and McBride	6.00	4.50	2.00
20 Falkenberg and Lajoie	12.00	8.75	4.00
21 Fitzpatrick and Killian	6.00	4.50	2.00
22 Gardener and Speaker	12.00	8.75	4.00
23 Gibson and Leach	6.00	4.50	2.00
24 Graham and Mattern	6.00	4.50	2.00
25 Hauser and Lush	6.00	4.50	2.00
26 Herzog and Miller	6.00	4.50	2.00
27 Hinchman and Hickman	6.00	4.50	2.00
28 Hofman and M. Brown	10.00	7.00	3.00
29 Jennings and Summers	10.00	7.00	3.00
30 Johnson and Ford	6.00	4.50	2.00
31 McCarty and McGinnity	10.00	7.00	3.00
32 McGlyn and Barrett	6.00	4.50	2.00
33 McLean and Grant	6.00	4.50	2.00
34 Merkle and Wiltse	6.00	4.50	2.00
35 Meyers and Doyle	6.00	4.50	2.00
36 Moore and Lobert	6.00	4.50	2.00
37 Odwell and Downs	6.00	4.50	2.00
38 Oldring and Bender	10.00	7.00	3.00
39 Payne and Walsh	10.00	7.00	3.00
40 Simon and Leifield	6.00	4.50	2.00
41 Starr and McCabe	6.00	4.50	2.00
42 Stephens and LaPorte	6.00	4.50	2.00
43 Stovall and Turner	6.00	4.50	2.00
44 Street and Johnson	20.00	15.00	6.50
45 Stroud and Donovan	6.00	4.50	2.00
46 Sweeney and Chase	6.00	4.50	2.00
47 Thoney and Cicotte	6.00	4.50	2.00
48 Wallace and Lake	10.00	7.00	3.00
49 Ward and Foster	6.00	4.50	2.00
50 Williams and Woodruff	6.00	4.50	2.00

1912 T202 TRIPLE FOLDERS (134)

2 1/4" X 5 1/4"

The 1912 T202 Hassan Triple Folder issue is perhaps the most ingenious baseball card ever issued. The two end cards of each panel are full color,

T205 individual cards whereas the black and white center panel pictures an action photo or a portrait. The end cards can be folded across the

center panel and stored in this manner. Seventy-six different center panels are known to exist; however, many of the center panels contain more than one combination of end cards. The center panel titles are listed below in alphabetical order while the different combinations of end cards are listed below each center panel as they appear left to right on the front of the card. A total of 134 different card fronts exist. The set price below includes all panel and player combinations listed in the checklist. Back color variations (red or black) also exist. The Birmingham's Home Run card is difficult to obtain as are other cards whose center panel exists with but one combination of end cards. The Devlin—Mathewson end panels on numbers 29(a) and 74(c) picture Devlin as a Giant. Devlin is pictured as a Rustler on 29(b) and 74(d).

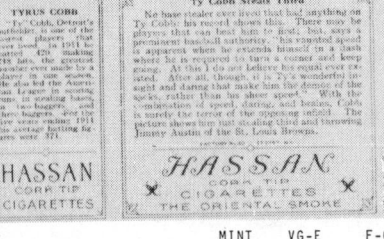 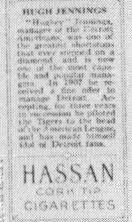

	MINT	VG-E	F-G
COMPLETE SET	2650.00	2000.00	800.00
COMMON PANEL	16.00	12.50	5.00

	MINT	VG-E	F-G
1 A Close Play Home			
a) Wallace-LaPorte	17.00	12.50	6.00
b) Wallace-Pelty	17.00	12.50	6.00
2 A Desperate Slide			
O'Leary-Cobb	35.00	26.00	12.00
3 A Great Batsman			
a) Barger-Bergen	16.00	12.50	5.00
b) Rucker-Bergen	16.00	12.50	5.00
4 Ambrose McConnell at Bat			
Blair-Quinn	17.00	12.50	6.00
5 A Wide Throw Saves Crawford			
Mullin-Stanage	17.00	12.50	6.00
6 Baker Gets His Man			
Collins-Baker	22.00	16.50	7.50
7 Birmingham Gets to Third			
Johnson-Street	23.00	17.00	8.00
8 Birmingham's Home Run			
Birmingham-Turner	75.00	55.00	24.00
9 Bush Just Misses Austin			
Moran-Magee	17.00	12.50	6.00
10 Carrigan Blocks His Man			
a) Gaspar-McLean	16.00	12.50	6.00
b) Wagner-Carrigan	16.00	12.50	6.00
11 Catching Him Napping			
Oakes-Bresnahan	18.00	13.50	6.00
12 Caught Asleep Off First			
Bresnahan-Harmon	18.00	13.50	6.00
13 Chance Beats Out a Hit			
a) Chance-Foxen	20.00	15.00	6.50
b) McIntire-Archer	16.00	12.50	5.00
c) Overall-Archer	16.00	12.50	5.00
d) Rowan-Archer	16.00	12.50	5.00
e) Shean-Chance	20.00	15.00	6.50
14 Chase Dives into Third			
a) Chase-Wolter	16.00	12.50	5.00
b) Gibson-Clarke	17.00	12.50	6.00
c) Phillippe-Gibson	16.00	12.50	5.00
15 Chase Gets Ball Too Late			
a) Egan-Mitchell	16.00	12.50	5.00
b) Wolter-Chase	16.00	12.50	5.00
16 Chase Guarding First			
a) Chase-Wolter	16.00	12.50	5.00
b) Gibson-Clarke	17.00	12.50	6.00
c) Leifield-Gibson	15.00	12.50	5.00
17 Chase Ready Squeeze Play			
Paskert-Magee	17.00	12.50	6.00
18 Chase Safe at Third			
Barry-Baker	20.00	15.00	6.50
19 Chief Bender Waiting			
Bender-Thomas	21.00	15.50	7.00
20 Clarke Hikes for Home			
Bridwell-Kling	17.00	12.50	6.00

	MINT	VG-E	F-G
21 Close at First			
Ball-Stovall	17.00	12.50	6.00
22 Close at the Plate			
a) Walsh-Payne	17.00	12.50	6.00
b) White-Payne	16.00	12.50	5.00
23 Close at Third(Speaker)			
Wood-Speaker	25.00	18.50	8.75
24 Close at Third(Wagner)			
Wagner-Carrigan	18.00	13.50	6.00
25 Collins Easily Safe			
a) Byrne-Clarke	17.00	12.50	6.00
b) Collins-Baker	18.00	13.50	6.00
c) Collins-Murphy	17.00	12.50	6.00
26 Crawford About to Smash			
Stanage-Summers	17.00	12.50	6.00
27 Cree Rolls Home			
Daubert-Hummell	17.00	12.50	6.00
28 Davy Jones' Great Slide			
Delahanty-Jones	17.00	12.50	6.00
29 Devlin Gets His Man			
a) Devlin-Mathewson	60.00	45.00	20.00
b) Devlin-Mathewson	25.00	18.50	8.75
c) Fletcher-Mathewson	20.00	15.00	6.50
d) Meyers-Mathewson	20.00	15.00	6.50
30 Donlin Out at First			
a) Camnitz-Gibson	16.00	12.50	5.00
b) Doyle-Merkle	16.00	12.50	5.00
c) Leach-Wilson	16.00	12.50	5.00
d) Magee-Dooin	16.00	12.50	5.00
e) Phillippe-Gibson	16.00	12.50	5.00
31 Dooin Gets His Man			
a) Dooin-Dollan	16.00	12.50	5.00
b) Lobert-Dooin	16.00	12.50	5.00
c) Titus-Dooin	16.00	12.50	5.00
32 Easy for Larry			
Doyle-Merkle	17.00	12.50	6.00
33 Elberfeld Beats			
Milan-Elberfeld	17.00	12.50	6.00
34 Elberfeld Gets His Man			
a) Milan-Elberfeld	17.00	12.50	6.00
b) Reulbach-Archer	xxx not verified		
35 Engle in a Close Play			
Speaker-Engle	24.00	18.00	8.50
36 Evers Makes a Safe Slide			
a) Archer-Evers	18.00	13.50	6.00
b) Evers-Chance	30.00	22.50	10.50
c) Overall-Archer	16.00	12.50	5.00
d) Reulbach-Archer	16.00	12.50	5.00
3) Tinker-Chance	28.00	21.00	10.00
37 Fast Work at Third			
O'Leary-Cobb	35.00	26.00	12.00
38 Ford Putting Over Spitter			
a) Ford-Vaughn	16.00	12.50	5.00
b) Sweeney-Ford	16.00	12.50	5.00

	MINT	VG-E	F-G
39 Good Play at Third			
Moriarty-Cobb	35.00	26.00	12.00
40 Grant Gets His Man			
Hoblitzel-Grant	17.00	12.50	6.00
41 Hal Chase Too Late			
a) McIntyre-McConnell	16.00	12.50	5.00
b) Suggs-McLean	16.00	12.50	5.00
42 Harry Lord at Third			
Lennox-Tinker	18.00	13.50	6.00
43 Hartzell Covering			
Scanlon-Dahlen	17.00	12.50	6.00
44 Hartzell Strikes Out			
Groom-Gray	17.00	12.50	6.00
45 Held at Third			
Tannehill-Lord	17.00	12.50	6.00
46 Jake Stahl Guarding			
a) Chase-Wolter	xxx not verified		
b) Cicotte-Stahl	17.00	12.50	6.00
47 Jim Delahanty at Bat			
Delahanty-Jones	17.00	12.50	6.00
48 Just Before the Battle			
a) Ames-Meyers	16.00	12.50	5.00
b) Bresnahan-McGraw	25.00	18.50	8.75
c) Crandall-Meyers	16.00	12.50	5.00
d) Devore-Becker	16.00	12.50	5.00
e) Fletcher-Mathewson	20.00	15.00	6.50
f) Marquard-Meyers	17.00	12.50	6.00
g) McGraw-Jennings	25.00	18.50	8.75
h) Meyers-Mathewson	20.00	15.00	6.50
i) Snodgrass-Murray	16.00	12.50	5.00
j) Wiltse-Meyers	16.00	12.50	5.00
49 Knight Catches Runner			
Knight-Johnson	16.00	12.50	5.00
50 Lobert Almost Caught			
a) Bridwell-Kling	16.00	12.50	5.00
b) Kling-Young	18.00	13.50	6.00
c) Mattern-Kling	16.00	12.50	5.00
d) Steinfelt-Kling	16.00	12.50	5.00
51 Lobert Gets Tenney			
Lobert-Dooin	17.00	12.50	5.00
52 Lord Catches His Man			
Tannehill-Lord	17.00	12.50	5.00
53 McConnell Caught			
Richie-Needham	17.00	12.50	5.00
54 McIntyre at Bat			
McIntyre-McConnell	17.00	12.50	5.00
55 Moriarty Spiked			
Willett-Stanage	17.00	12.50	5.00
56 Nearly Caught			
Bates-Bescher	22.00	16.50	7.50
57 Oldring Almost Home			
Lord-Oldring	17.00	12.50	5.00

	MINT	VG-E	F-G
58 Schaefer on First			
McBride-Milan	17.00	12.50	6.00
59 Schaefer Steals Second			
McBride-Griffiths	17.00	12.50	6.00
60 Scoring from Second			
Lord-Oldring	17.00	12.50	6.00
61 Scrambling Back			
a) Barger-Bergen	16.00	12.50	5.00
b) Wolter-Chase	16.00	12.50	5.00
62 Speaker Almost Caught			
Miller-Clarke	20.00	15.00	6.50
63 Speaker Rounding Third			
Wood-Speaker	25.00	18.50	8.75
64 Speaker Scores			
Speaker-Engle	24.00	18.00	8.50
65 Stahl Safe			
Stovall-Austin	17.00	12.50	6.00
66 Stone About to Swing			
Sheckard-Schulte	17.00	12.50	6.00
67 Sullivan Puts Up High			
a) Evans-Huggins	18.00	13.50	6.00
b) Groom-Gray	16.00	12.50	5.00
68 Sweeney Gets Stahl			
a) Ford-Vaughn	16.00	12.50	5.00
b) Sweeney-Ford	16.00	12.50	5.00
69 Tenney Lands Safely			
Raymond-Latham	17.00	12.50	6.00
70 The Athletic Infield			
a) Barry-Baker	18.00	13.50	6.00
b) Brown-Graham	16.00	12.50	5.00
c) Hauser-Konetchy	16.00	12.50	5.00
d) Krause-Thomas	16.00	12.50	5.00
71 The Pinch Hitter			
Hoblitzel-Egan	16.00	12.50	5.00
72 The Scissors Slide			
Birmingham-Turner	17.00	12.50	6.00
73 Tom Jones at Bat			
a) Fromme-McLean	16.00	12.50	5.00
b) Gaspar-McLean	16.00	12.50	5.00
74 Too Late for Devlin			
a) Ames-Meyers	16.00	12.50	5.00
b) Crandall-Meyers	16.00	12.50	5.00
c) Devlin-Mathewson	60.00	45.00	20.00
d) Devlin-Mathewson	25.00	18.50	8.75
e) Marquard-Meyers	17.00	12.50	6.00
f) Wiltse-Meyers	16.00	12.50	5.00
75 Ty Cobb Steals Third			
a) Jennings-Cobb	65.00	48.00	22.00
b) Moriarty-Cobb	65.00	48.00	22.00
c) Stovall-Austin	50.00	38.00	17.00
76 Wheat Strikes Out			
Dahlen-Wheat	19.00	14.50	6.50

1909 T204 RAMLY (121)

2″ X 2 1/2″

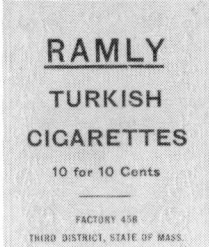

RAMLY

TURKISH

CIGARETTES

10 for 10 Cents

FACTORY 458
THIRD DISTRICT, STATE OF MASS.

The T204 Ramly set contains 121 unnumbered cards. This set is one of the most distinguished sets ever produced containing ornate gold borders around an oval portrait of the player. Two different players named Ball appear in the set and are noted in the checklist.

	MINT	VG-E	F-G
COMPLETE SET	8200.00	6500.00	2700.00
COMMON PLAYER	60.00	45.00	20.00

	MINT	VG-E	F-G			MINT	VG-E	F-G
1 Alperman, Whitey	60.00	45.00	20.00	62 Kahoe		60.00	45.00	20.00
2 Anderson	60.00	45.00	20.00	63 Karger, Ed		60.00	45.00	20.00
3 Archer, Jimmy	60.00	45.00	20.00	64 Keeler, Willie		175.00	135.00	60.00
4 Arrelanes	60.00	45.00	20.00	65 Kenotchey(sic)		60.00	45.00	20.00
5 Ball* Jim (BostonNL)	60.00	45.00	20.00	66 Kleiman		60.00	45.00	20.00
6 Ball* Neal (NYAL)	60.00	45.00	20.00	67 Knight, John		60.00	45.00	20.00
7 Bancroft, Dave	90.00	70.00	30.00	68 Lindeman, Vive		60.00	45.00	20.00
8 Bates, Johnny	60.00	45.00	20.00	69 Loebert(sic)		60.00	45.00	20.00
9 Beebe	60.00	45.00	20.00	70 Lord		60.00	45.00	20.00
10 Bell, George	60.00	45.00	20.00	71 Lumley, Harry		60.00	45.00	20.00
11 Bender, Chief	100.00	70.00	30.00	72 Lush, Ernie		60.00	45.00	20.00
12 Blair	60.00	45.00	20.00	73 Manning, Rube		60.00	45.00	20.00
13 Blankenship	60.00	45.00	20.00	74 McAleer		60.00	45.00	20.00
14 Boweman	60.00	45.00	20.00	75 McConnell, Amby		60.00	45.00	20.00
15 Bransfield, Kitty	60.00	45.00	20.00	76 McCormick, Moose		60.00	45.00	20.00
16 Bresnahan, Roger	100.00	70.00	30.00	77 McIntyre		60.00	45.00	20.00
17 Bridwell, Al	60.00	45.00	20.00	78 McLean, Larry		60.00	45.00	20.00
18 Brown, Mordecai	100.00	70.00	30.00	79 Merkle, Fred		60.00	45.00	20.00
19 Burchell	60.00	45.00	20.00	80 Milan, Clyde		60.00	45.00	20.00
20 Burkett, Jesse	120.00	85.00	40.00	81 Mitchell		60.00	45.00	20.00
21 Byrnes	60.00	45.00	20.00	82 Moran		60.00	45.00	20.00
22 Carrigan, Bill	60.00	45.00	20.00	83 Morgan		60.00	45.00	20.00
23 Chance, Frank	120.00	85.00	40.00	84 Murnane		60.00	45.00	20.00
24 Chech	60.00	45.00	20.00	85 Murphy, Danny		60.00	45.00	20.00
25 Cicotte, Eddie	60.00	45.00	20.00	86 Murray, Red		60.00	45.00	20.00
26 Clymer, Otis	60.00	45.00	20.00	87 Newton		60.00	45.00	20.00
27 Coakley	60.00	45.00	20.00	88 Nichols(sic)		60.00	45.00	20.00
28 Collins	60.00	45.00	20.00	89 Niles, Harry		60.00	45.00	20.00
29 Ed Collins	100.00	70.00	30.00	90 O'Hara, Bill		60.00	45.00	20.00
30 Conroy, Wid	60.00	45.00	20.00	91 O'Leary, Charley		60.00	45.00	20.00
31 Coombs, Jack	60.00	45.00	20.00	92 Paskert, Dode		60.00	45.00	20.00
32 Crandall, Doc	60.00	45.00	20.00	93 Pelty, Barney		60.00	45.00	20.00
33 Criger, Lou	60.00	45.00	20.00	94 Pfeister, Jack		60.00	45.00	20.00
34 Davis	60.00	45.00	20.00	95 Plank, Eddie		120.00	85.00	40.00
35 Devlin, Art	60.00	45.00	20.00	96 Powell, Jack		60.00	45.00	20.00
36 Dineen, Bill	60.00	45.00	20.00	97 Raymond, Bugs		60.00	45.00	20.00
37 Donahue	60.00	45.00	20.00	98 Reilly		60.00	45.00	20.00
38 Donlin, Mike	60.00	45.00	20.00	99 Ritchie		60.00	45.00	20.00
39 Donovan, Wild Bill	60.00	45.00	20.00	100 Rucker, Nap		60.00	45.00	20.00
40 Dorner	60.00	45.00	20.00	101 Ruelbach(sic)		60.00	45.00	20.00
41 Dunn, Joe	60.00	45.00	20.00	102 Sallee, Slim		60.00	45.00	20.00
42 Elberfield(sic)	60.00	45.00	20.00	103 Schaefer, Germany		60.00	45.00	20.00
43 Evers, Johnny	110.00	80.00	35.00	104 Schekard(sic)		60.00	45.00	20.00
44 Ewing	60.00	45.00	20.00	105 Schlei, Admiral		60.00	45.00	20.00
45 Ferguson, George	60.00	45.00	20.00	106 Schulte, Frank		60.00	45.00	20.00
46 Ferris, Hobe	60.00	45.00	20.00	107 Sebring		60.00	45.00	20.00
47 Freeman	60.00	45.00	20.00	108 Shipke, Bill		60.00	45.00	20.00
48 Fromme, Art	60.00	45.00	20.00	109 Smith		60.00	45.00	20.00
49 Ganley, Bob	60.00	45.00	20.00	110 Spencer, Tubby		60.00	45.00	20.00
50 Gessler	60.00	45.00	20.00	111 Stahl, Jake		60.00	45.00	20.00
51 Graham	60.00	45.00	20.00	112 Steinfeldt, Harry		60.00	45.00	20.00
52 Griffith, Clark	100.00	70.00	30.00	113 Stephens, Jim		60.00	45.00	20.00
53 Hartzell	60.00	45.00	20.00	114 Street, Gabby		60.00	45.00	20.00
54 Hemphill, Charlie	60.00	45.00	20.00	115 Sweeney		60.00	45.00	20.00
55 Hoblitzel, Dick	60.00	45.00	20.00	116 Tenney, Fred		60.00	45.00	20.00
56 Howard	60.00	45.00	20.00	117 Thomas, Ira		60.00	45.00	20.00
57 Howell, Harry	60.00	45.00	20.00	118 Tinker, Joe		110.00	80.00	35.00
58 Huggins, Miller	120.00	85.00	40.00	119 Unglaub, Bob		60.00	45.00	20.00
59 Hummel, John	60.00	45.00	20.00	120 Wagner, Heine		60.00	45.00	20.00
60 Johnson, Walter	225.00	160.00	70.00	121 Wallace, Bobby		90.00	70.00	30.00
61 Jones	60.00	45.00	20.00					

T—205 GOLD BORDER (208)   1 1/2" X 2 1/2"

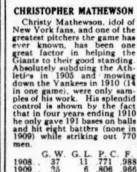

The T-205 set, also known as the "Gold Border" set, was issued with American Beauty, Broadleaf, Cyde, Drum, Hassan, Honest Long Cut, Piedmont, Polar Bear, Sovereign and Sweet Caperal Cigarettes in 1911. There are 12 scarce minor league players in the set.

	MINT	VG-E	F-G
COMPLETE SET	1500.00	1100.00	400.00
COMMON PLAYERS	5.00	3.50	1.50
1 Frank Baker	15.00	11.00	5.00
2 John J. Barry	5.00	3.50	1.50
3 Charles A. Bender	15.00	11.00	5.00
4 Edward T. Collins (mouth closed)	15.00	11.00	5.00
5 Edward T. Collins (mouth opened)	45.00	34.00	15.00
6 James H. Dygert	5.00	3.50	1.50
7 Frederick T. Hartsel	5.00	3.50	1.50
8 Harry Krause	5.00	3.50	1.50
9 Pat'k J. Livingston	5.00	3.50	1.50
10 Briscoe Lord	5.00	3.50	1.50
11 Daniel Murphy	5.00	3.50	1.50
12 Reuben N. Oldring	5.00	3.50	1.50
13 Ira Thomas	5.00	3.50	1.50
14 William Bailey	5.00	3.50	1.50
15 Daniel J. Hoffman	5.00	3.50	1.50
16 Frank LaPorte	5.00	3.50	1.50
17 B. Pelty	5.00	3.50	1.50
18 George Stone	5.00	3.50	1.50
19 Roderick J. Wallace (with cap)	14.00	10.50	4.75
20 Roderick J. Wallace (without cap)	40.00	30.00	13.00
21 Roger Bresnahan (mouth closed)	14.00	10.50	4.75
22 Roger Bresnahan (mouth open)	40.00	30.00	13.00
23 Frank J. Corridon	5.00	3.50	1.50
24 Louis Evans	5.00	3.50	'1.50
25 Robert Harmon (both ears)	6.00	4.50	2.00
26 Robert Harmon (left ear only)	25.00	18.50	8.75
27 Arnold J. Hauser	5.00	3.50	1.50
28 Miller Huggins	16.00	12.00	5.50
29 Edward Konetchy	5.00	3.50	1.50
30 John Lush	5.00	3.50	1.50
31 "Rebel" Oakes	5.00	3.50	1.50
32 Edward Phelps	5.00	3.50	1.50
33 James P. Archer	5.00	3.50	1.50
34 Mordecai Brown	15.00	11.00	5.00
35 Frank L. Chance	20.00	15.00	6.50
36 John J. Evers	16.00	12.00	5.50
37 William A. Foxen	5.00	3.50	1.50
38 George F. Graham	35.00	26.00	12.00
39 John Kling	5.00	3.50	1.50
40 Floyd M. Kroh	5.00	3.50	1.50
41 Harry McIntire	5.00	3.50	1.50
42 Thomas J. Needham	5.00	3.50	1.50
43 Orval Overall	5.00	3.50	1.50
44 John A. Pfiester	5.00	3.50	1.50
45 Edward M. Reulbach	5.00	3.50	1.50
46 Lewis Richie	5.00	3.50	1.50
47 Frank M. Schulte	5.00	3.50	1.50
48 David Shean (Cubs)	35.00	26.00	12.00
49 James T. Sheckard	5.00	3.50	1.50
50 Harry Steinfeldt	5.00	3.50	1.50
51 Joseph B. Tinker	16.00	12.00	5.50
52 Leon Ames	5.00	3.50	1.50
53 Beals Becker	5.00	3.50	1.50
54 Albert Bridwell	5.00	3.50	1.50
55 Otis Crandall	5.00	3.50	1.50
56 Arthur Devlin	5.00	3.50	1.50
57 Joshua Devore	5.00	3.50	1.50
58 W. R. Dickson	5.00	3.50	1.50
59 Lawrence Doyle	5.00	3.50	1.50
60 Arthur Fletcher	5.00	3.50	1.50
61 W. A. Latham	5.00	3.50	1.50

	MINT	VG-E	F-G
62 Richard Marquard	14.00	10.50	4.75
63 Christopher Mathewson	30.00	22.50	10.50
64 John J. McGraw	25.00	18.50	8.75
65 Fred Merkle	5.00	3.50	1.50
66 John T. Meyers	5.00	3.50	1.50
67 John J. Murray	5.00	3.50	1.50
68 Arthur L. Raymond	25.00	18.50	8.75
69 George H. Schlei	5.00	3.50	1.50
70 Frederick C. Snodgrass	5.00	3.50	1.50
71 George Wiltse (both ears)	6.00	4.50	2.00
72 George Wiltse (right ear only)	25.00	18.50	8.75
73 Neal Ball	5.00	3.50	1.50
74 Joseph Birmingham	5.00	3.50	1.50
75 A. Joss	40.00	30.00	13.00
76 George T. Stovall	5.00	3.50	1.50
77 Terence Turner	25.00	18.50	8.75
78 Denton T. Young	30.00	22.50	10.50
79 John W. Bates	5.00	3.50	1.50
80 Wm. E. Bransfield	5.00	3.50	1.50
81 Charles S. Dooin	5.00	3.50	1.50
82 Michael Doolan	5.00	3.50	1.50
83 Robert Ewing	5.00	3.50	1.50
84 Fred Jacklitsch	5.00	3.50	1.50
85 John Lobert	5.00	3.50	1.50
86 Sherwood R. Magee	5.00	3.50	1.50
87 Patrick J. Moran	5.00	3.50	1.50
88 George Paskert	5.00	3.50	1.50
89 John A. Rowan	25.00	18.50	8.75
90 John Titus	5.00	3.50	1.50
91 Robert Byrne	5.00	3.50	1.50
92 Howard Camnitz	5.00	3.50	1.50
93 Fred Clarke	14.00	10.50	4.75
94 John Flynn	5.00	3.50	1.50
95 George Gibson	5.00	3.50	1.50
96 Thomas W. Leach	5.00	3.50	1.50
97 Sam Leever	5.00	3.50	1.50
98 Albert P. Leifield	5.00	3.50	1.50
99 Nicholas Maddox	5.00	3.50	1.50
100 John D. Miller	5.00	3.50	1.50
101 Charles Phillippe	5.00	3.50	1.50
102 Kirb White	25.00	18.50	8.75
103 J. Owen Wilson	5.00	3.50	1.50
104 Robert H. Bescher	5.00	3.50	1.50
105 Thomas W. Downey	5.00	3.50	1.50
106 Richard J. Egan	5.00	3.50	1.50
107 Arthur Fromme	5.00	3.50	1.50
108 Harry L. Gaspar	5.00	3.50	1.50
109 Edward L. Grant	25.00	18.50	8.75
110 Clark Griffith	14.00	10.50	4.75
111 Richard Hoblitzell	5.00	3.50	1.50
112 John B. McLean	5.00	3.50	1.50
113 Michael Mitchell	5.00	3.50	1.50
114 George Suggs	5.00	3.50	1.50
115 William Carrigan	5.00	3.50	1.50
116 Edward V. Cicotte	5.00	3.50	1.50
117 Clyde Engle	5.00	3.50	1.50
118 Edward Karger	15.00	11.00	5.00
119 John Kleinow	5.00	3.50	1.50
120 Tris Speaker	30.00	22.50	10.50
121 Jacob G. Stahl	5.00	3.50	1.50
122 Charles Wagner	5.00	3.50	1.50
123 Edw'd J. Abbaticchio	5.00	3.50	1.50
124 Frederick T. Beck	5.00	3.50	1.50
125 G. C. Ferguson	5.00	3.50	1.50
126 Wilbur Good	5.00	3.50	1.50
127 George F. Graham	6.00	4.50	2.00
128 Charles L. Herzog	5.00	3.50	1.50
129 A. A. Mattern	5.00	3.50	1.50
130 Bayard H. Sharpe	5.00	3.50	1.50
131 David Shean (Boston)	6.00	4.50	2.00

		MINT	VG-E	F-G
32	Norman Elberfeld	5.00	3.50	1.50
33	Gray	5.00	3.50	1.50
34	Robert Groom	5.00	3.50	1.50
35	Walter Johnson	50.00	38.00	17.00
36	George F. McBride	5.00	3.50	1.50
37	J. Clyde Milan	5.00	3.50	1.50
38	Herman Schaefer	5.00	3.50	1.50
39	Charles E. Street	5.00	3.50	1.50
40	Edward B. Barger (full B)	4.00	3.00	1.40
41	Edward B. Barger (part B)	25.00	18.50	8.75
42	George G. Bell	5.00	3.50	1.50
43	William Bergen	5.00	3.50	1.50
44	William Dahlen	5.00	3.50	1.50
45	Jacob Daubert	5.00	3.50	1.50
46	John E. Hummell	5.00	3.50	1.50
47	Edgar Lennox	5.00	3.50	1.50
48	Pryor McElveen	5.00	3.50	1.50
49	G. N. Rucker	5.00	3.50	1.50
50	W. D. Scanlan	6.00	4.50	2.00
51	Tony Smith	5.00	3.50	1.50
52	Zach D. Wheat	15.00	11.00	5.00
53	Irvin N. Wilhelm	5.00	3.50	1.50
54	Tyrus Raymond Cobb	125.00	90.00	40.00
55	James Delahanty	5.00	3.50	1.50
56	Hugh Jennings	15.00	11.00	5.00
57	David Jones	5.00	3.50	1.50
58	Thomas Jones	5.00	3.50	1.50
59	Edward Killian	5.00	3.50	1.50
60	George Moriarity	5.00	3.50	1.50
61	George J. Mullin	5.00	3.50	1.50
62	Charles O'Leary	5.00	3.50	1.50
63	Charles Schmidt	5.00	3.50	1.50
64	George Simmons	5.00	3.50	1.50
65	Oscar Stanage	5.00	3.50	1.50
66	Edgar Summers	5.00	3.50	1.50
67	Edgar Willett	5.00	3.50	1.50
68	Russell A. Blackburne	5.00	3.50	1.50
69	J. Donohue	15.00	11.00	5.00
70	Pat'k H. Dougherty (white stocking)	6.00	4.50	2.00
70a	Pat'k H. Dougherty (red stocking)	25.00	18.50	8.75
71	Hugh Duffy	20.00	15.00	6.50
72	Frank Lang	5.00	3.50	1.50

		MINT	VG-E	F-G
173	Harry D. Lord	5.00	3.50	1.50
174	Ambrose McConnell	5.00	3.50	1.50
175	Matthew McIntyre	5.00	3.50	1.50
176	Frederick Olmstead	5.00	3.50	1.50
177	F. Parent	5.00	3.50	1.50
178	Fred Payne	5.00	3.50	1.50
179	James Scott	5.00	3.50	1.50
180	Lee Ford Tannehill	5.00	3.50	1.50
181	Edward Walsh	40.00	30.00	13.00
182	G. H. White	5.00	3.50	1.50
183	James Austin	5.00	3.50	1.50
184	Harold W. Chase (Chase only)	60.00	45.00	20.00
185	Harold W. Chase (Hal Chase)	4.00	3.00	1.40
186	Louis Criger	5.00	3.50	1.50
187	Ray Fisher	10.00	7.00	3.00
188	Russell Ford (dark cap)	4.00	3.00	1.40
189	Russell Ford (light cap)	25.00	18.50	8.75
190	Earl Gardner	5.00	3.50	1.50
191	Charles Hemphill	5.00	3.50	1.50
192	Jack Knight	5.00	3.50	1.50
193	John Quinn	5.00	3.50	1.50
194	Edward Sweeney	5.00	3.50	1.50
195	James Vaughn	25.00	18.50	8.75
196	Harry Wolter	5.00	3.50	1.50
197	Doctor Merle T. Adkins Baltimore	18.00	13.50	6.00
198	John Dunn-Baltimore	20.00	15.00	6.50
199	George Merritt-Buffalo	18.00	13.50	6.00
200	Charles Hanford-Jersey City	18.00	13.50	6.00
201	Forrest D. Cady-Newark	18.00	13.50	6.00
202	James Frick-Newark	18.00	13.50	6.00
203	Wyatt Lee-Newark	18.00	13.50	6.00
204	Lewis McAllister-Newark	18.00	13.50	6.00
205	John Nee-Newark	18.00	13.50	6.00
206	James Collins-Providence	40.00	30.00	13.00
207	James Phelan-Providence	18.00	13.50	6.00
208	Henry Batch-Rochester	18.00	13.50	6.00

T-206 WHITE BORDER (524) 1 1/2" X 2 1/2"

The T-206 set was the most popular of all the tobacco issues. The set was issued from 1909-1911 with six-teen different brands of cigarettes; American Beauty, Broadleaf, Cycle, Carolina Brights, Drum, El Principe de Gales, Hindu, Lenox, Old Mill, Piedmont, Polar Bear, Sovereign, Sweet Caporal, Tolstoi, Ty Cobb, and Uzit. The Ty Cobb brand back is scarce. The minor league cards are more difficult to obtain than the cards of the major leaguers, with the Southern League player cards being the most difficult. The set price does not include Wagner, Plank or Magie.

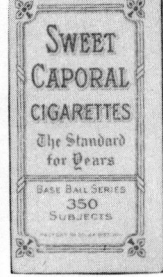
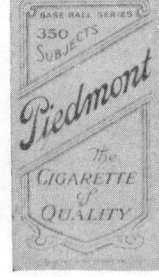
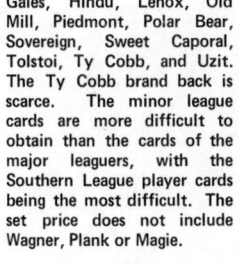

	MINT	VG-E	F-G
COMPLETE SET	3500.00	2500.00	1000.00
MAJOR LEAGUERS	4.50	3.00	1.50
MINOR LEAGUERS	5.50	4.00	1.50
SOUTHERN LEAGUERS	14.00	10.00	4.00
Abbaticchio-Pitt., Batting follow thru	4.50	3.00	1.50
Abbaticchio-Pitt., Batting waiting pitch	4.50	3.00	1.50
Abstein-Pitt.	4.50	3.00	1.50
Alperman-Brooklyn	4.50	3.00	1.50
Ames-Giants, Portrait	4.50	3.00	1.50
Ames-Giants, Hands over head	4.50	3.00	1.50
Ames-Giants, Hands in front of chest	4.50	3.00	1.50
Arellanes-Boston Am.	4.50	3.00	1.50
Atz-Chicago Am.	4.50	3.00	1.50
Baker-Phila. Am.	16.00	12.00	5.50
Ball-Cleveland	4.50	3.00	1.50
Ball-N. Y. Am.	4.50	3.00	1.50
Barbeau-St. Louis Nat.	4.50	3.00	1.50
Barry-Phila. Am.	4.50	3.00	1.50
Bates-Boston Nat.	4.50	3.00	1.50
Beaumont-Boston Nat.	4.50	3.00	1.50

		MINT	VG-E	F-G
17	Beck-Boston Nat.	4.50	3.00	1.50
18	Becker-Boston Nat.	4.50	3.00	1.50
19	Bell-Brooklyn (pitching) following thru	4.50	3.00	1.50
20	Bell-Brooklyn, Hands over head	4.50	3.00	1.50
21	Bender-Phila Am., Portrait	16.00	12.00	5.50
22	Bender-Phila. Am., (pitching) shows complete glove	16.00	12.00	5.50
23	Bender-Phila. Am., (pitching) shows part of glove	16.00	12.00	5.50
24	Bergen-Brooklyn, Catching	4.50	3.00	1.50
25	Bergen-Brooklyn, Batting	4.50	3.00	1.50
26	Berger, Cleveland	4.50	3.00	1.50
27	Bescher-Cinn., catching fly ball	4.50	3.00	1.50
28	Bescher-Cinn., Portrait	4.50	3.00	1.50
29	Birmingham-Cleveland	4.50	3.00	1.50
30	Bliss-St. Louis Nat.	4.50	3.00	1.50

	MINT	VG-E	F-G
31 Bowerman-Bost. Nat.	4.50	3.00	1.50
32 Bradley-Cleveland, Portrait	4.50	3.00	1.50
33 Bradley-Cleveland, Batting	4.50	3.00	1.50
34 Bransfield-Phila. Nat	4.50	3.00	1.50
35 Bresnahan-St. Louis Nat., Portrait	15.00	11.00	5.00
36 Bresnahan-St. Louis Nat., Batting	15.00	11.00	5.00
37 Bridwell-N. Y. Nat., Portrait	4.50	3.00	1.50
38 Bridwell-N.Y. Nat., Wearing sweater	4.50	3.00	1.50
39 G. Brown-Chicago Nat.	4.50	3.00	1.50
40 G. Brown-Washington	75.00	55.00	24.00
41 M. Brown-Chicago Nat Portrait	16.00	12.00	5.50
42 M. Brown-Chicago Nat Chicago letters down front of shirt	16.00	12.00	5.50
43 M. Brown-Chicago Nat Cubs lettered on shirt	16.00	12.00	5.50
44 Burch-Brooklyn, Fielding	4.50	3.00	1.50
45 Burch-Brooklyn, Batting	4.50	3.00	1.50
46 Burns-Chicago Am.	4.50	3.00	1.50
47 Bush-Detroit	4.50	3.00	1.50
48 Byrne-St. Louis Nat.	4.50	3.00	1.50
49 Camnitz-Pitt., Arms folded over chest	4.50	3.00	1.50
50 Camnitz-Pitt., Hands over head	4.50	3.00	1.50
51 Camnitz-Pitt., Throwing	4.50	3.00	1.50
52 Campbell, Cinn.	4.50	3.00	1.50
53 Carrigan-Boston Am.	4.50	3.00	1.50
54 Chance-Chicago Nat. Cubs lettered across chest	20.00	15.00	6.50
55 Chance-Chicago Nat. Chicago Cubs lettered on shirt	20.00	15.00	6.50
56 Chance-Chicago Nat. Batting	20.00	15.00	6.50
57 Charles-St. Louis Nat	4.50	3.00	1.50
58 Chase-N. Y. Am., Portrait, blue background	8.00	6.00	2.50
59 Chase-N. Y. Am., Portrait, pink background	8.00	6.00	2.50
60 Chase-N. Y. Am., Holding cap	8.00	6.00	2.50
61 Chase N. Y. Am., Throwing his blue cap	8.00	6.00	2.50
62 Chase-N. Y. Am., Fielding with white cap	16.00	12.00	5.50
63 Chesbro-N. Y. Am.	16.00	12.00	5.50
64 Cicotte-Boston Am.	4.50	3.00	1.50
65 Clarke-Pitt., Portrait	15.00	11.00	5.00
66 F. Clarke-Pitt., Bat in hands	15.00	11.00	5.00
67 J. J. Clarke-Cleve Fielding	4.50	3.00	1.50
68 Cobb-Detroit, Portrait red background	90.00	70.00	30.00
69 Cobb-Detroit, Portrait green background	150.00	110.00	50.00
70 Cobb-Detroit, Bat on shoulder	120.00	85.00	40.00
71 Cobb-Detroit, Bat away from shoulder	120.00	85.00	40.00
72 Collins-Phila. Am.	17.00	12.50	6.00
73 Conroy-Wash., Fielding	4.50	3.00	1.50
74 Conroy-Wash., Bat on shoulder	4.50	3.00	1.50
75 Covaleski-Phil. Nat.	6.00	4.50	2.00
76 Crandall-N. Y. Nat., Portrait without cap	4.50	3.00	1.50
77 Crandall-N. Y. Nat., Portrait with cap	4.50	3.00	1.50
78 Crawford-Detroit, Batting	15.00	11.00	5.00

	MINT	VG-E	F-G
79 Crawford-Detroit, Throwing	15.00	11.00	5.00
80 Cree-N. Y. Am.	4.50	3.00	1.50
81 Criger-St. Louis Am.	4.50	3.00	1.50
82 Criss-St. Louis Am.	4.50	3.00	1.50
83 Dahlen-Brooklyn	16.00	12.00	5.50
84 Dahlen-Bost. Nat.	4.50	3.00	1.50
85 Davis-Phila. Am.	4.50	3.00	1.50
86 G. Davis-Chicago Am.	4.50	3.00	1.50
87 H. Davis-Phila. Am.	4.50	3.00	1.50
88 Delehanty-Washington	4.50	3.00	1.50
89 Demmitt-St. Louis Am	175.00	125.00	60.00
90 Demmitt-N. Y. Am.	4.50	3.00	1.50
91 Devlin-N. Y. Nat.	4.50	3.00	1.50
92 Devore-N. Y. Nat.	4.50	3.00	1.50
93 Dineen-St. Louis Am.	4.50	3.00	1.50
94 Donlin-N. Y. Nat., Fielding	4.50	3.00	1.50
95 Donlin-N. Y. Nat., Sitting with hands on knees	4.50	3.00	1.50
96 Donlin-N. Y. Nat., Batting	4.50	3.00	1.50
97 Donohue-Chicago Am.	4.50	3.00	1.50
98 Donovan-Detroit, Portrait	4.50	3.00	1.50
99 Donovan-Detroit, Throwing	4.50	3.00	1.50
100 Doolin-Phila. Nat.	4.50	3.00	1.50
101 Doolan-Phila. Nat., Fielding	4.50	3.00	1.50
102 Doolan-Phila. Nat. Batting	4.50	3.00	1.50
103 Doolin-Phila. Nat.	4.50	3.00	1.50
104 Dougherty-Chicago Am., Portrait	4.50	3.00	1.50
105 Dougherty-Chicago Am., Fielding	4.50	3.00	1.50
106 Downey-Cinn., Bat	4.50	3.00	1.50
107 Downey-Cinn., Field	4.50	3.00	1.50
108 Doyle-N. Y. Am.	8.00	6.00	2.50
109 Doyle-N. Y. Nat., Portrait	4.50	3.00	1.50
110 Doyle-N. Y. Nat., (pitching) following thru	4.50	3.00	1.50
111 Doyle-N. Y. Nat., Bat on shoulders	4.50	3.00	1.50
112 Dubuc-Cinn.	4.50	3.00	1.50
113 Duffy-Chicago Am.	16.00	12.00	5.50
114 Dunn-Brooklyn	4.50	3.00	1.50
115 Durham-N. Y. Nat.	4.50	3.00	1.50
116 Dygert-Phila. Am.	4.50	3.00	1.50
117 Easterly-Cleveland	4.50	3.00	1.50
118 Egan-Cinn.	4.50	3.00	1.50
119 Elberfeld-Washington Fielding	4.50	3.00	1.50
120 Elberfeld-Wash Portrait	125.00	90.00	40.00
121 Elberfeld-N. Y. Am., Portrait	4.50	3.00	1.50
122 Engle-N. Y. Am.	4.50	3.00	1.50
123 Evans-St. Louis Nat.	4.50	3.00	1.50
124 Evers-Chicago Nat., Portrait	18.00	13.50	6.00
125 Evers-Chicago Nat., Cubs lettered across chest	18.00	13.50	6.00
126 Evers-Chicago Nat., Chicago lettered down shirt	18.00	13.50	6.00
127 Ewing-Cinn.	4.50	3.00	1.50
128 Ferguson-Bost. Nat.	4.50	3.00	1.50
129 Ferris-St. Louis Am.	4.50	3.00	1.50
130 Fiene-Chicago Am., Portrait	4.50	3.00	1.50
131 Fiene-Chicago Am., Throwing	4.50	3.00	1.50
132 Fletcher-N. Y. Nat.	4.50	3.00	1.50
133 Flick-Cleveland	15.00	11.00	5.00
134 Ford-N. Y. Am.	4.50	3.00	1.50
135 Frill-N. Y. Am.	4.50	3.00	1.50
136 Fromme-Cinn.	4.50	3.00	1.50
137 Gandil-Chicago Am.	4.50	3.00	1.50
138 Ganley-Washington	4.50	3.00	1.50
139 Gasper-Cinn.	4.50	3.00	1.50
140 Geyer-St. Louis Nat.	4.50	3.00	1.50
141 Gibson-Pitt.	4.50	3.00	1.50
142 Gilbert-St. Louis Nat.	4.50	3.00	1.50
143 Goode-Cleveland	4.50	3.00	1.50
144 Graham-Bost. Nat.	4.50	3.00	1.50
145 Graham-St. Louis Am	4.50	3.00	1.50
146 Gray-Washington	4.50	3.00	1.50

		MINT	VG-E	F-G
147	Griffith-Cinn., Portrait	15.00	11.00	5.00
148	Griffith-Cinn., Batting	15.00	11.00	5.00
149	Groom-Washington	4.50	3.00	1.50
150	Hahn-Chicago Am.	4.50	3.00	1.50
151	Hartsel-Phila. Am.	4.50	3.00	1.50
152	Hemphill-N. Y. Am.	4.50	3.00	1.50
153	Herzog-N. Y. Nat	4.50	3.00	1.50
154	Herzog-Bost. Nat.	4.50	3.00	1.50
155	Hinchman-Cleveland	4.50	3.00	1.50
156	Hoblitzell-Cinn.	4.50	3.00	1.50
157	Hoffman-St. Louis Am.	4.50	3.00	1.50
158	Hofman - Chicago Nat	4.50	3.00	1.50
159	Howard-Chicago Nat.	4.50	3.00	1.50
160	Howell-St. Louis Am. Portrait	4.50	3.00	1.50
161	Howell-St. Louis Am. Left hand on hips	4.50	3.00	1.50
162	Huggins-Cinn., Portrait	15.00	11.00	5.00
163	Huggins-Cinn., Hands up to mouth	15.00	11.00	5.00
164	Hulswitt-St. Louis Nat.	4.50	3.00	1.50
165	Hummel-Brooklyn	4.50	3.00	1.50
166	Hunter-Brooklyn	4.50	3.00	1.50
167	Isbell-Chicago Am.	4.50	3.00	1.50
168	Jacklitsch-Phila. Nat.	4.50	3.00	1.50
169	Jennings-Detroit, Portrait	15.00	11.00	5.00
170	Jennings-Detroit, Yelling	15.00	11.00	5.00
171	Jennings-Detroit, Dancing for joy	15.00	11.00	5.00
172	Johnson-Washington, Portrait	30.00	22.50	10.50
173	Johnson-Washington, Ready to pitch	30.00	22.50	10.50
174	Jones-St. Louis Am.	4.50	3.00	1.50
175	Jones-Detroit	4.50	3.00	1.50
176	F. Jones-Chicago Am., Portrait	4.50	3.00	1.50
177	F. Jones-Chicago Am., Hands on hips	4.50	3.00	1.50
178	Jordan-Brooklyn, Portrait	4.50	3.00	1.50
179	Jordan-Brooklyn, Batting	4.50	3.00	1.50
180	Joss-Cleveland, Portrait	18.00	13.50	6.00
181	Joss-Cleveland, Ready to pitch	18.00	13.50	6.00
182	Karger-Cinn.	4.50	3.00	1.50
183	Keeler-N. Y. Am., Portrait	18.00	13.50	6.00
184	Keeler-N. Y. Am., Batting	18.00	13.50	6.00
185	Killian-Detroit, Portrait	4.50	3.00	1.50
186	Killian-Detroit, Pitching	4.50	3.00	1.50
187	Kleinow-N. Y. Am., Batting	4.50	3.00	1.50
188	Kleinow-N. Y. Am., Catching with mask on	4.50	3.00	1.50
189	Kleinow-Bost. Am., Catching with mask on	35.00	26.00	12.00
190	Kling-Chicago Nat.	4.50	3.00	1.50
191	Knabe-Phila. Nat.	4.50	3.00	1.50
192	Knight-N. Y. Am., Portrait	4.50	3.00	1.50
193	Knight-N. Y. Am., Batting	4.50	3.00	1.50
194	Konetchy-St. Louis Nat., Fielding ground ball	4.50	3.00	1.50
195	Konetchy-St. Louis Nat., Reaching for high throw	4.50	3.00	1.50
196	Krause-Phila. Am., Portrait	4.50	3.00	1.50
197	Krause-Phila. Am., Pitching	4.50	3.00	1.50
198	Kroh-Chicago Nat.	4.50	3.00	1.50
199	Lajoie-Cleveland, Portrait	25.00	18.50	8.75
200	Lajoie-Cleveland, Batting	25.00	18.50	8.75
201	Lajoie-Cleveland, Throwing	25.00	18.50	8.75
202	Lake-N. Y. Am.	4.50	3.00	1.50
203	Lake-St. Louis Am., Hands over head	4.50	3.00	1.50
204	Lake-St. Louis Am., Throwing	4.50	3.00	1.50
205	La Porte-N. Y. Am.	4.50	3.00	1.50
206	Latham-N. Y. Nat.	4.50	3.00	1.50
207	Leach-Pitt., Portrait	4.50	3.00	1.50
208	Leach-Pitt., In fielding position	4.50	3.00	1.50
209	Leifield-Pitt., Batting	4.50	3.00	1.50
210	Leifield-Pitt., Hands behind head	4.50	3.00	1.50
211	Lennox-Brooklyn	4.50	3.00	1.50
212	Liebhardt-Cleveland	4.50	3.00	1.50
213	Lindaman-Boston Nat.	4.50	3.00	1.50
214	Livingstone-Phila. Am.	4.50	3.00	1.50
215	Lobert-Cinn.	4.50	3.00	1.50
216	Lord-Bost. Am.	4.50	3.00	1.50
217	Lumley-Brooklyn	4.50	3.00	1.50
218	Lundgren-Chicago Nat	40.00	30.00	13.00
219	Maddox-Pitt.	4.50	3.00	1.50
220	Magee-Phila. Nat., Portrait	4.50	3.00	1.50
221	Magee-Phila. Nat., Batting	4.50	3.00	1.50
222	*Magie-Phila. Nat., Portrait name misspelled*	1500.00	1100.00	500.00
223	Manning-N. Y. Am., Batting	4.50	3.00	1.50
224	Manning-N. Y. Am., Hands over head	4.50	3.00	1.50
225	Marquard-N. Y. Nat. Portrait	15.00	11.00	5.00
226	Marquard-N. Y. Nat. (pitching) following thru	15.00	11.00	5.00
227	Marquard-N. Y. Nat. Standing	15.00	11.00	4.00
228	Marshall-Brooklyn	4.50	3.00	1.50
229	Mathewson-N. Y. Nat. Portrait	28.00	21.00	10.00
230	Mathewson-N. Y. Nat. Pitching position white cap	35.00	26.00	12.00
231	Mathewson-N. Y. Nat. Pitching position dark cap	28.00	21.00	10.00
232	Mattern-Bost. Nat.	4.50	3.00	1.50
233	McAleese-St. Louis Am.	4.50	3.00	1.50
234	McBride-Washington	4.50	3.00	1.50
235	McCormick-N. Y. Nat.	4.50	3.00	1.50
236	McElveen-Brooklyn	4.50	3.00	1.50
237	McGraw-N. Y. Nat., Portrait without cap	20.00	15.00	6.50
238	McGraw-N. Y. Nat., Portrait with cap	20.00	15.00	6.50
239	McGraw-N. Y. Nat., One finger pointed over head	20.00	15.00	6.50
240	McGraw-N. Y. Nat., Standing glove hand on hip	20.00	15.00	6.50
241	McIntyre-Detroit	4.50	3.00	1.50
242	McIntyre-Brooklyn	4.50	3.00	1.50
243	McIntyre-Brooklyn & Chicago Nat.	4.50	3.00	1.50
244	McLean-Cinn.	4.50	3.00	1.50
245	McQuillan-Phila. Nat., Throwing	4.50	3.00	1.50
246	McQuillan-Phila. Nat., Batting	4.50	3.00	1.50
247	Merkle-N. Y. Nat., Portrait	4.50	3.00	1.50
248	Merkle-N. Y. Nat., Throwing	4.50	3.00	1.50
249	Meyers-N. Y. Nat.	4.50	3.00	1.50
250	Milan-Washington	4.50	3.00	1.50
251	Miller-Pitt.	4.50	3.00	1.50
252	Mitchell-Cinn.	4.50	3.00	1.50
253	Moran-Chicago Nat.	4.50	3.00	1.50
254	Moriarty-Detroit	4.50	3.00	1.50

	MINT	VG-E	F-G
255 Mowrey-Cinn.	4.50	3.00	1.50
256 Mullen-Detroit	4.50	3.00	1.50
257 Mullin-Detroit, Throwing	4.50	3.00	1.50
258 Mullin-Detroit, Batting	4.50	3.00	1.50
259 Murphy-Phila. Am., Throwing	4.50	3.00	1.50
260 Murphy-Phila. Am., Bat on shoulder	4.50	3.00	1.50
261 Murray-N. Y. Nat., Portrait	4.50	3.00	1.50
262 Murray-N. Y. Nat., Bat on shoulder	4.50	3.00	1.50
263 Myers-N. Y. Nat., Fielding	4.50	3.00	1.50
264 Myers-N. Y. Nat., Batting	4.50	3.00	1.50
265 Needham-Chicago Nat.	4.50	3.00	1.50
266 Niles-Bost. Am.	4.50	3.00	1.50
267 Nicholls - Phila. Am.	4.50	3.00	1.50
268 Nichols - Phila. Am	4.50	3.00	1.50
269 Oakes-Cinn.	4.50	3.00	1.50
270 O'Hara-St. Louis Nat	225.00	165.00	75.00
271 O'Hara-N. Y. Nat.	4.50	3.00	1.50
272 Oldring-Phila. Am., Fielding	4.50	3.00	1.50
273 Oldring-Phila. Am., Bat on shoulder	4.50	3.00	1.50
274 O'Leary-Detroit, Portrait	4.50	3.00	1.50
275 O'Leary-Detroit, Hands on knees	4.50	3.00	1.50
276 Overall-Chicago Nat. Portrait	4.50	3.00	1.50
277 Overall-Chicago Nat. Pitching following thru	4.50	3.00	1.50
278 Overall-Chicago Nat. Pitching hiding ball in glove	4.50	3.00	1.50
279 Owen-Chicago Am.	4.50	3.00	1.50
280 Parent-Chicago Am.	4.50	3.00	1.50
281 Paskert-Cinn.	4.50	3.00	1.50
282 Pastorius-Brooklyn	4.50	3.00	1.50
283 Pattee-Brooklyn	4.50	3.00	1.50
284 Payne-Chicago Am.	4.50	3.00	1.50
285 Pelty-St. Louis Am. Pitching ball in hand	4.50	3.00	1.50
286 Pelty-St. Louis Am. Pitching following thru	4.50	3.00	1.50
287 Perring-Cleveland	4.50	3.00	1.50
288 Pfeffer-Chicago Nat.	4.50	3.00	1.50
289 Pfeister-Chicago Nat., sitting down with bat in hands	4.50	3.00	1.50
290 Pfeister-Chicago Nat., Pitching	4.50	3.00	1.50
291 Phelps-St. Louis Nat	4.50	3.00	1.50
292 Phillippe - Pitt.	4.50	3.00	1.50
293 Plank-Phila., Am.	5000.00	3750.00	1750.00
294 Powell-St. Louis Am	4.50	3.00	1.50
295 Powers-Phil. Am.	4.50	3.00	1.50
296 Purtell-Chicago Am.	4.50	3.00	1.50
297 Quinn-N. Y. Am.	4.50	3.00	1.50
298 Raymond-N. Y. Nat.	4.50	3.00	1.50
299 Reulbach-Chicago Nat., Pitching	4.50	3.00	1.50
300 Reulbach-Chicago Nat., Standing hands at side	4.50	3.00	1.50
301 Rhoades-Cleveland, Pitching following thru	4.50	3.00	1.50
302 Rhoades-Cleveland, Hand in front of chest	4.50	3.00	1.50
303 Rhodes-St. Louis Nat	4.50	3.00	1.50
304 Ritchey-Boston Nat.	4.50	3.00	1.50
305 Rossman-Detroit	4.50	3.00	1.50
306 Rucker-Brooklyn, Portrait	4.50	3.00	1.50
307 Rucker-Brooklyn, Pitching	4.50	3.00	1.50
308 Schaefer-Washington	4.50	3.00	1.50
309 Schaefer-Detroit	4.50	3.00	1.50
310 Schlei-N. Y. Nat., Portrait	4.50	3.00	1.50

	MINT	VG-E	F-G
311 Schlei-N. Y. Nat., Batting	4.50	3.00	1.50
312 Schlei-N. Y. Nat., Fielding	4.50	3.00	1.50
313 Schmidt-Detroit, Portrait	4.50	3.00	1.50
314 Schmidt-Detroit, Throwing	4.50	3.00	1.50
315 Schulte-Chicago Nat. Batting with back turned	4.50	3.00	1.50
316 Schulte-Chicago Nat. Batting front pose	4.50	3.00	1.50
317 Scott-Chicago Am.	4.50	3.00	1.50
318 Seymour-N. Y. Nat., Portriat	4.50	3.00	1.50
319 Seymour-N. Y. Nat., Throwing	4.50	3.00	1.50
320 Seymour-N. Y. Nat., Batting	4.50	3.00	1.50
321 Shaw-St. Louis Nat.	4.50	3.00	1.50
322 Sheckard-Chicago Nat. Throwing	4.50	3.00	1.50
323 Sheckard-Chicago Nat. Side view walking	4.50	3.00	1.50
324 Shipke-Washington	4.50	3.00	1.50
325 Smith-Chicago Am.	4.50	3.00	1.50
326 Smith-Chicago & Boston Am.	60.00	45.00	20.00
327 F. Smith-Chicago Am.	4.50	3.00	1.50
328 Happy Smith-Brooklyn	4.50	3.00	1.50
329 Snodgrass-N. Y. Nat. Batting	4.50	3.00	1.50
330 Snodgrass-N. Y. Nat. Catching	4.50	3.00	1.50
331 Spade-Cinn.	4.50	3.00	1.50
332 Speaker-Boston Am.	25.00	18.50	8.75
333 Spencer-Boston Am.	25.00	18.50	8.75
334 Stahl-Bost. Am., Catching fly ball	4.50	3.00	1.50
335 Stahl-Bost. Am, Standing arms down	4.50	3.00	1.50
336 Starr-Bost. Nat.	4.50	3.00	1.50
337 Steinfeldt-Chicago Nat., Portrait	6.00	4.50	2.00
338 Steinfeldt-Chicago Nat., Batting	6.00	4.50	2.00
339 Stephens-St. Louis Am.	4.50	3.00	1.50
340 Stone-St. Louis Am.	4.50	3.00	1.50
341 Stovall-Cleveland, Portrait	4.50	3.00	1.50
342 Stovall-Cleveland, Batting	4.50	3.00	1.50
343 Stanage - Detroit	4.50	3.00	1.50
344 Street-Washington, Portrait	4.50	3.00	1.50
345 Street-Washington, Catching	4.50	3.00	1.50
346 Sullivan-Chicago Am.	4.50	3.00	1.50
347 Summers-Detroit	4.50	3.00	1.50
348 Sweeney-N. Y. Am.	4.50	3.00	1.50
349 Sweeney-Bost. Nat., Plain white uniform	4.50	3.00	1.50
350 Sweeney-Bost. Nat., Red trimmed uniform with letter "B" on shirt	4.50	3.00	1.50
351 L. Tannehill-Chicago Am.	4.50	3.00	1.50
352 Tannehill-Chicago Am	4.50	3.00	1.50
353 Tannehill-Washington	4.50	3.00	1.50
354 Tenney-N. Y. Nat.	4.50	3.00	1.50
355 Thomas-Phila. Am.	4.50	3.00	1.50
356 Tinker-Chicago Nat., Bat held away from shoulder	17.00	12.50	6.00
357 Tinker-Chicago Nat. Bat on shoulder	17.00	12.50	6.00
358 Tinker-Chicago Nat. Portrait	17.00	12.50	6.00
359 Tinker-Chicago Nat. Hands on knees	17.00	12.50	6.00
360 Titus-Phila. Nat.	4.50	3.00	1.50
361 Turner-Cleveland	4.50	3.00	1.50
362 Unglaub-Washington	4.50	3.00	1.50
363 Waddell-St. Louis Am Portrait	16.00	12.00	5.50
364 Waddell-St. Louis Am Pitching	16.00	12.00	5.00
365 Wagner-Boston Am., Plain uniform no lettering	10.00	7.00	3.00

T-206 (CONTINUED)

	MINT	VG-E	F-G
366 Wagner-BostonAm., Lettering on cap and uniform	10.00	7.00	3.00
387 *Wagner-Pitt.*	15000.00	9500.00	4500.00
368 Wallace- St. Louis Am.	15.00	11.00	5.00
369 Walsh-Chicago Am.	15.00	11.00	5.00
370 Warhop-N. Y. Am.	4.50	3.00	1.50
371 Weimer - N.Y. Nat.	4.50	3.00	1.50
372 Wheat-Brooklyn	15.00	11.00	5.00
373 White-Chicago Am., Portrait	4.50	3.00	1.50
374 White-Chicago Am., Pitching	4.50	3.00	1.50
375 Wilhelm-Brooklyn, Batting	4.50	3.00	1.50
376 Wilhelm-Brooklyn, Hands to chest	4.50	3.00	1.50
377 Willett - Detroit, Pitching	4.50	3.00	1.50
378 Willett - Detroit, Batting	4.50	3.00	1.50
379 Williams-St. Louis Am.	4.50	3.00	1.50
380 Willis-Pitt.	4.50	3.00	1.50
381 Willis-St. Louis Nat. Pitching	4.50	3.00	1.50
382 Willis-St. Louis Nat. Batting	4.50	3.00	1.50
383 Wilson-Pitt.	4.50	3.00	1.50
384 Wiltse-N. Y. Nat., Portrait without cap	4.50	3.00	1.50
385 Wiltse-N. Y. Nat., Portrait with cap	4.50	3.00	1.50
386 Wiltse-N. Y. Nat., Pitching	4.50	3.00	1.50
387 Young-Cleveland, Portrait	25.00	18.50	8.75
388 Young-Cleveland, Pitching front view	25.00	18.50	8.75
389 Young-Cleveland, Pitching side view	25.00	18.50	8.75
390 Zimmerman, Chicago Nat.	4.50	3.00	1.50
391 Abbott-Toledo	5.50	4.00	1.50
392 Armbruster-St. Paul	5.50	4.00	1.50
393 Barry-Milwaukee	5.50	4.00	1.50
394 Beckley, Jake-K.C.	16.00	12.00	5.50
395 Brashear-Kansas City	5.50	4.00	1.50
396 Burke-Indianapolis	5.50	4.00	1.50
397 Carr-Indianapolis	5.50	4.00	1.50
398 Clark-Columbus	5.50	4.00	1.50
399 Clymer-Columbus	5.50	4.00	1.50
400 Collins, Jimmy-Minn.	18.00	13.50	6.00
401 Congalton-Columbus	5.50	4.00	1.50
402 Cravath-Minneapolis	5.50	4.00	1.50
403 Cross-Indianapolis	5.50	4.00	1.50
404 Davidson-Indianapolis	5.50	4.00	1.50
405 Delehanty, Frank-Lou.	5.50	4.00	1.50
406 Dorner-Dansas City	5.50	4.00	1.50
407 Downs-Minneapolis	5.50	4.00	1.50
408 Freeman-Toledo	5.50	4.00	1.50
409 Hallman-Kansas City	5.50	4.00	1.50
410 Hayden-Indianapolis	5.50	4.00	1.50
411 Hinchman-Toledo	5.50	4.00	1.50
412 Kruger-Columbus	5.50	4.00	1.50
413 Lattimore-Toledo	5.50	4.00	1.50
414 Lundgren-Kansas City	5.50	4.00	1.50
415 Pickering-Minneapolis	5.50	4.00	1.50
416 McGann-Milwaukee	5.50	4.00	1.50
417 McGlynn-Milwaukee	5.50	4.00	1.50
418 Oberlin-Minneapolis	5.50	4.00	1.50
419 O'Brien-St. Paul	5.50	4.00	1.50
420 O'Neil-Minneapolis	5.50	4.00	1.50
421 Puttman-Louisville	5.50	4.00	1.50
422 Quillen-Minneapolis	5.50	4.00	1.50
423 Randall-Milwaukee	5.50	4.00	1.50
424 Ritter-Kansas City	5.50	4.00	1.50
425 Schreck-Columbus	5.50	4.00	1.50
426 Shannon-Kansas City	5.50	4.00	1.50
427 Thielman-Louisville	5.50	4.00	1.50
428 Wright-Toledo	5.50	4.00	1.50
429 Young, I.M.-Minn.	5.50	4.00	1.50
430 Adkins-Baltimore	5.50	4.00	1.50
431 Anderson-Providence	5.50	4.00	1.50
432 Arndt-Providence	5.50	4.00	1.50
433 Barger-Rochester	5.50	4.00	1.50
434 Batch-Rochester	5.50	4.00	1.50
435 Blackburne-Providence	5.50	4.00	1.50
436 Brain-Buffalo	5.50	4.00	1.50
437 Burchell-Buffalo	5.50	4.00	1.50

	MINT	VG-E	F-G
438 Butler-Rochester	5.50	4.00	1.50
439 Casey-Montreal	5.50	4.00	1.50
440 Cassidy-Baltimore	5.50	4.00	1.50
441 Chappelle-Rochester	5.50	4.00	1.50
442 Clancy-Buffalo	5.50	4.00	1.50
443 Dessau-Baltimore	5.50	4.00	1.50
444 Dunn-Baltimore	5.50	4.00	1.50
445 Flanagan-Buffalo	5.50	4.00	1.50
446 Ganzel-Rochester	5.50	4.00	1.50
447 Grimshaw-Toronto	5.50	4.00	1.50
448 Hall - Baltimore	5.50	4.00	1.50
449 Hannifan - Jersey City	5.50	4.00	1.50
450 Hoffman-Providence	5.50	4.00	1.50
451 Jackson, James-Balt.	5.50	4.00	1.50
452 Kelley, Joe-Tor.	18.00	13.50	6.00
453 Kisinger-Buffalo	5.50	4.00	1.50
454 Lavender-Providence	5.50	4.00	1.50
455 Malarkey-Buffalo	5.50	4.00	1.50
456 Maloney-Rochester	5.50	4.00	1.50
457 McGinley-Toronto	5.50	4.00	1.50
458 McGinnity, Joe-New.	20.00	15.00	6.50
459 Merritt-Jersey City	5.50	4.00	1.50
460 Milligan-Jersey City	5.50	4.00	1.50
461 Mitchell-Toronto	5.50	4.00	1.50
462 Moeller-Jersey City	5.50	4.00	1.50
463 Moran-Providence	5.50	4.00	1.50
464 Nattress-Buffalo	5.50	4.00	1.50
465 Phelan-Providence	5.50	4.00	1.50
466 Poland-Baltimore	5.50	4.00	1.50
467 Rudolph-Toronto	5.50	4.00	1.50
468 Schirm-Buffalo	5.50	4.00	1.50
469 Schlafly-Newark	5.50	4.00	1.50
470 Sharpe-Newark	5.50	4.00	1.50
471 Shaw-Providence	5.50	4.00	1.50
472 Slagle-Baltimore	5.50	4.00	1.50
473 Smith-Buffalo	5.50	4.00	1.50
474 Strang - Baltimore	5.50	4.00	1.50
475 Taylor-Buffalo	5.50	4.00	1.50
476 White-Buffalo	5.50	4.00	1.50
477 Coles-Augusta	14.00	10.00	4.00
478 Foster-Charleston	14.00	10.00	4.00
479 Helm-Columbus	14.00	10.00	4.00
480 Howard-Savannah	14.00	10.00	4.00
481 Kiernan-Columbia	14.00	10.00	4.00
482 LaFitte-Macon	14.00	10.00	4.00
483 Manion-Columbia	14.00	10.00	4.00
484 Mullaney-Jacksonville	14.00	10.00	4.00
485 Paige-Charleston	14.00	10.00	4.00
486 Violat-Jacksonville	14.00	10.00	4.00
487 Bay-Nashville	14.00	10.00	4.00
488 Bernhard-Nashville	14.00	10.00	4.00
489 Breitenstein-New Orleans	14.00	10.00	4.00
490 Carey-Memphis	14.00	10.00	4.00
491 Cranston-Memphis	14.00	10.00	4.00
492 Ellam-Nashville	14.00	10.00	4.00
493 Firtz-New Orleans	14.00	10.00	4.00
494 Greminger-Montgomery	14.00	10.00	4.00
495 Hart-Little Rock	14.00	10.00	4.00
496 F. Hart-Montgomery	14.00	10.00	4.00
497 Hickman-Mobile	14.00	10.00	4.00
498 Jordan, A. O. - Atlanta	14.00	10.00	4.00
499 Lentz-Little Rock	14.00	10.00	4.00
500 Molesworth- Birmingham	14.00	10.00	4.00
501 Perdue-Nashville	14.00	10.00	4.00
502 Persons-Montgomery	14.00	10.00	4.00
503 Reagan-New Orleans	14.00	10.00	4.00
504 Rockenfeld-Montgomery	14.00	10.00	4.00
505 Sid Smith-Atlanta	14.00	10.00	4.00
506 Thornton-Mobile	14.00	10.00	4.00
507 Bastion-San Antonio	14.00	10.00	4.00
508 Miller-Dallas	14.00	10.00	4.00
509 Smith-Shreveport	14.00	10.00	4.00
510 Stark-San Antonio	14.00	10.00	4.00
511 Thebo Waco	14.00	10.00	4.00
512 White-Houston	14.00	10.00	4.00
513 Guiheen-Portsmouth	14.00	10.00	4.00
514 Hooker-Lynchburg	14.00	10.00	4.00
515 King-Danville	14.00	10.00	4.00
516 Lipe-Richmond	14.00	10.00	4.00
517 McCavley-Portsmouth	14.00	10.00	4.00
518 Orth-Lynchburg	14.00	10.00	4.00
519 Otey-Norfolk	14.00	10.00	4.00
520 Revelle-Richmond	14.00	10.00	4.00
521 Ryan-Roanoke	14.00	10.00	4.00
522 Seitz-Norfolk	14.00	10.00	4.00
523 Shaughnessy-Roanoke	14.00	10.00	4.00
524 West Lake-Danville	14.00	10.00	4.00

T–207 BROWN BACKGROUND (200)   1 1/2" X 2 1/2"

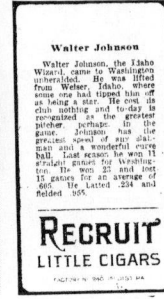

The T–207 set, also known as the "Brown Background" set was issued with Broadleaf, Cycle, Napoleon, Recruit and anonymous (Factories no. 2, 3 or 25) backs in 1912. Broadleaf, Cycle and anonymous backs are difficult to obtain. Although many scarcities and cards with degrees of difficulty to obtain exist (see prices below), the Loudermilk, Lewis (Bos.–N.L.) and Miller (Chi.–N.L.) cards are the rarest.

	MINT	VG-E	F-G
COMPLETE SET	4500.00	3500.00	1500.00
COMMON PLAYER	7.25	5.50	2.50
Adams, Cle-AL	50.00	38.00	17.00
Ainsmith, Wash-AL	7.25	5.50	2.50
Almeida, Cin-NL	30.00	22.50	10.50
Austin, StL-AL	10.00	7.00	3.00
with StL on shirt			
Austin, StL-AL	35.00	26.00	12.00
without StL on shirt			
Ball, Cle-AL	7.25	5.50	2.50
Barger, Brk-NL	7.25	5.50	2.50
Barry, Phil-AL	7.25	5.50	2.50
Bauman, Det-AL	50.00	38.00	17.00
Becker, NY-NL	7.25	5.50	2.50
Bender, Phil-AL	15.00	11.00	5.00
Benz, Chi-AL	30.00	22.50	10.50
Bescher, Cin-NL	7.25	5.50	2.50
Birmingham, Cle-AL	50.00	38.00	17.00
Blackburne, Chi-AL	50.00	38.00	17.00
Blanding, Cle-AL	30.00	22.50	10.50
Block, Chi-AL	7.25	5.50	2.50
Bodie, Chi-AL	7.25	5.50	2.50
Bradley, Bos-AL	10.00	7.00	3.00
Bresnahan, StL-NL	15.00	11.00	5.00
Bushelman, Bos-AL	50.00	38.00	17.00
Butcher, Cle-AL	30.00	22.50	10.50
Byrne, Pit-NL	7.25	5.50	2.50
Callahan, Chi-AL	7.25	5.50	2.50
Camnitz, Pit-NL	7.25	5.50	2.50
Carey, Pit-NL	15.00	11.00	5.00
Carrigan, Bos-AL	10.00	7.00	3.00
correct back			
Carrigan, Bos-AL	50.00	38.00	17.00
Wagner back			
Chalmers, Phil-NL	7.25	5.50	2.50
Chance, Chi-NL	20.00	15.00	6.50
Cicotte, Bos-AL	7.25	5.50	2.50
Clarke, Cin-NL	7.25	5.50	2.50
Cole, Chi-NL	7.25	5.50	2.50
Collins, Chi-AL	22.00	16.50	7.50
Coulson, Brk-NL	7.25	5.50	2.50
Covington, Det-AL	7.25	5.50	2.50
Crandall, NY-NL	7.25	5.50	2.50
Cunningham, Wash-AL	30.00	22.50	10.50
Danforth, Phil-AL	7.25	5.50	2.50
Daniels, NY-AL	7.25	5.50	2.50
Daubert, Brk-NL	7.25	5.50	2.50
Davis, Cle-AL	7.25	5.50	2.50
Delahanty, Det-AL	7.25	5.50	2.50
Derrick, Phil-AL	7.25	5.50	2.50
Devlin, Bos-NL	7.25	5.50	2.50
Devore, NY-NL	7.25	5.50	2.50
Donlin, Pit-NL	35.00	26.00	12.00
Donnelly, Bos-NL	35.00	26.00	12.00
Dooin, Phil-NL	7.25	5.50	2.50
Downey, Phil-NL	35.00	26.00	12.00
Doyle, NY-NL	7.25	5.50	2.50
Drake, Det-AL	7.25	5.50	2.50
Easterly, Cle-AL	7.25	5.50	2.50
Ellis, StL-NL	7.25	5.50	2.50
Engle, Bos-AL	10.00	7.00	3.00
Erwin, Brk-NL	7.25	5.50	

	MINT	VG-E	F-G
Evans, StL-NL	7.25	5.50	2.50
Ferry, Pit-NL	7.25	5.50	2.50
Fisher, NY-AL	25.00	18.50	8.75
white letters on cap			
Fisher, NY-AL	25.00	18.50	8.75
blue letters on cap			
Fletcher, NY-NL	7.25	5.50	2.50
Fournier, Chi-AL	50.00	38.00	17.00
Fromme, Cin-NL	7.25	5.50	2.50
Gainor, Det-AL	7.25	5.50	2.50
Gardner, Bos-AL	10.00	7.00	3.00
George, Cle-AL	7.25	5.50	2.50
Golden, StL-NL	7.25	5.50	2.50
Gowdy, Bos-NL	7.25	5.50	2.50
Graham, Phil-NL	12.00	8.75	4.00
Graney, Cle-AL	7.25	5.50	2.50
Gregg, Cle-AL	25.00	18.50	8.75
Hageman, Bos-AL	10.00	7.00	3.00
Hall, Bos-AL	10.00	7.00	3.00
Hallinan, StL-AL	7.25	5.50	2.50
Hamilton, StL-AL	7.25	5.50	2.50
Harmon, StL-NL	7.25	5.50	2.50
Hartley, NY-NL	30.00	22.50	10.50
Henriksen, Bos-AL	10.00	7.00	3.00
Henry, Wash-AL	7.25	5.50	2.50
Herzog, NY-NL	35.00	26.00	12.00
Higgins, NY-NL	7.25	5.50	2.50
Hoff, NY-AL	30.00	22.50	10.50
Hogan, StL-AL	7.25	5.50	2.50
Hooper, Bos-AL	18.00	13.50	6.00
Houser, Bos-NL	50.00	38.00	17.00
Hyatt, Pit-NL	35.00	26.00	12.00
Johnson, Wash-AL	50.00	38.00	17.00
Kaler, Cleve-AL	7.25	5.50	2.50
Kelly, Pit-NL	30.00	22.50	10.50
Kirke, Bos-NL	30.00	22.50	10.50
Kling, Bos-NL	7.25	5.50	2.50
Knabe, Phil-NL	7.25	5.50	2.50
Knetzer, Brk-NL	7.25	5.50	2.50
Konetchy, StL-NL	7.25	5.50	2.50
Krause, Phil-AL	7.25	5.50	2.50
Kuhn, Chi-AL	50.00	38.00	17.00
Kutina, StL-AL	35.00	26.00	12.00
Lange, Chi-AL	50.00	38.00	17.00
Lapp, Phil-AL	7.25	5.50	2.50
Latham, NY-NL	7.25	5.50	2.50
Leach, Pit-NL	7.25	5.50	2.50
Leifield, Pit-NL	7.25	5.50	2.50
Lennox, Chi-NL	7.25	5.50	2.50
Lewis, Bos-AL	10.00	7.00	3.00
Lewis, Bos-NL	500.00	400.00	200.00
Lively, Det-AL	7.25	5.50	2.50
Livingston, Cleve-AL	90.00	70.00	30.00
"A" shirt			
Livingston, Cleve-AL	90.00	70.00	30.00
"C" shirt			
Livingston, Cleve-AL	35.00	26.00	12.00
"C" shirt			
Lord, Phil-AL	7.25	5.50	2.50
Lord, Chi-AL	7.25	5.50	2.50
Loudermilk, StL-NL	500.00	400.00	200.00
Marquard, NY-NL	15.00	11.00	5.00
Marsans, Cin-NL	7.25	5.50	2.50

	MINT	VG-E	F-G		MINT	VG-E	F-G
McBride, Wash-AL	7.25	5.50	2.50	Schaefer, Wash-AL	7.25	5.50	2.50
McCarthy, Pit-NL	80.00	60.00	25.00	Schardt, Brk-NL	7.25	5.50	2.50
McDonald, Bos-NL	7.25	5.50	2.50	Schulte, Chi-NL	7.25	5.50	2.50
McGraw, NY-NL	25.00	18.50	8.75	Scott, Chi-AL	7.25	5.50	2.50
McIntire, Chi-NL	7.25	5.50	2.50	Severold, Cin-NL	7.25	5.50	2.50
McIntyre, Chi-NL	12.00	8.75	4.00	Simon, Pit-NL	7.25	5.50	2.50
McKechnie, Pit-NL	50.00	38.00	17.00	Smith, StL-NL	7.25	5.50	2.50
McLean, Cin-NL	7.25	5.50	2.50	Smith, Cin-NL	7.25	5.50	2.50
Milan, Wash-AL	7.25	5.50	2.50	Snodgrass, NY-NL	7.25	5.50	2.50
Miller, Pit-NL	7.25	5.50	2.50	Speaker, Bos-AL	75.00	55.00	24.00
Miller, Chi-NL	500.00	400.00	200.00	Spratt, Bos-NL	7.25	5.50	2.50
Miller, Brk-NL	30.00	22.50	10.50	Stack, Brk-NL	7.25	5.50	2.50
Miller, Bos-NL	30.00	22.50	10.50	Stanage, Det-AL	7.25	5.50	2.50
Mitchell, Cin-NL	12.00	8.75	4.00	Steele, StL-NL	7.25	5.50	2.50
Mitchell, Cle-AL	7.25	5.50	2.50	Steinfeldt, StL-NL	7.25	5.50	2.50
Mogridge, Chi-AL	30.00	22.50	10.50	Stovall, StL-AL	7.25	5.50	2.50
Moore, Phil-NL	20.00	15.00	6.50	Street, NY-AL	7.25	5.50	2.50
Moran, Phil-NL	7.25	5.50	2.50	Strunk, Phil-AL	7.25	5.50	2.50
Morgan, Phil-AL	7.25	5.50	2.50	Sullivan, Chi-AL	7.25	5.50	2.50
Morgan, Wash-AL	7.25	5.50	2.50	Sweeney, Bos-NL	50.00	38.00	17.00
Moriarity, Det-AL	30.00	22.50	10.50	Tannehill, Chi-AL	7.25	5.50	2.50
Mullin, Det-AL	25.00	18.50	8.75	Thomas, Bos-Al	10.00	7.00	3.00
with "D" on cap				Tinker, Chi-NL	16.00	12.00	5.50
Mullin, Det-AL	25.00	18.50	8.75	Tooley, Brk-NL	7.25	5.50	2.50
without "D" on cap				Turner, Cle-AL	7.25	5.50	2.50
				Tyler, Bos-NL	120.00	85.00	40.00
Needham, Chi-NL	7.25	5.50	2.50	Vaughn, NY-AL	7.25	5.50	2.50
Nelson, StL-AL	30.00	22.50	10.50	Wagner, Bos-AL	10.00	7.00	3.00
Northen, Brk-NL	7.25	5.50	2.50	correct back			
Nunamaker, Bos-AL	10.00	7.00	3.00	Wagner, Bos-AL	50.00	38.00	17.00
Oakes, StL-NL	7.25	5.50	2.50	Carrigan back			
O'Brien, Bos-AL	10.00	7.00	3.00	Walker, Wash-AL	7.25	5.50	2.50
Oldring, Phil-AL	7.25	5.50	2.50	Wallace, StL-AL	14.00	10.50	4.75
Olson, Cle-AL	7.25	5.50	2.50	Warhop, NY-AL	7.25	5.50	2.50
O'Toole, Pit-NL	7.25	5.50	2.50	Weaver, Chi-AL	30.00	22.50	10.50
Paskart, Phil-NL	7.25	5.50	2.50	Wheat, Brk-NL	16.00	12.00	5.50
Pelty, StL-AL	30.00	22.50	10.50	White, Chi-AL	30.00	22.50	10.50
Perdue, Bos-NL	7.25	5.50	2.50	Wilie, StL-NL	7.25	5.50	2.50
Peters, Chi-AL	30.00	22.50	10.50	Williams, NY-AL	7.25	5.50	2.50
Phelan, Cin-NL	50.00	38.00	17.00	Wilson, NY-NL	7.25	5.50	2.50
Quinn, NY-AL	7.25	5.50	2.50	Wilson, Pit-NL	30.00	22.50	10.50
Ragan, Brk-NL	120.00	85.00	40.00	Wiltse, NY-NL	7.25	5.50	2.50
Rasmussen, Phil-NL	90.00	70.00	30.00	Wingo, StL-NL	7.25	5.50	2.50
Rath, Chi-AL	30.00	22.50	10.50	Wolverton, NY-AL	7.25	5.50	2.50
Reulbach, Chi-NL	7.25	5.50	2.50	Wood, Bos-AL	12.00	8.75	4.00
Rucker, Brk-NL	7.25	5.50	2.50	Woodburn, StL-NL	50.00	38.00	17.00
Ryan, Cle-AL	30.00	22.50	10.50	Works, Det-AL	70.00	50.00	23.00
Saier, Chi-NL	120.00	85.00	40.00	Yerkes, Bos-AL	10.00	7.00	3.00
Scanlon, Phil-NL	7.25	5.50	2.50	Zeider, Chi-AL	35.00	26.00	12.00

20th CENTURY TOBACCO BOX

20th CENTURY TOBACCO BOX

1958 UNION OIL (10)

2 1/2" X 3 1/2"

AL HEIST, Centerfielder

Age 27, Ht. 6'2", Wt. 160

Sacramento '57   166 games

Bat. Avg. .257   R.B.I. 62

This Players Card entitles 1 person under
18 to free admission in bleacher section for
game of May 9, '58, against San Diego.

76 SPORTS CLUB

AL HEIST
SACRAMENTO SOLONS, Centerfielder

The 1958 Union Oil set of 10 black and white, unnumbered cards features the Sacramento Solons only. The set is distinguished by a white strip below the picture with the players name, team, and position printed on the front. The backs of the cards mention that the card is redeemable for a free admission to the July 11, 1958 game. The ACC designation is UO-29.

	MINT	VG-E	F-G			MINT	VG-E	F-G
COMPLETE SET	105.00	80.00	35.00	5 Nippy Jones		11.00	8.25	3.50
COMMON PLAYER	11.00	8.25	3.50	6 Carlos Paula		11.00	8.25	3.50
				7 Kal Segrist		11.00	8.25	3.50
1 Marshall Bridges	20.00	15.00	6.50	8 Sibbi Sisti		11.00	8.25	3.50
2 Dick Cole	11.00	8.25	3.50	9 Joe Stanka		11.00	8.25	3.50
3 Jim Greengrass	11.00	8.25	3.50	10 Bud Watkins		15.00	11.00	5.00
4 Al Heist	11.00	8.25	3.50					

1960 UNION OIL (9)

3 1/8" X 3 1/8" X 4"

Thumb-Nail Sketches — LOU SKIZAS

Lou Skizas has been one of the most impressive looking hitters in the Seattle Rainier spring camp. Skeezix is considered one of the best batters on the squad. Manager Dick Sisler plans to use Skizas in the lineup either at third base or in rightfield primarily to have that "good bat in there." Lou's average for Seattle last year was .272. He hit nine homers and had 37 runs batted in. He joined the Rainiers shortly past mid-season. Lou, who is a journalism graduate of the University of Illinois and has his eye alert for the good story, broke into baseball to help form half of baseball's best infield. He started in Joplin in 1950 as a third sacker. And the guy next to him at shortstop signed his autographs Mickey Mantle. Lou's best year was with the 1955 Denver club when he hit .350. He batted .316 the next season with the American League Kansas City club.

LOU SKIZAS—No. 15   Position: 3B, outfield
Nickname: Skeezix
Bats: R. Throws: R.   Home: Berwyn, Ill.
Born: July 2, 1932   Wife's name: Jean
Size: 5'10", 170 lb.   Children: None

76 Union Oil Company

PETE LUTHER PHOTO

The 1960 Union Oil se[t] nine full color, skip-numb[er] cards features the Se[attle] Rainiers. The cards were [given] away by Union Oil sta[tions] in the Seattle area. The f[ront] feature full body a[ction] photos taken at [Sick's] Stadium. Ripplemeyer an[d, to] a lesser extent, Obregon [are] more difficult to obtain [than] other cards in the set. [The] ACC designation is UO-13[.]

	MINT	VG-E	F-G		MINT	VG-E	F-G
COMPLETE SET	60.00	45.00	18.00	10 Ray Ripplemeyer	40.00	30.00	13.00
COMMON PLAYER	3.50	2.75	1.25	13 Joe Taylor	3.50	2.75	1.25
				15 Lou Skizas	3.50	2.75	1.25
4 Francisco Obregon	8.00	6.00	2.50	17 Don Rudolph	3.50	2.75	1.25
6 Drew Gilbert	3.50	2.75	1.25	19 Gordy Coleman	3.50	2.75	1.25
7 Bill Hain	3.50	2.75	1.25	22 Hal Bevan	3.50	2.75	1.25

The 1961 Union Oil set of 67 sepia, unnumbered cards contains players from nine Pacific Coast League teams. Individual player cards were available only in their respective cities at Union 76 stations. The backs are in blue print and give player biographies and depict the Union 76 logo. Spokane players are more difficult to obtain than players from other teams. The Gomez and Prescott cards are scarce. The Mike Hershberger card actually depicts Bobby Knoop.

	MINT	VG-E	F-G
COMPLETE SET	225.00	160.00	70.00
COMMON PLAYER	2.50	1.80	.80

		MINT	VG-E	F-G
H 1	Ray Jablonski	6.50	5.00	2.25
H 2	Jim McManus	6.50	5.00	2.25
H 3	George Prescott	25.00	18.50	8.75
H 4	Diego Segui	6.50	5.00	2.25
H 5	Rachel Slider	6.50	5.00	2.25
H 6	Jim Small	6.50	5.00	?.25
H 7	Milt Smith	6.50	5.00	2.25
H 8	Dave Thies	6.50	5.00	2.25
H 9	Jay Ward	6.50	5.00	2.25
H10	Bill Werle	6.50	5.00	2.25
P 1	Ed Bauta	2.50	1.80	.80
P 2	Vern Benson	2.50	1.80	.80
P 3	Jerry Buchek	2.50	1.80	.80
P 4	Bob Burda	2.50	1.80	.80
P 5	"Duke" Carmel	2.50	1.80	.80
P 6	Don Choate	2.50	1.80	.80
P 7	Phil Gagliano	2.50	1.80	.80
P 8	Jim Hickman	2.50	1.80	.80
P 9	Ray Katt	2.50	1.80	.80
P10	Mel Nelson	2.50	1.80	.80
P11	Jim Schaffer	2.50	1.80	.80
P12	Mike Shannon	3.25	2.40	1.10
P13	Clint Stark	2.50	1.80	.80
SD 1	Dick Barone	3.25	2.40	1.10
SD 2	Jim Bolger	3.25	2.40	1.10
SD 3	Kent Hadley	3.25	2.40	1.10
SD 4	Norman Hershberger	4.00	3.00	1.40
SD 5	Stan Johnson	3.25	2.40	1.10
SD 6	Dick Lines	3.25	2.40	1.10
SD 7	Jim Napier	3.25	2.40	1.10
SD 8	Tony Roig	3.25	2.40	1.10
SD 9	Herb Score	10.00	7.00	3.00
SD 10	Harry Simpson	4.00	3.00	1.40

		MINT	VG-E	F-G
SD11	Joe Taylor	3.25	2.40	1.10
SD12	Ben Wade	3.25	2.40	1.10
S 1	Galen Cisco	2.50	1.80	.80
S 2	Lou Clinton	2.50	1.80	.80
S 3	Marlan Coughtry	2.50	1.80	.80
S 4	Harry Malmberg	2.50	1.80	.80
S 5	Dave Mann	2.50	1.80	.80
S 6	Derrell Martin	2.50	1.80	.80
S 7	Erv Palica	2.50	1.80	.80
S 8	John Pesky	4.00	3.00	1.40
S 9	Bob Tillman	2.50	1.80	.80
S10	Marv Toft	2.50	1.80	.80
S11	Tom Umphlett	2.50	1.80	.80
SP 1	Doug Camilli	8.00	6.00	2.50
SP 2	Ramon Conde	8.00	6.00	2.50
SP 3	Bob Giallombardo	8.00	6.00	2.50
SP 4	Mike Goliat	8.00	6.00	2.50
SP 5	Preston Gomez	30.00	22.50	10.50
SP 6	Rod Graber	8.00	6.00	2.50
SP 7	Tim Harkness	8.00	6.00	2.50
SP 8	Jim Harwell	8.00	6.00	2.50
SP 9	Howie Reed	8.00	6.00	2.50
SP10	Curt Roberts	8.00	6.00	2.50
SP11	Rene Valdes	8.00	6.00	2.50
T10	Red Davis	3.25	2.40	1.10
T12	Dick Phillips	3.25	2.40	1.10
T17	Gil Garrido	3.25	2.40	1.10
T20	Georges Maranda	3.25	2.40	1.10
T25	John Orsino	3.25	2.40	1.10
T26	Dusty Rhodes	5.00	3.75	1.75
T28	Ron Herbel	3.25	2.40	1.10
T29	Gaylord Perry	16.00	12.00	5.50
T30	Rafael Alomar	3.25	2.40	1.10
T34	Bob Farley	3.25	2.40	1.10

VERNON STEPHENS—RED SOX

UNCLASSIFIED REGIONAL

The 1932 U.S. Caramels Famous Athletes set contains 32 numbered, red background cards. The ACC designation is R328. This set is one of the most difficult of the R card sets to complete.

	MINT	VG-E	F-G
COMPLETE SET	4500.00	3600.00	1600.00
COMMON PLAYER (BASEBALL)	125.00	90.00	80.00
COMMON NON-BB	40.00	30.00	12.00

#	Player	MINT	VG-E	F-G
1	Edw. T.(Eddie) Collins	150.00	110.00	50.00
2	Paul(Big Poison) Waner	150.00	110.00	50.00
3	Robert T.(Bobby) Jones	50.00	38.00	17.00
4	William (Bill) Terry	175.00	125.00	60.00
5	Earl B. Combs	140.00	100.00	45.00
6	William (Bill) Dickey	200.00	150.00	65.00
7	Joseph (Joe) Cronin	150.00	110.00	50.00
8	Charles (Chick) Hafey	140.00	100.00	45.00
9	Gene Sarazen	40.00	30.00	12.00
10	Rabbit Maranville	140.00	100.00	45.00
11	Rogers Hornsby	225.00	160.00	70.00
12	Mickey Cochrane	175.00	125.00	60.00
13	Lloyd(Little Poison) Waner	150.00	110.00	50.00
14	Tyrus (Ty) Cobb	400.00	325.00	150.00
15	Eugene (Gene) Tunney	60.00	45.00	20.00
16	Joe Kuhel	has not been verified		

#	Player	MINT	VG-E	F-G
17	Al Simmons	150.00	110.00	50.00
18	Anthony (Tony) Lazzeri	140.00	100.00	45.00
19	Walter (Wally) Berger	125.00	90.00	40.00
20	Charles Ruffing	140.00	100.00	45.00
21	Charles (Chuck) Klein	140.00	100.00	45.00
22	Jack Dempsey	80.00	60.00	25.00
23	Jimmy Foxx	250.00	175.00	80.00
24	Lefty O'Doul	125.00	90.00	40.00
25	Jack Sharkey	40.00	30.00	12.00
26	Henry (Lou) Gehrig	500.00	375.00	175.00
27	Robert (Lefty) Grove	225.00	160.00	70.00
28	Edward Brandt	125.00	90.00	40.00
29	George Earnshaw	125.00	90.00	40.00
30	Frank (Frankie) Frisch	175.00	125.00	60.00
31	Vernon (Lefty) Gomez	175.00	125.00	60.00
32	George (Babe) Ruth	500.00	375.00	175.00

1952 WHEATIES (60)

2" X 2 3/4"

The 1952 Wheaties set of 60 orange, blue and white, un-numbered cards was issued in panels of eight or ten cards on the backs of Wheaties cereal boxes. Each player appears in an action pose, designated in the checklist with an "a", and as a portrait, listed in the checklist with a "b". The ACC designation is F272-4.

	MINT	VG-E	F-G
COMPLETE SET	350.00	260.00	100.00
COMMON BASEBALL	5.50	4.25	2.00
COMMON NON-BASEBALL	2.75	2.00	1.00

	MINT	VG-E	F-G
1a Alice Bauer	2.75	2.00	1.00
2a Marlene Bauer	2.75	2.00	1.00
3a Patty Berg	2.75	2.00	1.00
4a Larry "Yogi" Berra	12.00	8.75	4.00
5a Roy Campanella	15.00	11.00	5.00
6a Bob Davies	2.75	2.00	1.00
7a Glenn Davis	4.00	3.00	1.40
8a Ned Day	2.75	2.00	1.00
9a Charles Diehl	2.75	2.00	1.00
10a Tom Fears	5.00	3.75	1.75
11a Bob Feller	12.00	8.75	4.00
12a Gretchen Fraser	2.75	2.00	1.00
13a Otto Graham	6.00	4.50	2.00
14a Ben Hogan	6.00	4.50	2.00
15a George Kell	6.00	4.50	2.00
16a Ralph Kiner	8.00	6.00	2.50
17a Jack Kramer	5.00	3.75	1.75
18a Bob Lemon	8.00	6.00	2.00
19a Johnny Lujack	5.00	3.75	1.75
20a Lloyd Mangrum	2.75	2.00	2.00
21a George Mikan	6.00	4.50	2.00
22a Stan Musial	20.00	15.00	6.50
23a Jimmy Patterson	2.75	2.00	1.00
24a Jim Pollard	2.75	2.00	1.00
25a Phil Rizzuto	9.00	6.75	3.00
26a Elwin "Preacher" Roe	7.00	5.25	2.50
27a Sam Snead	5.00	3.75	1.75
28a Doak Walker	4.00	3.00	1.40
29a Bob Waterfield	4.00	3.00	1.40
30a Ted Williams	25.00	18.50	8.75

	MINT	VG-E	F-G
1b Alice Bauer	2.75	2.00	1.00
2b Marlene Bauer	2.75	2.00	1.00
3b Patty Berg	2.75	2.00	1.00
4b Larry "Yogi" Berra	12.00	8.75	4.00
5b Roy Campanella	15.00	11.00	5.00
6b Bob Davies	2.75	2.00	1.00
7b Glenn Davis	4.00	3.00	1.40
8b Ned Day	2.75	2.00	1.00
9b Charles Diehl	2.75	2.00	1.00
10b Tom Fears	5.00	3.75	1.75
11b Bob Feller	12.00	8.75	4.00
12b Gretchen Fraser	2.75	2.00	1.00
13b Otto Graham	6.00	4.50	2.00
14b Ben Hogan	6.00	4.50	2.00
15b George Kell	6.00	4.50	2.00
16b Ralph Kiner	8.00	6.00	2.50
17b Jack Kramer	5.00	3.75	1.75
18b Bob Lemon	8.00	6.00	2.00
19b Johnny Lujack	5.00	3.75	1.75
20b Lloyd Mangrum	2.75	2.00	2.00
21b George Mikan	6.00	4.50	2.00
22b Stan Musial	20.00	15.00	6.50
23b Jimmy Patterson	2.75	2.00	1.00
24b Jim Pollard	2.75	2.00	1.00
25b Phil Rizzuto	9.00	6.75	3.00
26b Elwin "Preacher" Roe	7.00	5.25	2.50
27b Sam Snead	5.00	3.75	1.75
28b Doak Walker	4.00	3.00	1.40
29b Bob Waterfield	4.00	3.00	1.40
30b Ted Williams	25.00	18.50	8.75

1951 WHEATIES (6)

2 1/2" X 3 1/4"

The ACC designation is F272-3. Cards consist of the whole back of small individual Wheaties boxes and represent top names in a variety of sports.

	MINT	VG-E	F-G
COMPLETE SET	225.00	150.00	70.00
COMMON PLAYER	20.00	14.00	6.00
1 Feller	60.00	40.00	18.00
2 Lujack	20.00	14.00	6.00

	MINT	VG-E	F-G
3 Mikan	20.00	14.00	6.00
4 Musial	75.00	50.00	22.50
5 Snead	20.00	14.00	6.00
6 Williams	75.00	50.00	22.50

The 1954 Wilson Wieners contains 20 full color, numbered cards. The cards Hack, McMillan, Stephens, White are more abundant t other cards in the set. card of Jablonski is somew more difficult to obtain t other cards in the set.

	MINT	VG-E	F-G
COMPLETE SET	1600.00	1200.00	500.00
COMMON PLAYER	55.00	40.00	18.00

	MINT	VG-E	F-G
Roy Campanella	125.00	90.00	30.00
Del Ennis	65.00	48.00	22.00
Carl Erskine	65.00	48.00	22.00
Ferris Fain	55.00	40.00	18.00
Bob Feller	125.00	90.00	30.00
Nelson Fox	65.00	48.00	22.00
Johnny Groth	55.00	40.00	18.00
Stan Hack	40.00	30.00	13.00
Gil Hodges	100.00	70.00	30.00
Ray Jablonski	55.00	40.00	18.00

	MINT	VG-E	F-G
Harvey Kuenn	65.00	48.00	22.00
Roy McMillan	40.00	30.00	13.00
Andy Pafko	55.00	40.00	18.00
Paul Richards	55.00	40.00	18.00
Hank Sauer	65.00	48.00	22.00
Red Schoendienst	85.00	65.00	30.00
Enos Slaughter	55.00	40.00	18.00
Vern Stephens	40.00	30.00	13.00
Sammy White	40.00	30.00	13.00
Ted Williams	600.00	450.00	200.00

1931 W517 (54)

3" X 4"

The 1931 W517 set contains 54 numbered, blank backed cards. Although the cards are found predominantly in a sepia color, cards have been seen in blue, green, yellow, black, and gray tints. The card numbers are found in a small circle on the front of the cards. The prices in the checklist below are for the sepia color cards. Cards of other colors are worth approximately 20% more than the listed price. The cards were issued in strips.

	MINT	VG-E	F-G
COMPLETE SET	850.00	625.00	260.00
COMMON PLAYER	12.00	8.75	4.00

		MINT	VG-E	F-G
1	Earl Combs	15.00	11.00	5.00
2	Pie Traynor	18.00	13.50	6.00
3	Eddie Rousch	15.00	11.00	5.00
4	Babe Ruth	125.00	90.00	40.00
5	Chalmer Cissell	12.00	8.75	4.00
6	Bill Sherdel	12.00	8.75	4.00
7	Bill Shore	12.00	8.75	4.00
8	Geo. Earnshaw	12.00	8.75	4.00
9	Bucky Harris	15.00	11.00	5.00
10	Charlie Klein	15.00	11.00	5.00
11	Geo. Kelly	15.00	11.00	5.00
12	Travis Jackson	12.00	8.75	4.00
13	Willie Kamm	12.00	8.75	4.00
14	Harry Heilman	15.00	11.00	5.00
15	Grover Alexander	18.00	13.50	6.00
16	Frank Frisch	18.00	13.50	6.00
17	Jack Quinn	12.00	8.75	4.00
18	Cy Williams	12.00	8.75	4.00
19	KiKi Cuyler	15.00	11.00	5.00
20	Babe Ruth	150.00	110.00	50.00
21	Jimmy Foxx	45.00	34.00	15.00
22	Jimmy Dykes	13.00	9.50	4.00
23	Bill Terry	18.00	13.50	6.00
24	Freddy Lindstrom	15.00	11.00	5.00
25	Hugh Critz	12.00	8.75	4.00
26	Pete Donahue	12.00	8.75	4.00
27	Tony Lazzeri	13.00	9.50	4.00

		MINT	VG-E	F-G
28	Heine Manush	15.00	11.00	5.00
29	Chick Hafey	15.00	11.00	5.00
30	Melvin Ott	20.00	15.00	6.50
31	Bing Miller	12.00	8.75	4.00
32	Geo. Haas	12.00	8.75	4.00
33	Lefty O'Doul	13.00	9.50	4.00
34	Paul Waner	15.00	11.00	5.00
35	Lou Gehrig	90.00	70.00	30.00
36	Dazzy Vance	15.00	11.00	5.00
37	Mickey Cochrane	18.00	13.50	6.00
38	Rogers Hornsby	40.00	30.00	13.00
39	Lefty Grove	20.00	15.00	6.50
40	Al Simmons	20.00	15.00	6.50
41	Rube Walberg	12.00	8.75	4.00
42	Hack Wilson	15.00	11.00	5.00
43	Art Shires	12.00	8.75	4.00
44	Sammy Hale	12.00	8.75	4.00
45	Ted Lyons	15.00	11.00	5.00
46	Joe Sewell	15.00	11.00	5.00
47	Goose Goslin	15.00	11.00	5.00
48	Lou Fonseca	12.00	8.75	4.00
49	Bob Muesel	12.00	8.75	4.00
50	Lu Blue	12.00	8.75	4.00
51	Earl Averill	15.00	11.00	5.00
52	Eddy Collins	15.00	11.00	5.00
53	Joe Judge	12.00	8.75	4.00
54	Mickey Cochrane	18.00	13.50	6.00

1938-39 W711-1 (32)

2" X 3"

ERNIE LOMBARDI
Catcher

The most feared batter in the National League. Has no apparent weakness at the plate and hits all pitchers equally well. Is always in the race for league leadership in hitting. He has a fine arm and makes a specialty of catching runners off first. Caught both of Vandy's no-hitters. Most valuable player and the league's leading hitter in 1938.

The W711-1 Cincinnati Reds orange and gray set features 32 unnumbered cards. Many back variations and two poses of Vander Meer exist. The set was sold at the Red's ballpark and the paper stock is quite thin. The Livengood card is particularly difficult to obtain.

	MINT	VG-E	F-G
COMPLETE SET	175.00	130.00	60.00
COMMON PLAYER	5.00	4.00	1.75
1 Wally Berger (2)	5.00	4.00	1.75
2 Nino Bongiovanni	10.00	7.00	3.00
3 "Frenchy" Bordagaray	15.00	11.00	5.00
4 Joe Cascarella	5.00	4.00	1.75
5 "Dusty" Cooke	5.00	4.00	1.75
6 Harry Craft	5.00	4.00	1.75
7 Ray "Peaches" Davis	5.00	4.00	1.75
8 Paul Derringer (2)	8.00	6.00	2.50
9 Linus Frey	5.00	4.00	1.75
10 Lee Gamble (2)	5.00	4.00	1.75
11 Ival Goodman (2)	5.00	4.00	1.75
12 Hank Gowdy	5.00	4.00	1.75
13 Lee Grissom (2)	5.00	4.00	1.75
14 Willard Hershberger	12.50	9.00	4.00
15 Eddie Joost	5.00	4.00	1.75

	MINT	VG-E	F-G
16 Wes Livengood	30.00	22.50	10.50
17 Ernie Lombardi(2)	8.00	6.00	2.50
18 Frank McCormick	6.00	4.50	2.00
19 Bill McKechnie	8.00	6.00	2.50
20 "Whitey" Moore(2)	5.00	4.00	1.75
21 Billy Myers(2)	5.00	4.00	1.75
22 Lew Riggs	5.00	4.00	1.75
23 Eddie Roush	8.00	6.00	2.50
24 Les Scarsella	5.00	4.00	1.75
25 Gene Schott	5.00	4.00	1.75
26 Eugene Thompson	5.00	4.00	1.75
27 Johnny VanderMeer (P)	10.00	7.00	3.00
28 Johnny Vander Meer(A)	10.00	7.00	3.00
29 Wm. "Bucky" Walters(2)	6.00	4.50	2.00
30 Jim Weaver	5.00	4.00	1.75
31 Bill Werber	5.00	4.00	1.75
32 Jimmy Wilson	5.00	4.00	1.75

1941 W711–2 (33)

2 1/8" X 2 5/8"

The W711–2 Cincinnati Reds set contains 33 unnumbered, black and white cards. This issue is sometimes called the "Harry Hartman" set.

WILLARD HERSHBERGER
CATCHER

Born: May 28, 1911, Lemon Cove, Calif.
Died: Aug. 3, 1940, Boston, Mass.

"Hershey" played an important part in the early stretch of the pennant race, and his untimely end left a void not only on the playing field but in the hearts of his fellow players. Stunned by the sudden tragedy, the team first faltered and then recovered by the memory of "Hershey's" own fighting spirit then played even better than ever, clinching the National League pennant on Sept. 18, 1940.

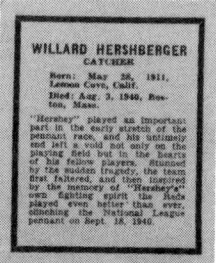

	MINT	VG-E	F-G
COMPLETE SET	200.00	150.00	65.00
COMMON PLAYER	6.50	5.00	2.00
1 Morris Arnovich	6.50	5.00	2.00
2 William (Bill) Baker	6.50	5.00	2.00
3 Joseph Beggs	6.50	5.00	2.00
4 Harry Craft	6.50	5.00	2.00
5 Paul Derringer	8.50	6.50	3.00
6 Linus Frey	6.50	5.00	2.00
7 Ival Goodman	6.50	5.00	2.00
8 (Hank) Gowdy	6.50	5.00	2.00
9 Witt Guise	6.50	5.00	2.00
10 Harry Hartman	6.50	5.00	2.00
11 Willard Hershberger	8.50	6.50	3.00
12 John Hutchings	6.50	5.00	2.00
13 Edwin Joost	6.50	5.00	2.00
14 Ernie Lombardi	7.50	5.75	2.50
15 Frank McCormick	7.50	5.75	2.50
17 Myron McCormick	6.50	5.00	2.00

	MINT	VG-E	F-G
18 William McKechnie	10.00	7.00	3.00
19 (Whitey) Moore	6.50	5.00	2.00
20 William (Bill) Myers	6.50	5.00	2.00
21 Elmer Riddle	6.50	5.00	2.00
22 Lewis Riggs	6.50	5.00	2.00
23 James A. Ripple	6.50	5.00	2.00
24 Milburn Shoffner	6.50	5.00	2.00
25 Eugene Thompson	6.50	5.00	2.00
26 James Turner	6.50	5.00	2.00
27 John Vander Meer	10.00	7.00	3.00
28 (Bucky) Walters	7.50	5.75	2.50
29 (Bill) Werber	6.50	5.00	2.00
30 James Wilson	6.50	5.00	2.00
31 Results 1940 World Series	6.50	5.00	2.00
32 The Cincinnati Reds (Title card)	6.50	5.00	2.00
33 The Cincinnati Reds World's Champions (Title Card)	6.50	5.00	2.00

1941 W753 (29)　　　　　　2 1/8" X 2 5/8"

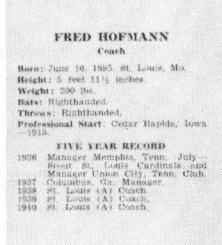

The 1941 W753 set features 29 unnumbered cards of the St. Louis Browns.

	MINI	VG-E	F-G			MINT	VG-E	F-G
COMPLETE SET	205.00	150.00	65.00	14	Robert A. Harris	7.00	5.25	2.25
COMMON PLAYER	7.00	5.25	2.25	15	Donald Henry Heffner	7.00	5.25	2.25
				16	Fred Hofmann	7.00	5.25	2.25
1 Johnny Allen	7.00	5.25	2.25	17	Walter F. Judnich	7.00	5.25	2.25
2 Elden Auker	7.00	5.25	2.25	18	Jack Kramer	7.00	5.25	2.25
3 Donald L. Barnes	7.00	5.25	2.25	19	Chester (Chet) Laabs	7.00	5.25	2.25
4 Johnny Beradino	8.00	6.00	2.50	20	John Lucadello	7.00	5.25	2.25
5 George Caster	7.00	5.25	2.25	21	George Hartley	7.00	5.25	2.25
6 Harland Clift	7.00	5.25	2.25	22	Robert C. Muncrief,Jr	7.00	5.25	2.25
7 Roy J. Cullenbine	7.00	5.25	2.25	23	John Niggeling	7.00	5.25	2.25
8 William O. DeWitt	8.00	6.00	2.50	24	Fritz Ostermueller	7.00	5.25	2.25
9 Robert Estalella	7.00	5.25	2.25	25	James (Luke) Sewell	8.00	6.00	2.50
10 Rick Ferrell	8.00	6.00	2.50	26	Alan C. Strange	7.00	5.25	2.50
11 Dennis W. Galehouse	7.00	5.25	2.25	27	Bob Swift	7.00	5.25	2.50
12 Joseph L. Grace	7.00	5.25	2.25	28	James (Zack) Taylor	7.00	5.25	2.50
13 Frank Grube	7.00	5.25	2.25	29	Bill Trotter	7.00	5.25	2.50

1941 W754 (29)　　　　　　2 1/8" X 2 5/8"

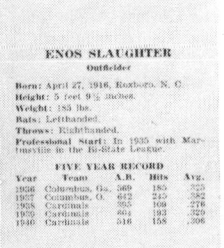

The 1941 W754 set of 29 unnumbered cards features St. Louis Cardinals.

	MINT	VG-E	F-G			MINT	VG-E	F-G
COMPLETE SET	215.00	160.00	70.00	14	Max Lanier	7.00	5.25	2.25
COMMON PLAYER	7.00	5.25	2.25	15	Gus Mancuso	7.00	5.25	2.25
				16	Marty Marion	12.00	8.75	4.00
1 Sam Breadon	8.00	6.00	2.50	17	Steve Mesner	7.00	5.25	2.25
2 Jimmy Brown	7.00	5.25	2.25	18	John Mize	15.00	11.00	5.00
3 Mort Cooper	7.00	5.25	2.25	19	Terry Moore	8.00	6.00	2.50
4 Walker Cooper	7.00	5.25	2.25	20	Sam Nahem	7.00	5.25	2.25
5 Estel Crabtree	7.00	5.25	2.25	21	Don Padgett	7.00	5.25	2.25
6 Frank Crespi	7.00	5.25	2.25	22	Branch Rickey	15.00	11.00	5.00
7 Bill Crouch	7.00	5.25	2.25	23	Clyde Shoun	7.00	5.25	2.25
8 Mike Gonzalez	7.00	5.25	2.25	24	Enos Slaughter	15.00	11.00	5.00
9 Harry Gumpert	7.00	5.25	2.25	25	Billy Southworth	8.00	6.00	2.50
10 John Hopp	7.00	5.25	2.25	26	Coaker Triplett	7.00	5.25	2.25
11 Ira Hutchinson	7.00	5.25	2.25	27	Buzzy Wares	7.00	5.25	2.25
12 Howie Krist	7.00	5.25	2.25	28	Lon Warneke	7.00	5.25	2.25
13 Eddie Lake	7.00	5.25	2.25	29	Ernie White	7.00	5.25	2.25

1928 YUENGLINGS ICE CREAM (60)   1 3/8" X 2 9/16"

SAVE THESE PICTURES

One ice cream novelty will be given free for each picture of Babe Ruth
ALSO

One gallon of Yuengling's ice cream will be delivered free to the holder of a complete set of sixty different Baseball Stars, upon surrender of same to any Yuengling dealer. Babe Ruth may be saved for quarts of ice cream or a $3.00 shooter.

This black & white, numbered set of 60 cards contain the same fronts as both E210 and W502. The Paul Waner card, No. 45, actually contains a picture of Clyde Barnhardt. The ACC designation is F50.

	MINT	VG-E	F-G
COMPLETE SET	420.00	330.00	150.00
COMMON PLAYER	6.50	5.00	2.50

		MINT	VG-E	F-G
1	Burleigh Grimes	10.00	8.00	4.00
2	Walter Reuther	6.50	5.00	2.50
3	Joe Dugan	6.50	5.00	2.50
4	Red Faber	10.00	8.00	4.00
5	Gabby Hartnett	10.00	8.00	4.00
6	Babe Ruth	50.00	40.00	16.00
7	Bob Meusel	6.50	5.00	2.50
8	Herb Pennock	10.00	8.00	4.00
9	George Burns	6.50	5.00	2.50
10	Joe Sewell	10.00	8.00	4.00
11	George Uhle	6.50	5.00	2.50
12	Bob O'Farrell	6.50	5.00	2.50
13	Rogers Hornsby	18.00	14.00	7.00
14	Pie Traynor	12.00	10.00	5.00
15	Clarence Mitchell	6.50	5.00	2.50
16	Eppa Rixey	10.00	8.00	4.00
17	Carl Mays	6.50	5.00	2.50
18	Adolfo Luque	6.50	5.00	2.50
19	Dave Bancroft	6.50	5.00	2.50
20	George Kelly	10.00	8.00	4.00
21	Earl Combs	10.00	8.00	4.00
22	Billy Herman	10.00	8.00	4.00
23	Ray Schalk	6.50	5.00	2.50
24	John Mostil	6.50	5.00	2.50
25	Hack Wilson	10.00	8.00	4.00
26	Lou Gehrig	30.00	25.00	12.50
27	Ty Cobb	30.00	25.00	12.50
28	Tris Speaker	15.00	12.00	6.00
29	Tony Lazzeri	8.00	6.50	3.00
30	Waite Hoyt	10.00	8.00	4.00

		MINT	VG-E	F-G
31	Sherwood Smith	6.50	5.00	2.50
32	Max Carey	10.00	8.00	4.00
33	Gene Hargrave	6.50	5.00	2.50
34	Miquel Gonzalez	6.50	5.00	2.50
35	Joe Judge	6.50	5.00	2.50
36	Sam Rice	10.00	8.00	4.00
37	Earl Sheeny	6.50	5.00	2.50
38	Sam Jones	6.50	5.00	2.50
39	Bibb Falk	6.50	5.00	2.50
40	Willie Kamm	6.50	5.00	2.50
41	Stan Harris (Bucky)	10.00	8.00	4.00
42	John McGraw	15.00	12.00	6.00
43	Art Nehf	6.50	5.00	2.50
44	Grover C. Alexander	15.00	12.00	6.00
45	Paul Waner	10.00	8.00	4.00
46	Bill Terry	12.00	10.00	5.00
47	Glenn Wright	6.50	5.00	2.50
48	Earl Smith	6.50	5.00	2.50
49	Goose Goslin	10.00	8.00	4.00
50	Frank Frisch	12.00	10.00	5.00
51	Joe Harris	6.50	5.00	2.50
52	Cy Williams	6.50	5.00	2.50
53	Eddie Roush	10.00	8.00	4.00
54	George Sisler	10.00	8.00	4.00
55	Ed Rommel	6.50	5.00	2.50
56	Roger Peckinpaugh	6.50	5.00	2.50
57	Stanley Coveleskie	10.00	8.00	4.00
58	Lester Bell	6.50	5.00	2.50
59	Lloyd Waner	10.00	8.00	4.00
60	John McInnis	6.50	5.00	2.50

BOXING EXHIBIT

EARLY EXHIBIT

413

 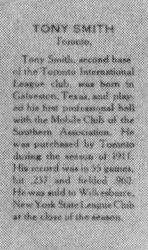

TONY SMITH
Toronto.

Tony Smith, second base of the Toronto International League club, was born in Galveston, Texas, and played his first professional ball with the Mobile Club of the Southern Association. He was purchased by Toronto during the season of 1911. His record was in 95 games, hit .237 and fielded .960. He was sold to Wilkesbarre, New York State League Club at the close of the season.

The 1912 C46 Canadian set features 90 numbered cards which were issued with an un-identified brand of cigarrettes. The set features International League players.

	MINT	VG-E	F-G
COMPLETE SET	1300.00	900.00	300.00
COMMON PLAYER	15.00	10.50	3.50
1 O'Hara	15.00	10.50	3.50
2 McGinley	15.00	10.50	3.50
3 Leclaire	15.00	10.50	3.50
4 White	15.00	10.50	3.50
5 James Murray	15.00	10.50	3.50
6 Ward	15.00	10.50	3.50
7 Alperman	15.00	10.50	3.50
8 Nattress	15.00	10.50	3.50
9 Sline	15.00	10.50	3.50
10 Rock	15.00	10.50	3.50
11 Demmitt	15.00	10.50	3.50
12 Schmidt	15.00	10.50	3.50
13 Frock	15.00	10.50	3.50
14 Burchell	15.00	10.50	3.50
15 Kelley, Joe	25.00	18.50	8.75
16 Barberich	15.00	10.50	3.50
17 Corridon	15.00	10.50	3.50
18 Adkins	15.00	10.50	3.50
19 Dunn	15.00	10.50	3.50
20 Walsh	15.00	10.50	3.50
21 Handford	15.00	10.50	3.50
22 Rudolph	15.00	10.50	3.50
23 Elston	15.00	10.50	3.50
24 Silton	15.00	10.50	3.50
25 French	15.00	10.50	3.50
26 Ganzel	15.00	10.50	3.50
27 Kelly	15.00	10.50	3.50
28 Meyers	15.00	10.50	3.50
29 Schirm	15.00	10.50	3.50
30 Purtell	15.00	10.50	3.50
31 Sharpe	15.00	10.50	3.50
32 Tony Smith	15.00	10.50	3.50
33 Lush	15.00	10.50	3.50
34 Collins	15.00	10.50	3.50
35 Phelan	15.00	10.50	3.50
36 Phelps	15.00	10.50	3.50
37 Vickers	15.00	10.50	3.50
38 Seymour	15.00	10.50	3.50
39 Carroll	15.00	10.50	3.50
40 Gettman	15.00	10.50	3.50
41 Taylor	15.00	10.50	3.50
42 Justis	15.00	10.50	3.50
43 Fisher	15.00	10.50	3.50
44 Parent	15.00	10.50	3.50

	MINT	VG-E	F-G
45 Dygert	15.00	10.50	3.50
46 Butler	15.00	10.50	3.50
47 Mitchell	15.00	10.50	3.50
48 Batch	15.00	10.50	3.50
49 Corcoran	15.00	10.50	3.50
50 Doescher	15.00	10.50	3.50
51 Wheeler	15.00	10.50	3.50
52 Jones	15.00	10.50	3.50
53 Truesdale	15.00	10.50	3.50
54 Beebe	15.00	10.50	3.50
55 Brocket	15.00	10.50	3.50
56 Wells	15.00	10.50	3.50
57 McAllister	15.00	10.50	3.50
58 Stroud	15.00	10.50	3.50
59 Manser	15.00	10.50	3.50
60 Holmes	15.00	10.50	3.50
61 Dessau	15.00	10.50	3.50
62 Jacklitsch	15.00	10.50	3.50
63 Graham	15.00	10.50	3.50
64 Henline	15.00	10.50	3.50
65 Gandil	15.00	10.50	3.50
66 Hughes	15.00	10.50	3.50
67 Delehanty	15.00	10.50	3.50
68 Pierce	15.00	10.50	3.50
69 Gaunt	15.00	10.50	3.50
70 Fitzpatrick	15.00	10.50	3.50
71 Lee	15.00	10.50	3.50
72 Kissinger	15.00	10.50	3.50
73 Malarkey	15.00	10.50	3.50
74 Byers	15.00	10.50	3.50
75 Simmons	15.00	10.50	3.50
76 Moeller	15.00	10.50	3.50
77 McGinnity	25.00	17.00	5.50
78 Hardy	15.00	10.50	3.50
79 Holmes	15.00	10.50	3.50
80 Baxter	15.00	10.50	3.50
81 Spencer	15.00	10.50	3.50
82 Kocher	15.00	10.50	3.50
83 Shaw	15.00	10.50	3.50
84 Yeager	15.00	10.50	3.50
85 Carlo	15.00	10.50	3.50
86 Abstein	15.00	10.50	3.50
87 Jordan	15.00	10.50	3.50
88 Breen	15.00	10.50	3.50
89 McCarty	15.00	10.50	3.50
90 Curtis	15.00	10.50	3.50

FC9 KELLOGG SPORT TIPS

1921 V61 NEILSON'S CHOCOLATES (120)   2" X 3 1/2"

NEILSON'S BIG LEAGUE BARS contain a photograph of a prominent player in action in either the American or National League. There are in all 120 photographs in this series.
NEILSON'S CHOCOLATE BARS are guaranteed absolutely pure. Made only from Pure Chocolate, Cane Sugar, Rich Milk and the best of Nuts.
Always ask for and insist on getting NEILSON'S.

Neilson's BIG LEAGUE BARS contain a photograph of a prominent player in action in either the American or National League. There are in all 120 photographs in this series.

Neilson's CHOCOLATE BARS are guaranteed absolutely pure. Made only from Pure Chocolate, Cane Sugar, Rich Milk and the best of Nuts. Always ask and insist on getting

Neilson's

105   OSCAR RAY GRIMES
FIRST BASE, CHICAGO NATIONALS

The 1921 Neilson's Chocolate set entitled "Big League Baseball Stars" contains 120 cards and is a reproduction of the E—120 set. There are two versions of this set. A numbered paper issue and an unnumbered cardboard issue. Cards of the unnumbered cardboard issue are worth approximately 50% more than the values listed in the checklist below. The ACC designation is V61.

	MINT	VG-E	F-G
COMPLETE SET	1200.00	900.00	400.00
COMMON PLAYER	9.00	6.75	3.00
1 George Burns	9.00	6.75	3.00
2 John Tobin	9.00	6.75	3.00
3 Tom Zachary	9.00	6.75	3.00
4 Bullet Joe Bush	9.00	6.75	3.00
5 Lu Blue	9.00	6.75	3.00
6 Tillie Walker	9.00	6.75	3.00
7 Carl Mays	9.00	6.75	3.00
8 Leon Goslin	14.00	10.50	4.75
9 Ed Rommel	9.00	6.75	3.00
10 Charles Robertson	9.00	6.75	3.00
11 Ralph Perkins	9.00	6.75	3.00
12 Joe Sewell	13.00	9.50	4.00
13 Harry Hooper	14.00	10.50	4.75
14 Urban Faber	13.00	9.50	4.00
15 Bib Falk	9.00	6.75	3.00
16 George Uhle	9.00	6.75	3.00
17 Emory Rigney	9.00	6.75	3.00
18 George Dauss	9.00	6.75	3.00
19 Herman Pillette	9.00	6.75	3.00
20 Wallie Schang	9.00	6.75	3.00
21 Lawrence Woodall	9.00	6.75	3.00
22 Steve O'Neill	9.00	6.75	3.00
23 Edmund Miller	9.00	6.75	3.00
24 Sylvester Johnson	9.00	6.75	3.00
25 Henry Severeid	9.00	6.75	3.00
26 Dave Danforth	9.00	6.75	3.00
27 Harry Heilman	15.00	11.00	5.00
28 Bert Cole	9.00	6.75	3.00
29 Eddie Collins	15.00	11.00	5.00
30 Ty Cobb	100.00	70.00	30.00
31 Bill Wambsganss	9.00	6.75	3.00
32 George Sisler	18.00	13.50	6.00
33 Bob Veach	9.00	6.75	3.00
34 Earl Sheely	9.00	6.75	3.00
35 Pat Collins	9.00	6.75	3.00
36 Frank Davis	9.00	6.75	3.00
37 Babe Ruth	150.00	110.00	50.00
38 Bryan Harris	9.00	6.75	3.00
39 Bob Shawkey	9.00	6.75	3.00
40 Urban Shocker	9.00	6.75	3.00
41 Martin McManus	9.00	6.75	3.00
42 Clark Pittenger	9.00	6.75	3.00
43 Sam Jones	9.00	6.75	3.00
44 Waite Hoyt	14.00	10.50	4.75
45 Johnny Mostil	9.00	6.75	3.00
46 Mike Menosky	9.00	6.75	3.00
47 Walter Johnson	50.00	38.00	17.00
48 Wallie Pipp	10.00	7.00	3.00
49 Walter Gerber	9.00	6.75	3.00
50 Ed Gharrity	9.00	6.75	3.00
51 Frank Ellerbe	9.00	6.75	3.00
52 Kenneth Williams	9.00	6.75	3.00
53 Joe Hauser	9.00	6.75	3.00
54 Carson Bigbee	9.00	6.75	3.00
55 Irish Meusel	9.00	6.75	3.00
56 Milton Stock	9.00	6.75	3.00
57 Wilbur Cooper	9.00	6.75	3.00
58 Tom Griffith	9.00	6.75	3.00
59 Butch Henline	9.00	6.75	3.00
60 Bubbles Hargrave	9.00	6.75	3.00

	MINT	VG-E	F-G
61 Russell Wrightstone	9.00	6.75	3.00
62 Frank Frisch	17.00	12.50	6.00
63 Jack Peters	9.00	6.75	3.00
64 Walter Ruether	9.00	6.75	3.00
65 Bill Doak	9.00	6.75	3.00
66 Marty Callaghan	9.00	6.75	3.00
67 Sammy Bohne	9.00	6.75	3.00
68 Earl Hamilton	9.00	6.75	3.00
69 Grover Alexander	30.00	22.50	10.50
70 George Burns	9.00	6.75	3.00
71 Max Carey	14.00	10.50	4.75
72 Adolph Luque	9.00	6.75	3.00
73 Dave Bancroft	13.00	9.50	4.00
74 Vic Aldridge	9.00	6.75	3.00
75 Jack Smith	9.00	6.75	3.00
76 Bob O'Farrell	9.00	6.75	3.00
77 Pete Donohue	9.00	6.75	3.00
78 Ralph Pinelli	9.00	6.75	3.00
79 Eddie Roush	14.00	10.50	4.75
80 Norman Boeckel	9.00	6.75	3.00
81 Rogers Hornsby	40.00	30.00	13.00
82 George Toporcer	9.00	6.75	3.00
83 Ivy Wingo	9.00	6.75	3.00
84 Virgil Cheeves	9.00	6.75	3.00
85 Vern Clemons	9.00	6.75	3.00
86 Lawrence Miller	9.00	6.75	3.00
87 Johnny Kelleher	9.00	6.75	3.00
88 Heinie Groh	9.00	6.75	3.00
89 Burleigh Grimes	14.00	10.50	4.75
90 Rabbit Maranville	13.00	9.50	4.00
91 Babe Adams	9.00	6.75	3.00
92 Lee King	9.00	6.75	3.00
93 Art Nehf	9.00	6.75	3.00
94 Frank Snyder	9.00	6.75	3.00
95 Raymond Powell	9.00	6.75	3.00
96 Wilbur Hubbell	9.00	6.75	3.00
97 Leon Cadore	9.00	6.75	3.00
98 Joe Oeschger	9.00	6.76	3.00
99 Jake Daubert	9.00	6.75	3.00
100 Will Sherdel	9.00	6.75	3.00
101 Hank DeBerry	9.00	6.75	3.00
102 Johnny Lavan	9.00	6.75	3.00
103 Jesse Haines	14.00	10.50	4.75
104 Joe (Goldie) Rapp	9.00	6.75	3.00
105 Oscar Ray Grimes	9.00	6.75	3.00
106 Ross Youngs	13.00	9.50	4.00
107 Art Fletcher	9.00	6.75	3.00
108 Clyde Barnhart	9.00	6.75	3.00
109 Louis (Pat) Duncan	9.00	6.75	3.00
110 Charlie Hollacher	9.00	6.75	3.00
111 Horace Ford	9.00	6.75	3.00
112 Bill Cunningham	9.00	6.75	3.00
113 Walter Schmidt	9.00	6.75	3.00
114 Joe Schultz	9.00	6.75	3.00
115 John Morrison	9.00	6.75	3.00
116 Jimmy Caveney	9.00	6.75	3.00
117 Zach Wheat	14.00	10.50	4.75
118 Fred (Cy) Williams	9.00	6.75	3.00
119 George Kelly	14.00	10.50	4.75
120 Jimmy Ring	9.00	6.75	3.00

1923 V100 WILLARDS CHOCOLATES (179)   2" X 3 1/4"

The 1923 Willard Chocolates set was issued in Canada and contains 179 unnumbered cards. The ACC designation is V100.

	MINT	VG-E	F-G
COMPLETE SET	3000.00	2200.00	900.00
COMMON PLAYER	14.00	10.00	4.00

	MINT	VG-E	F-G			MINT	VG-E	F-G
1 Adams, Charles B.	14.00	10.00	4.00	61 Heilmann, Harry		24.00	18.00	8.50
2 Alexander, Grover C.	35.00	26.00	12.00	62 Henline, Walter		14.00	10.00	4.00
3 Austin, J. P.	14.00	10.00	4.00	63 Holke, Walter		14.00	10.00	4.00
4 Bagby, Jim	14.00	10.00	4.00	64 Hollocher, Charles		14.00	10.00	4.00
5 Baker, J. Franklin	24.00	18.00	8.50	65 Hooper, Harry		22.00	16.50	7.50
6 Bancroft, Dave	20.00	15.00	6.50	66 Hornsby, Roger		40.00	30.00	13.00
7 Barber, Turner	14.00	10.00	4.00	67 Hoyt, Waite		21.00	15.50	7.00
8 Barnes, Jesse L.	14.00	10.00	4.00	68 Huggins, Miller		24.00	18.00	8.50
9 Bassler, John	14.00	10.00	4.00	69 Jacobson, W. C.		14.00	10.00	4.00
10 Blue, Lu	14.00	10.00	4.00	70 Jamieson, Charlie		14.00	10.00	4.00
11 Boeckel, Norman	14.00	10.00	4.00	71 E. Johnson		14.00	10.00	4.00
12 F. L. Brazil	14.00	10.00	4.00	72 W. Johnson		50.00	38.00	17.00
13 G. H. Burns	14.00	10.00	4.00	73 Johnston, James H.		14.00	10.00	4.00
14 G. J. Burns	14.00	10.00	4.00	74 R. Jones		14.00	10.00	4.00
15 Cadore, Leon	14.00	10.00	4.00	75 S. Jones		14.00	10.00	4.00
16 Carey, Max	21.00	15.50	7.00	76 Judge, J. I.		14.00	10.00	4.00
17 Carlson, Harold G.	14.00	10.00	4.00	77 Keenan, James W.		14.00	10.00	4.00
18 Christenberry, Lloyd	14.00	10.00	4.00	78 Kelly, Geo. L.		20.00	15.00	6.50
19 Clemons, Vernon J.	14.00	10.00	4.00	79 Kilduff, Peter J.		14.00	10.00	4.00
20 Cobb, Ty	100.00	70.00	30.00	80 Killefer, William		14.00	10.00	4.00
21 Cole, Bert	14.00	10.00	4.00	81 King, Lee		14.00	10.00	4.00
22 Collins, John F.	14.00	10.00	4.00	82 Kolp, Ray		14.00	10.00	4.00
23 Coveleski, Stan	20.00	15.00	6.50	83 Lavan, John		14.00	10.00	4.00
24 Cruise, Walton E.	14.00	10.00	4.00	84 Leibold, H. L.		14.00	10.00	4.00
25 Cutshaw, George W.	14.00	10.00	4.00	85 Mack, Connie		30.00	22.50	10.50
26 Daubert, Jake	14.00	10.00	4.00	86 Mails, J. W.		14.00	10.00	4.00
27 Dauss, George	14.00	10.00	4.00	87 Maranville, Walter		20.00	15.00	6.50
28 Davis, F. T.	14.00	10.00	4.00	88 Marquard, Richard W.		20.00	15.00	6.50
29 Deal, Charles A.	14.00	10.00	4.00	89 Mays, C.W.		14.00	10.00	4.00
30 Doak, William L.	14.00	10.00	4.00	90 McBride, Geo. F.		14.00	10.00	4.00
31 Donovan, Wild Bill	14.00	10.00	4.00	91 McClellan, H.M.		14.00	10.00	4.00
32 Duffy, Hugh	21.00	15.50	7.00	92 McGraw, John J.		30.00	22.50	10.50
33 Dugan, Joe	14.00	10.00	4.00	93 McHenry, Austin B.		14.00	10.00	4.00
34 Duncan, Louis B.	14.00	10.00	4.00	94 McInnis, J.		14.00	10.00	4.00
35 Dykes, Jimmy	15.00	11.00	5.00	95 McWeeny, Douglas		14.00	10.00	4.00
36 Ehmke, Howard	14.00	10.00	4.00	96 Menosky, M.		14.00	10.00	4.00
37 Ellerbe, Francis R.	14.00	10.00	4.00	97 Meusel, Emil F.		14.00	10.00	4.00
38 Erickson, E. G.	14.00	10.00	4.00	98 Meusel, R.		14.00	10.00	4.00
39 Evers, Johnny	21.00	15.50	7.00	99 Meyers, Henry W.		14.00	10.00	4.00
40 Faber, Urban	20.00	15.00	6.50	100 Milan, J.C.		14.00	10.00	4.00
41 Falk, Bibb	14.00	10.00	4.00	101 Miljus, John K.		14.00	10.00	4.00
42 Flack, Max	14.00	10.00	4.00	102 Miller, Elmer		14.00	10.00	4.00
43 Fohl, Lee	14.00	10.00	4.00	103 Miller, Otto L.		14.00	10.00	4.00
44 Fournier, Jack	14.00	10.00	4.00	104 Mitchell, Fred		14.00	10.00	4.00
45 Frisch, Frank	30.00	22.50	10.50	105 Mogridge, Geo.		14.00	10.00	4.00
46 Galloway, C. E.	14.00	10.00	4.00	106 Moran, Patrick J.		14.00	10.00	4.00
47 Gardner, W. C.	14.00	10.00	4.00	107 Morrison, John D.		14.00	10.00	4.00
48 Gharrity, Edward	14.00	10.00	4.00	108 Mostil, J.A.		14.00	10.00	4.00
49 Gibson, George	14.00	10.00	4.00	109 Mueller, Clarence F.		14.00	10.00	4.00
50 Gleason, Wm.	14.00	10.00	4.00	110 Neale, A. Earle		14.00	10.00	4.00
51 Gleason, William	14.00	10.00	4.00	111 Oeschger, Joseph		14.00	10.00	4.00
52 Gowdy, Hank	14.00	10.00	4.00	112 O'Farrell, Robert J.		14.00	10.00	4.00
53 Griffin, I. M.	14.00	10.00	4.00	113 Oldham, J.C.		14.00	10.00	4.00
54 Griffith	14.00	10.00	4.00	114 Olson, I.M.		14.00	10.00	4.00
55 Grimes, Burleigh	21.00	15.50	7.00	115 O'Neil, Geo. M.		14.00	10.00	4.00
56 Grimm, Charlie	15.00	11.00	5.00	116 O'Neill, S.F.		14.00	10.00	4.00
57 Haines, Jesse	20.00	15.00	6.50	117 Parkinson, Frank J.		14.00	10.00	4.00
58 S. Harris	20.00	15.00	6.50	118 Paskert, Geo. H.		14.00	10.00	4.00
59 W. Harris	14.00	10.00	4.00	119 Peckinpaugh, R.T.		14.00	10.00	4.00
60 Hasty, Robert	14.00	10.00	4.00	120 Pennock, H.J.		21.00	15.50	7.00

		MINT	VG-E	F-G			MINT	VG-E	F-G
121	Perkins, Ralph	14.00	10.00	4.00	151	Smith, Earl L.	14.00	10.00	4.00
122	Pfeffer, Edw. J.	14.00	10.00	4.00	152	Smith, Earl S.	14.00	10.00	4.00
123	Pipp, W.C.	15.00	11.00	5.00	153	Smith, Geo. A.	14.00	10.00	4.00
124	Ponder, Charles Elmer	14.00	10.00	4.00	154	Smith, J.W.	14.00	10.00	4.00
125	Powell, Raymond R.	14.00	10.00	4.00	155	Speaker, Tris E.	30.00	22.50	10.50
126	Pratt, D.B.	14.00	10.00	4.00	156	Staatz, Arnold	14.00	10.00	4.00
127	Rapp, Joseph	14.00	10.00	4.00	157	Stephenson, J.R.	14.00	10.00	4.00
128	Rawlings, John H.	14.00	10.00	4.00	158	Stock, Milton J.	14.00	10.00	4.00
129	Rice, E.S.	20.00	15.00	6.50	159	Sullivan, John L.	14.00	10.00	4.00
130	Rickey	25.00	18.50	8.75	160	Thormahlen, H.F.	14.00	10.00	4.00
131	Ring, James J.	14.00	10.00	4.00	161	Tierney, Jas. A.	14.00	10.00	4.00
132	Rixey, Eppa J.	20.00	15.00	6.50	162	Tobin, J.T.	14.00	10.00	4.00
133	Robertson, Davis A.	14.00	10.00	4.00	163	Vaughn, Jas. L.	14.00	10.00	4.00
134	Rommel, Edwin	14.00	10.00	4.00	164	Veach, R.H.	14.00	10.00	4.00
135	Roush, Ed J.	20.00	15.00	6.50	165	Walker, C.W.	14.00	10.00	4.00
136	Ruel, Harold	14.00	10.00	4.00	166	Ward, A.L.	14.00	10.00	4.00
137	Russell, Allen	14.00	10.00	4.00	167	Wheat, Zack D.	20.00	15.00	6.50
138	Ruth, G.H.	150.00	110.00	50.00	168	Whitted, George B.	14.00	10.00	4.00
139	Ryan, Wilfred D.	14.00	10.00	4.00	169	Wilhelm, Irvin K.	14.00	10.00	4.00
140	Sallee, Henry F.	14.00	10.00	4.00	170	Wilkinson, Roy H.	14.00	10.00	4.00
141	Schang, W.H.	14.00	10.00	4.00	171	Williams, Fred C.	14.00	10.00	4.00
142	Schmandt, Raymond H.	14.00	10.00	4.00	172	Williams, K.R.	14.00	10.00	4.00
143	Scott, Everett	14.00	10.00	4.00	173	Wilson, Samuel W.	14.00	10.00	4.00
144	Severeid, Henry	14.00	10.00	4.00	174	Wingo, Ivy B.	14.00	10.00	4.00
145	Sewell, Joseph W.	20.00	15.00	6.50	175	Witt, L.W.	14.00	10.00	4.00
146	Shanks, Howard S.	14.00	10.00	4.00	176	Wood, Joseph	15.00	11.00	5.00
147	Sheely, E.H.	14.00	10.00	4.00	177	Yaryan, E.	14.00	10.00	4.00
148	Shinners, Ralph	14.00	10.00	4.00	178	Young, R.S.	14.00	10.00	4.00
149	Shocker, U.J.	14.00	10.00	4.00	179	Youngs, Ross	20.00	15.00	6.50
150	Sisler, G.H.	25.00	18.50	8.75					

1937 V300 O–PEE–CHEE (40)
CANADIAN BATTER–UPS

2 1/2" X 3"

CHARLES (BUDDY) MYER

Is 32 years old, Signed by Cleveland in 1925 and sold in 1926 to Washington. Went to Boston in a trade in 1927 and traded back in 1928. Led American League in batting in 1935. Played in two World's Series. Bats left, throws right. Weight 165 lbs. Height 5' 10½".

A 32 ans. Signé par Cleveland en 1925 il fut vendu à Washington en 1926. Fut échangé à Boston en 1927 et échangé de nouveau en -1928. Premier batteur de la Ligue Americaine en 1935. Joua dans deux Séries Mondiales. Batte à gauche, lance à droite. Pèse 165 lbs. Mesure 5' 10½".

Series A—No. 114

"BUDDY" MYER
Second base, Washington Senators

The 1937 (or 1936) O-Pee-Chee set contains 40 unumbered, die-cut cards. The set is peculiar in that the numbers begin with number 101. The set is sometimes called the Canadian Batter Up set and is designated in ACC as V300.

		MINT	VG-E	F-G
	COMPLETE SET	1350.00	1100.00	400.00
	COMMON PLAYER	35.00	27.00	10.00

		MINT	VG-E	F-G			MINT	VG-E	F-G
101	John Lewis	35.00	27.00	10.00	121	Harry Kelley	35.00	27.00	10.00
102	Jack Hayes	35.00	27.00	10.00	122	Johnny Allen	35.00	27.00	10.00
103	Earl Averill	40.00	30.00	13.00	123	Bob Johnson	35.00	27.00	10.00
104	Harland Clift	35.00	27.00	10.00	124	Joe Cronin	40.00	30.00	13.00
105	Beau Bell	35.00	27.00	10.00	125	Rip Radcliff	35.00	27.00	10.00
106	Jimmy Foxx	90.00	70.00	30.00	126	Cecil Travis	35.00	27.00	10.00
107	Hank Greenberg	65.00	48.00	22.00	127	Joe Kuhel	35.00	27.00	10.00
108	George Selkirk	35.00	27.00	10.00	128	Odell Hale	35.00	27.00	10.00
109	Wally Moses	35.00	27.00	10.00	129	Sam West	35.00	27.00	10.00
110	Gerry Walker	35.00	27.00	10.00	130	Ben Chapman	35.00	27.00	10.00
111	Goose Goslin	40.00	30.00	13.00	131	Monte Pearson	35.00	27.00	10.00
112	Charlie Gehringer	45.00	34.00	15.00	132	Rick Ferrell	35.00	27.00	10.00
113	Hal Trosky	35.00	27.00	10.00	133	Tommy Bridges	35.00	27.00	10.00
114	Buddy Myer	35.00	27.00	10.00	134	Schoolboy Rowe	35.00	27.00	10.00
115	Luke Appling	40.00	30.00	13.00	135	Vernon Kennedy	35.00	27.00	10.00
116	Zeke Bonura	35.00	27.00	10.00	136	Red Ruffing	40.00	30.00	13.00
117	Tony Lazzeri	35.00	27.00	10.00	137	Lefty Grove	65.00	48.00	22.00
118	Joe DiMaggio	200.00	150.00	65.00	138	Wes Ferrell	35.00	27.00	10.00
119	Bill Dickey	80.00	60.00	25.00	139	Buck Newsom	35.00'	27.00	10.00
120	Bob Feller	100.00	70.00	30.00	140	Rogers Hornsby	80.00	60.00	25.00

1933 V353 CANADIAN GOUDEY (94)   2 3/8" X 2 7/8"

The 1933 Canadian Goudey set of 94 numbered cards was issued by World Wide Gum Company. The set is quite similar to the 1933 American Goudey issue with Nos. 49 to 94 renumbered and different than the 1933 American Goudey Nos. 49 to 94. Two backs exist for each card. The more common contain both French and English biographies while a back containing only English biographies is somewhat more difficult to obtain. The ACC designation is V353.

		MINT	VG-E	F-G
	COMPLETE SET	1250.00	900.00	350.00
	COMMON PLAYER	9.00	6.50	2.50
1	Benny Bengough	12.00	8.00	3.00
2	Dazzy Vance	16.00	12.00	5.50
3	Hugh Critz	9.00	6.50	2.50
4	Heine Schuble	9.00	6.50	2.50
5	Babe Herman	9.00	6.50	2.50
6	Jimmy Dykes	9.00	6.50	2.50
7	Ted Lyons	16.00	12.00	5.50
8	Roy Johnson	9.00	6.50	2.50
9	Dave Harris	9.00	6.50	2.50
10	Glenn Myatt	9.00	6.50	2.50
11	Billy Rogell	9.00	6.50	2.50
12	George Blaeholder	9.00	6.50	2.50
13	Lafayette Thompson	9.00	6.50	2.50
14	Henry Johnson	9.00	6.50	2.50
15	Victor Sorrell	9.00	6.50	2.50
16	George Blaeholder	9.00	6.50	2.50
17	Watson Clark	9.00	6.50	2.50
18	Muddy Ruel	9.00	6.50	2.50
19	Bill Dickey	30.00	22.50	10.50
20	Bill Terry	22.00	16.50	7.50
21	Phil Collins	9.00	6.50	2.50
22	Pie Traynor	20.00	15.00	6.50
23	Kiki Cuyler	16.00	12.00	5.50
24	Horace Ford	9.00	6.50	2.50
25	Paul Waner	18.00	13.50	6.00
26	Chalmer Cissell	9.00	6.50	2.50
27	George Connally	9.00	6.50	2.50
28	Dick Bartell	9.00	6.50	2.50
29	Jimmy Foxx	60.00	45.00	20.00
30	Frank Hogan	9.00	6.50	2.50
31	Tony Lazzeri	12.50	9.00	4.00
32	Bud Clancy	9.00	6.50	2.50
33	Ralph Kress	9.00	6.50	2.50
34	Bob O'Farrell	9.00	6.50	2.50
35	Al Simmons	20.00	15.00	6.50
36	Tommy Thevenow	9.00	6.50	2.50
37	Jimmy Wilson	9.00	6.50	2.50
38	Fred Bickell	9.00	6.50	2.50
39	Mark Koenig	9.00	6.50	2.50
40	Taylor Douthit	9.00	6.50	2.50
41	Gus Mancuso	9.00	6.50	2.50
42	Eddie Collins	18.00	13.50	6.00
43	Lew Fonseca	9.00	6.50	2.50
44	Jim Bottomley	16.00	12.00	5.50
45	Larry Benton	9.00	6.50	2.50
46	Ethan Allen	9.00	6.50	2.50
47	Heine Manush	16.00	12.00	5.50

		MINT	VG-E	F-G
48	Marty McManus	9.00	6.50	2.50
49	Frank Frisch	22.00	16.50	7.50
50	Ed Brandt	9.00	6.50	2.50
51	Charlie Grimm	10.00	7.00	3.00
52	Andy Cohen	9.00	6.50	2.50
53	Jack Quinn	9.00	6.50	2.50
54	Urban Faber	16.00	12.00	5.50
55	Lou Gehrig	150.00	110.00	50.00
56	John Welch	9.00	6.50	2.50
57	Bill Walker	9.00	6.50	2.50
58	Lefty O'Doul	10.00	7.00	3.00
59	Bing Miller	9.00	6.50	2.50
60	Waite Hoyt	16.00	12.00	5.50
61	Max Bishop	9.00	6.50	2.50
62	Pepper Martin	10.00	7.00	3.00
63	Joe Cronin	18.00	13.50	6.00
64	Burleigh Grimes	16.00	12.00	5.50
65	Milt Gaston	9.00	6.50	2.50
66	George Grantham	9.00	6.50	2.50
67	Guy Bush	9.00	6.50	2.50
68	Willie Kamm	9.00	6.50	2.50
69	Mickey Cochrane	20.00	15.00	6.50
70	Adam Comorosky	9.00	6.50	2.50
71	Alvin Crowder	9.00	6.50	2.50
72	Willis Hudlin	9.00	6.50	2.50
73	Eddie Farrell	9.00	6.50	2.50
74	Leo Durocher	12.50	9.00	4.00
75	Walter Stewart	9.00	6.50	2.50
76	George Walberg	9.00	6.50	2.50
77	Glenn Wright	9.00	6.50	2.50
78	Charles (Buddy) Myer	9.00	6.50	2.50
79	James (Zack) Taylor	9.00	6.50	2.50
80	George Herman (Babe) Ruth (#144 American Pose)	225.00	160.00	70.00
81	D'Arcy (Jake) Flowers	9.00	6.50	2.50
82	Ray Kolp	9.00	6.50	2.50
83	Oswald Bluege	9.00	6.50	2.50
84	Morris (Moe) Berg	9.00	6.50	2.50
85	Jimmy Foxx	50.00	38.00	17.00
86	Sam Byrd	9.00	6.50	2.50
87	Danny MacFayden	9.00	6.50	2.50
88	Joe Judge	9.00	6.50	2.50
89	Joe Sewell	16.00	12.00	5.50
90	Lloyd Waner	16.00	12.00	5.50
91	Luke Sewell	9.00	6.50	2.50
92	Leo Mangum	9.00	6.50	2.50
93	George Herman "Babe" Ruth (#149 American Pose)	225.00	160.00	70.00
94	Al Spohrer	9.00	6.50	2.50

1934 V354 CANADIAN GOUDEY (96)   2 3/8″ X 2 7/8″
WORLD WIDE GUM CO.

The 1934 Canadian Goudey issue of 96 cards was issued by World Wide Gum Company. Cards Nos. 1 to 48 have the same format as the 1933 American Goudey issue while cards Nos. 49 to 96 have the same format as the 1934 American Goudey issue. Cards

Nos. 49 to 96 all have the "Lou Gehrig Says" endorsement on the front of the cards. No Chuck Klein endorsement exists as it does in the 1934 American issue. The backs are either in English or in English and French. The ACC designation is V354.

No. 62 – 1934 Series –
ED BRANDT
BOSTON BRAVES
Edward Arthur Brandt is a State of Washington boy, who came out of the 1933 season with the reputation of having been one of the leading batters of the National League. And Brandt is a pitcher, who started in his home state on the Seattle team in 1923. Five years later the Boston Braves signed him and he quickly became one of their ace pitchers a southpaw at that.

Edward Brandt est un garçon de l'État de Washington qui termina la saison de 1933 avec la réputation d'avoir été l'un des meilleurs frappeurs de la Ligue Nationale. Et Brandt est aussi lanceur, après avoir commencé à jouer avec l'équipe de Seattle, dans son État, en 1923. Cinq ans plus tard, les "Boston Braves" l'engagèrent et il devint bientôt un de comme lanceur. Et remarquez qu'il est gaucher.

BIG LEAGUE
CHEWING GUM
WORLD WIDE GUM CO., LTD. MONTREAL
Printed in Canada.

	MINT	VG-E	F-G
COMPLETE SET	1250.00	900.00	350.00
COMMON PLAYER	9.00	6.50	2.50

		MINT	VG-E	F-G
1	Rogers Hornsby	40.00	30.00	13.00
2	Eddie Morgan	9.00	6.50	2.50
3	Valentine J. (Val) Picinich	9.00	6.50	2.50
4	Walter (Rabbit) Maranville	16.00	12.00	5.50
5	Flint Rhem	9.00	6.50	2.50
6	Jim Elliott	9.00	6.50	2.50
7	Fred (Red) Lucas	9.00	6.50	2.50
8	Fred Marberry	9.00	6.50	2.50
9	Clifton Earl Heathcote	9.00	6.50	2.50
10	Bernie Friberg	9.00	6.50	2.50
11	Elwood (Woody) English	9.00	6.50	2.50
12	Carl Reynolds	9.00	6.50	2.50
13	Ray Benge	9.00	6.50	2.50
14	Ben Cantwell	9.00	6.50	2.50
15	Irving (Bump) Hadley	9.00	6.50	2.50
16	Herb Pennock	18.00	13.50	6.00
17	Fred Lindstrom	16.00	12.00	5.50
18	Edgar (Sam) Rice	16.00	12.00	5.50
19	Fred Frankhouse	9.00	6.50	2.50
20	Fred Fitzsimmons	9.00	6.50	2.50
21	Earl Coombs	16.00	12.00	5.50
22	George Uhle	9.00	6.50	2.50
23	Richard Coffman	9.00	6.50	2.50
24	Travis C. Jackson	9.00	6.50	2.50
25	Robert J. Burke	9.00	6.50	2.50
26	Randy Moore	9.00	6.50	2.50
27	John Henry (Heinie) Sand	9.00	6.50	2.50
28	George Herman (Babe) Ruth	225.00	160.00	70.00
29	Tris Speaker	30.00	22.50	10.50
30	Perce (Pat) Malone	9.00	6.50	2.50
31	Sam Jones	9.00	6.50	2.50
32	Eppa Rixey	16.00	12.00	5.50
33	Floyd (Pete) Scott	9.00	6.50	2.50
34	Pete Jablonowski	9.00	6.50	2.50
35	Clyde Manion	9.00	6.50	2.50
36	Dibrell Williams	9.00	6.50	2.50
37	Glenn Spencer	9.00	6.50	2.50
38	Ray Kremer	9.00	6.50	2.50
39	Phil Todt	9.00	6.50	2.50
40	Russell Rollings	9.00	6.50	2.50
41	Earl Clark	9.00	6.50	2.50
42	Jess Petty	9.00	6.50	2.50
43	Frank O'Rourke	9.00	6.50	2.50
44	Jesse Haines	16.00	12.00	5.50
45	Horace Lisenbee	9.00	6.50	2.50
46	Owen Carroll	9.00	6.50	2.50

		MINT	VG-E	F-G
47	Tom Zachary	9.00	6.50	2.50
48	Charlie Ruffing	16.00	12.00	5.50
49	Ray Benge	9.00	6.50	2.50
50	Elwood (Woody) English	9.00	6.50	2.50
51	Ben Chapman	9.00	6.50	2.50
52	Joe Kuhel	9.00	6.50	2.50
53	Bill Terry	22.00	16.50	7.50
54	Robert (Lefty) Grove	25.00	18.50	8.75
55	Jerome (Dizzy) Dean	60.00	45.00	20.00
56	Charles (Chuck) Klein	16.00	12.00	5.50
57	Charley Gehringer	20.00	15.00	6.50
58	Jimmy Foxx	60.00	45.00	20.00
59	Gordon (Mickey) Cochrane	22.00	16.50	7.50
60	Willie Kamm	9.00	6.50	2.50
61	Charlie Grimm	9.00	6.50	2.50
62	Ed Brandt	9.00	6.50	2.50
63	Tony Piet	9.00	6.50	2.50
64	Frank Frisch	22.00	16.50	7.50
65	Alvin Crowder	9.00	6.50	2.50
66	Frank Hogan	9.00	6.50	2.50
67	Paul Waner	18.00	13.50	6.00
68	Henry (Heinie) Manush	16.00	12.00	5.50
69	Leo Durocher	12.50	9.00	4.00
70	Floyd Vaughan	10.00	7.00	3.00
71	Carl Hubbell	22.00	16.50	7.50
72	Hugh Critz	9.00	6.50	2.50
73	John (Blondy) Ryan	9.00	6.50	2.50
74	Roger Cramer	9.00	6.50	2.50
75	Baxter Jordan	9.00	6.50	2.50
76	Ed Coleman	9.00	6.50	2.50
77	Julius Solters	9.00	6.50	2.50
78	Charles (Chick) Hafey	16.00	12.00	5.50
79	Larry French	9.00	6.50	2.50
80	Frank (Don) Hurst	9.00	6.50	2.50
81	Gerald Walker	9.00	6.50	2.50
82	Ernie Lombardi	11.00	8.00	3.50
83	Walter (Huck) Betts	9.00	6.50	2.50
84	Luke Appling	16.00	12.00	5.50
85	John Frederick	9.00	6.50	2.50
86	Fred Walker	9.00	6.50	2.50
87	Tom Bridges	9.00	6.50	2.50
88	Dick Porter	9.00	6.50	2.50
89	John Stone	9.00	6.50	2.50
90	James (Tex) Carleton	9.00	6.50	2.50
91	Joe Stripp	9.00	6.50	2.50
92	Lou Gehrig	150.00	110.00	50.00
93	George Earnshaw	9.00	6.50	2.50
94	Oscar Melillo	9.00	6.50	2.50
95	Oral Hildebrand	9.00	6.50	2.50
96	John Allen	9.00	6.50	2.50

1936 V355 CANADIAN GOUDEY (135)   2 1/2" X 3"
WORLD WIDE GUM CO.

No. 23 HAL SCHUMACHER

No. 23
Harold Henry (Hal) Schumacher,
NEW YORK GIANTS

Pitcher   Lanceur

Harold Schumacher, star member of the New York Giants twirling staff. He attended the St. Lawrence University where he starred as a right-handed slab ace. He achieved the longest consecutive winning streak among National League flingers in 1935, topping eleven stars.

Harold Schumacher, une étoile parmis les lanceurs des Giants de New York. Il étudia à l'Université St. Laurent ou il fût une vedette comme lanceur droitier en 1935 il eût la plus longue série de victoires consécutives parmis les lanceurs de la Ligue Nationale dévançant onze autres lanceurs étoiles.

BIG LEAGUE CHEWING GUM

World Wide Gum Co. Ltd. Granby, Que.

Printed in Canada.

The 1936 Candian Goudey set was issued by World Wide Gum Company and contains 135 black and white cards. This issue is the most difficult to obtain of the Canadian Goudeys. The ACC designation is V355.

	MINT	VG-E	F-G
COMPLETE SET	3700.00	2800.00	1300.00
COMMON PLAYER	26.00	20.00	9.00

		MINT	VG-E	F-G
1	Jimmy Dykes	30.00	20.00	9.00
2	Paul Waner	45.00	34.00	15.00
3	Cy Blanton	26.00	20.00	9.00
4	Sam Leslie	26.00	20.00	9.00
5	Johnny Louis Vergez	26.00	20.00	9.00
6	Arky Vaughn	30.00	22.50	10.50
7	Bill Terry	50.00	38.00	17.00
8	Joe Moore	26.00	20.00	9.00
9	Gus Mancuso	26.00	20.00	9.00
10	Fred Marberry	26.00	20.00	9.00
11	George Selkirk	26.00	20.00	9.00
12	Spud Davis	26.00	20.00	9.00
13	Chuck Klein	40.00	30.00	13.00
14	Fred Fitzsimmons	26.00	20.00	9.00
15	Bill DeLancey	26.00	20.00	9.00
16	Billy Herman	40.00	30.00	13.00
17	George Davis	26.00	20.00	9.00
18	Rip Collins	26.00	20.00	9.00
19	Dizzy Dean	100.00	70.00	30.00
20	Roy Parmelee	26.00	20.00	9.00
21	Vic Sorrell	26.00	20.00	9.00
22	Harry Danning	26.00	20.00	9.00
23	Hal Schumacher	26.00	20.00	9.00
24	Cy Perkins	26.00	20.00	9.00
25	Speedy Durocher	35.00	26.00	12.00
26	George Myatt	26.00	20.00	9.00
27	Bob Seeds	26.00	20.00	9.00
28	Jimmy Ripple	26.00	20.00	9.00
29	Al Schacht	26.00	20.00	9.00
30	Pete Fox	26.00	20.00	9.00
31	Del Baker	26.00	20.00	9.00
32	Feal Clifton	26.00	20.00	9.00
33	Tommy Bridges	26.00	20.00	9.00
34	Bill Dickey	65.00	48.00	22.00
35	Wally Berger	26.00	20.00	9.00
36	Slick Castleman	26.00	20.00	9.00
37	Dick Bartell	26.00	20.00	9.00
38	Red Rolfe	26.00	20.00	9.00
39	Waite Hoyt	40.00	30.00	13.00
40	Wes Ferrell	26.00	20.00	9.00
41	Hank Greenberg	50.00	38.00	17.00
42	Charlie Gehringer	50.00	38.00	17.00
43	Goose Goslin	40.00	30.00	13.00
44	Schoolboy Rowe	30.00	22.50	10.50
45	Mickey Cochrane	50.00	38.00	17.00
46	Joe Cronin	50.00	38.00	17.00
47	Jimmy Foxx	80.00	60.00	25.00
48	Jerry Walker	26.00	20.00	9.00
49	Charlie Gelbert	26.00	20.00	9.00
50	Ray Hayworth	26.00	20.00	9.00
51	Joe DiMaggio	200.00	150.00	65.00
52	Billy Rogell	26.00	20.00	9.00
53	John McCarthy	26.00	20.00	9.00
54	Phil Cavaretta	30.00	22.50	10.50
55	KiKi Cuyler	40.00	30.00	13.00
56	Lefty Gomez	50.00	38.00	17.00
57	Gabby Hartnett	45.00	34.00	15.00
58	John Marcum	26.00	20.00	9.00
59	Burgess Whitehead	26.00	20.00	9.00
60	Whitey Whitehill	26.00	20.00	9.00

		MINT	VG-E	F-G
61	Bucky Walters	26.00	20.00	9.00
62	Luke Sewell	26.00	20.00	9.00
63	Joey Kuhel	26.00	20.00	9.00
64	Lou Finney	26.00	20.00	9.00
65	Fred Lindstrom	40.00	30.00	13.00
66	Paul Derringer	30.00	22.50	10.50
67	Steve O'Neill	26.00	20.00	9.00
68	Mule Haas	26.00	20.00	9.00
69	Freck Owen	26.00	20.00	9.00
70	Bill Hallahan	26.00	20.00	9.00
71	Billy Urbanski	26.00	20.00	9.00
72	Dan Taylor	26.00	20.00	9.00
73	Heine Manush	40.00	30.00	13.00
74	Jo-Jo White	26.00	20.00	9.00
75	Mickey Medwick	45.00	34.00	15.00
76	Joe Vosmik	26.00	20.00	9.00
77	Al Simmons	45.00	34.00	15.00
78	Shaug Shaugnessy	26.00	20.00	9.00
79	Harry Smythe	26.00	20.00	9.00
80	Benny Tate	26.00	20.00	9.00
81	Billy Rhiel	26.00	20.00	9.00
82	Lauri Myllykangas	26.00	20.00	9.00
83	Ben Sankey	26.00	20.00	9.00
84	Crip Poli	26.00	20.00	9.00
85	Jim Bottomley	40.00	30.00	13.00
86	Watson Clark	26.00	20.00	9.00
87	Ossie Bluege	25.00	20.00	9.00
88	Lefty Grove	65.00	48.00	22.00
89	Charlie Grimm	26.00	20.00	9.00
90	Ben Chapman	26.00	20.00	9.00
91	Frank Crosetti	30.00	22.50	10.50
92	John Pomorski	26.00	20.00	9.00
93	Jess Haines	40.00	30.00	13.00
94	Chick Hafey	50.00	38.00	17.00
95	Tony Piet	26.00	20.00	9.00
96	Lou Gehrig	250.00	150.00	65.00
97	Billy Jurges	26.00	20.00	9.00
98	Smead Jolley	26.00	20.00	9.00
99	Jimmy Wilson	26.00	20.00	9.00
100	Lon Warneke	26.00	20.00	9.00
101	Vito Tamulis	26.00	20.00	9.00
102	Charlie Ruffing	40.00	30.00	13.00
103	Earl Grace	26.00	20.00	9.00
104	Rox Lawson	26.00	20.00	9.00
105	Stan Hack	30.00	22.50	10.50
106	Augie Galan	26.00	20.00	9.00
107	Frank Frisch	45.00	34.00	15.00
108	Bill McKechnie	35.00	26.00	12.00
109	Bill Lee	26.00	20.00	9.00
110	Connie Mack	60.00	45.00	20.00
111	Frank Reiber	26.00	20.00	9.00
112	Zeke Bonura	26.00	20.00	9.00
113	Luke Appling	40.00	30.00	13.00
114	Monte Pearson	26.00	20.00	9.00
115	Bob O'Farrell	26.00	20.00	9.00
116	Marvin Duke	26.00	20.00	9.00
117	Paul Florence	26.00	20.00	9.00
118	John Berley	26.00	20.00	9.00
119	Tom Oliver	26.00	20.00	9.00
120	Norman Kies	26.00	20.00	9.00

```
1936 CANADIAN GOUDEY (CONT)
          MINT    VG-E    F-G                              MINT    VG-E    F-G
121 Hal King       26.00   20.00    9.00    129 Rabbit Maranville   35.00   26.00   12.00
122 Tom Abernathy  26.00   20.00    9.00    130 Bucky Harris        35.00   26.00   12.00
123 Phil Hensich   26.00   20.00    9.00    131 Al Lopez            35.00   26.00   12.00
124 Ray Schalk     35.00   26.00   12.00    132 Buddy Myer          26.00   20.00    9.00
125 Paul Dunlap    26.00   20.00    9.00    133 Cliff Bolton        26.00   20.00    9.00
126 Benny Bates    26.00   20.00    9.00    134 Estel Crabtree      26.00   20.00    9.00
127 George Puccinelli 26.00 20.00   9.00    135 Phil Weintrab       26.00   20.00    9.00
128 Stevie Stevenson 26.00 20.00    9.00
```

1950 V362 BIG LEAGUE STARS (48)   2 1/2" X 3 1/4"
WORLD WIDE GUM CO.

The 1950 World Wide Gum Company V362 set contains 48 numbered cards. The set depicts International League players only; however, it is entitled "Big League Stars".

```
                MINT    VG-E    F-G
COMPLETE SET   750.00  600.00  250.00
COMMON PLAYER   16.00   12.50    5.00
```

```
                   MINT    VG-E    F-G                           MINT    VG-E    F-G
 1 Rocky Bridges   16.00   12.50   5.00    25 Ronnie Lee          16.00   12.50   5.00
 2 Chuck Connors   75.00   55.00  24.00    26 Clyde King          16.00   12.50   5.00
 3 Jake Wade       16.00   12.50   5.00    27 Harry Heslet        16.00   12.50   5.00
 4 Al Cihocki      16.00   12.50   5.00    28 Jerry Scala         16.00   12.50   5.00
 5 John Simmons    16.00   12.50   5.00    29 Boris Woyt          16.00   12.50   5.00
 6 Frank Trechock  16.00   12.50   5.00    30 Jack Collum         16.00   12.50   5.00
 7 Steve Lembo     16.00   12.50   5.00    31 Chet Laabs          16.00   12.50   5.00
 8 Johnny Welaj    16.00   12.50   5.00    32 Carden Gillenwater  16.00   12.50   5.00
 9 Seymour Block   16.00   12.50   5.00    33 Irving Medlinger    16.00   12.50   5.00
10 Pat McGlothlin  16.00   12.50   5.00    34 Toby Atwell         16.00   12.50   5.00
11 Bryan Stephans  16.00   12.50   5.00    35 Charlie Marshall    16.00   12.50   5.00
12 Clarence Podbelian 16.00 12.50  5.00    36 Johnny Mayo         16.00   12.50   5.00
13 Clem Hausmann   20.00   15.00   6.50    37 Gene Markland       16.00   12.50   5.00
14 Turk Lown       16.00   12.50   5.00    38 Russ Kerns          16.00   12.50   5.00
15 Joe Payne       16.00   12.50   5.00    39 Jim Prendergast     16.00   12.50   5.00
16 Coaker Triplett 16.00   12.50   5.00    40 Lou Welaj           16.00   12.50   5.00
17 Nick Strincevich 16.00  12.50   5.00    41 Clyde Kluttz        16.00   12.50   5.00
18 Charlie Thompson 16.00  12.50   5.00    42 Bill Glynn          16.00   12.50   5.00
19 Erick Silverman 16.00   12.50   5.00    43 Don Richmond        16.00   12.50   5.00
20 George Schmees  16.00   12.50   5.00    44 Hank Biasatti       16.00   12.50   5.00
21 George Binks    16.00   12.50   5.00    45 Tom Lasorda         50.00   38.00  17.00
22 Gino Cimoli     16.00   12.50   5.00    46 Al Roberge          16.00   12.50   5.00
23 Marty Tabacheck 16.00   12.50   5.00    47 George Byam         16.00   12.50   5.00
24 Al Gionfriddo   16.00   12.50   5.00    48 Dutch Mele          16.00   12.50   5.00
```

1952 V338-1 PARKHURST/FROSTADE (100) 2" X 2 1/2"

The 1952 Parkhurst/Frostade set contains 100 black and white, numbered cards. The set depicts players from the three Canadian International League teams - Montreal Royals, Ottawa Athletics, and Toronto Maple Leafs. The backs have a red print and include player information and an ad for Frostade. The set also includes a number of playing tip cards.

	MINT	VG-E	F-G
COMPLETE SET	700.00	525.00	250.00
COMMON PLAYER	7.00	5.25	2.50

#	Player	MINT	VG-E	F-G
1	Joe Becker	8.00	6.00	2.50
2	Aaron Silverman	7.00	5.25	2.50
3	Bobby Rhown	7.00	5.25	2.50
4	Russ Bauers	7.00	5.25	2.50
5	William Jennings	7.00	5.25	2.50
6	Grover Bowers	7.00	5.25	2.50
7	Vic Lombardi	7.00	5.25	2.50
8	William DeMars	7.00	5.25	2.50
9	Frank Colman	7.00	5.25	2.50
10	Charles Grant	7.00	5.25	2.50
11	Irving Medlinger	7.00	5.25	2.50
12	Burke McLaughlin	7.00	5.25	2.50
13	Lew Morton	7.00	5.25	2.50
14	Red Barrett	7.00	5.25	2.50
15	Leon Foulk	7.00	5.25	2.50
16	Neil Sheridan	7.00	5.25	2.50
17	Andy Anderson	7.00	5.25	2.50
18	Roy Shore	7.00	5.25	2.50
19	Duke Markell	7.00	5.25	2.50
20	Robert Balcena	7.00	5.25	2.50
21	Wilmer Fields	7.00	5.25	2.50
22	Charles White	7.00	5.25	2.50
23	Gerald Fahr	7.00	5.25	2.50
24	Jose Bracho	7.00	5.25	2.50
25	Edward Stevens	7.00	5.25	2.50
26	Maple Leaf Stadium	7.00	5.25	2.50
27	Throwing Home	7.00	5.25	2.50
28	Baseball Diamond	7.00	5.25	2.50
29	Gripping the Bat	7.00	5.25	2.50
30	Hiding Kind of Pitch	7.00	5.25	2.50
31	Catcher's Stance	7.00	5.25	2.50
32	Quiz Question	7.00	5.25	2.50
33	Finger/Arm Exercises	7.00	5.25	2.50
34	First Baseman	7.00	5.25	2.50
35	Pitcher's Stance	7.00	5.25	2.50
36	Swinging Bats	7.00	5.25	2.50
37	Quiz Question	7.00	5.25	2.50
38	Watch the Ball	7.00	5.25	2.50
39	Quiz Question	7.00	5.25	2.50
40	Quiz Question	7.00	5.25	2.50
41	How to Bunt	7.00	5.25	2.50
42	Wrist Snap	7.00	5.25	2.50
43	Pitching Practice	7.00	5.25	2.50
44	Stealing Bases	7.00	5.25	2.50
45	Pitching 1	7.00	5.25	2.50
46	Pitching 2	7.00	5.25	2.50
47	Signals	7.00	5.25	2.50
48	Regulation Baseballs	7.00	5.25	2.50
49	Albert Ronning	7.00	5.25	2.50
50	William C. Lane	7.00	5.25	2.50

#	Player	MINT	VG-E	F-G
51	William Samson	7.00	5.25	2.50
52	Charles Thompson	7.00	5.25	2.50
53	Ezra McGlothin	7.00	5.25	2.50
54	Forest Jacobs	7.00	5.25	2.50
55	Arthur Fabbro	7.00	5.25	2.50
56	James Hughes	7.00	5.25	2.50
57	Donald Hoak	8.00	6.00	2.50
58	Thomas Lasorda	20.00	15.00	6.50
59	Gilbert Mills	7.00	5.25	2.50
60	Malcolm Mallette	7.00	5.25	2.50
61	Glenn Nelson	7.00	5.25	2.50
62	John Simmons	7.00	5.25	2.50
63	R. S. Alexander	7.00	5.25	2.50
64	Daniel Bankhead	7.00	5.25	2.50
65	Solomon Coleman	7.00	5.25	2.50
66	Walter Alston	12.00	8.75	4.00
67	Walter Fiala	7.00	5.25	2.50
68	James Gilliam	16.00	12.00	5.50
69	James Pendleton	7.00	5.25	2.50
70	Gino Cimoli	7.00	5.25	2.50
71	Carmen Mauro	7.00	5.25	2.50
72	Walter Moryn	7.00	5.25	2.50
73	James Romano	7.00	5.25	2.50
74	Rollin Lutz	7.00	5.25	2.50
75	Edward Roebuck	7.00	5.25	2.50
76	John Podres	12.00	8.75	4.00
77	Walter Novick	7.00	5.25	2.50
78	Lefty Gohl	7.00	5.25	2.50
79	Thomas Kirk	7.00	5.25	2.50
80	Robert Betz	7.00	5.25	2.50
81	Bill Hockenbury	7.00	5.25	2.50
82	Albert Rubeling	7.00	5.25	2.50
83	Julius Watlington	7.00	5.25	2.50
84	Frank Fanovich	7.00	5.25	2.50
85	Hank Foiles	7.00	5.25	2.50
86	Lou Limmer	7.00	5.25	2.50
87	Edward Hrabcsak	7.00	5.25	2.50
88	Bale Gardner	7.00	5.25	2.50
89	John Metkovich	7.00	5.25	2.50
90	Jean-Pierre Roy	7.00	5.25	2.50
91	Frank Skaff	7.00	5.25	2.50
92	Harry Desert	7.00	5.25	2.50
93	Stanley Jok	7.00	5.25	2.50
94	Russ Swingle	7.00	5.25	2.50
95	Bob Wellman	7.00	5.25	2.50
96	John Conway	7.00	5.25	2.50
97	George Maskovich	7.00	5.25	2.50
98	Charles Bishop	7.00	5.25	2.50
99	Joseph Murray	7.00	5.25	2.50
100	Mike Kume	7.00	5.25	2.50

V410 CRACKER JACK

1953 CANADIAN EXHIBITS (64)   3 1/4" X 5 1/4"

This numbered, blank-back set depicts both major league players — reprinted from American Exhibit sets — and International League Montreal Royals. The cards are slightly smaller than regular Exhibit issues and are printed on gray stock. Numbers 1–32 are found in green or wine—red color, while 33–64 are blue or reddish—brown. Cards 1–32 are numbered in a small, diamond—shaped white box at lower right; cards 33–64 have a large, hand—lettered number at upper right.

	MINT	VG-E	F-G
COMPLETE SET	180.00	135.00	60.00
COMMON PLAYER (1-32)	3.00	2.25	1.00
COMMON PLAYER (33-64)	1.00	.70	.30

	MINT	VG-E	F-G
1 Preacher Roe	4.00	3.00	1.40
2 Luke Easter	3.00	2.25	1.00
3 Gene Bearden	3.00	2.25	1.00
4 Chico Carrasquel	3.00	2.25	1.00
5 Vic Raschi	4.00	3.00	1.40
6 Monte Irvin	5.00	3.75	1.75
7 Henry Sauer	3.00	2.25	1.00
8 Ralph Branca	3.00	2.25	1.00
9 Eddie Stanky	3.00	2.25	1.00
10 Sam Jethroe	3.00	2.25	1.00
11 Larry Doby	4.00	3.00	1.40
12 Hal Newhouser	4.00	3.00	1.40
13 Gil Hodges	6.00	4.50	2.00
14 Harry Brecheen	3.00	2.25	1.10
15 Ed Lopat	4.00	3.00	1.40
16 Don Newcombe	4.00	3.00	1.40
17 Bob Feller	12.00	8.75	4.00
18 Tommy Holmes	4.00	3.00	1.40
19 Jackie Robinson	12.00	8.75	4.00
20 Roy Campanella	12.00	8.75	4.00
21 Pee Wee Reese	6.00	4.50	2.00
22 Ralph Kiner	6.00	4.50	2.00
23 Dom DiMaggio	6.00	4.50	2.00
24 Bobby Doerr	4.00	3.00	1.40
25 Phil Rizzuto	6.00	4.50	2.00
26 Bob Elliott	3.00	2.25	1.00
27 Tom Henrich	4.00	3.00	1.40
28 Joe DiMaggio	25.00	18.50	8.75
29 Harry Lowery (sic)	3.00	2.25	1.00
30 Ted Williams	20.00	15.00	6.50
31 Bob Lemon	5.00	3.75	1.75
32 Warren Spahn	6.00	4.50	2.00

	MINT	VG-E	F-G
33 Don Hoak	1.00	.70	.30
34 Bob Alexander	1.00	.70	.30
35 Simmons	1.00	.70	.30
36 Steve Lembo	1.00	.70	.30
37 Norman Larker	1.00	.70	.30
38 Bob Ludwick	1.00	.70	.30
39 Walter Moryn	1.00	.70	.30
40 Charlie Thompson	1.00	.70	.30
41 Ed Roebuck	1.00	.70	.30
42 Rose	1.00	.70	.30
43 Edmundo Amoros	1.00	.70	.30
44 Bob Milliken	1.00	.70	.30
45 Art Fabbro	1.00	.70	.30
46 Forrest Jacobs	1.00	.70	.30
47 Carmen Mauro	1.00	.70	.30
48 Walter Fiala	1.00	.70	.30
49 Rocky Nelson	1.00	.70	.30
50 Tom Lasorda	2.50	1.80	.80
51 Ronnie Lee	1.00	.70	.30
52 Hampton Coleman	1.00	.70	.30
53 Frank Marchio	1.00	.70	.30
54 Samson	1.00	.70	.30
55 Gil Mills	1.00	.70	.30
56 Al Ronning	1.00	.70	.30
57 Stan Musial	4.00	3.00	1.40
58 Walker Cooper	1.00	.70	.30
59 Mickey Vernon	1.00	.70	.30
60 Del Ennis	1.00	.70	.30
61 Walter Alston	1.50	1.10	.50
62 Dick Sisler	1.00	.70	.30
63 Billy Goodman	1.00	.70	.30
64 Alex Kellner	1.00	.70	.30

M130-1 PHILADELPHIA BULLETIN

1962 CANADIAN POST CEREAL (200)   2 1/2" X 3 1/2"

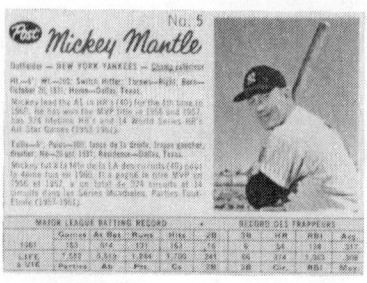

The 1962 Canadian Post Cereal set contains 200 numbered cards quite similar in appearance to the 1962 American Post Cereal set. The Maris card number 6, and the Mays card number 142, are of limited distribution as are others marked in the checklist with an asterisk. Two Ford cards exist. The correct version is more scarce as the correction was not made until late in the year.

	MINT	VG-E	F-G
COMPLETE SET	350.00	250.00	100.00
COMMON PLAYER	1.25	.90	.40

#	Player	MINT	VG-E	F-G
1	Bill Skowron	1.75	1.25	.55
2	Bobby Richardson	1.75	1.25	.55
3	Cletis Boyer	1.25	.90	.40
4	Tony Kubek	1.75	1.25	.55
5	Mickey Mantle	15.00	11.00	5.00
6	Roger Maris*	10.00	7.00	3.00
7	Yogi Berra	4.00	3.00	1.40
8	Elston Howard	2.00	1.50	.60
9A	Whitey Ford (Dodgers)	5.00	3.75	1.75
9B	Whitey Ford (Yankees)	20.00	15.00	6.50
10	Ralph Terry	1.25	.90	.40
11	John Blanchard	1.25	.90	.40
12	Luis Arroyo	1.25	.90	.40
13	Bill Stafford	1.25	.90	.40
14	Norm Cash	1.50	1.10	.50
15	Jake Wood	1.25	.90	.40
16	Steve Boros	1.25	.90	.40
17	Chico Fernandez	1.25	.90	.40
18	Bill Bruton	1.25	.90	.40
19	Ken Aspromonte	1.25	.90	.40
20	Al Kaline	4.00	3.00	1.40
21	Dick Brown	1.25	.90	40
22	Frank Lary *	5.00	3.75	1.75
23	Don Mossi	1.25	.90	.40
24	Phil Regan	1.25	.90	.40
25	Charley Maxwell	1.25	.90	.40
26	Jim Bunning	1.75	1.25	.55
27	Jim Gentile	1.25	.90	.40
28	Marv Breeding	1.25	.90	.40
29	Brooks Robinson	4.00	3.00	1.40
30	Ron Hansen	1.25	.90	.40
31	Jackie Brandt	1.25	.90	.40
32	Dick Williams	1.50	1.10	.50
33	Gus Triandos	1.25	.90	.40
34	Milt Pappas	1.25	.90	.40
35	Hoyt Wilhelm *	6.00	4.50	2.00
36	Chuck Estrada	1.25	.90	.40
37	Vic Power	1.25	.90	.40
38	Johnny Temple	1.25	.90	.40
39	Bubba Phillips	1.25	.90	.40
40	Tito Francona *	5.00	3.75	1.75
41	Willie Kirkland	1.25	.90	.40
42	John Romano	1.25	.90	.40
43	Jim Perry	1.50	1.10	.50
44	Woodie Held	1.25	.90	.40
45	Chuck Essegian	1.25	.90	.40
46	Roy Sievers	1.25	.90	.40
47	Nellie Fox	1.75	1.25	.55
48	Al Smith	1.25	.90	.40
49	Luis Aparicio *	6.00	4.50	2.00
50	Jim Landis	1.25	.90	.40
51	Minnie Minoso	1.75	1.25	.55
52	Andy Carey	1.25	.90	.40
53	Sherman Lollar	1.25	.90	.40
54	Bill Pierce	1.50	1.10	.50
55	Early Wynn	2.50	1.80	.80
56	Chuck Schilling	1.25	.90	.40
57	Pete Runnels	1.25	.90	.40
58	Frank Malzone	1.25	.90	.40
59	Don Buddin	1.25	.90	.40
60	Gary Geiger	1.25	.90	.40
61	Carl Yastrzemski	8.00	6.00	2.50
62	Jackie Jensen	1.50	1.10	.50
63	Jim Pagliaroni	1.25	.90	.40
64	Don Schwall *	5.00	3.75	1.75
65	Dale Long	1.25	.90	.40
66	Chuck Cottier	1.25	.90	.40
67	Billy Klaus	1.25	.90	.40
68	Coot Veal	1.25	.90	.40
69	Marty Keough	1.25	.90	.40
70	Willie Tasby	1.25	.90	.40
71	Gene Woodling	1.25	.90	.40
72	Gene Green	1.25	.90	.40
73	Dick Donovan	1.25	.90	.40
74	Steve Bilko	1.25	.90	.40
75	Rocky Bridges	1.25	.90	.40
76	Eddie Yost	1.25	.90	.40
77	Leon Wagner*	5.00	3.75	1.75
78	Albie Pearson	1.25	.90	.40
79	Ken Hunt	1.25	.90	.40
80	Earl Averill	1.25	.90	.40
81	Ryne Duren	1.25	.90	.40
82	Ted Kluszewski	1.75	1.25	.55
83	Bob Allison	1.50	1.10	.50
84	Billy Martin	2.25	1.65	.75
85	Harmon Killebrew	2.50	1.80	.80
86	Zoilo Versalles	1.25	.90	.40
87	Lenny Green *	5.00	3.75	1.75
88	Bill Tuttle	1.25	.90	.40
89	Jim Lemon	1.25	.90	.40
90	Earl Battey	1.25	.90	.40
91	Camilo Pascual	1.25	.90	.40
92	Norm Sieburn	1.25	.90	.40
93	Jerry Lumpe	1.25	.90	.40
94	Dick Howser	1.75	1.25	.55
95	Gene Stephens	1.25	.90	.40
96	Leo Posada	1.25	.90	.40
97	Joe Pignatano	1.25	.90	.40
98	Jim Archer	1.25	.90	.40
99	Haywood Sullivan	1.50	1.10	.50
100	Art Ditmar	1.25	.90	.40
101	Gil Hodges	3.00	2.25	1.00
102	Charlie Neal	1.25	.90	.40
103	Daryl Spencer	1.25	.90	.40
104	Maury Wills	1.75	1.25	.55
105	Tommy Davis *	6.00	4.50	2.00
106	Willie Davis	1.25	.90	.40
107	John Roseboro	1.25	.90	.40
108	John Podres	1.50	1.10	.50
109	Sandy Koufax	8.00	6.00	2.50
110	Don Drysdale	2.50	1.80	.80
111	Larry Sherry	1.25	.90	.40
112	Jim Gilliam *	6.00	4.50	2.00
113	Norm Larker	1.25	.90	.40
114	Duke Snider	5.00	3.75	1.75
115	Stan Williams	1.25	.90	.40
116	Gordy Coleman	1.25	.90	.40
117	Don Blasingame *	5.00	3.75	1.75
118	Gene Freese	1.25	.90	.40
119	Ed Kasko	1.25	.90	.40
120	Gus Bell	1.25	.90	.40

Most serious collectors subscribe to at least one of the hobby papers. Read the ads in this Guide for The Trader Speaks (for advanced collectors), Sports Collectors Digest, and Baseball Hobby News to determine which one or more appeal to you.

1962 CANADIAN POST (CONTINUED)

		MINT	VG-E	F-G			MINT	VG-E	F-G
121	Vada Pinson	1.50	1.10	.50	161	Carl Warwick *	5.00	3.75	1.75
122	Frank Robinson	4.00	3.00	1.40	162	Carl Sawatski	1.25	.90	.40
123	Bob Purkey *	5.00	3.75	1.75	163	Lindy McDaniel	1.25	.90	.40
124	Joey Jay	1.25	.90	.40	164	Ernie Broglio	1.25	.90	.40
125	Jim Brosnan	1.25	.90	.40	165	Larry Jackson	1.25	.90	.40
126	Jim O'Toole	1.25	.90	.40	166	Curt Flood	1.50	1.10	.50
127	Jerry Lynch	1.25	.90	.40	167	Curt Simmons	1.25	.90	.40
128	Wally Post	1.25	.90	.40	168	Alex Grammas	1.25	.90	.40
129	Ken Hunt	1.25	.90	.40	169	Dick Stuart	1.25	.90	.40
130	Jerry Zimmerman	1.25	.90	.40	170	Bill Mazeroski	1.50	1.10	.50
131	Willie McCovey	3.00	2.25	1.00	171	Don Hoak	1.25	.90	.40
132	Jose Pagan	1.25	.90	.40	172	Dick Groat	1.50	1.10	.50
133	Felipe Alou	1.50	1.10	.50	173	Roberto Clemente	8.00	6.00	2.50
134	Jim Davenport	1.25	.90	.40	174	Bob Skinner	1.25	.90	.40
135	Harvey Kuenn	1.50	1.10	.50	175	Bill Virdon	1.75	1.25	.55
136	Orlando Cepeda	2.00	1.50	.60	176	Smokey Burgess *	5.00	3.75	1.75
137	Ed Bailey *	5.00	3.75	1.75	177	Elroy Face	1.50	1.10	.50
138	Sam Jones	1.25	.90	.40	178	Bob Friend	1.25	.90	.40
139	Mike McCormick	1.25	.90	.40	179	Vernon Law	1.50	1.10	.50
140	Juan Marichal	2.00	1.50	.60	180	Harvey Haddix	1.25	.90	.40
141	Jack Sanford	1.25	.90	.40	181	Hal Smith	1.25	.90	.40
142	Willie Mays *	25.00	18.50	8.75	182	Ed Bouchee *	5.00	3.75	1.75
143	Stu Miller	1.25	.90	.40	183	Don Zimmer	1.50	1.10	.50
144	Joe Amalfitano	1.25	.90	.40	184	Ron Santo	1.75	1.25	.55
145	Joe Adcock	1.25	.90	.40	185	Andre Rodgers	1.25	.90	.40
146	Frank Bolling	1.25	.90	.40	186	Richie Ashburn	1.75	1.25	.55
147	Ed Mathews	3.50	2.50	1.20	187	George Altman	1.25	.90	.40
148	Roy McMillan	1.25	.90	.40	188	Ernie Banks	6.00	4.50	2.00
149	Hank Aaron	10.00	7.00	3.00	189	Sam Taylor	1.25	.90	.40
150	Gino Cimoli	1.25	.90	.40	190	Don Elston	1.25	.90	.40
151	Frank Thomas	1.25	.90	.40	191	Jerry Kindall	1.25	.90	.40
152	Joe Torre	1.75	1.25	.55	192	Pancho Herrera	1.25	.90	.40
153	Lew Burdette	1.50	1.10	.50	193	Tony Taylor	1.25	.90	.40
154	Bob Buhl	1.25	.90	.40	194	Ruben Amaro	1.25	.90	.40
155	Carlton Willey	1.25	.90	.40	195	Don Demeter	1.25	.90	.40
156	Lee Maye	1.25	.90	.40	196	Bobby Gene Smith	1.25	.90	.40
157	Al Spangler	1.25	.90	.40	197	Clay Dalrymple	1.25	.90	.40
158	Bill White	1.25	.90	.40	198	Robin Roberts	2.50	1.80	.80
159	Ken Boyer	1.75	1.25	.55	199	Art Mahaffey	1.25	.90	.40
160	Joe Cunningham	1.25	.90	.40	200	John Buzhardt	1.25	.90	.40

O-PEE-CHEE

O-Pee Chee issued cards so similar to Topps from 1965 to 1976, that reference is made below to the Topps sets of the same year with only notable changes listed. Superstar, star and special card prices are approximately the same as for Topps cards of the same year.

O-PEE-CHEE CO. LTD.

	VALUES					
	COMPLETE SET			COMMON PLAYER		

1965 (283) same as Topps 1-283.
125.00 100.00 40.00   .25   .20   .08

1966 (196) same as Topps 1-196.
90.00 70.00 30.00   .22   .17   .07

1967 (196) same as Topps 1-196.
85.00 65.00 30.00   .21   .16   .07

1968 (196) same as Topps 1-196.
75.00 55.00 25.00   .18   .14   .06

1969 (218) same as Topps 1-218.
CHANGES
    Dalrymple - Phillies
    Clendennon - Expos
75.00 55.00 25.00   .17   .13   .06

1970 (546) same as Topps (French and English text).
110.00 85.00 40.00   .15   .11   .05

1971 (752) #1-523 have French and English text, with photo on back centered betweeen text.
    #524-752 English text only. Same back style as Topps only gold back, instead of green.
CHANGES
    #31 John Bateman (different pose)
    #32 with Orioles
    #73 with Cardinals
    #144 with Pirates
    #151 with Athletics
    #161 Ron Hunt (different pose)
    #172 with Dodgers
    #182 with Dodgers
    #191 with White Sox
    #202 Claude Raymond (different pose)
    #207 with Indians
    #248 with Braves
    #289 Rusty Staub (different pose)
    #578 Eddie Kasko
140.00 100.00 40.00   .15   .11   .05

1972 (525) Hodges card has note about death on 4-2-72 same as Topps 1-525. French and English text.
90.00 70.00 30.00   .14   .10   .04

1973 (660) same as Topps. French and English text.
70.00 50.00 20.00   .10   .07   .03

1974 (660) no traded set. French and English text.
CHANGES
    #3 shows Aaron cards 1958 and 1959.
    #4 shows Aaron cards 1960 and 1961.
    #5 shows Aaron cards 1962 and 1963.
    #6 shows Aaron cards 1964 and 1965.
    #7 shows Aaron cards 1966 and 1967.
    #8 shows Aaron cards 1968 and 1969.
    #9 shows Aaron cards 1970 to 1973.
    #99 George Theodore
    #166 Mickey Lolich
    #196 Jim Hunter
60.00 45.00 20.00   .08   .06   .02

1975 (660) same as Topps. French and English text.
50.00 38.00 18.00   .06   .04   .02

1976 (660) same as Topps. French and English text.
40.00 30.00 13.00   .06   .04   .02

The 1977 O-Pee-Chee set of 264 cards differs considerably from the Topps set of 1977. Many different poses and the existence of many more players from the two Canadian teams than the Topps set are the two most significant discrimination features.

	MINT	VG-E	F-G
COMPLETE SET	18.00	14.00	6.00
COMMON PLAYER	.05	.03	.01

	MINT	VG-E	F-G
1 '76 Batting Leaders	.10	.07	.03
2 '76 Home Run Ldrs.	.10	.07	.03
3 '76 RBI Leaders	.10	.07	.03
4 '76 SB Leaders	.10	.07	.03
5 '76 Victory Leaders	.10	.07	.03
6 '76 SO Leaders	.10	.07	.03
7 '76 ERA Leaders	.10	.07	.03
8 '76 Leading Firemen	.10	.07	.03
9 Mike Jorgensen	.05	.03	.01
10 Jim Hunter	.20	.15	.06
11 Ken Griffey	.15	.11	.05
12 Bill Campbell	.05	.03	.01
13 Otto Velez	.05	.03	.01
14 Mitt May	.05	.03	.01
15 Dennis Eckersley	.08	.06	.02
16 John Mayberry	.08	.06	.02
17 Larry Bowa	.15	.11	.05
18 Don Carrithers	.05	.03	.01
19 Ken Singleton	.15	.11	.05
20 Bill Stein	.05	.03	.01
21 Ken Brett	.05	.03	.01
22 Gary Woods	.05	.03	.01
23 Steve Swisher	.05	.03	.01
24 Don Sutton	.20	.15	.06
25 Willie Stargell	.35	.27	.12
26 Jerry Koosman	.08	.06	.02
27 Del Unser	.05	.03	.01
28 Bob Grich	.08	.06	.02
29 Jim Slaton	.05	.03	.01
30 Thurman Munson	.40	.30	.13
31 Dan Driessen	.05	.03	.01
32 Tom Bruno	.05	.03	.01
33 Larry Hisle	.08	.06	.02
34 Phil Garner	.05	.03	.01
35 Mike Hargrove	.05	.03	.01
36 Jackie Brown	.05	.03	.01
37 Carl Yastrzemski	.40	.30	.13
38 Dave Roberts	.05	.03	.01
39 Ray Fosse	.05	.03	.01
40 Dave McKay	.05	.03	.01
41 Paul Splittorff	.05	.03	.01
42 Garry Maddox	.08	.06	.02
43 Phil Niekro	.10	.07	.03
44 Roger Metzger	.05	.03	.01
45 Gary Carter	.20	.15	.06
46 Jim Spencer	.05	.03	.01
47 Ross Grimsley	.05	.03	.01
48 Bob Bailor	.05	.03	.01
49 Chris Chambliss	.05	.03	.01
50 Will McEnaney	.05	.03	.01
51 Lou Brock	.30	.25	.10
52 Rollie Fingers	.15	.11	.05
53 Chris Speier	.05	.03	.01
54 Bombo Rivera	.05	.03	.01
55 Pete Broberg	.05	.03	.01
56 Bill Madlock	.05	.03	.01
57 Rick Rhoden	.05	.03	.01
58 Blue Jays: Coaches	.10	.07	.03
59 John Candelaria	.05	.03	.01
60 Ed Kranepool	.05	.03	.01

	MINT	VG-E	F-G
61 Dave LaRoche	.05	.03	.01
62 Jim Rice	.40	.30	.13
63 Don Stanhouse	.05	.03	.01
64 Jason Thompson	.05	.03	.01
65 Nolan Ryan	.30	.25	.10
66 Tom Poquette	.05	.03	.01
67 Leon Hooten	.05	.03	.01
68 Bob Boone	.05	.03	.01
69 Mickey Rivers	.08	.06	.02
70 Gary Nolan	.05	.03	.01
71 Sixto Lezcano	.08	.06	.02
72 Larry Parrish	.10	.07	.03
73 Dave Goltz	.05	.03	.01
74 Bert Campaneris	.05	.03	.01
75 Vida Blue	.15	.11	.05
76 Rick Cerone	.08	.06	.02
77 Ralph Garr	.05	.03	.01
78 Ken Forsch	.05	.03	.01
79 Willie Montanez	.05	.03	.01
80 Jim Palmer	.30	.25	.10
81 Jerry White	.05	.03	.01
82 Gene Tenace	.05	.03	.01
83 Bobby Murcer	.08	.06	.02
84 Garry Templeton	.30	.25	.10
85 Bill Singer	.05	.03	.01
86 Buddy Bell	.15	.11	.05
87 Luis Tiant	.10	.07	.03
88 Rusty Staub	.15	.11	.05
89 Sparky Lyle	.08	.06	.02
90 Jose Morales	.05	.03	.01
91 Dennis Leonard	.10	.07	.03
92 Tommy Smith	.05	.03	.01
93 Steve Carlton	.30	.25	.10
94 John Scott	.05	.03	.01
95 Bill Bonham	.05	.03	.01
96 Dave Lopes	.08	.06	.02
97 Jerry Reuss	.08	.06	.02
98 Dave Kingman	.20	.15	.06
99 Dan Warthen	.05	.03	.01
100 Johnny Bench	.40	.30	.13
101 Bert Blyleven	.10	.07	.03
102 Cecil Cooper	.15	.11	.05
103 Mike Willis	.05	.03	.01
104 Dan Ford	.05	.03	.01
105 Frank Tanana	.10	.07	.03
106 Bill North	.05	.03	.01
107 Joe Ferguson	.05	.03	.01
108 Dick Williams	.08	.06	.02
109 John Denny	.05	.03	.01
110 Willie Randolph	.10	.07	.03
111 Reggie Cleveland	.05	.03	.01
112 Doug Howard	.05	.03	.01
113 Randy Jones	.08	.06	.02
114 Rico Carty	.08	.06	.02
115 Mark Fidrych	.10	.07	.03
116 Darrell Porter	.15	.11	.05
117 Wayne Garrett	.05	.03	.01
118 Greg Luzinski	.15	.11	.05
119 Jim Barr	.05	.03	.01
120 George Foster	.20	.15	.06

		MINT	VG-E	F-G
121	Phil Roof	.05	.03	.01
122	Bucky Dent	.08	.06	.02
123	Steve Braun	.05	.03	.01
124	Checklist: 1-132	.05	.03	.01
125	Lee May	.05	.03	.01
126	Woodie Fryman	.05	.03	.01
127	Jose Cardenal	.05	.03	.01
128	Doug Rau	.05	.03	.01
129	Rennie Stennett	.05	.03	.01
130	Pete Vuckovich	.05	.03	.01
131	Cesar Cedeno	.20	.15	.06
132	Jon Matlack	.08	.06	.02
133	Don Baylor	.15	.11	.05
134	Darrel Chaney	.05	.03	.01
135	Tony Perez	.15	.11	.05
136	Aurelio Rodriguez	.05	.03	.01
137	Carlton Fisk	.20	.15	.06
138	Wayne Garland	.05	.03	.01
139	Dave Hilton	.05	.03	.01
140	Rawly Eastwick	.05	.03	.01
141	Amos Otis	.10	.07	.03
142	Tug McGraw	.08	.06	.02
143	Rod Carew	.40	.30	.13
144	Mike Torrez	.08	.06	.02
145	Sal Bando	.10	.07	.03
146	Dock Ellis	.05	.03	.01
147	Jose Cruz	.10	.07	.03
148	Alan Ashby	.05	.03	.01
149	Gaylord Perry	.25	.20	.08
150	Keith Hernandez	.35	.27	.12
151	Dave Pagan	.05	.03	.01
152	Richie Zisk	.10	.07	.03
153	Steve Rogers	.10	.07	.03
154	Mark Belanger	.05	.03	.01
155	Andy Messersmith	.08	.06	.02
156	Dave Winfield	.40	.30	.13
157	Chuck Hartenstein	.05	.03	.01
158	Manny Trillo	.05	.03	.01
159	Steve Yeager	.05	.03	.01
160	Cesar Geronimo	.05	.03	.01
161	Jim Rooker	.05	.03	.01
162	Tim Foli	.05	.03	.01
163	Fred Lynn	.40	.30	.13
164	Ed Figueroa	.05	.03	.01
165	Johnny Grubb	.05	.03	.01
166	Pedro Garcia	.05	.03	.01
167	Ron LeFlore	.15	.11	.05
168	Rich Hebner	.05	.03	.01
169	Larry Herndon	.05	.03	.01
170	George Brett	.50	.40	.18
171	Joe Kerrigan	.05	.03	.01
172	Bud Harrelson	.05	.03	.01
173	Bobby Bonds	.10	.07	.03
174	Bill Travers	.05	.03	.01
175	John Lowenstein	.05	.03	.01
176	Butch Wynegar	.05	.03	.01
177	Pete Falcone	.05	.03	.01
178	C. Washington	.05	.03	.01
179	Checklist: 133-264	.05	.03	.01
180	Dave Cash	.05	.03	.01
181	Fred Norman	.05	.03	.01
182	Roy White	.05	.03	.01
183	Marty Perez	.05	.03	.01
184	Jesse Jefferson	.05	.03	.01
185	Jim Sundberg	.10	.07	.03
186	Dan Meyer	.05	.03	.01
187	Fergie Jenkins	.10	.07	.03
188	Tom Veryzer	.05	.03	.01
189	Dennis Blair	.05	.03	.01
190	Rick Manning	.05	.03	.01
191	Doug Bird	.05	.03	.01
192	Al Bumbry	.05	.03	.01

		MINT	VG-E	F-G
193	Dave Roberts	.05	.03	.01
194	Larry Christenson	.05	.03	.01
195	Chet Lemon	.10	.07	.03
196	Ted Simmons	.25	.20	.08
197	Ray Burris	.05	.03	.01
198	Expos: Coaches	.10	.07	.03
199	Ron Cey	.10	.07	.03
200	Reggie Jackson	.40	.30	.13
201	Pat Zachry	.05	.03	.01
202	Doug Ault	.05	.03	.01
203	Al Oliver	.20	.15	.06
204	Robin Yount	.15	.11	.05
205	Tom Seaver	.35	.27	.12
206	Joe Rudi	.08	.06	.02
207	Barry Foote	.05	.03	.01
208	Toby Harrah	.05	.03	.01
209	Jeff Burroughs	.08	.06	.02
210	George Scott	.05	.03	.01
211	Jim Mason	.05	.03	.01
212	Vern Ruhle	.05	.03	.01
213	Fred Kendall	.05	.03	.01
214	Rick Reuschel	.12	.08	.04
115	Hal McRae	.05	.03	.01
216	Chip Lang	.05	.03	.01
217	Craig Nettles	.10	.07	.03
218	George Hendrick	.10	.07	.03
219	Glenn Abbott	.05	.03	.01
220	Joe Morgan	.15	.11	.05
221	Sam Ewing	.05	.03	.01
222	George Medich	.05	.03	.01
223	Reggie Smith	.15	.11	.05
224	Dave Hamilton	.05	.03	.01
225	Pepe Frias	.05	.03	.01
226	Jay Johnstone	.05	.03	.01
227	J.R. Richard	.30	.25	.10
228	Doug DeCinces	.05	.03	.01
229	Dave Lemanczyk	.05	.03	.01
230	Rick Monday	.08	.06	.02
231	Manny Sanguillen	.05	.03	.01
232	John Montefusco	.05	.03	.01
233	Duane Kuiper	.05	.03	.01
234	Ellis Valentine	.10	.07	.03
235	Dick Tidrow	.05	.03	.01
236	Ben Oglivie	.05	.03	.01
237	Rick Burleson	.10	.07	.03
238	Roy Hartsfield	.05	.03	.01
239	Lyman Bostock	.15	.11	.05
240	Pete Rose	.45	.35	.15
241	Mike Ivie	.05	.03	.01
242	Dave Parker	.30	.25	.10
243	Bill Greif	.05	.03	.01
244	Freddie Patek	.05	.03	.01
245	Mike Schmidt	.35	.27	.12
246	Brian Downing	.08	.06	.02
247	Steve Hargan	.05	.03	.01
248	Dave Collins	.08	.06	.02
249	Felix Millan	.05	.03	.01
250	Don Gullett	.05	.03	.01
251	Jerry Royster	.05	.03	.01
252	Earl Williams	.05	.03	.01
253	Frank Duffy	.05	.03	.01
254	Tippy Martinez	.05	.03	.01
255	Steve Garvey	.35	.27	.12
256	Alvis Woods	.05	.03	.01
257	John Hiller	.05	.03	.01
258	Dave Concepcion	.10	.07	.03
259	Dwight Evans	.05	.03	.01
260	Pete Mackannin	.05	.03	.01
261	'76 Record: G. Brett	.40	.30	.13
262	'76 Record: Minoso	.10	.07	.03
263	'76 Record: Morales	.10	.07	.03
264	'76 Record: N. Ryan	.20	.15	.06

STEVE ROGERS

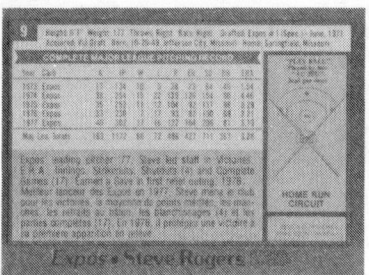

Expos • Steve Rogers

The 1978 O-Pee-Chee set of 242 cards follows the pattern set in 1977 as this Canadian issue differs from the Topps set of this year by the inclusion of many more players from the two Canadian teams. The backs are in both French and English. The asterisk cards have an extra line on the front indicating team change.

	MINT	VG-E	F-G
COMPLETE SET	13.00	10.00	4.00
COMMON PLAYER	.05	.03	.01
1 '77 Batting Ldrs.	.10	.07	.03
2 '77 H.R. Ldrs.	.10	.07	.03
3 '77 R.B.I. Ldrs	.10	.07	.03
4 '77 Stolen Base Ldrs.	.10	.07	.03
5 '77 Victory Ldrs.	.10	.07	.03
6 '77 Strikeout Ldrs.	.10	.07	.03
7 '77 E.R.A. Ldrs.	.10	.07	.03
8 '77 Firemen Ldrs.	.10	.07	.03
9 Steve Rogers	.10	.07	.03
10 Graig Nettles	.08	.06	.02
11 Doug Capilla	.05	.03	.01
12 George Scott	.05	.03	.01
13 Gary Woods	.05	.03	.01
14 Tom Veryzer*	.05	.03	.01
15 Wayne Garland	.05	.03	.01
16 Amos Otis	.10	.07	.03
17 Larry Christenson	.05	.03	.01
18 Dave Cash	.05	.03	.01
19 Jim Barr	.05	.03	.01
20 Ruppert Jones	.05	.03	.01
21 Eric Soderholm	.05	.03	.01
22 Jesse Jefferson	.05	.03	.01
23 Jerry Morales	.05	.03	.01
24 Doug Rau	.05	.03	.01
25 Rennie Stennett	.05	.03	.01
26 Lee Mazzilli	.10	.07	.03
27 Dick Williams	.08	.06	.02
28 Joe Rudi	.08	.06	.02
29 Robin Yount	.10	.07	.03
30 Don Gullett	.05	.03	.01
31 Roy Howell	.05	.03	.01
32 Cesar Geronimo	.05	.03	.01
33 Rick Langford	.05	.03	.01
34 Dan Ford	.05	.03	.01
35 Gene Tenace	.05	.03	.01
36 Santo Alcala	.05	.03	.01
37 Rick Burleson	.10	.07	.03
38 Dave Rozema	.05	.03	.01
39 Duane Kuiper	.05	.03	.01
40 Ron Fairly*	.05	.03	.01
41 Dennis Leonard	.08	.06	.02
42 Greg Luzinski	.15	.11	.05
43 Willie Montanez*	.05	.03	.01
44 Enos Cabell	.05	.03	.01
45 Ellis Valentine	.10	.07	.03
46 Steve Stone	.08	.06	.02
47 Lee May	.05	.03	.01
48 Roy White	.05	.03	.01
49 Jerry Garvin	.05	.03	.01
50 Johnny Bench	.30	.25	.10
51 Garry Templeton	.20	.15	.06
52 Doyle Alexander	.05	.03	.01
53 Steve Henderson	.10	.07	.03
54 Stan Bahnsen	.05	.03	.01
55 Dan Meyer	.05	.03	.01
56 Rick Reuschel	.10	.07	.03
57 Reggie Smith	.15	.11	.05
58 Blue Jays Team	.10	.07	.03
59 John Montefusco	.05	.03	.01
60 Dave Parker	.25	.20	.08
61 Jim Bibby	.08	.06	.02
62 Fred Lynn	.25	.20	.08
63 Jose Morales	.05	.03	.01
64 Aurelio Rodriguez	.05	.03	.01
65 Frank Tanana	.10	.07	.03
66 Darrell Porter	.10	.07	.03
67 Otto Velez	.05	.03	.01
68 Larry Bowa	.10	.07	.03
69 Jim Hunter	.15	.11	.05

	MINT	VG-E	F-G
70 George Foster	.15	.11	.05
71 Cecil Cooper	.12	.08	.04
72 Gary Alexander	.05	.03	.01
73 Paul Thormodsgard	.05	.03	.01
74 Toby Harrah	.05	.03	.01
75 Mitchell Page	.05	.03	.01
76 Alan Ashby	.05	.03	.01
77 Jorge Orta	.05	.03	.01
78 Dave Winfield	.25	.20	.08
79 Andy Messersmith*	.08	.06	.02
80 Ken Singleton	.12	.08	.04
81 Will McEnaney	.05	.03	.01
82 Lou Piniella	.08	.06	.02
83 Bob Forsch	.05	.03	.01
84 Dan Driessen	.05	.03	.01
85 Dave Lemanczyk	.05	.03	.01
86 Paul Dade	.05	.03	.01
87 Bill Campbell	.05	.03.	.01
88 Ron LeFlore	.12	.08	.04
89 Bill Madlock	.05	.03	.01
90 Tony Perez	.12	.08	.04
91 Freddie Patek	.05	.03	.01
92 Glenn Abbott	.05	.03	.01
93 Garry Maddox	.08	.06	.02
94 Steve Staggs	.05	.03	.01
95 Bobby Murcer	.08	.06	.02
96 Don Sutton	.15	.11	.05
97 Al Oliver*	.15	.11	.05
98 Jon Matlack *	.08	.06	.02
99 Sam Mejias	.05	.03	.01
100 Pete Rose	.35	.27	.12
101 Randy Jones	.08	.06	.02
102 Sixto Lezcano	.08	.06	.02
103 Jim Clancy	.05	.03	.01
104 Butch Wynegar	.05	.03	.01
105 Nolan Ryan	.25	.20	.08
106 Wayne Gross	.05	.03	.01
107 Bob Watson	.05	.03	.01
108 Joe Kerrigan*	.05	.03	.01
109 Keith Hernandez	.25	.20	.08
110 Reggie Jackson	.30	.25	.10
111 Denny Doyle	.05	.03	.01
112 Sam Ewing	.05	.03	.01
113 Bert Blyleven*	.10	.07	.03
114 Andre Thornton	.08	.06	.02
115 Milt May	.05	.03	.01
116 Jim Colborn	.05	.03	.01
117 Warren Cromartie	.05	.03	.01
118 Ted Sizemore	.05	.03	.01
119 Check List 1-121	.05	.03	.01
120 Tom Seaver	.25	.20	.08
121 Luis Gomez	.05	.03	.01
122 Jim Spencer*	.05	.03	.01
123 Leroy Stanton	.05	.03	.01
124 Luis Tiant	.08	.06	.02
125 Mark Belanger	.05	.03	.01
126 Jackie Brown	.05	.03	.01
127 Bill Buckner	.12	.08	.04
128 Bill Robinson	.05	.03	.01
129 Rick Cerone	.08	.06	.02
130 Ron Cey	.10	.07	.03
131 Jose Cruz	.08	.06	.02
132 Len Randle	.05	.03	.01
133 Bob Grich	.08	.06	.02
134 Jeff Burroughs	.08	.06	.02
135 Gary Carter	.12	.08	.04
136 Milt Wilcox	.05	.03	.01
137 Carl Yastrzemski	.30	.25	.10
138 Dennis Eckersley	.08	.06	.02
139 Tim Nordbrook	.05	.03	.01
140 Ken Griffey	.08	.06	.02
141 Bob Boone	.05	.03	.01

	MINT	VG-E	F-G			MINT	VG-E	F-G
142 Dave Goltz	.04	.02	.01	193 Tom Murphy		.04	.02	.01
143 Al Cowens	.04	.02	.01	194 Rich Hebner		.04	.02	.01
144 Bill Atkinson	.04	.02	.01	195 Ralph Garr		.04	.02	.01
145 Chris Chambliss	.04	.02	.01	196 Bruce Sutter		.20	.15	.06
146 Jim Slaton*	.04	.02	.01	197 Tom Poquette		.04	.02	.01
147 Bill Stein	.04	.02	.01	198 Wayne Garrett		.04	.02	.01
148 Bob Bailor	.04	.02	.01	199 Pedro Borbon		.04	.02	.01
149 J.R. Richard	.25	.20	.08	200 Thurman Munson		.30	.25	.10
150 Ted Simmons	.25	.20	.08	201 Rollie Fingers		.15	.11	.05
151 Rick Manning	.04	.02	.01	202 Doug Ault		.04	.02	.01
152 Lerrin LaGrow	.04	.02	.01	203 Phil Garner		.04	.02	.01
153 Larry Parrish	.10	.07	.03	204 Lou Brock		.25	.20	.08
154 Eddie Murray	.12	.08	.04	205 Ed Kranepool		.04	.02	.01
155 Phil Niekro	.12	.08	.04	206 Bobby Bonds*		.10	.07	.03
156 Bake McBride	.08	.06	.02	207 Expos Team		.10	.07	.03
157 Pete Vuckovich	.04	.02	.01	208 Bump Wills		.04	.02	.01
158 Ivan DeJesus	.04	.02	.01	209 Gary Matthews		.08	.06	.02
159 Rick Rhoden	.04	.02	.01	210 Carlton Fisk		.15	.11	.05
160 Joe Morgan	.12	.08	.04	211 Jeff Byrd		.04	.02	.01
161 Ed Ott	.04	.02	.01	212 Jason Thompson		.04	.02	.01
162 Don Stanhouse	.04	.02	.01	213 Larvell Blanks		.04	.02	.01
163 Jim Rice	.30	.25	.10	214 Sparky Lyle		.08	.06	.02
164 Bucky Dent	.08	.06	.02	215 George Brett		.35	.27	.12
165 Jim Kern	.04	.02	.01	216 Del Unser		.04	.02	.01
166 Doug Rader	.04	.02	.01	217 Manny Trillo		.04	.02	.01
167 Steve Kemp	.08	.06	.02	218 Roy Hartsfield		.04	.02	.01
168 John Mayberry	.08	.06	.02	219 Carlos Lopez		.04	.02	.01
169 Tim Foli*	.04	.02	.01	220 Dave Concepcion		.08	.06	.02
170 Steve Carlton	.25	.20	.08	221 John Candelaria		.04	.02	.01
171 Pepe Frias	.04	.02	.01	222 Dave Lopes		.08	.06	.02
172 Pat Zachry	.04	.02	.01	223 Tim Blackwell*		.04	.02	.01
173 Don Baylor	.12	.08	.04	224 Chet Lemon		.08	.06	.02
174 Sal Bando	.08	.06	.02	225 Mike Schmidt		.25	.20	.08
175 Alvis Woods	.04	.02	.01	226 Cesar Cedeno		.12	.08	.04
176 Mike Hargrove	.04	.02	.01	227 Mike Willis		.04	.02	.01
177 Vida Blue	.15	.11	.05	228 Willie Randolph		.08	.06	.02
178 George Hendrick	.10	.07	.03	229 Doug Bair		.04	.02	.01
179 Jim Palmer	.25	.20	.08	230 Rod Carew		.25	.20	.08
180 Andre Dawson	.10	.07	.03	231 Mike Flanagan		.10	.07	.03
181 Paul Moskau	.04	.02	.01	232 Chris Speier		.04	.02	.01
182 Mickey Rivers	.08	.06	.02	233 Don Aase*		.04	.02	.01
183 Check List 122-242	.04	.02	.01	234 Buddy Bell		.12	.08	.04
184 Jerry Johnson	.04	.02	.01	235 Mark Fidrych		.10	.07	.03
185 Willie McCovey	.15	.11	.05	236 '77 Rec. Breaker		.10	.07	.03
186 Enrique Romo	.04	.02	.01	237 '77 Rec. Breaker		.10	.07	.03
187 Butch Hobson	.04	.02	.01	238 '77 Rec. Breaker		.10	.07	.03
188 Rusty Staub	.10	.07	.03	239 '77 Rec. Breaker		.10	.07	.03
189 Wayne Twitchell	.04	.02	.01	240 '77 Rec. Breaker		.10	.07	.03
190 Steve Garvey	.30	.25	.10	241 '77 Rec. Breaker		.10	.07	.03
191 Rick Waits	.04	.02	.01	242 '77 Rec. Breaker		.10	.07	.03
192 Doug DeCinces	.04	.02	.01					

1979 O—PEE—CHEE (374)　　　2 1/2″ X 3 1/2″

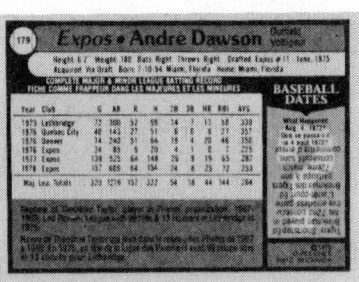

The 1979 O-Pee-Chee set is the largest (374) baseball card set ever issued by O-Pee-Chee The fronts have an O-Pee-Chee logo in the lower left corner comparable to the Topps logo on the 1979 American Set.

	MINT	VG-E	F-G			MINT	VG-E	F-G
COMPLETE SET	14.00	11.00	5.00	15 Dale Murphy		.04	.03	.01
COMMON PLAYER	.04	.03	.01	16 Dennis Eckersley		.07	.05	.02
				17 Ron Blomberg		.04	.03	.01
1 Lee May	.04	.03	.01	18 Wayne Twitchell		.04	.03	.01
2 Dick Drago	.04	.03	.01	19 Al Hrabosky		.07	.05	.02
3 Paul Dade	.04	.03	.01	20 Fred Norman		.04	.03	.01
4 Ross Grimsley	.04	.03	.01	21 Steve Garvey		.25	.20	.08
5 Joe Morgan	.10	.07	.03	22 Willie Stargell		.20	.15	.06
6 Kevin Kobel	.04	.03	.01	23 John Hale		.04	.03	.01
7 Terry Forster	.07	.05	.02	24 Mickey Rivers		.07	.05	.02
8 Paul Molitor	.10	.07	.03	25 Jack Brohamer		.04	.03	.01
9 Steve Carlton	.15	.11	.05	26 Tom Underwood		.04	.03	.01
10 Dave Goltz	.04	.03	.01	27 Mark Belanger		.04	.03	.01
11 Dave Winfield	.20	.15	.06	28 Elliott Maddox		.04	.03	.01
12 Dave Rozema	.04	.03	.01	29 John Candelaria		.04	.03	.01
13 Ed Figueroa	.04	.03	.01	30 Shane Rawley		.04	.03	.01
14 Alan Ashby	.04	.03	.01	31 Steve Yeager		.04	.03	.01

		MINT	VG-E	F-G			MINT	VG-E	F-G
32	Warren Cromartie	.04	.03	.01	124	Jeff Burroughs	.10	.07	.03
33	Jason Thompson	.04	.03	.01	125	Willie Randolph	.10	.07	.03
34	Roger Erickson	.04	.03	.01	126	Bob Stinson	.04	.03	.01
35	Gary Matthews	.07	.05	.02	127	Rick Wise	.04	.03	.01
36	Pete Falcone	.04	.03	.01	128	Luis Gomez	.04	.03	.01
37	Dick Tidrow	.04	.03	.01	129	Tommy John	.15	.11	.05
38	Bob Boone	.04	.03	.01	130	Richie Zisk	.10	.07	.03
39	Jim Bibby	.07	.05	.02	131	Mario Guerrero	.04	.03	.01
40	Len Barker	.07	.05	.02	132	Oscar Gamble	.05	.03	.01
41	Robin Yount	.10	.07	.03	133	Don Money	.05	.03	.01
42	Sam Mejias	.04	.03	.01	134	Joe Rudi	.05	.03	.01
43	Ray Burris	.04	.03	.01	135	Woodie Fryman	.04	.03	.01
44	Tom Seaver	.25	.20	.08	136	Butch Hobson	.04	.03	.01
45	Roy Howell	.04	.03	.01	137	Jim Colborn	.04	.03	.01
46	Jim Todd	.04	.03	.01	138	Tom Grieve	.04	.03	.01
47	Frank Duffy	.04	.03	.01	139	Andy Messersmith	.07	.05	.02
48	Joel Youngblood	.04	.03	.01	140	Andre Thornton	.05	.03	.01
49	Vida Blue	.15	.11	.05	141	Ken Kravec	.04	.03	.01
50	Cliff Johnson	.04	.03	.01	142	Bobby Bonds	.10	.07	.03
51	Nolan Ryan	.20	.15	.06	143	Jose Cruz	.07	.05	.02
52	Ozzie Smith	.07	.05	.02	144	Dave Lopes	.07	.05	.02
53	Jim Sundberg	.07	.05	.02	145	Jerry Garvin	.04	.03	.01
54	Mike Paxton	.04	.03	.01	146	Pepe Frias	.04	.03	.01
55	Lou Whitaker	.07	.05	.02	147	Mitchell Page	.04	.03	.01
56	Dan Schatzeder	.04	.03	.01	148	Ted Sizemore	.04	.03	.01
57	Rick Burleson	.10	.07	.03	149	Rich Gale	.04	.03	.01
58	Doug Bair	.04	.03	.01	150	Steve Ontiveros	.04	.03	.01
59	Ted Martinez	.04	.03	.01	151	Rod Carew	.30	.25	.10
60	Bob Watson	.05	.03	.01	152	Lary Sorensen	.07	.05	.02
61	Jim Clancy	.04	.03	.01	153	Willie Montanez	.04	.03	.01
62	Rowland Office	.04	.03	.01	154	Floyd Bannister	.04	.03	.01
63	Bobby Murcer	.07	.05	.02	155	Bert Blyleven	.10	.07	.03
63	Don Gullett	.05	.03	.01	156	Ralph Garr	.04	.03	.01
65	Tom Paciorek	.04	.03	.01	157	Thurman Munson	.30	.25	.10
66	Rick Rhoden	.04	.03	.01	158	Bob Robertson	.04	.03	.01
67	Duane Kuiper	.04	.03	.01	159	Jon Matlack	.05	.03	.01
68	Bruce Boisclair	.04	.03	.01	160	Carl Yastrzemski	.30	.25	.10
69	Manny Sarmiento	.04	.03	.01	161	Gaylord Perry	.15	.11	.05
70	Wayne Cage	.04	.03	.01	162	Mike Tyson	.04	.03	.01
71	John Hiller	.04	.03	.01	163	Cecil Cooper	.12	.08	.04
72	Rick Cerone	.05	.03	.01	164	Pedro Borbon	.04	.03	.01
73	Dwight Evans	.04	.03	.01	165	Art Howe	.04	.03	.01
74	Buddy Solomon	.04	.03	.01	166	Joe Coleman	.04	.03	.01
75	Roy White	.04	.03	.01	167	George Brett	.35	.27	.12
76	Mike Flanagan	.07	.05	.02	168	Gary Alexander	.04	.03	.01
77	Tom Johnson	.04	.03	.01	169	Chet Lemon	.07	.05	.02
78	Glenn Burke	.04	.03	.01	170	Craig Swan	.07	.05	.02
79	Frank Taveras	.04	.03	.01	171	Chris Chambliss	.05	.03	.01
80	Don Sutton	.12	.08	.04	172	John Montague	.04	.03	.01
81	Leon Roberts	.04	.03	.01	173	Ron Jackson	.04	.03	.01
82	George Hendrick	.10	.07	.03	174	Jim Palmer	.20	.15	.06
83	Aurelio Rodriguez	.04	.03	.01	175	Willie Upshaw	.04	.03	.01
84	Ron Reed	.04	.03	.01	176	Tug McGraw	.08	.06	.02
85	Alvis Woods	.04	.03	.01	177	Bill Buckner	.10	.07	.03
86	Jim Beattie	.04	.03	.01	178	Doug Rau	.04	.03	.01
87	Larry Hisle	.10	.07	.03	179	Andre Dawson	.10	.07	.03
88	Mike Garman	.04	.03	.01	180	Jim Wright	.04	.03	.01
89	Tim Johnson	.04	.03	.01	181	Garry Templeton	.15	.11	.05
90	Paul Splittorff	.04	.03	.01	182	Bill Bonham	.04	.03	.01
91	Darrel Chaney	.04	.03	.01	183	Lee Mazzilli	.10	.07	.03
92	Mike Torrez	.07	.05	.02	184	Alan Trammell	.07	.05	.02
93	Eric Soderholm	.04	.03	.01	185	Amos Otis	.10	.07	.03
94	Ron Cey	.07	.05	.02	186	Tom Dixon	.04	.03	.01
95	Randy Jones	.07	.05	.02	187	Mike Cubbage	.04	.03	.01
96	Bill Madlock	.05	.03	.01	188	Sparky Lyle	.07	.05	.02
97	Steve Kemp	.10	.07	.03	189	Juan Bernhardt	.04	.03	.01
98	Bob Apodaca	.04	.03	.01	190	Bump Wills	.25	.20	.08
99	Johnny Grubb	.04	.03	.01	191	Dave Kingman	.15	.11	.05
100	Larry Milbourne	.04	.03	.01	192	Lamar Johnson	.04	.03	.01
101	Johnny Bench	.30	.25	.10	193	Lance Rautzhan	.04	.03	.01
102	Dave Lemanczyk	.04	.03	.01	194	Ed Herrmann	.04	.03	.01
103	Reggie Cleveland	.04	.03	.01	195	Bill Campbell	.04	.03	.01
104	Larry Bowa	.10	.07	.03	196	Gorman Thomas	.07	.05	.02
105	Denny Martinez	.04	.03	.01	197	Paul Moskau	.04	.03	.01
106	Bill Travers	.04	.03	.01	198	Dale Murray	.04	.03	.01
107	Willie McCovey	.20	.15	.06	199	John Mayberry	.07	.05	.02
108	Wilbur Wood	.04	.03	.01	200	Phil Garner	.04	.03	.01
109	Dennis Leonard	.07	.05	.02	201	Dan Ford	.04	.03	.01
110	Roy Smalley	.07	.05	.02	202	Gary Thomasson	.04	.03	.01
111	Cesar Geronimo	.04	.03	.01	203	Rollie Fingers	.10	.07	.03
112	Jesse Jefferson	.04	.03	.01	204	Al Oliver	.10	.07	.03
113	Dave Revering	.04	.03	.01	205	Doug Ault	.04	.03	.01
114	Rich Gossage	.12	.08	.04	206	Scott McGregor	.07	.05	.02
115	Steve Stone	.08	.06	.02	207	Dave Cash	.04	.03	.01
116	Doug Flynn	.04	.03	.01	208	Bill Plummer	.04	.03	.01
117	Bob Forsch	.04	.03	.01	209	Ivan DeJesus	.04	.03	.01
118	Paul Mitchell	.04	.03	.01	210	Jim Rice	.25	.20	.08
119	Toby Harrah	.04	.03	.01	211	Ray Knight	.04	.03	.01
120	Steve Rogers	.10	.07	.03	212	Paul Hartzell	.04	.03	.01
121	Checklist 1-125	.04	.03	.01	213	Tim Foli	.04	.03	.01
122	Balor Moore	.04	.03	.01	214	Butch Wynegar	.04	.03	.01
123	Rick Reuschel	.10	.07	.03	215	Darrell Evans	.04	.03	.01

	MINT	VG-E	F-G
216 Ken Griffey	.10	.07	.03
217 Doug. DeCinces	.04	.03	.01
218 Ruppert Jones	.05	.03	.01
219 Bob Montgomery	.04	.03	.01
220 Rick Manning	.04	.03	.01
221 Chris Speier	.04	.03	.01
222 Bobby Valentine	.04	.03	.01
223 Dave Parker	.20	.15	.06
224 Larry Biittner	.04	.03	.01
225 Ken Clay	.04	.03	.01
226 Gene Tenace	.05	.03	.01
227 Frank White	.05	.05	.02
228 Rusty Staub	.07	.05	.02
229 Lee Lacy	.04	.03	.01
230 Doyle Alexander	.04	.03	.01
231 Bruce Bochte	.04	.03	.01
232 Steve Henderson	.07	.05	.02
233 Jim Lonborg	.05	.03	.01
234 Dave Concepcion	.07	.05	.02
235 Jerry Morales	.04	.03	.01
236 Len Randle	.04	.03	.01
237 Bill Lee	.04	.03	.01
238 Bruce Sutter	.15	.11	.05
239 Jim Essian	.04	.03	.01
240 Graig Nettles	.07	.05	.02
241 Otto Velez	.04	.03	.01
242 Checklist 126-250	.04	.03	.01
243 Reggie Smith	.10	.07	.03
244 Stan Bahnsen	.04	.03	.01
245 Garry Maddox	.07	.05	.02
246 Joaquin Andujar	.04	.03	.01
247 Dan Driessen	.04	.03	.01
248 Bob Grich	.05	.03	.01
249 Fred Lynn	.25	.29	.08
250 Skip Lockwood	.04	.03	.01
251 Craig Reynolds	.04	.03	.01
252 Willie Horton	.05	.03	.01
253 Rick Waits	.04	.03	.01
254 Bucky Dent	.07	.05	.02
255 Bob Knepper	.05	.03	.01
256 Miguel Dilone	.05	.03	.01
257 Bob Owchinko	.04	.03	.01
258 Al Cowens	.05	.03	.01
259 Bob Bailor	.04	.03	.01
260 Larry Christenson	.04	.03	.01
261 Tony Perez	.10	.07	.03
262 Blue Jays Checklist	.08	.06	.02
263 Glenn Abbott	.04	.03	.01
264 Ron Guidry	.20	.15	.06
265 Ed Kranepool	.04	.03	.01
266 Charlie Hough	.04	.03	.01
267 Ted Simmons	.15	.11	.05
268 Jack Clark	.12	.08	.04
269 Enos Cabell	.04	.03	.01
270 Gary Carter	.12	.08	.04
271 Sam Ewing	.04	.03	.01
272 Tom Burgmeier	.04	.03	.01
273 Freddie Patek	.04	.03	.01
274 Frank Tanana	.07	.05	.02
275 Leroy Stanton	.04	.03	.01
276 Ken Forsch	.04	.03	.01
277 Ellis Valentine	.10	.07	.03
278 Greg. Luzinski	.10	.07	.03
279 Rick Bosetti	.04	.03	.01
280 John Stearns	.04	.03	.01
281 Enrique Romo	.04	.03	.01
282 Bob Bailey	.04	.03	.01
283 Sal Bando	.07	.05	.02
284 Matt Keough	.04	.03	.01
285 Biff Pocoroba	.04	.03	.01
286 Mike Lum	.04	.03	.01
287 Jay Johnstone	.04	.03	.01
288 John Montefusco	.04	.03	.01
289 Ed. Ott	.04	.03	.01
290 Dusty Baker	.07	.05	.02
291 Rico Carty	.07	.05	.02
292 Nino Espinosa	.04	.03	.01
293 Rich Hebner	.04	.03	.01
294 Cesar Cedeno	.10	.07	.03
295 Darrell Porter	.10	.07	.03
296 Rod Gilbreath	.04	.03	.01
297 Jim Kern	.04	.03	.01
298 Claudell Washington	.04	.03	.01
299 Luis Tiant	.07	.05	.02
300 Mike Parrott	.04	.03	.01
301 Pete Broberg	.04	.03	.01
302 Greg Gross	.04	.03	.01
303 Darold Knowles	.04	.03	.01
304 Paul Blair	.04	.03	.01
305 Julio Cruz	.04	.03	.01
306 Hal McRae	.04	.03	.01
307 Ken Reitz	.04	.03	.01
308 Tom Murphy	.04	.03	.01
309 Terry Whitfield	.04	.03	.01
310 J.R. Richard	.20	.15	.06
311 Mike Hargrove	.04	.03	.01
312 Rick Dempsey	.04	.03	.01
313 Phil Niekro	.10	.07	.03
314 Bob Stanley	.04	.03	.01
315 Jim Spencer	.04	.03	.01
316 George Foster	.15	.11	.05
317 Dave LaRoche	.04	.03	.01
318 Rudy May	.04	.03	.01
319 Jeff Newman	.04	.03	.01
320 Rick Monday	.05	.03	.01
321 Omar Moreno	.07	.05	.02
322 Dave McKay	.04	.03	.01
323 Mike Schmidt	.20	.15	.06
324 Ken Singleton	.10	.07	.03
325 Jerry Remy	.04	.03	.01
326 Bert Campaneris	.05	.03	.01
327 Pat Zachry	.04	.03	.01
328 Larry Herndon	.04	.03	.01
329 Mark Fidrych	.07	.05	.02
330 Del Unser	.04	.03	.01
331 Gene Garber	.04	.03	.01
332 Bake McBride	.07	.05	.02
333 Jorge Orta	.04	.03	.01
334 Don Kirkwood	.04	.03	.01
335 Don Baylor	.10	.07	.03
336 Bill Robinson	.04	.03	.01
337 Manny Trillo	.05	.03	.01
338 Eddie Murray	.12	.08	.04
339 Tom Hausman	.04	.03	.01
340 George Scott	.05	.03	.01
341 Rick Sweet	.04	.03	.01
342 Lou Piniella	.07	.05	.02
343 Pete Rose	.30	.25	.10
344 Stan Papi	.04	.03	.01
345 Jerry Koosman	.07	.05	.02
346 Hosken Powell	.04	.03	.01
347 George Medich	.04	.03	.01
348 Ron LeFlore	.10	.07	.03
349 Expos Team Checklist	.10	.07	.03
350 Lou Brock	.25	.20	.08
351 Bill North	.04	.03	.01
352 Jim Hunter	.10	.07	.03
353 Checklist 251-374	.04	.03	.01
354 Ed Halicki	.04	.03	.01
355 Tom Hutton	.04	.03	.01
356 Mike Caldwell	.07	.05	.02
357 Larry Parrish	.10	.07	.03
358 Geoff. Zahn	.04	.03	.01
359 Derrel Thomas	.04	.03	.01
360 Carlton Fisk	.12	.08	.04
361 John Henry Johnson	.04	.03	.01
362 Dave Chalk	.04	.03	.01
363 Dan Meyer	.04	.03	.01
364 Sixto Lezcano	.07	.05	.02
365 Rennie Stennett	.04	.03	.01
366 Mike Willis	.04	.03	.01
367 Buddy Bell	.10	.07	.03
368 Mickey Stanley	.04	.03	.01
369 Dave Radar	.04	.03	.01
370 Burt Hooton	.05	.03	.01
371 Keith Hernandez	.20	.15	.06
372 Bill Stein	.04	.03	.01
373 Hal Dues	.04	.03	.01
374 Reggie Jackson	.25	.20	.08

1980-81 HOCKEY CARD CHECKLIST AND PRICE GUIDE

by Andrew Pywowarczuk

96 pages loaded with information and illustrations about hockey cards 1910-1980.

Features:
1. Cigarette cards.
2. 1920's and 1930's issues.
3. Bee Hive Photos
4. Parkhurst/Topps/O-Pee-Chee and much more.

ONLY

$3.95 PPD.

HOCKEY CARD SETS FOR SALE

Mint, Postpaid. Quebec Residents add 8% sales tax.
Allow 3-5 weeks for delivery. Prices in effect until Aug. 31/81.

1980-81 O-Pee-Chee (396) ... $14.00

1979-80 O-Pee-Chee (396) ... $14.00

1978-79 O-Pee-Chee (396) ... $15.00

1977-78 O-Pee-Chee NHL (396) $16.00

1977-78 O-Pee-Chee WHA (66) $6.00

1976-77 O-Pee-Chee NHL (396) $17.00

1976-77 O-Pee-Chee WHA (132) $9.00

1975-76 O-Pee-Chee NHL (396) $18.00

1974-75 O-Pee-Chee NHL (396) $20.00

1974-75 O-Pee-Chee WHA (66) $8.00

1973-74 O-Pee-Chee WHA
Posters (20) $5.00

1973-74 O-Pee-Chee NHL
133-264 .... $10.00

1971-72 O-Pee-Chee NHL
133-264 .... $12.00

1970-71 Dad's Cookies (144) $12.00

CARTOPHILIUM
DEPT PG3
**3681 MASSON ST.
MONTREAL, QUE.
H1X 1S4**

(Detailed price list on request)

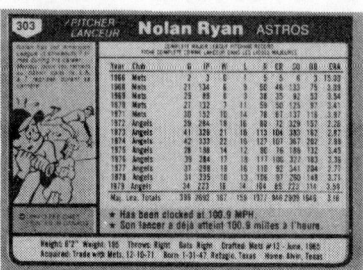

The 1980 baseball set i
by O—Pee—Chee for «
bution in Canada cor
374 cards. They are pr
on white stock rather
the gray stock used by T
The backs contain biogra
in both English and Fr
Cards marked with a
terisk in the checklist d«
players with the line '
with (new team na
on the front. Color chang
correspond to the new
are apparent on the pen
name and frame on the fr

	MINT	VG-E	F-G
COMPLETE SET	12.50	9.00	4.00
COMMON PLAYER	.03	.02	.01
1 Craig Swan	.05	.03	.01
2 Denny Martinez	.03	.02	.01
3 Dave Cash*	.03	.02	.01
4 Bruce Sutter	.10	.07	.03
5 Ron Jackson	.03	.02	.01
6 Balor Moore	.03	.02	.01
7 Dan Ford	.03	.02	.01
8 Pat Putnam	.03	.02	.01
9 Derrel Thomas	.03	.02	.01
10 Jim Slaton	.03	.02	.01
11 Lee Mazzilli	.05	.03	.01
12 Del Unser	.03	.02	.01
13 Mark Wagner	.03	.02	.01
14 Vida Blue	.10	.07	.03
15 Jay Johnstone	.03	.02	.01
16 Julio Cruz	.03	.02	.01
17 Tony Scott	.03	.02	.01
18 Jeff Newman	.03	.02	.01
19 Luis Tiant	.05	.03	.01
20 Carlton Fisk	.10	.07	.03
21 Dave Palmer	.03	.02	.01
22 Bombo Rivera	.03	.02	.01
23 Bill Fahey	.03	.02	.01
24 Frank White	.05	.03	.01
25 Rico Carty	.05	.03	.01
26 Bill Bonham	.03	.02	.01
27 Rick Miller	.03	.02	.01
28 J. R. Richard	.05	.03	.01
29 Joe Ferguson	.03	.02	.01
30 Bill Madlock	.05	.03	.01
31 Pete Vuckovich	.03	.02	.01
32 Doug Flynn	.03	.02	.01
33 Bucky Dent	.05	.03	.01
34 Mike Ivie	.03	.02	.01
35 Bob Stanley	.03	.02	.01
36 Al Bumbry	.03	.02	.01
37 Gary Carter	.10	.07	.03
38 John Milner	.03	.02	.01
39 Sid Monge	.03	.02	.01
40 Bill Russell	.03	.02	.01
41 John Stearns	.03	.02	.01
42 Dave Stieb	.03	.02	.01
43 Ruppert Jones*	.03	.02	.01
44 Bob Owchinko	.03	.02	.01
45 Ron LeFlore*	.10	.07	.03
46 Ted Sizemore	.03	.02	.01
47 Ted Simmons	.10	.07	.03
48 Pepe Frias*	.03	.02	.01
49 Ken Landreaux	.03	.02	.01
50 Manny Trillo	.03	.02	.01
51 Rick Dempsey	.03	.02	.01
52 Cecil Cooper	.05	.03	.01
53 Bill Lee	.05	.03	.01
54 Victor Cruz	.03	.02	.01
55 Johnny Bench	.25	.20	.08
56 Rich Dauer	.03	.02	.01
57 Frank Tanana	.05	.03	.01

	MINT	VG-E	F-G
58 Francisco Barrios	.03	.02	.01
59 Bob Horner	.10	.07	.03
60 Fred Lynn	.25	.20	.08
61 Bob Knepper	.03	.02	.01
62 Sparky Lyle	.05	.03	.01
63 Larry Cox	.03	.02	.01
64 Dock Ellis*	.03	.02	.01
65 Phil Garner	.03	.02	.01
66 Greg Luzinski	.10	.07	.03
67 Checklist 1-125	.03	.02	.01
68 Dave Lemanczyk	.03	.02	.01
69 Tony Perez*	.10	.07	.03
70 Gary Thomasson	.03	.02	.01
71 Craig Reynolds	.03	.02	.01
72 Amos Otis	.05	.03	.01
73 Biff Pocoroba	.03	.02	.01
74 Matt Keough	.03	.02	.01
75 Bill Buckner	.05	.03	.01
76 John Castino	.03	.02	.01
77 Rich Gossage	.05	.03	.01
78 Gary Alexander	.03	.02	.01
79 Phil Huffman	.03	.02	.01
80 Bruce Bochte	.03	.02	.01
81 Darrell Evans	.03	.02	.01
82 Terry Puhl	.05	.03	.01
83 Jason Thompson	.05	.03	.01
84 Larry Sorenson	.03	.02	.01
85 Jerry Remy	.03	.02	.01
86 Tony Brizzolara	.03	.02	.01
87 Willie Wilson	.10	.07	.03
88 Eddie Murray	.05	.03	.01
89 Larry Christenson	.03	.02	.01
90 Bob Randall	.03	.02	.01
91 Greg Pryor	.03	.02	.01
92 Glenn Abbott	.03	.02	.01
93 Jack Clark	.05	.03	.01
94 Rick Waits	.03	.02	.01
95 Luis Gomez*	.03	.02	.01
96 Burt Hooton	.05	.03	.01
97 John Henry Johnson	.03	.02	.01
98 Ray Knight	.05	.03	.01
99 Rick Reuschel	.05	.03	.01
100 Champ Summers	.03	.02	.01
101 Ron Davis	.03	.02	.01
102 Warren Cromartie	.05	.03	.01
103 Ken Reitz	.03	.02	.01
104 Hal McRae	.03	.02	.01
105 Alan Ashby	.03	.02	.01
106 Kevin Kobel	.03	.02	.01
107 Buddy Bell	.10	.07	.03
108 Dave Goltz*	.03	.02	.01
109 John Montefusco	.03	.02	.01
110 Lance Parrish	.05	.03	.01
111 Mike LaCoss	.03	.02	.01
112 Jim Rice	.25	.20	.08
113 Steve Carlton	.20	.15	.06
114 Sixto Lezcano	.10	.07	.03
115 Ed Halicki	.05	.03	.01
116 Jose Morales	.03	.02	.01
117 Dave Concepcion	.05	.03	.01

#	Name	MINT	VG-E	F-G	#	Name	MINT	VG-E	F-G
118	Joe Cannon	.03	.02	.01	209	George Foster	.15	.11	.05
119	Willie Montanez*	.03	.02	.01	210	Dwight Evans	.03	.02	.01
120	Lou Piniella	.05	.03	.01	211	Paul Molitor	.10	.07	.03
121	Bill Stein	.03	.02	.01	212	Tony Solaita	.03	.02	.01
122	Dave Winfield	.25	.20	.08	213	Bill North	.03	.02	.01
123	Alan Trammell	.05	.03	.01	214	Paul Splittorf	.03	.02	.01
124	Andre Dawson	.05	.03	.01	215	Bobby Bonds*	.10	.07	.03
125	Marc Hill	.03	.02	.01	216	Butch Hobson	.03	.02	.01
126	Don Aase	.03	.02	.01	217	Mark Belanger	.03	.02	.01
127	Dave Kingman	.10	.07	.03	218	Grant Jackson	.03	.02	.01
128	Checklist 126-250	.03	.02	.01	219	Tom Hutton	.03	.02	.01
129	Dennis Lamp	.03	.02	.01	220	Pat Zachry	.03	.02	.01
130	Phil Niekro	.10	.07	.03	221	Duane Kuiper	.03	.02	.01
131	Tim Foli	.03	.02	.01	222	Larry Hisle	.05	.03	.01
132	Jim Clancy	.03	.02	.01	223	Mike Krukow	.03	.02	.01
133	Bill Atkinson*	.03	.02	.01	224	Johnnie LeMaster	.03	.02	.01
134	Paul Dade	.03	.02	.01	225	Billy Almon*	.03	.02	.01
135	Dusty Baker	.05	.03	.01	226	Joe Niekro	.05	.03	.01
136	Al Oliver	.10	.07	.03	227	Dave Revering	.03	.02	.01
137	Dave Chalk	.03	.02	.01	228	Don Sutton	.10	.07	.03
138	Bill Robinson	.03	.02	.01	229	John Hiller	.05	.03	.01
139	Robin Yount	.10	.07	.03	230	Alvis Woods	.03	.02	.01
140	Dan Schatzeder*	.03	.02	.01	231	Mark Fidrych	.05	.03	.01
141	Mike Schmidt	.20	1.50	.60	232	Duffy Dyer	.03	.02	.01
142	Ralph Garr*	.03	.02	.01	233	Nino Espinosa	.03	.02	.01
143	Dale Murphy	.05	.03	.01	234	Doug Bair	.03	.02	.01
144	Jerry Koosman	.05	.03	.01	235	George Brett	.25	.20	.08
145	Tom Veryzer	.03	.02	.01	236	Mike Torrez	.05	.03	.01
146	Rick Bosetti	.03	.02	.01	237	Frank Taveras	.03	.02	.01
147	Jim Spencer	.03	.02	.01	238	Bert Blyleven	.05	.03	.01
148	Gaylord Perry	.15	.11	.05	239	Willie Randolph	.05	.03	.01
149	Paul Blair	.03	.02	.01	240	Mike Sadek	.03	.02	.01
150	Don Baylor	.15	.11	.05	241	Jerry Royster	.03	.02	.01
151	Dave Rozema	.03	.02	.01	242	John Denny*	.03	.02	.01
152	Steve Garvey	.20	.15	.06	243	Rick Monday	.05	.03	.01
153	Elias Sosa	.03	.02	.01	244	Jesse Jefferson	.03	.02	.01
154	Larry Gura	.05	.03	.01	245	Aurelio Rodriguez*	.03	.02	.01
155	Tim Johnson	.03	.02	.01	246	Bob Boone	.03	.02	.01
156	Steve Henderson	.03	.02	.01	247	Cesar Geronimo	.03	.02	.01
157	Ron Guidry	.15	.11	.05	248	Bob Shirley	.03	.02	.01
158	Mike Edwards	.03	.02	.01	249	Expos checklist	.05	.03	.01
159	Butch Wynegar	.03	.02	.01	250	Bob Watson*	.05	.03	.01
160	Randy Jones	.05	.03	.01	251	Mickey Rivers	.05	.03	.01
161	Denny Walling	.03	.02	.01	252	Mike Tyson*	.03	.02	.01
162	Mike Hargrove	.03	.02	.01	253	Wayne Nordhagen	.03	.02	.01
163	Dave Parker	.20	.15	.06	254	Roy Howell	.05	.03	.01
164	Roger Metzger	.03	.02	.01	255	Lee May	.03	.02	.01
165	Johnny Grubb	.03	.02	.01	256	Jerry Martin	.03	.02	.01
166	Steve Kemp	.10	.07	.03	257	Bake McBride	.05	.03	.01
167	Bob Lacey	.03	.02	.01	258	Silvio Martinez	.03	.02	.01
168	Chris Speier	.03	.02	.01	259	Jim Mason	.03	.02	.01
169	Dennis Eckersley	.05	.03	.01	260	Tom Seaver	.20	.15	.06
170	Keith Hernandez	.15	.11	.05	261	Rich Wortham	.03	.02	.01
171	Claudell Washington	.05	.03	.01	262	Mike Cubbage	.03	.02	.01
172	Tom Underwood*	.03	.02	.01	263	Gene Garber	.03	.02	.01
173	Dan Driessen	.03	.02	.01	264	Bert Campaneris	.05	.03	.01
174	Al Cowens*	.03	.02	.01	265	Tom Buskey	.03	.02	.01
175	Rich Hebner*	.03	.02	.01	266	Leon Roberts	.03	.02	.01
176	Willie McCovey	.20	.15	.06	267	Ron Cey	.05	.03	.01
177	Carney Lansford	.05	.03	.01	268	Steve Ontiveros	.03	.02	.01
178	Ken Singleton	.10	.07	.03	269	Mike Caldwell	.05	.03	.01
179	Jim Essian	.03	.02	.01	270	Nelson Norman	.03	.02	.01
180	Mike Vail	.03	.02	.01	271	Steve Rogers	.10	.07	.03
181	Randy Lerch	.03	.02	.01	272	Jim Morrison	.03	.02	.01
182	Larry Parrish	.05	.03	.01	273	Clint Hurdle	.03	.02	.01
183	Checklist 251-374	.03	.02	.01	274	Dale Murray	.03	.02	.01
184	George Hendrick	.05	.03	.01	275	Jim Barr	.03	.02	.01
185	Bob Davis	.03	.02	.01	276	Jim Sundberg	.05	.03	.01
186	Gary Matthews	.05	.03	.01	277	Willie Horton	.05	.03	.01
187	Lou Whitaker	.05	.03	.01	278	Andre Thornton	.03	.02	.01
188	Darrell Porter	.05	.03	.01	279	Bob Forsch	.03	.02	.01
189	Wayne Gross	.03	.02	.01	280	Joe Strain	.03	.02	.01
190	Bobby Murcer	.05	.03	.01	281	Rudy May*	.05	.03	.01
191	Willie Aikens*	.05	.03	.01	282	Pete Rose	.25	.20	.08
192	Jim Kern	.03	.02	.01	283	Jeff Burroughs	.05	.03	.01
193	Cesar Cedeno	.10	.07	.03	284	Rick Langford	.03	.02	.01
194	Joel Youngblood	.03	.02	.01	285	Ken Griffey	.05	.03	.01
195	Ross Grimsley	.03	.02	.01	286	Bill Nahorodny*	.03	.02	.01
196	Jerry Mumphrey*	.03	.02	.01	287	Art Howe	.03	.02	.01
197	Kevin Bell	.03	.02	.01	288	Ed Figueroa	.03	.02	.01
198	Garry Maddox	.05	.03	.01	289	Joe Rudi	.05	.03	.01
199	Dave Freisleben	.03	.02	.01	290	Alfredo Griffin	.05	.03	.01
200	Ed Ott	.03	.02	.01	291	Dave Lopes	.05	.03	.01
201	Enos Cabell	.03	.02	.01	292	Rick Manning	.03	.02	.01
202	Pete LaCock	.03	.02	.01	293	Dennis Leonard	.05	.03	.01
203	Fergie Jenkins	.10	.07	.03	294	Bud Harrelson	.03	.02	.01
204	Milt Wilcox	.03	.02	.01	295	Skip Lockwood*	.03	.02	.01
205	Ozzie Smith	.03	.02	.01	296	Roy Smalley	.03	.02	.01
206	Ellis Valentine	.10	.07	.03	297	Kent Tekulve	.05	.03	.01
207	Dan Meyer	.03	.02	.01	298	Scot Thompson	.03	.02	.01
208	Barry Foote	.03	.02	.01	299	Ken Kravec	.03	.02	.01

	MINT	VG-E	F-G
300 Blue Jays Checklist	.05	.03	.01
301 Scott Sanderson	.03	.02	.01
302 Charlie Moore	.03	.02	.01
303 Nolan Ryan*	.15	.11	.05
304 Bob Bailor	.03	.02	.01
305 Bob Stinson	.03	.02	.01
306 Al Hrabosky*	.05	.03	.01
307 Mitchell Page	.03	.02	.01
308 Garry Templeton	.10	.07	.03
309 Chet Lemon	.05	.03	.01
310 Jim Palmer	.20	.15	.06
311 Rick Cerone*	.05	.03	.01
312 Jon Matlack	.05	.03	.01
313 Don Money	.05	.03	.01
314 Reggie Jackson	.20	.15	.06
315 Brian Downing	.03	.02	.01
316 Woodie Fryman	.03	.02	.01
317 Alan Bannister	.03	.02	.01
318 Ron Reed	.03	.02	.01
319 Willie Stargell	.15	.11	.05
320 Jerry Garvin	.03	.02	.01
321 Cliff Johnson	.03	.02	.01
322 Doug DeCinces	.03	.02	.01
323 Gene Richards	.03	.02	.01
324 Joaquin Andujar	.03	.02	.01
325 Richie Zisk	.05	.03	.01
326 Bob Grich	.05	.03	.01
327 Gorman Thomas	.10	.07	.03
328 Chris Chambliss	.05	.03	.01
329 Blue Jay's Prospects	.05	.03	.01
330 Larry Bowa	.10	.07	.03
331 Barry Bonnell*	.03	.02	.01
332 John Candelaria	.05	.03	.01
333 Toby Harrah	.03	.02	.01
334 Larry Biittner	.03	.02	.01
335 Mike Flanagan	.05	.03	.01
336 Ed Kranepool	.03	.02	.01

	MINT	VG-E	F-G
337 Ken Forsch	.05	.03	.01
338 John Mayberry	.05	.03	.01
339 Rick Burleson	.05	.03	.01
340 Milt May*	.03	.02	.01
341 Roy White	.03	.02	.01
342 Joe Morgan*	.15	.11	.05
343 Rollie Fingers	.05	.03	.01
344 Mario Mendoza	.03	.02	.01
345 Stan Bahnsen	.03	.02	.01
346 Tug McGraw	.05	.03	.01
347 Rusty Staub	.10	.07	.03
348 Tommy John	.15	.11	.05
349 Ivan DeJesus	.03	.02	.01
350 Reggie Smith	.10	.07	.03
351 Expos Prospects	.05	.03	.01
352 Floyd Bannister	.03	.02	.01
353 Rod Carew	.20	.15	.06
354 Otto Velez	.03	.02	.01
355 Gene Tenace	.05	.03	.01
356 Freddie Patek*	.03	.02	.01
357 Elliott Maddox	.03	.02	.01
358 Pat Underwood	.03	.02	.01
359 Craig Nettles	.05	.03	.01
360 Rodney Scott	.03	.02	.01
361 Terry Whitfield	.03	.02	.01
362 Fred Norman*	.03	.02	.01
363 Sal Bando	.05	.03	.01
364 Greg Gross	.03	.02	.01
365 Carl Yastrzemski	.20	.15	.06
366 Paul Hartzell	.03	.02	.01
367 Joe Cruz	.03	.02	.01
368 Shane Rawley	.03	.02	.01
369 Jerry White	.03	.02	.01
370 Rick Wise*	.05	.03	.01
371 Steve Yeager	.03	.02	.01
372 Omar Moreno	.03	.02	.01
373 Bump Wills	.03	.02	.01
374 Craig Kusick*	.03	.02	.01

PRICE GUIDE FOR OTHER SETS

Listed below are retail prices for an average card (very good to excellent condition) in the set listed.

en & Ginter N28 Baseball	60.00
en & Ginter N28 Boxers	6.00
en & Ginter N28 Others	3.00
en & Ginter N29 Baseball	100.00
en & Ginter N29 Boxers	10.00
en & Ginter N29 Others	5.00
en & Ginter N43	160.00
our Coins 1955	3.00
our Coins 1959	1.50
our Coins 1960	1.50
Blankets	4.00
hner Gold Coin N284	40.00
hner St. Louis N284	60.00
2 Cloverleaf	12.00
e Tips 1952	36.00
gan's Chips E254	6.00
ton Daily News	2.00
7-38 Dixie Lids Baseball	25.00
7-38 Dixie Lids Non-BB	10.00
2-54 Dixie Lids	11.00
nand Post Cards	3.00
e N135	10.00
e Cabinets N142	500.00
Coast League	35.00
D Bishop	30.00
4 Nadja	15.00
5 Mello Mints	18.00
6 Amer. Car.	16.00
7 Williams	27.00
2 Amer. Car.	7.50
5 Amer. Car.	12.00
D York Car.	7.50
D National Car.	7.50
3 Oxford Conf.	42.00
5 Rittenhouse	15.00
ibits 4-in-1	15.00
staff F224	10.00
D Fleer W.S.	.11
1 Fleer W.S.	.10
r Base Hit	200.00
dwin & Co. N162	90.00
Pirates 1963	.30
amazoo Bats N690	175.00
all N184 Baseball	175.00
all N184 Others	15.00
o N300	60.00
sboy N566	300.00

N321 Creole	100.00
N338-1 S.F. Hess	150.00
N338-2 S.F. Hess	200.00
N370 Lone Jack	300.00
N403 Aug. Beck	175.00
Old Judge N172	17.00
Old Judge N172-1 Spotted Tie	80.00
Old Judge N172-2 Browns	70.00
Old Judge Cabinets Minors	100.00
Old Judge Cabinets Majors	150.00
Old London Coins	1.25
Omaha Dodgers	.39
P2 Pins Small Letters	2.50
P2 Pins Large Letters	5.00
PR2 Orbit Pins	4.00
PR3 Orbit Pins	6.50
PR4 Pins	6.00
1978 Pepsi Reds	.07
1978 Pepsi Stars	.08
1955 Rawlings Musial	30.00
1964 Rawlings	12.00
R301 Overland Candy	25.00
R303 Goudey 1939	10.00
R308 Self Develop	25.00
R309-2 Premiums	7.00
R315 Premiums	6.00
R332 Schutter-Johnson	12.00
R342 Thum Movies	30.00
R344 Secrets	12.00
RC Cans	.14
S74 Silks	8.00
1936 S & S	1.30
Salada Coins	1.00
1957 Sohio Reds	1.75
1957 Sohio Indians	1.75
Star-Cal Decals	7.00
1910 Tip-Top	50.00
1913 Tom Barker	10.00
1956 Topps Pins	5.00
1961 Topps Stamps	.18
1962 Topps Stamps	.18
1963 Topps Stick-Ons	.35
1964 Topps Coins	.75
1964 Topps A-S Coins	1.00
1965 Topps Press Ons	.30
1966 Topps Rub-offs	.25
1971 Topps Coins	.40

T208 Fireside	100.00
T209 Contentnea	9.00
T210 Old Mill	6.00
T211 Obak red	5.00
T212 Obak blue	4.00
T212 Obak old Eng.	10.00
T213 Coupon	15.00
T214 Victory	30.00
T215 Red Cross	20.00
T216	16.00
T222 Fatima Players	40.00
V89 Patterson	12.50
V117 Maple Crispette	9.50
Wheaties Panels 1930's Baseball	10.00
Wheaties Panels 1930's Non-Baseball	6.00
1951 Wheaties F272-3	14.00
1911 Zeenuts	6.00
1912 Zeenuts	6.00
1912 Home Run Kisses	25.00
1913 Zeenuts	6.00
1914 Zeenuts	5.00
1915 Zeenuts	6.00
1916 Zeenuts	5.00
1917 Zeenuts	4.00
1918 Zeenuts	6.00
1919 Zeenuts	3.00
1920 Zeenuts	3.00
1921 Zeenuts	2.75
1922 Zeenuts	2.75
1923 Zeenuts B&W	2.75
1923 Sepia	5.00
1924 Zeenuts	2.50
1925 Zeenuts	2.50
1926 Zeenuts	3.00
1927 Zeenuts	2.00
1928 Zeenuts	2.00
1929 Zeenuts	2.50
1930 Zeenuts	2.00
1931 Zeenuts	2.00
1932 Zeenuts	2.75
1933 Zeenuts	3.00
1934-1936 Zeenuts	3.25
1937-1938 Zeenuts	5.50

437

HALL OF FAME AUTOGRAPH PRICE GUIDE

An alphabetical listing of all members of the Baseball Hall of Fame (HOF) is given below. Also listed is the retail price of that member's autograph. This listing is essentially an abridgement and revision of the HOF autograph price survey performed by Gordon Ruiter with assistance from Bill Zekus, Jack Smalling, and others. Please direct any autograph inquiries or questions to Dr. Beckett (with a self-addressed stamped envelope) at P.O. Box 332, Bowling Green, Ohio 43402.

Alexander, Grover C.	60.00	Frisch, Frankie	5.00	Mathewson, Christy	150.00
Anson, Cap	250.00	Galvin, Pud	350.00	Mays, Willie	5.00
Appling, Luke	1.00	Gehrig, Lou	150.00	McCarthy, Joe	3.00
Averill, Earl	1.00	Gehringer, Charlie	1.00	McCarthy, Tommy	300.00
Baker, Home Run	20.00	Gibson, Bob	3.00	McGinnity, Joe	300.00
Bancroft, Dave	4.00	Gibson, Josh	175.00	McGraw, John	110.00
Banks, Ernie	2.00	Giles, Warren	5.00	McKechnie, Bill	20.00
Barrow, Ed	25.00	Gomez, Lefty	1.50	Medwick, Joe	4.00
Beckley, Jake	275.00	Goslin, Goose	5.00	Musial, Stan	1.00
Bell, Cool Papa	3.00	Greenberg, Hank	1.50	Nichols, Kid	30.00
Bender, Chief	55.00	Griffith, Clark	25.00	O'Rourke, Jim	250.00
Berra, Yogi	2.00	Grimes, Burleigh	1.00	Ott, Mel	25.00
Bottomley, Jim	50.00	Grove, Lefty	4.00	Paige, Satchel	3.00
Boudreau, Lou	1.00	Hafey, Chick	4.00	Pennock, Herb	50.00
Bresnahan, Roger	175.00	Haines, Jesse	4.00	Plank, Eddie	275.00
Brouthers, Dan	300.00	Hamilton, Billy	250.00	Radbourn, Old Hoss	250.00
Brown, Mordecai	90.00	Harridge, Will	20.00	Rice, Sam	4.00
Bulkeley, Morgan	225.00	Harris, Bucky	3.00	Rickey, Branch	25.00
Burkett, Jesse	150.00	Hartnett, Gabby	5.00	Rixey, Eppa	15.00
Campanella, Roy	45.00	Heilmann, Harry	90.00	Roberts, Robin	1.00
Carey, Max	4.00	Herman, Billy	1.00	Robinson, Jackie	15.00
Cartwright, Alexander	275.00	Hooper, Harry	3.00	Robinson, Wilbert	150.00
Chadwick, Henry	250.00	Hornsby, Roger	30.00	Roush, Edd	2.00
Chance, Frank	200.00	Hoyt, Waite	1.00	Ruffing, Red	3.00
Charleston, Oscar	80.00	Hubbard, Cal	10.00	Rusie, Amos	300.00
Chesbro, Jack	225.00	Hubbell, Carl	1.50	Ruth, Babe	135.00
Clarke, Fred	25.00	Huggins, Miller	225.00	Schalk, Ray	5.00
Clarkson, John	250.00	Irvin, Monte	1.00	Sewell, Joe	1.00
Clemente, Roberto	25.00	Jennings, Hughey	175.00	Simmons, Al	35.00
Cobb, Ty	25.00	Johnson, Ban	100.00	Sisler, George	5.00
Cochrane, Mickey	25.00	Johnson, Judy	1.00	Snider, Duke	1.00
Collins, Eddie	30.00	Johnson, Walter	70.00	Spahn, Warren	1.00
Collins, Jimmy	275.00	Joss, Addie	275.00	Spalding, Albert	175.00
Combs, Earle	4.00	Kaline, Al	1.00	Speaker, Tris	30.00
Comiskey, Charles	100.00	Keefe, Tim	250.00	Stengel, Casey	6.00
Conlan, Jocko	1.00	Keeler, Willie	225.00	Terry, Bill	1.00
Connolly, Tom	35.00	Kelley, Joe	175.00	Thompson, Sam	350.00
Connor, Roger	225.00	Kelly, George	1.50	Tinker, Joe	150.00
Covaleskie, Stan	1.00	Kelly, King	300.00	Traynor, Pie	8.00
Crawford, Sam	15.00	Kiner, Ralph	1.00	Vance, Dazzy	25.00
Cronin, Joe	1.00	Klein, Chuck	50.00	Waddell, Rube	325.00
Cummings, Candy	275.00	Klem, Bill	85.00	Wagner, Honus	35.00
Cuyler, Kiki	55.00	Koufax, Sandy	1.00	Wallace, Bobby	50.00
Dean, Dizzy	4.00	Lajoie, Napoleon	30.00	Walsh, Ed	35.00
Delahanty, Ed	300.00	Landis, Kenesaw M.	45.00	Waner, Lloyd	1.00
Dickey, Bill	1.50	Lemon, Bob	1.00	Waner, Paul	20.00
Dihigo, Martin	150.00	Leonard, Buck	1.00	Ward, John Montgomery	225.00
Dimaggio, Joe	3.00	Lindstrom, Fred	1.00	Weiss, George	15.00
Duffy, Hugh	65.00	Lloyd, John Henry	150.00	Welch, Mickey	250.00
Evans, Billy	55.00	Lopez, Al	1.00	Wheat, Zach	6.00
Evers, Johnny	150.00	Lyons, Ted	2.00	Williams, Ted	10.00
Ewing, Buck	350.00	Mack, Connie	25.00	Wilson, Hack	120.00
Faber, Red	3.00	MacPhail, Larry	10.00	Wright, George	175.00
Feller, Bob	1.00	Mantle, Mickey	10.00	Wright, Harry	150.00
Flick, Elmer	5.00	Manush, Heine	4.00	Wynn, Early	5.00
Ford, Whitey	2.50	Maranville, Rabbit	50.00	Yawkey, Tom	12.00
Foxx, Jimmie	25.00	Marquard, Rube	3.00	Young, Cy	30.00
Frick, Ford	5.00	Mathews, Eddie	1.00	Youngs, Ross	225.00

GLOSSARY

This glossary defines many common terms frequently used in the collecting hobby of baseball cards and closely associated material. There are exceptions to some of the definitions presented; however, to list all of the exceptions would only tend to confuse the reader and detract from the usefulness of the glossary.

AD CARD—See Display Card.

ALL STAR CARD—A card portraying an All Star Player of the previous year that says "ALL STAR" on its face.

AUTOGRAPHED CARD—A card that has been signed (usually on the front of the card) by the player portrayed on the card with a fountain pen, felt tip. magic marker, or ball-point pen. This term does not include stamped or facsimile autographed cards.

BLANKET—A felt square (normally 5" − 6") portraying a baseball player.

BRICK—A group of cards, usually 50 or more and having some common characteristic, that is intended to be bought, sold or traded as a unit.

CABINETS—Very popular and highly valuable large cards on thick card stock produced in the 19th and early 20th century.

CHECKLIST—a) A list of the cards contained in a particular set. The list is always in numerical order if the cards are numbered but in alphabetical or by team and alphabetical within team if the particular set is unnumbered.

b) A book containing a number of set checklists.

COIN—A small disc of metal or plastic portraying a baseball player in its center.

COLLECTOR—A person who engages in the hobby of collecting baseball cards for his own enjoyment, without a profit motive.

COLLECTOR ISSUE—A set produced for the sake of the card itself, with no product or service sponsor. It derives its name from the fact that most of these sets are produced by collector - dealers.

CONVENTION—A large weekend gathering at one location of dealers and collectors for the purpose of buying, selling. and sometimes trading of sports memorabilia items. Conventions are open to the public and sometimes feature celebrities, door prizes, films, contests, etc.

CONVENTION ISSUE—A set produced in conjunction with a sports collectibles convention to commemorate or promote the show.

COUPON—See Tab.

CREASE—A wrinkle on the card, usually caused by bending the card.

DEALER—A person who engages in the buying, selling and trading of sports collectibles or supplies who antcipates a profit, direct or indirect, from each transaction. A dealer may also be a collector, but as a dealer, he anticipates a profit.

DIE-CUT—A card which by design has its stock partially cut through for removal or folding of one or more parts to the card. After removal of these parts and appropriate folding, the remaining part of the card can be made to stand-up.

DISC—A circular shaped card.

DISPLAY CARD—A sheet, usually containing three to seven cards, that is printed and used by the manufacturer to advertise and/or display the packages containing his product and cards. The backs of display cards are blank or contain advertisements.

ERROR CARD—A card with erroneous information, spelling, or depiction on either side of the card.

EXHIBIT—The generic name given to thick stock, postcard sized cards with single color obverse pictures. The name is derived from the Exhibit Supply Co. of Chicago, the principal manufacturer of this type of card.

FULL SHEET—(Also called uncut sheet) A complete sheet of cards that has not been cut up into individual cards by the manufacturer.

HALL OF FAMER—(HOF'er) A card which portrays a player who has been inducted into the Baseball Hall Of Fame.

HIGH NUMBER—The cards in the last series of numbers in a year in which these higher numbered cards were printed or distributed in significantly fewer amounts than the lower numbered cards. The high number designation refers to a scarcity of the high numbered cards. Not all years have high numbers in terms of this definition.

INSERT—A card of a different type, a poster, or any other sports collectible contained and sold in the same package along with a card or cards of a major set.

ISSUE—Synonomous with set, but usually used in conjunction with a manufacturer, e.g. a Topps issue.

LAYERING—The separation or peeling of one or more layers of the card stock, usually at the corner of the card.

LEGITIMATE ISSUE—A set produced to promote or boost sales of a product or service, e.g. bubble gum, cereal, cigarettes, etc. Most collector issues are not legitimate issues in this sense.

LID—A circular (possibly with tab) shaped card that forms the top of the container for the product being promoted.

MAJOR SET—A set produced by a national manufacturer of cards containing a large number of cards. "Usually" 100 or more different cards are in the set.

MINOR LEAGUER—A card that portrays a minor league player, the card belonging to a set predominantly composed of major league players,e.g. Southern League player card in the T—206 series.

MISCUT—A card that has been cut particularly unevenly at the manufacturer's cutting stage.

NON-SPORT CARD—A card from a set whose major theme is a subject other than a sports subject. A card of a sports figure or event that is part of a non-sport set is still a non-sport card, e.g., while the Look'N See non-sport card set contains a card of Babe Ruth, a sports figure, the card is a non-sport card.

NOTCHING—The grooving of the edge of a card, usually caused by the fingernail, rubber bands, or bumping the edge against another object.

OBVERSE—The front, face or pictured side of the card.

PANEL—An extended card that is composed of two or more individual cards. Often the panel forms the back part of the container for the product being promoted, e.g. a Hostess panel, a Bazooka panel, an Esskay meat panel.

PLASTIC SHEET—A clear vinyl page (normally using 6—8 mil plastic and punched for insertion into a binder with standard 3—ring spacing) containing pockets for insertion of cards. Many different styles of sheets exist with pockets of varying sizes to hold different sizes of cards.

PREMIUM—A card, possibly on photograph stock, that is purchased or obtained in conjunction with or redemption for another card or product. The premium is not packaged in the same unit as the primary item.

RARE—A card or series of cards of very limited availability. Unfortunately "rare" is a subjective and rather nebulous term sometimes used indiscriminantly. "Rare" cards are harder to obtain than "scarce" cards.

REGIONAL—A card issued and distributed only in a limited area of the country. The producer is not a major, national producer of baseball cards.

REPRINT—A reproduction of an original card, usually produced by a maker other than the original manufacturer from a source other than the original artwork or negative.

REVERSE—The back or narrative side of the card.

ROOKIE CARD—a) The first card from a particular issuer of a particular player. Usually only star or superstar players are associated with the "rookie card" term, e.g., both 1951 Bowman no.253 or 1952 Topps no.311 are considered rookie cards of Mickey Mantle. The first card of a star often holds unusually high value.

b) A card which portrays one or more players with the notation on the card that these players are Rookies.

SCARCE—A card or series of cards of limited availability. A subjective and nebulous term sometimes used indiscriminately to promote value. Scarce cards are not as difficult to obtain as rare cards.

SERIES—a) The entire set of cards issued by a particular producer in a particular year, e.g., the 1933 Goudey series.

b) Within a particular set, a group of consecutively numbered cards printed at the same time, e.g., the first series of the 1951 Bowman issue (nos. 1-36).

SET—One each of the entire run of cards of the same type produced by a particular manufacturer during a single year. If the same type card is printed over a period of years, a set refers to the span of years, e.g., a 1976 Topps set (nos. 1–660) or the T–206 set (524 different cards printed between 1909 and 1911). A complete set does not include extra error or variation cards unless specified.

SKIP-NUMBERED—A set that has many card numbers not issued between the lowest number in the set and the highest number in the set. A major set in which a few numbers were not printed is not considered to be skip-numbered, e.g., six numbers of the 1953 Topps set were not issued; this set is not skip-numbered. The 1948–49 Leaf set contains 98 cards which are skip-numbered from no. 1 to no. 168.

SPECIAL CARD—A card that portrays something other than a single player or team, e.g., a card that portrays the previous year's, RBI Leaders or previous year's World Series Games.

STAMP—Adhesive backed paper depicting a baseball player. The stamp may be indiviual or in a sheet of many stamps. Moisture must be applied to the adhesive in order for the stamp to be attached to another surface.

STAR CARD—A card that portrays a player of some repute, usually determined by his ability as a baseball player; however, sometimes referring to sheer popularity, e.g., Ted Kluszewski, Mark Fidrych, Joe Garagiola.

STICKER—A card with a removable layer that can be adhered to (stuck onto) another surface.

STOCK—The cardboard or paper on which the card is printed.

STRIP CARDS—A sheet or strip of cards, particularly popular in the 1920's and 1930's, with the individual cards separated by a broken or dotted line.

SUPERSTAR CARD—A card that portrays a superstar, e.g., A Hall Of Fame member (Ruth, Mantle, Williams), or a probable future Hall Of Fame member (Aaron, Brooks Robinson, Pete Rose).

TAB—a) A part of a card set off from the rest of the card, usually with perforations, that may be removed without damaging the central character or event depicted by the card.

    b) The grasping nib of a lid.

TEAM CARD—A card which depicts an entire team.

TEST SET—A set, usually containing a small number of cards, issued by a national card producer and distributed in a limited section or sections of the country. Presumably, the purpose of a test set is to "test" market appeal for this particular type of card.

TRIMMED—A card cut down from its original size.

VARIATION— One of two or more cards from the same series with the same number (or player with indentical pose if the series is unnumbered) differing from one other by some aspect, the different feature stemming from the printing or stock of the card, not from an alteration.

ABBREVIATIONS

ABC   — The Sport Americana Alphabetical Baseball Card Checklist
ACC   — The American Card Catalog
ATG   — All Time Greats
BHN   — Baseball Hobby News
dp   — Double-printed
E(card) — The ACC reference letter for pre-1930 candy and gum cards
IWC   — The Illustrated Wrapper Checklist
N(card) — The SCB reference letter denoting 19th Century tobacco cards
PG   — The Sport Americana Baseball Card Price Guide
SCB   — The Sports Collectors Bible
SCD   — Sports Collectors Digest
SSPC   — Sports Stars Publishing Company
T(card) — The ACC reference letter for 20th Century tobacco cards
TCMA — The Card Memorabilia Associates
tp   — Triple-printed
TSN   — The Sporting News
TTS   — The Trader Speaks
V(card) — The ACC reference letter for Canadian candy and gum cards
2-D   — Two-dimensional-used to denote 1973 Kellogg set only
3-D   — Three-dimensional

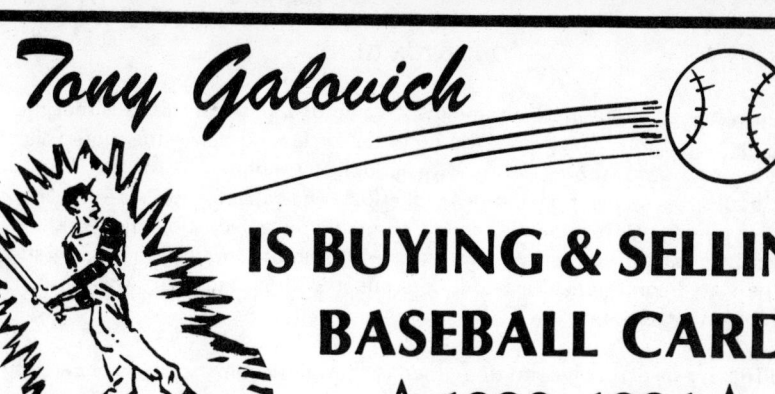

CONDITION GUIDE

If there is one absolute in determining the value of a baseball card it is that the better the condition of the card, the more desirable, and hence the more valuable the card. Each hobby has its own grading terminology — stamps, coins, comic books, beer cans, right on down the line. The collectors of baseball cards are no exception. Unfortunately, condition grading is a very subjective task. Individual baseball card dealers and collectors differ in the strictness of their grading. The stated condition of a card is determined without regard to whether it is being bought or sold.

The difficulty in defining condition grade is that, although the physical defects which lower the conditions of a card are quite apparent when one looks at the card, each individual places his own value (negative value in this case) on the defects.

Rather than confuse the issue further let us present the condition guide used for values in the Sport Americana Baseball Card Price Guide.

ALTERATIONS

The defects listed in the condition guide are those defects either placed in the card at the time of printing of the card (uneven borders, focus) or those defects that occur to a card under normal handling (corner sharpness, gloss, edge wear) and environmental conditions (browning). Other defects found on cards are inflicted by human carelessness and in all cases should be noted separately and in addition to the condition grade. Among the more common alterations are tape, tape stains, rubber band marks, water damage, smoke damage, trimming, paste, tears, writing, pin or tack holes, any back damage, and missing parts (tabs, tops, coupons, backgrounds).

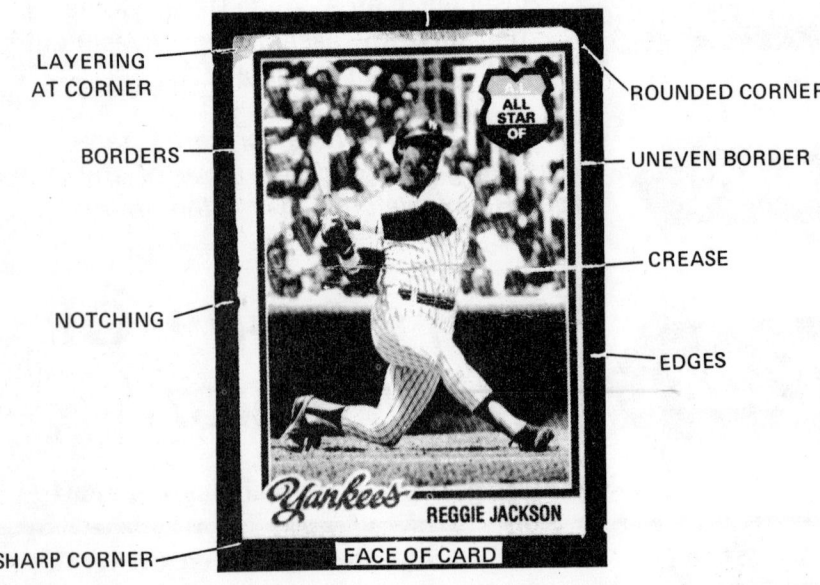

BROWNING OF BORDER

LAYERING AT CORNER

BORDERS

NOTCHING

SHARP CORNER

ROUNDED CORNER

UNEVEN BORDER

CREASE

EDGES

REGGIE JACKSON

FACE OF CARD